Fundamentals of Structural Geology

Fundamentals of Structural Geology provides a new framework for the investigation of geological structures by integrating field mapping and mechanical analysis. It emphasizes the observational data, modern mapping technology, principles of continuum mechanics, and the mathematical and computational skills, necessary to map, describe, model, and explain deformation in the Earth's lithosphere quantitatively.

Assuming a basic knowledge of physical geology, introductory calculus, and physics, this advanced textbook builds on more traditional courses that emphasize descriptive terminology, geometric techniques, and kinematics. In a significant departure from conventional textbooks on the subject, differential geometry is introduced and applied to quantify descriptions of geological structures. Differential geometry integrates the spatial information conventionally found on maps with orientation data from stereograms to provide reproducible descriptions of geological structures. By starting from the fundamental conservation laws of mass and momentum, the constitutive laws of material behavior, and the kinematic relationships for strain and rate of deformation, the authors demonstrate the relevance of solid and fluid mechanics to structural geology. The constitutive relations used in the book are sufficiently elementary to enable students to gain physical insight from analytical solutions, but are adequately realistic to provide compelling correlations to observational data.

This book offers a modern quantitative approach to structural geology for advanced undergraduate and graduate students and researchers in structural geology and tectonics. It will also interest those working in related disciplines, including geophysics, rock mechanics, field mapping, hydrogeology, petroleum and geotechnical engineering, and natural hazard mitigation. The book is supported by a website (www.cambridge.org/ 0521839270) hosting images from the book, additional colour images, student exercises and MATLAB® scripts. Solutions to the exercises are available to instructors.

DAVID POLLARD is the Morris Professor of Earth Sciences in the Department of Geological and Environmental Sciences at Stanford University where he co-directs the program in Structural Geology and Geomechanics. He and his students are using quantitative field data and principles of structural geology, combined with laboratory and computer modeling, to address questions about processes of faulting, fracturing, and rock deformation. The research aims to understand how faults and fractures evolve in the Earth's crust; how they affect the flow of magma, groundwater, and hydrocarbons; and what role fractures play in earthquake generation and volcanic eruption

RAYMOND FLETCHER is a Research Professor in the Department of Geosciences at the Pennsylvania State University. He and his collaborators study the continuous deformation of rock as in the emplacement of mantled gneiss domes, rock folding, and basin and range necking. He also works on processes linking chemical aspects of mineral growth or dissolution in rocks and deformation. Currently he is studying folding near the base of ice sheets, and the evolution of structures and rheological behavior of composite rock masses.

Fundamentals of Structural Geology

David D. Pollard
Stanford University

and

Raymond C. Fletcher
The Pennsylvania State University

CAMBRIDGE
UNIVERSITY PRESS

CAMBRIDGE UNIVERSITY PRESS
Cambridge, New York, Melbourne, Madrid, Cape Town, Singapore, São Paulo

Cambridge University Press
The Edinburgh Building, Cambridge CB2 2RU, UK
Published in the United States of America by Cambridge University Press, New York

www.cambridge.org
Information on this title: www.cambridge.org/9780521839270

First published 2005
Reprinted with corrections 2006

Printed in the United Kingdom at the University Press, Cambridge

A catalogue record for this book is available from the British Library

ISBN-13   978-0-521-83927-0 hardback
ISBN-10   0-521-83927-3 hardback

Contents

Chapter 12 | Model development and methodology 456

Preface

Fundamentals of Structural Geology is a textbook that emphasizes modern techniques of field data acquisition and analysis, the principles of continuum mechanics, and the mathematical and computational skills necessary to describe, model, and explain quantitatively the deformation of rock in Earth's lithosphere.

With precise location data now available from the Global Positioning System (GPS) and powerful computer systems now transportable in a backpack, the quantity of reproducible field data has increased dramatically. These new data sets demand better methods for describing the geometry of structures, and we address this demand by introducing the basic concepts of differential geometry, which provide unambiguous descriptions of curved lineations and surfaces in three dimensions. Data sets from a variety of field areas are provided via the textbook website to promote the practice of opening field "notebooks" to the entire community of researchers, and as input for student exercises (see below).

Textbooks in structural geology provide elements of continuum mechanics (e.g. separate chapters on stress and strain), but rarely are these concepts tied together with constitutive laws or formulated into equations of motion or equilibrium to solve boundary or initial value problems. These textbooks largely beg the questions: what methodology should one adopt to solve the problems of structural geology; and what are the fundamental constructs that must be acknowledged and honored? These constructs are the conservation laws of mass, momentum, and energy, combined with the constitutive laws for material behavior and the kinematic relationships for strain and rate of deformation. We use these constructs to build a rational methodology for the investigation of tectonic processes and their structural products.

This textbook is designed for senior undergraduate students and graduate students who have taken an introductory physical geology course, mathematics courses that include differential and integral calculus in several variables, and a physics course covering mechanics and heat. We consider these courses to be the essential mathematical and scientific pre-requisites for a course using this textbook. Elementary concepts of vector analysis, matrix theory, linear algebra, ordinary and partial differential equations, and computer programming with MATLAB® are used throughout, but are introduced in such a way that a formal course in these subjects, while helpful, should not be considered a pre-requisite. The authors view this textbook as appropriate for a first course in structural geology, but recognize that many students will come to a course using this book after a traditional course that emphasizes the descriptive terminology, geometric techniques, and kinematic concepts of the discipline.

Although designed as a text for students, this book also should be useful as a reference for researchers in structural geology, and as an aid for updating instructors and professionals who have been exposed only to traditional courses and textbooks on the subject. Furthermore, this book should be attractive to scientists in related disciplines (geophysics, rock mechanics, tectonics, geotechnical engineering, and petroleum engineering) who are looking for a modern summary of the fundamentals of structural geology. We encourage students and professionals from these disciplines to learn about the modern methods and tools of structural geology so that they can effectively interact with geologists on multi-disciplinary projects.

One of the opportunities and challenges of publishing a textbook in the twenty-first century is the fact that the printed volume is no longer the only vehicle for communication between authors and readers. Accordingly, we have prepared a homepage for *Fundamentals of Structural Geology* that is available on the World Wide Web (www.cambridge.org/0521839270) and provides the following supplementary materials for readers, instructors, and students:

- Full color images for all outcrop photographs used in the text

- Full color images for key graphical results used in the text
- Supplementary outcrop photographs, maps, and cross sections
- A repository for supplementary images contributed by readers
- Exercises for students that reinforce the concepts introduced in the text
- Data sets from field mapping campaigns for use in the exercises
- Solutions to the exercises for instructors with password protection
- Sample MATLAB® m-files for the exercises
- Sample MATLAB® m-files for recreation of graphical figures found in the text
- A repository for exercises and MATLAB® m-files contributed by readers
- Errata

With a laptop connected to the Web and an LCD projector instructors can use the color outcrop images in the classroom to illustrate geological concepts, and run the m-files with their own choice of parameters for a dynamic demonstration of the mechanical concepts. We envision readers of the textbook having this website open on their desktop to enhance their learning experience. Today desktop PCs provide the necessary CPU power, 3D graphics cards provide the visualization environment and speed, and professional programmers have written applications such as MATLAB® that provide most of the computational tools needed by structural geologists.

For the authors of this textbook, it is not sufficient to focus on understanding the structural history of the Earth as an arcane academic exercise. We believe that structural geologists can make important contributions in natural resource recovery (including water, oil, gas, and minerals), in the assessment of natural hazards (including earthquakes, landslides, and volcanic eruptions), and in the management of the environment (for example the long-term storage of radioactive materials and the contamination of fractured aquifers by hazardous chemicals). It is the authors' hope that students and instructors alike will be as captivated as we have been by the remarkable opportunities and challenges of structural geology. Great satisfaction in the practice of this science is achieved when one successfully brings together the beauty of the natural world and the physical world of continuum mechanics to achieve a better understanding of rock deformation and the development of structures. By doing so one contributes to the knowledge of Earth's remarkable history and to the solution of important practical problems facing society today.

Acknowledgments

David Pollard would like to acknowledge four teachers who shaped his understanding of structural geology as an undergraduate and graduate student. Donald B. McIntyre of Pomona College provided the spark that ignited his curiosity about the subject and put it in an historical context. Arvid M. Johnson of Stanford University introduced him to the tools of mechanics and to a rational way to approach physical processes in the field and laboratory. John G. Ramsay of Imperial College taught him how to measure deformation in outcrop and investigate the geometry and kinematics of rock subject to ductile deformation. Neville J. Price of Imperial College introduced him to rock mechanics and the analysis of rock subject to brittle deformation. These teachers provided a diversity of viewpoints of structural geology that was fascinating as well as challenging, and the origins of many of the themes played out in this textbook can be traced directly to their classrooms. Arvid Johnson's role in the formative stages of work on the textbook was particularly important.

David Pollard was privileged to study with students who were colleagues at Pomona College, Stanford University, and Imperial College, and later to work with students in a teaching and advisory capacity at the University of Rochester, the US Geological Survey (Menlo Park), and Stanford University. Many of these students have participated in research that helped to shape the concepts and methods described in this book. They include: Atilla Aydin, Ze'ev Reches, Gary R. Holzhausen, John W. Cosgrove, Otto H. Muller, David R. Dockstader, Paul T. Delaney, Paul Segall, Jon H. Fink, J. Russell Dyer, Russell K. Davies, Laurie L. Erickson, Marie D. Jackson, Peter C. Wallmann, Stephen J. Martel, Allan M. Rubin, Larry G. Mastin, Jon E. Olson, Sarah D. Saltzer, Scott S. Zeller, Andrew L. Thomas, Carl E. Renshaw, Roland Bürgmann, Pauline M. Mollema, Marco Antonellini, Haiqing Wu, Peter P. Christiansen, Stephen K. Mathäi, Joshua J. Roering, J. Ramón Arrowsmith, George Hilley, Emanuel J. M. Willemse, Michele L. Cooke, Elissa Koenig, Juliet G. Crider, W. Lansing Taylor, Simon A. Kattenhorn, Taixu Bai, Laurent Maerten, Scott S. Young, Frantz Maerten, Stephan Bergbauer, Peter Eichhubl, Phillip G. Resor, Kurt R. Sternlof, Patricia E. Fiore, Ian W. Mynatt, W. Ashley Griffith, Nicolas Bellahsen, Gaurav Chopra, and J. Ole Kaven.

David Pollard would like to thank John Suppe of Princeton University and Patience A. Cowie of Edinburgh University for hosting sabbaticals that provided important time for development of the materials presented here. He gratefully acknowledges the help of the staff of the Department of Geological and Environmental Sciences and the Branner Earth Sciences Library at Stanford University. Also, he extends special thanks to the Seeley G. Mudd Science Library at Pomona College and to the National Cello Institute for providing an idyllic venue for preparation of the manuscript.

Raymond Fletcher would like to acknowledge several people who contributed to his education as a structural geologist. William F. Brace (MIT) awarded him a C in the undergraduate structural geology course, giving useful incentive for further study of a subject that Bill's treatment showed to consist of an intriguing combination of field observation and mechanical analysis. Bill Brace also gave excellent advice on what not to do as a Ph.D. research project prior to the arrival at Brown University of his Ph.D. advisor William M. Chapple. Bill Chapple provided guidance in formulating a tractable complete mechanical model for the emplacement of a gneiss dome and M. A. Jaswon pointed him toward a method of analysis. Interaction with Bill Chapple over many years continued to enrich his experience. The foundation for his understanding of continuum mechanics was provided by the lucid presentation of this subject in a two-semester course at Brown University by E. T. Onat. Arvid M. Johnson introduced him to the disciplined mapping of small-scale structures in the field interspersed with more freewheeling discussions of mechanical modeling. Memorable discussions over coffee and pastry with Bernard Hallet continue to provide him with imaginative ideas, such as treating the Basin-and-Range Province as a string of blood sausages. He has benefited from and enjoyed collaborations with former graduate students Judi Chester, Russell Davies, Jon Fink, George Gazonas, Bill Kilsdonk, Frank Irwin, Duncan Mardon, and Tom Patton.

Chapter 1

Motivations and opportunities

Mt. Hillers, southern Henry Mountains, UT. The mountain is cored by igneous rock and surrounded by upturned beds of sandstone and shale. G. K. Gilbert coined the term "laccolite" for these structures in the late 1870s and proposed models for this process of mountain building based on mechanical principles. Inset: Frontispiece from G. K. Gilbert's *Report on the Geology of the Henry Mountains* (Gilbert, 1877). To the rear of this illustration the sedimentary strata form the structural dome of Mt. Ellsworth, and to the front the eroded remnant of the dome represents the current topography of this mountain. Photograph by D. D. Pollard.

The sciences do not try to explain, they hardly even try to interpret, they mainly make models. By a model is meant a mathematical construct which, with the addition of certain verbal interpretations, describes observed phenomena. The justification of such a mathematical construct is solely and precisely that it is expected to work (quote from John von Neumann; Gleick, 1987, p. 273).

In this chapter we motivate the study of structural geology by introducing selected topics that illustrate the extraordinary breadth of interesting problems and important practical applications of this discipline. For example, we use the Imperial Valley earthquake of 1979 along the San Andreas Fault zone to describe techniques for geological hazard analysis. In a second example the lineaments visible in radar images of Venus provide the data for investigating tectonic processes on a planet other than our own. This is followed by an investigation of normal faulting in a hydrocarbon reservoir under the North Sea, off the coast of Norway, to introduce an application to petroleum exploration and production. Then we describe the pattern of small faults, veins, and solution surfaces from an exposure in southern France, an example that demonstrates the practice of structural geology at the human scale. The concept of "anticracks" that emerged from this academic investigation is now being used to help explain the origin of huge earthquakes a hundred kilometers below Earth's surface. Finally, we describe a mechanism for mountain building that was discovered in the Henry Mountains of southern Utah in the late nineteenth century by one of the pioneers of structural geology, G. K. Gilbert.

The frontispiece for this chapter is a photograph of Mt. Hillers in the southern Henry Mountains. Like all the photographs that appear as grayscale images in this book, a color image of this photograph is available at the textbook website along with images of related exposures and scenes. These are presented as monitor resolution images for quick viewing with a web browser or for LCD projection in the classroom for teaching purposes.

1.1 | Earthquake hazards in southern California

Academic researchers have learned that society may not be content to continue funding the arcane studies of ancient rocks that have been the mainstay of the National Science Foundation's Tectonics Program in the past. Darrel Cowan, then President of the Geological Society of America's Structural Geology and Tectonic Division, concluded:

We are at the end of the era when an unquestioning public belief in the benefits of basic scientific research almost automatically led to increased budgets at the NSF (National Science Foundation) Program level. Already, NSF management and the Congress want to hear arguments about how research, and especially new programs, will address important social issues: environmental changes and hazards, exploitation, waste, and recycling of natural resources, and the like (Cowan, 1992).

Thus, whether a career in the Earth sciences takes one to industry or to academia or to a government laboratory, the structural geologist should know how to address problems of social importance. To this end, we integrate aspects of active tectonics, engineering geology, and petroleum geology into this book to show how structural geology can contribute to solving problems in these areas.

Most inhabitants of southern California are familiar with earthquakes and the geological hazard associated with living in an active tectonic province, although the recurrence time of major events is great enough to instill a sense of complacency in many citizens. On the other hand, Earth scientists and government officials are acutely aware that destructive earthquakes could occur at any moment. Teams of scientists and engineers supported by federal and local governments are monitoring the continuing activity of the faults in this area and have tools in place to capture data from the next significant event (Yeats et al., 1997).

What are the data that these scientists and engineers are hoping to capture? Perhaps the most fundamental aspect of faulting is the fact that the rock and soil on either side of the fault slip past one another. There is relative motion of these two masses more or less parallel to the fault surface. For example, Fig. 1.1 is a photograph taken across the trace of the Imperial Fault in the Imperial Valley of southern California shortly after a magnitude 6.5 earthquake struck on October 15, 1979. The vertical surface just behind the observer's feet is one surface of the fault exposed at the time of the earthquake. Relative to the ground on which the observer is standing, slip on the fault offset the two small drainage channels upward and to the right. By identifying soil particles (say in the bottom of the drainage channel) that were adjacent before the slip, one can make precise measurements of the offset. Using a tape measure, the geologist records the horizontal, *strike slip* component of relative motion as about 5 cm, and the upward, *dip slip* component as about 20 cm.

To characterize the behavior of a fault, one would like to know the magnitudes and directions of this relative motion in terms of the displacements, velocities, and accelerations of originally adjacent particles over the entire fault. The relative motion of particles is directly measurable only at (or very near) the surface of the Earth for active faults, and yet the fault might extend to depths of 10 km or more. Furthermore, one would like to know the distributions of these quantities over the entire time the two surfaces of the fault were in relative motion. In other words one would like to know the spatial and temporal distributions of displacement, velocity, and acceleration for particles of rock or soil in the vicinity of the fault. Given such information we could begin to understand the mechanisms that control fault slip and, perhaps, be in a position to be predictive about such events.

1.1.1 Contributions from geology, geodesy, and geophysics

Figure 1.2 is a schematic illustration of some of the tools used to monitor the slip across faults in active tectonic regions (Thatcher and Bonilla, 1989). The illustration in Fig. 1.2a represents a vertical cross section along the fault with contours of slip magnitude. The tools used to estimate the *slip distribution* fall within three different disciplines in the Earth sciences: namely geology, geodesy, and geophysics. The geologist measures the offset of geological structures and formations across a fault at the surface as well as the offset of whatever cultural markers might be present (Fig. 1.2b). By walking along the surface trace of the fault, the structural geologist can gather data on many different types of geological and cultural features and plot a graph of fault slip at the surface versus distance along the fault. Usually the geologist records only the total slip between a time before

Fig 1.1 Ground rupture along the northern trace of the Imperial Fault in southern California after the October 15, 1979, magnitude 6.5 earthquake. View is to the southwest. The strike and dip components of slip are identified based on the offsets of the small stream channels. The relative motion is right-lateral strike slip (~5 cm) and dip slip (~20 cm) down to the northeast. See website for color image. Photograph by D. D. Pollard.

the earthquake and a time after the earthquake, and cannot measure the velocities or accelerations that occurred during the slip event.

Although the data gathered by geologists provide the most direct measurement of slip at the Earth's surface, they only record the slip at certain points along the fault and these data may not be similar to the distribution of slip at depth. For example, the offset of a fence line at the surface may be strongly influenced by a thick layer of relatively soft soil or unconsolidated sediments overlying the more rigid rock below. Models are required to interpolate the surface slip between these data points and to extrapolate these surface measurements to the sub-surface. Using elasticity theory, one could specify remote stresses and stresses along the fault as boundary conditions and solve for the slip distribution over the fault surface. One could search for boundary conditions that produced a slip distribution best matching the slip measured at the surface. Of course the model parameters themselves may be poorly constrained, and there may be many possible slip distributions at depth that are consistent with data from the surface. None-the-less, such modeling exercises are the only way for the geologist to extrapolate data from the surface to the sub-surface.

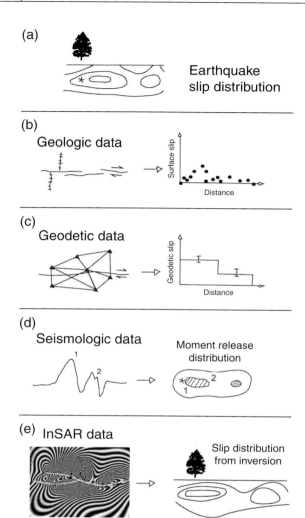

(a)

Earthquake slip distribution

(b) Geologic data

Surface slip

Distance

(c) Geodetic data

Geodetic slip

Distance

(d) Seismologic data

Moment release distribution

(e) InSAR data

Slip distribution from inversion

Fig 1.2 Schematic diagram of four different methods for estimating the slip on a fault (Thatcher and Bonilla, 1989). The actual slip is contoured on the fault surface in (a). Illustrations (b)–(d) show how geologists, geodesists, and seismologists gather data (left column), and graphical representations of these data are shown to the right. (e) Interferometric synthetic aperture radar (InSAR) data provide the field of displacement at the surface near a fault which can be inverted to estimate the slip distribution.

The geodesist measures the changes in lengths, angles, and/or elevations between surveyed benchmarks usually located at scattered points some distance from the fault (Fig. 1.2c). Such measurements are often more precise than geological measurements because high-precision instruments are used to gather the data and the bench marks are fixed to carefully designed and stable monuments. In some cases the instruments are permanently mounted at the survey locations and record data that can be used to calculate velocities and accelerations. In these respects the geodetic data can provide a better constraint on the deformation associated with faulting.

On the other hand the benchmarks usually are not located at the fault itself, so they do not directly record fault slip, even at the surface. Rather, a model (usually based on elasticity theory) is employed that requires as input the location and geometry of the fault and the mechanical behavior of the rock mass underlying the geodetic network. These models usually treat the fault as a set of segments, each with a constant slip, so the output is slip at the surface for different segments of the fault (Fig. 1.2c). The geodetically inferred slip is consistent with the changes in line lengths or angles between the benchmarks of the array, but clearly depends upon the chosen segment geometry and the other model parameters. More elaborate models are capable of calculating slip distributions at depth from the geodetic data. Because the geodetic data come from widely scattered locations away from the fault, the geometry and mechanical behavior of the sub-surface materials over a large volume of rock must be provided as model input.

The third category of data is taken from seismograms recorded both in the vicinity of the fault and at distant stations at the time of the earthquake (Fig. 1.2d). Although the locations of the seismographs may be even more remote from the fault than the geodetic benchmarks, these instruments continuously record the shaking of the ground due to the passage of *seismic waves* generated at the fault. Therefore, they can provide a wealth of data for inferring the behavior of the fault. In this example pulses on the seismogram are correlated to areas on the fault at depth that slipped at slightly different times or at different distances from the recording instrument. What is actually calculated is the *seismic moment* on the fault over these areas, but this can, in principle, be related to the average slip. By combining data from many seismographs a picture of the moment release distribution on the fault can be constructed. In practice the instruments may not be ideally located, and there may not be as many as one would desire.

Models of the sub-surface fault geometry are needed as well as the mechanical properties (seismic wave velocities) of the rock from the fault to the location of the seismographs.

The use of interferometric synthetic aperture radar (InSAR) for the detection of ground displacements associated with earthquakes was highlighted in articles appearing in the early 1990s (Massonnet *et al.*, 1993; Prescott, 1993; Zebker *et al.*, 1994). The radar signal is transmitted from a satellite to the ground surface where it is reflected back to the satellite and recorded as a set of pixels making up an image of the surface. Knowledge of the travel time and speed of the signal provide the information necessary to calculate the range, or distance, from the satellite to each reflective site on the surface. If the same region is imaged at two different times, for example before and after the earthquake, the difference between the two images can be used to calculate the component of the surface displacement directed toward the satellite. The resulting image (Fig. 1.2e), called an *interferogram*, is similar to a contour map of the displacement component on which the white and black bands (called *fringes*) are the contours. The fault segments are shown as fine white lines superimposed on this image. By invoking a model (usually based on elasticity theory) for the location and geometry of the fault segments and the mechanical behavior of the rock mass, one may use this displacement distribution on Earth's surface to calculate the corresponding slip distribution on the fault. The abundance of data provides considerable constraint on the unknown slip distribution below Earth's surface and very exciting avenues for new research on faulting.

It should be obvious from this discussion that the different disciplines contribute information that is based on different observations in different locations and over different length and time scales. Yet scientists from all three disciplines are studying the same physical phenomenon, faulting, and they are using the same tools to build their models, namely elasticity theory. In this textbook we focus on the geological data and the models that are used to relate measurements of slip to fault behavior. On the other hand each discipline is providing important pieces of the puzzle, so structural geologists should be aware of

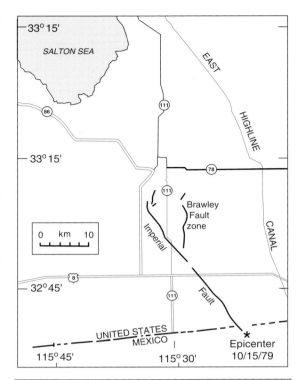

Fig 1.3 Map of the region affected by the October 15, 1979, earthquake in southern California (Wosser *et al.*, 1982). The epicenter is shown as a star in the lower right-hand corner.

the concepts and contributions from geophysics and geodesy to the study of faulting. In addition important insights are attained from studying the effects of faulting on the geomorphology of the landscape (Arrowsmith *et al.*, 1996; Arrowsmith *et al.*, 1998). The most comprehensive view of faults and the faulting process will come from an integration of all these data and that integration will be most effective in the context of building well-constrained models.

1.1.2 Conceptual and mechanical models for the 1979 earthquake rupture

On October 15, 1979, the magnitude 6.5 earthquake rupture began just south of the US–Mexico border and spread approximately 35 km to the north into southern California (Fig. 1.3), breaking ground along the trace of the Imperial Fault (Johnson *et al.*, 1982; Wosser *et al.*, 1982). Many agricultural features such as fence lines and canals provided markers to measure the slip

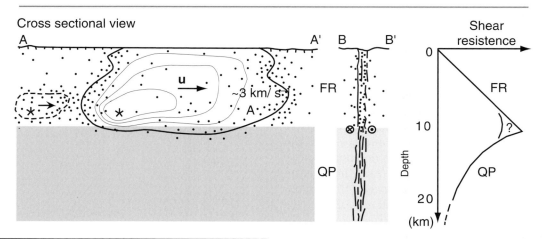

Map view

Cross sectional view

Fig 1.4 Three views of a crustal-scale strike slip fault. Map view illustrates the fault as a zone of deformation. Cross section A–A′ in the fault plane includes a contour map of the slip (**u**) which goes to zero at the fault tipline and is greatest near the hypocenter (star). Cross section B–B′ perpendicular to the fault plane suggests that slip mechanisms are frictional resistance (FR) in the upper part of the crust and localized quasi-plastic flow (QP) in the lower part. The graph at the right indicates a linearly increasing resistance to shearing with depth to the brittle–ductile transition, and then a non-linear decreasing resistance to shearing with depth. Reprinted from Sibson (1989) with permission from Elsevier.

across the fault trace. The farmers, homeowners, businesses, and municipalities in the Imperial Valley, mostly around the town of El Centro, sustained over twenty million dollars in damage. Fortunately, there was no loss of life and few catastrophic failures of man-made structures in this event. On the other hand, earthquakes of similar magnitude often are accompanied by many deaths in regions with less stringent building codes, or no building codes at all. These events testify to the destructive power of earthquakes and to the need to understand such hazards. Because earthquakes are generated by sudden slip on faults, we need to understand the mechanisms and behaviors of faults in order to develop informed hazard mitigation policy. Just what are the causes and consequences of dynamic rupture

on faults? Some answers to this question have come from research by scientists and engineers over the past few decades, but much remains to be understood.

In the previous section we described how geologists, geodesists, and geophysicists use models to extrapolate information on displacements or accelerations from the locations where data are measured on the Earth's surface to the fault in the sub-surface. These models help us to understand the behavior of faults where they cannot be observed directly and they provide insights concerning earthquake faulting as a structural process. The faulting process is conceptualized at the crustal scale in Fig. 1.4 for a vertical fault with strike slip motion (Sibson, 1989). Each view of this conceptual fault model reveals different aspects of faulting at the crustal scale. The map view shows a zone of fractures and deformation, rather than two surfaces in contact. This suggests that faults can be more complex than a single fracture and that shearing of material in a fault zone may characterize the deformation rather than slip between two surfaces. The vertical cross section viewed parallel to the fault indicates that frictional resistance (labeled "FR" in Fig. 1.4) to slip on a fault operates to depths of perhaps 10 km and plastic flow (labeled "QP") is associated with distributed shearing in a zone at deeper levels. Thus, the mechanisms of faulting may change with depth as temperature and pressure increase, such that brittle fracture and friction dominate at shallow depths and ductile flow dominates at greater depths. In this conceptual model the resistance to shearing increases with depth to this transition and then decreases with depth. In a vertical section viewed perpendicular to the fault (A–A'), dynamic shearing begins at depth, near the *brittle–ductile transition* and spreads out over the fault surface at a velocity of about $3 \, \mathrm{km \, s^{-1}}$, eventually reaching the Earth's surface.

The Imperial Valley earthquake is noteworthy because it occurred within a dense array of geodetic and geophysical instruments and there were abundant cultural features for the geologists to measure at the surface (Savage *et al.*, 1979). The mechanical model reviewed here was constructed using data from the seismographs and strong motion instruments that monitored this event (Archuleta, 1984). The results are not unique and the choice of model parameters could be debated, but that is not the issue here. This model provides an excellent example of the insight one can gain about phenomena that are otherwise totally inaccessible to direct observation.

Figure 1.5a is a map of the rupture traces for both the Imperial and Brawley Faults as compiled by geologists from observations at the Earth's surface. The photograph shown in Fig. 1.1 was taken near the northern end of the Imperial Fault. The map also shows rupture traces along the Brawley Fault that trend oblique to the Imperial Fault. Apparently the Brawley Fault slipped at about the same time as the Imperial Fault, but the relative motion on the Brawley Fault was primarily dip slip. Note that the southern half of the Imperial Fault rupture trace is drawn as continuous, whereas it is drawn as composed of discrete segments in the northern half. Also shown on Fig. 1.5a is the rupture *epicenter*, the point at the surface of the Earth immediately above the point where rupture initiated, as inferred by geophysicists from seismic records. This location is dependent upon a model for the seismic wave velocities of the crustal rocks. Note that the epicenter was approximately 5 km south of the southernmost surface break.

Each of the observations made in the previous

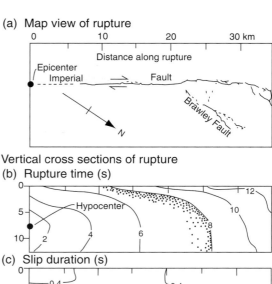

(a) Map view of rupture

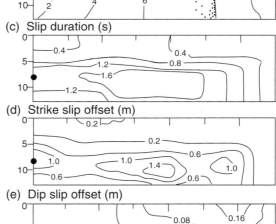

Fig 1.5 Map and cross sections of the Imperial Fault and the Brawley Fault for the October 15, 1979, earthquake in southern California (Archuleta, 1984): (a) map of the rupture trace; (b)–(e) vertical cross sections parallel to the fault trace with contours of the model rupture time, slip duration, strike slip offset, and dip slip offset.

paragraph brings up interesting questions about faulting. Why did the rupture not break to the surface immediately over the epicenter? Why would a second fault rupture at the same time as the Imperial Fault, and why is the trace of the second fault obliquely oriented? What does the discontinuous nature of the rupture trace tell us about faulting? Some of these questions can be addressed with models for the rupture process.

The mechanical model for the October 15, 1979, earthquake event considers only the rupture along the Imperial Fault (Archuleta, 1984). The lower four panels of Fig. 1.5 are graphs of different physical quantities calculated using the model and plotted on a vertical planar section that approximates the more complex geometry of the actual fault as suggested by the mapped trace in the first panel. The model fault is about 12 km in depth (ordinate) and 35 km in length (abscissa). The physical quantities (rupture time, slip duration, strike slip, and dip slip) are represented by contours of equal magnitude on these graphs. Together these panels provide a remarkable visualization of the model slip event from the Earth's surface to the bottom of the rupture.

Figure 1.5b illustrates the position of the leading edge of the model rupture to the north of the point of rupture initiation, the *hypocenter*, at times measured in seconds after initiation. What happened to the south of the hypocenter is ignored on these panels. At a given time, say 4 s, that portion of the fault between the hypocenter and the 4-s contour has slipped, while elsewhere on the fault no slip has occurred. Clearly, slip on the model fault does not initiate everywhere simultaneously. Rather, the model rupture initiated at a point, at the hypocentral depth of about 8 km. Then, the rupture front advanced rapidly to the north and less rapidly upward toward the surface. The rupture took a total time of about 12 s to spread the 35 km to the north end of the model fault. Thus, the average *rupture velocity* was about 3 km s^{-1} toward the north, approximately the speed of seismic shear waves.

Figure 1.5c shows the total time that originally adjacent particles on the two surfaces of the model fault were in relative motion. For example, along the contour labeled "1.6 s" the two surfaces slipped for a total time of less than 2 s. You might find this surprising given the fact that the total duration of faulting was about 12 s. Clearly all parts of the model fault were not slipping at the same time. This is illustrated in the previous panel by the pattern of dots next to the 8-s contour. These dots cover the relatively small portion of the fault that has already slipped and is still in the process of slipping at the moment that the rupture front lies along the 8-s contour. Between these dots and the hypocenter the model fault has slipped and stopped, whereas to the north and above the 8-s contour the fault has not yet slipped. At any particular location on the model fault the slipping occurred over a period of time ranging from a fraction of a second to almost 2 s as the rupture front passed, and then slipping stopped.

Figures 1.5d and e show, respectively, two components of slip between the model fault surfaces after the rupture has completed its propagation from the hypocenter to the northern termination. Strike slip varies from 1.4 m near the bottom center of the fault to a few decimeters or less at the surface. The strike slip is zero along the southern portion of the fault at the surface and this is consistent with the observations shown on the map in the first panel. Note that the surface measurements of slip, amounting to about 20 cm, under-represent the slip at depth by a factor of eight or more. The model fault slipped much more at depth than at the surface. Dip slip is concentrated near the surface at the northern end of the model fault with magnitudes approaching a few decimeters. This is consistent with the geological observations (see Fig. 1.1) that indicate the rocks on the northeastern side of this part of the Imperial Fault went down relative to those on the southwestern side. The amount of dip slip at the surface (up to about 20 cm) also is consistent with the field observations. The relative motion on the Brawley Fault was also nearly pure dip slip with the northwestern side down. In fact, the region between the Imperial and Brawley Faults is a topographic depression occupied by a (usually) dry lake-bed. This suggests that the relative motion experienced during the 1979 earthquake is typical of the recent geological history of this fault system.

This mechanical model gives us a picture of active faulting that is reasonably consistent with the available surficial and seismic data from the 1979 event. It informs our intuition about the physical process of faulting and provides a glimpse into possible behavior along the Imperial Fault at depth. Building models such as this one and using these models to understand the process of faulting is an exciting area of research in which structural geologists can participate (Segall and Pollard, 1980; Aydin and Schultz, 1990; Cowie and

Scholz, 1992; Dawers *et al.*, 1993; Bürgmann *et al.*, 1994; Muller *et al.*, 2003).

1.2 | Radar lineaments on Venus

In his book *The Assayer* Galileo Galilei apparently wrote the following:

The Universe, which stands continually open to our gaze, cannot be understood unless one first learns to comprehend the language and read the letters in which it is composed. It is written in the language of mathematics ... (Gregory, 1990).

Today the power of modern telescopes and satellite exploration of the planets provides countless opportunities to investigate structures in rock beyond Earth.

The Magellan mission to Venus produced radar images of much of the planet's surface and many of the structures observed on these images apparently are related to volcanism (Head *et al.*, 1992). One of the most interesting classes of structures is composed of radar *lineaments* (paired bright and dark lines or single bright lines on the image) that appear to radiate from a central focal point like spokes on a bicycle wheel (Fig. 1.6). Grosfils and Head (1994) have identified more than 160 such radial systems on Venus and have interpreted the lineaments as fractures cutting the surface of the Venusian crust. At first glance the patterns are reminiscent of radial fracture patterns you might have seen in a pane of tempered glass where it has been struck by a rock; however, these lineament patterns are enormous. The pattern at (15°S, 215°E), shown in more detail in Fig. 1.7, is about 200 km in diameter and the average diameter for all such patterns identified on Venus is 325 km, with some as great as 2000 km! These patterns are intriguing in their symmetry and awe inspiring in their size; they clearly warrant our attention as structural geologists.

Grosfils and Head (1994) developed conceptual models to distinguish and interpret two types of radial lineament patterns. For the first type they suggest the fractures are formed by doming and stretching of the Venusian crust over a body of molten rock, *magma*, that flows upward from a source reservoir at depth. The fractures them-

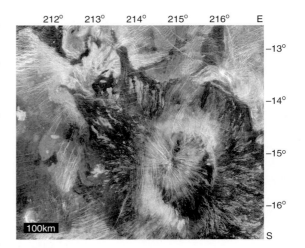

Fig 1.6 Left-looking F-MIDR 15s214 radar image of the surface of Venus from the Magellan mission (Koenig and Pollard, 1998). Look angle is approximately 40°. Note radial pattern of lineaments centered at 15°S, 215°E. One degree of latitude or longitude is about 100 km.

selves are not filled with magma; rather they are the ephemeral manifestation of a large rising body of magma beneath the surface. The second type of lineament pattern is interpreted as having formed as magma-filled fractures, *dikes*, that propagated upward and radially outward from a central magma conduit at shallow depths under the volcanic edifice. The dikes act as the passageways for magma flow to the surface from the central conduit. Here we only consider the second type, which apparently makes up more than 70% of the radial patterns identified on Venus.

1.2.1 Conceptual and mechanical models for graben formation

The volcanic edifice at (15°S, 215°E) stands about 1 km above the surrounding plains. Elongate and lobate gray regions (labeled "rlf" on Fig. 1.7) on the surface of this edifice are interpreted as lava flows (Koenig and Pollard, 1998), which spread down the flanks of this large volcano before solidifying. Also visible on the radar image are paired radial bright and dark lines that extend up to 50 km down the slope (labeled "g" on Fig. 1.7). These are interpreted as *graben*, linear depressions about 1 to 2 km in width bounded by normal faults along which the central block of rock has moved downward. When obliquely incident radar signals are

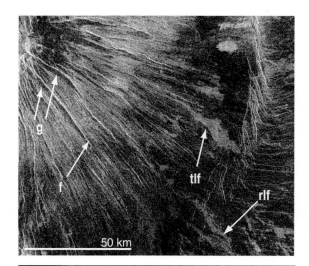

Fig 1.7 Left-looking F-MIDR 15s214 radar image of the southeast quadrant of the volcanic edifice centered at 15°S, 215°E. Surface structures are identified (Koenig and Pollard, 1998) as graben (g), fractures (f), terminal lava flows (tlf), and radial lava flows (rlf). The graben and fractures radiate from the volcanic center in the upper left corner of the image.

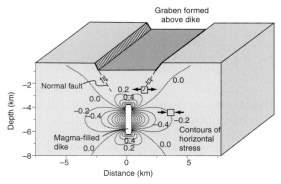

Fig 1.8 Schematic block diagram of a graben bounded by two normal faults and underlain by a dike (Rubin and Pollard, 1988; Koenig and Pollard, 1998). The horizontal stress component induced by opening of the dike is contoured on the front view showing a stress shadow (negative, compressive stress) to either side of the dike and a stress concentration (positive, tensile stress) near the dike tips.

reflected off the fault surface on one side of the graben, returning a bright lineament, the fault surface on the other side of the graben lies in a radar shadow and forms a dark lineament. Thus the surface topography accounts for the closely spaced pairs of bright and dark lines on the image.

Figure 1.8 illustrates the conceptual model for the development of graben over igneous dikes. The pairs of normal faults bounding graben on Venus are interpreted as having formed because of the local horizontal stretching of the rock immediately over or ahead of vertical dikes. Because the dikes apparently propagated upward and outward from a central magma chamber located under the summit of the edifice at (15°S, 215°E), the graben form a radial pattern on the flanks of this volcano.

A couple of questions come to mind when thinking about the origin of graben as described in the previous paragraph. Does the opening of a dike actually lead to stretching at the surface? If it does, why should two normal faults form to either side of the dike instead of one immediately over the dike? These questions have been addressed by studying the physical relationships between normal faults and dikes (Rubin and Pollard, 1988; Rubin, 1990).

Horizontal stretching is caused by tensile stresses that tend to pull the rock apart. Therefore, one needs to determine if dike opening at depth could induce tensile stresses near the Earth's surface, where normal faults bound the graben. Such associations are found in volcanic regions on Earth, including those in Iceland and Afar.

The mechanical model of this phenomenon is based on principles that are formulated into a set of mathematical equations known as the *theory of elasticity* (Timoshenko and Goodier, 1970). This theory and the relevant equations are described in detail later in this textbook. For the moment you only need to know that these equations can, for example, be solved to determine the stress distribution in the rock mass surrounding a dike. This formulation is called a *boundary value problem* because one prescribes the stresses on the boundaries of a body and the governing equations of elasticity theory are used to calculate the stresses in the interior. In this case one boundary represents Earth's surface, which is free of stress, and the other boundaries represent the dike walls that are subjected to stresses equal to the outward-directed pressure of the magma. The magma pressure pushes the dike walls apart and distorts the surrounding rock mass, thereby inducing a change in the stress distribution that is not easy to imagine without the aid of elasticity theory.

On the front face of the block diagram in Fig. 1.8 values of the horizontal stress are shown using a contour plot. This illustrates quantitatively how the opening of a model dike changes the stress field in the surrounding rock. To either side of the dike negative (compressive) stresses are induced that push inward on any small element of rock. These induced compressive stresses would tend to prevent normal faults from forming because they increase the frictional resistance to sliding. However, immediately over the dike, positive (tensile) stresses are induced. These tensile stresses stretch the rock and could contribute to the formation of normal faults. The distribution of horizontal stress at the surface has two maxima located symmetrically about the plane of the model dike. These two maxima correlate with the two normal faults that develop to either side of the dike plane. In this way the model has successfully addressed the questions we asked about the relationship between dikes and graben.

Does the success of the model provide all one needs to know to interpret the radar lineaments on Venus? Certainly it is supportive of the concept that dikes can induce slip on normal faults, but it does not prove that dikes actually exist beneath the graben. Some of the paired radial bright and dark lines on the radar image at (15°S, 215°E) can be traced down the flanks of the volcano where they merge into a single bright radar lineament (labeled "f" on Fig. 1.7). These single lineaments are interpreted as open fissures that formed as dikes neared the surface (Koenig and Pollard, 1998). This interpretation is consistent with the presence of dark lobate regions, interpreted as lava flows, emerging from near the distal end of some fissures and extending outward in a radial direction (labeled "tlf" on Fig. 1.7). These flows provide compelling evidence that dikes underlie the radial fractures and graben, and are the conduits for the escape of magma from beneath the volcano.

1.3 | Faulting in a North Sea hydrocarbon reservoir

R. N. Farvolden and J. A. Cherry (1991) wondered if geology departments are preparing their students for the twenty-first century:

After many years of observing geology departments, our experience indicates that they have adjusted to the scientific revolution of recent decades, but have largely ignored the technical, economic, and social changes that influence the practice of geology and thereby have ignored the professional lives of their students.

Structural geologists can make important contributions to natural resource recovery, including water, oil, gas, and minerals. They can play key roles in the management of the environment, for example in the long-term storage of radioactive materials and the contamination of fractured aquifers by hazardous chemicals.

One of the most interesting new areas of research in structural geology related to natural resources is the investigation of folds and faults using data from seismic reflection surveys (Kattenhorn and Pollard, 2001). These data are gathered by the petroleum industry to image hydrocarbon reservoirs (Sheriff and Geldart, 1995). To carry out a reflection survey in a sedimentary basin, seismic waves are generated by impulsively striking the surface of the Earth. Depending upon the depth of investigation required, these waves are generated using explosive charges, mechanically driven vibrators, or simply a hand-held hammer. Some of the waves travel down into the Earth, reflect off sedimentary layers or other structures, and travel back to the surface where they are recorded by a string of portable seismographs laid out along the survey line. The depth to different reflecting horizons can be computed by identifying the two-way travel time (down and back) for each reflection, and by knowing the velocity for acoustic waves in the rock. A series of impulses is generated along the survey line and reflections are recorded at each seismograph. The abundant data help to reduce the uncertainty in identifying and locating the reflecting horizons using a variety of data processing techniques.

The output of this processing is a seismic reflection cross section (*seismic section*) of the Earth immediately under the survey line. For example, consider the northern part of the North Sea (Fig. 1.9a) on the Norwegian Continental Shelf (Maerten *et al.*, 2000; Maerten *et al.*, 2002). Figure 1.9b is a seismic section taken from approximately 150 km west of the Norwegian coast (Faerseth

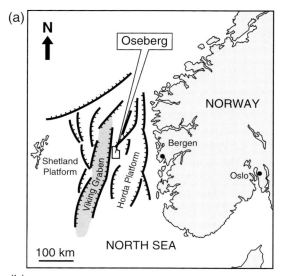

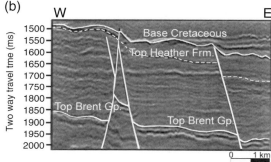

Fig 1.9 (a) Regional map showing the location of Oseberg Syd Field on the Norwegian Continental Shelf.
(b) Interpreted seismic data from the northern part of the North Sea approximately 150 km west of the Norwegian coast. Two-way travel time plotted versus distance along section. Interpreted horizons include the base of the Cretaceous, the top of the Heather Formation, and the top of the Brent Group. Reprinted from Maerten et al. (2002) and Faerseth et al. (1997) with permission from Elsevier.

et al., 1997). For offshore surveys the seismographs are towed in long strings behind a ship and the sources for the acoustic waves are implosions created by submerged devices called air guns. The seismic section plots position from west to east along the survey line (see kilometer scale) versus two-way travel time measured in milliseconds (ms). For a typical wave velocity of $2\,\mathrm{km\,s^{-1}}$, the bottom of the section at $2000\,\mathrm{ms} = 2\,\mathrm{s}$ represents a depth of about 4 km. The processed data appear as a series of bright and dark stripes representing the reflectors in the pile of sedimentary layers. Note that these reflectors are not continuous across the section from west to east, suggesting that they have been offset by normal faults or truncated by unconformities.

Specific sedimentary horizons are interpreted in Fig. 1.9b including the top of the Brent Group, the top of the Heather Formation, and the base of the Cretaceous. Interpretations of the normal faults (thick steeply inclined white lines) were drawn and labeled by Faerseth and his colleagues from the Norwegian oil company Norsk Hydro ASA. The faults strike approximately north–south so seismic sections along east–west trends such as in Fig. 1.9b should display these faults as viewed along their strike. The two east-dipping faults offset the top of the Brent Group, but do not offset the overlying base of the Cretaceous. Because these faults offset formations of upper Jurassic age, but do not extend into the overlying Cretaceous strata, they are interpreted as having formed during Jurassic extension of the basin. The west-dipping fault interpreted in Fig. 1.9b cuts the top of the Brent and extends slightly above the base of the Cretaceous. It also offsets one of the east-dipping faults. Because the west-dipping faults in this region systematically offset the east-dipping faults, Faerseth and his colleagues conclude that the west-dipping faults are younger.

A combination of factors, some related to improved equipment for acquiring such data and others related to improved software and hardware for processing such data, have changed the quality and resolution of seismic imaging technology dramatically in the past few decades. These developments are largely driven by the need for oil and gas companies to improve their exploration strategies through better images of sedimentary basins, and to improve their production strategies through better characterizations of particular reservoirs within these basins. The older technique is essentially two dimensional, providing an image of the strata on a vertical cross section along the survey line. By capturing numerous closely spaced parallel lines in two orthogonal directions, enough information is gathered to interpolate the reflecting horizons between these two-dimensional surveys and produce a three-dimensional image of the horizons within a volume of rock. The seismic section in Fig. 1.9 has been combined with hundreds of additional sections surveyed both parallel and perpendicular to this one. Using such three-dimensional surveys the opportunity exists to characterize and map the three-dimensional geometry of the faults.

Both the acquisition and the processing of seismic reflection data are in the domain of geophysics so we will not dwell on this aspect of the subject. On the other hand the images captured by these surveys illuminate both the sedimentological and the structural heterogeneities in the rock mass. These images have provided us with the challenging problem of understanding folding and faulting in three dimensions, no longer limited by poor exposure and arbitrary erosional slices through these structures. Instead of searching for the few exposures of a poorly revealed fault, hoping to measure the offset of one or two geological markers, we are able to measure the offset of continuous reflecting horizons at many points across a fault. Instead of locating the two points in space that represent the *fault terminations* at either end of an exposed fault trace, we are able to locate the *fault tipline* at many points in three dimensions. Of course there is a limit to the resolution of these images, now about 10-m offset for good reflectors, but the techniques are improving yearly.

1.3.1 Conceptual and mechanical models for fault linkage

As an example of using structural geology to analyze three-dimensional seismic data we turn to the Oseberg Syd Field operated by the Norwegian company Norsk Hydro (Faerseth *et al.*, 1997). The faulting in two parts of this field, called Omega North and Omega South (Fig. 1.10), has been investigated using a three-dimensional seismic survey (Maerten, 2000; Maerten *et al.*, 2000, 2002). The map depicts the base of the Brent Formation, one of the hydrocarbon reservoirs. The black stripes of variable width represent the normal faults that cut this formation and separate pieces of the Brent Formation in map view. The major faults in this field strike approximately north–south and dip to the west. A second set of faults is less well developed, striking approximately northwest–southeast and dipping to the southwest.

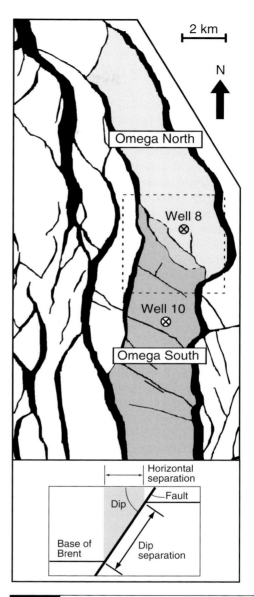

Fig 1.10 Map of normal faults in part of the Oseberg Syd Field in the northern North Sea based on the structural separation of the base of the Brent Formation. Wells No. 8 and No. 10 penetrate the producing reservoir and data from these wells suggest the Omega North and Omega South regions are isolated from one another by sealing faults. The dashed square indicates the area of faulting investigated by modeling. Inset: Schematic vertical cross section that illustrates how the width of the fault stripe on the map (gray on cross section) depends upon the dip of the normal fault and the dip separation of a particular horizon. Reprinted from Maerten *et al.* (2000) by permission of the AAPG whose permission is required for future use.

The inset on Fig. 1.10 illustrates in cross section how the horizontal component of separation (sometimes called the *heave*) and the dip of the normal fault are represented by the width of the black stripes on maps. Greater stripe widths (gray on the inset) imply greater horizontal separations of two points that originally were adjacent to one another at the base of the Brent Formation. Two faults with the same dip are displayed as stripes with lesser and greater widths (horizontal separations) corresponding to lesser and greater dip separation. Two faults with the same dip separation are displayed as stripes with lesser and greater widths corresponding to greater and lesser dips. In regions where the dips of all the normal faults are about the same, the widths of the stripes on the structure map are used to infer the relative magnitude of dip separations. Similarly, if the dip does not vary along the length of a fault, the changing width of the stripe is used to infer changes in the distribution of dip separation.

From information gathered by drilling and recovering core samples, measuring a variety of indicators in the wells, and running flow and pressure tests in the sub-surface, it is believed that the rocks in the fault zones shown in Fig. 1.10 are relatively impermeable to fluid flow compared to the unfaulted portions of the sandstone reservoir. Therefore these are referred to as *sealing faults*. A number of mechanisms for changing the permeability of rock in a fault zone have been identified (Jones *et al.*, 1998). For example, the crushing of sandstone grains during shearing in the fault zone can fill the pores with fragments, thereby decreasing the porosity and the permeability (Antonellini and Aydin, 1994, 1995; Antonellini *et al.*, 1994). Also, it is possible for very fine-grained clays to be dragged or injected into the fault zone to form a seal (Aydin and Eyal, 2002). If the faults are all of the sealing type, then they can divide the reservoir into a number of isolated compartments with little or no fluid communications between compartments. The map shown in Fig. 1.10 suggests that the Brent Formation could be divided into many compartments separated by the sealing faults.

The presence of fault-sealed compartments has important implications for locating wells and producing the hydrocarbons from this reservoir (Maerten *et al.*, 1999, 2000). For example, if part of the target reservoir is separated from a well by a sealing fault those hydrocarbons beyond the fault cannot be produced and another well must be drilled. If the second well is drilled and it turns out that the compartments do have a fluid connection because the faults are not continuous, or do not extend as far as originally interpreted, the unnecessary expense can be significant. Drilling one additional well in these offshore settings can be a multi-million dollar proposition. Clearly the design of the production strategy is dependent upon accurate interpretation of the fault geometry and sealing properties. Here we demonstrate how models of fault slip distributions developed by structural geologists can be helpful in making such design decisions.

The two compartments of the Brent reservoir in the Oseberg Syd Field are labeled in Fig. 1.10 as Omega North and South. Both are bounded to the west and east by major faults, presumed to be sealing. Data from well No. 8, which intersects the Brent Formation in Omega North, and data from well No. 10, which intersects the formation in Omega South, suggest that there is a fluid pressure difference between the northern and southern compartments. However, the interpreted fault pattern does not define a complete compartment. The two northwest–southeast striking faults just to the southwest of Well No. 8 do not form a complete barrier between Omega South and Omega North. Perhaps there are other explanations for the pressure difference, but the hypothesis investigated here is that these two faults are actually linked and thereby separate the reservoir into two compartments.

This hypothesis was tested using a mechanical model that relates fault geometry, rock properties, and tectonic loading to fault slip (Crider and Pollard, 1998; Maerten *et al.*, 2000; Crider, 2001). The modeling method subdivides faults into many small triangular elements, as seen for a non-planar fault with irregular tipline in Fig. 1.11, and these elements approximate the three-dimensional geometry. The model is based on elasticity theory and the numerical method used to solve the governing equations is called the *boundary element method* (Crouch and Starfield, 1983). Each element

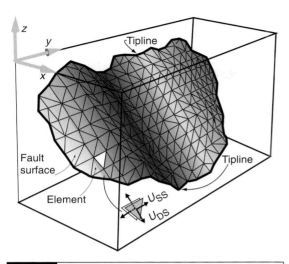

Fig 1.11 Model of a normal fault taken from seismic data and analyzed using the boundary element code Poly3D. In this illustration the fault has an irregular tipline and an irregular surface. The fault surface is divided into many small triangular boundary elements. Inset: Dip slip, U_{DS}, and strike slip, U_{SS}, are constant on an element but vary from element to element to model the slip distribution on the fault. Reprinted from Maerten et al. (2002) with permission from Elsevier.

may be assigned a strike slip, U_{SS}, and a dip slip, U_{DS}, component (Fig. 1.11, inset) based on the available data, or the magnitude and direction of the shear stress drop during slip may be assigned. Given these local boundary conditions and the state of stress or strain in the region before slip on the faults, the numerical method solves the elastic boundary value problem for the displacement, strain, and stress fields in the region surrounding the fault.

The basis for the investigation was the three-dimensional seismic data set used for the original interpretation of the faults and the sedimentary horizons in the Oseberg Syd Field. From this interpretation the geometries of faults A, B, and C were defined and visualized (Fig. 1.12). These faults are not planar structures, nor are their tiplines simple elliptical shapes. The slip on model fault A, as interpreted using the offset of reflecting horizons on the seismic data, was examined and contoured to produce the slip distribution in Fig. 1.12a. This slip distribution is somewhat unusual in that it has three distinct maxima, each defined by a set of

closed contours distributed along the fault at about mid-height. On a single fault that is isolated from its neighbors one would expect a single maximum in slip located more or less at the center of the fault.

The geometry of faults A, B, and C were represented in the model as originally interpreted from the seismic data. The slip distribution on fault A (Fig. 1.12b) was computed by imposing boundary conditions on the model that are consistent with the overall deformation recorded by the fault heaves across the entire Oseberg Syd Field. The interpreted slip distribution on fault A and the computed slip distribution on model fault A are roughly similar, but only two of the three maxima are seen in the model distribution. The fact that the intersection of faults A and C produced two maxima suggests that fault B extends to the southeast until it truncates against fault A. The computed slip distribution for this new model geometry (Fig. 1.12c) has three maxima, one on each side of the two lines of intersection of faults B and C with fault A. The model slip distribution and the interpreted slip distribution are not identical, but the major features are remarkably similar. This correspondence suggests that it would be well worth the effort to look again at the seismic data to determine if the linkage of fault B with fault A is permitted by the data. Fault B could extend and link, but have slip that is below the resolution of the data. Or, the seismic interpreter could have overlooked the linkage. It would also be worth checking to see if the slip distribution on fault B is suggestive of linkage with fault A.

The mechanical models described here provide encouraging results for the further evaluation of the geometry of sealing faults. In addition, as small-scale opening fractures, and their counterpart compaction bands, propagate through reservoirs they can have a significant effect on bulk permeability (Taylor et al., 1999; Aydin, 2000; Taylor and Pollard, 2000). Working out the relationships among the faults that can be imaged using seismic techniques and these sub-seismic fractures is a challenging task. One can easily imagine how structural geologists and geophysicists, working together with high-quality three-dimensional seismic data, could improve the

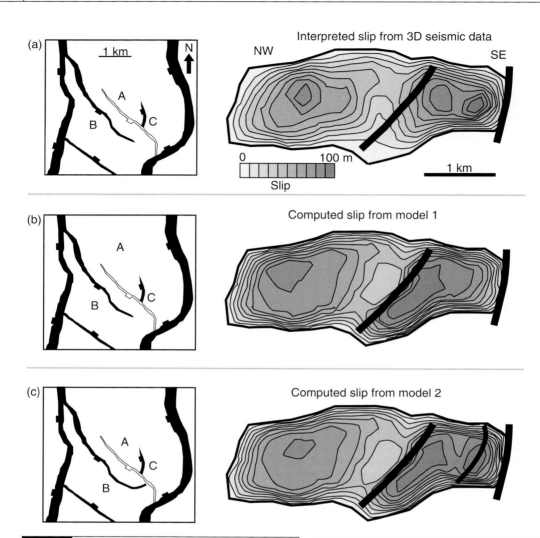

Fig 1.12 Fault maps and slip distributions on fault A between Omega North and Omega South in the Oseberg Syd Field in the northern North Sea. (a) Slip as determined by interpretation of seismic reflection data. (b) Slip from a boundary element model that includes faults A, B, and C as interpreted. (c) Slip for a boundary element model that extends fault B to link with fault A. See website for color image. Reprinted from Maerten *et al.* (2002) with permission from Elsevier.

interpretation of fault and fracture geometries and provide input for a more effective production strategy. Using models to clarify the geometry of faults in hydrocarbon reservoirs is a timely example of an application of modern structural geology to a problem of economic importance to society.

1.4 | Anticracks in southern France

Mapping, describing, and analyzing geologic structures can help one appreciate new and beautiful facets of the natural world. One of the great scientists of the early twentieth century, Henri Poincaré, said it this way:

The scientist does not study nature because it is useful to do so. He studies it because he takes pleasure in it; and he takes pleasure in it because it is beautiful. If nature were not beautiful, it would not be worth knowing and life would not be worth living ... It is because simplicity and vastness are both beautiful that we seek by preference simple facts and vast facts; that we take delight, now in following the giant courses of the stars, now in scrutinizing with a microscope that prodigious small-

Fig 1.13 Outcrop photograph from Les Matelles in southern France showing three small faults with traces parallel to the top of the photograph. Each fault has an antisymmetric distribution of veins (filled with white calcite) and solution surfaces (dark wavy bands). See website for color image. Photograph by J.-P. Petit. Reprinted from Petit and Mattauer (1995) with permission from Elsevier.

ness which is also a vastness, and now in seeking in geological ages the traces of the past that attracts us because of its remoteness (Chandrasekhar, 1979).

Once bitten by the "bug" of structural geology it is impossible to walk up to an outcrop displaying a particularly ornate structure or complex structural relationship (for example, as pictured in Fig. 1.13) and not exclaim: "WOW, look at this!" Such was the reaction of the authors of this textbook to the outcrops of Jurassic limestone exposed at Les Matelles in the Languedoc region of southern France (Petit and Mattauer, 1995). Actually, our first glimpse of these structures came by way of an article in the journal *Tectonophysics* (Rispoli, 1981). We were working at the US Geological Survey in Menlo Park, California, when the article appeared and both of us were immediately captivated by the systematic geometrical relationships among the structures illustrated on the published maps. Despite the fact that we were working on quite different problems for the Earthquake Studies Branch of the Survey at the time, we resolved to seek an explanation for the systematic relationships among these small structures.

1.4.1 Cracks and anticracks

The structures pictured in Fig. 1.13 include three small faults, each about 20 cm in trace length and

oriented parallel to the bottom of the photograph. Parts of these faults are highlighted in the photograph because they contain a thin layer of white calcite between the two surfaces of the faults. Near the left termination of the middle fault two thin white structures extend toward the lower left-hand corner of the photograph. They have tapered shapes, being thickest at the fault and thinning with distance from the fault to zero at their distal terminations. These structures are interpreted as *veins* that broke open the limestone and propagated away from the fault. Each vein filled with groundwater from the surrounding rock mass because opening reduced the local fluid pressure, and the mineral calcite was precipitated from this solution. Note that a few veins also trend toward the upper right-hand corner of the photograph from near the right-hand termination of this small fault.

Very different looking structures extend from near the left-hand termination of the fault toward the upper left-hand corner of the photograph. Instead of smoothly tapered cracks with white fillings, these structures are less regular and are marked by dark blotches. The dark material is made up of insoluble minerals, probably clays that are found dispersed throughout the limestone in minor quantities. Here they are concentrated within what is called a *solution seam*, composed of two surfaces of limestone on either side of the insoluble material. As the name implies this structure is interpreted as forming where the limestone has dissolved and the soluble components (calcium carbonate) have been transported away in the groundwater, either by diffusion within stagnant groundwater or by groundwater flow, leaving the insoluble minerals (Rutter, 1983; Mardon, 1988).

1.4.2 Conceptual and mechanical models for veins and solution surfaces near a fault

The combination of veins, solution surfaces, and fault is depicted in the conceptual model shown schematically in Fig. 1.14. We understand that vein surfaces move away from one another as the vein opens. On the other hand, we can think of the solution surfaces as closing or *anticracks*. As limestone dissolved at the surfaces and was transported away

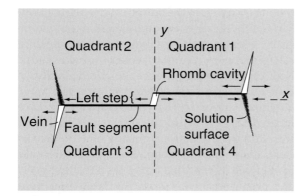

Fig 1.14 Schematic illustration of a left-lateral fault with veins and solution surfaces emanating from the fault tips in an antisymmetric pattern (Fletcher and Pollard, 1981). Pairs of arrows indicate stretching or shortening of the rock associated with slip on the fault. This deformation is accommodated by the formation of the veins and solution surfaces, respectively.

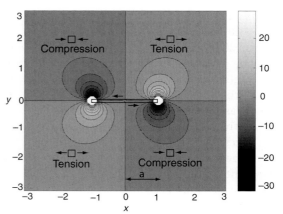

Fig 1.15 Contour map of the normal stress acting parallel to a fault modeled as a surface of displacement discontinuity with uniform left-lateral slip (Crouch and Starfield, 1983). Note the pattern of tensile stress (positive) in the first and third quadrants, and compressive stress (negative) in the second and fourth quadrants. Also note that the stress magnitudes increase toward the model fault tips. See website for color image.

in the groundwater, the material to either side of the solution surface moved inward. Note how the veins and solution surfaces are distributed into the four quadrants defined by a coordinate system centered on the fault with the x-axis parallel to the trace of the fault. The conceptual model consists of a system of cracks and anticracks distributed about the small fault in what is called an anti-symmetric configuration. The presence of veins and solution surfaces with this particular anti-symmetric arrangement is diagnostic of *left-lateral slip* on the fault. If the veins are in the second and fourth quadrants, and the solution surfaces are in the first and third quadrants, the arrangement is diagnostic of *right-lateral slip*.

Our conceptual model for the relative motion of the surfaces of the cracks and anticracks (Fig. 1.14) suggests that the limestone in the first and third quadrants extended parallel to the fault and the limestone in the second and fourth quadrants contracted parallel to the fault. How do these deformations relate to the state of stress? Why do these structures initiate near the fault termina-tions and propagate outward into these quad-rants? Why do the structures stop propagating at a short distance from the fault? These and other questions can be addressed with a mechanical model for the state of stress near a fault.

Laboratory investigations have shown that the mechanical response of rock to stress is, in part, dependent upon the magnitude of the normal stress. For example, modest positive values of the normal stress (on the order of 1 to 10 MPa) corre-late with extension of the rock mass and the devel-opment of opening cracks. As the normal stress becomes more compressive, pressure solution may become an active deformation mechanism in rocks with soluble components. Although the exact magnitudes of the tensile and compressive stresses necessary to induce these structures is not well known, it is clear that tension is neces-sary to induce opening cracks and compression is necessary to induce solution surfaces.

The mechanical model we employ consists of a single two-dimensional fault (Fig. 1.15) with left-lateral relative motion (Pollard and Segall, 1987). The normal stress acting on planes perpendicular to the model fault is calculated on a grid of points, and these values are contoured to produce the figure. The contours appear symmetric about the model fault, but note that the stress is, in fact, dis-continuous across the fault surfaces, having the same magnitude but opposite sign for adjacent points on the two surfaces. The stress, as indicated by the values associated with each contour, is positive (tensile) in the first and third quadrants and negative (compressive) in the second and fourth quadrants. Furthermore there is a *stress concentration* at the terminations of the model fault: the values associated with the contours increase toward the fault tip and the spacing between contours decreases. In fact the stress becomes so great very near the model fault tips that the contours merge into a pattern that is no longer distinguishable at the scale of this figure. Thus we have omitted the contouring in a small region around each tip.

Figure 1.15 is an example of a plot prepared using MATLAB®, the computational and graphics engine that we employ throughout this textbook. The m-file used to compute the values of the stress component at the grid points and to prepare the contour plot is available at the textbook website. There, a color version of the contour plot is viewable along with contour plots of other stress components. This procedure is followed throughout the textbook where grayscale figures are used to reduce printing costs and color versions are available at the website.

To relate the veins and solution surfaces at the Les Matelles outcrop to the left-lateral faults we have to recognize that the veins and solution surfaces are *secondary structures* and the faults are the *primary structures*. In other words, the veins and solution surfaces formed in response to the stress changes in the rock mass as slip developed on the faults. We can correlate the symmetry of these secondary structures with the symmetry of the stress field about the model fault (Fig. 1.15). The veins are cracks that are pulled open by tensile stresses and therefore are associated with the field of tensile stress in quadrants 1 and 3. Conversely, the solution surfaces form in response to elevated compressive stresses and therefore are associated with the field of compressive stress in quadrants 2 and 4.

The correlation between the model and the exposure observations is supported by the fact that the veins and solution surfaces do not cross the fault surfaces where the model indicates a discontinuity (change in sign) of the stress. Furthermore, the model provides an explanation for the initiation of these secondary structures near the terminations of the faults. This is the region of greatest stress concentration, and therefore is the locality where secondary structures are most likely to form. Finally, the stress distribution offers an explanation for the limited extent of the secondary structures. The stress decreases away from the fault tips toward much lower values at a distance that scales with the length of the fault. This decrease in stress is consistent with the termination of the veins and solution surfaces at modest distances from the fault tips. Although this two-dimensional model provides important insights, additional understanding of the faulting process may be achieved using three-dimensional models (Willemse *et al.*, 1996; Willemse, 1997; Martel and Boger, 1998).

The authors became intrigued by the structures at Les Matelles over twenty years ago and, in the course of investigating models for their formation, conceived of the concept of anticracks. At that time we had no practical applications for this concept in mind. Nor, to our knowledge, did the exposure at Les Matelles figure significantly in the solution of any problem relevant to society. For us this was an academic exercise, motivated by a strong (and inexplicable) urge to understand these structures, and nothing more. However, explanations for certain features of very deep and large-magnitude earthquakes now utilize the concept of anticracks (Green and Burnley, 1989). Also, the evolution of fault zones in limestone through a complex sequence of vein development, solution surface development, and slip on solution surfaces has been documented and interpreted using the anticrack concept (Willemse *et al.*, 1996). In addition, the development of compaction bands in porous sandstone has been explained using the anticrack concept (Mollema and Antonellini, 1996). These tabular zones of localized compaction appear to propagate as anticracks in response to elevated compression, and they also have a significant effect on the permeability of reservoirs and aquifers in porous sandstone (Sternlof *et al.*, 2004). Perhaps the time and the taxpayers' dollars spent working on the seemingly arcane concept of anticracks at the Earthquake Studies Branch of the US Geological Survey can be justified in light of these applications.

1.5 | Mountain building on the Colorado Plateau

We are geologists because we love beautiful mineral specimens or fine fossils or magnificent mountains (Woodford, 1956).

Many structural geologists would argue that the premier research topic in this discipline is mountain building. Mountain building produces many of the most dramatic landscapes on our planet and provides countless opportunities to escape from urban settings into the wilderness for different forms of recreation. Mountains profoundly affect local climates and provide challenges to builders of roads and dams. Few can say that their lives are not affected in some way by mountains. The obvious question is: why are they there? No single answer is credible and geologists have identified several tectonic processes that lead to mountain building. Here we describe one such process because it is rather simple to understand and because it informs us about an interesting chapter in the development of structural geology in the latter half of the nineteenth century.

Our story begins when John Wesley Powell stopped briefly on one of his harrowing boat trips down the Colorado River (1869–71) and climbed up out of the deep canyon to look around. Across the plateau country of southern Utah Powell saw several mountain peaks, capped with massive gray rock that clearly was not sedimentary. One of the nearby peaks, later named Mt. Hillers, is shown on the frontispiece for this chapter. Powell gave the range a name, the Henry Mountains, in honor of the distinguished physicist Joseph Henry. In hindsight it is fitting that this range, which would reveal to others one of the fundamental physical processes of mountain building, should be named for a physicist.

Figure 1.16 is a geological map of the region Powell could see from his perch on the side of the nearby canyon. The Mesozoic strata of this region range in age from the Permian Cutler Formation through the Upper Cretaceous Mancos Group. Throughout much of the nearby plateau they are inclined just a few degrees to the west, so progressively younger rocks crop out from east to west across this map. Disturbing this simple

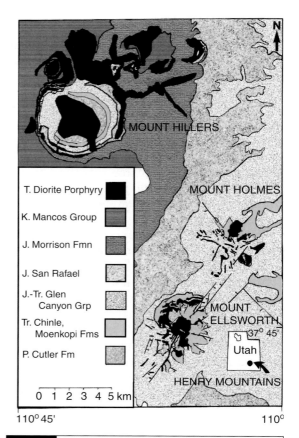

T. Diorite Porphyry

K. Mancos Group

J. Morrison Fmn

J. San Rafael

J.-Tr. Glen Canyon Grp

Tr. Chinle, Moenkopi Fms

P. Cutler Fm

0 1 2 3 4 5 km

110° 45'   110°

Fig 1.16 Simplified geological map of the southern Henry Mountains. Mt. Holmes, Mt. Ellsworth, and Mt. Hillers are structural domes. T, Tertiary; K, Cretaceous; J, Jurassic; Tr, Triassic; P, Permian. Reprinted from Jackson and Pollard (1988) with permission from The Geological Society of America.

"layer-cake" geology are three mountains, Mt. Holmes, Mt. Ellsworth, and Mt. Hillers, each associated with igneous rocks (black on the map). Note how the strata circle Mt. Hillers, with older sedimentary units exposed toward the center of the mountain. This is a clear indication that the mountain is a *structural dome*: the strata have been elevated over the center of the mountain relative to the flanks.

Powell wondered about the origin of these spectacular mountains, but his primary mission was exploration of the river so he did little more than gaze at them from a distance. A few years later, as Chief of the Geological Survey in Washington, DC, Powell sent a young geologist,

Grove Karl Gilbert, to investigate the Wasatch Plateau, just west of the Henry Mountains, and to carry out a topographic and geologic survey of the region. Gilbert's career and his many contributions to geology are described in the book *Grove Karl Gilbert: A Great Engine of Research* (Pyne, 1980). Gilbert worked from horseback covering an area from Salina, Utah, to the western edge of the Henry Mountains from late June to mid August of 1875 (Gilbert, 1877). The chronicle of this trip is clearly laid out in his field notebooks and these have been reproduced and annotated by Charles Hunt (Hunt, 1988a).

The frontispiece from Gilbert's *Report on the Geology of the Henry Mountains*, published in 1877, is reproduced as an inset on the frontispiece for this chapter. This drawing illustrates the form of the displaced (and now eroded) sedimentary strata forming the structural dome that is M. Ellsworth. The base of this diagram is taken at modern sea level and the strata are broadly divided into four layers: the upper Paleozoic at the bottom, followed by the Triassic and Jurassic, then the Cretaceous, and finally the Tertiary at the top. The near half of the diagram displays the current topography of Mt. Ellsworth and the remote half shows the form of the strata in the structural dome. In the preface to this report Gilbert comments as follows:

Two months would be far too short a period in which to survey a thousand square miles in Pennsylvania or Illinois, but among the Colorado Plateaus it proved sufficient. A few comprehensive views from mountain tops gave the general distribution of the formations, and the remainder of the time was spent in the examination of the localities which best displayed the peculiar features of the structure. So thorough was the display and so satisfactory the examination, that in preparing my report I have felt less than ever before the desire to revisit the field and prove my conclusions by more extended observation (Gilbert, 1877, p. vii).

Those "peculiar features of the structure" revealed the two major processes that shaped the Henry Mountains, upward displacement of the strata and the progress of erosion that carved the mountains as we know them today. As structural geologists it is the first of these processes that captures our attention, while the geomorphologist would naturally focus on the second.

(a)

(b)

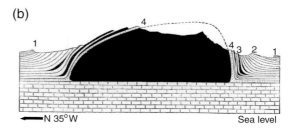

Fig 1.17 Cross sections of Mt. Hillers (Gilbert, 1877, Figs. 25, 26). (a) Only the exposed formations are depicted with appropriate inclinations. (b) Idealized representation of the sub-surface structure showing the bottom of the laccolith and the bending of strata onto the flanks of the dome.

1.5.1 Conceptual and mechanical models for laccolith formation

Although exposures in the three southern Henry Mountains do not reveal the bottoms of the larger masses of igneous rock or the conduits that fed magma into them (Fig. 1.17a), some of the smaller bodies on the flanks of these mountains have well-exposed floors. Based in part on analogy to the smaller intrusions, Gilbert concluded that the uplifted strata of the major domes formed as magma flowed upward from an unknown source, perhaps in dikes, and then spread laterally between two strata as thin sills. Some of these sills continued to thicken by pushing up the overlying strata into structural domes (Fig. 1.17b). The resulting structure was named a laccolite by Gilbert and is now called a *laccolith*. The progression from feeder dike to sill to laccolith, and the concomitant formation of a structural dome, was the new conceptual model for mountain building offered by Gilbert in his 1877 report (Gilbert, 1877).

Gilbert wondered if there was a systematic relationship between the depth of emplacement of a laccolith and its diameter. One might imagine that magma, insinuating between horizontal strata, would find it easier to spread laterally at shallow depths, because there is less overburden. If this conjecture were correct, one would expect to find laccoliths with lesser diameters exposed lower in the stratigraphic sequence. On the other hand one might imagine that magma would have to spread farther at greater depth to gain the leverage necessary to push the overburden upward. If this conjecture were correct, one would expect to find laccoliths with greater diameters exposed lower in the stratigraphic sequence. Both conjectures cannot be correct.

To evaluate these conjectures and thereby clarify the mechanics of laccolith formation Gilbert idealized the laccolith as a cylindrical chamber of magma pushing upward on a rigid piston representing the overlying strata (Fig. 1.18). The mechanical model considers the piston of overburden alone and ignores the dynamics of the magma and the surrounding rock. The boundary of the piston is a cylindrical and vertical fault. The relevant geometric parameters are the diameter of the piston, 2a, and the depth of overburden, d, above the base of the laccolith. This depth is equal to the height of the rock piston and the surrounding fault. Note that the slip on this fault would be equal to the thickness of the laccolith. The cylindrical fault is an idealization of what is observed to be a flexure of the strata. We describe the procedure of idealization in the development of mechanical models in the last chapter of this book.

To derive a mechanical relationship between the diameter and depth Gilbert considered the forces acting on the piston and sought a relationship among these forces based on Newton's Laws of Motion (Newton, 1687), in particular Newton's Second Law, $\mathbf{F} = m\mathbf{a}$, where $\mathbf{F}$ is the net force, m is the mass, and $\mathbf{a}$ is the linear acceleration. He simplified this equation by considering the acceleration to be zero. Of course the piston must accelerate as slip develops on the fault, but Gilbert chose to consider the moment just before slip begins, when the upward force due to the magma pressure is just sufficient to balance the weight of the overburden and the shear force resisting slip on the fault. In other words the system is in a state of *mechanical equilibrium*.

The magnitude of the upward force on the

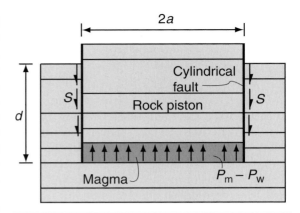

Fig 1.18 Gilbert's piston-cylinder mechanical model for laccolith formation: 2a, piston diameter; d, depth to laccolith bottom; S, shear strength of cylindrical fault; $P_m - P_w$, driving pressure.

base of the piston (Fig. 1.18) is evaluated as the magma pressure, P_m, times the surface area of the piston, πa^2. Recall that pressure is a force per unit area, so this force is simply the pressure times the surface area. The magnitude of the downward directed force along the fault is given by the shear strength, S, times the area of the cylindrical fault, $2\pi a d$. The shear strength is defined as the shear stress acting on the fault just before slip and shear stress is the force per unit area. Finally, the magnitude of the downward directed force due to gravity is given by the pressure, P_w, due to the weight of the piston times the surface area of the piston, πa^2. In these expressions upward directed forces are taken as positive.

Newton's Second Law, for the case of zero acceleration, requires the net force acting on the piston to be zero. Summing the forces identified in the previous paragraph and setting this sum to zero we have the equilibrium equation:

$$(P_m - P_w)\pi a^2 - 2S\pi a d = 0 \tag{1.1}$$

The first term in this equation is the driving force for upward motion of the piston. Clearly the magma pressure must exceed the lithostatic pressure for uplift. The second term is the resisting force due to the shear strength of rock along the fault. Note that the driving force increases as the square of the piston radius, whereas the resisting force increases only in proportion to the radius. For small radii there may be insufficient driving

Table 1.1.	Gilbert's field data on laccolite diameter.		
Zone	Formations	Laccolite name	Diameter (miles)
Upper	Blue Gate Shale	Sentinel	0.7
	Tununk Shale	Geikie	0.8
		A	0.9
		Marvin	1.0
		Jukes	1.4
		Peale	1.8
	Flaming Gorge Shale	Steward	1.0
		B	1.1
		Newberry	1.8
		C	1.9
Lower		Dana	2.0
		Greater Holmes	2.1
		Lesser Holmes	2.1
		Ellsworth	2.3
		Pulpit	2.3
		Maze	2.8
		Crescent	3.6
		Hillers	3.9

force to overcome the resistance to faulting. This does not preclude the lateral growth of a sill, but does preclude the development of the laccolith. From this relationship Gilbert inferred that short sills would be incapable of producing a structural dome of the kind observed in the Henry Mountains. On the other hand if the magma were able to spread far enough laterally as a sill, the driving force would equal the resisting force and, in the next increment of growth, the fault would develop and the overburden would begin to displace upward to form a laccolith.

Solving the equilibrium equation for the radius of the piston, Gilbert found:

$$a = \frac{2dS}{P_m - P_w} \tag{1.2}$$

He noted the linear relationship between piston radius, a, and depth of overburden, d, and inferred that, for a given (positive) driving pressure, $P_m - P_w$, and fault shear strength, S, magma must spread to a greater radius at a greater depth in order for the overburden to be pushed upward along the fault. The second conjecture made above (laccoliths with greater diameters should be found lower in the stratigraphic sequence) is correct according to this model for laccolith formation.

The conceptual and mechanical models formulated by Gilbert for laccolith formation provided him with a linear relationship between the diameter of laccoliths and their depth of burial. He devoted much of his time in the field to gathering data (Table 1.1) on the horizontal dimensions of laccoliths and their stratigraphic positions in order to test this relationship (Gilbert, 1877, p. 86). Although the diameters given in this table are uncertain because of incomplete exposure of the larger laccoliths in the Henry Mountains, Gilbert came to the conclusion that these data were consistent with the relationship he had derived. None of the diameters of laccoliths from the upper zone exceed the diameters of those from the lower zone. For its simplicity and the insight gained from it, this model is remarkably successful.

Many questions about laccolith formation cannot be addressed with Gilbert's model. What are the feeder conduits? How does the sill propagate laterally from this feeder to a diameter where the laccolith can form? At what rate did the magma flow in these conduits? How might one account for the resistance to bending of the strata over the laccolith? How did the temperature vary as the hot magma invaded the cold sedimentary strata? We develop other models in later chapters to address some of these questions.

Because the bottom contacts of the larger igneous intrusions are not exposed, other conceptual models for the development of the structural domes could be viable. Based on geological mapping of the Henry Mountain range and surrounding plateau country, Hunt (1953) proposed that each of the major mountain peaks is underlain by a cylindrical stock of igneous rock that extends well below the bottom contacts that were inferred by Gilbert. This hypothesis has been challenged, based on more recent geological mapping in the southern Henry Mountains and cross sections that were constructed from new structural data (Jackson and Pollard, 1988). The two hypotheses for the shape of the magma chamber, stock or laccolith, were debated in the literature and a variety of geological and geophysical evidence brought to bear on the subject (Hunt, 1988b).

1.6 | Concluding remarks

One of our objectives for this chapter was to introduce a strategy for comprehending complex tectonic processes and their products over relevant length and time scales by combining observational data with both conceptual and mechanical models. For each of the examples given we described the phenomenon and then offered a simple conceptual model that illustrates the key elements of the physical process. Then we described a mechanical model used to understand the physical process. A second objective for this chapter was to illustrate *reductionism*, a scientific methodology in which complex processes are broken up into their (relative few) fundamental elements in order to understand each element in isolation. Then, the elements are put back together to understand how the whole system operates. This methodology is espoused throughout the book.

Some of the topics in the introduction satisfy our objective of demonstrating the possible roles a structural geologist can take in society. For example, career opportunities may be available undertaking geological hazard assessment with the US Geological Survey (USGS), being a member of a production analysis team for an international oil company, or participating in planetary exploration with the National Aeronautics and Space Administration (NASA). We hope that these examples motivate students to learn more about the fundamentals of structural geology by reading this textbook.

Chapter 2

Structural mapping techniques and tools

Structural geologists use a GPS receiver to determine the UTM coordinates of the point under their feet on this outcrop of Aztec sandstone in the Valley of Fire, NV. Photograph by D. D. Pollard.

'You think these raindrops are random?' his uncle had asked. And Leaphorn had been surprised. He'd said of course they were random. Didn't his uncle think they were random?

'The stars,' Haskie Jim said. 'We have a legend about how First Man and First Woman, over by Huerfano Mesa, had the stars in their blanket and were placing them carefully in the sky. And then Coyote grabbed the blanket and whirled it around and flung them into the darkness and that is how the Milky Way was formed. Thus order in the sky became chaos. Random. But even then ... Even then, what Coyote did was evil, but was there not a pattern, too, in the evil deed?'

That had not been the time in Leaphorn's life when he had patience for the old metaphysics. He remembered telling Haskie Jim about modern astronomy and the cosmic mechanics of gravity and velocity. Leaphorn had said something like 'Even so, you couldn't expect to find anything except randomness in the way the rain fell.' And Haskie Jim had watched the rain awhile, silently. And then he had said, and Joe Leaphorn still remembered not just the words but the old man's face when he said them: 'I think from where we stand the rain seems random. If we could stand somewhere else, we would see the order in it.' (Hillerman, 1990, pp. 213–14.)

nlike the laboratory-bound physicist, structural geologists usually make measurements and gather data in the field, where, because of poor exposures and the limited view that erosion provides, structures may seem chaotically arranged. Yet, when each measurement is tied to a particular geographic location and represented on a map, and when sets of measurements are organized by orientation and plotted on an appropriate graph, systematic relationships and patterns emerge that can be interpreted. In making such interpretations we have achieved what Haskie Jim was alluding to, we have found where to stand to view the structures to bring order to what otherwise appears to be a random phenomenon.

In pursuit of this objective we begin this chapter by "finding our bearings" in terms of the coordinate systems commonly employed to locate outcrops in the field and to construct maps of geological structures. This includes an introduction to the geographic coordinate systems used for the Global Positioning System (GPS), which is becoming the standard tool for structural mapping (see frontispiece to Chapter 2). Also, we introduce the Universal Transverse Mercator (UTM) projection, used to project geographic information from the curved surface of the Earth onto a flat piece of paper. Structural geologists should be capable of measuring the location of key exposures where field data are taken, and then constructing the map projections that record the spatial distributions of these data. Structural maps should convey the geometry of structures to other geologists in a form that is quantitatively precise and readily visualized and analyzed.

A position vector uniquely determines the location of every exposure and every point at which structural data are collected in the field. Vectors have many uses in structural geology, from locating an exposure, to describing the shape of folded strata, to representing quantities such as displacement and velocity in the physical laws that underlie the modeling of tectonic processes. The position vector is introduced here along with some of the vector concepts and notations useful for structural mapping. Position vectors are defined with reference to a particular coordinate system. UTM coordinates may not be the best choice during a mapping campaign, and usually they are not the most convenient for modeling and data analysis. To change from one coordinate system to another one uses transformation equations, which make use of vector concepts and operations.

Because much of the structural information recorded at exposures can be reduced to the orientations in space of planar or linear elements, we introduce the techniques to measure, record, and analyze these orientations. Special projections are used to depict a set of orientations on a flat piece of paper – a common one being the stereographic projection. Here, the basic procedures for plotting orientation data on a stereogram are described in such a way that they can be implemented on a computer. Combinations of structural maps and stereograms are used to visualize, respectively, the spatial distributions and the orientations of geological structures. Examples are provided to illustrate how this can be done.

Finally we describe a modern mapping campaign that utilizes GPS technology to create a precise structure contour map in a region where four sets of faults intersect to disrupt and fold the surrounding strata. With new technology the mapping was accomplished in a fraction of the time required using traditional methods, with much greater control on the shapes of the deformed strata and on the fault offsets and slip directions because of the abundance of quantitative data. The GPS technology is rapidly evolving so we anticipate a new generation of structural maps that will provide the impetus for more specific modeling of tectonic processes and the data better to constrain those models.

2.1 | Geographic coordinates and map projections

2.1.1 Geographic coordinates: the Global Positioning System (GPS)

The first order of business for any mapping project is to locate oneself on Earth's surface, either to identify the positions of outcrops or sampling localities, or simply to avoid getting lost! For mapping or sampling on the Earth's surface it is common to use a geographic coordinate system based on lines of constant *latitude* and *longitude* (Fig. 2.1a). Lines of constant latitude trend from east to west and are numbered in degrees, 0 to 90°, both north and south from the equator to the poles. Lines of constant longitude trend from north to south and pass through the poles. They are numbered in degrees, 0 to 180°, both east and west from Greenwich, UK, so there are 360° in total. To be more precise in locating position on the Earth's surface, each degree is subdivided into sixty minutes ($1° = 60'$) and each minute is sub-divided into sixty seconds ($1' = 60''$).

The scheme of subdividing circles, such as the lines of latitude or longitude, into 360 sectors dates back at least to the ancient Babylonians (Beckmann, 1971), who used a base 60 numbering system. Imagine having to recall sixty different names for your basic counting numbers! The Babylonians knew that the perimeter of a hexagon is exactly equal to six times the radius, R, of the cir-cumscribed circle (Fig. 2.1c). Apparently thinking that each equilateral triangle with side length R defines a "unit" sector of the circle, they divided each of the six sectors of the circumscribed circle into 60 sub-sectors, based upon their numbering system, and this results in 360 sub-sectors for the entire circle. This system defies the simple power of ten relationships of a metric system, but we are stuck with it.

We indicate latitude and longitude on the edges of some of the maps used in this text when they cover sufficient area to warrant this coordi-nate system (Fig. 2.1b). Note how the lines of con-stant longitude in this example are designated to be west (W) of Greenwich and the lines of constant latitude are designated to be north (N) of the equator. Distance above or below the chosen *datum* usually is indicated on such a map using *topographic contours*, lines of equal elevation, to produce a topographic map. Here the contour interval is 100 m and the datum is mean sea level. The two geographic coordinates, elevation, and datum completely define the location of the outcrop at the point Q:

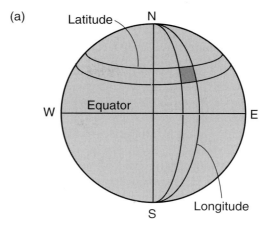
(a)

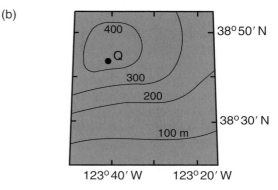
(b)

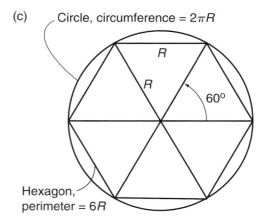
(c)

Fig 2.1 Geographic coordinates consisting of latitude, longitude, and elevation. (a) Lines of constant latitude and longitude. (b) Topographic map with a datum of mean sea level and contour interval of 100 m. (c) Hexagon with circumscribed circle used by Babylonians to divide the circle into 360 sectors.

Latitude: 38° 45′ N
Longitude: 123° 42′ W
Elevation (mean sea level datum): 425 m

Note that the precision of the location given here is only to the nearest degree and the elevation is extrapolated from contours with 100 m intervals (not very precise).

The convention in geodesy is to use a mathematical model for the Earth's shape that is oblate ellipsoidal: a three-dimensional surface formed by rotating an ellipse about its minor axis. If the semi-major and semi-minor axes of the ellipse are called a and b, respectively, the compression or flattening of the ellipsoid at the poles is defined as $f = (a - b)/a$. The rotation of the Earth does cause some extension of the equatorial radius and some flattening at the poles so $a > b$, and the semi-major axis is the radius of the equatorial circle of the ellipsoid. A standard model used by geodesists is called the Geodetic Reference System 1980 ellipsoid, or GRS-80 for short (Hofmann-Wellenhof *et al.*, 1997, p. 293). The center of GRS-80 is located at the true center of the Earth and the semi-minor axis is parallel to the Earth's axis of rotation (Fig. 2.2a). The length of the semi-minor axis is $b = 6\,356\,752.3$ m, and the length of the semi-major axis, extending from the center of the Earth to the equator, is $a = 6\,378\,137.0$ m. Note that this ellipsoid is flattened only by 21 384.7 m (about 21 km) so $f = 0.003\,352\,8$. In other words the ellipsoid is only about 0.3% different than a perfect sphere. An early ellipsoidal model for Earth was calculated in 1830 by Everest, working in India, where he estimated $a = 6\,377\,276$ m and $b = 6\,356\,075$ m, so the flattening is $f = 0.003\,324\,4$ (Richardus and Adler, 1972, p. 23). Different ellipsoids are used in different regions because they minimize discrepancies with the local geoid.

To put the degree–minute–second measures of distance in perspective we use the semi-major axis of GRS-80 as the radius, R, of the equatorial circle, and calculate the circumference as $C = 2\pi R = 40\,075\,016.7$ m. The following relationships are found for distances along this equator:

1 degree = 111 319.5 m
1 minute = 1 855.3 m
1 second = 30.9 m

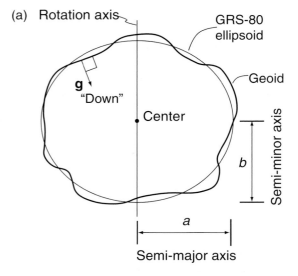

(a)

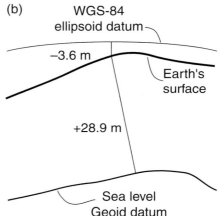

(b)

Different elevations of the geology building at Stanford University

Fig 2.2 Cross section of Earth. (a) Mathematical model ellipsoid and physically defined geoid. Local gravitational acceleration vector, **g**, defines "down". (b) Elevations of Geology Building at Stanford University relative to different datums.

These odd values and the awkwardness of converting degrees–minutes–seconds to standard distance units make this geographic coordinate system less than ideal, but it is conventional to use it and conventions of this long standing (perhaps three to four thousand years) are difficult to abandon.

The third coordinate in the geographic system is approximately parallel to a radial line from Earth's center and is referred to as *elevation*. Often, elevation is referenced to a *sea level datum*, that is mean sea level as determined by tidal gauges. This is not an unreasonable choice, but it is subject to perturbations caused by water temperature variations and currents, and it is limited in applications to the coastline. So-called *leveling surveys* are performed to determine elevations away from the coast as heights above (or below) another datum called the *geoid*. The geoid is a physically defined surface (Fig. 2.2a) that is everywhere perpendicular to the local direction of the acceleration of gravity, **g**, so it is everywhere perpendicular to the direction we call "down" from observations of falling objects. Leveling instruments (for example a bubble level) are capable of very precise determinations of the local direction of gravity and therefore can determine the shape of the geoid. For a fluid Earth, the geoid would be a perfect ellipsoid, but the Earth's geoid has a very irregular shape. These irregularities mean that the local direction of gravitational acceleration ("down") does not point directly toward the center of the Earth. Indeed, this acceleration varies from place to place, because of topography and variable rock density. In some applications the particular geoid chosen as the datum is the one that best approximates mean sea level at the nearest coastline.

Thus, an important question to ask about elevations is: what is the datum? Is it a mathematically defined ellipsoid or a physically defined geoid (see Fig. 2.2a)? This information should be provided on any map that depicts elevation. On many older maps in the continental United States, for example, the datum used is the North American Datum for 1927 (NAD-27). This coincides with the ellipsoid that closely approximates the geoid in North America, but the center of this ellipsoid is about 100 m from the actual center of the Earth. Another familiar datum is the North American Datum for 1983 (NAD-83) that appears, for example, on many topographic and geologic maps published by the US Geological Survey. Today the datum used for the *Global Positioning System* (GPS) is the World Geodetic

System datum for 1984 (WGS-84) and this is almost identical to the ellipsoid called GRS-80. However, this ellipsoid may be separated from the mean sea level geoid by a considerable distance. For example, the WGS-84 ellipsoid is about 32.5 m above the mean sea level geoid at Stanford University in central California (Fig. 2.2b). Thus, the reported elevation relative to the WGS-84 datum for a location just outside the Geology Building at Stanford University using a high-precision GPS receiver is −3.6 m, but the building clearly is not below sea level! The elevation relative to the mean sea level geoid is about +28.9 m. This difference is not due to errors in measurement, but rather to use of the different datums.

A metric coordinate system for location on the Earth's surface is becoming popular because of the accessibility of inexpensive receivers for the GPS and the fact that a metric system is easier to manipulate. The GPS provides locations by measuring the times of travel of radio signals from a set of satellites to a receiving antenna held at the desired location (Hofmann-Wellenhof *et al.*, 1997). The travel time measurement requires very precise (atomic) clocks on the satellites and sophisticated electronic techniques for synchronizing the clock in the receiver to the satellite clocks. Using these clocks, the time of sending and receiving a radio signal from a particular satellite can be differenced to compute the travel time, t, for the signal from that satellite. Knowing the velocity of the radio signal, v, corrected for atmospheric delays, and the travel time, t, the distance from the antenna to that satellite is computed as $d = vt$. Knowing the positions of all the satellites (provided by the government operators of the system) and the respective distances from the antenna to each satellite, the location of the antenna can be computed. A minimum of three satellite distances is required for one location, but most systems use four or more distances. The redundant data are used to refine the precision of the location.

Locations can be determined to better than ±1 m using portable receivers, and these are an excellent choice for mapping most geological structures (Chapter 2 Frontispiece). The two geologists shown on the frontispiece for this chapter are standing on an exposure of Aztec sandstone in the Valley of Fire, Utah. The GPS antenna, seen just above the left-hand shoulder of one of the geologists, is on a short mast extending from the geologist's backpack. In the geologist's hands is the computer used to enter data and control the receiver. The most precise (geodetic grade) GPS provide locations to about ± 0.01 m using equipment transported in vehicles and set up over stable benchmarks. The more precise measurements are done using a technique of *differential corrections* that reduces errors by comparing the signal received by the roving antenna to the signal received at a nearby base station where the location is fixed and well known.

At the time of publication of this book the GPS is the preferred technology for locating one's position on Earth's surface while mapping geological structures. Because this is a rapidly developing technology we have only described the rudimentary features of the system and refer interested readers to books and manufacturers' manuals for details concerning usage, precision, and instrumentation (Committee on the Future of the Global Positioning System, 1995; Hofmann-Wellenhof *et al.*, 1997).

2.1.2 Map projections: the Universal Transverse Mercator (UTM) projection

Different forms of *map projections* are used to depict geographic information located on Earth's curved surface on a flat piece of paper (Alpha *et al.*, 1988). This procedure is a necessary and crucial part of making maps that accurately record and convey the field data of structural geology. In this section we describe what is meant by map projection, discuss some of the complications of this procedure, and provide some illustrative examples. In particular we describe the UTM projection, which is becoming the standard for geological and topographical maps.

A curved surface is taken as the datum, either a spherical or an ellipsoidal model of Earth, and the projection surface is taken as a plane, cone, or cylinder that is tangent to the datum (Richardus and Adler, 1972). The cone and cylinder are wrapped around the datum for projec-

tion and then are "unwrapped" to a flat sheet for display. The projection is done primarily for convenience, to avoid having to use three-dimensional representations such as globes. Ideally one would want the map projection to represent geographic information without distortion. For example, any two curves of equal length on the sphere (or ellipsoid) should project to two curves of equal length on the flat map. This cartographic criterion is called *equidistance* because such a projection correctly represents distances. The cartographic criterion called *conformality* refers to the correct representation of shapes on the map and requires that angles on the sphere (or ellipsoid) project to the same angles on the map. The third cartographic criterion, *equivalency*, requires the correct representation of areas from the sphere (or ellipsoid) to the map. Unfortunately, it is generally not possible to achieve undistorted representations that meet all three criteria simultaneously; so different projections (apparently there are about two hundred in use) are chosen for different purposes with the objective of minimizing the distortion or honoring one or other of the three cartographic criteria (Richardus and Adler, 1972).

To illustrate the procedure of projection we consider a spherical datum of radius R, take the so-called perspective point (view point) as the center of the sphere, C, and project points from the sphere onto a plane that is tangent to the sphere at the point O (Fig. 2.3a). The point O should be centrally located within the region where structural mapping is planned. The north pole of the sphere is labeled N. Points on the sphere are projected to the plane along straight lines that emanate from the perspective point. This is called the *gnomonic projection* and it is one member of the class of azimuthal projections that provide images similar to what one would observe on a photograph taken from space along a line of sight coincident with the normal to the datum ellipsoid or sphere at the point O (Richardus and Adler, 1972, Chapter 4). Among the attributes of the gnomonic projection is the fact that directions from the point O are not distorted. Also, straight lines from this point represent arcs of great circles (the intersections of the sphere with planes that pass

(a)

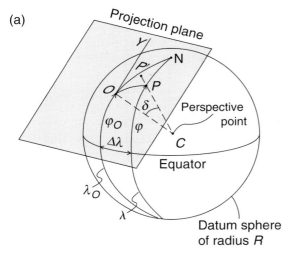

(b)

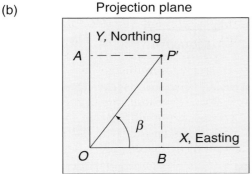

Fig 2.3 The gnomonic projection (Richardus and Adler, 1972). (a) Spherical datum with projection plane tangent to the sphere at point O. Symbols are identified in the text. (b) Cartesian coordinates (X, Y) of the projection plane.

define the Cartesian coordinates (X, Y) of projected points in terms of the geographic coordinates of points on the sphere.

Consider an arbitrary point, $P(\varphi, \lambda)$, on the sphere (Fig. 2.3a) with latitude, φ, and longitude, λ. Since the origin may lie on any meridian, the relative longitude of P is determined by the difference, $\Delta\lambda = \lambda - \lambda_0$, between the longitude of the meridian passing through the origin and that passing through the point P. Use is made of the angle δ measured from the radial line CO to the radial line CP'. The point P' is the projection of the point P onto the projection plane. The angle β is measured in the projection plane from OX to the line OP' (Fig. 2.3b). The Cartesian coordinates of the projected point, $P'(X, Y)$, are derived from the trigonometry of Fig. 2.3 as functions of the radius, R, and the two angles δ and β (Richardus and Adler, 1972, p. 59):

$$X = OB = OP' \cos \beta = R \tan \delta \cos \beta = \frac{R \sin \delta \, \cos \beta}{\cos \delta}$$

$$Y = OA = OP' \sin \beta = R \tan \delta \sin \beta = \frac{R \sin \delta \, \sin \beta}{\cos \delta} \tag{2.1}$$

In terms of the geographic coordinates, latitude and longitude, the Cartesian coordinates of the point P' on the projection plane are (Richardus and Adler, 1972, p. 59):

$$X = \frac{R(\cos \varphi \sin \Delta\lambda)}{\sin \varphi_0 \sin \varphi + \cos \varphi_0 \cos \varphi \cos \Delta\lambda}$$

$$Y = \frac{R(\cos \varphi_0 \sin \varphi - \sin \varphi_0 \cos \varphi \cos \Delta\lambda)}{\sin \varphi_0 \sin \varphi + \cos \varphi_0 \cos \varphi \cos \Delta\lambda} \tag{2.2}$$

Equations (2.2) are the mapping equations for the gnomonic projection from a spherical datum as illustrated in Fig. 2.3. Given the radius of the datum and the geographic coordinates (latitude, φ, and longitude, λ) of any point on the datum, and the latitude, φ_0, and relative longitude, $\Delta\lambda$, of the origin of the projection plane, these equations provide the Cartesian coordinates of that point on the projection plane (the map). For $\varphi_0 = \pi/2$ the point O is at the north pole and this is referred to as a polar gnomonic projection. For $\varphi_0 = 0$ the point O is on the equator and this is referred to as a transverse gnomonic projection. If the point O is

through the center of the sphere) and therefore the shortest paths from this point to any other on the sphere.

The point $O(\varphi_0, \lambda_0)$ has a latitude φ_0 and longitude λ_0 and lies on an arbitrary meridian of the sphere. This point is the origin of a two-dimensional Cartesian coordinate system on the projection plane (Fig. 2.3b). The X-axis is coincident with the projection of a great circle through O and perpendicular to the central meridian with positive X pointing to the east. The Y-axis is coincident with the projection of this central meridian and positive Y points to the north. The X- and Y-axes are referred to as *easting* and *northing*, respectively. The objective is to

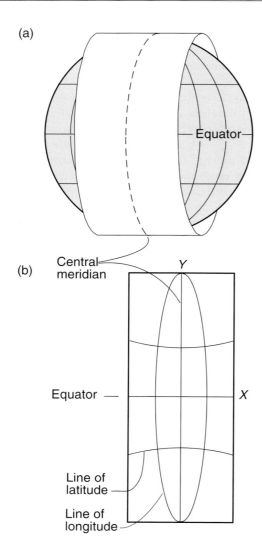

(a)

(b)

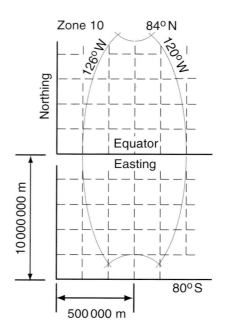

(c)

Fig 2.4 The Transverse Mercator (TM) projection (Hofmann-Wellenhof *et al.*, 1997). (a) Spherical or ellipsoidal datum with right circular cylinder used for projection. (b) Cylinder unwrapped to form the projection plane with lines of latitude and longitude. (c) Universal Transverse Mercator (UTM) grid (dashed lines) superimposed on projection.

on the Greenwich meridian $\Delta\lambda = \lambda$. All forms of this projection are limited in that an entire hemisphere cannot be projected: the boundary of the hemisphere would plot at an infinite distance from the origin.

One of the more common projections in use today is the Transverse Mercator (TM) projection in which a spherical or ellipsoidal datum is projected onto a right circular cylinder. The mathematical procedure used to accomplish the projection is called conformal mapping (Hofmann-Wellenhof *et al.*, 1997, p. 287). As the name implies this transformation and others in this class preserve the angular relations of curves on the datum. The TM projection maps sections of the spherical or ellipsoidal datum onto a cylinder with its axis parallel to the plane of the equator (Fig. 2.4a). The cylinder is tangent to the ellipsoid along a particular line of longitude known as the central meridian. For this projection the equator and the central meridian are straight lines whereas all other lines of longitude and latitude are curved (Fig. 2.4b). Lines of longitude to either side of the central line are concave toward this line. Lines of latitude, other than the equator, are concave toward their respective poles. Because this is a conformal projection the lines of longitude are everywhere orthogonal to the lines of latitude.

Taking a simple example for the sake of illustration consider the TM projection for a spherical datum of radius R. The Cartesian coordinates are chosen so the X-axis is coincident with the equator and Y-axis is coincident with the central meridian. They are related to the latitude, φ, and longitude, λ, as (Richardus and Adler, 1972, p. 101):

$$X = R\tan^{-1}(-\cot\varphi\sin\lambda)$$
$$Y = \frac{1}{2}R\ln\left(\frac{1 + \cos\varphi\cos\lambda}{1 - \cos\varphi\cos\lambda}\right) \tag{2.3}$$

This projection is most appropriate where the mapped objects are organized along a particular meridian, or where the datum can be mapped separately in narrow strips aligned with different lines of longitude.

Most GPS receivers have onboard computers that are capable of reporting locations using the so-called *Universal Transverse Mercator* (UTM) projection, which is a modification of the TM projection. The UTM system was designed to meet a number of criteria including conformality to minimize directional errors, a minimum number of zones, limited errors in scale, a common referencing grid, and limited convergence of lines of longitude toward the poles (Richardus and Adler, 1972, p. 138). The design of this system has proved to be quite good so UTM coordinates are found on most modern maps. To set up the UTM system the Earth is divided into 60 zones (the ancient Babylonians would like this choice!), each spanning 6° of longitude and each extending from 80°S to 84°N, and these zones are individually projected (e.g. Fig. 2.4c). The zones are numbered consecutively toward the east from M1, which spans from 180° W to 174° W longitude, with a central line of longitude at 177° W. Thus, for example, zones M10 through M19 span the United States from just off the west coast (126° W line of longitude) to just off the east coast (66° W line of longitude). The central meridian of zone M10 is 123°W and the central meridian of zone M19 is 69°W. The projection cylinder is tangent to the central meridian if the datum is taken as a sphere.

To establish the UTM coordinates within a particular zone, the central line of longitude and the equator are used as *reference lines* because both of these lines are projected as straight lines and they are orthogonal to one another (Fig. 2.4c). Recall that the other lines of longitude and latitude are projected as curved lines. The *UTM grid* is a Cartesian (rectangular) metric grid overlaid on this projection. The western edge of the UTM grid is a line drawn parallel to the central meridian but 500 000 m (about 4.5°) to the west. The eastern edge of the UTM grid is 500 000 m to the east of the central meridian. Values along this axis are referred to as false eastings because of the shift in origin, and these values are measured parallel to the equator, starting at the western edge of the UTM grid. Thus, the central line of longitude is at a false easting (X-coordinate value) of 500 000 m. Northing is measured in the northern hemisphere from the equator toward the north and parallel to the central line of longitude. In the southern hemisphere the zero northing is shifted to the south, so the equator is at a false northing of 10 000 000 m. Note that for the depiction of zone 10 shown in Fig. 2.4c the easting axis is stretched relative to the northing axis. At true scale the zone in each hemisphere would be a very thin strip that is ten times taller than it is wide.

To specify the UTM coordinates of a particular point on Earth's surface, the hemisphere and the zone number and the datum must be identified, along with the appropriate easting, northing, and elevation. Thus, for example, the UTM coordinates of a location just outside the Geology Building at Stanford University are reported as follows:

Northern hemisphere
Zone M10
Datum WGS-84
Easting: 573 218.49 m
Northing: 4 142 572.31 m
Elevation: −3.6 m

The horizontal precision of the measured coordinates is about ±3 cm for easting and northing and the vertical precision is about ±10 cm. Recall that the mean sea level elevation is about +28.9 m and the negative elevation listed here is referenced to the WGS-84 ellipsoid (Fig. 2.2b).

At the time of writing of this book the UTM projection is the preferred coordinate system for the preparation of geological and structural maps. Formulae to compute the coordinates on the UTM grid given geographic coordinates on an ellipsoidal datum, and to calculate the geographic coordinates on the ellipsoidal datum given the UTM coordinates have been derived (Richardus and Adler, 1972). These take several pages to write down and are not repeated here. Many GPS systems have these formulae built in and make the computations at the push of a button.

2.2 | Local coordinates and position vectors

Points and sets of points can be defined only relative to (i.e., as functions of) a coordinate system, never absolutely. The coordinate system is the unavoidable residue of the eradication of the ego in that geometrico-physical world which reason sifts from the given using "objectivity" as its standard – a final scanty token in this objective sphere that existence is only given and can only be given as the intentional content of the processes of consciousness of a pure, sense-giving ego (Weyl, 1987).

Students first learn to deal with points and sets of points described relative to a chosen coordinate system in elementary courses in mathematics. This procedure was apparently conceived by René Descartes in the early seventeenth century and has become one of the most powerful tools ever developed for scientists and engineers (Davis and Hersh, 1986; Aczel, 2000). In honor of Descartes' contribution the most familiar coordinate system we use is referred to as the *Cartesian coordinate system*. With this coordinate system and the concept of a position vector one can locate outcrops or the point where samples are collected in the field relative to a local origin. In other words the origin is located in the region being mapped or on the actual outcrop for very large-scale mapping, instead of at an arbitrary point determined by a global projection such as the UTM grid. To put the map or data in a global context one transforms the position vectors from the local coordinate system to the UTM system. Here we introduce the position vector, several local coordinate systems, and equations for the transformation from one coordinate system to another because these are basic tools for structural mapping.

It is useful to understand the concept of vectors in general, and to be familiar with specific techniques for manipulating vectors, because structural geologists employ them for modeling as well as mapping. This should come as no surprise because the evolution of geologic structures is primarily a physical process and the physical laws that describe such a process are written as vector equations. This section focuses on position vectors, but also serves as a summary of some general vector concepts that we build upon in later sections where, for example, we use vectors to characterize the shapes of folded geological surfaces and to visualize velocity fields within a deforming rock mass. Other general vector concepts are introduced as needed in later sections and chapters.

2.2.1 Locating data using local coordinates and position vectors

Geographical coordinates, based on the UTM grid, may not be the best choice for mapping in the field, but their use is becoming universal for the final presentation of structural maps. For large-scale maps awkwardness arises because the central line of longitude for each UTM zone is 500 000 m to the east of the origin (Fig. 2.4c), so a typical easting would have six digits with meter precision and eight digits if centimeter precision were required. Similar numbers of digits are required for the northing unless, for example, the location is near the equator in the northern hemisphere. To reduce this cumbersome number of digits it is practical to select a local origin within the mapped region. Local origins are also commonly employed in modeling and data analysis. Furthermore, a local origin may be necessitated by the use of surveying equipment that references locations to the instrument itself rather than the UTM system. Topographical, geological, and structural maps can be prepared using a coordinate system consisting of the easting, northing, and elevation for which the datum is the local elevation of the instrument and the easting and northing are measured in the horizontal plane from a local origin at the instrument site. These maps also can be prepared using a local Cartesian coordinate system with x- and y-axes in the local (horizontal) datum and the z-axis vertical.

As an example consider the region (Fig. 2.5a) near Ship Rock, New Mexico, where volcanic necks and associated igneous dikes crop out in the Mancos Shale of the San Juan Basin (Delaney and Pollard, 1981). In this photograph, taken from the largest volcanic edifice called Ship Rock, three smaller volcanic necks are seen in the foreground and three dikes crop out along low ridges that trend out into the basin to the northeast. A rough scale for the photograph is provided by a one-lane dirt track, about 2 to 3 m wide, that scars the desert landscape just to the south (to the right) of the middle dike. As read from the topographic map for this quadrangle, the UTM coordinates of a point near the western (proximal) termination of this dike, called the northeastern dike, are:

Northern hemisphere
Zone M12
Datum NAD-29
Easting: 694 000 m
Northing: 4 063 000 m
Elevation: 1675 m

The precision of these coordinates is about ±30 m for easting and northing and the vertical precision is about ±5 m. To map the dikes and volcanic necks with greater precision a surveying instrument, such as a *total station*, could be set up at this location and a new origin and datum established at the instrument site. On Fig. 2.5a we have positioned a Cartesian coordinate system there with the (x, y)-plane as the datum. Total stations are capable of determining the local coordinates of points relative to the instrument location over distances up to a few kilometers with precisions ranging from a few centimeters to about a decimeter.

On most geological maps dikes are represented as solid lines with a uniform thickness determined by the diameter of the pen or the minimum line width of the printer used to produce the map, rather than the scaled thickness of the exposed dike. Because dike thickness

(a)

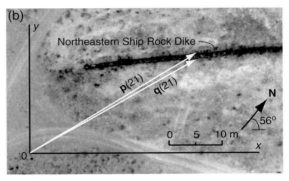

(b)

Fig 2.5 Structural mapping at Ship Rock, NM, using local coordinates and position vectors (Delaney and Pollard, 1981). (a) Photograph of volcanic necks and igneous dikes with local Cartesian coordinate system. (b) Aerial photograph of dike outcrop with local coordinate system and position vectors, **p**(21) and **q**(21), marking contact. Photograph by D. D. Pollard.

plays a crucial role in the mechanics of dike formation this kind of representation is inadequate for structural investigations. The northeastern dike at Ship Rock is composed of thirty-five discrete segments ranging from less than 1 m to about 7 m in thickness with an average of about 2.3 m (Delaney and Pollard, 1981). Therefore, to achieve a precision of about ten percent of the average thickness, say ±20 cm, the two adjacent contacts must be located to within about a decimeter. Instruments were not available in 1980 to survey the contacts directly. Instead, vertical photographs were taken from a low-flying aircraft and the central portions enlarged eight times to yield a map scale of about 1 : 228. Mapping was done directly on the enlarged photos with a pen diameter of about 0.24 mm, equivalent to about 5 cm on the ground. Although the exposure of the

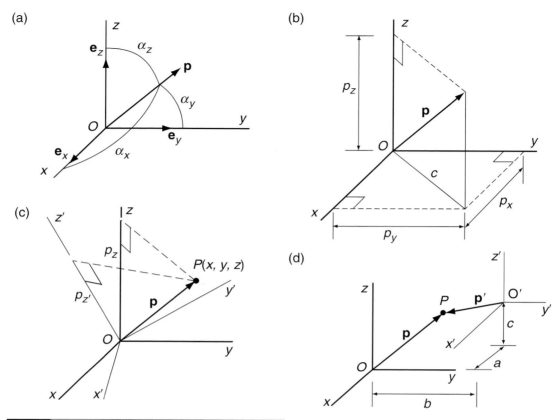

Fig 2.6 The position vector, **p**. (a) Base vectors, **e**, and direction angles, α. (b) Components (p_x, p_y, p_z) of the position vector. (c) Rotation from the (x, y, z) coordinate system to $(x'\,y'\,z')$. (d) Translation of the coordinate system.

dike introduced some uncertainty in locating the contact, this procedure generally provided the required precision. A portion of the first photograph in the series is shown in Fig. 2.5b along with the local coordinate system.

Every point in three-dimensional space is uniquely determined by a *position vector*, **p**, that specifies the position of the point relative to a fixed origin, O (Fig. 2.6a). The position vector is visualized as an arrow extending from the origin to the point. In other words the tail of this vector is at the origin and the head is at the designated point. As with all vectors, the position vector has both a magnitude and a direction. The length of the arrow is drawn proportional to the magnitude, and the shaft and head of the arrow prescribe the direction. In this text, vector quantities are written in boldface type to distinguish them

from scalar quantities, which have a magnitude, and possibly both positive and negative values, but scalars lack a specific direction.

In general, a vector may be written as a linear combination of three *base vectors* and three quantities called the *scalar components* of the vector. For position vectors we choose a set of three mutually orthogonal base vectors $(\mathbf{e}_x, \mathbf{e}_y, \mathbf{e}_z)$ each of unit magnitude and each directed, respectively, from the origin along the positive axes (Ox, Oy, Oz) of a right-handed Cartesian coordinate system (Fig. 2.6a):

$$\mathbf{e}_x = (1, 0, 0), \quad \mathbf{e}_y = (0, 1, 0), \quad \mathbf{e}_z = (0, 0, 1) \qquad (2.4)$$

These equations give the values of the three scalar components for each unit base vector where it is understood that the respective components are for the three coordinate directions (Ox, Oy, Oz). Mutually orthogonal unit base vectors are said to form an *orthonormal basis* (Malvern, 1969). In some notations different symbols are used to distinguish each base vector (e.g. **i**, **j**, **k**), but here a common symbol is used with subscripts to associate each base vector with a particular coordinate direction. Most vector quantities used in this book, such as the position vector or velocity vector, are free to take on any orientation and therefore do not carry subscripts. The coordinate axes, and therefore the base vectors, comprise a right-handed system. By right handed we mean that the axes (Ox, Oy, Oz) extend, respectively, in the same mutual orientations as the thumb, index finger, and middle finger of the right hand when these fingers are directed orthogonal to one another. Base vectors need not be orthogonal to one another nor of unit magnitude, and Cartesian coordinates can be left-handed, but these alternatives are not employed in this book.

The scalar components of a vector are quantities that can be visualized as the orthogonal projections of the vector arrow onto lines in arbitrary but designated directions. In general, scalar components are written with the same symbol as the vector, but the type is not bold and each component has a subscript that identifies the line projected upon. For the position vector, $\mathbf{p}$, the designated directions are parallel to the base vectors (Fig. 2.6b), in other words lines parallel to the respective coordinate axes. The three components of the position vector are written (p_x, p_y, p_z). Thus, the equation for the position vector with the basis ($\mathbf{e}_x$, $\mathbf{e}_y$, $\mathbf{e}_z$) is written as the following linear combination of scalar components and base vectors:

$$\mathbf{p} = p_x\mathbf{e}_x + p_y\mathbf{e}_y + p_z\mathbf{e}_z \qquad (2.5)$$

Although it is convenient to speak of a position vector simply as $\mathbf{p}$, and this notation is useful for writing compact vector equations, most calculations are done using the scalar components. Apparently Descartes introduced the notion of using vector components, defined with respect to a coordinate system in order to develop analytical geometry (Fung, 1969, p. 22).

An arbitrary vector, $\mathbf{v}$, may have its tail at any point (x_1, y_1, z_1) and its head at any other point (x_2, y_2, z_2) so this vector is written:

$$\begin{aligned} \mathbf{v} &= (x_2 - x_1)\mathbf{e}_x + (y_2 - y_1)\mathbf{e}_y + (z_2 - z_1)\mathbf{e}_z \\ &= v_x\mathbf{e}_x + v_y\mathbf{e}_y + v_z\mathbf{e}_z \end{aligned} \qquad (2.6)$$

The quantities (v_x, v_y, v_z) are the scalar components of the vector, which can be interpreted as the orthogonal projections of $\mathbf{v}$ onto lines drawn parallel to the base vectors ($\mathbf{e}_x$, $\mathbf{e}_y$, $\mathbf{e}_z$), respectively. If the two points are coincident $\mathbf{v} = \mathbf{0} = (0, 0, 0)$ is the zero vector.

The meter (m) is the physical unit used to measure distance, and this is carried by the position vector components, not the base vectors. Thus one would write, for example, $p_y = 22.5$ m and $|\mathbf{e}_y| = 1$. Each base vector has a magnitude of one but does not carry a physical unit. The base vectors provide the directional information necessary to compose a position vector. The three-dimensional space defined in terms of position vector components using the basis ($\mathbf{e}_x$, $\mathbf{e}_y$, $\mathbf{e}_z$) is referred to as *Euclidean space* (Lipschutz, 1969).

When the base vectors change direction because of a rotation of the coordinate system about the origin (Fig. 2.6c), the components of the position vector $\mathbf{p}$ for an arbitrary point P change, but the magnitude and direction of the position vector do not change. For example, the projection p_z' of $\mathbf{p}$ onto the rotated coordinate axis Oz' is different from the projection p_z onto the original coordinate axis Oz. Thus we say that (p_x, p_y, p_z) are the components of $\mathbf{p}$ with respect to a particular basis ($\mathbf{e}_x$, $\mathbf{e}_y$, $\mathbf{e}_z$), and this basis must be defined in order to interpret the components. On the other hand if the base vectors and coordinate system are translated to a new origin, O', but not rotated (Fig. 2.6d), a new position vector, $\mathbf{p}'$, extends to the given point, P, and this vector has a different magnitude and/or direction than $\mathbf{p}$. In general, two vectors are equal only if they have the same magnitude and direction, so the position vectors for the point P referred to different origins are not equal, despite the fact that they define the location of the same point. In this sense position vectors are so-called *fixed vectors* (Malvern, 1969): they emanate from a particular point, the origin of the coordinate system, and the location of this origin must be specified in order to define a set of position vectors. Position vectors are useful quantities for defining the locations of points, but they lack the attributes of those vectors that we think of as physical entities, such as force or velocity, which are independent of an arbitrarily defined coordinate system.

The magnitude of any vector is calculated as the square root of the sum of the squares of its scalar components and this quantity is written with the same symbol as the vector but not in boldface type. For the position vector this relationship may be deduced from Fig. 2.6b and the theorem of Pythagoras. The squared length of the position vector is $p^2 = (p_z)^2 + c^2$, but $c^2 = (p_x)^2 + (p_y)^2$. Thus, the magnitude, p, of the position vector $\mathbf{p}$ is:

$$p = |\mathbf{p}| = \sqrt{p_x^2 + p_y^2 + p_z^2} \geq 0 \qquad (2.7)$$

The magnitude of a vector, written symbolically using $|\ |$, is equivalent to the scaled length of the vector arrow, and is always greater than or equal to zero. The components of the position vector are proportional to the vector magnitude and the cosines of the angles that the vector makes with the positive coordinate axes (Fig. 2.6a):

$$p_x = p\cos\alpha_x, \ \ p_y = p\cos\alpha_y, \ \ p_z = p\cos\alpha_z \qquad (2.8)$$

The set of three angles $(\alpha_x, \alpha_y, \alpha_z)$ are called the *direction angles* of the position vector, and the cosines of these angles are referred to as the *direction cosines*. The direction angles are measured in the planes defined by the vector and the respective coordinate axis, and each is taken as the smaller of the two angles between the vector and the positive coordinate axis.

At Ship Rock (Fig. 2.5a), the UTM coordinates of the local origin near the western (proximal) termination of the middle dike are given above. The local Cartesian coordinate system is oriented with the z-axis vertical (upward) and the x-axis directed in an azimuth of 056°, which is approximately parallel to the outcrop trace of the dike. Two sets of position vectors, $\mathbf{p}(i)$ and $\mathbf{q}(i)$, trace out the contact between the Mancos Shale and the igneous rock of the dike with $\mathbf{p}(i)$ along the northwestern side and $\mathbf{q}(i)$ along the southeastern side (Fig. 2.5b). The spacing is about 1 m between members of a given set and there are 2724 members of each set that define the shapes of the thirty-five dike segments. The first few and last few members are given in Table 2.1 and the entire data set is provided at the textbook website.

The z-components of the position vectors are not listed in Table 2.1. In fact the dike outcrop varies in elevation by about 55 m over the nearly 3-km distance from the southwestern to the northeastern termination, and these elevation differences were not measured. In effect one can

Table 2.1. Position vectors for ship rock dike.

Counter, i	p_x (m)	p_y (m)	q_x (m)	q_y (m)
1	3.9	15.7	3.9	15.7
2	4.6	15.4	4.6	16.0
3	5.8	15.4	5.8	16.0
4	7.0	15.3	7.0	16.1
5	8.1	15.2	8.1	16.0
...	...	...	...	...
2720	2900.2	−6.1	2900.2	−4.4
2721	2901.4	−6.2	2901.4	−4.7
2722	2902.5	−6.4	2902.5	−5.0
2723	2903.7	−6.5	2903.7	−5.2
2724	2904.8	−5.9	2904.8	−5.9

think of the photograph-based map as the projection of the dike outcrop onto the (x, y)-datum plane of the local coordinate system. Then, for example, the position vector for the counter $i = 21$, shown in Fig. 2.5b, is written in the form of (2.5) as:

$$\mathbf{p} = p_x\mathbf{e}_x + p_y\mathbf{e}_y = (26.7\,\text{m})\mathbf{e}_x + (18.2\,\text{m})\mathbf{e}_y \qquad (2.9)$$

Because all of the vectors used to quantify the dike contact lie in the (x, y)-plane, the direction angle $\alpha_z = \pi/2$ (Fig. 2.6a) and, for example, using (2.8) and $i = 21$ we have:

$$p_y = p\cos\alpha_y = p\cos\left(\frac{\pi}{2} - \alpha_x\right) = p\sin\alpha_x$$

and

$$p_x = p\cos\alpha_x \qquad (2.10)$$

so

$$\alpha_x = \tan^{-1}(p_y/p_x) = 34.3°$$

For two-dimensional cases only one independent direction angle is required to orient the position vectors.

Digitization of the dike map from Ship Rock is carried out such that the x-components of $\mathbf{p}$ and $\mathbf{q}$ are identical for each value of the counter. Also, the dike segments are approximately parallel to the x-axis of the local coordinate system. Therefore, for a given value of the counter, the dike thickness, $t(i)$, is approximately equal to the difference between the y-components of the two position vectors, which is equal to the magnitude of the vector difference:

$$t(i) \approx p_y(i) - q_y(i) = |\mathbf{p}(i) - \mathbf{q}(i)| \qquad (2.11)$$

This can be understood by considering the general expression for the sum of two vectors:

$$\text{if} \quad \mathbf{r} = \mathbf{v} + \mathbf{w}, \quad \text{then} \quad r_x = v_x + w_x,$$
$$r_y = v_y + w_y, \quad r_z = v_z + w_z \qquad (2.12)$$

The difference of the two vectors may be thought of as $\mathbf{r} = \mathbf{v} + (-\mathbf{w})$. In other words the sum (or difference) of two vectors is a vector with scalar components that are the sum (or difference) of the respective components. This result can be generalized to the sum or difference of any number of vectors. For a given value of the counter the x-components of the position vectors from Table 2.1 are equal, and the z-components are zero for all these vectors, so the magnitude (2.7) of the vector difference reduces to the difference of the y-components. The set of thickness values so determined is used in a mechanical model for the opening of the dike segments that leads to estimates for the stiffness of the host rock (Delaney and Pollard, 1981).

Several segments of the northeastern Ship Rock dike are shown on Fig. 2.7, a structure map using local Cartesian coordinates (Fig. 2.5b). The precise mapping method described above brings out a host of structural features (Delaney and Pollard, 1981) that otherwise would be unrecorded on typical quadrangle-scale maps where thin constant-width lines only display the location and trace of dikes. Instead we note that the dike is composed of sub-parallel but offset segments forming an echelon array. Segments numbered 13 to 15 are offset by a few meters and have blunt, rounded terminations, whereas segments 15 to 21 are offset by as much as 15 m and have more tapered terminations. The contacts of overlapping segments have a distinct asymmetry such that adjacent contacts curve toward their respective terminations and distal contacts are relatively straight. At $x = 1000$ m, on segment 12, both contacts bulge outward to form a putative volcanic neck; and at $x = 1310$ m, on segment 19, one contact bulges outward such that the total thickness almost doubles. Both of these structures are associated with breccias that suggest the local increases in thickness are related to fracturing and brecciation of the host rock and transport of the breccia by flowing magma. At these locations the dike apparently did not attain its final thickness simply by opening a large crack. The physical insights and new data gained through precise quantitative mapping are the reward for the effort required to learn and implement the techniques.

2.2.2 Transformation of position and basis vectors, and coordinate systems

For the presentation and publication of maps and structural data sets it is appropriate to reference locations to the UTM grid (Fig. 2.4). For example, the local Cartesian coordinate system (x, y, z) used to define the position vectors for the contact of the northeastern Ship Rock dike (Fig. 2.7) can be transformed to the UTM grid through a two-step procedure starting with a clockwise rotation through 34° about a vertical axis to align the x-axis and y-axis with the easting and northing directions on the grid. This is followed by a translation of the local origin to the origin for the northern hemisphere of zone 12, which is 694 000 m to the west, 4 063 000 m to the south, and 1675 m down.

In general, changing (transforming) from one rectangular coordinate system to another may involve three independent operations: a *rotation* about a fixed origin (Fig. 2.6c) without changing the orthogonality or sense of the axes; a *translation* of the origin (Fig. 2.6d) without changing the orientation or sense of the axes; and a *reflection* that only changes the sense of the axes (right handed to left handed or vice versa) while maintaining their orientation and the origin. Because we utilize only right-handed coordinate systems, the operation of reflection is not considered further. Here we illustrate rotation and translation using the Ship Rock example and then generalize these operations for the transformation of vectors and rectangular coordinate systems in three dimensions.

The azimuth of the local x-axis at Ship Rock is 56° measured clockwise from north in the horizontal plane (Fig. 2.5). Therefore, the transformation to a new Cartesian coordinate system (x', y') that shares the same origin but is aligned with the UTM grid axes is a clockwise rotation of 34° about the vertical z-axis. This is a two-dimensional transformation in which every point, $P(x, y)$, referred to the old coordinate system on the map takes on

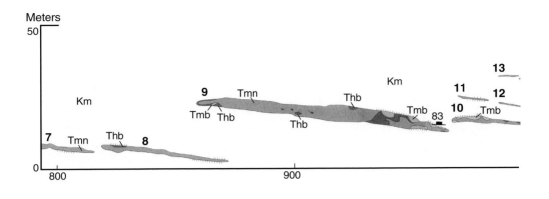

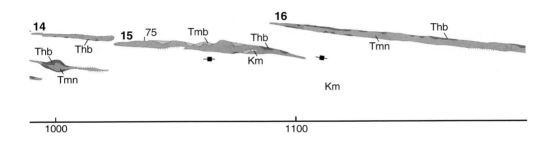

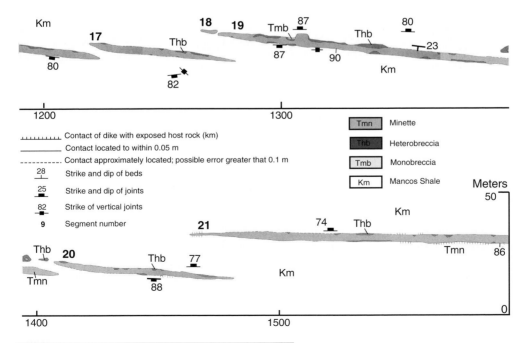

Fig 2.7 Structural map of several segments of the northeastern Ship Rock dike (Delaney and Pollard, 1981).

new coordinates, $P(x', y')$, which are found using the following equations:

$$x' = x\cos\alpha + y\sin\alpha$$
$$y' = -x\sin\alpha + y\cos\alpha \qquad (2.13)$$

The angle α is the counterclockwise angle from the Ox to Ox' and the trigonometry used to derive these equations is illustrated in Fig. 2.8a. For the local coordinate system at Ship Rock the angle $\alpha = -34°$.

The x- and y-components of position vectors $\mathbf{p}$ and $\mathbf{q}$ (Fig. 2.8b) change under the rotational transformation just described, but the position vectors themselves are unchanged. Because the components of an arbitrary position vector, $\mathbf{p}$, that locates a point, $P(x, y)$, are equivalent to the coordinates of that point, the two-dimensional rotational transformation of position vectors about the z-axis follows directly from (2.13):

$$p_{x'} = p_x\cos\alpha + p_y\sin\alpha$$
$$p_{y'} = -p_x\sin\alpha + p_y\cos\alpha \qquad (2.14)$$

Here $p_{x'}$ and $p_{y'}$ are the components of the same position vector, $\mathbf{p}$, locating the same point, $P(x, y)$, but this vector is referred to the new (x', y') coordinate system.

For a two-dimensional rotational transformation the basis for the new (x', y') coordinate system is not the same as that for the old (x, y)-system (Fig. 2.8c). However, the base vector $\mathbf{e}_x$ only has an x-component, and $\mathbf{e}_y$ only has a y-component, so the rotational transformation to the new base vectors $(\mathbf{e}_{x'}, \mathbf{e}_{y'})$ may be taken directly from (2.13):

$$\mathbf{e}_{x'} = \mathbf{e}_x\cos\alpha + \mathbf{e}_y\sin\alpha$$
$$\mathbf{e}_{y'} = -\mathbf{e}_x\sin\alpha + \mathbf{e}_y\cos\alpha \qquad (2.15)$$

These are vector equations that relate two different pairs of orthogonal unit vectors. One pair aligns with the positive axes of the old coordinate system and the other with the positive axes of the new system. The fact that both $\mathbf{e}_{x'}$ and $\mathbf{e}_{y'}$ are unit vectors follows from the Pythagorean relation $\sin^2\alpha + \cos^2\alpha = 1$. In contrast to the vector equations (2.15), the rotational transformation illustrated in Fig. 2.8b is for the single position vector, $\mathbf{p}$, and utilizes scalar equations (2.14) for the components of that vector referred to the new coordinate system.

Transforming the coordinates of a point from

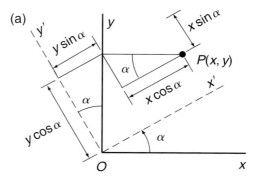

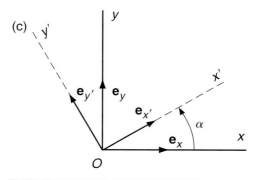

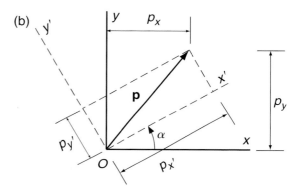

Fig 2.8 Rotation of Cartesian coordinates in two dimensions. (a) New coordinates of the point P. (b) Components of the position vector under the old (x, y) and new $(x'\ y')$ coordinate systems. (c) Base vectors, $\mathbf{e}$, for the old and new coordinate system.

the new (x', y')-coordinate system back to the old (x, y)-system merely reverses the operation just described. The inverse form of the rotation equations is found by solving (2.13) for x and y:

$$x = x'\cos\alpha - y'\sin\alpha$$
$$y = x'\sin\alpha + y'\cos\alpha \qquad (2.16)$$

The inverse transformation for the components of a position vector, or for the base vectors, follows from (2.16) by analogy with (2.14) and (2.15).

Coordinates of points on the Ship Rock map in the rotated local system (x', y', z'), and components of position vectors referred to that system, are transformed to the UTM grid by a translation of the origin using the following equations:

$$\text{Easting} = x' + 694\,000\,\text{m}$$
$$\text{Northing} = y' + 4\,063\,000\,\text{m} \qquad (2.17)$$
$$\text{Elevation} = z' + 1675\,\text{m}$$

Notice that the transformation is accomplished by adding to the local coordinates the coordinates of the local origin referred to the UTM system.

The transformation of local coordinates at the Ship Rock site to the UTM grid is an example of a *translation* from one rectangular (Cartesian) system to another rectangular system with parallel axes (Fig. 2.6d). For the purpose of generalizing this discussion we refer to (x, y, z) as the old system and (x', y', z') as the new system, with origins at O and O', respectively. For every point, $P(x, y, z)$, referred to the old coordinate system, the rectangular coordinates in the new system are found using the following expressions:

$$x' = x - a$$
$$y' = y - b \qquad (2.18)$$
$$z' = z - c$$

Here the constants $(a, b, \text{and } c)$ are the coordinates of the origin, O', of the new system as written with respect to the old system. That is, the origin of the old system is translated a distance a along x and a distance b along y and a distance c along z from the origin of the old system (Fig. 2.6d). The inverse of this transformation is found algebraically by rearranging the three equations to solve for x, y, and z, respectively.

The two-dimensional rotational transformation (2.13) can be generalized to three dimensions if the old and new coordinate systems share a common origin. The coordinate axes (Ox, Oy, Oz) of the old system are related to the coordinate axes (Ox', Oy', Oz') of the new system using nine *direction angles*. For example, in Fig. 2.9a the positive x-axis is related to the positive x'-axis by the smaller of

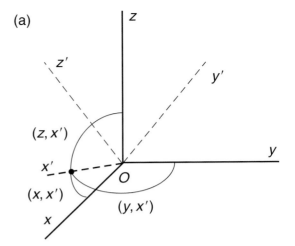

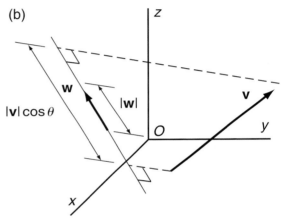

Fig 2.9 Rotation of Cartesian coordinates in three dimensions. (a) Direction angles relating old (x, y, z) and new $(x'\ y'\ z')$ axes. (b) Geometric interpretation of scalar product of two arbitrary vectors, **v** and **w**.

the two angles in the plane defined by Ox and Ox'. This direction angle is referred to as (x, x'). Similarly, the direction angle (y, x') relates the y-axis to the x'-axis, and the direction angle (z, x') relates the z-axis to the x'-axis. Three direction angles are defined similarly for the y'-axis and for the z'-axis, bringing the total to nine angles.

The old and new coordinate systems (Fig. 2.9a) have bases $(\mathbf{e}_x, \mathbf{e}_y, \mathbf{e}_z)$ and $(\mathbf{e}_{x'}, \mathbf{e}_{y'}, \mathbf{e}_{z'})$, respectively. To calculate the new basis vectors from the old we need to define the *scalar product* of two vectors. For two arbitrary vectors, **v** and **w**, the scalar product is:

$$\mathbf{v} \cdot \mathbf{w} = |\mathbf{v}| |\mathbf{w}| \cos \theta, \qquad \text{for } 0 \le \theta \le \pi$$
$$= v_x w_x + v_y w_y + v_z w_z \qquad (2.19)$$

Because the scalar product is written with a dot between the two vectors, it is referred to as the dot product. Here θ is the smaller of the two angles between the lines directed parallel to $\mathbf{v}$ and $\mathbf{w}$ measured in the plane defined by the two vectors (Fig. 2.9b), so the product $|\mathbf{v}| \cos \theta$ is the orthogonal projection of $\mathbf{v}$ onto the line parallel to $\mathbf{w}$. In other words $|\mathbf{v}| \cos \theta$ is the component of $\mathbf{v}$ in the direction of $\mathbf{w}$. Therefore, the scalar product may be interpreted geometrically as the product of the component of $\mathbf{v}$ along $\mathbf{w}$ and the magnitude of $\mathbf{w}$. Alternatively, the scalar product may be interpreted as the product of the component of $\mathbf{w}$ along $\mathbf{v}$ and the magnitude of $\mathbf{v}$.

Two important relationships among the vectors defining a basis are expressed conveniently using the scalar product (2.19):

$$\mathbf{e}_x \cdot \mathbf{e}_x = \mathbf{e}_y \cdot \mathbf{e}_y = \mathbf{e}_z \cdot \mathbf{e}_z = 1$$
$$\mathbf{e}_x \cdot \mathbf{e}_y = \mathbf{e}_y \cdot \mathbf{e}_z = \mathbf{e}_z \cdot \mathbf{e}_x = 0 \qquad (2.20)$$

These relations are interpreted by recalling that orthonormal basis vectors are of unit magnitude and they are mutually orthogonal to one another.

For the rotational transformation we want, for example, to project $\mathbf{e}_x$, $\mathbf{e}_y$, and $\mathbf{e}_z$ onto the line parallel to $\mathbf{e}_{x'}$ (Fig. 2.9a). These projections are accomplished using the scalar product (2.19) and recalling that the base vectors are unit vectors:

$$\mathbf{e}_x \cdot \mathbf{e}_{x'} = |\mathbf{e}_x| |\mathbf{e}_{x'}| \cos(x, x') = \cos(x, x') = m_{xx'}$$
$$\mathbf{e}_y \cdot \mathbf{e}_{x'} = |\mathbf{e}_y| |\mathbf{e}_{x'}| \cos(y, x') = \cos(y, x') = m_{yx'} \qquad (2.21)$$
$$\mathbf{e}_z \cdot \mathbf{e}_{x'} = |\mathbf{e}_z| |\mathbf{e}_{x'}| \cos(z, x') = \cos(z, x') = m_{zx'}$$

Analogous procedures are used to project $\mathbf{e}_x$, $\mathbf{e}_y$, and $\mathbf{e}_z$ onto lines parallel to $\mathbf{e}_{y'}$ and $\mathbf{e}_{z'}$ and these operations define nine *direction cosines* that relate the old basis to the new basis:

$$m_{xx'} = \cos(x, x'), \quad m_{xy'} = \cos(x, y'), \quad m_{xz'} = \cos(x, z')$$
$$m_{yx'} = \cos(y, x'), \quad m_{yy'} = \cos(y, y'), \quad m_{yz'} = \cos(y, z')$$
$$m_{zx'} = \cos(z, x'), \quad m_{zy'} = \cos(z, y'), \quad m_{zz'} = \cos(z, z')$$
$$(2.22)$$

Here the double subscripts on the direction cosines refer to the reference (old) axis and the transformed (new) axis, respectively.

The direction cosines and basis vectors may be organized into a table that facilitates rotational transformations in three dimensions:

	$\mathbf{e}_{x'}$	$\mathbf{e}_{y'}$	$\mathbf{e}_{z'}$
$\mathbf{e}_x$	$m_{xx'}$	$m_{xy'}$	$m_{xz'}$
$\mathbf{e}_y$	$m_{yx'}$	$m_{yy'}$	$m_{yz'}$
$\mathbf{e}_z$	$m_{zx'}$	$m_{zy'}$	$m_{zz'}$

$$(2.23)$$

The new and old basis vectors are listed in the first row and first column, respectively, and the direction cosines fill out the table such that their two subscripts match the subscript of the basis vector heading the row and the column, respectively. Each new basis vector is composed of a linear combination of the old basis vectors and the direction cosines in the corresponding column of (2.23):

$$\mathbf{e}_{x'} = m_{xx'}\mathbf{e}_x + m_{yx'}\mathbf{e}_y + m_{zx'}\mathbf{e}_z$$
$$\mathbf{e}_{y'} = m_{xy'}\mathbf{e}_x + m_{yy'}\mathbf{e}_y + m_{zy'}\mathbf{e}_z \qquad (2.24)$$
$$\mathbf{e}_{z'} = m_{xz'}\mathbf{e}_x + m_{yz'}\mathbf{e}_y + m_{zz'}\mathbf{e}_z$$

Each old basis vector is composed of a linear combination of the new basis vectors and the direction cosines in the corresponding row of (2.23):

$$\mathbf{e}_x = m_{xx'}\mathbf{e}_{x'} + m_{xy'}\mathbf{e}_{y'} + m_{xz'}\mathbf{e}_{z'}$$
$$\mathbf{e}_y = m_{yx'}\mathbf{e}_{x'} + m_{yy'}\mathbf{e}_{y'} + m_{yz'}\mathbf{e}_{z'} \qquad (2.25)$$
$$\mathbf{e}_z = m_{zx'}\mathbf{e}_{x'} + m_{zy'}\mathbf{e}_{y'} + m_{zz'}\mathbf{e}_{z'}$$

This is the inverse rotational transformation. The basis vectors are unit vectors so (2.7) requires that the sum of the squares of the direction cosines in any row or column of (2.23) equal one. For example:

$$|\mathbf{e}_{y'}| = \sqrt{(m_{xy'})^2 + (m_{yy'})^2 + (m_{zy'})^2} = 1,$$
so
$$(m_{xy'})^2 + (m_{yy'})^2 + (m_{zy'})^2 = 1 \qquad (2.26)$$

The direction cosines as arranged in (2.23) comprise a square matrix and the rotational transformation will be described in terms of matrix operations later.

It was pointed out with respect to the two-dimensional form of the rotational transformation that basis vectors and components of position vectors and coordinates of points all transform using similar equations. This principle extends to three dimensions so we can construct a table of directional cosines for rotation of position vector components using (2.23) as a template:

$$
\begin{array}{cccc}
 & p_{x'} & p_{y'} & p_{z'} \\
p_x & m_{xx'} & m_{xy'} & m_{xz'} \\
p_y & m_{yx'} & m_{yy'} & m_{yz'} \\
p_z & m_{zx'} & m_{zy'} & m_{zz'}
\end{array}
\tag{2.27}
$$

For example, one uses $m_{zx'}$ for the orthogonal projection of the z-component of the position vector onto the x'-axis. Each new component of the position vector is composed of a linear combination of the old components and the direction cosines in the corresponding column of (2.27). Each old component of the position vector is composed of a linear combination of the new components and the direction cosines in the corresponding row of (2.27).

Because the coordinates of an arbitrary point, $P(x, y, z)$, are equivalent to the components of the position vector, $\mathbf{p}$, for that point, the coordinates can replace the components in (2.27) to form a table of direction cosines for the rotational transformation of coordinates:

$$
\begin{array}{cccc}
 & x' & y' & z' \\
x & m_{xx'} & m_{xy'} & m_{xz'} \\
y & m_{yx'} & m_{yy'} & m_{yz'} \\
z & m_{zx'} & m_{zy'} & m_{zz'}
\end{array}
\tag{2.28}
$$

From this table we understand, for example, that the direction cosine $m_{yz'}$ is used for the orthogonal projection of the y-coordinate of P onto the z'-axis. Each new coordinate of P is composed of a linear combination of the old coordinates and the direction cosines in the corresponding column of (2.28). The inverse transformation equations are formed using the rows of this table. In summary (2.23), (2.27), and (2.28) provide the equations for both forward (old to new) and inverse (new to old) rotational transformations for orthonormal base vectors, for components of position vectors, and for coordinates of points referred to rectangular Cartesian coordinate systems.

Transformation equations that commonly are employed in modeling structures include those for the *cylindrical coordinate system*. As an example consider the volcanic neck shown in the lower-right corner of the photograph from Ship Rock (Fig. 2.5a). This edifice, once a conduit for magma, is about 30 m in diameter and roughly circular in map view (Fig. 2.10a, c). The neck is composed pri-

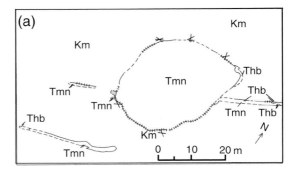

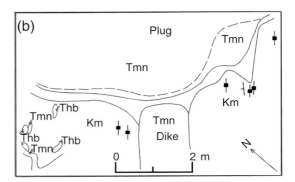

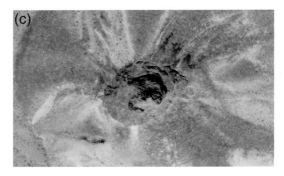

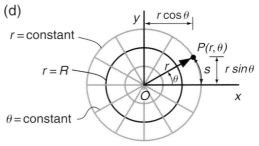

Fig 2.10 Volcanic neck near Ship Rock, NM (Delaney and Pollard, 1981). (a) Structural map of the neck and associated dikes. (b) Detailed map of the neck and a dike. (c) Aerial photograph of the neck. (d) Polar coordinate system used in models of volcanic necks.

marily of a volcanic igneous rock called minette, but breccias of minette and Mancos Shale crop out around the perimeter. From the side of the neck a thin dike extends about 440 m to the northeast along a gently curving outcrop (Fig. 2.5a), and a dike with similar trend extends from the opposite side of the neck a few meters to the southwest. The crosscutting relationships (Fig. 2.10b) between the minette of the dike and the minette and breccias of the neck suggest that the dike formed first and solidified while local brecciation and erosion of the Mancos Shale and the dike rock enabled the neck to grow in diameter to its present size (Delaney and Pollard, 1981). This interpretation is surprising because the analogy to hydraulic fracturing of wells (Hubbert and Willis, 1957) would suggest that the neck formed first and that pressurized magma in the neck fractured the contact, initiating dike propagation into the Mancos Shale. The interpretation that dikes form first and necks grow from them is supported by observations on active volcanoes where short-lived fissure eruptions precede longer-lived eruptions from cylindrical vents located along the fissure.

The forms of the volcanic necks at Ship Rock motivate the choice of a cylindrical coordinate system for idealizing the geometry and facilitating modeling (Fig. 2.11a). For reference consider the Cartesian axes (Ox, Oy, Oz) with Oz parallel to the cylindrical axis. The basic elements of the cylindrical system are an origin, O, a radial distance, r, measured from the origin, an angle, θ, measured from the line Ox, and an axial distance, z, measured from the origin. Both r and θ are measured in the plane perpendicular to the cylindrical axis and the angle is positive if clockwise when looking in the positive direction of Oz. Given an arbitrary point $P(r, \theta, z)$ in cylindrical coordinates, the Cartesian coordinates are found using the following transformation equations (Selby, 1975, p. 385):

$$x = r\cos\theta, \ y = r\sin\theta, \ z = z$$

$$r = \sqrt{x^2 + y^2}, \ \theta = \tan^{-1}\left(\frac{y}{x}\right), \ z = z \tag{2.29}$$

The second line of (2.29) contains the corresponding inverse transformation equations. Note that

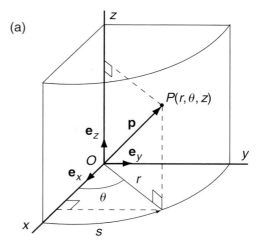

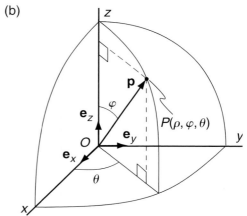

Fig 2.11 Position vector, **p**, and base vector, **e**, for two coordinate systems. (a) Cylindrical coordinate system. (b) Spherical coordinate system.

the axial coordinate z is identical for the two transformations. Following standard conventions the positive square root is used so r is always a positive number. The line Ox in the Cartesian system and that in the polar system must be identical, sharing the same origin and direction.

The position vector, **p**, used to locate the point $P(r, \theta, z)$ in the cylindrical coordinate system (Fig. 2.11a) is written as a linear combination of the scalar components and the three mutually orthogonal unit base vectors ($\mathbf{e}_x$, $\mathbf{e}_y$, $\mathbf{e}_z$) of the Cartesian system:

$$\mathbf{p} = p_x\mathbf{e}_x + p_y\mathbf{e}_y + p_z\mathbf{e}_z$$

$$= (r\cos\theta)\mathbf{e}_x + (r\sin\theta)\mathbf{e}_y + (z)\mathbf{e}_z \tag{2.30}$$

The Cartesian coordinates defined in the first line of (2.29) are the scalar components of the position vector. These scalar components carry the units of length (meters) as do the radius, r, and axial length, z. The angle, θ, is measured in radians which may be thought of as the ratio of arc length to radial length, s/r.

For modeling purposes it is helpful to reduce the number of coordinates from three to two by idealizing the structure as one that is perfectly cylindrical. For the volcanic neck at Ship Rock (Fig. 2.10c), we would say that it has a similar geometry for any horizontal cross section within several tens of meters of the current outcrop, so we can ignore spatial variations in geometry, material properties, and boundary conditions with the axial coordinate z. Then we focus on the two-dimensional *polar coordinates* (r, θ) and define the problem in terms of these two coordinates (Fig. 2.10d). Radial lines of constant θ and circles of constant r form an orthogonal network centered on the origin. The contact between the minette of the neck and the Mancos Shale is defined as a particular circle, $r = R = 15\,\text{m}$, with a radius that best approximates that of the neck. The alternative would be to define the contact in terms of the Cartesian coordinates as the circle $(x^2 + y^2)^{1/2} = R$, but this is mathematically more cumbersome.

Similarly, the boundary (BC) and initial (IC) conditions for models of the volcanic neck are simplified using polar rather than Cartesian coordinates. For example consider a model for the conductive heat flow from the hot magma into the cold host rock. The cylindrical geometry of the volcanic neck dictates a temperature field that varies spatially only in the radial coordinate direction, thereby reducing the problem to one spatial dimension. Because the governing equation for heat conduction is written with temperature as the dependent variable, the initial conditions typically constrain the temperature field at some specified time and the boundary conditions constrain the temperature field at specified locations on the surface(s) of the body. Here we consider initial conditions at the time $t = 0$, such that the temperature is uniform, T_{m}, throughout the neck and zero throughout the host rock. Then let the temperature field, $T(r, t)$ evolve with time according to the governing equations for heat conduction with the boundary condition that the temperature far from the neck remains zero:

$$
\text{IC: for } t = 0 \begin{cases} T = T_{\text{m}} \ \text{at } r < R \\ T = 0 \ \text{at } r \geq R \end{cases}
$$

$$
\text{BC: at } r = \infty \ \ T = 0 \text{ for } t > 0 \tag{2.31}
$$

A uniform temperature could be added everywhere to account for the ambient temperature before the development of the volcanic neck.

The natural symmetry of some geological structures motivates use of a coordinate system that bears some resemblance to the cylindrical system, but admits very eccentric shapes. The map of dike segments (Fig. 2.7) suggests that an elliptical cross section may be a good approximation for some of these. Segment 16, for example, is 136 m long, has a maximum thickness of 3.4 m, and is approximately symmetric about planes that pass through its middle parallel to its length and thickness (Fig. 2.12a). The contact between the minette and the Mancos Shale is relatively smooth and slowly tapers toward the distal terminations. We have scant information about the extent or shape of this segment with depth, or with height above the current outcrop. Unlike the necks which stand well above the surrounding shale, the dike segments reveal little of their three-dimensional geometry. Over the few meters of local relief the contact maintains a near vertical dip and this is consistent over the 55 m of elevation change from one end of the dike to the other. Where exposed the terminations of individual segments are steeply plunging. Based on this limited information we adopt two-dimensional *elliptical coordinates*, which may be visualized as a set of confocal ellipses and hyperbolae (Fig. 2.12b).

For reference consider the Cartesian axes (Ox, Oy, Oz) with Oz perpendicular to the plane of interest. We postulate that the dike segment has a similar geometry for any horizontal cross section within several tens of meters of the current outcrop, so we can ignore spatial variations in geometry, material properties, and boundary conditions with the coordinate z. Then the basic elements of the two-dimensional elliptical system are an origin, 0, the line Ox, a coordinate ξ, a coordinate η, and a focal length, f, measured from the

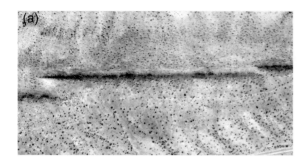

(a)

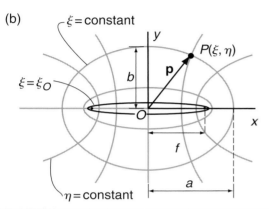

(b)

Fig 2.12 (a) Aerial photograph of one segment of the northeastern dike at Ship Rock (Delaney and Pollard, 1981). (b) Elliptical coordinate system used in models of dike segments.

origin along the line Ox (Fig. 2.12b). The ellipses and hyperbolae are called confocal because they share common foci located at $x = \pm f$.

Given an arbitrary point $P(\xi, \eta)$ in elliptical coordinates, the Cartesian coordinates are found using the following transformation equations (Timoshenko and Goodier, 1970):

$$x = f \cosh \xi \cos \eta, \quad y = f \sinh \xi \sin \eta \qquad (2.32)$$

The functions cosh and sinh are *hyperbolic functions*. Just as in the polar coordinate system where any circle centered at the origin would be represented by a constant value of r, each of the family of confocal ellipses is represented by a constant value of ξ. However, unlike the coordinate r, which is a length measured in meters, the coordinate ξ is just a number. Also, as each radial line in the polar system is associated with a particular value of the angle θ, each of the family of confocal hyperbolae is associated with a particular value of the angle η.

The position vector, **p**, used to locate the point $P(\xi, \eta)$ in the two-dimensional elliptical coordinate system (Fig. 2.12b) is written as a linear combination of the scalar components (2.32) and the two mutually orthogonal unit base vectors $(\mathbf{e}_x, \mathbf{e}_y)$ of the Cartesian system:

$$\begin{aligned} \mathbf{p} &= p_x \mathbf{e}_x + p_y \mathbf{e}_y \\ &= (f \cosh \xi \cos \eta) \mathbf{e}_x + (f \sinh \xi \sin \eta) \mathbf{e}_y \end{aligned} \qquad (2.33)$$

The scalar components carry the units of length (meters) because f has units of length. Thus the focal length determines the length scale of this coordinate system.

For a given hyperbola ($\eta =$ constant), as ξ ranges from numbers much less than one to numbers greater than one the ellipses range from very eccentric to nearly circular. In the limit, as $\xi \to 0$ the ellipse collapses down onto the x-axis, extending from one focus to the other. Later we use such highly eccentric ellipses as models for fractures and faults in rock. For a given ellipse ($\xi =$ constant), as the angle η ranges from 0° to 360°, points vary in position around the ellipse in a counterclockwise direction starting at the intersection with the positive x-axis where $\eta = 0°$. The angle $\eta = 90°$ at the intersection of the ellipse and the positive y-axis; $\eta = 180°$ at the intersection with the negative x-axis, and so forth.

The semi-major axis, a, and semi-minor axis, b, of a particular ellipse ($\xi =$ constant) are:

$$a = f \cosh \xi, \quad b = f \sinh \xi \qquad (2.34)$$

For segment 16 of the Ship Rock dike (Fig. 2.12a) we have $a = 68$ m and $b = 1.7$ m, so the particular ellipse, ξ_0, defining the contact is:

$$\xi_0 = \tanh^{-1}\left(\frac{b}{a}\right) = \tanh^{-1}(0.025) = 0.025 \qquad (2.35)$$

The specification of boundary conditions for problems related to dike segments is particularly simple using elliptical coordinates. For example, if the magma pressure, p_m, exerts traction, **t**, only perpendicular to the contact, we write:

$$\text{BC: on } \xi = \xi_0 \begin{cases} t_\xi = p_m \\ t_\eta = 0 \end{cases} \qquad (2.36)$$

Here t_ξ is the traction component acting on the elliptical surface, ξ_0, in the ξ-coordinate direction

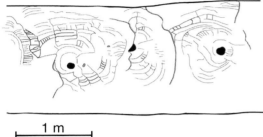

1 m

Fig 2.13 Cavities that served as nucleation sites for joints in the Soreq Dolomite, Israel. (a) Photograph of cliff face with joints and cavities. (b) Map of outcrop. Reprinted from Weinberger (2001) with permission from Elsevier.

and t_η is the traction component acting on that surface in the η-coordinate direction.

The last coordinate system we consider here is motivated by geological structures that are approximately spherical in shape. A good example comes from the Soreq Formation, a stack of dolomite layers separated by thin marls that crops out in central Israel and contains two systematic sets of joints (Weinberger, 2001). The west-striking joint set is older than the north–northwest-striking set and is spatially associated with cavities that apparently are dissolved anhydrite nodules (Fig. 2.13). The surfaces of joints of this set are decorated with both plumose structures and rib markings (Hodgson, 1961; DeGraff and Aydin, 1987; Aydin and DeGraff, 1988; Bahat, 1991) indicating that each joint nucleated at a particular cavity and propagated vertically and laterally away from it. The three semi-axes of 14 cavities in a single layer were measured and provide the following statistics:

$$C_h = 45 \pm 20\,\text{mm}, \quad C_v = 43 \pm 20\,\text{mm},$$
$$C_d = 45 \pm 23\,\text{mm} \tag{2.37}$$

Here C_h and C_v are the horizontal and vertical semi-axes of the cavities measured from the center to the periphery in the plane of the intersecting joint, and C_d is the horizontal semi-axis measured perpendicular to this plane. Although the mean values are nearly identical for the three semi-axes, the standard deviations indicate that the semi-axes can be quite different for any particular cavity. None-the-less the cavities may be idealized as spherical in shape as a first approximation in the procedure of modeling their mechanical behavior.

Again for reference we consider the Cartesian axes (Ox, Oy, Oz). The basic elements of the spherical system are an origin, O, a radial distance, ρ, measured from the origin, an angle φ measured from the line Oz, and an angle, θ, measured from the line Ox (Fig. 2.11b). The angle φ is measured in the plane defined by the Oz-axis and the position vector for the point in question and is the smaller of the two angles between these directions in that plane. The angle θ is measured in the (x, y)-plane and is positive if clockwise when looking in the positive direction of Oz. Curves of constant φ are analogous to lines of latitude and curves of constant θ are analogous to lines of longitude. Together these curves form an orthogonal network on any sphere of constant radius ρ.

Given an arbitrary point $P(\rho, \varphi, \theta)$ in spherical coordinates, the Cartesian coordinates are found using the following transformation equations (Selby, 1975, p. 385):

$$x = \rho \cos\theta \sin\varphi, \; y = \rho \sin\theta \sin\varphi, \; z = \rho \cos\varphi$$
$$\rho = \sqrt{x^2 + y^2 + z^2}, \; \varphi = \cos^{-1}\left(\frac{z}{\sqrt{x^2 + y^2 + z^2}}\right),$$
$$\theta = \tan^{-1}\left(\frac{y}{x}\right) \tag{2.38}$$

The second and third lines contain the inverse transformation equations. The position vector, **p**, used to locate an arbitrary point $P(\rho, \varphi, \theta)$ in spherical coordinates (Fig. 2.11b) is written using the first line of (2.38) as:

$$\mathbf{p} = p_x \mathbf{e}_x + p_y \mathbf{e}_y + p_z \mathbf{e}_z$$
$$= (\rho \cos \theta \sin \varphi)\mathbf{e}_x + (\rho \sin \theta \sin \varphi)\mathbf{e}_y + (\rho \cos \varphi)\mathbf{e}_z$$

$$(2.39)$$

In other words $\mathbf{p}$ is a linear combination of the Cartesian coordinates from (2.38) and the base vectors $(\mathbf{e}_x, \mathbf{e}_y, \mathbf{e}_z)$.

Points on a particular sphere, such as the perimeter of one of the cavities in the Soreq Formation (Fig. 2.13) are identified by specifying $\rho = \rho_0 = 45$ mm, where ρ_0 is the cavity radius. If the cavities contained no fluid at the time of joint formation, the traction, $\mathbf{t}$, acting on the perimeter was identically zero and the boundary conditions are written:

$$\text{BC: on } \rho = \rho_0, \quad t_\rho = t_\varphi = t_\theta = 0 \qquad (2.40)$$

The three traction components act on the surface of the spherical cavity in the directions of increasing coordinates ρ, φ, and θ, respectively.

2.2.3 Indicial and matrix notations and equations

The systematics of (2.28) motivate a notation, referred to as *indicial notation*, that greatly reduces the effort of writing the rotational transformation equations and facilitates recalling them from memory. This notation also applies to many of the equations from continuum mechanics that are used for a variety of different purposes in structural geology, so it is important to understand how to read, formulate, and decompose equations written using indicial notation. Some of the basic elements of indicial notation are introduced here as they specifically relate to coordinate transformations; others are introduced as needed throughout the text.

Rather than naming the Cartesian coordinates (x, y, z) they are named (x_1, x_2, x_3) in which a single letter, x, is used with subscripts 1, 2, and 3 to distinguish the three axes. Although this appears to have made the notation more cumbersome, efficiency is achieved in that one can refer to the three coordinates simply as x_i where it is understood that i ranges from 1 to 3. In this context the subscript i is called an *index*. Similarly, one can refer to the three basis vectors as $\mathbf{e}_i$ and the three components of the position vector as p_i.

The direction cosines of (2.28) are referred to as m_{ij} where both indices i and j range from 1 to 3, so the double index implies nine quantities that can be arranged in a table as:

	x'_1	x'_2	x'_3
x_1	m_{11}	m_{12}	m_{13}
x_2	m_{21}	m_{22}	m_{23}
x_3	m_{31}	m_{32}	m_{33}

$$(2.41)$$

Note that the first subscript on the direction cosines refers to the reference (old) axis and the second subscript refers to the transformed (new) axis. Thus, one uses m_{31} for the orthogonal projection of the x_3-coordinate of a point onto the x'_1-axis. Similarly, one uses m_{23} for the orthogonal projection of the x_2-coordinate of a point onto the x'_3-axis.

Additional efficiency is gained in writing equations with indicial notation by introducing the so-called *summation convention*. This convention establishes that a repeated subscript in any given term of an equation implies summation with respect to that index over its range. Using (2.41) the equations for the rotational transformation from old coordinate, x_i, to new coordinates, x'_i, are written:

$$x'_1 = m_{11}x_1 + m_{21}x_2 + m_{31}x_3 = \sum_{i=1}^{3} m_{i1}x_i = m_{i1}x_i$$

$$x'_2 = m_{12}x_1 + m_{22}x_2 + m_{32}x_3 = \sum_{i=1}^{3} m_{i2}x_i = m_{i2}x_i \quad (2.42)$$

$$x'_3 = m_{13}x_1 + m_{23}x_2 + m_{33}x_3 = \sum_{i=1}^{3} m_{i3}x_i = m_{i3}x_i$$

In the last step of each equation the summation symbol is replaced by the summation convention. Recognizing the pattern of subscripts in these equations, one may compose the forward and inverse rotational transformation equations as:

$$x'_j = m_{ij}x_i, \quad x_i = m_{ij}x'_j \qquad (2.43)$$

A repeated subscript in any term is called a *dummy index*: any letter may be used for this subscript because it only functions to inform the reader that summation is required over the specified range. In contrast any non-repeated subscript in a given term is called a *free index* because the reader is free to choose any particular value within the specified range. Because there is one free index which ranges from 1 to 3 in each of these equations, each may be expanded into the three equations. The forward and inverse rotational transformations for the components of the old and new position vectors (p_i, p'_j) and the old and new basis vectors $(\mathbf{e}_i, \mathbf{e}'_j)$ are constructed similarly.

The definition of the direction cosines in terms of the base vectors is written using indicial notation and the scalar product (2.19) as:

$$m_{ij} \equiv \mathbf{e}_i \cdot \mathbf{e}'_j \qquad (2.44)$$

Here there are no repeated indices but both i and j range from 1 to 3, so this equation expands into nine equations for the direction cosines. The scalar product of two arbitrary vectors, $\mathbf{v}$ and $\mathbf{w}$ (Fig. 2.9b), is expressed using indicial notation as:

$$\mathbf{v} \cdot \mathbf{w} \equiv v_i w_i \qquad (2.45)$$

Here the repeated index requires summation of the product of the components over the range 1 to 3.

The facts that the base vectors are of unit magnitude and orthogonal to one another are expressed by the two equations:

$$\mathbf{e}_1 \cdot \mathbf{e}_1 = \mathbf{e}_2 \cdot \mathbf{e}_2 = \mathbf{e}_3 \cdot \mathbf{e}_3 = 1$$
$$\mathbf{e}_1 \cdot \mathbf{e}_2 = \mathbf{e}_2 \cdot \mathbf{e}_3 = \mathbf{e}_3 \cdot \mathbf{e}_1 = 0 \qquad (2.46)$$

These conditions motivate the definition of a new quantity, δ_{ij} called the *Kronecker delta* that finds considerable usage with indicial notation:

$$\delta_{ij} \equiv \begin{cases} 1, & \text{if } i = j \\ 0, & \text{if } i \neq j \end{cases}, \quad \text{for } (i, j = 1, 2, 3) \qquad (2.47)$$

The conditions of unit magnitude and orthogonal orientations (2.46) are succinctly written using the Kronecker delta:

$$\mathbf{e}_i \cdot \mathbf{e}_j = \delta_{ij} \qquad (2.48)$$

Furthermore, the conditions that the squares of direction cosines in each row and each column of (2.41) sum to one are written:

$$m_{ki} m_{kj} = \delta_{ij}, \quad m_{ik} m_{jk} = \delta_{ij} \qquad (2.49)$$

The first equation applies to the direction cosines in each column (sum over the first index) and the second equation applies to each row (sum over the second index).

The arrangement of direction cosines in (2.41)

as a table or array of numbers motivates consideration of the concept and mathematical properties of a matrix. This is further motivated by the fact that the computational engine, MATLAB®, used for the exercises and many of the graphical illustrations in this text, treats all data sets as arrays of numbers and offers many useful functions that operate on matrices. Furthermore, many of the constructs of continuum mechanics can be described and manipulated as matrices. As we have just done with indicial notation, some of the basic concepts of matrices are introduced here as they specifically relate to coordinate transformations; others are introduced as needed throughout the text.

A *matrix* is a rectangular array of numbers with each element of the array designated by its position in the array according to the row and column number: an m by n matrix has m rows and n columns. For example, consider the position vectors that were used to describe the contact of the dike at Ship Rock (Fig. 2.5). In general, a position vector, $\mathbf{p}$, is written using indicial notation and in expanded form as follows:

$$\mathbf{p} = p_i \mathbf{e}_i = p_1 \mathbf{e}_1 + p_2 \mathbf{e}_2 + p_3 \mathbf{e}_3 \qquad (2.50)$$

The three components (p_1, p_2, p_3) of the position vector can be thought of as either a 1 by 3 *row matrix* or a 3 by 1 *column matrix*:

$$P = [P_1 \ P_2 \ P_3], \quad \text{or} \quad P = \begin{bmatrix} P_1 \\ P_2 \\ P_3 \end{bmatrix} \qquad (2.51)$$

Notice that the single subscript for each vector component, p_i, is replaced by a double subscript and that these subscripts refer, respectively, to the row number and column number. There are no restrictions on the number of elements in a row or column matrix, or on the relationships among those elements, although our example happens to use three elements that are components of a position vector. Sometimes row and column matrices are referred to as "vectors," but we restrict that term to quantities in which the elements have the properties of vectors.

As a second example consider the set of direction cosines used to relate the old and new basis vectors for a rotational transformation of coordinates (2.41). Using indicial notation and in expanded form these direction cosines are written:

$$m_{ij} = \begin{matrix} m_{11} & m_{12} & m_{13} \\ m_{21} & m_{22} & m_{23} \\ m_{31} & m_{32} & m_{33} \end{matrix} \qquad (2.52)$$

The matrix representation of the direction cosines follows quite naturally because the row and column numbers of the matrix, M, are the same as the indices of m_{ij}:

$$M = \begin{bmatrix} M_{11} & M_{12} & M_{13} \\ M_{21} & M_{22} & M_{23} \\ M_{31} & M_{32} & M_{33} \end{bmatrix} \qquad (2.53)$$

This is a 3 by 3 matrix and any matrix where the number of rows and columns are identical, $m = n$, is termed a *square matrix*. The number of rows and columns is referred to as the order of a matrix and, in general, there are no restrictions on the order of a matrix.

Just as two vectors are added (or subtracted) component by component (2.12) two matrices are added (or subtracted) element by element. For example, the addition of two 3 by 2 matrices, Q and R, is carried out as:

$$Q + R = \begin{bmatrix} Q_{11} + R_{11} & Q_{12} + R_{12} \\ Q_{21} + R_{21} & Q_{22} + R_{22} \\ Q_{31} + R_{31} & Q_{32} + R_{32} \end{bmatrix} \qquad (2.54)$$

This results in a row matrix of exactly the same order, 3 by 2. The addition (or subtraction) of matrices requires that they be of the same order.

The 3 by 2 matrix R is scaled by a constant numerical factor as follows:

$$kR = \begin{bmatrix} kR_{11} & kR_{12} \\ kR_{21} & kR_{22} \\ kR_{31} & kR_{32} \end{bmatrix} \qquad (2.55)$$

In general, the multiplication of a matrix by a constant is accomplished by multiplying each element of the matrix by that constant. The division of a matrix by a constant is equivalent to multiplying by the reciprocal of that constant.

The multiplication of two matrices follows rules that are similar, in part, to those for the scalar product of two vectors (2.19), but there are important distinctions that restrict the order of

the two matrices and the sequence in which they can be multiplied. As an example, consider the 2 by 3 matrix, Q, and the 3 by 1 matrix, R:

$$Q = \begin{bmatrix} Q_1 & Q_2 & Q_3 \\ Q_1 & Q_2 & Q_3 \end{bmatrix}, \quad R = \begin{bmatrix} R_1 \\ R_2 \\ R_3 \end{bmatrix} \qquad (2.56)$$

These may be multiplied in the sequence QR and the multiplication is carried out as though each row of Q and the column of R are vectors and one wishes to form their scalar products:

$$QR = \begin{bmatrix} Q_{11}R_{11} + Q_{12}R_{21} + Q_{13}R_{31} \\ Q_{21}R_{11} + Q_{22}R_{21} + Q_{23}R_{31} \end{bmatrix} = S \qquad (2.57)$$

The result is the matrix S of order 2 by 1: a matrix with the same number of rows as the first matrix, Q, and the same number of columns as the second matrix, R. The two matrices, Q and R, cannot be multiplied in the sequence RQ.

Now consider the general case of a matrix Q of order m by l and a matrix R of order l by n. The multiplication of these two matrices can be symbolized as follows:

$$QR = [m \text{ by } l][l \text{ by } n] = [m \text{ by } n] = S \qquad (2.58)$$

Note that the order of the resulting matrix S is m by n. In general, two matrices can be multiplied in the sequence QR if the number of columns of Q is equal to the number of rows of R. Indicial notation provides a succinct way to describe the elements of the matrix S (Malvern, 1969, p. 41):

$$S_{ij} = Q_{ik} R_{kj}, \quad \text{for} \begin{cases} i = 1, \dots, m \\ j = 1, \dots, n \\ k = 1, \dots, l \end{cases} \qquad (2.59)$$

Here S_{ij} is the element in the ith row and jth column of the matrix S. Because of the repeated index k, each element is the sum of l terms. If the number of rows of Q is the same as the number of columns of R, $m = n$, the multiplication can proceed in the reverse sequence, RQ, but the two products are not equal, $QR \neq RQ$.

Multiplication with square matrices is commonly encountered in applications to physical problems and they have special properties that can be illustrated using the rotational transformation equations. Recall the table (2.41) that relates the old, x_i, and new, x'_j, Cartesian coordinates using the direction cosines, m_{ij}. These three quantities may be written as two column matrices and one square matrix:

$$X = \begin{bmatrix} X_1 \\ X_2 \\ X_3 \end{bmatrix}, \ X' = \begin{bmatrix} X'_1 \\ X'_2 \\ X'_3 \end{bmatrix}, \ M = \begin{bmatrix} M_{11} & M_{12} & M_{13} \\ M_{21} & M_{22} & M_{23} \\ M_{31} & M_{32} & M_{33} \end{bmatrix} \quad (2.60)$$

The inverse rotational transformation, $x_i = m_{ij}x'_j$, may be constructed directly by matrix multiplication, $X = MX'$, because the number of columns of M is the same as the number of rows of X', and the summation required by the indicial notation is consistent with that of matrix multiplication:

$$\begin{bmatrix} X_1 \\ X_2 \\ X_3 \end{bmatrix} = \begin{bmatrix} M_{11} & M_{12} & M_{13} \\ M_{21} & M_{22} & M_{23} \\ M_{31} & M_{32} & M_{33} \end{bmatrix} \begin{bmatrix} X'_1 \\ X'_2 \\ X'_3 \end{bmatrix}$$

$$= \begin{bmatrix} M_{11}X'_{11} + M_{12}X'_{21} + M_{13}X'_{31} \\ M_{21}X'_{11} + M_{22}X'_{21} + M_{23}X'_{31} \\ M_{31}X'_{11} + M_{32}X'_{21} + M_{33}X'_{31} \end{bmatrix} \quad (2.61)$$

However, the forward rotational transformation, $x'_j = m_{ij}x_i$, is not represented as $X' = MX$, despite the fact that the number of columns of M is the same as the number of rows of X, because the summation implied by the indicial notation is not consistent with matrix multiplication. Instead one must first take the transpose of M, symbolized as M^T, and then compute the product as $X' = M^TX$:

$$\begin{bmatrix} X'_1 \\ X'_2 \\ X'_3 \end{bmatrix} = \begin{bmatrix} M_{11} & M_{21} & M_{31} \\ M_{12} & M_{22} & M_{32} \\ M_{13} & M_{23} & M_{33} \end{bmatrix} \begin{bmatrix} X_1 \\ X_2 \\ X_3 \end{bmatrix}$$

$$= \begin{bmatrix} M_{11}X_{11} + M_{21}X_{21} + M_{31}X_{31} \\ M_{12}X_{11} + M_{22}X_{21} + M_{32}X_{31} \\ M_{13}X_{11} + M_{23}X_{21} + M_{33}X_{31} \end{bmatrix} \quad (2.62)$$

Note that the transpose, M^T, is found by interchanging the rows and columns of M.

2.3 | Orientations of structural elements

Given the complete UTM geographic coordinates for the position of a particular outcrop, the next step in most structural studies is to measure and describe the structures underfoot. Most geological structures may be idealized as three-dimensional curved surfaces or curved lines. Examples are surfaces that truncate older formations such as a fault offsetting sedimentary bedding, or a dike that cuts across an igneous contact. Or there may be surfaces within a mass of rock defined by the alignment of platy minerals, as in an igneous or metamorphic foliation. Curvilinear structures also may be composed of aligned mineral grains, as in a metamorphic lineation. The intersection of two curved surfaces, for example the intersection of two faults, would define a curved linear structure. Regardless of the specific nature of these curved surfaces and lines we need techniques for measuring their orientations in the field and for recording these orientations on a map at the position determined by the UTM coordinates. Techniques are introduced here along with a projection that is useful for visualizing the relative orientations of such structures.

2.3.1 Orientations of linear and planar structural elements

Most curved structural surfaces may be approximated locally by a *planar element* that is tangential to the surface at the point of measurement. Similarly, most curvilinear structures may be approximated locally by a *linear element* that is tangential to the curve at the point of measurement. What are actually recorded by the structural geologist at an exposure are the orientations of these structural elements. The exposure photographs in Fig. 2.14 show a number of geological structures that can be approximated in this way with planar and linear elements. These exposures are from the northern part of the San Rafael Swell in the Colorado Plateau province of central Utah (Kelly, 1955). In Fig. 2.14a a member of the Chimney Rock fault system juxtaposes beds of limestone, siltstone, and mudstone of the Middle Jurassic Carmel Formation (to the left) against the massive Jurassic Navajo Sandstone (to the right). Because the Carmel Formation immediately overlies the Navajo Sandstone in the normal stratigraphic sequence, we deduce that the Carmel Formation exposed in this photograph has moved downward on the fault relative to the Navajo Sandstone.

The fault pictured in Fig. 2.14a is a steeply

Carmel Formation

Fault surface

Navajo Sandstone

Slickenline

Fault surface

Fig 2.14 Outcrop in Navajo Sandstone and Carmel Formation near Chimney Rock, UT (Maerten et al., 2001). (a) Fault surface that can be approximated locally using a planar structural element. (b) Slickenlines that can be approximated using a linear element. Photograph by D. D. Pollard.

is not a good approximation. Many such elements positioned along the exposed trace of the fault could provide a good representation at the scale of the trace length. For smaller areas at this exposure there is a roughness associated with undulations and small steps on the exposed surfaces within the fault zone (Fig. 2.14b). To capture this roughness a map at the outcrop scale with many individual planar elements properly positioned and oriented, could provide a good representation. For still smaller areas individual grains of sand provide a roughness that precludes approximation as a single planar element. Similarly, beds of the Carmel Formation appear to be roughly planar at a scale of several square meters and are gently inclined toward the left-hand side of the photograph (Fig. 2.14a). They too have undulations at both larger and smaller scales that would require a redefinition of the size of the planar element. For our purposes the orientations of the fault and the beds at this outcrop can be represented by the orientations of planar elements that locally approximate these structures at the scale of about a square meter.

On many exposures of the Navajo Sandstone, where a member of the Chimney Rock fault system cuts it, curvilinear structures are visible called *slickenlines* or slickensides (Fig. 2.14b). These structures apparently resulted from the frictional sliding of the two rock masses over one another along the fault. If this is a correct interpretation the slickenlines trend in the direction of relative motion. Although the slickenlines are gently curved in detail, we can approximate them with linear elements with lengths from a few centimeters to several decimeters. The orientations of the slickenlines at this exposure are represented by the orientations of these linear elements. Because there is a range of orientations over the exposure, the question being addressed might require a detailed map of the surface with many distinct orientations at different locations on the surface. For our purposes we will take a single (average) orientation to represent the population.

The orientations of the planar and linear elements that approximate geologic structures in outcrop are defined relative to a local geographic coordinate system composed of east, north, and up (Fig. 2.15). Structural geologists use a small

inclined and somewhat undulating tabular zone of deformed rock. Within that zone are surfaces that can be approximated as planar over areas of a few square meters. If we were to consider a much larger area, we would find that the fault bends and even is segmented, so a single planar element hand-held instrument that combines a compass and an inclinometer with bubble levels to measure the necessary angles between the planar or linear elements and this coordinate system. Instructions for the use of such instruments are found in books on geological field methods (Compton, 1962; Davis and Reynolds, 1996) and most students will be introduced to their use at geological field camps. For the local coordinate system "up" is determined as the opposite direction to the local gravitational acceleration using the bubble levels, and this determines the horizontal plane that contains north and east. North is measured with the compass (corrected for the magnetic declination) and east is 90° clockwise from north when looking down on the horizontal plane.

Consider first the planar element that approximates the fault zone at the outcrop shown in Fig. 2.14a. Imagine a small lake lapping up against the fault. Because the water surface is a geoid (everywhere perpendicular to the down direction), the intersection of the water and the planar element defines a horizontal line that is referred to as the *line of strike*. Of course this line, and any line for that matter, points in two directions, so we must establish a convention to specify which of the two directions to measure. The convention is one of many so-called *right-hand rules* that are used in structural geology. Position yourself on the structure in the field (or imagine positioning yourself on the planar element that approximates that structure) and look along the line of strike such that the structure (planar element) slopes down to your right. The *dip direction* is the direction the outstretched fingers of your right hand would point if you raised your right arm to the horizontal plane (Fig. 2.15a). In other words the strike direction is along the line of strike such that the dip direction is to the right. The strike and dip directions are orthogonal to one another in the horizontal plane.

Either the azimuth of the strike direction or the azimuth of the dip direction is used to relate these directions to the local geographic coordinate system. The *azimuth* is the clockwise angle, α, looking down on the horizontal plane, measured from north to that direction. Thus, azimuths vary from 000° (north) to 090° (east) to 180° (south) to

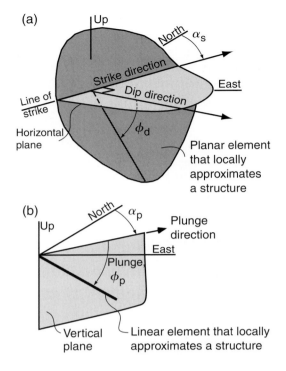

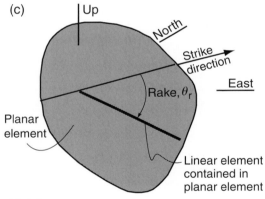

Fig 2.15 Diagrams used to define orientations of structural elements. Different azimuth angles, α, and angles of inclination, ϕ, are distinguished by appropriate subscripts. (a) Strike and dip of a planar element. (b) Plunge direction and plunge of a linear element. (c) Rake of a linear element in a planar element.

270° (west) to just less than 360°, and it is a convention to use three digits when specifying any azimuth. The azimuth of the strike direction, α_s, is the *strike* of the planar element that approximates the structure (Fig. 2.15a). In casual conversation this would be referred to as the strike of the structure. For the example illustrated in Fig. 2.14a we would refer to the "strike of the fault," and the fact that the fault is not simply a plane in space would be left unspoken. To understand what someone means by the strike of a fault, both the nature of the surface within the fault zone and the size of the planar element should be identified.

Knowing the strike of a planar element enables one to identify the orientation of the line of intersection of that element with a horizontal plane. There are an infinite number of elements that share the same strike, but vary in inclination, so we have to define a second angle that is a measure of this inclination in order to determine uniquely the orientation of a particular planar element relative to the local geographic coordinate system. This angle, ϕ_d, is measured in a vertical plane that contains the dip direction, from the dip direction to the planar element in question (Fig. 2.15a). This angle is referred to as the *dip* of the planar element that approximates the structure, and by convention two digits are used to specify the dip. Thus, a dip of seven degrees would be written 07°. Note that the angle measured from the horizontal plane to the planar element in vertical planes of other orientations would be smaller than the dip. Such an angle is referred to as an *apparent dip*. Apparent dips are commonly observed and measured in the field where exposures cut obliquely across structures.

Only two angles are necessary to reference a planar element to the local geographic coordinate system. Some use the strike and dip (α_s, ϕ_d), whereas others use the dip direction and dip (α_d, ϕ_d). Because of the construction of some field instruments it may be more convenient to measure and record the strike. On the other hand, the dip direction and dip require the identification of only one direction and that direction corresponds more directly to the inclination of the planar element that is measured. If the dip direction and dip were used, the number pair (085, 37) would indicate a planar element with a dip direction just 5° to the north of east and an inclination of 37° in that same direction. The degree symbol is left off for recording convenience. The number pair (355, 37), plus the right-hand rule, would identify the same planar

element using strike and dip. The relations between dip direction and strike direction are:

$$\alpha_d = \alpha_s + 90°, \quad 0° < \phi_d \leq 90° \quad (2.63)$$

Two special cases are noteworthy. For a horizontal planar element the dip is zero, so the strike and dip direction are undefined and we would write (UDF, 00) for the strike (or dip) direction and dip:

$$\alpha_s = UDF = \alpha_d, \quad \phi_d = 0° \quad (2.64)$$

For a vertical planar element the dip is 90°, but there are two possible strike (and dip) directions, and either one is suitable. For example, the strike and dip of a vertical plane with line of strike recorded in the field as (136, 90) could equally well be recorded as (316, 90).

Next consider the orientations of linear elements that approximate structures such as the slickenlines in Fig. 2.14b. These also are defined with respect to the local geographic coordinate system composed of east, north, and up (Fig. 2.15b). The first step is to imagine a vertical plane that contains the linear element. Position yourself over the structure at the exposure (or imagine positioning yourself over the line segment) such that the structure (line segment) is inclined downward in front of you. The *plunge direction* is the direction of your view in the horizontal plane. The azimuth of the plunge direction, α_p, is sometimes referred to as the *trend* of the linear element and it is specified using three digits. The angle ϕ_p measured in the vertical plane from the plunge direction down to the linear element is defined as the *plunge* and it is specified using two digits.

Two angles, the plunge direction and the plunge (α_p, ϕ_p) are necessary to reference a linear element to the local geographic coordinate system and these would be recorded, for example, as (356, 58) indicating a linear trend just a few degrees west of north and plunging 58° in that direction. Again, two special cases are noteworthy. For a vertical linear element the plunge is 90°, so the plunge direction is undefined:

$$\alpha_p = UDF, \quad \phi_p = 90° \quad (2.65)$$

This line would be recorded as (UDF, 90). For a horizontal element the plunge is 0°, so there are two possible plunge directions and either one can be used. Thus, the same horizontal linear element could be recorded as (022, 00) or (202, 00).

Some curvilinear structures lie in curved surfaces that are well-defined structures themselves. For example, the slickenlines shown in Fig. 2.14b are in the surface of a fault. For these cases the strike and dip of the planar element that represents the surface are recorded, along with an angle known as the *rake* that can be measured on the exposure with a protractor (Fig. 2.15c). The rake is the angle, θ_r, measured in the plane of the element from the strike direction down to the linear element. It is recorded using three digits and can vary from 000° (the linear element is parallel to the line of strike of the planar element) to just less than 180°:

$$000° \leq \theta_r < 180° \qquad (2.66)$$

For $\theta_r = 090°$ the linear element is inclined directly down the dip of the planar element. Of course one could measure the plunge direction and plunge of this line, but often it is simpler to measure the strike and dip of the planar element and the rake angle in this planar element.

Structural geologists refer to the *attitude of a structure* and by that they mean the orientation in space, relative to the local geographic coordinate system, of the planar or linear element that approximates (is tangential to) the structure at the point of measurement. Thus, the attitude of a fault at a particular location would be recorded as the strike and dip, or the dip direction and dip. The attitude of a slickenline on that fault would be recorded as the plunge direction and the plunge. These measurements are represented on maps using symbols and numbers placed at the appropriate location. Some of the symbols used on structural maps are illustrated in Fig. 2.16, extracted from a more extensive table of symbols in a manual of field geology (Compton, 1962). For most of these symbols, longer line segments are drawn parallel to the strike direction so the azimuth can be determined with reference to the north direction on the map. Shorter line segments indicate the dip direction and arrows indicate the plunge direction. Numbers set near the shorter line segments record the dip or plunge angle. The style of the line segments is used to distinguish different structures that are approximated as planar or linear elements. For example, note the different symbols for joints and veins or dikes. In this way a lot of information is conveyed in a compact form on the map, and structures can be related to one another in terms of their locations.

2.3.2 Stereographic projection of structural elements

It is useful to have a graphical means to visualize the attitudes of planar and linear structural elements. The most effective tools for this purpose are a family of projections that create an image of the elements on a flat piece of paper. The locations of the structures are not recorded in this image, but their orientations relative to the geographic coordinate system are recorded. Here we introduce one of these projections, the so-called *stereographic projection*. Details concerning the use of this projection, and other members of this family of projections, can be found in books devoted to the subject (Phillips, 1954; Ragan, 1985; Marshak and Mitra, 1988). In some courses in structural geology much of the student's time is committed to the manipulation of these projections by hand and many of the geometric problems encountered in fieldwork are described in these reference works. Here we adopt the more analytical approach described by Goodman and Shi (1985, p. 56) that avoids the tedium and inaccuracy of hand constructions. We also take advantage of the visualization power of modern computer applications for plotting quantitative field data.

We begin by reviewing the basic concepts and present the analytical expressions necessary to plot stereographic projections of planar and linear structural elements. Consider a linear element fixed in space at the center, *C*, of a transparent sphere called the *reference sphere* (Fig. 2.17a). Only the part of the linear element extending from *C* to the point *P* on the sphere is shown. Points such as *P* are projected onto the equatorial plane of this sphere and the intersection of the sphere and this plane is called the *reference circle*. Points on the reference circle represent the four compass directions (north, east, south, and west), and the axis perpendicular to the equatorial plane intersects the top of the sphere at the zenith, *Z*. In the view shown in this figure the sphere is rotated

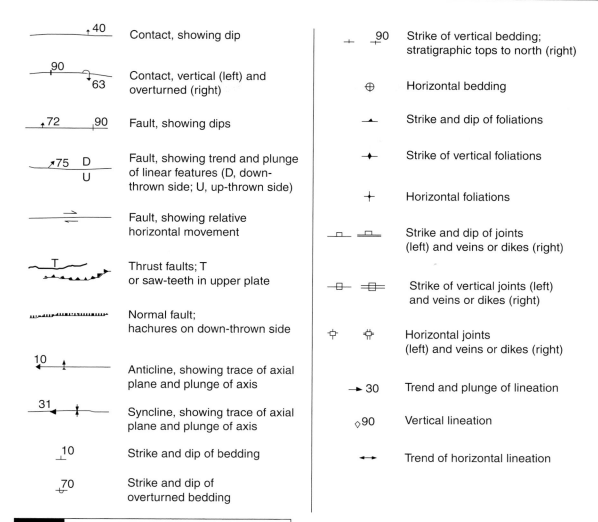

Fig 2.16 Selection of symbols used on structural maps to indicate type of structure and orientation (Compton, 1962).

somewhat about the east–west axis, so the upper surface of the equatorial plane inside the reference circle is visible as a shaded elliptical surface. Thus, the zenith has moved toward the observer and appears somewhat below what appears as the top of the sphere. The zenith is chosen as the perspective point for the stereographic projections described here. One also may choose the bottom of the reference sphere as the perspective point. The intersection of the linear element with the lower hemisphere is a point, P, and this point is projected to the point P' on the equatorial plane along the line ZP from the zenith. By convention

only the intersection of the linear element with the lower hemisphere is projected. The point where the linear element would intersect the upper hemisphere projects to a point on the equatorial plane that is outside the reference circle.

The scales for plotting the point representing the linear element are provided by the *meridional stereographic net*, sometimes called the Wulff net after G. V. Wulff who published a version in 1902, or the equal angle net, or the stereonet (Phillips, 1954). Later in this section we show how to construct the stereonet itself, but we start with a simpler construction, which provides the technique for plotting linear elements. An example of a stereonet is given in Fig. 2.17b where we note that the net is composed of a family of arcs of

(a)

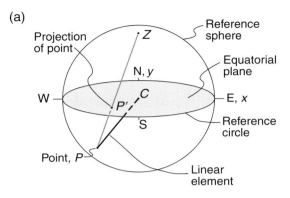

(b)

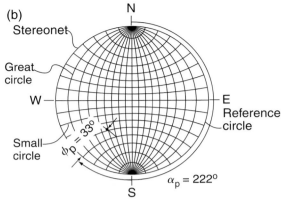

(c)

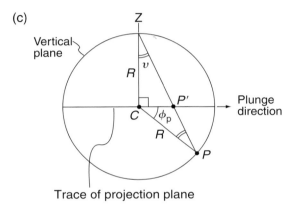

(d)

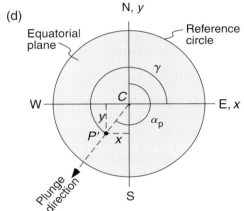

Fig 2.17 Stereographic projection of linear element.
(a) Reference sphere. (b) Meridional stereographic projection or equal angle net. (c) Vertical plane passing through center of reference sphere and containing linear element.
(d) Equatorial plane.

---

great circles (meridians) running from north to south and an orthogonal family of arcs of small circles. Both the great and small circular arcs are restricted to the interior of the reference circle. The plunge direction, α_p, of the linear element is measured from north clockwise around the reference circle. The plunge angle, ϕ_p, is measured from the reference circle toward the center to the appropriate point along the radial line that is coincident with the plunge direction. Thus, linear elements with shallow plunges project as points lying close to, but just inside the reference circle, whereas steeply plunging linear elements project as points near the center, C.

An example of a linear element with plunge direction and plunge of (222, 33) is plotted on the stereonet in Fig. 2.17b. Plotting the point representing the element by hand is accomplished on a sheet of transparent material pinned through the center of the net and marked with the north direction at the top of the net. The overlay is rotated counterclockwise through an angle equal to the azimuth of the plunge direction and the plunge angle is scaled off from the reference circle at north toward the center using the small circles for a scale. On this net the small circles are drawn every 10°. The point so identified is marked on the overlay and the overlay is rotated back to the original orientation as shown in Fig. 2.17b.

Locating the point representing a linear element on a stereographic projection may be done analytically, so a computer can plot the projection rather than your hand. Consider a vertical plane passing through the center of the sphere and containing the plunge direction (Fig. 2.17c). The radius of the sphere is R. The angle

PCP' is the plunge, ϕ_p, and we define the angle CZP as ν. The distance from the center, C, to the projected point is:

$$CP' = R \tan \nu \qquad (2.67)$$

Because $CP = CZ = R$, the triangle $CZPC$ is isosceles and the angle ZPC also is ν. Therefore, the two angles are related as:

$$\nu = 45° - \frac{1}{2}\phi_p \qquad (2.68)$$

Substituting for ν in the previous equation we write the distance of the projected point from the center as:

$$CP' = R \tan\left(45° - \frac{1}{2}\phi_p\right) \qquad (2.69)$$

CP' varies from R to 0 as the plunge angle varies from $0°$ to $90°$.

The next step is to determine the coordinates of the projected point, P', relative to a Cartesian coordinate system with center at C and the x-axis and y-axis positive toward east and north respectively (Fig. 2.17d). The point representing the linear element is located along the radial line in the plunge direction at the distance CP' from the center. In the Cartesian system the coordinates of the point P' are related to the angle γ, measured counterclockwise from Ox to the line CP', as:

$$x = CP'\cos\gamma, \ y = CP'\sin\gamma \qquad (2.70)$$

Furthermore, the angle γ is related to the plunge direction, α_p, as $\gamma = 90° - \alpha_p$, so the coordinates of the point P' are:

$$x = CP'\sin\alpha_p, \ y = CP'\cos\alpha_p \qquad (2.71)$$

Utilizing (2.69) to substitute for the distance CP', we have:

$$x = R \tan\left(45° - \frac{1}{2}\phi_p\right)\sin\alpha_p$$
$$\qquad (2.72)$$
$$y = R \tan\left(45° - \frac{1}{2}\phi_p\right)\cos\alpha_p$$

These are the equations used to plot the projection of a linear element on a stereonet of radius R, given the azimuth of plunge, α_p, and angle of plunge, ϕ_p.

Next consider a planar element fixed in space at the center, C, of the transparent reference sphere (Fig. 2.18a). For the sake of an example we take the dip direction and dip as (118, 26). The intersection of the planar element with the sphere is a so-called *great circle*, because it is a circle and because this circle has the largest possible radius of all those formed by planes of this orientation intersecting the sphere. In fact it has the same radius as the reference sphere, R. A planar element not passing through the center of the sphere also intersects the sphere to form a circle, but this is called a *small circle*, because it has a radius that is less than the radius of the reference sphere. Only the intersection of the planar element with the lower hemisphere is drawn and a straight line marks the intersection of this element with the equatorial plane. The stereographic projection is constructed by connecting lines of sight from the zenith, Z, to points such as G on the half great circle. The line ZG intersects the equatorial plane at the point G', which is the projection of the point G. All possible lines ZG from the zenith to the half great circle intersect the equatorial plane along a circular arc, and this arc is the stereographic projection of the half great circle. Note that the radius of this circular arc is greater than the radius of the reference circle, R, unless the dip of the planar element is zero. In this special case the half great circle representing the planar element is coincident with the reference circle.

The line of strike, $\alpha_s = 28°$, connects the end points of the projected half great circle at the reference circle (Fig. 2.18b). The strike direction is that direction viewed along the line of strike with the trace of the circular arc to the right. Any azimuth, such as the strike direction, α_s, or the dip direction, α_d, is measured from north clockwise around the reference circle. The dip angle, ϕ_d, is measured from the reference circle to the circular arc along a radial line in the equatorial plane that is coincident with the dip direction. Thus, planar elements with shallow dips project as nearly complete half circular arcs lying close to the reference circle, whereas steeply dipping planar elements project as nearly straight lines approaching the line of strike. Constructing the circular arc by hand is accomplished on a sheet of transparent material pined through the center

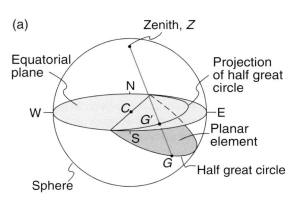

(a)

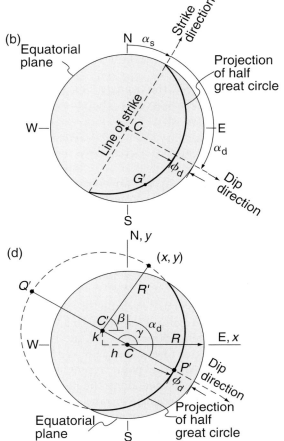

(b)

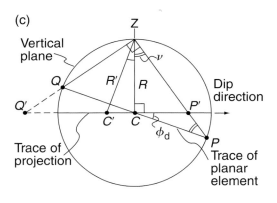

(c)

(d)

Fig 2.18 Stereographic projection of planar element.
(a) Reference sphere. (b) Projection of half great circle onto
equatorial plane. (c) Vertical plane passing through center
of reference sphere and containing the dip direction.
(d) Equatorial plane with projection of whole circle.

of the stereonet and marked with the north
direction at the top of the net. The overlay is then
rotated counterclockwise through the angle of
strike and the dip is scaled off from the reference
circle at east toward the center using the great
circles of the net for a scale. The great circle so
identified is traced on the overlay and the overlay
is rotated back to the original orientation to
produce the graphical representation of the
planar element shown in Fig. 2.18b.

To avoid the tedious and inaccurate process of
hand construction we seek analytical expressions
for plotting the circular arc representing a planar
element on a stereographic projection by com-

puter. Consider a vertical plane passing through
the center of the sphere, C, and containing the
dip direction (Fig. 2.18c). The horizontal line is the
trace of the projection (equatorial) plane and the
line segment PQ is the trace of the planar
element. The point P' is the projection of P onto
the equatorial plane from a perspective at the
zenith, Z, and the point Q' is the projection of the
point Q. The points P' and Q' lie on the projected
circle and the line segment $P'Q'$ is a diameter of
that circle. An arc of this circle is the stereographic projection of the half great circle, so we
seek the center and radius of this projected circle
in order to plot it.

The angle PCP' is the dip, ϕ_d, of the planar
element and the angle CZP is defined as ν. By the
same argument leading to (2.68), the two angles
are related as $\nu = 45° - \phi_d/2$. Using this relation
and the triangle $CZP'C$, the angle $ZP'C$ is related to
the dip as:

angle $ZP'C = 90° - \nu = 45° + \dfrac{1}{2}\phi_d$ (2.73)

Because PQ is a diameter of the sphere, QZP is a right angle, so $Q'ZP'Q'$ is a right triangle. If the line segment $C'Z$ bisects the hypotenuse of this right triangle, then $C'P' = C'Z$ and we define this length as R', which is the radius of the projected circle. Furthermore, because the triangle $C'ZP'C'$ is isosceles, the angles $ZP'C'$ and $C'ZP'$ are equal. Using this fact and the previous equation we have:

$$45° + \frac{1}{2}\phi_d = \text{angle } C'ZC + \nu$$ (2.74)

Solving for the angle $C'ZC$ we find that this angle must be equal to the angle of dip, ϕ_d. The trigonometry of the right triangle $C'ZCC'$ provides the distance, CC', from the center of the sphere to the center of the projected circle and the radius of that circle, R':

$$CC' = R\tan\phi_d, \ R' = \frac{R}{\cos\phi_d}$$ (2.75)

As the dip of the planar element varies from $0°$ to $90°$, the distance CC' varies from $0°$ to ∞, and the radius of the projected circle varies from R to ∞. Thus, the projected arc of the half great circle varies from being coincident with half the reference circle to being coincident with the straight line of strike.

For plotting purposes a Cartesian coordinate system is established with origin at the center, C, of the equatorial plane and the x-axis and y-axis are taken as positive toward east and north, respectively (Fig. 2.18d). The coordinates of points on the projected circle are given by:

$$\left. \begin{array}{l} x = h + R'\cos\beta \\ y = k + R'\sin\beta \end{array} \right\} \quad 0 \le \beta < 2\pi$$ (2.76)

Here (h, k) are the coordinates of the center, C', of the projected circle and R' is the radius. The point C' is at a distance CC' on a radial line oriented at $180°$ from the dip direction. The coordinates (h, k) are related to the angle γ, measured counterclockwise from Ox to this radial line:

$$h = CC'\cos\gamma = -CC'\sin\alpha_d$$
$$k = CC'\sin\gamma = -CC'\cos\alpha_d$$ (2.77)

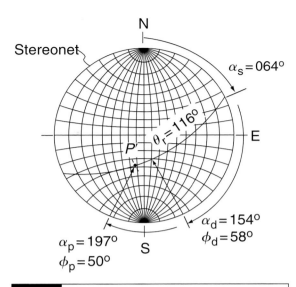

$\alpha_s = 064°$

$\theta_r = 116°$

$\alpha_d = 154°$
$\phi_d = 58°$

$\alpha_p = 197°$
$\phi_p = 50°$

Fig 2.19 Meridional stereographic net with projection of linear element within planar element.

The second step in each of these equations follows from the fact that the angle γ is related to the dip direction, α_d, as $\gamma = 270° - \alpha_d$. Substituting (2.75) and (2.77) in (2.76) we have:

$$x = -R\tan\phi_d\sin\alpha_d + (R/\cos\phi_d)\cos\beta$$
$$y = -R\tan\phi_d\cos\alpha_d + (R/\cos\phi_d)\sin\beta$$ (2.78)

These are the equations used to plot the projected circle representing the orientation of a planar element on a stereonet of radius R, given the azimuth of dip, α_d, and the angle of dip, ϕ_d. To plot the whole circle one uses the range $0 \le \beta < 2\pi$. To restrict the plot to the circular arc lying within the reference circle (Fig. 2.18d), in other words the projection of the half great circle, the further condition on the coordinates is $(x^2 + y^2)^{1/2} \le R$.

Slickenlines lying in the plane of a fault (Fig. 2.14) are idealized as linear elements contained within planar elements on a stereographic projection (Fig. 2.19). The linear element projects to the point P' and falls on the great circle representing the planar element. The rake angle, θ_r, is measured from the point on the reference circle, representing the strike direction of the planar element, along the great circle to the point P'. The example shown in Fig. 2.19 is for a linear element

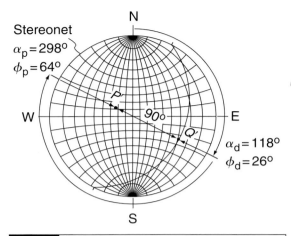

Fig 2.20 Meridional stereographic net with projection of linear element that is perpendicular to a planar element.

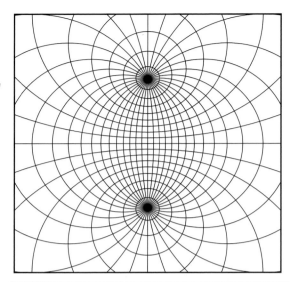

Fig 2.21 Meridional stereographic net plotted both inside and outside the reference circle.

with a rake of 116 lying in a planar element with strike and dip of (064, 58).

Any plane can be oriented in three-dimensional space by identifying the orientation of the perpendicular line, referred to as the *normal to a planar element*. Consider, for example, the planar element with strike and dip (028, 26) shown in Fig. 2.20. To understand the relationship of the normal to the other attributes of planar elements consider a line element that lies in the planar element and plunges with the same angle as the dip. This line element is represented by the point Q' on the stereonet whereas the normal plots at point P'. These points lie along a straight line, oriented in the dip direction that passes through the center of the stereonet. The smaller of the two angles between the normal and the linear element measured in this vertical plane is 90°. The point P' sometimes is referred to as the *pole of a planar element*.

The final topic in our discussion of stereographic projections is the construction of the meridional stereographic net itself (Fig. 2.21). The net is composed of two sets of great circles representing the projections of planes with common dip directions either to the east or to the west, and dip angles between 0° and 90°:

$$\alpha_d = 90°, \quad 0° \le \phi_d \le 90° \text{ and}$$

$$\alpha_d = 270°, \quad 0° \le \phi_d \le 90° \tag{2.79}$$

The dip interval between successive great circles is arbitrary and is taken as $\Delta\phi_d = 10°$ for the construction of this net. For plotting purposes the number of great circles in each set is $n = (90°/\Delta\phi_d) + 1$. For these two sets of great circles the general plotting equations for planar elements (2.78) reduce to:

$$x = \mp R\tan\phi_d + (R/\cos\phi_d)\cos\beta$$

$$y = (R/\cos\phi_d)\sin\beta \tag{2.80}$$

To plot great circles covering the full stereonet (with the exception of points near the zenith) one uses the range $0 \le \beta \le 2\pi$. To restrict the plot to the interior of the reference circle the further condition on the coordinates is $(x^2 + y^2)^{1/2} \le R$.

There are two sets of small circles on the meridional stereonet. In general any small circle on the stereonet can be thought of as the projection of the intersection of a cone with the reference sphere (Goodman and Shi, 1985, p. 71). The apex of the cone is at the center of the sphere and the cone itself can be generated by a set of lines that make a common angle, γ, with a vector, Rv/v that extends from the center to the perimeter of the reference sphere (Fig. 2.22). The vector is normalized by dividing each component by the vector

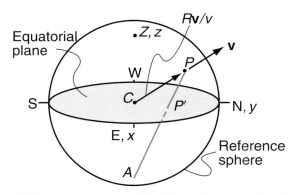

Fig 2.22 Reference sphere with arbitrary vector **v** and normalized vector $R\mathbf{v}/v$ extending from center to perimeter.

magnitude, v. This produces a unit vector, which then is scaled by the radius of the sphere, R. This normalized vector is related to its components as:

$$\frac{R\mathbf{v}}{v} = \left(\frac{Rv_x}{v}\right)\mathbf{e}_x + \left(\frac{Rv_y}{v}\right)\mathbf{e}_y + \left(\frac{Rv_z}{v}\right)\mathbf{e}_z \qquad (2.81)$$

The radius of the small circle, R', and the coordinates of the center of the small circle (h, k) are (Goodman and Shi, 1985, p. 75):

$$R' = \frac{R\sin\gamma}{(Rv_z/v) + \cos\gamma}, \quad h = \frac{(Rv_x/v)}{(Rv_z/v) + \cos\gamma},$$

$$k = \frac{(Rv_y/v)}{(Rv_z/v) + \cos\gamma} \qquad (2.82)$$

Substituting these equations into (2.76) we find the coordinates of points on a projected small circle centered on the vector $R\mathbf{v}/v$ with apical angle 2γ.

For the two sets of small circles on the meridional stereonet, all of the vectors are directed north or south, along the y-axis, so $Rv_y/v = \pm R$ and $Rv_x/v = 0 = Rv_z/v$. Therefore the coordinates of points on these small circles are:

$$x = R\tan\gamma\cos\beta$$
$$y = \pm(R/\cos\gamma) + R\tan\gamma\sin\beta \qquad (2.83)$$

The angular interval between successive small circles is arbitrary and is taken as $\Delta\gamma = 10°$ for the construction of this net (Fig. 2.21).

There are many applications for stereographic projections in structural geology, and some of

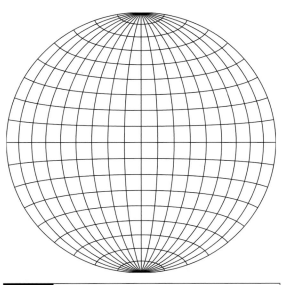

Fig 2.23 Lambert equal area projection or Schmidt net.

these require more elaborate techniques for plotting structural data on stereonets. Most of these graphical constructions can be derived from the elementary concepts and procedures introduced here and therefore can be implemented on a computer rather than a piece of paper. For example, common problems include determining true dip from apparent dip of a planar element, and determining the orientation of the line of intersection of two planar elements (Marshak and Mitra, 1988, Chapter 5). An example of a more complicated problem is based on the fact that the poles to bedding surfaces within a cylindrical fold follow a path along a small circle, as the surfaces are unfolded or refolded about the fold axis (Marshak and Mitra, 1988, p. 119). For additional coverage of these and other graphical constructions using the stereonet, one should refer to specialized books on geometric techniques (Phillips, 1954; Ragan, 1985; Marshak and Mitra, 1988).

2.3.3 Equal area projection and graphical orientation statistics

Projections other than the stereographic projection have been invoked to solve important geometrical problems in structural geology. For example, the *Lambert equal area projection* is associated with the so-called *Schmidt net* (Fig. 2.23), which

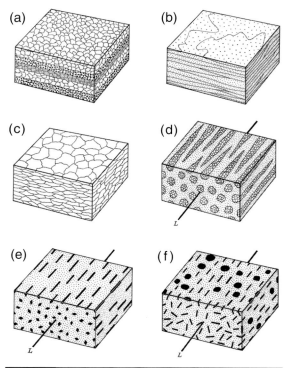

Fig 2.24 Schematic illustrations of rock fabrics. Planar fabrics consisting of (a) different rock types, (b) sub-parallel fractures, and (c) platy mineral grains. Linear fabrics consisting of (d) elongate clusters of mineral grains, (e) prismatic grains, and (f) platy mineral grains with common direction. Reprinted from Turner and Weiss (1963) with permission from McGraw-Hill.

statistics of structural elements that define a *rock fabric*. Fabric in this context refers to the internal arrangement of the physical constituents that make up the rock mass. For example, planar fabrics in metamorphic rocks (Turner and Weiss, 1963, p. 97) can be composed of layers of different rock types (Fig. 2.24a), a set of sub-parallel fractures (Fig. 2.24b), or a set of similarly oriented platy mineral grains (Fig. 2.24c). In metamorphic rocks such structures are referred to as a *metamorphic foliation*, but planar fabrics can be found in sedimentary and igneous rocks. In these illustrations there is little doubt that the constituents are arranged in a very orderly manner such that the normals to the different layers or fractures or platy mineral grains are oriented in almost exactly the same direction. The constituents of a rock mass also may be arranged to form a *metamorphic lineation* (Turner and Weiss, 1963, p. 102). Examples include elongate clusters of mineral grains (Fig. 2.24d) and individual prismatic grains (Fig. 2.24e) that point in almost the same direction. Platy mineral grains (Fig. 2.24f) that contain a particular direction form a lineation.

It is not uncommon, however, for rock fabrics to be less obvious than the schematic illustrations of Fig. 2.24. In these instances it is necessary to analyze the orientations of the constituents and determine whether or not these data could have resulted from a random sampling of a population that has no *preferred orientation*. In cases such as slickenlines the lineation may have a direction that must be considered (Davis, 1986). An analysis of orientation or direction data can be purely graphical, in which case the Lambert equal area projection and the Schmidt net are well suited to the task of preparing the so-called *fabric diagram*. Methods have been devised for hand contouring the number of points per unit area on the Schmidt net (Marshak and Mitra, 1988, p. 148). For example, a counting circle with an area that is 1% of the area of the net is positioned at every intersection of a regular grid covering the net. The number of points in the counter is associated with each grid intersection and these numbers are contoured. A nested set of contours encloses a cluster of points and serves to identify a direction of preferred orientation. Graphical methods that

looks very much like the stereonet, but has the desirable feature that areas bounded by pairs of adjacent great and small circles, each separated by the same number of degrees, have the same surface area (Phillips, 1954). In other words this net satisfies the cartographic criterion of *equivalency*, i.e. the correct representation of areas. Note that such areas clearly are not of equal size on the stereonet (Fig. 2.21), where pairs of great and small circles are separated by 10°. For example, a 10° by 10° area near the center of this net is smaller than one near east or west along the reference circle. Therefore, a set of points plotted near the center of the stereonet would appear to be more densely clustered than a set with the same angular relations plotted near the reference circle.

The need for equivalency is most apparent in structural studies that address the orientation include considerations of statistics (Fisher, 1953) have advantages over these contouring methods, so examples are presented after we describe how to prepare the fabric diagram.

The first step in the preparation of the fabric diagram is the plotting of points that represent the orientations of line elements (e.g. the normals to foliations or the lineations) on the Schmidt net. Consider a reference sphere of radius R with an arbitrarily oriented line segment passing through the center, C, and intersecting the lower hemisphere at the point P. We view the line segment CP in a vertical plane that contains the plunge direction (Fig. 2.25a). Unlike the stereographic projection, the equal area projection plane is tangent to the sphere at the antipode, A. Given the relation (2.68) between the angle ν and the plunge angle, ϕ_p, the angle ACP is:

$$\text{Angle } ACP = 180° - 90° - \phi_p = 90° - \phi_p = 2\nu \tag{2.84}$$

Because $AC = CP = R$, the triangle $ACPA$ is isosceles and angle CPA is equal to angle PAC, so:

$$\text{Angle } CPA = \frac{1}{2}(180° - 2\nu) = 90° - \nu \tag{2.85}$$

Because the angle ZPC is ν, the angle ZPA is a right angle and the triangle $AZPA$ is a right triangle with hypothenuse $2R$. Using this right triangle the distance, AP, from the antipode to the point in question is:

$$AP = 2R \sin \nu \tag{2.86}$$

It is a property of the Lambert equal area projection that the distance AP' from the antipode to the projected point, P', is equal to the distance AP. Substituting for the angle ν using (2.68) we relate this distance to the plunge angle:

$$AP' = AP = 2R \sin\left(45° - \frac{1}{2}\phi_p\right) \tag{2.87}$$

Geometrically this step in the Lambert projection can be accomplished by turning a circle with center at A through the point in question onto the projection plane (Ragan, 1985, p. 273).

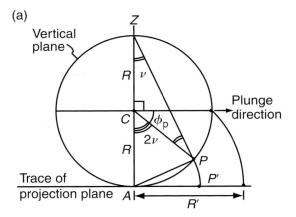

(a)

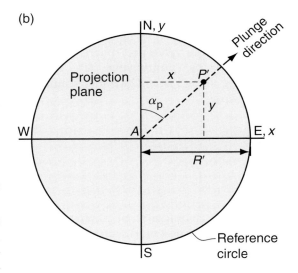

(b)

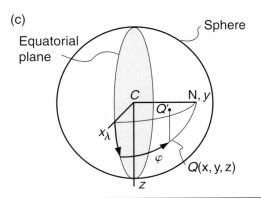

(c)

Fig 2.25 Lambert equal area projection of a linear element. (a) Vertical plane containing the linear element. (b) Equatorial projection plane. (c) Reference sphere.

The next step in the projection procedure considers the projection plane itself (Fig. 2.25b). Linear elements with zero plunge project onto the reference circle in this view, so (2.87) gives the radius of the reference circle as:

$$R' = 2R\sin(45°) = R\sqrt{2} \qquad (2.88)$$

The arbitrarily oriented point P' is associated with a plunge direction, α_p, measured clockwise from north. Taking a Cartesian coordinate system with x- and y-axes coincident with east and north, respectively, the coordinates of the point P' are:

$$x = AP'\sin\alpha_p, \quad y = AP'\cos\alpha_p \qquad (2.89)$$

It is convenient to scale the reference circle of the equal area projection so its radius, R', is equal to the radius of the reference sphere, R. This is accomplished by multiplying AP' by $\frac{1}{2}\sqrt{2}$. Substituting for AP' from (2.87) and scaling the radius we have:

$$x = R\sqrt{2}\sin\left(45° - \frac{1}{2}\phi_p\right)\sin\alpha_p$$

$$\qquad (2.90)$$

$$y = R\sqrt{2}\sin\left(45° - \frac{1}{2}\phi_p\right)\cos\alpha_p$$

These are the coordinates of a point on the Schmidt net of radius R representing the orientation of a linear element with plunge direction, α_p, and plunge angle, ϕ_p. For foliations or other planar fabrics the azimuth and plunge of the normal, α_n and ϕ_n, are substituted in these equations to prepare the fabric diagram.

The Schmidt net itself is plotted as the meridians and parallels of a sphere of radius R, oriented such that the poles, north and south, are on the horizontal y-axis (Fig. 2.25c). Note that this illustration of the sphere is rotated slightly about the vertical z-axis so the equatorial plane is visible. Longitude angles, λ, are measured from the horizontal x-axis around the equatorial perimeter and latitude angles, φ, are measured along a meridian from the equator toward the poles. The equations relating longitude and latitude to the Cartesian coordinates are:

$$x = R\cos\varphi\cos\lambda, \quad y = R\sin\varphi, \quad z = R\cos\varphi\sin\lambda \quad (2.91)$$

An arbitrary point, $Q(x, y, z)$, at the intersection of a particular meridian and parallel corresponds to a linear element through the center of the sphere. This point projects onto the horizontal (x, y)-plane at Q' and the distance $CQ' = (x^2 + y^2)^{1/2}$. Furthermore, the cosine of the plunge angle, ϕ_p, is CQ'/R. Using these relationships as shown in Fig. 2.25c, the plunge direction and plunge are:

$$\alpha_p = \frac{1}{2}\pi - \tan^{-1}(y/x),$$

$$\phi_p = \cos^{-1}[(x^2 + y^2)^{1/2}/R] \qquad (2.92)$$

Given the longitude and latitude of points on a particular meridian or parallel, the first set of equations establishes the Cartesian coordinates and the second provides the plunge direction and plunge. These two angles are used in (2.90) to project and plot the points. The longitude intervals between successive meridians is arbitrary and is taken as $\Delta\lambda = 10°$ for the construction of Fig. 2.23. The range of longitudes is $0° \le \lambda \le 180°$ to cover the lower hemisphere. Similarly the latitude intervals between successive parallels is taken as $\Delta\varphi = 10°$, and the range of latitudes is $-90° < \varphi < 90°$.

Given the equations to construct the Schmidt net and to plot points representing linear elements on a fabric diagram, the most important question is whether or not the distribution of points has a statistically significant preferred orientation (Kamb, 1959a). This question is addressed graphically by relating the area of the counter used in the construction of contours on the diagram to the total number of points, N, in the population. The counter is a circle with area A_c that is some fraction, $0 \le f \le 1$, of the total area A_n of the Schmidt net:

$$f = \frac{A_c}{A_n} = \frac{\pi r^2}{\pi R^2} \qquad (2.93)$$

The center of the counting circle is positioned at every intersection of an r by r square grid laid over the projection. The number of points within the counter is recorded for each intersection and these numbers are contoured. What distinguishes this method from those mentioned earlier is the choice of the radius, r, of the counting circle.

To understand how r is determined consider a set of N points that have statistically uniform orientations over the entire net. In other words this population has no preferred orientation. As the counter is randomly positioned on the net the number of points within the counter, n, varies. The distribution of n is a *binomial distribution* because the counting circle divides the population into two mutually exclusive sets: those inside the counter and those outside. On average the number of points in the counter will be fN because the area of the counter is a fraction f of the area of the net. The mean, m, and standard deviation, s, of this binomial distribution are (Krumbein and Graybill, 1965, p. 102):

$$m = fN, \quad s = [fN(1-f)]^{1/2} \tag{2.94}$$

Recall that the standard deviation is a measure of the spread of the distribution about the mean. As the counter gets very small, $f \to 0$, $m \to 0$, and $s \to (fN)^{1/2}$. As the counter approaches the size of the net, $f \to 1$, $m \to N$, and $s \to 0$.

It is recommended (Kamb, 1959a) that the radius of the counter be chosen such that $m = 3s$. In other words, for the population with no preferred orientation, the number of points within the counter, on average, would be three times the standard deviation. The fabric diagrams can be contoured at values of 0, $2s$, $4s$, $6s$, etc. Contours drawn from counts using this prescription are very smooth. If such large counts cluster in one region of the fabric diagram and produce closed contours with values greater than $3s$, one can interpret the population as having a preferred orientation. Substituting the expressions for the mean and standard deviation from (2.94) into the condition $m = 3s$ and solving for f, we find:

$$f = \frac{9}{N+9} \tag{2.95}$$

Note that a 1% counter area, sometimes chosen arbitrarily for the contouring of fabric diagrams, corresponds to $N = 891$. This is an unusually large number of points for fabric studies. Implementations using a 1% area and fewer than 891 points are likely to produce irregular contours that have no statistical significance because the counter area is too small.

Substituting the ratio of areas for f in the previous equation, and solving for the radius of the counter, r, we have:

$$r = \frac{3R}{\sqrt{N+9}} \tag{2.96}$$

Given the radius of the Schmidt net, R, and the number of points, N, in the population (2.96) provides the radius of the counter and the distance between the intersection points of the square grid that overlays the net. Using the counter and grid so defined one can construct the orientation density diagram to display graphically the statistical significance of a data set containing the orientations of a linear fabric or the normals to a planar fabric.

2.3.4 Field and model angles and analytical orientation statistics

We turn now to the relationships between geographic angles and coordinates, and the angles and coordinates used in data analysis and model construction. Recall that the orientations of planar and linear elements that approximate geological structures are measured in the field using two geographic angles, the azimuth, α, and the inclination, ϕ. Different terms are associated with the azimuth of strike (α_s), dip (α_d), plunge (α_p), and normal (α_n), and appropriate subscripts distinguish these. Similarly, different subscripts for the inclination angle, ϕ, distinguish the dip (ϕ_d), plunge (ϕ_p), and plunge of the normal (ϕ_n). For any planar element the azimuth and plunge of the normal line (pole) may be used to specify the orientation, so in fact we only need to consider how line segments are oriented in three-dimensional space to account for the orientations of all linear and planar elements that approximate geological structures. For data analysis and model computations it is convenient to describe the orientation of any line segment using three *direction angles* (α_x, α_y, α_z) that relate the line to a Cartesian coordinate system, rather than the geographic system. Here we introduce the relationships that transform field data in the geographic coordinate system to a Cartesian system using these direction angles. The textbook by Groshong (1999) provides additional discussion of these and other techniques of three-dimensional geometry as used in structural geology.

Consider the orientation of the line segment OP relative to the orthogonal geographic coordinate system composed of the axes east, north, and up (Fig. 2.26a). Regardless of their specific geological (a)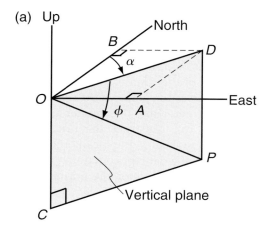

(b)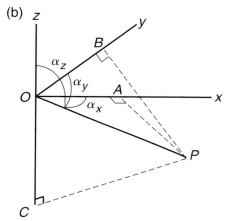

Fig 2.26 Field and model angles. (a) Geographic coordinate system with plunge direction, α, and plunge angle, ϕ, of line element. (b) Cartesian coordinate system with direction angles $(\alpha_x, \alpha_y, \alpha_z)$ of line element.

upward directed line segment (Goodman, 1980, p. 145), whereas structural geologists take the downward directed segment and refer to the angle as the plunge. Perhaps geologists typically gaze downward to observe structures in outcrops and mining engineers gaze upward to observe blocks of rock that may fall on their heads!

The line OP (Fig. 2.26a) projects onto the horizontal (east, north) plane as the line OD, and this line in turn projects onto the east and north axes as the lines OA and OB, respectively. The following three trigonometric equations relate these lines to the geographic angles:

$$\sin \alpha = \frac{OA}{OD}, \quad \cos \alpha = \frac{OB}{OD}, \quad \cos \phi = \frac{OD}{OP} \quad (2.98)$$

Here it is understood that OP and OD are inherently positive and OC is negative, but OA and OB are positive or negative depending upon their location on the positive or negative extensions of the respective coordinate axes. This accounts for the range of the azimuth and plunge.

Now consider a Cartesian coordinate system composed of axes x, y, and z (Fig. 2.26b) that shares the origin at O with the geographic system, and is oriented such that the respective axes are coincident with east, north, and up. The line OP projects onto the x-, y-, and z-axes as the lines OA, OB, and OC. The direction angle α_x is measured in the plane POA; the angle α_y is measured in the plane POB; and the angle α_z is measured in the plane POC. Each direction angle is the smaller of the two possible angles from the line OP to the positive extensions of the respective coordinate axis. Thus, the ranges of the direction angles are:

$$0 \leq \alpha_x \leq \pi, \quad 0 \leq \alpha_y \leq \pi, \quad \frac{\pi}{2} \leq \alpha_z \leq \pi \quad (2.99)$$

The following three trigonometric equations relate the projections of OP onto the coordinate axes and the line OP itself:

$$\cos \alpha_x = \frac{OA}{OP}, \quad \cos \alpha_y = \frac{OB}{OP}, \quad \cos \alpha_z = \frac{OC}{OP} \quad (2.100)$$

These are the *direction cosines* for the line OP with respect to the Cartesian coordinate system.

meaning, all azimuths, α, are defined as angles measured clockwise from north in the horizontal plane to the vertical plane $(ODPC)$ that contains the line. All plunges, ϕ, are defined as the angle measured downward in this vertical plane from the horizontal plane to the line. Thus the ranges of these two geographic angles are restricted as follows:

$$0 \leq \alpha < 2\pi, \quad 0 \leq \phi \leq \frac{\pi}{2} \quad (2.97)$$

It is interesting to note that mining engineers define the normal to planar elements as the

The transformation equations are constructed from the preceding trigonometric identities as follows:

$$\cos \alpha_x = \frac{OA}{OD}\frac{OD}{OP} = \sin \alpha \, \cos \phi$$

$$\cos \alpha_y = \frac{OB}{OD}\frac{OD}{OP} = \cos \alpha \, \cos \phi \qquad (2.101)$$

$$\cos \alpha_z = \frac{OC}{OP} = \cos\left(\frac{\pi}{2} + \phi\right) = -\sin \phi$$

In this way the direction cosines for the line OP are calculated from the azimuth and plunge of the linear element. The azimuth and plunge are recovered from the direction cosines using:

$$\alpha = \tan^{-1}\left[\frac{\cos \alpha_x}{\cos \alpha_y}\right], \quad \phi = \sin^{-1}[-\cos \alpha_z] \qquad (2.102)$$

To compute the full range for the azimuth, the signs of both the numerator and the denominator in the arctangent function must be used. Most computer languages offer a function such as ATAN2(XNUM, YNUM) that explicitly uses the two arguments with their signs.

The relationships we have just derived are used to develop an analytical method for determining the "mean" direction for a set of n linear elements or normals to planar elements (Davis, 1986). Consider each member of the set to be a *unit vector*, $\mathbf{u}(i)$, where $i = 1$ to n. For example, the line segment OP (Fig. 2.26) could represent one such unit vector:

$$\mathbf{u}(i) = u_x(i)\mathbf{e}_x + u_y(i)\mathbf{e}_y + u_z(i)\mathbf{e}_z$$

$$u(i) = [u_x^2(i) + u_y^2(i) + u_z^2(i)]^{1/2} = 1 \qquad (2.103)$$

The components of any vector are equal to the vector magnitude times the respective direction cosine (2.8), so in the case of a unit vector the components are the direction cosines. Using this relationship and (2.101) the components of the unit vector may be related to the azimuth, $\alpha(i)$, and plunge, $\phi(i)$, of the line element or normal.

The mean direction for a set of linear elements or normals taken as unit vectors is defined as the direction of the resultant vector, $\mathbf{U}$:

$$\mathbf{U} = U_x\mathbf{e}_x + U_y\mathbf{e}_y + U_z\mathbf{e}_z$$

$$U = [U_x^2 + U_y^2 + U_z^2]^{1/2} \qquad (2.104)$$

Note that the magnitude of the resultant vector does not have a unit value. The components of the resultant vector are found as the sums of the respective components of the set of unit vectors:

$$U_x = \sum_{i=1}^{n} u_x(i), \quad U_y = \sum_{i=1}^{n} u_y(i), \quad U_z = \sum_{i=1}^{n} u_z(i) \qquad (2.105)$$

The direction cosines of the resultant vector are given by the ratios of the components to the magnitude of this vector:

$$\cos \alpha_x = U_x/U, \quad \cos \alpha_y = U_y/U,$$

$$\cos \alpha_z = U_z/U \qquad (2.106)$$

The azimuth and plunge of the resultant vector ("mean" direction) are found using (2.102). If the unit vectors representing the direction data are widely scattered the magnitude U is small compared to n, whereas for tightly clustered data the magnitude of U approaches n. The spherical variance is defined (Davis, 1986, p. 334):

$$s_s^2 = (n - U)/n \qquad (2.107)$$

This is a measure of the clustering of the direction data about the mean.

2.4 | Structural mapping using GPS technology

2.4.1 The Chimney Rock fault array

The Chimney Rock fault array crops out on the northern San Rafael Swell (Fig. 2.27) and is exposed over an area of about 25 km² where the local stratigraphy (Fig. 2.28) is composed of the Jurassic Navajo Sandstone and overlying Carmel Formation (Maerten, 2000; Maerten *et al.*, 2001; Davatzes and Aydin, 2003). The lower Carmel is predominantly shale, sandy shale, and limestone beds. The top of the Navajo and three resistant limestone layers in the lower Carmel provided excellent marker horizons for mapping in this region and for determining the location, orientation, and offset on the faults. The traces of the

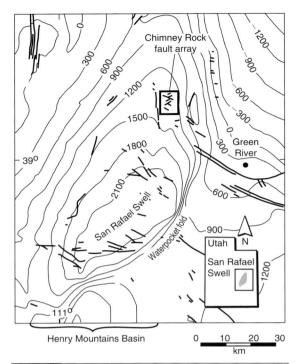

Fig 2.27 Structure contour map of San Rafael Swell region of south central Utah (Maerten, 2000). Contour interval is 300 feet. Location of Chimney Rock fault array indicated within rectangle.

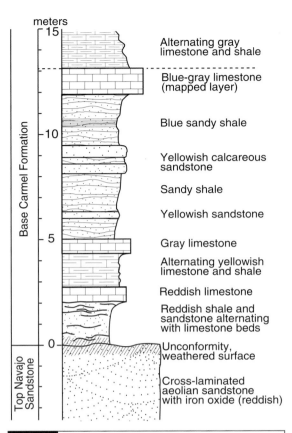

Fig 2.28 Local stratigraphic section at top of Navaho Sandstone and base of Carmel Formation in Chimney Rock area. Reprinted from Maerten et al. (2001) with permission from Elsevier.

faults are shown on a map (Fig. 2.29) to trend predominantly to the northwest or to the northeast. One might suppose that the fault system is composed of two sets based upon these two strike directions; however, this view does not take into consideration the dip of the faults. Some of these faults dip to the north (solid lines), but others with a similar strike dip to the south (dotted lines). Therefore, based on the three-dimensional orientations of these faults, there are a total of four different sets (Krantz, 1988).

The traces of the Chimney Rock faults range in length from a few hundred meters to as much as 5 km, and the offsets of the sedimentary marker horizons range up to almost 40 m, measured in the fault plane and down the dip of the fault (Fig. 2.30a). As depicted in this sketch, the block of rock above the fault, referred to as the *hangingwall*, has apparently moved down relative to the block below the fault, which is referred to as the *footwall*. Slickenlines on the fault surfaces (Fig. 2.14b) indi-

cate that the slip was approximately down the dip of these faults. Therefore they are referred to as *dip slip faults*. Furthermore, because the hangingwall moved downward relative to the footwall these are referred to as *normal faults*. If the hangingwall moved up relative to the footwall they would be called *reverse faults*.

The structure contour map (Fig. 2.29) is based on the elevation of the top of the blue-gray limestone near the bottom of the Carmel Formation (Fig. 2.28). This resistant layer is about a meter thick and forms prominent ledges throughout the mapped region. The elevation of the top of the blue-gray limestone gradually decreases from west to east across the map, so it is inclined to the east. To estimate a typical dip angle, compare the following points on Fig. 2.29:

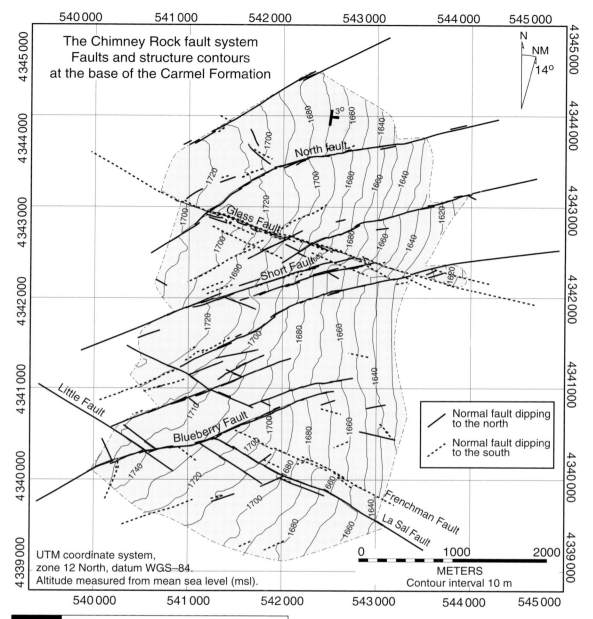

Fig 2.29 Structural contour map of blue-gray limestone unit near base of Carmel Formation illustrating offset by faults of the Chimney Rock array (Maerten, 2000).

Easting: 542 000 m
Northing: 4 344 000 m
Elevation: 1693 m

Easting: 543 000 m
Northing: 4 344 000 m
Elevation: 1644 m

The complete positions would include information from the map that indicates it is in the northern hemisphere, Zone M12, and the datum is WGS-84. Noting the positions of these points along the northing grid line 4 344 000 m and the fact that they are separated by 1000 m horizontally and 49 m vertically with no intervening faults, we calculate:

$$\phi_{\rm d} = \tan^{-1}\left(\frac{1693\,{\rm m} - 1644\,{\rm m}}{1000\,{\rm m}}\right) \approx 3° \qquad (2.108)$$

The strike of the blue-gray limestone is everywhere parallel to the structure contours so the

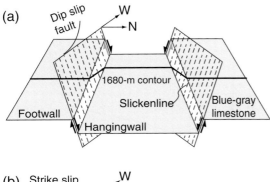

(a)

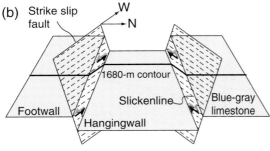

(b)

Fig 2.30 Schematic illustration of a pair of faults bounding a graben. (a) Dip slip. (b) Strike slip.

strike at the intersection of the 1670 contour and the 4 344 000 m northing grid line is due north (Fig. 2.29). The map symbol for strike and dip of bedding (Fig. 2.16) is placed at this intersection and recorded as (000, 03). One can judge from the spacings and orientations of the structure contours that this is a typical strike and dip, at least over the eastern portion of the map. If the blue-gray limestone were planar, the contours would be straight lines and uniformly spaced. The undulations in these lines suggest that this limestone layer is locally folded, perhaps as a result of the faulting or the development of the San Rafael Swell (Fig. 2.27).

The sense in which the structure contours on Fig. 2.29 are discontinuous across the normal faults depends upon the direction of inclination of the faults. For example, follow the 1680-m contour from near the southeast corner of the mapped region toward the north and note that this contour steps about 300 m to the west across the La Sal Fault. The La Sal Fault dips to the north and the relative downward motion of the hangingwall block on the north side of this fault is responsible for the discontinuity in this and other

contours that intersect the trace of the fault (shown schematically in Fig. 2.30a). Now continue following the 1680-m contour to the north on Fig. 2.29 until it encounters the Frenchman Fault and note that this fault dips to the south. The 1680-m contour steps a total of about 150 m to the east across this fault. The relative upward motion of the footwall block on the north side of the Frenchman Fault is responsible for this discontinuity in the contour (Fig. 2.30a).

The sense of relative motion of the footwall and hangingwall need not be oriented along the dip of the fault. Another possibility is illustrated in Fig. 2.30b where the slickenlines are oriented parallel to the strike direction. The fault on the left side of this figure is a *strike slip fault* and has slipped such that the hangingwall block moved to the west relative to the footwall block. The fault on the left side of this figure is a *left-lateral fault* because, when looking across the fault, the block on the opposite side appears to have moved to the left. The fault on the right side of this figure is a *right-lateral fault*. Given sufficient slip in the strike direction across the fault on the left side of Fig. 2.30b, the 1680-m contour would step to the west as much as the same contour steps to the west on the dip slip fault illustrated on the left in Fig. 2.30a. Thus, the sense and magnitude of offset of the structure contours are not diagnostic of the direction or magnitude of slip.

On the other hand the slickenline directions and the offset of sedimentary horizons are diagnostic of the slip direction and magnitude of dip slip on the Chimney Rock faults (Fig. 2.31). The magnitude of the dip slip increases from zero at the eastern termination of the Blueberry Fault to about 16 m and then jumps to about 30 m across the intersection of the La Sal Fault. Between the La Sal and Little Faults the dip slip increases to about 35 m and then decreases to just less than 30 m before jumping to about 16 m across the Little Fault. The rake of slickenlines is about 90° (pure dip slip) near the eastern termination of the Blueberry Fault and decreases to about 70° at the intersection with the La Sal Fault. Across the La Sal Fault the rake jumps to about 105° and then decreases toward the Little Fault, across which the rake jumps to 65° and then increases back to 90°.

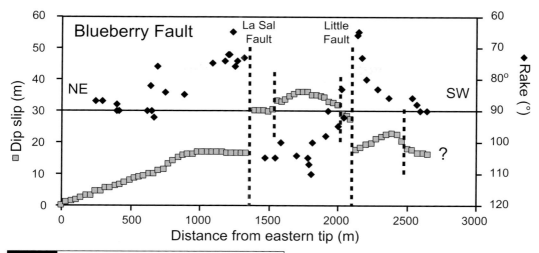

Fig 2.31 Distribution of dip slip magnitude and rake of slickenlines on Blueberry Fault of the Chimney Rock array (Maerten, 2000).

These data demonstrate that the Chimney Rock faults have a systematic variation of slip magnitude and direction and that the intersections of faults are associated with discontinuities in both magnitude and direction. While one could characterize the Blueberry Fault as a normal fault with about 30 m of dip slip, this would not reveal the interesting slip variations that provide important insights regarding the mechanical behavior of this fault and its neighbors. The data necessary to quantify these slip variations are obtainable using GPS technology.

2.4.2 GPS technology and mapping techniques

The combination of fault traces and structure contours on Fig. 2.29 provide considerable insight about the geometry of the structures in the Chimney Rock region. The construction of this map was facilitated by a sub-meter precision GPS receiver combined with a data collector and a laptop computer (Maerten *et al.*, 2001). This is a remarkable tool for modern structural investigations. Specifically, the ProXL System™ manufactured by Trimble Navigation Limited was used to receive the GPS signals and process the coordinate data to determine locations to within less than 1 m, given sufficient satellite signals. These data were combined with other field measurements in the TDC1™ data collector running Asset Surveyor™ software that prompts the user for particular field measurements using a data dictionary. The receiver and data collector are carried in the field in a small backpack (frontispiece, Chapter 2) and the data are later downloaded to a laptop computer running the PathFinder Office™ software. This software is used to create a custom data dictionary, visualize the map data, process the coordinate data using a technique called differential correction, and export the final data to other software or to a printer. Coordinate data can be collected at preset time intervals as the geologist walks throughout the field area, or at specific sites where particular structures crop out.

The Asset Surveyor™ software enables the structural geologist to create a data dictionary specifically tailored to the structures and terrain in the region being mapped. In terms of recording quantitative data, keyed to locations, this is a significant improvement on the traditional geologist notebook. For this region the basic "features" were the four distinctive sedimentary layers and the faults, so a data dictionary could contain the entries shown in Table 2.2 (Maerten *et al.*, 2001). Each feature can be recorded at a particular site as "point data" or at many sites along a traverse as "line data." For example, as the geologist walks along the ledge (Fig. 2.28) formed by one of the resistant limestone layers (C1, C2, C3) or the top of the Navajo Formation (Nav), the receiver can collect location coordinates every few steps,

Table 2.2. Data dictionary.

Features	Attributes	Options
Layer (point)	Type	C1, C2, C3, Nav
	Strike	0 to 360°
	Dip	0 to 90°
	comments	
Layer (line)	Type	C1, C2, C3, Nav
	comment	
Fault (point)	Strike	0 to 360°
	Dip	0 to 90°
	Rake of	0 to 180°
	slickenline	
	Surface	Good,
	quality	medium,
		poor
	Fault offset	0 m to 100 m
	Faulted layer	C1, C2, C3, Nav
	comments	
Fault (line)	Faulted layer	C1, C2, C3, Nav
	comments	

creating a very dense data set along the traverse. For each "feature" there are a number of common "attributes" such as the type of layer (C1 or Nav), the orientation (strike and dip), and comments. The "options" determine such things as the names of the layer types, or the magnitude of the offset on a fault. At particular sites, the orientation of a layer or a fault can be measured using a compass and inclinometer, and these numbers are recorded as the strike and dip angles. The definitions of these angles were given earlier in this chapter.

A single geologist collected the data necessary to construct the map shown in Fig. 2.29 in fifteen days using the GPS system (Maerten *et al.*, 2001). A total of 14 863 locations (easting, northing, elevation) were collected to define the tops of the four sedimentary layers. The thickness of the local stratigraphic section (Fig. 2.28) was used to extrapolate from a given measurement to the elevation of the top of the blue-gray limestone at each location. These combined data were used to construct the structure contour map. In addition, a total of 1768 locations were collected to define the traces of the faults, and the orientations of these faults were measured at 537 locations. By precisely and efficiently digitizing the three-dimensional geometry of the deformed layers and the faults in this region, the GPS mapping technology provides an effective mapping tool for the structural geologist.

2.5 | Concluding remarks

A number of new technologies are transforming structural mapping. These include the Global Positioning System (GPS), used to locate outcrops and structures on Earth's surface more rapidly and precisely than one could have imagined when the authors of this textbook began their careers. High-resolution aerial photography and scanning technologies enable one to create digital images with pixel widths of a few centimeters on the ground. Airbourne Laser Swath Mapping (ALSM) produces topographic maps with decimeter precision. These technologies are remarkable and they are rapidly evolving. There is no doubt that this revolution in our ability to image Earth's surface will usher in a new generation of structural maps and data.

Chapter 3

Characterizing structures using differential geometry

Two aerial views of the southeastern margin of the San Rafael Swell, UT. Mesozoic clasitic sedimentary rocks are upturned in the Waterpocket monocline. Photographs by D. D. Pollard.

The strange combination of mathematics and physics is a Greek invention, pioneered by Archimedes. Modern science is a mythical monster: half-goat, half-bird. The student of physics is led simultaneously to the laboratory, to face the phenomena of physical reality; and to the math course, to forget about the phenomena and to contemplate pure abstractions. That this hybrid existence is at all fertile is amazing: we use it, because we have discovered its effectiveness through experience.

The structure of the application of mathematics to physics by Archimedes, then, is this: by making explicit, clear assumptions, one draws the logical implications of the assumptions, which then have to hold for the world – as long as the assumptions themselves do.

Mathematics may have little to say, directly, about the physical world, but it is the only way to say anything at all with any certainty. The bet of modern science – following on Archimedes – is that we are willing to say very little, as long as what we say is well argued. Good arguments are good starting points for truly productive discussion, and so it is not surprising that the mathematical route has been so productive in modern science (Netz, 2000).

In the previous chapter we illustrated examples of geological surfaces, such as the top of the Triassic Chinle Formation throughout the San Rafael Swell in southern Utah, using structure contours (Fig. 2.27). The more detailed shape of the top of the blue-gray limestone bed near the bottom of the Carmel Formation in the Chimney Rock area is shown by the structure contours in Fig. 2.29. The frontispiece of this chapter shows two aerial photographs of the exposed surfaces of Jurassic sandstone formations on the flank of the Waterpocket Fold that defines the southeastern margin of the San Rafael Swell. Notice how the sandstone formations bend over the monoclinal flexure and also bend as the strike of the beds changes along the length of the fold. Monoclinal flexures are a continuing focus of structural investigation in this region (Reches, 1978; Reches and Johnson, 1978; Cooke *et al.*, 2000; Johnson and Johnson, 2000). Clearly these surfaces are not planar, but what is their shape? A primary task for structural geologists is to describe and characterize such surfaces and this may be accomplished in a mathematically rigorous and complete manner using concepts and tools from *differential geometry*, the branch of mathematics that brings the power of vector calculus to geometry (Gauss, 1827). Here we review some of the elementary concepts of differential geometry that are helpful to quantify the departure of geological surfaces from a plane (Mallet, 2002).

Structural data typically are gathered at scattered exposures as point measurements and the locations of these points should be identified using geographic or local coordinates and position vectors. The measured data include the local attitudes of planar and linear elements that approximate, for example, a foliation (Figs. 2.24a–c) or lineation (Figs. 2.24d–f) at the point of measurement (Cloos, 1946; Turner and Weiss, 1963). Plotting the attitudes of a set of structural elements on a stereographic projection enables one to compare the orientations of different members of the set. While serving a useful purpose in their own right, stereographic projections provide an incomplete characterization of foliations and lineations, because these projections lack any information about the spatial variations of orientations. It may be clear that a particular lineation has a different plunge direction and plunge at different exposures, but how does the attitude vary from one location to the next? The lineation may approximate a three-dimensional curve, so we need to understand how to describe the shape of such curves. The spatial variation of plunge direction and plunge can be inferred qualitatively from the distribution of attitude symbols on a structural map, but differential geometry provides the tools for the quantification and analysis of these spatial variations.

Relatively little use of differential geometry is found in the twentieth-century literature of structural geology, despite the obvious need to describe the complex shapes of curved lineations and surfaces, and the attractiveness of accomplishing this in a quantitative manner (Mallet, 2002). This literature provides few examples that we can use to illustrate the concepts introduced here. Furthermore, field techniques for deducing the shapes of curves or surfaces from scattered location and orientation data are just now being devised and tested. Therefore this chapter focuses on the principles and methods of differential geometry that appear to have the greatest potential for application to structural geology. This introduction is meant to encourage the use of these principles and methods and thereby provide, in the words of Reveil Netz (2000), "good starting points for truly productive discussion" of the geometry of geological structures.

Position vectors are used to describe points, curves, and surfaces in differential geometry. Many other vector quantities, such as the tangent and curvature vector, are derived from the position vector and used extensively in this chapter. Therefore it is necessary to understand the basic concepts of vectors, and to be familiar with specific techniques for manipulating vectors as introduced in the previous chapter before reading this chapter. For in-depth treatments of differential geometry that provide a rigorous mathematical basis, the reader is referred to textbooks on the subject (Struik, 1961; Stoker, 1969). In particular, the book by Lipschutz (1969) is a source for much of the material in this chapter and provides many useful exercises and worked examples.

3.1 | The concept and description of lineations

3.1.1 Discrete, superficial, and penetrative lineations

Before proceeding to the analytical description of lineations using differential geometry it is useful to step back and review some qualitative aspects of these structures. Some lineations are defined by the intersection of two geological surfaces that separate one volume of rock from another. For example, a fault (F–F′, Fig. 3.1a) separates the relatively young and undeformed rocks of a sedimentary basin from the older and more deformed sedimentary or metamorphic rocks of the adjacent mountain range. An igneous contact (I–I′, Fig. 3.1b) separates older deformed sedimentary or metamorphic rocks from the younger rocks of an igneous intrusion. An angular unconformity (U–U′, Fig. 3.1c) separates older sedimentary or metamorphic rocks from the overlying sedimentary strata. In these two-dimensional illustrations, taken from the textbook by Turner and Weiss (1963), the fault is shown as a straight line and the igneous contact and unconformity are shown as curved lines. In general such structures are three-dimensional surfaces that may be roughly planar or highly curved. The intersections of these surfaces with other similar surfaces, or with the surfaces of the sedimentary strata or metamorphic foliations, are curved lineations in three-dimensional space.

To generalize these concepts consider two roughly planar and continuous geological surfaces, say an igneous contact and an unconformity that intersect one another. To the extent that the surfaces are planar, the intersection defines a straight line (Fig. 3.2a). At points along the intersection the attitudes, measured as the plunge direction and plunge, would be approximately equal and the resulting points would plot in a very tight cluster on a stereogram. The type of lineation we have just described is called a *discrete lineation* because it is made up of the set of points common to two discrete surfaces. Unlike the lineations shown in Figs. 2.24d–f this type does not permeate the rock mass and there-

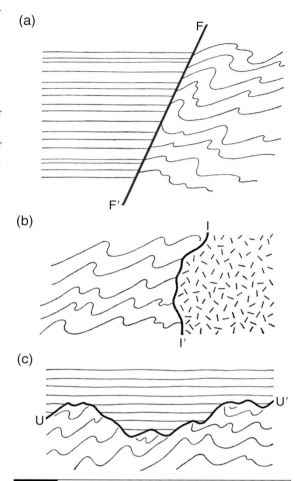

(a)

(b)

(c)

Fig 3.1 Two distinct rock volumes separated across geological surfaces including: (a) a fault, F–F′; (b) an igneous contact, I–I′; and (c) an angular unconformity, U–U′. Intersections of sedimentary or metamorphic layers with these surfaces define discrete lineations. Reprinted from Turner and Weiss (1963) with permission from McGraw-Hill.

fore is sometimes referred to as a non-penetrative lineation.

The igneous contact and unconformity may be continuous curved surfaces and in this case their intersection defines a continuous curve in three-dimensional space (Fig. 3.2b). Measures of plunge direction and plunge at discrete outcrops along such a curved lineation would result in distinctly different attitudes and the set of points would plot along an arc across the stereogram. Because the

(a)

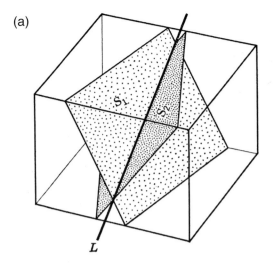

(b)

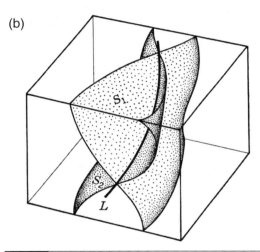

Fig 3.2 Discrete lineations defined by intersections of geological surfaces. (a) Straight lineation at intersection of two planar surfaces. (b) Curved lineation at intersection of curved surfaces. Reprinted from Turner and Weiss (1963) with permission from McGraw-Hill.

spatial relations of these outcrops are not depicted on the stereogram one could not reconstruct the curved intersection from these data. However, if the geographic coordinates of these points were recorded along with the attitudes one could reconstruct the curved intersection and study its geometric attributes using differential geometry.

A second type of lineation exists only on discrete surfaces such as the surfaces of a fault or

intrusive contact. An example (Fig. 3.3a) is taken from a small fault in the Lake Edison granodiorite in the Sierra Nevada of central California. There a set of opening fractures formed in the granodiorite, presumably due to contraction during cooling (Bergbauer and Martel, 1999), and these fractures were filled with hydrothermal minerals, predominantly quartz, epidote, and chlorite (Segall and Pollard, 1983a). During a later tectonic event sufficient shear stress was resolved across these weak surfaces to promote slip and the consequent shearing of the hydrothermal minerals between the two fault surfaces generated the slickenlines (Segall and Pollard, 1983b; Martel *et al.*, 1988). A second example (Fig. 3.3b) is taken from the intrusive contact of a diorite porphyry sill in the Henry Mountains, Utah. Here shearing of the highly viscous magma against the sandstone host rock generated the slickenlines (Johnson and Pollard, 1973), which are composed of fragmented feldspar grains.

Both examples of slickenlines in Fig. 3.3 are taken from individual exposures but nearby exposures also display these structures. If one could observe the entire fault surface or igneous contact surface, we suggest that the lineations would cover much if not all of these surfaces. This type of lineation is called a *superficial lineation* because it is only found on a discrete surface. Furthermore we suggest that the linear elements observed locally would form coherent patterns over these surfaces, reflecting the continuous relative motion of the two sides of the fault and the continuous relative motion of the magma against the host rock. That is, one could define a set of three-dimensional curves lying in these surfaces that are everywhere parallel to the local directions of the slickenlines. These curves are the trajectories of the relative motion of the surfaces. As with any continuous curve the geometric attributes of these trajectories can be defined and analyzed using differential geometry.

In contrast consider foliations composed of lithologic layering (Fig. 2.24a) or a set of subparallel fractures (Fig. 2.24b), or the preferred orientation of tabular mineral grains (Fig. 2.24c). Where two roughly planar foliations with different attitudes exist in the same rock mass, say litho-

Fig 3.3 Superficial lineations on geological surfaces. (a) Slickenlines on fault surface in granitic rock of the Sierra Nevada, California (Segall and Pollard, 1983b). (b) Lineations on igneous contact in Henry Mountains, UT (Johnson and Pollard, 1973). Photographs by D. D. Pollard.

logic layering and a set of fractures, the mutual intersections define a *penetrative lineation* that permeates the rock mass (Fig. 3.4a). To the extent that both foliations are planar, the intersections define straight lineations. Attitudes gathered at different outcrops would be approximately equal and the resulting points would plot in a very tight cluster on a stereogram. A possible alternative is that the lithologic layering is folded and the fractures are roughly planar (Fig. 3.4b). In this case the intersections define continuous curves in three-dimensional space that permeate the rock mass, so attitudes from different outcrops would plot at scattered locations on the stereogram.

An outstanding challenge for structural geologists is the development of procedures to define individual curves in three-dimensional space from scattered measurements of the attitudes and outcrop locations of a penetrative lineation. The underlying presumption is that the linear fabric elements from scattered outcrops are part of a coherent and continuous pattern of curves in three dimensions, much like the flow lines of a three-dimensional steady-state flow problem in fluid mechanics. The flow lines are everywhere parallel to the local velocity vector. We are not presuming that penetrative lineations have any particular relationship to a velocity field. Rather we are advocating the study of such lineations in a three-dimensional spatial context that could lead to their quantitative characterization using differential geometry. With such a characterization in hand one could model the structures using continuum mechanics and test hypotheses concerning relationships between the fabric and the velocity field.

3.1.2 Parametric representation of curves

Given the intuitive concept that a curve is a set of points, arranged "side by side" in some orderly and continuous distribution, it should not be surprising that position vectors, which define the locations of points, are used to define curves. To distinguish individual points clearly from the set of points composing a curve we use the symbol **p** for the position vector of a point and **c** for the curve. The spatial continuity of the set of points composing a curve is achieved by defining **c** as a continuous function. Because **c** is a vector quantity these functions are called *vector functions*. Curves in three-dimensional Euclidean space are

(a)

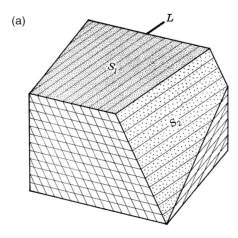

(b)

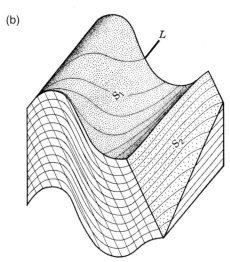

Fig 3.4 Penetrative lineations. (a) Intersections of two penetrative planar foliations define straight lineations. (b) Intersections of two penetrative curved foliations define curved lineations. Reprinted from Turner and Weiss (1963) with permission from McGraw-Hill.

defined in terms of vector functions of a single real variable, t, such that:

$$\mathbf{c}(t) = c_x(t)\mathbf{e}_x + c_y(t)\mathbf{e}_y + c_z(t)\mathbf{e}_z \tag{3.1}$$

The three scalar functions ($c_x(t)$, $c_y(t)$, $c_z(t)$) are the components of the vector function with respect to the base vectors ($\mathbf{e}_x$, $\mathbf{e}_y$, $\mathbf{e}_z$). These functions, along with the base vectors, determine the position vectors for all points on the curve: as t varies smoothly from one value to another, the points

trace out the curve. The vector equation (3.1) is called the *parametric representation* of the curve, and the real variable t is an arbitrary parameter for this representation.

For example, consider the parametric representation for a circular helix (Fig. 3.5a) defined as (Lipschutz, 1969, p. 63):

$$\mathbf{c}(t) = a(\cos t)\mathbf{e}_x + a(\sin t)\mathbf{e}_y + bt\mathbf{e}_z$$
$$\text{(circular helix)} \tag{3.2}$$

The components of this vector function and the ranges of the constants, a and b, are:

$$c_x(t) = a(\cos t), \quad c_y(t) = a(\sin t), \quad c_z(t) = bt,$$
$$a > 0, \quad -\infty < b < +\infty \tag{3.3}$$

The points on this curve lie on a right cylinder of radius a with the cylindrical axis coincident with the z-axis. As the parameter increases from $t = 0$ to $t = 2\pi$ the point on the curve "advances" in the z-direction a distance $2\pi|b|$, and the x and y components return to their original values. As t continues to increase the points continue to "advance" in the z-direction encircling the z-axis. For $a > 0$ and $b = 0$, (3.2) reduces to the special case of a circle of radius a in the (x, y)-plane (Fig. 3.5b):

$$\mathbf{c}(t) = a(\cos t)\mathbf{e}_x + a(\sin t)\mathbf{e}_y \quad \text{(circle)} \tag{3.4}$$

In this representation of a circle the parameter t is the counterclockwise angle measured in radians from 0 at the positive x-axis.

As we review the concepts of differential geometry the circular helix (3.2) and the circle (3.4) are used as examples because they are well known and because they are easily visualized. In the classic review of lineations by Ernst Cloos (1946) geological lineations are not reported with shapes that approximate a complete circle or the full cycle of a circular helix. However, lineations are reported that lie on surfaces or within layers of sedimentary or metamorphic rock that approximate a *cylindrical fold* (Turner and Weiss, 1963, pp. 123–9). Folds are termed cylindrical if a straight line moving parallel to itself can generate the surfaces of the layers. The straight-line generator is called the *fold axis*. In Fig. 3.6a the idealized shape of a folded surface containing a lineation is

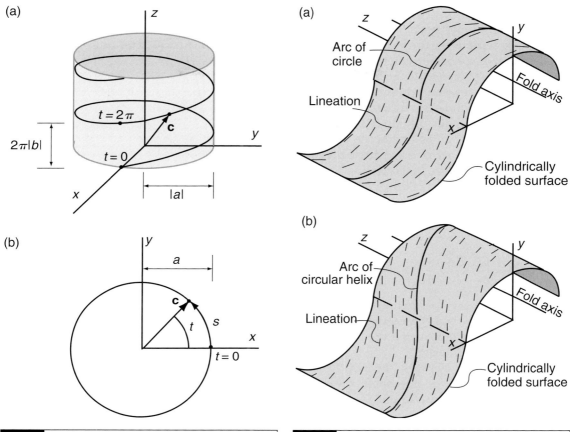

Fig 3.5 (a) Circular helix, defined by position vector **c**, with radius a and pitch b. (b) Special case of a circle where $b = 0$. Arbitrary parameter is t; arc length is s.

Fig 3.6 (a) Lineations on cylindrical fold with circular profile shape lie on arcs of circles. (b) Lineations oblique to fold axis lie on arcs of a circular helix.

composed of two halves of a circular cylinder joined along the dashed line. This is just one of the many possible shapes for a cylindrical fold. For this special case, lineations that are perpendicular to the fold axis approximate the arc of a circle. Lineations that are not perpendicular to the fold axis may approximate the arc of a circular helix (Fig. 3.6b). Thus even these elementary examples of curved lines from differential geometry may have application to geological lineations.

The lineations illustrated in Fig. 3.6 are shown as short tick marks on the folded surface. This is in keeping with the fact that field measurements usually are limited to orientations determined at isolated exposures. Not much is known about the continuity of lineations from exposure to exposure, or about the three-dimensional shapes of lin-

eations where they are continuous. Can the arc of a circle or circular helix approximate a given lineation, or is a more complex shape required? In part our inability to address this question is due to poor exposure and therefore inadequate data, but in part it is due to the lack of quantitative tools to describe and analyze curved lines in three-dimensional space. Differential geometry provides these tools.

3.1.3 The unit tangent vector

Recall that the local orientation of a curvilinear structure at the exposure is measured as the orientation of the line element that is tangential to the lineation. It should come as no surprise, then, that we make use of the *unit tangent vector*, **t**, along a curve. Some care is needed to distinguish the symbol for the arbitrary parameter of a curve, t, from that for the unit tangent vector, **t**. This vector is defined by considering the position vector to be a function of a special parameter, s, such that $|d\mathbf{c}/ds| = 1$. This parameter is the length of an arc of the curve from some arbitrary initial point where $s = 0$ (Fig. 3.7a), so it is referred to as the *arc length*. Now consider the difference between the positive vectors for two points on the curve, say s and $s + \Delta s$. Notice that this is a secant to the curve between these two points. Dividing this difference by the arc length, Δs, and taking the limit as this length goes to zero, we are left with the definition of the derivative of the vector function **c** with respect to the arc length s (Lipschutz, 1969, p. 61):

$$\lim_{\Delta s \to 0} \frac{\mathbf{c}(s + \Delta s) - \mathbf{c}(s)}{\Delta s} = \frac{d\mathbf{c}}{ds} = \mathbf{t}(s) \qquad (3.5)$$

In the limit, as Δs goes to zero the secant becomes parallel to the curve and of the same length as the arc. Therefore, this derivative is the unit tangent vector, $\mathbf{t}(s)$, at the point $\mathbf{c}(s)$.

The relationship between the unit tangent vector and the curve at any point $\mathbf{c}(s)$ can be thought of intuitively in terms of a straight line passing through that point called the tangent line. To envision the tangent line, first consider the secant line (Fig. 3.7b) that passes through the two points, $\mathbf{c}(s)$ and $\mathbf{c}(s + \Delta s)$ on the curve. In the limit, as Δs goes to zero the secant line becomes the tangent line, and becomes parallel to the unit tangent vector at the point $\mathbf{c}(s)$. In this sense the tangent line is the one straight line, of an infinite number of differently oriented straight lines through the point, that has the closest contact with the curve and best quantifies the orientation of the curve at that point. One can say that it is the "best fitting" straight line to the curve at that point.

When the arc length, s, is used as the parameter, the equation for the curve is called the *natural representation* of the curve. For the circular helix the natural representation is (Lipschutz, 1969, p. 52):

$$\mathbf{c}(s) = a\cos[(a^2 + b^2)^{-1/2}s]\mathbf{e}_x$$
$$+ a\sin[(a^2 + b^2)^{-1/2}s]\mathbf{e}_y + b(a^2 + b^2)^{-1/2}s\mathbf{e}_z \qquad (3.6)$$

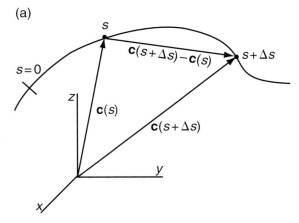

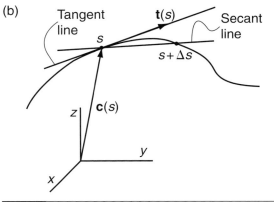

Fig 3.7 Diagrams to define unit tangent vector **t**. (a) Difference between two position vectors, $\mathbf{c}(s + \Delta s)$ and $\mathbf{c}(s)$, for curve defines vector parallel to the secant line. (b) In the limit, as the arc length, Δs, goes to zero the secant line is parallel to the tangent line.

Comparing this equation with (3.2), we note that, despite being called "natural," this representation is somewhat more cumbersome to write down because the arbitrary parameter, t, is replaced with $(a^2 + b^2)^{-1/2}s$. For $a > 0$ and $b = 0$ the equation for the circular helix reduces to the natural representation of the circle:

$$\mathbf{c}(s) = a\cos(s/a)\mathbf{e}_x + a\sin(s/a)\mathbf{e}_y \qquad (3.7)$$

In comparing this equation with (3.4) recall that the central angle of a sector of a circle measured in radians is equal to the ratio of the arc length to the radius, that is $t = s/a$ (Fig. 3.5b).

The natural representation of a curve permits a direct calculation of the unit tangent vector by taking the derivative with respect to the arc length, $\mathbf{t} = d\mathbf{c}/ds$. For an arbitrary parameter, t, the unit tangent vector is defined using the chain rule and the fact that $ds/dt = |d\mathbf{c}/dt|$ (Lipschutz, 1969, p. 61):

$$\mathbf{t} = \frac{d\mathbf{c}}{ds} = \frac{d\mathbf{c}}{dt}\frac{dt}{ds} = \frac{d\mathbf{c}}{dt}\Big/\frac{ds}{dt} = \frac{d\mathbf{c}}{dt}\Big/\left|\frac{d\mathbf{c}}{dt}\right| \quad (3.8)$$

This is a more general equation for the unit tangent vector because it does not depend upon the parameter being the arc length. Recalling that $\mathbf{c}$ is a vector function of a single real variable, t or s, how does one take the derivative of such a function? The answer is that one takes the derivative of each component with respect to the variable and uses these as the components of a new vector. For example, given $\mathbf{c}(t)$ as in (3.1), then:

$$\frac{d\mathbf{c}(t)}{dt} = \frac{dc_x(t)}{dt}\mathbf{e}_x + \frac{dc_y(t)}{dt}\mathbf{e}_y + \frac{dc_z(t)}{dt}\mathbf{e}_z \quad (3.9)$$

The function $\mathbf{c}(t)$ is differentiable at some particular value of the variable, say $t = t_0$, if each component is differentiable at that point. Note that the derivative of a vector function is a vector function: higher-order derivatives may be calculated following the same procedure, and the standard formulae for derivatives of the common functions apply (Selby, 1975).

For the circular helix (Fig. 3.8a) the derivative and absolute value of the derivative of the vector function are found using (3.2):

$$\frac{d\mathbf{c}}{dt} = -a(\sin t)\mathbf{e}_x + a(\cos t)\mathbf{e}_y + b\mathbf{e}_z,$$
$$\left|\frac{d\mathbf{c}}{dt}\right| = (a^2 + b^2)^{1/2} \quad (3.10)$$

Equations (3.10) are substituted into (3.8) to find the unit tangent vector for the circular helix:

$$\mathbf{t}(t) = (a^2 + b^2)^{-1/2}[-a(\sin t)\mathbf{e}_x + a(\cos t)\mathbf{e}_y + b\mathbf{e}_z] \quad (3.11)$$

As b goes to zero the helix collapses into a circle on the (x, y)-plane (Fig. 3.8b) and the unit tangent vector becomes:

$$\mathbf{t}(t) = -(\sin t)\mathbf{e}_x + (\cos t)\mathbf{e}_y \quad (3.12)$$

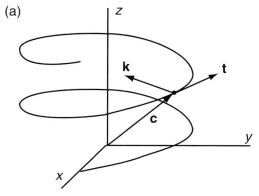

(a)

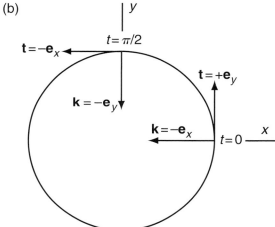

(b)

Fig 3.8 (a) Unit tangent vector, $\mathbf{t}$, and curvature vector, $\mathbf{k}$, on circular helix. (b) Unit tangent and curvature vectors on a circle.

By substitution, notice that the tangent vector for the circle varies with the parameter t as:

$t =$	0	$\pi/2$	π	$3\pi/2$	
$\mathbf{t} =$	$+\mathbf{e}_y$	$-\mathbf{e}_x$	$-\mathbf{e}_y$	$+\mathbf{e}_x$	(3.13)

This describes a set of unit vectors that are, indeed, tangent to the circle (Fig. 3.8b).

The unit tangent vector for the circular helix maintains a constant angular relationship to the z-axis for any position along the circular helix (Fig. 3.8a). This angle is found using the scalar product of the tangent vector (3.11) and the base vector $\mathbf{e}_z$:

$$\mathbf{t} \cdot \mathbf{e}_z = b(a^2 + b^2)^{-1/2} = |\mathbf{t}||\mathbf{e}_z|\cos\theta = \cos\theta \quad (3.14)$$

In the last step we used the fact that both vectors have unit magnitude, so the product of their absolute values is one. Solving for the angle θ:

$$\theta = \cos^{-1}(\mathbf{t} \cdot \mathbf{e}_z) = \cos^{-1}[b(a^2 + b^2)^{-1/2}] = \text{constant} \tag{3.15}$$

As b goes to zero the helix collapses into a circle on the (x, y)-plane and the angle θ goes to $\pi/2$. This special relationship is illustrated in Fig. 3.8b where it is seen that $\mathbf{t}$ is perpendicular to the z-axis for all values of the arbitrary parameter t.

For a lineation observed at exposure, such as the slickenlines in Fig. 3.3, the orientation determined in the field using geographic angles can be related to the unit tangent vector, $\mathbf{t}$. Although slickenlines may be curved, they are approximated locally with linear elements whose orientation is measured using the plunge direction, α_p, and plunge, ϕ_p. We assert that such a linear element is parallel to the unit tangent vector of a three-dimensional curve that passes through the point of measurement, so it has the same direction angles. Furthermore, because $\mathbf{t}$ is a unit vector, the scalar components are equivalent to the direction cosines. We find using (2.101):

$$\begin{aligned} t_x &= \cos \alpha_x = \sin \alpha_p \cos \phi_p \\ t_y &= \cos \alpha_y = \cos \alpha_p \cos \phi_p \\ t_z &= \cos \alpha_z = -\sin \phi_p \end{aligned} \tag{3.16}$$

In this way we relate the orientation data taken at scattered exposures on a continuous geological lineation to the components of the unit tangent vectors at correlative points on a three-dimensional curve.

As an example, consider the lineation described by the plunge direction, $\alpha_p = 222°$, and plunge, $\phi_p = 33°$ (Fig. 2.17). Substituting these values into (3.16) we have $t_x = -0.561$, $t_y = -0.623$, $t_z = -0.545$ and $|\mathbf{t}| = 1$. Recall that the geographic coordinates (east, north, up) correspond to the Cartesian coordinates (x, y, z), as shown in Fig. 2.15, to reconcile the three negative components of the tangent vector with the orientation of this lineation as plotted on the stereogram. Also note that these components combine to give a unit magnitude, as expected for the tangent vector.

3.1.4 The curvature vector and the scalar curvature

Although the unit tangent vector is an important geometric quantity for the characterization of curves it is not one of the two fundamental properties that uniquely determine the shape of a curve. The first of these fundamental geometric quantities is the curvature. The *curvature vector*, $\mathbf{k}$, is defined for a natural representation of a curve, $\mathbf{c}(s)$, as the derivative of the unit tangent vector with respect to the natural parameter s. This derivative is defined using the standard limiting procedure from calculus (Lipschutz, 1969, p. 62):

$$\lim_{\Delta s \to 0} \frac{\mathbf{t}(s + \Delta s) - \mathbf{t}(s)}{\Delta s} = \frac{d\mathbf{t}}{ds} = \mathbf{k}(s) \tag{3.17}$$

This definition, and the earlier definition of the unit tangent vector (3.5), imply that the curvature vector is equivalent to the second derivative of the vector function $\mathbf{c}$ with respect to the natural parameter: $\mathbf{k}(s) = d^2\mathbf{c}/ds^2$. Therefore, definition of the curvature vector requires that the curve, $\mathbf{c}(s)$, have a continuous second derivative over the interval of interest. In general, the curvature vector is directed away from the curve on its concave side (Fig. 3.8). In other words the curvature vector points in the direction that the curve is turning.

The specific orientation of the curvature vector is determined by the fact that the tangent vector is constant in magnitude; in fact it is a unit vector. In general, if $\mathbf{v}$ is an arbitrary vector function such that $|\mathbf{v}| = \text{constant}$ (not necessarily a unit vector), then from the properties of the scalar product we have $\mathbf{v} \cdot \mathbf{v} = |\mathbf{v}||\mathbf{v}| \cos 0 = \text{constant}$. Differentiating this scalar product using the standard product rule (Selby, 1975):

$$\mathbf{v} \cdot \frac{d\mathbf{v}}{dt} + \frac{d\mathbf{v}}{dt} \cdot \mathbf{v} = 0, \quad \text{so} \quad \mathbf{v} \cdot \frac{d\mathbf{v}}{dt} = 0 \tag{3.18}$$

Given that neither $\mathbf{v}$ nor $d\mathbf{v}/dt$ is zero, a zero scalar product implies that $\cos\theta = 0$ and $\theta = \pi/2$. Thus, the curvature vector is orthogonal to the unit tangent vector.

Consider Fig. 3.9a to understand how the magnitude of the curvature vector is related to the change in orientation of the tangent vector with respect to position along a curve (Lipschutz,

(a)

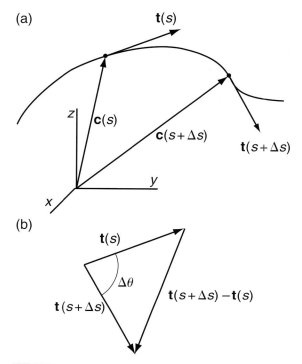

(b)

Fig 3.9 Diagrams to define scalar curvature, κ. (a) Two tangent vectors, $\mathbf{t}(s + \Delta s)$ and $\mathbf{t}(s)$, on curve separated by arc length Δs. (b) Change in angle, $\Delta\theta$, between two tangent vectors with respect to arc length Δs defines scalar curvature in limit as arc length goes to zero.

1969, p. 73). Here the parameter is the arc length, s, and the unit tangent vectors $\mathbf{t}(s)$ and $\mathbf{t}(s + \Delta s)$ are shown with different orientations at their respective points on the curve, separated by some small (differential) arc length Δs. Bringing the tails of these two unit vectors together forms an isosceles triangle (Fig. 3.9b) with sides of unit length, a base of length $|\mathbf{t}(s + \Delta s) - \mathbf{t}(s)|$, and a differential angle between the sides, $\Delta\theta$. The general relationship among the sides of equal length, a, the base, b, and the angle between the sides, θ, for an isosceles triangle is $b/a = 2\sin(\theta/2)$. Substituting $b = |\mathbf{t}(s + \Delta s) - \mathbf{t}(s)|$ and $a = 1$ we have, for small angles:

$$|\mathbf{t}(s + \Delta s) - \mathbf{t}(s)| = 2\sin(\Delta\theta/2) \cong \Delta\theta \qquad (3.19)$$

Here we have used the first term of the series expansion for the sine function (Selby, 1975,

p. 472) to approximate the function for small angles. Dividing both sides of this equation by the differential arc length, Δs, and taking the limit as this length goes to zero:

$$\left| \lim_{\Delta s \to 0} \frac{\mathbf{t}(s + \Delta s) - \mathbf{t}(s)}{\Delta s} \right| = \lim_{\Delta s \to 0} \frac{\Delta\theta}{\Delta s} = \frac{d\theta}{ds} = \kappa(s) \qquad (3.20)$$

The left-hand side of this equation is the magnitude of the curvature vector (3.17), $|\mathbf{k}(s)| = \kappa(s)$, a quantity known as the *scalar curvature*. From this relationship one can understand that the scalar curvature is equivalent to the spatial rate of change of the orientation of the unit tangent vector with arc length along the curve. The scalar curvature, $\kappa(s)$, is called an intrinsic property of a curve (Lipschutz, 1969) because it is one of two quantities that uniquely defines the shape of a curve. Where the orientation of the unit tangent vector changes more rapidly with position along the curve, the curvature is greater. A point on the curve where the curvature is zero is called an *inflection point*.

For an arbitrary parametric representation of a curve, $\mathbf{c}(t)$, the curvature vector and the scalar curvature are calculated using (Lipschutz, 1969, p. 65):

$$\mathbf{k}(t) = \frac{d\mathbf{t}}{dt} \bigg/ \left| \frac{d\mathbf{c}}{dt} \right|, \quad \kappa = |\mathbf{k}(t)| = \sqrt{k_x^2 + k_y^2 + k_z^2} \qquad (3.21)$$

That is, one first calculates the unit tangent vector using (3.8) and then calculates the derivative of that vector function. To calculate the scalar curvature one takes the absolute value of the curvature vector.

To calculate the curvature vector and the scalar curvature for the circular helix (3.2) we take the derivative of the unit tangent vector (3.11) and use (3.21) to find:

$$\mathbf{k}(t) = -a(a^2 + b^2)^{-1}[(\cos t)\mathbf{e}_x + (\sin t)\mathbf{e}_y],$$
$$\kappa = a(a^2 + b^2)^{-1} \qquad (3.22)$$

Note that the curvature vector lies in the (x, y)-plane (there is no component in the z-direction), it is orthogonal to the tangent vector, and it points away from the curve on its concave side toward the z-axis (Fig. 3.8a). Unlike the tangent vector, **t**, the curvature vector, **k**, is not generally a unit vector and here it has a magnitude given by κ that is a constant related to the radius, a, and the pitch, b, of the helix. For the circle in the (x, y)-plane (Fig. 3.8b), the curvature vector and scalar curvature are found from (3.22) by letting b go to zero:

$$\mathbf{k}(t) = -(1/a)[(\cos t)\mathbf{e}_x + (\sin t)\mathbf{e}_y], \quad \kappa = 1/a \quad (3.23)$$

By substitution, notice that the curvature vector for the circle varies with the parameter t as:

$$
\begin{array}{ccccc}
t = & 0 & \pi/2 & \pi & 3\pi/2 \\
k = & -\mathbf{e}_x/a & -\mathbf{e}_y/a & +\mathbf{e}_x/a & +\mathbf{e}_y/a
\end{array} \quad (3.24)
$$

This curvature vector is orthogonal to the circle and directed toward the center of the circle (Fig. 3.8b). It is not a unit vector unless $a = 1$. The scalar curvature is inversely proportional to the radius of the circle.

A positive scalar quantity called the *radius of curvature*, ρ, is motivated by (3.23) and is defined for an arbitrary parametric representation of a curve, $\mathbf{c}(t)$, as the reciprocal of the scalar curvature (Lipschutz, 1969, p. 63):

$$\rho(t) = \frac{1}{\kappa(t)} \quad (3.25)$$

From (3.23) we have $\rho = a$, so the radius of curvature of a circle is the radius of that circle. For the circular helix (Fig. 3.8) the geometric relationship is not so obvious, but using (3.22) we see that the radius of curvature is a constant everywhere along the helix with a value $\rho = (a^2 + b^2)/a$. The radius of curvature for the circular helix is the radius of a circle that is tangent to the helix and lies in the plane defined by the unit tangent vector and the curvature vector. In general, for an arbitrary curved line, the radius of curvature is a function of the parameter t, and therefore must be calculated for every point along the curve. For any straight line or segment of a straight line, and also for any point of inflection along a curve the radius of curvature is infinite because the scalar curvature is zero.

To acquire a more intuitive understanding of the radius of curvature consider once again the natural parametric representation of a curve, $\mathbf{c}(s)$,

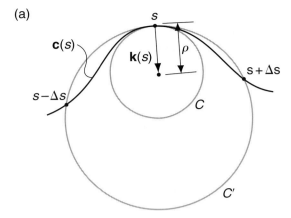

(a)

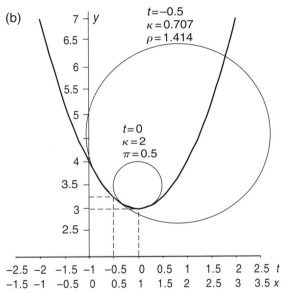

(b)

Fig 3.10 Diagram to define radius of curvature (Lipschutz, 1969). (a) Radius of curvature, ρ, defined as radius of best-fitting circle to curve at point s. (b) Scalar curvature, κ, and radius of curvature, ρ, at two points on a parabola.

for the curve illustrated in Fig. 3.10a (Lipschutz, 1969, p. 1). Given the radius of curvature, $\rho(s) = 1/\|\mathbf{k}(s)\|$, at any point along this curve, for what circle is this the radius? To address this question consider a circle, C', that passes through the curve at the three points, $\mathbf{c}(s - \Delta s)$, $\mathbf{c}(s)$, and $\mathbf{c}(s + \Delta s)$. In the limit, as Δs goes to zero the circle C' becomes the circle C and the radius of C is equal to the radius of curvature of the curve at the point $\mathbf{c}(s)$. This circle lies on the concave side of the curve and the curvature vector for the circle, C, and the curve are identical at the point $\mathbf{c}(s)$. The circle C is the one circle, of an infinite number of different circles that pass through this point, that has the closest contact with the curve, and therefore provides a geometric visualization of the radius of curvature. One can say that it is the "best-fitting" circle to the curve at that point.

For the natural representation of a curve, $\mathbf{c}(s)$, recall that the curvature vector is the second derivative of the position vector: $\mathbf{k}(s) = d^2\mathbf{c}/ds^2$, so the scalar curvature is defined as $\kappa(s) = |d^2\mathbf{c}/ds^2|$. Given this definition, one might be tempted to associate curvature with the second derivative of a function, say $y = f(x)$, representing a plane curve. In fact, this is commonly done in casual conversations where one says the first derivative, dy/dx, is the slope of the curve, and the second derivative, d^2y/dx^2, is the curvature. However, such statements involve special conditions and approximations that are spelled out in the following paragraphs.

If $\mathbf{c} = \mathbf{c}(t)$ is the arbitrary parametric representation of a curve, as in (3.1), then a general definition of the scalar curvature is (Lipschutz, 1969, p. 64):

$$\kappa(t) = \left| \frac{d\mathbf{c}}{dt} \times \frac{d^2\mathbf{c}}{dt^2} \right| \bigg/ \left| \frac{d\mathbf{c}}{dt} \right|^3 \qquad (3.26)$$

When a curve is defined using a parameter other then the arc length, s, the scalar curvature is not simply the absolute value of the second derivative of the vector function $\mathbf{c}(t)$. Compare (3.26) to the earlier definition of the scalar curvature (3.21): both are useful definitions.

To calculate the scalar curvature using (3.26) one uses the *cross product* of two vectors, say $\mathbf{v}$ and $\mathbf{w}$, found from the components of these vectors as (Selby, 1975, p. 556):

$$\mathbf{v} \times \mathbf{w} = (v_y w_z - v_z w_y)\mathbf{e}_x + (v_z w_x - v_x w_z)\mathbf{e}_y \\ + (v_x w_y - v_y w_x)\mathbf{e}_z \qquad (3.27)$$

The cross (or vector) product also may be evaluated as the determinant of the matrix formed by the base vectors and components as follows:

$$\mathbf{v} \times \mathbf{w} = \det \begin{pmatrix} \mathbf{e}_x & v_x & w_x \\ \mathbf{e}_y & v_y & w_y \\ \mathbf{e}_z & v_z & w_z \end{pmatrix} \qquad (3.28)$$

The magnitude of the cross product is proportional to the magnitudes of the two vectors and the sine of the smaller angle, θ, between these vectors measured in the plane that they define:

$$|\mathbf{v} \times \mathbf{w}| = |\mathbf{v}||\mathbf{w}|\sin\theta, \quad 0 \le \theta \le \pi \qquad (3.29)$$

These general relationships for the cross (or vector) product are used extensively in differential geometry and are used here to calculate the scalar curvature.

Again taking the circular helix (3.2) as an example we use (3.26) to calculate the scalar curvature. The second derivative of the vector function $\mathbf{c}(t)$ for the helix is:

$$\frac{d^2\mathbf{c}}{dt^2} = -a(\cos t)\mathbf{e}_x - a(\sin t)\mathbf{e}_y \qquad (3.30)$$

The absolute value of the cross product of the two derivatives is found using (3.27):

$$\frac{d\mathbf{c}}{dt} \times \frac{d^2\mathbf{c}}{dt^2} = ab(\sin t)\mathbf{e}_x - ab(\cos t)\mathbf{e}_y + a^2\mathbf{e}_z$$
$$\left| \frac{d\mathbf{c}}{dt} \times \frac{d^2\mathbf{c}}{dt^2} \right| = a(a^2 + b^2)^{1/2} \qquad (3.31)$$

Then the quotient in (3.26) is:

$$\kappa(t) = \frac{a(a^2 + b^2)^{1/2}}{[(a^2 + b^2)^{1/2}]^3} = a(a^2 + b^2)^{-1} \qquad (3.32)$$

This is exactly the result found in (3.22): the scalar curvature of the circular helix is a constant depending upon both the radius and the pitch.

The general equation for the scalar curvature (3.26) may be specialized for a plane curve, for example a curve that lies entirely within the (x, y)-plane:

$$\mathbf{c}(t) = c_x(t)\mathbf{e}_x + c_y(t)\mathbf{e}_y \qquad (3.33)$$

Here the vector function $\mathbf{c}(t)$ lacks any component along the z-axis and the two non-zero components are functions of the arbitrary parameter, t. Substituting into (3.26) we find the scalar curvature for this parametric representation of the plane curve (Varberg and Purcell, 1992, p. 623):

$$\kappa(t) = \left| \frac{dc_x}{dt}\frac{d^2c_y}{dt^2} - \frac{dc_y}{dt}\frac{d^2c_x}{dt^2} \right| \bigg/ \left[\left(\frac{dc_x}{dt}\right)^2 + \left(\frac{dc_y}{dt}\right)^2 \right]^{3/2} \qquad (3.34)$$

Again we see that the curvature is not simply related to the second derivative of the vector function $\mathbf{c}(t)$.

The circular helix is not a planar curve, so we turn to the parametric representation of a parabolic curve that lies entirely in the (x, y)-plane (Fig. 3.10b):

$$\mathbf{c}(t) = (t + 1)\mathbf{e}_x + (t^2 + 3)\mathbf{e}_y \qquad (3.35)$$

Taking the first and second derivatives of the components, the scalar curvature is found using (3.34):

$$\kappa(t) = \frac{|2 - 0|}{[(1)^2 + (2t)^2]^{3/2}} = \frac{2}{(1 + 4t^2)^{3/2}} \qquad (3.36)$$

For $t = -0.5$ we find $\kappa = 0.707$ so $\rho = 1.414$ and a circle of this radius is shown tangent to the parabola at this point in Fig. 3.10b. For $t = 0$ the scalar curvature $\kappa = 2$ and the radius of curvature is $\rho = 0.5$. A circle with this radius of curvature is shown tangent to the point at the base of the parabola. Clearly there is a significant change in curvature along a relatively short arc of the parabola.

We further specialize the representation of the curve such that $c_x(x) = x$ and $c_y(x) = y$. In other words the arbitrary parameter in (3.33) is the x-coordinate, and the derivatives of the two components of $\mathbf{c}$ may be rewritten:

$$\frac{dc_x}{dt} = \frac{dx}{dx} = 1, \quad \frac{d^2c_x}{dt^2} = 0, \quad \frac{dc_y}{dt} = \frac{dy}{dx}, \quad \frac{d^2c_y}{dt^2} = \frac{d^2y}{dx^2} \qquad (3.37)$$

Upon substitution into (3.34) the curvature takes the form often introduced in calculus textbooks (Varberg and Purcell, 1992, p. 623):

$$\kappa(x) = \left| \frac{d^2y}{dx^2} \right| \bigg/ \left[1 + \left(\frac{dy}{dx} \right)^2 \right]^{3/2} \qquad (3.38)$$

Again note that the scalar curvature is not simply the absolute value of the second derivative of the function $y = f(x)$. The parabolic plane curve illustrated in Fig. 3.10b may be written in this form using $x = t + 1$ and substituting for t in $y = t^2 + 3$ to find:

$$y = x^2 - 2x + 4 \qquad (3.39)$$

The curvature for this function is found using (3.38) as:

$$\kappa(x) = 2/(4x^2 - 8x + 5)^{3/2} \qquad (3.40)$$

For $x = t + 1$, this is identical to the curvature of the parabola found in (3.36) using the parametric representation as a function of t.

If the squared slope of the function, $y = f(x)$ in the denominator of (3.38) is small compared to one, then the curvature may be approximated as:

$$\kappa(x) \approx \left| \frac{\partial^2 y}{\partial x^2} \right|, \quad \text{for} \left(\frac{dy}{dx} \right)^2 \ll 1 \qquad (3.41)$$

For the parabola of Fig. 3.10b this approximation gives a constant value, $\kappa = 2$, for all x. This is exact at the base of the parabola where $x = 1$ and the slope is zero, but is in error by 182% where $\kappa = 0.707$ at $x = 0.5$ and the slope is 45°. For plane curves described by functions of the form $y = f(x)$, with squared slopes that are not small compared to one, (3.38) is the appropriate equation for scalar curvature. For the general parametric representation of a plane curve (3.34) is the appropriate equation. For the general parametric representation of a curve that is not confined to a plane (3.26) must be used.

3.1.5 The unit principal normal vector and binormal vector

We have already mentioned that the curvature vector is not generally a unit vector, that it is orthogonal to the unit tangent vector, and that it is directed away from the curve on the concave side. As the curve $\mathbf{c}(s)$ passes through an inflection point (Fig. 3.11a), the curvature vector, $\mathbf{k}(s)$, goes to zero magnitude and thereafter switches direction to the other side of the curve. In the interest of working with a geometric quantity that is less erratic in both magnitude and direction, a unit vector is defined as parallel to the curvature vector, but directed to remain continuous along the curve wherever possible (Fig. 3.11b):

$$\mathbf{n}(s) = \frac{\pm \mathbf{k}(s)}{|\mathbf{k}(s)|} \qquad (3.42)$$

This vector is called the *unit principal normal vector* for the natural representation of the curve $\mathbf{c}(s)$ (Lipschutz, 1969, p. 64). The choice of sign in the numerator is used to keep this normal vector from switching direction arbitrarily from one side of the curve to the other at points of inflection. For

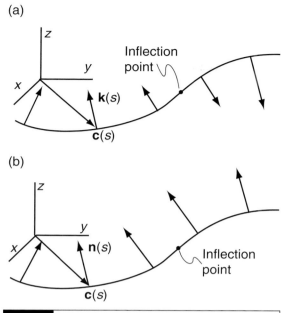

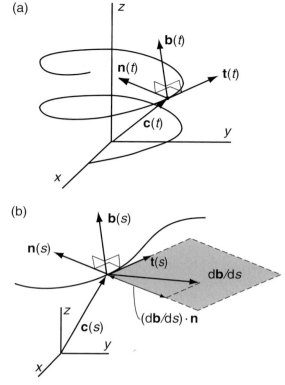

Fig 3.11 Diagrams to define unit principal normal vector, **n**. (a) Curve with curvature vectors, **k**(s). (b) Same curve with unit principal normal vectors, **n**(s).

Fig 3.12 (a) Circular helix with moving trihedron defined by unit tangent, principal normal, and binormal vectors (**t**, **n**, **b**) all functions of the arbitrary parameter t. (b) Derivative of the binormal vector, d**b**/ds, used to define the scalar torsion, τ.

example, in Fig. 3.11b the positive sign is used to the left of the inflection point so **n**(s) and **k**(s) are similarly directed away from the concave side of the curve. However, to the right of the inflection point the negative sign is used so **n**(s) and **k**(s) are oppositely directed. Although **k**(s) varies in magnitude and remains directed away from the concave side, **n**(s) is a unit vector directed consistently to one side of the curve.

For an arbitrary parametric representation of a curve, **c**(t), the unit principal normal vector is (Lipschutz, 1969, p. 66):

$$\mathbf{n}(t) = \frac{\pm\mathbf{k}(t)}{|\mathbf{k}(t)|} = \frac{\pm\mathbf{k}(t)}{\kappa(t)} \tag{3.43}$$

For the circular helix, using (3.22) in (3.43) with the positive sign we have:

$$\mathbf{n}(t) = -[(\cos t)\mathbf{e}_x + (\sin t)\mathbf{e}_y] \tag{3.44}$$

Note that **n**(t) is independent of the pitch, b, of the helix, so the principal normal vector given here is the same as that for the circle. This unit vector is directed toward the z-axis and away from the curve on its concave side for all values of the parameter t (Fig. 3.12a). Also, note that this vector lies

in the (x,y)-plane. However, as determined by (3.11), the unit tangent vector for the circular helix is not in the (x, y)-plane unless $b = 0$. Because there are no inflection points along the helix or the circle the choice of signs is arbitrary.

In order to identify the second property that uniquely describes curves we again consider the natural parametric representation of a curve, **c**(s), and define a unit vector, **b**(s), called the *unit binormal vector*, which is normal to the plane containing the unit tangent vector, **t**(s), and the unit principal normal vector, **n**(s):

$$\mathbf{b}(s) = \mathbf{t}(s) \times \mathbf{n}(s) \tag{3.45}$$

The three unit vectors [**t**(s), **n**(s), **b**(s)] form the so-called *moving trihedron* for the curve (Fig. 3.12b), which can be thought of as traveling along the curve with change in arc length, s. The binormal vector is directed following the conventional right-hand rule for vector (cross) products: curl the fingers of your right hand from $\mathbf{t}$ toward $\mathbf{n}$ and your thumb points in the direction of $\mathbf{b}$.

For an arbitrary parametric representation of a curve, $\mathbf{c}(t)$, the unit binormal vector is the cross product of the tangent and principal normal vectors, both written as functions of the parameter t (Lipschutz, 1969, p. 68):

$$\mathbf{b}(t) = \mathbf{t}(t) \times \mathbf{n}(t) \qquad (3.46)$$

Referring back to (3.29) and recalling that the tangent vector, $\mathbf{t}(t)$, and the principal normal vector, $\mathbf{n}(t)$, are mutually orthogonal, the smaller angle between them is $\theta = \pi/2$, so $\sin\theta = 1$. Furthermore, both of these vectors have unit magnitudes, so the binormal vector, $\mathbf{b}(t)$, also is a unit vector. The moving trihedron (Fig. 3.12b) is composed of three orthogonal unit vectors.

For the circular helix (Fig. 3.12a) the unit binormal vector is found using (3.11) and (3.44) in (3.46):

$$\mathbf{b}(t) = (a^2 + b^2)^{-1/2}[b(\sin t)\mathbf{e}_x - b(\cos t)\mathbf{e}_y + a\mathbf{e}_z] \qquad (3.47)$$

For the special case where b goes to zero, resulting in a circle, the unit binormal vector is $\mathbf{b}(t) = \mathbf{e}_z$. The circle lies in the (x,y)-plane, which also contains the tangent vector and the principal normal vector, and the unit binormal vector is parallel to the z-axis.

3.1.6 The scalar torsion

The unit binormal vector is used to define the second intrinsic geometric property of curves, namely the *torsion*. For the natural parametric representation of a curve, $\mathbf{c}(s)$, the torsion is defined as (Lipschutz, 1969, p. 69):

$$\tau(s) = -\left(\frac{d\mathbf{b}}{ds}\right) \cdot \mathbf{n} \qquad (3.48)$$

Because $\mathbf{b}(s)$ is a constant (unit) vector function, the derivative $d\mathbf{b}/ds$ is orthogonal to $\mathbf{b}(s)$, and therefore lies in the plane containing $\mathbf{t}(s)$ and $\mathbf{n}(s)$ (Fig. 3.12b). The scalar product of $d\mathbf{b}/ds$ and $\mathbf{n}$ determines the component of the vector $d\mathbf{b}/ds$ on an axis for which $\mathbf{n}$ is the base vector. Thus, the torsion is a measure of the change in orientation

of the binormal vector, $\mathbf{b}$, with arc length, s, but only that part of the change in orientation that projects onto the plane normal to the tangent vector, $\mathbf{t}$. In other words the torsion describes the component of rotation of the binormal vector about the tangent line with change in position along the curve. The torsion is called an intrinsic property of a curve because it serves, along with the scalar curvature, to define the shape of the curve uniquely.

For an arbitrary parametric representation of the curve $\mathbf{c}(t)$ the torsion is (Lipschutz, 1969, pp. 69–70):

$$\tau(t) = -\left(\frac{d\mathbf{b}}{dt} \middle/ \left|\frac{d\mathbf{c}}{dt}\right|\right) \cdot \mathbf{n} \qquad (3.49)$$

The torsion also may be calculated in terms of the first three derivatives of the vector function $\mathbf{c}(t)$:

$$\tau(t) = \left[\frac{d\mathbf{c}}{dt} \cdot \left(\frac{d^2\mathbf{c}}{dt^2} \times \frac{d^3\mathbf{c}}{dt^3}\right)\right] \middle/ \left|\frac{d\mathbf{c}}{dt} \times \frac{d^2\mathbf{c}}{dt^2}\right|^2 \qquad (3.50)$$

This property of the curve depends upon the arbitrary representation of the curve having derivatives of order 3 or greater that are continuous. The numerator of (3.50) is sometimes written without the scalar and vector product symbols and without the inner parenthesis. In this form it is referred to as a *triple scalar product*. The following determinant provides a handy way to evaluate a triple scalar product:

$$[\mathbf{uvw}] = \mathbf{u} \cdot (\mathbf{v} \times \mathbf{w}) = \det\begin{pmatrix} u_x & v_x & w_x \\ u_y & v_y & w_y \\ u_z & v_z & w_z \end{pmatrix} \qquad (3.51)$$

Here $\mathbf{u}$, $\mathbf{v}$, and $\mathbf{w}$ are arbitrary vectors and the determinant is composed of their components.

For the circular helix the torsion is calculated using (3.49). Taking the derivative of the unit binormal vector (3.47) and (3.10) we have:

$$\frac{d\mathbf{b}}{dt} = (a^2 + b^2)^{-1/2}[b(\cos t)\mathbf{e}_x + b(\sin t)\mathbf{e}_y],$$

$$\left|\frac{d\mathbf{c}}{dt}\right| = (a^2 + b^2)^{1/2} \qquad (3.52)$$

Taking the scalar product of the ratio of these two quantities with the unit principal normal vector (3.44), the torsion of the circular helix is:

$$\tau = -(a^2 + b^2)^{-1}[b(\cos t)\mathbf{e}_x + b(\sin t)\mathbf{e}_y]$$
$$[-(\cos t)\mathbf{e}_x - (\sin t)\mathbf{e}_y] = b(a^2 + b^2)^{-1} \quad (3.53)$$

The torsion is constant and proportional to the pitch, b. For $b > 0$, $\tau > 0$ and the circular helix is called right handed, that is the axis of the helix is parallel to the thumb of your right hand when your fingers bend to follow the curve (Fig. 3.12a). For $b < 0$, $\tau < 0$ and the helix is left handed. Because $b = 0$ for the circle, (3.53) demonstrates that the torsion is zero for that special case. A curve with zero torsion lies entirely within a single plane, and that plane contains both the unit tangent vector and unit principal normal vector. Such a curve is called a *plane curve* and the torsion for all plane curves is zero (Lipschutz, 1969, p. 70).

In summary, we have introduced the parametric representation of curves as defined by the vector function, $\mathbf{c}(t)$, where t is an arbitrary parameter. The shape of such curves is determined by the curvature, $\kappa(t)$, and the torsion, $\tau(t)$, both of which are scalar functions of position along the curve. The curvature measures the change in orientation of the unit tangent vector, $\mathbf{t}(t)$, and the torsion measures the rotation of the binormal vector, $\mathbf{b}(t)$, about the tangent line. These two vectors, along with the principal unit normal vector, $\mathbf{n}(t)$, form a mutually orthogonal set of unit vectors called the moving trihedron of the curved line.

We have shown how the geographic angles used to measure the orientation of lineations at the exposure are related to the components of the unit tangent vector (3.16), and how to calculate the curvature from the spatial variation of the tangent vector (3.26). To apply the concepts of curved lines from differential geometry to curvilinear structures observed at exposure, lineations must be sufficiently continuous so that the tangent, normal, and binormal vector functions and their first derivatives with respect to the natural parameter can be defined. Data that would be suitable for such a study are available in the geological record, but the common measurements of lineation attitudes at discrete points are not sufficient. The tools we have introduced here are suitable for an analysis of the spatial variations of lineations, so the gathering of field data must address the continuity and spatial variation of these structures. In this way field data can be put in the context of differential geometry and one can begin to analyze the shapes of lineations in nature. Some of the tools developed to analyze curves are used to describe and analyze curved surfaces, the subject of the next section of this chapter.

3.2 | The concept and description of curved surfaces

3.2.1 Discrete, folded, and penetrative geological surfaces

Curved surfaces are found in a wide variety of geological contexts making up many different kinds of structures. For example, discrete geological surfaces include faults (Fig. 3.1a), igneous contacts (Fig. 3.1b), and unconformities (Fig. 3.1c) all of which locally resemble a planar surface, but viewed more broadly are curved surfaces that can be characterized using the principles of differential geometry introduced in this section. In each case the curvature of these surfaces has implications for their origin and the physical processes involved in their evolution. For example, faults may be curved because they evolved from discrete segments that do not lie in a plane (Segall and Pollard, 1983b; Martel *et al.*, 1988). Furthermore, the curvature of a fault surface may constrain the direction and magnitude of slip during an earthquake (Carena and Suppe, 2002). The curvature of the contact of an igneous dike may be used to deduce the stiffness of the surrounding host rock and the distribution of magma pressure (Delaney and Pollard, 1981). The curvature of an angular unconformity provides information about the sedimentary processes that shaped that surface. To make the appropriate deductions about the physical processes involved in the formation of faults, igneous contacts, unconformities, and other discrete geological surfaces one must quantitatively characterize the shapes of these surfaces.

Sedimentary and metamorphic layering commonly is folded and the shapes of the surfaces of the folded layers have been the subject of many

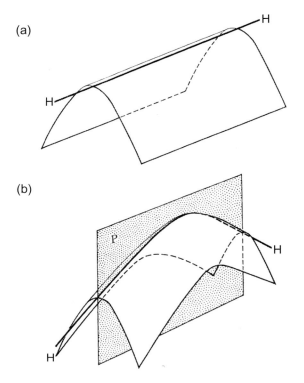

Fig 3.13 Some geometric attributes of folded geological surfaces. (a) Cylindrical fold with straight fold hinge, H–H. (b) Non-cylindrical fold with hinge that is a plane curve. Reprinted from Turner and Weiss (1963) with permission from McGraw-Hill.

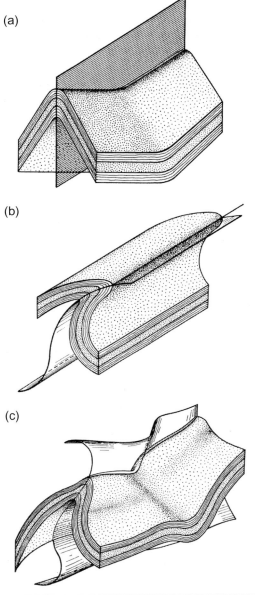

Fig 3.14 More geometric attributes of folded geological surfaces. Successive hinges define axial surfaces that may be (a) planar, (b) cylindrical, or (c) non-cylindrical. Reprinted from Turner and Weiss (1963) with permission from McGraw-Hill.

geometric classification schemes (Turner and Weiss, 1963; Fleuty, 1964; Ramsay, 1967; Hudleston, 1973; Twiss and Moores, 1992). For example, structural geologists identify the line or curve joining points of greatest curvature on such surfaces as the *fold hinge* (Fig. 3.13). Where the hinge is approximately a straight line and that line is capable of generating the folded surface when moved perpendicular to itself (Fig. 3.13a), the direction of the line is termed the *fold axis* and the surface is called a *cylindrical fold*. The hinge may be a plane curve (Fig. 3.13b) or may curve in three dimensions. For a stack of layers in a fold the surface that contains successive hinges is referred to as the *axial surface*. The shape of the axial surface may be approximately planar (Fig. 3.14a), cylindrical (Fig. 3.14b), or non-cylindrical (Fig. 3.14c). Other geometric attributes of folded surfaces include the crest line, trough line, dip isogon, fold tightness, and limb to hinge ratio. While descriptions of folded surfaces and layers may be enhanced using these attributes, the resulting classification schemes are not mathematically rigorous, they do not provide the data necessary to reproduce the surface, and they do not provide adequate measures for quantitatively comparing the shapes of the different surfaces or the spatial variations in shape of a single surface. Descriptions of folded surfaces using differential geometry do not have these shortcomings.

Metamorphic rocks composed of the systematic arrangement of layers of different rock types (Fig. 2.24a), a set of sub-parallel fractures (Fig. 2.24b), or a set of similarly oriented platy mineral grains (Fig. 2.24c) are said to have a penetrative planar fabric (Turner and Weiss, 1963, p. 97). The name indicates that the constituents locally define a surface that resembles a plane, but the normal to this planar fabric may systematically change orientation from exposure to exposure. In these cases it may be possible to represent this spatial variation in orientation with a set of curved surfaces such that a given surface is everywhere tangent to the locally planar fabric. Procedures to define individual continuous surfaces in three-dimensional space from scattered measurements of a penetrative planar fabric have not been devised, so that is a noteworthy challenge for structural geologists. With such a characterization in hand one could model fabrics using continuum mechanics and test hypotheses concerning their orientation using differential geometry.

3.2.2 Parametric representations of curved surfaces

We began our discussion of curved lines by appealing to the intuitive notion of a set of points arranged in an orderly and continuous fashion to form a curve in three-dimensional space. Because individual points in three-dimensional space are identified by their position vectors, $\mathbf{p}$, this led to the definition of a curved line as a continuous vector function of a single scalar variable t, called the arbitrary parameter of the curve, such that $\mathbf{c} = \mathbf{c}(t)$. As t increases in value the heads of successive position vectors trace out the curved line. The analytical description of curved surfaces also may be approached from the intuitive notion of a set of points arranged in some continuous fashion in three-dimensional space. However, sufficiently close to any particular point, the neighboring points are distributed such that they resemble a

plane, not a line. This leads to the definition of a curved surface as a continuous vector function of two scalar variables (u, v), called the parameters of the surface, such that $\mathbf{s} = \mathbf{s}(u, v)$. The two parameters may be thought of as the coordinates of points on a plane, called the parameter plane, and those points map onto the surface according to the vector function $\mathbf{s}(u, v)$. As the two parameters vary, the heads of the successive position vectors sweep out the curved surface in three-dimensional space.

To understand the analytical definition of a curved surface we begin by describing the coordinate systems used for the two-dimensional parameter plane and the three-dimensional curved surface (Fig. 3.15). The two Cartesian axes (Ou, Ov) and the associated base vectors $(\mathbf{e}_u, \mathbf{e}_v)$ define the parameter plane on which the two coordinates are the parameters u and v. The three Cartesian axes (Ox, Oy, Oz) and the associated base vectors $(\mathbf{e}_x, \mathbf{e}_y, \mathbf{e}_z)$ comprise the system for the curved surface. The position vectors, $\mathbf{s}$, for the curved surface can be written as a function of the two parameters (Lipschutz, 1969, p. 128):

$$\mathbf{s}(u, v) = s_x(u, v)\mathbf{e}_x + s_y(u, v)\mathbf{e}_y + s_z(u, v)\mathbf{e}_z \qquad (3.54)$$

The three scalar functions $[s_x(u, v), s_y(u, v), s_z(u, v)]$ are the components of the vector function, $\mathbf{s}(u, v)$, with respect to the base vectors $(\mathbf{e}_x, \mathbf{e}_y, \mathbf{e}_z)$. These functions, along with the base vectors, determine the position vectors for all points on the curved surface. The vector equation (3.54) is called the *parametric representation* of the surface. Compare the facts that a single variable parameterizes the curved line (3.1) and a pair of variables parameterizes the curved surface (3.54).

Any point in the parameter plane (Fig. 3.15a) may be defined by a two-dimensional position vector $\mathbf{w} = u\mathbf{e}_u + v\mathbf{e}_v$ with respect to the base vectors $\mathbf{e}_u$ and $\mathbf{e}_v$. Thus, the position vectors for the curved surface, $\mathbf{s}$, in three-dimensional space are determined by a vector function of the two-dimensional vector variable, $\mathbf{w}$, that is $\mathbf{s} = \mathbf{s}(\mathbf{w})$. However, because the components of the vector $\mathbf{w}$ are the two parameters (u, v), we can speak of the surface as a function of these two scalar parameters, $\mathbf{s} = \mathbf{s}(u, v)$, and that is what we will do in the following discussion. An individual point (u_o, v_o) in the parameter plane (Fig. 3.15a) maps onto the surface (Fig. 3.15b) using the position vector $p(u_o, v_o)$. Similarly, the coordinate lines $u = u_o$ and $v = v_o$ in the parameter plane map onto the curves $c(u_o, v)$ and $c(u, v_o)$ on the surface. This hierarchy of points, curves and a surface is fundamental to the concepts of differential geometry.

For example, consider the parametric representation of a particular curved surface (Fig. 3.16) in three-dimensional space (Lipschutz, 1969, p. 151):

$$s = (u + v)e_x + (u - v)e_y + 2(u^2 + v^2)e_z \qquad (3.55)$$

The components of this vector function are equal to the coordinates x, y, and z in the three-dimensional space containing the surface:

$$x = u + v, \quad y = u - v, \quad z = 2(u^2 + v^2) \qquad (3.56)$$

Adding and then subtracting the first two equations to eliminate v and then u, and then substituting the resulting equations into the third equation, we have:

$$u = \frac{1}{2}(x + y), \quad v = \frac{1}{2}(x - y), \quad \text{so } z = x^2 + y^2 \qquad (3.57)$$

The last of these equations is in the standard form of an elliptic paraboloid (Selby, 1975, p. 400) and is the special case where sections parallel to the (x, y)-plane are circles. In the geological context the patch of this surface near the origin is similar in shape to the surfaces of formations that are deformed into a basin-shaped fold.

How do the coordinate lines $u = u_o$ and $v = v_o$ in the parameter plane map onto this elliptic paraboloid? In other words what are the curves $c(u_o, v)$ and $c(u, v_o)$ on the surface $s(u, v)$? For example, setting $v = v_o$ we have $x - y = 2v_o$, so $y = x - 2v_o$. This equation defines a plane that is parallel to the z-axis and intersects the (x, y)-plane along a line with a unit positive slope. This plane intersects the surface along a parabola to form the curve $c(u, v_o)$ which is referred to as a u-parameter curve on the surface (Fig. 3.16a). As the value of v_o varies, the set of u-parameter curves is defined. Similarly, by setting $u = u_o$ one defines a plane that is parallel to the z-axis and intersects the (x, y)-plane along a line with a unit negative slope. This plane also intersects the surface along a parabola, forming the curve $c(u_o, v)$ which is referred to as a v-parameter curve on the surface (Fig. 3.16b). As the

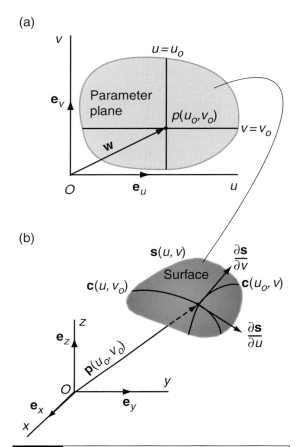

Fig 3.15 Parametric representation of a curved surface (a) Two-dimensional parameter plane with parameters u and v. Lines $u = u_o$ and $v = v_o$ in the parameter plane map to v- and u-parameter curves on the surface. (b) Three-dimensional surface defined by vector function of two parameters, $s(u, v)$. Reprinted from Pollard et al. (2004) with permission from The Geological Society of London.

value of u_o varies, the set of v-parameter curves is defined. In this way the two sets of coordinate lines, $v = $ constant and $u = $ constant, that cover the parameter plane map to the two sets of curves that cover the three-dimensional surface.

All three components of the vector function $s(u, v)$ in (3.54) may be complicated functions of u and v, subject only to constraints that insure the functions are continuous and can be differentiated, and that the surface has a well-defined tangent plane at each point (Lipschutz, 1969, p. 150). However, in many cases of interest in structural geology a simpler form of the parametric

(a)

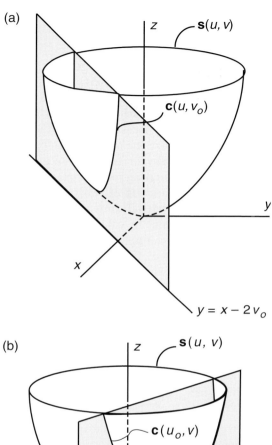

(b)

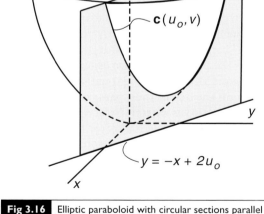

Fig 3.16 Elliptic paraboloid with circular sections parallel to the (x, y)-plane. (a) The u-parameter curve, $c(u, v_0)$, is a parabola. (b) The v-parameter curve, $c(u_0, v)$, also is a parabola.

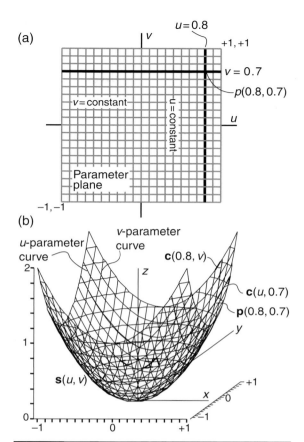

Fig 3.17 The same elliptic paraboloid shown in Fig. 3.16 but represented as a Monge patch with parameter plane superimposed on the (x, y)-plane so u and v are equivalent to x and y. (a) Parameter plane. (b) Wire-frame diagram of elliptic paraboloid: the u- and v-parameter curves, $c(u, v_0)$ and $c(u_0, v)$, are parabolas in (x, z)- and (y, z)-planes, respectively, that define two of the sets of wires.

representation of a surface, or of a patch of a surface, may be found such that:

$$s(u, v) = u e_x + v e_y + g(u, v) e_z \qquad (3.58)$$

Note that the components, s_x and s_y, of s are equated to the parameters u and v, and only s_z is a function of the two parameters, $g(u, v)$. A parametric representation of a surface in which two of the components of s are the parameters and the third component is a function of the parameters is referred to as a Monge patch, named after the French mathematician Gaspard Monge who lived from 1746 to 1818 and is regarded as one of the founders of differential geometry.

Practical applications of the Monge patch to structural mapping become obvious if one thinks of the parameter plane as superimposed on the (x, y)-plane in three-dimensional space (Fig. 3.17a), so the parameters u and v are equivalent to the coordinates x and y. Then the vector function for a surface that is the target for mapping may be written:

$$\mathbf{s}(x,y) = x\mathbf{e}_x + y\mathbf{e}_y + g(x,y)\mathbf{e}_z \tag{3.59}$$

Here we consider the (x,y)-plane as the horizontal plane of a local Cartesian coordinate system established in the region being mapped, and values of $g(x,y)$ are the measured elevations of exposures of the surface relative to the local origin. Similarly, the parameter plane can be superimposed on the UTM grid for the region in which case (3.58) is transformed such that s_x = easting, s_y = northing, and s_z = elevation.

To gain further insights about the Monge patch consider the parameter plane (Fig. 3.17a) with a rectangular grid of lines, u = constant and v = constant, parallel to the coordinate axes and use the following parametric representation of a curved surface which is in the form (3.58) of a Monge patch (Lipschutz, 1969, p. 185):

$$\mathbf{s}(u,v) = u\mathbf{e}_x + v\mathbf{e}_y + (u^2 + v^2)\mathbf{e}_z \tag{3.60}$$

Using the first two components to eliminate the parameters u and v from the expression for the third component, and noting that the components of the vector are equivalent to the coordinates, the equation $z = x^2 + y^2$ is found which is the same elliptic paraboloid illustrated in Fig. 3.16. However, in contrast to that representation, the u- and v-parameter curves for (3.60) are the intersections of the surface with planes parallel to the (x,z)-plane and the (y,z)-plane, respectively.

Note how three sets of curved lines are used to represent the elliptic paraboloid in the wireframe diagram (Fig. 3.17b). The intersections of the curved surface with planes parallel to the (x,z)-plane form a set of parabolas, as do the intersections of the curved surface with planes parallel to the (y,z)-plane. The intersections of the curved surface with planes parallel to the (x,y)-plane form a set of circles. A particular u-parameter curve, defined by the vector function $\mathbf{c}(u,0.7)$, and a particular v-parameter curve, defined by $\mathbf{c}(0.8, v)$, are highlighted in Fig. 3.17b. The point $(0.8, 0.7)$ on the parameter plane maps to the point $\mathbf{p}(0.8, 0.7)$ on the curved surface at the intersection of the two highlighted curves. In this way every coordinate line and every point in the two-dimensional parameter plane have a corresponding curve and a corresponding point on the curved surface in three-dimensional space.

3.2.3 The tangent plane, tangent vector, and unit normal vector

We continue to use the more general parametric representation of a surface (3.54) to develop the theoretical concepts necessary to characterize surfaces, but recognize the Monge patch (3.58) as a useful representation for mapping. Because the parametric representation of a surface, $\mathbf{s}(u,v)$, describes a vector function of two variable parameters, there is a partial derivative associated with each parameter. To calculate the partial derivative $\partial\mathbf{s}/\partial u$, for example, one takes the derivative with respect to u of each component of the vector function while holding v constant, and then uses these as the components of a new vector function. Thus, the partial derivatives of $\mathbf{s}(u,v)$ with respect to the two parameters are (Lipschutz, 1969, p. 126):

$$\begin{aligned} \frac{\partial\mathbf{s}(u,v)}{\partial u} &= \frac{\partial s_x}{\partial u}\mathbf{e}_x + \frac{\partial s_y}{\partial u}\mathbf{e}_y + \frac{\partial s_z}{\partial u}\mathbf{e}_z \\ \frac{\partial\mathbf{s}(u,v)}{\partial v} &= \frac{\partial s_x}{\partial v}\mathbf{e}_x + \frac{\partial s_y}{\partial v}\mathbf{e}_y + \frac{\partial s_z}{\partial v}\mathbf{e}_z \end{aligned} \tag{3.61}$$

Recall from (3.8) that for the natural representation of a curve, $\mathbf{c}(s)$, the derivative with respect to the arc length, s, is the unit tangent vector. Because the partial derivative $\partial\mathbf{s}/\partial u$ is taken with v = constant, this is equivalent to taking the derivative along any one of the u-parameter curves, for example, $\mathbf{c}(u, 0.7)$ as shown in Fig. 3.17b. Thus, the partial derivative, $\partial\mathbf{s}/\partial u$, is a vector that is tangent to a u-parameter curve and points in the direction of increasing u. Similarly, $\partial\mathbf{s}/\partial v$, is a vector that is tangent to a v-parameter curve and points in the direction of increasing v. These tangent vectors are not necessarily unit vectors because the u- and v-parameter curves are not necessarily the natural representations of these curves.

As an example consider the partial derivatives of the parametric representation for the elliptic paraboloid (3.60) illustrated in Fig. 3.17b:

$$\frac{\partial\mathbf{s}}{\partial u} = \mathbf{e}_x + 2u\mathbf{e}_z, \quad \frac{\partial\mathbf{s}}{\partial v} = \mathbf{e}_y + 2v\mathbf{e}_z \tag{3.62}$$

Note that the tangent vectors, $\partial\mathbf{s}/\partial u$, for the u-parameter curves lie in planes that are parallel to the (x,z)-plane. Consider the particular u-parameter

(a)

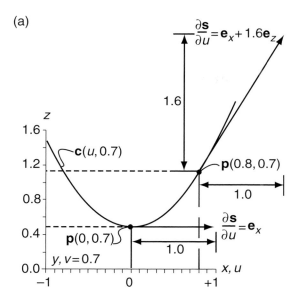

(b)

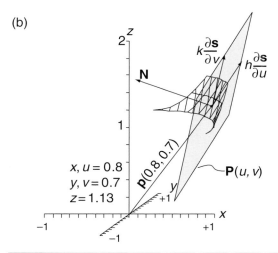

Fig 3.18 Tangent vectors and tangent planes to a curved surface. (a) Tangent vector to the elliptic paraboloid in the direction of a u-parameter curve. (b) Tangent plane, $\mathbf{P}(u, v)$, to the elliptic paraboloid with unit normal vector, $\mathbf{N}$.

$\mathbf{s}(u, v)$ are not generally one. The tangent vectors, $\partial \mathbf{s}/\partial v$, for the v-parameter curves have a similar form, but all lie in planes parallel to the (y, z)-plane.

The two partial derivatives (3.61) of the vector function for a curved surface are used to define the parametric representation of planes, $\mathbf{P}$, that are tangent to the surface. In general, the family of *tangent planes* for the surface, $\mathbf{s}(u, v)$, are defined as (Lipschutz, 1969, p. 158):

$$\mathbf{P} = \mathbf{s} + h\frac{\partial \mathbf{s}}{\partial u} + k\frac{\partial \mathbf{s}}{\partial v}, \quad -\infty \leq h, k \leq +\infty \qquad (3.63)$$

This equation may be understood intuitively by considering the vector function for the tangent plane at the arbitrary point on the surface designated by the point $p(u_o, v_o)$ on the parameter plane:

$$\mathbf{P}(u_o, v_o) = \mathbf{s}(u_o, v_o) + h\frac{\partial \mathbf{s}}{\partial u}\bigg|_{u_o, v_o} + k\frac{\partial \mathbf{s}}{\partial v}\bigg|_{u_o, v_o},$$
$$-\infty \leq h, k \leq +\infty \qquad (3.64)$$

The first term on the right-hand side is the position vector for the point on the curved surface. The second and third terms extend the position vector parallel to the tangent vectors at this point by arbitrary distances proportional to the variables h and k. As h and k range over the entire set of real numbers, this equation defines all possible points on the tangent plane.

For example, consider the particular point on the parameter plane $p(0.8, 0.7)$, and its mapping onto the curved surface $\mathbf{s}(u, v)$ illustrated in Fig. 3.17b. The parametric representation of the tangent plane, $\mathbf{P}$, to this elliptic paraboloid (3.60) at the designated point is:

$$\mathbf{P}(0.8, 0.7) = 0.8\mathbf{e}_x + 0.7\mathbf{e}_y + 1.13\mathbf{e}_z + h(\mathbf{e}_x + 1.6\mathbf{e}_z)$$
$$+ k(\mathbf{e}_y + 1.4\mathbf{e}_z), \quad -\infty \leq h, k \leq +\infty$$
$$(3.65)$$

A portion of this tangent plane is illustrated along with a portion of the wire-frame diagram for the surface in Fig. 3.18b. Note that the first three terms of the right-hand side of this vector equation locate the designated point, $\mathbf{p}(0.8, 0.7)$, on the surface. The fourth term is the tangent vector to the u-parameter curve, $\partial \mathbf{s}/\partial u$, evaluated at this point and scaled by the arbitrary variable h. The fifth term is the tangent vector to the v-parameter curve, $\partial \mathbf{s}/\partial v$, evaluated at this point and scaled by

curve, $\mathbf{c}(u, 0.7)$, as shown in Fig. 3.18a. At the point $\mathbf{p}(0, 0.7)$ on this curve the slope is zero and the magnitude of the tangent vector is one, because $\partial \mathbf{s}/\partial u = \mathbf{e}_x$. As u increases from 0, the inclinations of the tangent vectors increase in proportion to u, just as the slope of the parabolic curve increases. Thus, at the point $\mathbf{p}(0.8, 0.7)$ that tangent vector is $\partial \mathbf{s}/\partial u = \mathbf{e}_x + 1.6\mathbf{e}_z$. Clearly, the magnitudes of the tangent vectors as calculated by the partial derivatives of the arbitrary variable k. As h and k vary, the sum of these terms defines vectors that cover the tangent plane, **P**.

The tangent plane plays an important role in describing any curved surface. Furthermore, any geological surface observed at exposure is approximated locally with planar elements whose orientations are measured using angles such as the strike, α_s, and dip, ϕ_d. These planar elements are tangent planes to the geological surface at the point of measurement and would be described quantitatively by (3.63) if a parametric representation of the geological surface were known.

Now we are in a position to bring the concepts of the curved line and curved surface together to understand the geometry of an arbitrary curved line lying on a particular surface. This concept is necessary because the curvature at a point on a surface may vary with direction, and these directions are defined in terms of curves passing through the point and lying on the curved surface. Consider an arbitrary curve (Fig. 3.19a) in the parameter plane (u, v) that is defined by the functions $u = u(t)$, $v = v(t)$ and passes through the point $p(u_o, v_o)$. The two coordinate lines, $u = u_o$ and $v = v_o$, are parallel to the axes and also pass through this point. The parametric representation of the surface, $s(u, v)$, along with the u-parameter curve, $c(u, v_o)$, and the v-parameter curve, $c(u_o, v)$, are shown in Fig. 3.19b. The arbitrary curve in the parameter plane is a function of the two "surface" parameters, u and v, and these are, in turn, functions of the one "curve" parameter, t. Thus, the parametric representation of the arbitrary curve is given by the vector function $c[u(t), v(t)]$.

The tangent vector, **T**, to the arbitrary curve is given by the derivative of the vector function $c[u(t), v(t)]$ with respect to the parameter, t. Unlike the unit tangent vector, **t**, defined in (3.8), this tangent vector is not normalized by its magnitude. Because **c** is a vector function of two variable parameters that are, in turn, functions of a single variable parameter, the derivative is evaluated using the chain rule as (Lipschutz, 1969, p. 158):

$$\mathbf{T} = \frac{d\mathbf{c}[u(t), v(t)]}{dt} = \frac{d\mathbf{c}(u, v_o)}{du}\frac{du}{dt} + \frac{d\mathbf{c}(u_o, v)}{dv}\frac{dv}{dt}$$
$$= \frac{\partial \mathbf{s}}{\partial u}\frac{du}{dt} + \frac{\partial \mathbf{s}}{\partial v}\frac{dv}{dt} \tag{3.66}$$

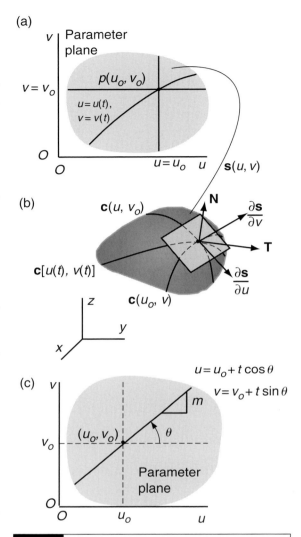

Fig 3.19 Diagrams to define the tangent vector, **T**, to a curved surface, $s(u, v)$, in the direction of an arbitrary curve, $c[u(t), v(t)]$. (a) Parameter plane. (b) Three-dimensional surface. (c) Parameter plane with line in arbitrary direction. Reprinted from Pollard et al. (2004) with permission from The Geological Society of London.

In the last step we use the fact that the partial derivatives, $\partial s/\partial u$ and $\partial s/\partial v$, are the tangent vectors to the u- and v-parameter curves, respectively (Fig. 3.19b). As we have shown in Fig. 3.18b, these two vectors lie in the tangent plane and, indeed, are used to define the tangent plane (3.63) to the curved surface at a designated point. Because the tangent vector **T** is linearly dependent upon these two partial derivatives, it also lies in the tangent plane. In this way the tangent vector to the surface $s(u,v)$ at an arbitrary point in any arbitrary direction is related to the partial derivatives of the parametric representation of the curved surface at that point.

The following example provides geometric interpretations for the quantities du/dt and dv/dt in (3.66) and further insight about the tangent vector T. Consider a straight line in the parameter plane through the arbitrary point $p(u_o, v_o)$ and having an arbitrary slope, m (Fig. 3.19c). The equation for this line, given in the standard point-slope form, is:

$$v - v_o = m(u - u_o) \qquad (3.67)$$

To write this equation in parametric form consider the parameter, t, to be the coordinate measured along the line from the arbitrary point $p(u_o, v_o)$. The parameters u and v are related to the parameter t by noting that the slope $m = \tan \theta$, where θ is the angle from the positive u-axis to the line, so:

$$u = u_o + t\cos \theta, \quad v = v_o + t\sin \theta \qquad (3.68)$$

By varying the angle, θ, lines with any orientation can be used to specify the direction of the tangent vector, T, at a point on the surface. The derivatives of $u(t)$ and $v(t)$ as used in the definition of the tangent vector (3.66) are:

$$\frac{du}{dt} = \cos \theta, \quad \frac{dv}{dt} = \sin \theta = \cos \left(\frac{\pi}{2} - \theta \right) \qquad (3.69)$$

These are the direction cosines of the angles between the arbitrary line and the two coordinate axes in the parameter plane. In (3.66) these two quantities scale the tangent vectors for the u- and v-parameter curves to determine the tangent vector, T, for the curve $c[u(t), v(t)]$. The ratio $(dv/dt)/(du/dt) = \tan \theta$ determines the direction of the tangent line to this curve.

Returning to the example of the elliptic paraboloid (3.60), the straight line in the parameter plane (Fig. 3.19c) maps onto this surface as the curve:

$$c[u(t), v(t)] = (u_o + t\cos \theta)e_x + (v_o + t\sin \theta)e_y$$
$$+ (u_o^2 + 2u_o t\cos \theta + v_o^2$$
$$+ 2v_o t\sin \theta + t^2)e_z \qquad (3.70)$$

The tangent vector anywhere along this curve is:

$$\frac{dc}{dt} = (\cos \theta)e_x + (\sin \theta)e_y$$
$$+ (2u_o \cos \theta + 2v_o \sin \theta + 2t)e_z \qquad (3.71)$$

At the arbitrary point $p(u_o, v_o)$ the curve and its derivative are found by setting $t = 0$ in these equations. The tangent vectors anywhere on the elliptic paraboloid (3.60) in the direction specified by the direction cosines of the arbitrary line are calculated using (3.66) as:

$$T(u,v) = (e_x + 2ue_z)\cos \theta + (e_y + 2ve_z)\sin \theta \qquad (3.72)$$

This is equivalent to the tangent vector calculated for the curved line in the preceding equation, given our definitions of the parameters u and v as functions of t.

The orientation of the tangent plane (3.63) is uniquely determined by either of the two unit normal vectors to that plane. The choice between these two oppositely directed vectors is determined by a right-hand rule: the unit normal vector, N, makes a right-handed orthogonal system with the two tangent vectors, $\partial s/\partial u$ and $\partial s/\partial v$ (Fig. 3.19b) and is defined as (Lipschutz, 1969, p. 158):

$$N = \frac{\dfrac{\partial s}{\partial u} \times \dfrac{\partial s}{\partial v}}{\left| \dfrac{\partial s}{\partial u} \times \dfrac{\partial s}{\partial v} \right|} \qquad (3.73)$$

Recall that the vector (cross) product of two arbitrary vectors, $v \times w$, is normal to the plane containing v and w and that the thumb of your right hand points in the direction of $v \times w$ when your fingers curl from v toward w. Using (3.73) the unit normal at any point on a surface can be calculated from its parametric representation $s(u,v)$.

As an example consider the unit normal vector for the elliptic paraboloid (3.60). Using (3.28) the vector product of the two tangent vectors is:

$$\frac{\partial s}{\partial u} \times \frac{\partial s}{\partial v} = \det \begin{pmatrix} e_x & 1 & 0 \\ e_y & 0 & 1 \\ e_z & 2u & 2v \end{pmatrix}$$
$$= -2ue_x - 2ve_y + 1e_z \qquad (3.74)$$

Therefore, the unit normal vector is:

$$N = (-2ue_x - 2ve_y + 1e_z)/(4u^2 + 4v^2 + 1)^{1/2} \qquad (3.75)$$

At the origin in the parameter plane, $u = 0 = v$, we find $\mathbf{N} = \mathbf{e}_z$. As expected, this is a unit vector pointed away from the concave side of the surface along the positive z-axis. For the point $p(0.8, 0.7)$ shown in Fig. 3.17, we calculate the unit normal vector as:

$$\mathbf{N}(0.8, 0.7) = -0.68101\,\mathbf{e}_x - 0.59588\,\mathbf{e}_y + 0.42563\,\mathbf{e}_z \tag{3.76}$$

Given the signs of the three components or the visualization of the surface near this point in Fig. 3.18b, one can conclude that $\mathbf{N}(0.8, 0.7)$ points away from the surface on its concave side and that it obeys the right-hand rule with respect to the two tangent vectors.

3.2.4 Dike and joint surfaces idealized as helicoids

Observations and mapping of opening fractures in rock, including basaltic dikes (Delaney and Pollard, 1981) and joints (Woodworth, 1896) suggest that the surfaces of some of these fractures can be idealized as helicoids (Pollard et al., 1982). Specifically, the traces of some echelon fractures are approximately straight when viewed in cross sectional exposures that are perpendicular to the propagation direction (e.g. Fig. 3.20c, d). However, exposures at different levels (serial cross sections) reveal different orientations, such that the surfaces appear to twist about an axis that is parallel to the propagation direction (Fig. 3.20a, b). A straight line that is perpendicular to the propagation axis would sweep out these fracture surfaces if it were rotated about the axis and translated along it. If the spatial rate of rotation is constant the twisted surface so produced is a helicoid. To understand how to test the hypothesis that some dike and joint surfaces approximate helicoids, we review the characteristics of this class of surfaces using differential geometry.

The parametric representation of helicoids is based on (3.54) where $v = $ constant and $u = $ constant are coordinate lines in the parameter plane that map onto the u- and v-parameter curves on the helicoidal surface defined by the following vector function:

$$\mathbf{s}(u, v) = (u \cos v)\mathbf{e}_x + (u \sin v)\mathbf{e}_y + (cv)\mathbf{e}_z \tag{3.77}$$

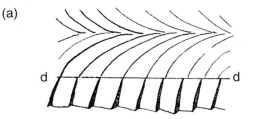

(a)

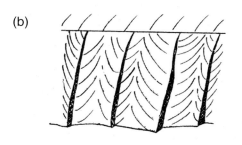

(b)

(c)

(d)

Fig 3.20 Surface structures of joints from pelitic rocks of the Mystic River region, MA. (a) Joint plane with plumose structure and fringe fracture surfaces. (b) Plumose structure on fringe fracture surfaces. (c) Cross section of fringe showing echelon fractures. (d) Cross section of fringe with echelon fractures and cross fractures. Reproduced from Woodworth (1986) with permission from The Museum of Science, Boston.

The u-parameter curves on the surface are straight lines that intersect and are perpendicular to the z-axis. Each v-parameter curve is a helix that intersects the x-axis and curves around the z-axis. The tangent vectors to the u- and v-parameter curves are found using (3.61) such that:

$$\frac{\partial \mathbf{s}}{\partial u} = (\cos v)\mathbf{e}_x + (\sin v)\mathbf{e}_y$$
$$\frac{\partial \mathbf{s}}{\partial v} = -(u \sin v)\mathbf{e}_x + (u \cos v)\mathbf{e}_y + (c)\mathbf{e}_z \tag{3.78}$$

Using these partial derivatives in (3.73) the unit normal vector at any point on the helicoid is:

$$\mathbf{N}(u, v) = (1/\sqrt{c^2 + u^2})[(c \sin v)\mathbf{e}_x - (c \cos v)\mathbf{e}_y + (u)\mathbf{e}_z] \tag{3.79}$$

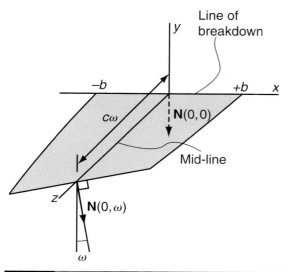

Fig 3.21 Patch of a helicoidal surface taken as a model for the surface of a fringe joint. **N** is the unit normal vector to the surface; $1/c$ is the spatial rate of twist; and ω is the twist angle at the distal edge. Reprinted from Pollard *et al.* (2004) with permission from The Geological Society of London.

For a given value of the constant c, the unit normal completely determines the orientation of the surface at any point specified by the parameters u and v.

The patch of a helicoidal surface used to model a fracture surface is illustrated in Fig. 3.21. To appreciate the geometric meaning of the parameters and constant associated with the helicoid consider the following special cases. For $u = 0$ the surface (3.77) is coincident with the z-axis such that the position vector and unit normal are:

$$\mathbf{s}(0,v) = (cv)\mathbf{e}_z, \quad \mathbf{N}(0,v) = (\sin v)\mathbf{e}_x - (\cos v)\mathbf{e}_y \quad (3.80)$$

Position on this part of the surface is determined by the value of v scaled by the constant c. The unit normal is independent of c and varies, for example, from $-\mathbf{e}_y$ for $v = 0$ to $+\mathbf{e}_x$ for $v = \pi/2$ as the local surface twists from the (x, z)-plane to the (y, z)-plane.

We define the twist of the helicoidal surface (Fig. 3.21) as the angle between the reference unit normal, $\mathbf{N}(0,0)$, and the unit normal at the point in question along the mid-line, $\mathbf{N}(0,v)$. The scalar product of these two unit vectors is:

$$\mathbf{N}(0,0) \cdot \mathbf{N}(0,v) = [-(1)\mathbf{e}_y] \cdot [(\sin v)\mathbf{e}_x$$
$$- (\cos v)\mathbf{e}_y] = \cos v \quad (3.81)$$

Because the scalar product of unit vectors is equal to the cosine of the angle between them, the twist angle is equal to the parameter v. The component of $\mathbf{s}(0,v)$ in the z-direction is $s_z = cv$, and this is equal to the z-coordinate, so $dz/dv = c$. The spatial *rate of twist* of the surface is defined as $dv/dz = 1/c$. The patch of the helicoidal surface (Fig. 3.21) that we take as an analytical description of a fracture surface, covers the range $0 \leq v \leq \omega$, so ω is the maximum twist angle at the distal edge.

For $v = 0$ the helicoidal surface (3.77) is coincident with the x-axis (Fig. 3.21) such that the position vector and unit normal are:

$$\mathbf{s}(u,0) = (u)\mathbf{e}_x, \quad \mathbf{N}(u,0) = (1/\sqrt{c^2 + u^2})$$
$$\times [-(c)\mathbf{e}_y + (u)\mathbf{e}_z] \quad (3.82)$$

Position on this part of the surface is given by the value of u. For the analytical description of a helicoidal fracture surface we take the range $-b \leq u \leq +b$ so the width of the fracture is $2b$ and the fracture mid-line is coincident with the z-axis. We take the x-axis as the intersection between a planar fracture surface that lies in the (x, z)-plane where $z \leq 0$ and a helicoidal fracture surface that twists about the positive z-axis. Thus, the x-axis is equivalent to the line of breakdown from a single parent (main) fracture to multiple echelon fractures (feather fractures, twist hackle) in the fringe of a joint or dike (Fig. 3.20a, line d–d).

For $u = 0$ and $v = 0$ the unit normal for the helicoidal surface is $\mathbf{N}(0,0) = -\mathbf{e}_y$, which is in the negative y-coordinate direction and is parallel to the unit normal for the planar fracture surface (Fig. 3.21). However, for all other points along the x-axis, $0 < |u| \leq b$ and $v = 0$, there is a component of the unit normal in the z-coordinate direction that is proportional to $u/(c^2 + u^2)^{1/2}$. Thus, the planar and helicoidal fracture surfaces may be continuous with one another along the line of breakdown (x-axis), but there is a discontinuity in the orientation of the two surfaces except at the mid-line of the helicoidal surface ($u = 0, v = 0$). This may have important implications for the growth of an echelon fracture surface.

The geometry of twist hackle has been hypothesized to be similar to a helicoidal surface (Pollard *et al.*, 2004). We test this hypothesis using an area (white rectangular box) on a joint surface found on a hand-sized sample of chert (Fig. 3.22). The

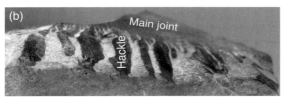

Fig 3.22 Photograph of the surface of a joint in chert with plumose structure merging into twist hackle. Reprinted from Pollard *et al.* (2004) with permission from The Geological Society of London.

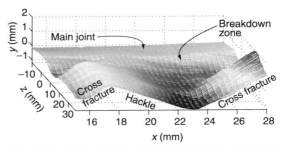

Fig 3.23 Oblique rendering of a portion of the joint fringe in Fig. 3.22 from scanned data. Reprinted from Pollard *et al.* (2004) with permission from The Geological Society of London.

data set consists of 5244 points measured with a laser scanner that cover a small portion of the main joint surface, a portion of the breakdown zone, most of one coarse hackle in the fringe region, and the adjacent cross fractures. An oblique rendering of this area (Fig. 3.23) depicts the local geometry of the main joint surface in the background, the breakdown zone, the hackle, and the two cross fractures. Note that this view foreshortens the *z*-axis but leaves the *x*- and *y*-axes approximately equal. This rendering of the surface does not capture the sharp discontinuity of the exposed surface where the cross fractures meet the hackle, but it does provide an accurate image of the main joint, the hackle, and the cross fractures. Also, it should be noted that a small piece of the hackle surface has been plucked away from the breakdown zone where the ridge along $x = 18$ mm would have intersected the main joint surface.

The centerline of the hackle (Fig. 3.23) lies somewhere between the lines $x = 19.5$ and 20.5 mm, and the elevation of the surface there is approximately zero, equal to the local elevation of the main joint surface. The elevation of the hackle is greater than zero for lines between $x = 17$ and 19.5 mm (except for the plucked portion), and less than zero for lines between $x = 20.5$ and 23 mm. Furthermore, the ridge along $x = 17$ mm increases in elevation and the trough along $x = 23$ mm decreases in elevation away from the main joint. These observations are consistent with the hypothesis that the hackle approximates a helicoidal surface.

Recall that the centerline of a helicoid is defined as the line along which the parameter $u = 0$. The difference between the orientation of the unit normal at the proximal edge of the helicoid and that at any position along the centerline was defined as the twist angle, which is equal to the parameter v. Using data for the twist hackle (Fig. 3.23; Pollard *et al.*, 2004) we calculate the change in orientation of the unit normal vector, **N**, relative to a reference point on the main joint surface, along the grid line $x = 20$ mm, our interpretation of the centerline (Fig. 3.24). The orientation of the unit normal relative to the reference value changes systematically with the *z*-coordinate. On the main joint surface ($z < 4$ mm) the change in angle is roughly constant and less than about $4°$. Over the breakdown zone ($4 < z < 19$ mm) the angle increases to about $25°$. For the distal portion of the hackle ($19 < z > 37$ mm) the angle oscillates about a more-or-less constant value. The spatial rate of twist ($1/c$) is the slope of the curve plotted on Fig. 3.24 in the breakdown zone. For the grid line $x = 20$ mm, the slope is roughly constant over the range $7 < z < 18$ mm and is about $2° \text{mm}^{-1}$ (0.035 mm^{-1}). A constant rate of twist is consistent

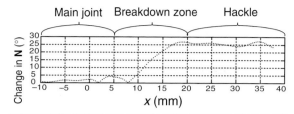

Fig 3.24 Graph of orientation of unit normal vector, **N**, versus distance along the mid-line of a fringe fracture surface from the joint pictured in Figs. 3.22 and 3.23. Reprinted from Pollard et al. (2004) with permission from The Geological Society of London.

with the hypothesis that the hackle approximates a helicoidal surface.

In summary, we have introduced the elementary concepts to describe quantitatively a surface (3.54) using a parametric representation defined by the vector function of two parameters, $\mathbf{s}(u,v)$. The partial derivatives of this function with respect to each parameter (3.61) are tangent vectors to the respective parameter curves on the surface and these serve to define the tangent planes for the surface. Structural geologists quantify the orientation of a geological surface at an exposure by measuring strike and dip or dip and dip direction, and these measurements use the concept of the tangent plane at a point on a surface. The tangent vector to an arbitrary curve on the surface (3.66) lies in the tangent plane. This concept will be used in the next two sections where we introduce measures of arc length and curvature. The normal vector (3.73) to the curved surface is equivalent to the pole to a geological surface as plotted on a stereogram. In this way we understand the relationships among the analytical descriptions of a curved surface and the everyday techniques used by structural geologists. For the particular example of twist hackle in the fringe region of a joint surface we have shown how the normal vector can be used to test the hypothesis that the hackle surface is helicoidal (Pollard et al., 2004).

3.2.5 The first fundamental form, arc length, and surface area

A continuous curved surface is completely described at an arbitrary point in terms of two differential quantities called the first and second fundamental forms. These quantities are introduced in this and the following sections. The first fundamental form, I, at an arbitrary point on a curved surface, $\mathbf{s}(u,v)$, is a measure of the differential arc length of curves lying on the surface and oriented in all possible directions at that point. To define this property of a curved surface consider the two points, $p(u,v)$ and $p(u+\mathrm{d}u, v+\mathrm{d}v)$, that lie along an arbitrary line, $u=u(t)$ and $v=v(t)$, in the parameter plane and are separated by an arbitrarily small distance (Fig. 3.25a). These points map onto the curved surface using the position vectors $\mathbf{p}(u,v)$ and $\mathbf{p}(u+\mathrm{d}u, v+\mathrm{d}v)$ along the curve $c[u(t), v(t)]$. A tangent vector to this arbitrary curve is defined using (3.66) such that (Lipschutz, 1969, p. 171):

$$\mathrm{d}\mathbf{c} = \mathbf{T}\mathrm{d}t = \frac{\partial \mathbf{s}}{\partial u}\mathrm{d}u + \frac{\partial \mathbf{s}}{\partial v}\mathrm{d}v \qquad (3.83)$$

Because this vector is a differential quantity that is parallel to $\mathbf{T}$, we refer to it as the differential tangent vector. As shown in Fig. 3.25b, the differential tangent vector is not exactly parallel to the secant line that passes through the two points $\mathbf{p}(u,v)$ and $\mathbf{p}(u+\mathrm{d}u, v+\mathrm{d}v)$ on the curve. However, recall from our discussion of Fig. 3.7 that, as the distance between the two points goes to zero, the tangent line and the secant line become parallel and the tangent line becomes the best-fitting line to the curve at the point in question. In this limit the magnitude of the differential tangent vector, $\mathrm{d}\mathbf{c}$, becomes equal to the arc length of the curve $c[u(t), v(t)]$ on the surface $\mathbf{s}(u,v)$.

The *first fundamental form*, I, is a differential quantity defined as the scalar product of the differential tangent vector, $\mathrm{d}\mathbf{c}$, with itself (Lipschutz, 1969, p. 171). Using (3.83) the first fundamental form is expanded as follows:

$$I = \mathrm{d}\mathbf{c} \cdot \mathrm{d}\mathbf{c} = \left(\frac{\partial \mathbf{s}}{\partial u}\mathrm{d}u + \frac{\partial \mathbf{s}}{\partial v}\mathrm{d}v\right) \cdot \left(\frac{\partial \mathbf{s}}{\partial u}\mathrm{d}u + \frac{\partial \mathbf{s}}{\partial v}\mathrm{d}v\right)$$

$$= \left(\frac{\partial \mathbf{s}}{\partial u} \cdot \frac{\partial \mathbf{s}}{\partial u}\right)\mathrm{d}u^2 + 2\left(\frac{\partial \mathbf{s}}{\partial u} \cdot \frac{\partial \mathbf{s}}{\partial v}\right)\mathrm{d}u\mathrm{d}v + \left(\frac{\partial \mathbf{s}}{\partial v} \cdot \frac{\partial \mathbf{s}}{\partial v}\right)\mathrm{d}v^2$$

$$(3.84)$$

The coefficients in this equation are scalar quantities with particular geometric interpretations. Because of their role in defining I, and in the calculation of useful quantities such as arc length

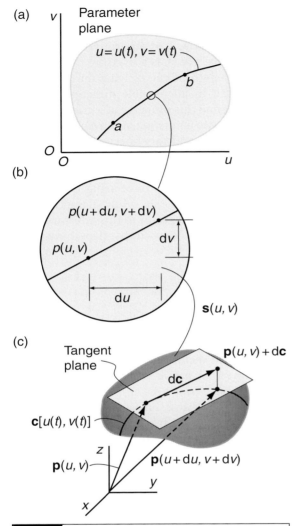

(a) Parameter plane

$v = v(t)$, $u = u(t)$

(b)

(c) Tangent plane

Fig 3.25 Diagrams to define first fundamental form for a surface. (a) Parameter plane with arbitrary curve $u = u(t)$, $v = v(t)$. (b) Fine-scale view of curve. (c) Three-dimensional view of surface and mapped curve, $\mathbf{c}[u(t), v(t)]$, with differential tangent vector, $d\mathbf{c}$, that approximates the arc of the curve. Reprinted from Pollard et al. (2004) with permission from The Geological Society of London.

The scalar quantities E, F, and G are called the coefficients of the first fundamental form. The values of the coefficients depend upon the choice of parameters used to represent the surface, but the first fundamental form itself (3.85) is invariant with respect to this choice (Lipschutz, 1969, p. 172). In this sense I is a property of the surface and plays a fundamental role in defining arc lengths on the surface.

Recall that the scalar product of any vector, $\mathbf{v}$, with itself is equal to the squared magnitude of the vector: $\mathbf{v} \cdot \mathbf{v} = |\mathbf{v}||\mathbf{v}| = |\mathbf{v}|^2$. Thus, the first fundamental form may be interpreted as:

$$I = |d\mathbf{c}|^2 \geq 0 \qquad (3.86)$$

In other words it is the square of the differential arc length (3.83) of the curve $\mathbf{c}[u(t), v(t)]$ on the surface $\mathbf{s}(u, v)$, so it is a positive quantity. The first fundamental form refers to the arc length of curves in all directions at a particular point on the surface, and the differential parameters du and dv in (3.85) are used to define a particular direction. In general, $I = 0$ if and only if $du = 0$ and $dv = 0$.

Recall that the scalar product of two arbitrary vectors, $\mathbf{v}$ and $\mathbf{w}$, may be written: $\mathbf{v} \cdot \mathbf{w} = |\mathbf{v}||\mathbf{w}| \cos \theta$, where θ is the smaller angle between the two vectors. The coefficients of the first fundamental form as defined in the second of (3.85) are scalar products of the tangent vectors to the u- and v-parameter curves. Therefore, they can be interpreted geometrically as:

$$E = \left| \frac{\partial \mathbf{s}}{\partial u} \right|^2, \quad F = \left| \frac{\partial \mathbf{s}}{\partial u} \right| \left| \frac{\partial \mathbf{s}}{\partial v} \right| \cos \theta,$$
$$G = \left| \frac{\partial \mathbf{s}}{\partial v} \right|^2 \qquad (3.87)$$

Here θ is the smaller angle between the two tangent vectors at a particular point on the surface. From these equations we understand that E and G are, respectively, the squares of the magnitudes (lengths) of the tangent vectors to the u- and v-parameter curves, so they satisfy the relationships $E > 0$ and $G > 0$. It is also the case that $EG - F^2 > 0$. Furthermore, the u- and v-parameter curves are orthogonal ($\theta = 90°$) if and only if $F = 0$ (Lipschutz, 1969, p. 173).

As an example we compute the coefficients of the first fundamental form for the elliptic paraboloid (3.60):

and area on the curved surface, they are denoted with the special symbols E, F, and G. Using this notation the first fundamental form is written (Lipschutz, 1969, p. 171):

$$I = E du^2 + 2F du dv + G dv^2$$
$$E = \frac{\partial \mathbf{s}}{\partial u} \cdot \frac{\partial \mathbf{s}}{\partial u}, \quad F = \frac{\partial \mathbf{s}}{\partial u} \cdot \frac{\partial \mathbf{s}}{\partial v}, \quad G = \frac{\partial \mathbf{s}}{\partial v} \cdot \frac{\partial \mathbf{s}}{\partial v} \qquad (3.85)$$

$$E = (\mathbf{e}_x + 2u\mathbf{e}_z) \cdot (\mathbf{e}_x + 2u\mathbf{e}_z) = 1 + 4u^2$$
$$F = (\mathbf{e}_x + 2u\mathbf{e}_z) \cdot (\mathbf{e}_y + 2v\mathbf{e}_z) = 4uv \qquad (3.88)$$
$$G = (\mathbf{e}_y + 2v\mathbf{e}_z) \cdot (\mathbf{e}_y + 2v\mathbf{e}_z) = 1 + 4v^2$$

Where $u = 0$ we have $E = 1$, so the tangent vectors to the u-parameter curves along $u = 0$ are unit vectors, a result we illustrated in Fig. 3.18a. A similar result is found for the v-parameter curves by noting that $G = 1$ for $v = 0$. Because F is not zero, the u- and v-parameter curves are not orthogonal, as is readily confirmed by glancing at Fig. 3.17b.

The first fundamental form (3.85) at a point on a surface, $\mathbf{s} = \mathbf{f}(u, v)$, is the square of the differential arc length of a curve through that point. To illustrate the geometric meaning of this quantity and to show how it is utilized in practical applications consider the points $t = a$ and $t = b$ along the arbitrary curve $u = u(t)$, $v = v(t)$ in the parameter plane (Fig. 3.25a). This curve maps onto the surface as $\mathbf{c}[u(t), v(t)]$ and the differential tangent vector, $d\mathbf{c}$, anywhere along this curve is defined by (3.83). Integrating the magnitude (length) of the differential tangent vector, $|d\mathbf{c}| = |d\mathbf{c}/dt| \, dt$, from a to b we find the arc length, s, of the curve on the surface (Lipschutz, 1969, p. 173):

$$s = \int_a^b \left| \frac{d\mathbf{c}}{dt} \right| dt = \int_a^b \left(\frac{d\mathbf{c}}{dt} \cdot \frac{d\mathbf{c}}{dt} \right)^{1/2} dt$$
$$= \int_a^b \left[E\left(\frac{du}{dt} \right)^2 + 2F\left(\frac{du}{dt}\frac{dv}{dt} \right) + G\left(\frac{dv}{dt} \right)^2 \right]^{1/2} dt \qquad (3.89)$$

Here the magnitude of $d\mathbf{c}/dt$ is taken as the square root of the scalar product of this vector with itself, and this scalar product is associated with the coefficients of the first fundamental form using (3.85). The derivatives du/dt and dv/dt establish the direction in which the arc length is measured: they are the direction cosines for the curve in the parameter plane that maps onto the surface as $\mathbf{c}[u(t), v(t)]$ (Fig. 3.19).

The coefficients of the first fundamental form also are useful for calculating the area of a surface, given its parametric representation. Consider adjacent members of the two families of coordinate lines on the parameter plane that are separated by small differential distances du and dv (Fig. 3.26a). These lines partition the parameter plane into a rectangular grid that is, in turn, mapped

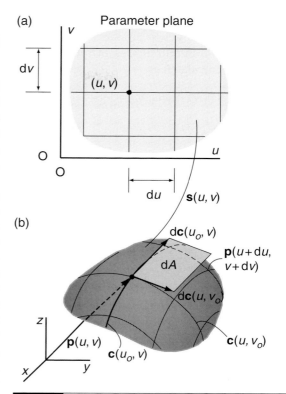

Fig 3.26 Diagrams to define the differential surface area. (a) Parameter plane with coordinate lines parallel to u and v. (b) Surface with u- and v-parameter curves and parallelogram approximating surface area between curves. Reprinted from Pollard et al. (2004) with permission from The Geological Society of London.

onto the surface as a curvilinear grid (Fig. 3.26b). The differential tangent vectors at the point $\mathbf{p}(u, v)$ in the directions of the u- and v-parameter curves are found from (3.83):

$$d\mathbf{c}(u, v_o) = \frac{\partial \mathbf{s}}{\partial u} du, \quad d\mathbf{c}(u_o, v) = \frac{\partial \mathbf{s}}{\partial v} dv \qquad (3.90)$$

These vectors form two sides of a small parallelogram and the differential area, dA, of this planar figure is used to approximate the area of the curved surface between the adjacent parameter curves. The differential area is:

$$dA = |d\mathbf{c}(u, v_o)||d\mathbf{c}(u_o, v)| \sin \theta \qquad (3.91)$$

This equation follows from the fact that the area of a parallelogram with sides a and b with included angle θ is $A = ab \sin \theta$.

The formula for dA is similar to (3.29) for the absolute value of the cross product of two vectors. Therefore, the differential area of the parallelogram can be calculated as:

$$dA = |dc(u,v_o) \times dc(u_o,v)| = \left| \frac{\partial s}{\partial u} \times \frac{\partial s}{\partial v} \right| dudv$$

$$= \left[\left(\frac{\partial s}{\partial u} \times \frac{\partial s}{\partial v} \right) \cdot \left(\frac{\partial s}{\partial u} \times \frac{\partial s}{\partial v} \right) \right]^{1/2} dudv \qquad (3.92)$$

An identity relating scalar and vector products can be used to convert this equation to an equation that involves the coefficients of the first fundamental form (Lipschutz, 1969, p. 10):

$$(\mathbf{a} \times \mathbf{b}) \cdot (\mathbf{c} \times \mathbf{d}) = (\mathbf{a} \cdot \mathbf{c})(\mathbf{b} \cdot \mathbf{d}) - (\mathbf{a} \cdot \mathbf{d})(\mathbf{b} \cdot \mathbf{c}) \quad (3.93)$$

Substituting the appropriate vector cross products into this identity yields:

$$\left(\frac{\partial s}{\partial u} \times \frac{\partial s}{\partial v} \right) \cdot \left(\frac{\partial s}{\partial u} \times \frac{\partial s}{\partial v} \right)$$

$$= \left(\frac{\partial s}{\partial u} \cdot \frac{\partial s}{\partial u} \right)\left(\frac{\partial s}{\partial v} \cdot \frac{\partial s}{\partial v} \right) - \left(\frac{\partial s}{\partial u} \cdot \frac{\partial s}{\partial v} \right)\left(\frac{\partial s}{\partial u} \cdot \frac{\partial s}{\partial v} \right)$$

$$= EG - F^2 \qquad (3.94)$$

Combining these results the differential area of the curved surface is $dA = [EG - F^2]^{1/2}dudv$. Because $EG - F^2 > 0$, the square root of this quantity is a real number. The area of a curved surface is found by integrating the differential area over the surface:

$$A = \iint (EG - F^2)^{1/2}dudv \qquad (3.95)$$

The surface area is a function of the coefficients of the first fundamental form and, in turn, of the parameters u and v.

Consider the helicoidal surface (3.77), which we have identified as a geometric model, for twist hackle (Figs. 3.22 and 3.23). The coefficients of the first fundamental form are found using (3.85) such that:

$$E = 1, \quad F = 0, \quad G = c^2 + u^2 \qquad (3.96)$$

In general E is the squared magnitude of the tangent vector to the u-parameter curves. This vector for the helicoid is a unit vector that lies in the (x, y)-plane and is not a function of u, so the u-parameter curve is a straight line perpendicular to the z-axis (Fig. 3.21). Similarly, G is the squared

magnitude of the tangent vector to the v-parameter curves. In this case the vector has a magnitude $(c^2 + u^2)^{1/2}$. From the general parametric representation for a circular helix (3.2) we consider a particular example that has a radius u_o and pitch c (Lipschutz, 1969, p. 63):

$$c(t) = (u_o \cos t)e_x + (u_o \sin t)e_y + (ct)e_z \qquad (3.97)$$

Here t is the single arbitrary parameter for the curve, and the tangent vector is:

$$\frac{dc}{dt} = -(u_o \sin t)e_x + (u_o \cos t)e_y + (c)e_z \qquad (3.98)$$

Comparing these equations to (3.77) and the second of (3.78) it is clear that each v-parameter curve on the helicoid is a helix with radius u_o and pitch c. Because neither tangent vector (3.78) is zero but the coefficient $F = 0$, the u- and v-parameter curves are orthogonal everywhere on the helicoidal surface. The set of straight lines and the set of helixes cover the helicoidal surface with an orthogonal network.

The arc length of any curve on a surface is calculated using (3.89) and for the helicoid this reduces to:

$$s = \int_{t_1}^{t_2} \left[\left(\frac{du}{dt} \right)^2 + (c^2 + u^2)\left(\frac{dv}{dt} \right)^2 \right]^{1/2} dt \qquad (3.99)$$

For a coordinate line $v = $ constant which maps onto the helicoid as a u-parameter curve with $u = t$, we have $du/dt = 1$, $dv/dt = 0$. Taking the limits as $t_1 = -b$ and $t_2 = +b$ we find $s = 2b$, just what is expected for a straight line. For a coordinate line $u = $ constant $= u_o$ that maps onto the helicoid as a v-parameter curve (a helix) with $v = t$, we have $du/dt = 0$, $dv/dt = 1$. Taking the limits as $t_1 = 0$ and $t_2 = \omega$ we find the length of this segment of the helix, $s = \omega(u_o^2 + c^2)^{1/2}$. Along the z-axis $u_o = 0$ and $s = \omega c$, which is the length of the surface (Fig. 3.21).

The area of the patch of a helicoid that we take as a fracture surface (Fig. 3.21) is found using the coefficients of the first fundamental form in (3.95) with the limits $-b \leq u \leq +b$ and $0 \leq v \leq \omega$. From symmetry this is equivalent to twice the area using the range $0 \leq u \leq +b$ such that:

$$A = 2\int_0^\omega \left[\int_0^b \sqrt{c^2 + u^2}\, du \right] dv \qquad (3.100)$$

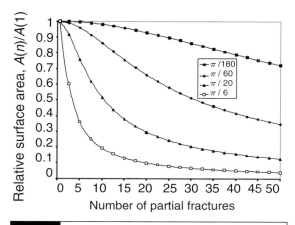

Fig 3.27 Graph of relative surface area versus number of partial fractures for helicoidal model of fringe fractures. Relative surface area decreases with number of fractures. Reprinted from Pollard et al. (1982) with permission from The Geological Society of America.

The inner integral is evaluated using (Selby, 1975, p. 424):

$$\int \sqrt{a^2 + x^2}\, dx = \frac{1}{2}\left[x\sqrt{a^2 + x^2} + a^2 \ln\left(x + \sqrt{a^2 + x^2}\right)\right] \tag{3.101}$$

The area of the helicoidal fracture surface is:

$$A = \omega\left[b\sqrt{b^2 + c^2} + c^2 \ln\left(\frac{b + \sqrt{b^2 + c^2}}{c}\right)\right] \tag{3.102}$$

As the spatial rate of twist goes to zero, $1/c \to 0$, the area goes to that of a rectangular plane, $A \to A_0$. For unit half-width ($b = 1$) and unit length ($\omega c = 1$), we have $A_0 = 2$, and the normalized area, A/A_0, increases slowly and non-linearly with rate of twist.

Using the dimensionless ratio b/c in (3.102), the area of the helicoidal fracture surface takes the form (Pollard et al., 2004):

$$A = \omega c^2\left[\frac{b}{c}\sqrt{\left(\frac{b}{c}\right)^2 + 1} + \ln\left(\frac{b}{c} + \sqrt{\left(\frac{b}{c}\right)^2 + 1}\right)\right] \tag{3.103}$$

This relationship demonstrates that the surface area of n helicoidal fractures, each of half-width b and length ωc, is less than the surface area of a single helicoidal fracture of half-width nb and

length ωc. Taking the n fractures as a model for the twist hackle in the fringe region of a joint (Fig. 3.22) the non-intuitive result is that the surface area decreases as the number of fractures increases (Fig. 3.27). On this figure each curve corresponds to a different twist angle, ω. For a twist angle of 1° ($\omega = \pi/180$) the surface area of ten fractures is 99.5% of that for the single fracture, only marginally less. However, for a twist angle of 30° ($\omega = \pi/6$) the surface area of ten fractures is 36.1% of that for the single fracture, dramatically less. Because the energy required to form a fracture in brittle materials scales with the fracture surface area (Lawn and Wilshaw, 1975) this result shows that the breakdown of joints into hackle with helicoidal shapes is consistent with a condition of lesser energy expended during propagation.

3.2.6 The second fundamental form, surface shape, and normal curvature

The second fundamental form provides a measure of the shape at any point on a continuous curved surface. To understand how this is accomplished we focus on a very small part of the parameter plane so lengths along the coordinate axes are measured using the differential quantities du and dv (Fig. 3.28a). Consider the arbitrary curve $u = u(t)$, $v = v(t)$ in the parameter plane which maps to the curve $c[u(t), v(t)]$ on the curved surface. At an arbitrary point along this curve the differential tangent vector, dc, is defined by (3.83) and this vector lies in the tangent plane to the surface (Fig. 3.28b). The unit vector, N, at this arbitrary point is a function of the two parameters u and v, such that the differential is:

$$dN = \frac{\partial N}{\partial u}du + \frac{\partial N}{\partial v}dv \tag{3.104}$$

The vector dN is a measure of the change in orientation of N with position along the curve on the surface and, in this sense, it is a measure of the shape of the surface. Also, because N is constant in magnitude, the vector dN is orthogonal to N and therefore lies in the tangent plane (Lipschutz, 1969).

Although dc and dN both lie in the tangent plane of the surface (Fig. 3.28b), these vectors

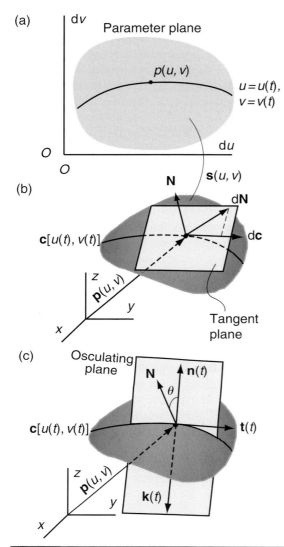

(a) Parameter plane

$p(u, v)$

$u = u(t), v = v(t)$

(b) $\mathbf{N}$ $\mathbf{s}(u, v)$ $d\mathbf{N}$

$\mathbf{c}[u(t), v(t)]$ $d\mathbf{c}$

$\mathbf{p}(u, v)$

Tangent plane

(c) Osculating plane $\mathbf{N}$ $\mathbf{n}(t)$

θ

$\mathbf{c}[u(t), v(t)]$ $\mathbf{t}(t)$

$\mathbf{p}(u, v)$

$\mathbf{k}(t)$

Fig 3.28 Diagrams to define second fundamental form for a surface. (a) Parameter plane with arbitrary curve $u = u(t)$, $v = v(t)$. (b) Surface with curve, $\mathbf{c}[u(t), v(t)]$, unit normal vector, $\mathbf{N}$, differential tangent vector, $d\mathbf{c}$, and differential normal vector, $d\mathbf{N}$. (c) Surface with osculating plane containing the unit binormal vector, $\mathbf{n}(t)$, and curvature vector, $\mathbf{k}(t)$. Reprinted from Pollard et al. (2004) with permission from The Geological Society of London.

$$II = -d\mathbf{N} \cdot d\mathbf{c} = -\left(\frac{\partial \mathbf{N}}{\partial u}du + \frac{\partial \mathbf{N}}{\partial v}dv\right) \cdot \left(\frac{\partial \mathbf{s}}{\partial u}du + \frac{\partial \mathbf{s}}{\partial v}dv\right)$$

$$= -\left(\frac{\partial \mathbf{N}}{\partial u} \cdot \frac{\partial \mathbf{s}}{\partial u}\right)du^2 - \left(\frac{\partial \mathbf{N}}{\partial u} \cdot \frac{\partial \mathbf{s}}{\partial v} + \frac{\partial \mathbf{N}}{\partial v} \cdot \frac{\partial \mathbf{s}}{\partial u}\right)dudv$$

$$-\left(\frac{\partial \mathbf{N}}{\partial v} \cdot \frac{\partial \mathbf{s}}{\partial v}\right)dv^2 \tag{3.105}$$

The coefficients in this equation are given particular symbolic names: L, M, and N. Using these symbols the second fundamental form is written:

$$II = Ldu^2 + 2Mdudv + Ndv^2$$

$$L = -\left(\frac{\partial \mathbf{N}}{\partial u} \cdot \frac{\partial \mathbf{s}}{\partial u}\right), \quad M = -\frac{1}{2}\left(\frac{\partial \mathbf{N}}{\partial u} \cdot \frac{\partial \mathbf{s}}{\partial v} + \frac{\partial \mathbf{N}}{\partial v} \cdot \frac{\partial \mathbf{s}}{\partial u}\right),$$

$$N = -\left(\frac{\partial \mathbf{N}}{\partial v} \cdot \frac{\partial \mathbf{s}}{\partial v}\right) \tag{3.106}$$

The quantities L, M, and N are functions of the two parameters u and v, and are called the coefficients of the second fundamental form of the surface. Do not confuse the scalar quantity N, and the vector quantity $\mathbf{N}$. The coefficients depend upon the choice of parameters used to represent the surface, but the second fundamental form itself is invariant with respect to this choice (Lipschutz, 1969), and in this sense II is a property of the surface. Note that II characterizes the changing shape of the surface in all directions at a particular point and that the differential parameters du and dv define the direction.

The coefficients of the second fundamental form (3.106) may be rewritten in a different way that is useful for computations. The unit normal vector, $\mathbf{N}$, to the surface $\mathbf{s}(u, v)$ is perpendicular to the vectors that are tangent to the u- and v-parameter curves (Fig. 3.19b). Therefore, for example, the scalar product of $\mathbf{N}$ and the tangent vector $\partial \mathbf{s}/\partial u$ is zero, and this product may be expanded as follows:

$$\mathbf{N} \cdot \frac{\partial \mathbf{s}}{\partial u} = 0 = \frac{\partial}{\partial u}\left(\mathbf{N} \cdot \frac{\partial \mathbf{s}}{\partial u}\right) = \mathbf{N} \cdot \frac{\partial^2 \mathbf{s}}{\partial u^2} + \frac{\partial \mathbf{N}}{\partial u} \cdot \frac{\partial \mathbf{s}}{\partial u} \tag{3.107}$$

Rearranging the right-hand side of this expression we have:

$$\mathbf{N} \cdot \frac{\partial^2 \mathbf{s}}{\partial u^2} = -\left(\frac{\partial \mathbf{N}}{\partial u} \cdot \frac{\partial \mathbf{s}}{\partial u}\right) = L \tag{3.108}$$

are not necessarily parallel to one another. The shape of the surface in the particular direction specified by $d\mathbf{c}$ is characterized by the scalar product of the two vectors, $d\mathbf{N}$ and $d\mathbf{c}$, and this product is used to define the second fundamental form, II:

Similar expansions yield the other coefficients of the second fundamental:

$$L = \mathbf{N} \cdot \frac{\partial^2 \mathbf{s}}{\partial u^2}, \quad M = \mathbf{N} \cdot \frac{\partial^2 \mathbf{s}}{\partial u \partial v}, \quad N = \mathbf{N} \cdot \frac{\partial^2 \mathbf{s}}{\partial v^2} \quad (3.109)$$

These coefficients are the scalar product of the unit normal vector and the respective second partial derivatives of the surface, $\mathbf{s}(u,v)$.

One can use the coefficients of the second fundamental form to characterize the shape of a surface in the vicinity of a particular point as follows (Lipschutz, 1969):

$$LN - M^2 \begin{cases} > 0, \text{ elliptic point} \\ = 0, \text{ parabolic point} \\ < 0, \text{ hyperbolic point} \end{cases} \quad (3.110)$$
$$L = M = N = 0, \quad \text{planar point}$$

For the parabolic point not all of the coefficients are zero but the combination $LN - M^2$ is zero. The three non-planar characteristic shapes are illustrated in Fig. 3.29. For the elliptic point the local surface lies entirely on one side of the tangent plane to that point. Planes that are parallel to the tangent plane and intersect the local surface cut out elliptical curves. For the parabolic point the local surface is cylindrical and may lie on one or both sides of the tangent plane to that point. Planes that are parallel to the tangent plane intersect the local surface in one or two straight lines. For the hyperbolic point the local surface lies on both sides of the tangent plane to that point. The local surface intersects the tangent plane along two lines where the surface passes from one side to the other of the tangent plane. For the special case where all the coefficients of the second fundamental form are zero, the local surface is planar.

As an example consider the coefficients of the second fundamental form for the helicoidal surface (Fig. 3.21). The unit normal vector is given in (3.79) and the second partial derivatives of $\mathbf{s}(u, v)$ are found from (3.78) to be:

$$\frac{\partial^2 \mathbf{s}}{\partial u^2} = 0, \quad \frac{\partial^2 \mathbf{s}}{\partial u \partial v} = -(\sin v)\mathbf{e}_x + (\cos v)\mathbf{e}_y,$$

$$\frac{\partial^2 \mathbf{s}}{\partial v^2} = -(u \cos v)\mathbf{e}_x - (u \sin v)\mathbf{e}_y \quad (3.111)$$

Taking the scalar product of the unit normal vector and the respective derivatives as indicated

(a)

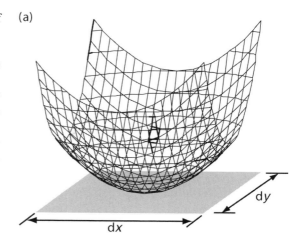

(b)

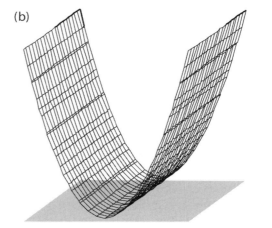

(c)

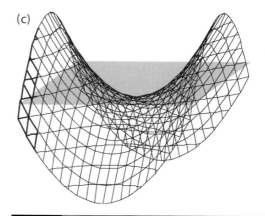

Fig 3.29 Wire-frame images of three characteristic shapes of a surface near an arbitrary point: (a) elliptic, (b) parabolic, and (c) hyperbolic. Reprinted from Pollard et al. (2004) with permission from The Geological Society of London.

in (3.109) the coefficients of the second fundamental form for the helicoidal surface are:

$$L = 0, \quad M = -c/\sqrt{c^2 + u^2}, \quad N = 0 \qquad (3.112)$$

Using (3.110) the local shape of the helicoidal surface is determined by the sign of $LN - M^2 = -c^2/(c^2 + u^2) \leq 0$. With the exception of the case $c = 0$, which describes a planar surface, the sign of this quantity is negative, so every point on the helicoidal surface is hyperbolic.

Recall from (3.21) that the shape of a curved line is characterized, in part, using the curvature vector, $\mathbf{k}$, and the scalar curvature, $\kappa = |\mathbf{k}|$. For a curve on a surface $\mathbf{s}(u, v)$ two analogous measures of shape are the normal curvature vector, $\mathbf{k}_n$, and the normal curvature, κ_n. Both of these quantities are defined by considering an arbitrary curve $u = u(t)$, $v = v(t)$ in the parameter plane (Fig. 3.28a) which maps to the curve $\mathbf{c}[u(t), v(t)]$ on the surface (Fig. 3.28c). At a point on this curve the curvature vector $\mathbf{k}$ is a function of the parameter t; it lies in the osculating plane of the curve; and it extends away from the concave side of the curve. The *osculating plane* of a curve is the plane that contains both the unit tangent vector, $\mathbf{t}(t)$, and the unit principal normal vector, $\mathbf{n}(t)$. The unit normal vector, $\mathbf{N}$, is perpendicular to the surface; it is a function of the parameters u and v; and it may not lie in the osculating plane of the curve. The normal curvature vector, $\mathbf{k}_n$, and the normal curvature, κ_n, are defined in terms of $\mathbf{k}(t)$ and $\mathbf{N}(u, v)$ as:

$$\mathbf{k}_n = (\mathbf{k} \cdot \mathbf{N})\mathbf{N}, \quad \kappa_n = \mathbf{k} \cdot \mathbf{N} \qquad (3.113)$$

Because $\mathbf{N}$ is a unit vector we understand from (3.113) that κ_n, is a scalar quantity equal to the component of $\mathbf{k}$ along $\mathbf{N}$. Also, $\mathbf{k}_n$ is a vector of magnitude κ_n with the same, or the opposite, direction as $\mathbf{N}$.

Recall that the direction of the unit principal normal vector, $\mathbf{n}(t)$, is chosen for consistency along the curve (Fig. 3.11). If we choose the direction of $\mathbf{n}(t)$ for the arbitrary curve $\mathbf{c}[u(t), v(t)]$ on the surface $\mathbf{s}(u, v)$ (Fig. 3.28c) such that the angle, θ, between $\mathbf{n}(t)$ and $\mathbf{N}(u, v)$ is in the range $0 \leq \theta < \pi/2$, then (Lipschutz, 1969):

$$\kappa_n = \kappa \cos \theta, \quad 0 \leq \theta < \pi/2 \qquad (3.114)$$

In other words, the normal curvature associated with a particular curve on a surface is equal to the curvature of this curve times the cosine of the angle between $\mathbf{n}$ and $\mathbf{N}$. If the osculating plane of the curve contains the unit normal vector for the surface, then $\mathbf{n}$ and $\mathbf{N}$ are parallel, and $\kappa_n = \kappa$. On the other hand, if the osculating plane of the curve is parallel to the tangent plane for the surface, then $\kappa_n = 0$.

The relationship given in (3.114) illustrates the fact that the curvature of an arbitrary curve at a point on a surface is greater than or equal to the normal curvature of the surface in the direction of the curve at that point. Familiar examples are the circles of latitude and longitude on a sphere of radius R (Fig. 2.1a). The normal curvature in any direction at any point on the sphere is a constant, $\kappa_n = 1/R$. Circles of longitude are the intersection of the sphere with planes that pass through the center and the poles. These curves have the same radius as the sphere and therefore their curvature is $\kappa = 1/R$. However, circles of latitude, except the equatorial circle, have a lesser radius, $\rho(\varphi) \leq R$, and therefore a greater curvature, $\kappa = 1/\rho(\varphi)$. These circles are the intersections of the sphere with planes that are parallel to the equatorial plane and do not pass through the center. The unit principal normal vector, $\mathbf{n}(t)$, for these circles and the unit normal vector, $\mathbf{N}$, for the sphere are not parallel. As the circles of latitude approach the poles of the sphere, their radii of curvature approach zero, the osculating plane of the circle approaches the tangent plane of the sphere, and the curvature of the circle becomes greater and greater. This exemplifies the fact that curves on surfaces provide the direction in which the normal curvature of the surface is measured, but the normal curvature is not necessarily equal to the curvature of the curve.

If one chooses two differently directed curves through the same point on a surface (Fig. 3.30a), the respective values of the normal curvature, κ_n, for the surface may be different. On the other hand, the curvature, κ, at a point on a curve is a unique property of the curve. The normal curvature, κ_n, at a point on a curved surface varies in a smooth and systematic manner with the direction of the tangent line through the point of interest, from a maximum value, κ_1, to a minimum value, κ_2. These two values of normal curvature, κ_1 and κ_2, are called the *principal normal curvatures*.

(a)

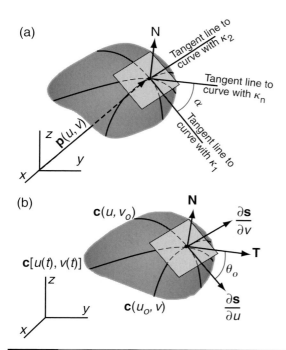

(b)

Fig 3.30 Diagrams to define variation of normal curvature with direction at a point on a surface. (a) Angle α measured in the tangent plane from direction of maximum principal normal curvature, κ_1, to direction of normal curvature κ_n. (b) Angle θ_o measured in the tangent plane from tangent to u-parameter curve to direction of principal normal curvature.

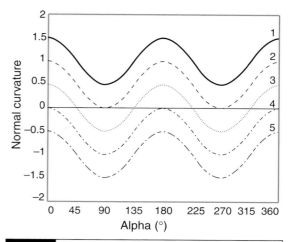

Fig 3.31 Graph of normal curvature versus angle α with examples for elliptical dome (1), parabolic antiform (2), hyperbolic saddle (3), parabolic synform (4), and elliptical basin (5). Reprinted from Pollard *et al.* (2004) with permission from The Geological Society of London.

The variation of normal curvature with direction is of the same form for all surfaces with continuous second partial derivatives such that (Lipschutz, 1969):

$$\kappa_n = \kappa_1 \cos^2\alpha + \kappa_2 \sin^2\alpha \qquad (3.115)$$

This relationship is known as *Euler's Theorem* and the angle α is measured in the tangent plane from the direction of the tangent line corresponding to the curvature κ_1 to that corresponding to κ_n. The directions of the tangent lines associated with the extreme values of normal curvature are called the *principal directions of normal curvature* and they are orthogonal.

The signs of the principal normal curvatures are related to the shape and orientation of a surface in the vicinity of a point as defined in (3.110). For example in Fig. 3.31 the distributions of normal curvature κ_n at a point as a function of the angle α are plotted for the fundamental shapes illustrated in Fig. 3.29. We use the Monge patch (3.58) where the (x, y)-plane is the horizontal plane to give the surface an orientation (up or down) and relate it to geological structures. For the sake of this illustration we consider particular cases where $\kappa_1 - \kappa_2 = 1$. The elliptic paraboloid (3.60) in this context is analogous to the surfaces of sedimentary beds in a basin-shaped structure (Fig. 3.17b). For points where both principal curvatures are positive (concave upward) or negative (concave downward) the shape is elliptical and the structure is a basin or a dome. For points where one principal curvature is zero and the other is positive or negative the shape is parabolic and the structure is a cylindrical synform or antiform. For points where the principal curvatures are of different signs the shape is hyperbolic and the structure is a saddle.

Because the normal curvature is a property of a surface at any point, we anticipate that it can be written as a function of the fundamental forms. The derivation uses (3.21) to replace the curvature vector in (3.113) with the derivative of the tangent vector written as a function of the arbitrary parameter t (Lipschutz, 1969):

$$\kappa_n = \mathbf{k} \cdot \mathbf{N} = \left(\frac{d\mathbf{t}}{dt} \cdot \mathbf{N} \right) \Big/ \left| \frac{d\mathbf{c}}{dt} \right| \qquad (3.116)$$

Because the tangent vector, **t**, is perpendicular to the normal vector, **N**, the derivative of their scalar product is zero:

$$\frac{d}{dt}(\mathbf{t} \cdot \mathbf{N}) = \frac{d\mathbf{t}}{dt} \cdot \mathbf{N} + \mathbf{t} \cdot \frac{d\mathbf{N}}{dt} = 0,$$

$$\text{so } \frac{d\mathbf{t}}{dt} \cdot \mathbf{N} = -\mathbf{t} \cdot \frac{d\mathbf{N}}{dt} \qquad (3.117)$$

Using the last equation in (3.116) and substituting (3.8) for the tangent vector we have:

$$\kappa_n = -\left(\mathbf{t} \cdot \frac{d\mathbf{N}}{dt}\right)\bigg/\left|\frac{d\mathbf{c}}{dt}\right| = -\left(\frac{d\mathbf{c}}{dt} \cdot \frac{d\mathbf{N}}{dt}\right)\bigg/\left(\frac{d\mathbf{c}}{dt} \cdot \frac{d\mathbf{c}}{dt}\right)$$

$$(3.118)$$

The derivatives of **c** and **N** with respect to t may be rewritten as derivatives of **s** and **N** with respect to u and v using (3.83) and (3.104). Comparing the results with the expressions for the coefficients of the fundamental forms, (3.85) and (3.106), leads to the definition of the normal curvature in terms of these coefficients:

$$\kappa_n = \frac{L(du/dt)^2 + 2M(du/dt)(dv/dt) + N(dv/dt)^2}{E(du/dt)^2 + 2F(du/dt)(dv/dt) + G(dv/dt)^2}$$

$$(3.119)$$

From the discussion of (3.66) and Fig. 3.19 recall that the ratio of the derivatives dv/dt and du/dt determine the direction of the tangent line to the arbitrary curve $\mathbf{c}[u(t), v(t)]$ at the point in question, so the normal curvature depends upon this direction. In addition the normal curvature depends upon the coefficients of the first and second fundamental forms.

The normal curvature may be written in terms of the differentials, du and dv, using (3.119) (Lipschutz, 1969):

$$\kappa_n = \frac{L\,du^2 + 2M\,du\,dv + N\,dv^2}{E\,du^2 + 2F\,du\,dv + G\,dv^2} = \frac{II}{I} \qquad (3.120)$$

The ratio of the differentials, $dv:du$, determines the direction of the tangent line to the arbitrary curve $\mathbf{c}[u(t), v(t)]$, and these differentials are referred to as the *direction numbers* of the tangent line. From (3.120) we understand that the normal curvature κ_n at an arbitrary point on the surface $\mathbf{s}(u, v)$ in the direction of this tangent line is equal to the ratio of the second to the first fundamental form.

To illustrate the concept of normal curvature, consider again the helicoidal surface (Fig. 3.21) as defined in (3.77). The coefficients of the first and second fundamental forms were derived from (3.85) and (3.106) above such that:

$$I = (du)^2 + (c^2 + u^2)(dv)^2, \quad II = \frac{-2c}{\sqrt{c^2 + u^2}}(du\,dv)$$

$$(3.121)$$

In the form of (3.119) the normal curvature for the helicoidal surface is:

$$\kappa_n = \frac{\dfrac{-2c}{\sqrt{c^2 + u^2}}\left(\dfrac{du}{dt}\dfrac{dv}{dt}\right)}{\left(\dfrac{du}{dt}\right)^2 + (c^2 + u^2)\left(\dfrac{dv}{dt}\right)^2} \qquad (3.122)$$

On a u-parameter curve $u = t$, $du/dt = 1$, and $dv/dt = 0$, so the normal curvature is $\kappa_n = 0$, just what one would expect for a straight line. Recall that such a straight line is the generating line for the helicoidal surface when it is moved perpendicular to itself and rotated about the z-axis which is the mid-line of the helicoid (Fig. 3.21).

A v-parameter curve on the helicoidal surface (Fig. 3.21) is a circular helix with radius u_o and pitch c. On this curve $v = t$, $du/dt = 0$, and $dv/dt = 1$, so the normal curvature is $\kappa_n = 0$. The curvature vector, **k**, for the helix is not zero (3.22) and is directed in the (x, y)-plane toward the z-axis. The unit normal vector, **N**, for the helicoidal surface along a v-parameter curve is orthogonal to the curvature vector, so the scalar product in (3.113) defines the normal curvature as $\mathbf{k} \cdot \mathbf{N} = \kappa_n = 0$. In other words the curvature vector for the helix does not resolve any component onto the line normal to the helicoidal surface. This result is non-intuitive because the v-parameter curve clearly has a non-zero curvature, but the normal curvature of the surface along the tangent line to this curve is zero.

3.2.7 Principal normal curvatures, Gaussian, and mean curvature

Euler's Theorem (3.115) is used to calculate the normal curvature κ_n in the direction of any line tangent to a surface, $\mathbf{s}(u, v)$, given the principal normal curvatures, κ_1 and κ_2, at a point on the surface. Here we describe how to calculate the magnitudes of the two principal normal curvatures and the principal directions. Recall from calculus that the maximum and minimum values of a function of two variables are found by setting the partial derivatives of the function to zero. From (3.120) we note that the normal curvature, κ_n, is a function of the two differential quantities, du and dv, which determine the direction of the tangent line on the surface at a particular point. Thus, the derivative of κ_n with respect to each of these direction numbers is set equal to zero and evaluated for the principal directions, identified by du_o and dv_o:

$$\left.\frac{\partial \kappa_n}{\partial du}\right|_{(du_o, dv_o)} = 0, \quad \left.\frac{\partial \kappa_n}{\partial dv}\right|_{(du_o, dv_o)} = 0 \qquad (3.123)$$

We substitute $\kappa_n = II/I$, use the formula for the derivative of a quotient, and write the partial derivatives of I and II in terms of their coefficients using (3.85) and (3.106). When the resulting expressions are evaluated for the principal directions, du_o and dv_o, the normal curvature takes on extreme values, $\kappa_o = II/I$, satisfying the following linear equations (Lipschutz, 1969):

$$(Ldu_o + Mdv_o) + (Edu_o + Fdv_o)(-\kappa_o) = 0$$
$$(Mdu_o + Ndv_o) + (Fdu_o + Gdv_o)(-\kappa_o) = 0 \qquad (3.124)$$

These equations have a simultaneous solution $(1, -\kappa_o)$ if the determinant made up of the coefficients on the left-hand side is zero. Expanding the determinant produces a quadratic equation in the direction numbers for the principal directions, du_o and dv_o:

$$(LF - ME)(du_o)^2 + (LG - NE)du_o dv_o + (MG - NF)(dv_o)^2 = 0 \qquad (3.125)$$

The ratio of the direction numbers, $dv_o : du_o = \tan \theta_o$, and this determines the angles, θ_o and $\theta_o + \pi/2$, between the tangent to the u-parameter curve and the tangent to the principal directions (Fig. 3.30b).

Dividing (3.125) by $(du_o)^2$ and substituting for the ratio of direction numbers, we find a quadratic equation in $\tan \theta_o$:

$$(MG - NF)\tan^2 \theta_o + (LG - NE)\tan \theta_o + (LF - ME) = 0 \qquad (3.126)$$

The principal directions for the normal curvature at a point on a surface are found from (3.126) using the standard formula for the solution of a quadratic equation. Using the helicoidal surface (3.77) as an example, the principal directions of the normal curvature are found by substituting

for the coefficients of the fundamental forms, (3.96) and (3.112), to find $\tan \theta_o = 1/\sqrt{c^2 + u^2}$. Here θ_o is the angle measured in the tangent plane to the surface from the tangent line for the u-parameter curve to the tangent line for the two principal directions (Fig. 3.30b). Along the midline, $u = 0$, of the helicoidal surface (Fig. 3.21) the tangent of the principal directions is equal to the spatial rate of twist, $1/c$.

The magnitudes of the principal normal curvatures, κ_1 and κ_2, are found by rearranging (3.124) to factor out the two differentials du_o and dv_o:

$$(L - \kappa_o E)du_o + (M - \kappa_o F)dv_o = 0$$
$$(M - \kappa_o F)du_o + (N - \kappa_o G)dv_o = 0 \qquad (3.127)$$

These two linear equations have a simultaneous solution (du_o, dv_o) if the determinant of the coefficients of the left side is zero. Expanding the determinant produces a quadratic equation in κ_o:

$$(EG - F^2)\kappa_o^2 + (-EN + 2FM - GL)\kappa_o + (LN - M^2) = 0 \qquad (3.128)$$

For example, the magnitudes of the principal normal curvatures for the helicoidal surface (3.77) are found by substitution of (3.96) and (3.112) to find $\kappa_1, \kappa_2 = \pm c/(c^2 + u^2)$. The two principal curvatures are equal in magnitude and opposite in sign. They are independent of the parameter v, and so are constant along any particular circular helix that is a v-parameter curve. Along the mid-line the principal curvatures are equal in magnitude to the spatial rate of twist, $1/c$. For a given rate of twist the principal curvatures decrease in magnitude with distance, u, from the mid-line.

Equation (3.128) may have two real and unequal roots, κ_1 and κ_2, or two real and equal non-zero roots, or two zero roots (Lipschutz, 1969). The second case pertains to elliptical points (Fig. 3.29a) at which the normal curvature is non-zero but the same in all directions and the ratios of respective fundamental coefficients are constant:

$$\kappa_n = \frac{L}{E} = \frac{M}{F} = \frac{N}{G} = \text{constant} \qquad (3.129)$$

This is referred to as an *umbilical point*. The third case is the planar point where the normal curvature is zero in all directions.

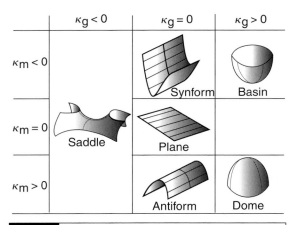

	$\kappa_g < 0$	$\kappa_g = 0$	$\kappa_g > 0$
$\kappa_m < 0$		Synform	Basin
$\kappa_m = 0$	Saddle	Plane	
$\kappa_m > 0$		Antiform	Dome

Fig 3.32 Table of six different characteristic shapes of geological surfaces near an arbitrary point categorized by the signs of the Gaussian curvature, κ_g, and mean normal curvature, κ_m. Reprinted from Bergbauer and Pollard (2003) with permission from Elsevier.

Dividing each term of (3.128) by the first term in parentheses we have:

$$\kappa_o^2 - 2\kappa_m\kappa_o + \kappa_g = 0 \qquad (3.130)$$

The first constant, κ_m, is the average of the two principal normal curvatures and is referred to as the *mean principal normal curvature*:

$$\kappa_m = \frac{(EN - 2FM + GL)}{2(EG - F^2)} = \frac{1}{2}(\kappa_1 + \kappa_2) \qquad (3.131)$$

The second constant, κ_g, is the product of the principal curvatures and is called the *Gaussian curvature*:

$$\kappa_g = \frac{(LN - M^2)}{(EG - F^2)} = \kappa_1\kappa_2 \qquad (3.132)$$

For example, the mean curvature for the helicoidal surface is found by substituting the coefficients of the fundamental forms, (3.96) and (3.112), into (3.131) to find $\kappa_m = 0$. The fact that the mean normal curvature is zero is consistent with the two principal curvatures being equal and opposite in sign. Surfaces that satisfy the condition of zero mean curvature are called *minimal surfaces*. The Gaussian curvature for the helicoidal surface is found by substituting (3.96) and (3.112) into (3.132) to find $\kappa_g = -c^2/(c^2 + u^2)^2$. The Gaussian curvature is not a function of the parameter v and therefore is constant along a given v-parameter

circular helix. Along the mid-line of the helicoidal surface, $u = 0$, the Gaussian curvature is a constant equal to the negative of the squared rate of twist.

We have identified the three possible non-planar shapes (hyperbolic, parabolic, and elliptic) in the vicinity of a particular point on a surface based on the sign of the numerator in (3.132) and these shapes are illustrated in Fig. 3.29. Because the denominator in (3.132) always is positive, the sign of the Gaussian curvature is determined by the numerator. Thus the sign of κ_g may be used to distinguish these three non-planar shapes. Taken together, the signs of the Gaussian and the mean curvature may be used to categorize surfaces with respect to orientation in keeping with geological conventions (Roberts, 2001). Consider the Monge patch (3.58) with the (x, y)-plane horizontal and positive z upward. Six shapes are distinguished in Fig. 3.32 by noting that the sign of the mean curvature is different for elliptic shapes that are domes and basins, and for parabolic shapes that are cylindrical antiforms and synforms (Bergbauer and Pollard, 2003). Therefore, for $\kappa_g > 0$ the surface is elliptic; it is a dome if $\kappa_m > 0$ and a basin if $\kappa_m < 0$. For $\kappa_g = 0$ the surface is parabolic; it is antiformal if $\kappa_m > 0$, planar if $\kappa_m = 0$, and synformal if $\kappa_m < 0$. For $\kappa_g < 0$ the surface is hyperbolic. This categorization provides a simple way to describe geological surfaces using the concepts of differential geometry.

3.3 | Applications of differential geometry to structural geology

In the introduction to this chapter we stated that a primary task for structural geologists is to describe and characterize the lineations and surfaces that make up the structures we use to unravel the history of deformation in a region and to understand how the rocks in Earth's crust deform. We noted, with some surprise, that relatively little use of differential geometry is found in the twentieth-century literature of structural geology, despite the fact that this mathematical subject provides the only rigorous, complete and self-consistent method to describe and characterize geological structures. A keyword search of GEOREF, a geological reference data base in July 2003 using the exact phrase "differential geometry" uncovered only fourteen references from 1963 to 2003. Of these ten are applications to other geoscience subjects such as gravity and geodesy, seismology, hydrogeology, and paleontology. The four remaining consider the three-dimensional geometry of folds, the deformation of Earth's surface due to neotectonic crustal motion (Zakarevicius, 2000; Grachev *et al.*, 2001), and the normal curvature of geological surfaces (Bergbauer and Pollard, 2003). A search on the phrase "Gaussian curvature" again uncovered fourteen references including three on the estimation of strain and the prediction of fractures within folds (Lisle, 1994, 2000; Ozkaya, 2002).

This section includes examples that provide insights into how differential geometry can be applied to problems in structural geology. These examples are works in progress and we expect more details to emerge during on-going studies. None-the-less we hope that these examples will encourage others to apply differential geometry to structural problems.

3.3.1 Characterizing the shapes of lineations on discrete surfaces

Lineations are found on discrete geological surfaces such as faults and intrusive contacts (Fig. 3.3). These superficial lineations typically are aligned on an exposure such that multiple measurements of the orientations of linear elements would have a standard deviation of few degrees. However, faults and intrusive contacts may pass through rocks with different mechanical properties, they may be influenced mechanically by adjacent faults or intrusions, and they may be curved surfaces. Thus one should expect superficial lineations to vary in orientation over the surfaces on which they are found. On a fault, for example, slickenlines should form a systematic pattern that reflects the relative motion of the two surfaces during frictional sliding. Of course the direction of relative motion at a point may change as a fault develops, leading to overprinting of slickenlines with different orientations. Where overprinting is not an issue, one should be able to define a set of three-dimensional curves lying on the fault

surface that are everywhere parallel to the local direction of relative motion, and then use the curvature and torsion to characterize the shapes of these curves.

To illustrate the fact that slickenlines do vary systematically with position on a fault, and to appreciate some of the challenges inherent to the investigation of superficial lineations we turn to a data set from the Chimney Rock fault array (Fig. 2.29). The four sets of faults in this region are displayed on the structure contour map constructed on the base of the Carmel Formation. Note, for example, that individual contours on this map are truncated by the Frenchman Fault. When traced to the north across the fault the sense of step is consistently to the east. However, the magnitude of the step decreases toward both terminations of this fault. This change in step magnitude suggests that the magnitude of the slip decreases from the mid-section of the Frenchman Fault toward the terminations and, indeed, the slip must go to zero at the terminations by definition.

The distribution of dip slip is plotted versus position along the trace of the Blueberry Fault in Fig. 2.31. Note how the magnitude of the dip slip (gray boxes) increases from zero at the eastern termination to more than 30 m near the middle of the fault. The slip distribution is not continuous, but jumps abruptly where members of other fault sets intersect the Blueberry Fault. The distribution of slickenline rake (black diamonds) is plotted versus position along the trace of the Blueberry Fault. The rakes are approximately 90° (down dip) near the northeastern and southwestern terminations of the fault, but decrease more or less systematically to about 70° as one approaches the intersections with the La Sal and Little Faults. Across these faults the rakes abruptly increase. The rakes are systematically greater than 90° (inclined toward the east) between the intersections with the La Sal and Little Faults, and less than 90° (inclined toward the west) on the distal sides of these intersections. These changes reflect the mechanical interaction of the faults and are consistent with elastic models of this interaction (Maerten, 2000).

Exposure of the faults at Chimney Rock are adequate to document the lateral variation in rake of the slickenlines over a distance of almost

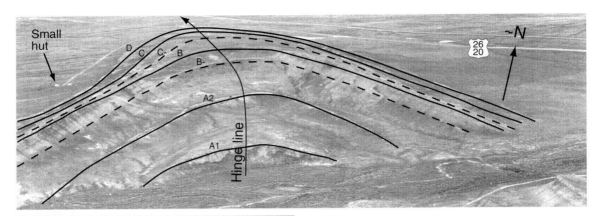

Fig 3.33 Oblique aerial photograph of the nose of the Emigrant Gap anticline, WY. Reprinted from Bergbauer and Pollard (2004) with permission from The Geological Society of America.

3 km, but inadequate to document the vertical variation. However, model fault surfaces can be constructed and elastic boundary value problems can be solved to find the variation in slip direction with position over the entire model fault surface. Then curves can be defined such that their tangent line is everywhere parallel to the local relative slip direction. The three-dimensional varia-

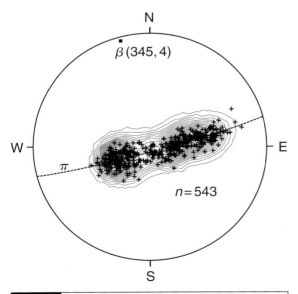

Fig 3.34 Stereographic projection of 543 poles to Frontier Formation sandstone beds on the Emigrant Gap anticline. Reprinted from Bergbauer and Pollard (2004) with permission from The Geological Society of America.

tion in curvature and torsion of these curved lines completely characterizes the geometry of relative slip on the model fault. The local orientations of these curves can be compared with the exposure data for consistency.

3.3.2 Characterizing the shapes of folded surfaces

The Emigrant Gap anticline is a doubly plunging fold exposed for about 30 km along a northwest–southeast trend near Casper, Wyoming (Bergbauer and Pollard, 2004). Sandstone beds of the Frontier Formation crop out on the fold limbs and are continuously exposed around the fold hinge (Fig. 3.33). The top of the lowest-most sandstone bed (labeled A1) of the Frontier Formation defines a somewhat asymmetric anticlinal surface, plunging gently to the north, with approximately planar limbs and a rounded hinge. The arc length of the exposed surface is on the order of 500 m, and the amplitude is about 75 m. On a stereographic projection (Fig. 3.34), 543 poles to bedding define a great circle (labeled π), with a tighter cluster of poles representing the eastern limb and a broader cluster representing the western limb. The pole to the great circle (labeled β) defines an approximate fold axis with trend and plunge of 345°, 04°.

The top of the A1 sandstone was sampled at 2529 points using a Trimble^{TM} Pro XL GPS receiver with a vertical precision of 0.5 to 1.5 m and horizontal precision of less than 0.7 m. Fig. 3.35a is a map of the GPS locations on the A1 surface with a local coordinate system in which $x = $ easting, $y = $ northing, and $z = $ up. The map region is about 500 m wide and 2300 m long. The limbs of the

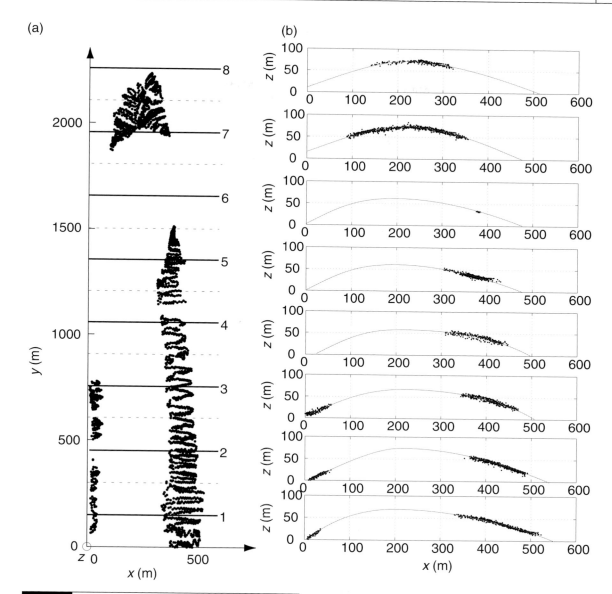

Fig 3.35 (a) Map view of Emigrant Gap anticline with 2529 GPS survey points (Bergbauer, 2002). (b) Eight profiles of fold shape constrained by GPS data.

folded surface could be sampled only in the southern part of the map area, and the hinge only is exposed and sampled near the northern termination of the outcrop. The GPS data were used to create a digital model of the surface, despite the limitation that the A1 sandstone is exposed only over about 25% of the map area. Clearly, sufficient data control is lacking to make conclusive statements about the geometry where the surface is

not exposed. Eight cross sections of the folded surface were used to constrain the shape of the surface (Fig. 3.35b). From these cross sections one can infer that the anticline is asymmetric, with the west flank exhibiting steeper dips than the east flank, and the hinge is rounded. The cross sections were constructed using GPS points located within 150 m of each cross section. Cross sections 1 through 6 are weakly constrained near the fold hinge, whereas cross sections 7 and 8 are weakly constrained on the fold limbs.

A model surface was constructed by interpolation and filtering (Bergbauer and Pollard, 2004)

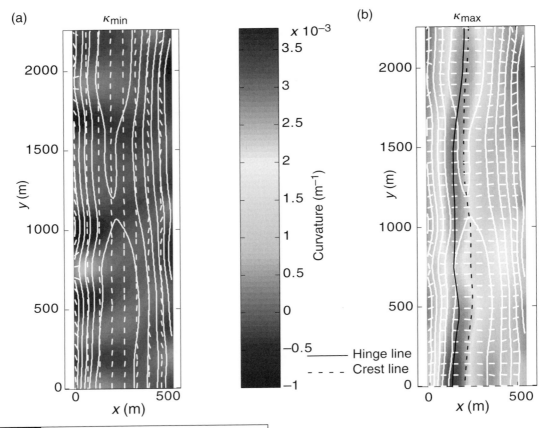

Fig 3.36 (a) Map view of Emigrant Gap anticline with contours of minimum principal normal curvature, κ_2, and tick marks parallel to direction of minimum curvature (Bergbauer, 2002). (b) Contours of maximum principal normal curvature, κ_1, and tick marks parallel to direction of maximum curvature.

that is approximately cylindrical in shape and exhibits a smoothly rounded hinge region. Gentle surface undulations, which trend obliquely to the hinge line, are superimposed on the more or less cylindrical shape. Apart from these gentle undulations, the limbs of the modeled surface are approximately planar. Fig. 3.36 shows the distributions of the maximum, κ_1, and minimum, κ_2, principal normal curvatures. Values of the minimum curvature range from $-1e^{-3}$ to $+1e^3$ m^{-1} and values of the maximum curvature range from $-1.7e^{-4}$ to $3.8e^3$ m^{-1}. Areas with elevated magnitudes of minimum curvature trend obliquely across the fold due to the gentle surface undulations. The directions of minimum curvature, shown as white ticks in Fig. 3.36a, are sub-

parallel to the trend of the fold hinge, and significantly change directions only across the gentle surface undulations. The directions of maximum curvature (white ticks, Fig. 3.36b) are approximately perpendicular to the fold hinge.

It is standard practice in structural geology to idealize folds as cylindrical structures. The principal normal curvatures provide a quantitative measure of the departure from a cylindrical shape. For a surface to be perfectly cylindrical one principal curvature must be zero everywhere, and the other principal curvature must have the same distribution on every cross section taken perpendicular to the fold axis. Not only is the minimum principal curvature non-zero across the modeled bedding surface (Fig. 3.36a), the maximum curvature distributions differ from one cross section to another (Fig. 3.36b). Discrimination of cylindrical and non-cylindrical areas across the surface is possible using the categorization depicted in Fig. 3.32. Based on the signs of the Gaussian and mean curvatures at every grid point, the surface can be decomposed into areas that are locally shaped like one or the other of the six different characteristic shapes (Bergbauer and Pollard, 2003). Performing this analysis on the modeled bedding surface shows that the surface is composed primarily of domal and saddle-like areas, which reflect the gentle undulations superimposed on the broader fold shape. The modeled bedding surface does not contain any cylindrically shaped areas of significant extent. We suggest that the characterization of folded surfaces using differential geometry will provide new insights concerning the process of folding (Fisher and Wiklerson, 2000; Lisle, 2000; Bergbauer and Pollard, 2004).

3.4 | Concluding remarks

The objective of this chapter is to introduce structural geologists to the elementary concepts of differential geometry that serve to characterize curves (lineations) and surfaces in three-dimensional space. One could imagine that these concepts and the tools that follow from them might capture the attention of structural geologists, much as the concepts and tools related to descriptive geometry and stereographic projection did in the second half of the twentieth century. This is not the intention of the authors. We view differential geometry as the appropriate mathematical machinery to characterize structures, but this characterization is just one step in an investigation which ultimately must include consideration of the constitutive properties of rock and models of deformation based on the equations of motion (Guiton et al., 2003).

Justifications for learning differential geometry are several. The structures encountered in Earth's crust are three dimensional with spatial variations in size and shape that only can be accounted for using a geometry that involves the spatial derivatives of such things as orientation and curvature. Plotting orientation data on a stereographic projection eliminates the opportunity to visualize and analyze these spatial changes. Furthermore, to proceed with modeling one needs to write boundary conditions that refer explicitly to geometry of surfaces. Finally, we now have precise field data on the three-dimensional shape of surfaces from new technology such as GPS and we need to know how to describe these surfaces and how to compare them to a model result.

Chapter 4

Physical quantities, fields, dimensions, and scaling

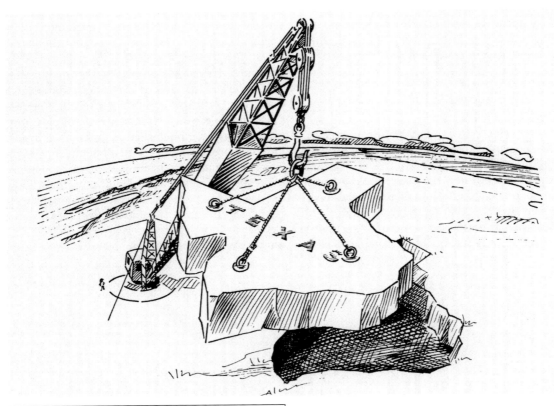

Earth's crust under the state of Texas being lifted by a crane. Scaling laws demonstrate that the good state of Texas is utterly incapable of self-support. Reprinted from Hubbert (1945) by permission of the AAPG whose permission is required for further use.

In physical science a first essential step in the direction of learning any subject is to find principles of numerical reckoning and practical methods for measuring some quality connected with it. I often say that when you can measure what you are speaking about, and express it in numbers you know something about it; but when you cannot measure it, when you cannot express it in numbers your knowledge is of a meager and unsatisfactory kind: it may be the beginning of knowledge, but you have scarcely, in your thoughts, advanced to the stage of science, whatever the matter may be (Thomson, 1891).

In an insightful article about research in geology in the early twentieth century M. King Hubbert refers to Sir William Thomson (Lord Kelvin) as the "Patron Saint" of geologists, including himself, who espouse a quantitative agenda, and he cites this quotation from Thomson as their "guiding credo" (Hubbert, 1974). Thomson is not advocating numeration purely for the sake of collecting numbers; rather this is a call to measure relevant physical quantities and express them as numbers. Thomson was a physicist, not a geologist, but Hubbert recognized the importance of quantification in the geological sciences and was a leader among geologists of his generation in this regard (Hubbert, 1972). In part, Hubbert was reacting to the popularity of descriptive taxonomy for geologists of the twentieth century, structural geologists being no exception: an introductory textbook published in 1987 provides a glossary of terms with over 350 entries that beginning students might be expected to master (Dennis, 1987). In a playful reaction to the plethora of terms for intrusive forms at mid-century Charles Hunt comments on the feeder to the Trachyte Mesa laccolith: "Because the form has certain resemblances to the woody structure of the cane cactus the name cactolith might be used and defined as a quasi-horizontal chonolith composed of anastomosing ductoliths whose distal ends curl like a harpolith, thin like a sphenolith, or bulge discordantly like an akmolith or ethmolith" (Hunt, 1953).

Here we introduce some of the concepts and the tools necessary to practice structural geology in a manner that Hubbert would have understood and Thomson would have appreciated. We begin this chapter by defining the basic physical quantities used to describe and measure Earth structures, and agree on their units of measure. This leads to a discussion of the continuum, the mathematical idealization that forms the basis for most of our thinking about the spatial and temporal variations of the relevant physical quantities. These so-called *field quantities* are defined at every point in the continuum and are inferred to be measurable in the rock mass. Next we consider physical dimensions and explain how dimensional analysis is used to check the consistency of equations and to construct graphs of physical quantities. Dimensional analysis provides the tools to understand the scaling of structural phenomena, and to set up scaled laboratory experiments to model the development of structures.

4.1 | Physical quantities and the continuum

4.1.1 Fundamental and derived quantities

Structural geology is concerned with deformation of rock and this is largely a physical process, although chemical processes can play important roles. Most of the physical quantities we use in this textbook can be described in terms of four *fundamental quantities* for mechanical systems, namely length, mass, time, and temperature. Associated with each fundamental quantity are actual objects (e.g. a cylinder of platinum–iridium alloy residing at Sèvres, France, and assigned a mass of one kilogram), or devices with prescribed procedures (e.g. a device to measure the duration of 9 192 631 770 periods of radiation corresponding to transitions of the cesium-133 atom and assigned a time of one second; Mechtly, 1973). These are used as standards to define the quantities, and copies of the standards are used for everyday measurement. For example, one would compare an unknown mass to a copy of the standard kilogram using a balance. For structural geologists most measurements are made using classical physical principles that predate relativity, quantum mechanics, and the physics of atomic and sub-atomic particles. As two modern physicists point out:

Observations are formulated in the language of classical physics because that is the language used to record measurements with macroscopic instruments. That statement does not imply that the measuring instruments follow classical physics instead of quantum physics, a wrong opinion some writers ascribe incorrectly to Bohr. Instead our statement implies that the special nature, in particular the larger size, of measuring instruments allows the description of their behavior in classical terms (Feshbach and Weisskopf, 1988).

Such measurements determine a numerical value for the physical quantity.

It is not the measured number itself that is useful, but rather that number in combination

Table 4.1. Physical quantities, units, and symbols.

Quantity	Unit	Symbol
Fundamental physical quantities and SI units		
Length	meter	m
Mass	kilogram	kg
Time	second	s
Temperature	kelvin	K
Some derived quantities and SI units		
Area	square meter	m^2
Volume	cubic meter	m^3
Displacement	meter	m
Velocity	meter per second	$m \cdot s^{-1}$
Acceleration	meter per second squared	$m \cdot s^{-2}$
Mass density	kilogram per cubic meter	$kg \cdot m^{-3}$
Force	newton	N
Traction, stress	pascal	Pa
Pressure	pascal	Pa
Work, energy	joule	J
Common quantities and units		
Time	year (annum)	a
Temperature	degree Celsius	°C
Plane angle	radian	rad

with appropriate *units of measure*. A myriad of units of measure for the fundamental quantities have been invented and many are in use today, but we will use those now recognized as part of the "Système Internationale d'Unités" or *SI system* (Table 4.1). Use of the four units (meter, kilogram, second, and kelvin) for the fundamental physical quantities and the development of an international regulatory system can be traced back historically about two hundred years. For example, the meter and the kilogram were created by members of the Paris Academy of Sciences and adopted by the National Assembly of France in 1795 (Mechtly, 1973). The annual review by R. A. Nelson in *Physics Today* (Nelson, 2003) provides a useful summary of metric practice, and the article by D. Kind and T. Quinn summarizes the status of *metrology* (the science of measurement) at the end of the twentieth century (Kind and Quinn, 1999).

The units for mechanical quantities commonly used in structural geology are derived using the units of the fundamental quantities. For example, reading the symbol [=] "has units of" we have:

$$\text{volume, } V [=] m^3 \tag{4.1}$$

$$\text{acceleration, } \mathbf{a} [=] m \cdot s^{-2} \tag{4.2}$$

$$\text{mass density, } \rho [=] kg \cdot m^{-3} \tag{4.3}$$

$$\text{thermal expansion, } \alpha [=] K^{-1} \tag{4.4}$$

These relationships illustrate how the units of derived quantities are made up of products and powers of the units for the fundamental quantities.

There are a few derived quantities that are particularly important and have been given special names, usually to honor a person responsible for introducing or clarifying the usage of the quantity. Perhaps the most famous person in this regard is the English natural philosopher Sir Isaac Newton (1642–1727) after whom the unit of force is named. Newton's second law $\mathbf{F} = m\mathbf{a}$ establishes the relationship among force, $\mathbf{F}$, mass, m, and acceleration, $\mathbf{a}$, from which the units follow:

$$\text{force, } \mathbf{F} [=] kg \cdot m \cdot s^{-2} = N \tag{4.5}$$

Note that proper names for the SI units, such as newton and kelvin, are not capitalized, but the corresponding units themselves, N and K, are capitalized. The unit of stress follows from the concept of a force per unit area:

$$\text{stress, } \sigma[=](\text{kg} \cdot \text{m} \cdot \text{s}^{-2}) \cdot \text{m}^{-2} = \text{N} \cdot \text{m}^{-2} = \text{Pa} \tag{4.6}$$

The SI unit for stress is the pascal, named after the French mathematician and physicist Blaise Pascal (1623–62). Equations (4.5) and (4.6) illustrate how the special units of derived quantities can be converted to products and powers of units of the fundamental quantities.

To put the newton and the pascal into a geological context consider the weight per unit volume of granite, one of the most common crustal rocks. Measurement of 155 different samples of granite produced a range from $2.516 \times 10^4 \, \text{N m}^{-3}$ to $2.809 \times 10^4 \, \text{N m}^{-3}$. These unit weights come from Table 4.1 of Memoir 97 of the Geological Society of America (Daly et al., 1966). Clearly not all rocks called granite have the same unit weight, but we take the reported mean value of $2.667 \times 10^4 \, \text{N m}^{-3}$ for this calculation. Thus, one cubic meter of this granite weighs $2.667 \times 10^4 \, \text{N}$ at sea level. The sea level weight of one of the authors of this textbook in *archaic units* is 140 pounds force, which is 6.23×10^2 N. Thus, the weight of the granite cube is greater than that of the author by a factor of 4.28×10^1.

Implicit in the preceding paragraph are two concepts, *scientific notation* and *significant figures* that are standard practice for a scientist working with numerical data. For example, the mean unit weight of granite is given in scientific notation with four significant figures. In scientific notation a value is represented by a number, with only one digit to the left of the decimal place, multiplied by a power of ten. The power indicates the *order of magnitude* of the quantity. The total number of digits to the left and right of the decimal place is the number of significant figures. They are called significant because they recur consistently during repeated measurements. The weight of the author has three significant figures.

When multiplying or dividing two quantities in scientific notation the number of significant figures of the result is the same as that of the

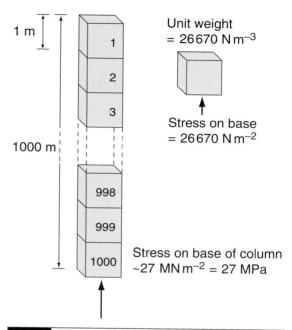

Fig 4.1 Stack of 1 m cubes of rock 1 km high results in a vertical stress of about 27 MPa.

quantity with the least significant figures. Thus, when the weight of the granite cube is divided by the author's weight, the quotient is rounded off to three significant figures. When adding or subtracting a set of numbers, they are arranged by place (hundreds, tens, ones, tenths, etc.) and the result is rounded off to the least place that contains significant figures in all the numbers of the set.

Now imagine the cube of granite positioned below 999 other such cubes (Fig. 4.1) and calculate the force per unit area (stress) acting on the bottom of this granite column:

$$\text{stress, } \sigma = (2.667 \times 10^4 \, \text{N m}^{-3})(1.000 \times 10^3 \, \text{m})$$

$$= 2.667 \times 10^7 \, \text{Pa} \tag{4.7}$$

The mean densities reported for sedimentary, metamorphic, and igneous rocks in Memoir 97 range from $1.44 \times 10^4 \, \text{N m}^{-3}$ (sand–silt–clay) to $3.392 \times 10^4 \, \text{N m}^{-3}$ (eclogite). We infer that the stress acting in the vertical direction at one thousand meters depth in the Earth is likely to fall in the range from about 14 to 34 million pascals. This inference neglects the possible mechanical constraints that the surrounding rock might place on such a column, but we will evaluate those lateral constraints in a later chapter. A handy rule of thumb is: the vertical stress in the Earth's crust due to the weight of overlying rock increases with depth at a rate of about 25 million pascals per thousand meters.

A few units, not part of the official SI system, are in such common usage in the geological literature that we refer to them throughout the text. The *annum*, a, is used for one year when measuring the age (time before present) of rocks and minerals. The unit *degree Celsius*, °C, is equivalent to the unit kelvin, but the scales are offset such that the number of degrees Celsius is less than the number of kelvin by the constant 273.15. Some important derived quantities are made up of ratios of fundamental quantities in which the units cancel out. For example, one measure of deformation called *stretch*, is defined as the final length of a material line segment divided by its original length, so the stretch is devoid of units. Because angles are defined as ratios of circular arc lengths to radial lengths, they too are devoid of units. However, it is customary to assign the unit *radian* to angles.

4.1.2 SI prefixes and conversion factors

One of the beauties of the SI system is the ease with which quantities are manipulated in simple powers of ten by placing different prefixes on the units (Table 4.2). Other prefixes exist that extend the range of values both upward and downward, but these are less commonly called for in structural geology. The prefixes and symbols from Table 4.2 are attached to the front of the respective unit or symbol. For example, using the symbols k and M the rule of thumb stated in the previous section says that the vertical stress increases with depth at a rate of 25 megapascals per kilometer or $25\,\mathrm{MPa\,km^{-1}}$. Because the ages of rock formations typically fall in the range of millions of years the units are written mega-annum (Ma).

Because there are many examples of archaic units in the literature of structural geology, one needs to be proficient converting to the SI system. The *CRC Handbook of Chemistry and Physics* (Lide, 2004) and *The International System of Units* (Mechtly, 1973) are useful references that contain extensive

Table 4.2. Selected SI prefixes and symbols.

Prefix	Symbol	Multiple of
giga	G	10^9
mega	M	10^6
kilo	k	10^3
deci	d	10^{-1}
centi	c	10^{-2}
milli	m	10^{-3}
micro	μ	10^{-6}
nano	n	10^{-9}

tables to facilitate unit conversion. These conversions take the form of the common examples shown in Table 4.3.

4.1.3 The material continuum

Geometric and physical quantities used in structural geology (e.g. strike and dip, mass density, stretch, displacement) usually are measured at scattered locations or isolated exposures and the values so obtained commonly are used to characterize a volume of rock that surrounds each location. For example, in their monograph on metamorphic tectonites Turner and Weiss (1963) emphasize that one of the foundations of structural analysis, as conceived by Bruno Sander in the second half of the twentieth century (Sander, 1970), is the concept that a deformed rock mass is separable into volumes of statistically homogeneous fabric that are investigated independently. One of the principal tools of such an investigation is the stereonet on which orientation data are plotted, devoid of any connection to location. This viewpoint begs the question: how does the physical quantity under investigation vary from one volume to an adjacent volume? The spatial variation of physical quantities is unapproachable using this method, in part because it avoids the use of calculus and the underlying principles of that mathematical discipline.

The alternative, advocated here, is to embrace calculus and use it to investigate how physical quantities such as the poles to planar elements, temperature, velocity, and stress vary in space and time as structures evolve. In this context physical quantities are defined at a mathematical point by a limiting process in which an element of the

Table 4.3.	Selected conversions from archaic to SI units.	
From	To	Multiply by
To convert length		
inch	meter	2.54×10^{-2}
foot	meter	3.048×10^{-1}
mile	meter	$1.609\,344 \times 10^{3}$
To convert mass		
kgf s^2 m^{-1}	kilogram	$9.806\,65$
pound mass (lbm)	kilogram	$4.535\,924 \times 10^{-1}$
To convert time		
hour	second	3.60×10^{3}
annum	second	3.1536×10^{7}
To convert temperature		
Celsius	kelvin	$T(\text{K}) = T(^\circ\text{C}) + 273.15$
Fahrenheit	kelvin	$T(\text{K}) = (5/9)[T(^\circ\text{F}) + 459.67]$
To convert force		
kilogram force (kgf)	newton	$9.806\,65$
pound force (lbf)	newton	$4.448\,222$
dyne	newton	1×10^{-5}
To convert pressure, traction, or stress		
atm	pascal	1.01×10^{5}
bar	pascal	1.00×10^{5}
dyne/cm^2	pascal	1×10^{-1}
lbf/in^2 (psi)	pascal	$6.894\,757 \times 10^{3}$
To convert angle		
degree	radian	$3.141\,59/180$

material is shrunk down about that point. We understand that such a viewpoint cannot be taken literally if the element becomes too small (e.g. smaller than a single pore in a sandstone), but the definition provides the necessary mathematical properties to interpret and explain geologic structures in which these point quantities vary continuously in space and time. In other words these are *field quantities* defined in a *material continuum*.

We feel we understand something when we can picture how the wheels and levers must fit together in order for it to work. Physicists were reluctant to abandon this level of understanding until they had no alternative. However, the development of physics in the twentieth century has been a progressive movement away from visualizable models and toward abstract mathematical models.

Physicists now talk of fields in a much more abstract way than Faraday or Maxwell did. A field is now thought of as a way of assigning numbers to a region of space, much as a temperature map assigns a temperature to every point on the earth's surface. Although this description makes a field seem very abstract, it proves to be a very rich way of talking about nature. In fact, physicists today talk about fields in exactly the same way as they talk about material objects (Gregory, 1990).

This viewpoint was of tremendous value to physicists and engineers throughout the twentieth century, but few structural geologists adopted this perspective.

Perhaps our most familiar experience with the concept of a continuum comes with the realization that given any two real numbers one can choose another that falls between the first two. Because of this property the set of real numbers is called continuous, or we would say it forms a *continuum*. This concept is applied every time we construct a graph of a continuous function and give a scale to the ordinate and abscissa. We know that we can choose any scale for the axes and the function will plot without gaps. Because physicists assert, based on intuition, that time and space can be represented by real numbers, it is natural to think of time and space as continuous. The fertile imaginations of mathematicians have come up with functions that are discontinuous and some of these have applications in structural geology. For example, faults may be modeled as a surface of discontinuity in a function for the displacement field. None-the-less, the displacement field is adequately represented as continuous in the rock surrounding the fault.

Structural geologists seek to describe the motion of particles in a rock mass as it deforms under the action of prescribed forces. It would be useful to assign material properties or calculate physical quantities at arbitrary points within the rock mass. For this endeavor we construct a *material continuum* for which the mass density, momentum, and energy are well defined at every

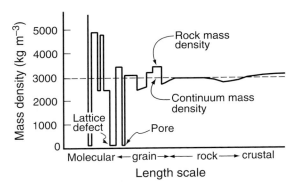

Fig 4.2 Mass density plotted versus length scale for rock over the range from crustal to molecular. Major discontinuities are caused by pore and lattice defects.

point. This can, however, present conceptual difficulties. For example, consider the mass density, ρ, of a sample of rock as determined by:

$$\rho = \frac{\delta M}{\delta V} \tag{4.8}$$

Here δM is the mass and δV is the volume of the sample. Mass is equivalent to weight divided by the known acceleration of gravity and it is a straightforward matter to weigh the sample. If the sample is cylindrical the volume is readily calculated after measuring the height and diameter. With these numbers in hand, (4.8) is used to calculate the mass density of the sample. Suppose we decide to use this density as representative of the rock mass under consideration. Plotting density as a function of volume for a homogeneous material continuum we have a continuous line of constant value (Fig. 4.2, dashed line). We must admit that this density may not represent the rock mass at scales of the lithosphere or at scales of individual grains: there our sample size would have to be adjusted to determine a meaningful density.

To characterize the mass density at a point P in the continuum consider a sequence of volumes, δV_i, of mass, δM_i, each containing the point and ordered from largest, $i = 1$, to smallest $i = n$, such that the volume approaches zero as n approaches infinity. In this limit the largest dimension of the sample approaches zero, so the volume converges to the point, not to a surface or a curve containing the point (Malvern, 1969). Using this procedure

the formal definition of the density at the point P in the material continuum is:

$$\rho = \operatorname*{limit}_{n \to \infty}\left(\frac{\delta M_n}{\delta V_n}\right) \tag{4.9}$$

If we could carry out measurements on a rock sample at smaller and smaller volumes we would plot an irregular curve (Fig. 4.2, solid line). Below a certain size particular mineral grains or pores might alter the result; below that size, lattice defects in a particular mineral could cause irregularities in the curve; and eventually individual molecules, atoms, or sub-atomic particles would become the important contributors to the mass density. For these small volumes we have lost sight of the density of the rock sample, yet our arbitrarily chosen point P is, in principle, even smaller.

The solution to this practical problem is to accept the material continuum as a description of the rock sample while recognizing that there are constraints on the volume below which the definition (4.9) has no meaningful application. For a physicist, examining a crystal of quartz or a drop of water, the continuum concept for mass density is reconciled with the concepts of particle physics by insisting that the ratio, $\delta M / \delta V$, should only be calculated for length scales, δL, much greater than the intermolecular spacing in quartz and much greater than the mean free molecular path in the water. That is, the volume must be much greater than a cube with sides of length about 10^{-10} m. For structural geologists this volume is a useful limit if we are considering deformation of individual mineral grains. However, the volume must include many of the different constituent grains to give a representative mass density for rock. Typically several cubic millimeters, perhaps up to several cubic centimeters, would be necessary to get meaningful densities for rock samples, depending on the grain size and heterogeneity of the sample. Thus, a few cubic centimeters might represent the lower limit in volume for application of the continuum model in terms of rock density.

Given what we have learned in the twentieth century from particle physicists about the basic building blocks of solids and fluids we must understand that the material continuum is an abstraction or *idealization* of nature and we must address its limitations. As John Wheeler reminds us in his forward to *The Continuum: A Critical Examination of the Foundation of Analysis* by Hermann Weyl:

For the advancing army of physics, battling for many a decade with heat and sound, fields and particles, gravitation and space–time geometry, the cavalry of mathematics, galloping out ahead, provided what it thought to be the rationale for the real number system. Encounter with the quantum has taught us, however, that we acquire our knowledge in bits; that the continuum is forever beyond our reach. Yet for daily work the concept of the continuum has been and will continue to be as indispensable for physics as it is for mathematics. In either field of endeavor, in any given enterprise, we can adopt the continuum and give up absolute rigor, or adopt rigor and give up the continuum, but we can't pursue both approaches at the same time in the same application (Weyl, 1987).

We refer to mathematical points at which density is defined in a continuum mechanical model of a faulted rock mass. Those "points" and the motions or material properties attributed to them, must be thought of as representative of a finite piece of rock, perhaps several cubic centimeters in volume.

4.2 | Physical dimensions and dimensional analysis

One can express physical quantities in terms of many different units of measure and a particular quantity can take on very different numerical values under the different systems of units. For example, $1\,\mathrm{m} \approx 2.85 \times 10^3$ printer points $\approx 3.94 \times 10^1$ inches $\approx 3.28 \times 10^0$ feet $\approx 4.97 \times 10^{-3}$ furlongs $\approx 6.21 \times 10^{-4}$ miles. However, the underlying physics must be independent of the choice of units: it can't depend on the length of the King's Foot! This leads us to the concept that there is something more fundamental than the units attached to a physical quantity and this is the *physical dimension* of that quantity. Regardless of the units chosen, for example, for mechanical work (newton · meter, pound force · foot, or dyne · centimeter) this physical quantity has the dimensions

of force times displacement. Thus, when analyzing the relationships among various quantities it is instructive to consider the dimensions of those quantities. In this section we introduce the dimensions commonly encountered in mechanical processes.

Dimensional analysis is a useful tool for working with and understanding theoretical constructs in all of science and engineering. The paper by M. K. Hubbert (1937) puts the use of dimensional analysis in a geological context and relies on the methods put forward in the book by P. W. Bridgman (1931). In this section we use dimensional analysis to understand whether a given equation, which reportedly describes some aspect of rock deformation, is consistent from a dimensional point of view. If not, the equation is invalid and should be discarded. Then we introduce the technique for plotting dimensionless graphs and illustrate why this is the preferred method to present scientific results.

4.2.1 Dimensionally homogeneous equations

The dimensions of the fundamental mechanical quantities (length, mass, time, and temperature) are given as: L, M, T, and Θ respectively. The dimensions of derived quantities are composed of products and powers of these fundamental dimensions. Reading $\{=\}$ "has dimensions of" we have, for example:

$$\text{area, } A\{=\}\mathrm{L}^2 \tag{4.10}$$

$$\text{volume, } V\{=\}\mathrm{L}^3 \tag{4.11}$$

$$\text{displacement, } \mathbf{u}\{=\}\mathrm{L} \tag{4.12}$$

$$\text{velocity, } \mathbf{v}\{=\}\mathrm{L\,T}^{-1} \tag{4.13}$$

$$\text{acceleration, } \mathbf{a}\{=\}\mathrm{L\,T}^{-2} \tag{4.14}$$

$$\text{mass density, } \rho\{=\}\mathrm{M\,L}^{-3} \tag{4.15}$$

$$\text{force, } \mathbf{F}\{=\}\mathrm{M\,L\,T}^{-2} \tag{4.16}$$

$$\text{stress, } \sigma\{=\}\mathrm{M\,L}^{-1}\mathrm{T}^{-2} \tag{4.17}$$

$$\text{thermal expansion, } \alpha\{=\}\Theta^{-1} \tag{4.18}$$

$$\text{stretch, } S\{=\}\mathrm{L\,L}^{-1}=\mathrm{L}^0=1 \tag{4.19}$$

$$3.141\,592\,65,\ldots,\pi\{=\}1 \tag{4.20}$$

Both the stretch and the angle are *dimensionless* physical quantities, but we use the symbol 1

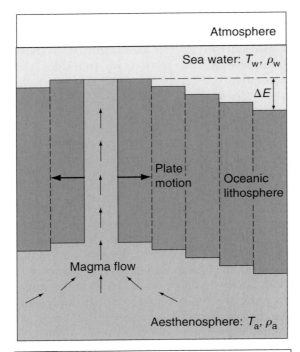

Fig 4.3 Schematic vertical cross section through oceanic lithosphere and upper aesthenosphere at a mid-ocean ridge and spreading center (Davis and Lister, 1974).

rather than 0, so quantities such as these can be included in the algebraic manipulation of dimensional equations (Obert and Duvall, 1967). Similarly, the symbol 1 is used for dimensionless constants such as π.

Dimensional analysis provides a procedure to evaluate equations involving physical quantities: those purporting to describe some physical object, event, or process. This procedure enables one to check whether an equation might be in error by being dimensionally inconsistent. This is probably the first thing you should do when confronted with an unfamiliar equation, especially a very complicated one. For example, suppose that you are reading the geological literature and you come across the following equation for the change in elevation, ΔE, of the seafloor due to cooling and thermal contraction of oceanic crust (Fig. 4.3) as it is transported away from a mid-ocean ridge by plate motion (Davis and Lister, 1974):

$$\Delta E = \left[\frac{\rho_a}{\rho_a - \rho_w}\right] 2\alpha (T_w - T_a) \sqrt{\frac{\kappa t}{\pi}} \qquad (4.21)$$

The subscripts, a and w, attached to density, ρ, and temperature, T, refer to that property of the *aesthenosphere* and of the *ocean water*, respectively. To evaluate (4.21) we assign the appropriate dimensions to each quantity:

change in elevation, $\Delta E \{=\} L$ (4.22)

mass density, ρ_a and $\rho_w \{=\} M L^{-3}$ (4.23)

temperature, T_a and $T_w \{=\} \Theta$ (4.24)

thermal expansion, $\alpha \{=\} \Theta^{-1}$ (4.25)

thermal diffusivity, $\kappa \{=\} L^2 T^{-1}$ (4.26)

time, $t \{=\} T$ (4.27)

A basic principle of dimensional analysis is: an equation is *dimensionally homogeneous* if every term has the same dimensions. To be meaningful in a physical context it is necessary for an equation to be dimensionally homogeneous. This is not sufficient because one could construct a dimensionally homogeneous equation that does not obey the fundamental laws of physics. Furthermore, being dimensionally homogeneous does not imply that the equation is the only, or even the best, description of the event or process under consideration. This test merely is a starting point in the evaluation of equations.

We apply the principle of dimensional homogeneity to (4.21) by noting that the left-hand side is the elevation change which has dimensions of length, $\Delta E \{=\} L$. The right-hand side is analyzed by substituting the dimensional symbols and canceling exponents where appropriate:

$$\left[\frac{\rho_a}{\rho_a - \rho_w}\right] 2\alpha (T_w - T_a) \sqrt{\frac{\kappa t}{\pi}} \{=\}$$

$$\frac{M L^{-3}}{M L^{-3} - M L^{-3}} (1)(\Theta^{-1})(\Theta - \Theta) \sqrt{\frac{L^2 T^{-1} T}{1}}$$

$$= (M L^{-3})(M^{-1} L^3)(\Theta^{-1})(\Theta) \sqrt{L^2 T^{-1} T}$$

$$= M^0 L^0 \Theta^0 \sqrt{L^2 T^0} = \sqrt{L^2} = L \qquad (4.28)$$

Note that the sum or difference of two terms with the same dimensions can be shortened to a single term with those same dimensions, so $(\Theta - \Theta)$ is written as (Θ). Also, exponents are added for terms that are multiplied, and these may cancel to produce a dimensionless term, as in $\Theta^{-1} \Theta = \Theta^0 = 1$. After simplifying the right-hand side we find dimensions of length: this equation is dimensionally homogeneous.

4.2.2 Dimensionless equations and graphs

Having corrected dimensional inconsistencies, the next step in the analysis of an unfamiliar equation is to plot it in graphical form so you can visualize the relationships between the different variables. For other than the simplest equations with one dependent and one independent variable, there are several possibilities for plotting graphs. Here we introduce the concept of *dimensionless* equations and graphs because they turn out to be a particularly instructive form for clarifying the relationships among the different variables. Fig. 4.4a shows an exposure of a fault in granitic rock with offset aplite dikes indicating apparent left-lateral separations of several tens of centimeters. By walking along this fault one could gather data on offset markers. A schematic map (Fig. 4.4b) illustrates such a fault trace with a few offset markers at different positions along the fault. The trace length of the fault is $W = 384$ m. The positions of each marker are determined by the field coordinate axis, X, oriented along the trace of the fault. A plot of the measured offset, O, versus position, X, is shown in Fig. 4.5a. Note that the offset is zero at either end of the fault by definition. These points may or may not be exposed, so their locations are not necessarily well defined.

The following equation, which we will learn more about later in the book, describes the relative displacement, Δu, or slip along a two-dimensional model fault in an elastic material (Pollard and Segall, 1987):

$$\Delta u = 2\Delta\sigma\left(\frac{1-\nu}{G}\right)\sqrt{a^2 - x^2} \tag{4.29}$$

The variables and their dimensions are given by:

relative displacement, $\Delta u \{=\} L$ (4.30)

shear stress drop, $\Delta\sigma \{=\} M L^{-1} T^{-2}$ (4.31)

Poisson's ratio, $\nu \{=\} 1$ (4.32)

shear modulus, $G \{=\} M L^{-1} T^{-2}$ (4.33)

half-length, $a \{=\} L$ (4.34)

spatial coordinate, $x \{=\} L$ (4.35)

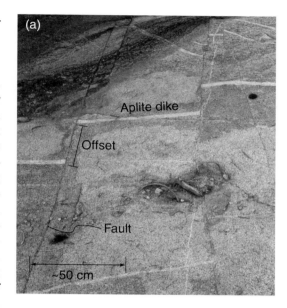

(a)

Aplite dike

Offset

Fault

~50 cm

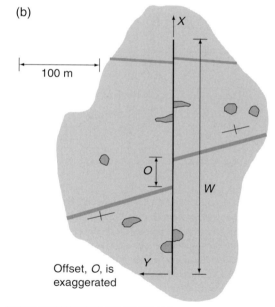

(b)

X

100 m

O

W

Y

Offset, O, is exaggerated

Fig 4.4 (a) Photograph of fault in granitic rock exposure offsetting aplite dikes from the Sierra Nevada, CA (Segall and Pollard, 1983b). (b) Schematic map of fault with offset dikes and zenoliths. Photograph by D. D. Pollard.

The relative displacement, Δu, is analogous to the offset, O, measured across the fault and the model fault length, $2a$, is analogous to the outcrop trace length of the fault, W. The shear stress drop, $\Delta\sigma$, is the change in shear stress acting on the model

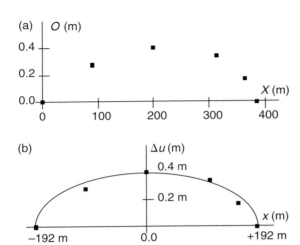

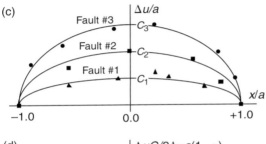

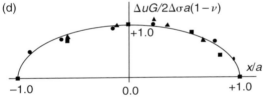

Fig 4.5 Graphs of offset or displacement discontinuity versus position along the trace of a fault. (a) Offset versus position using field coordinate system. (b) Displacement discontinuity versus position with origin at fault middle. (c) Normalized displacement discontinuity versus normalized position. (d) Generic plot of dimensionless displacement discontinuity versus dimensionless distance.

fault during slip. Poisson's ratio, ν, and the shear modulus, G, are two properties of the elastic material surrounding the model fault. The combination $G/(1 - \nu)$ can be thought of as the stiffness of this material. Inspection of (4.29) shows that the equation is dimensionally homogeneous. The actual distribution of slip on faults and models to explain these are part of a growing literature (Cowie and Scholz, 1992; Dawers et al., 1993; Bürgmann et al., 1994; Cowie and Shipton, 1998).

Because the origin of the coordinate system for (4.29) is at the model fault center, the field coordinate, X, must be transformed to have an origin at the center of the natural fault (Fig. 4.5b). This is done using $x = X - (W/2)$. The solid curve on this graph represents the relative displacements for the model. This curve was calculated using $a = 192$ m and noting that the offset at $x = 0$ is about 0.4 m. Substituting these values, we find:

$$0.4 \text{ m} \approx 2\Delta\sigma\left(\frac{1 - \nu}{G}\right)(192 \text{ m}),$$

$$\text{so } 2\Delta\sigma\left(\frac{1 - \nu}{G}\right) \approx 0.002 \tag{4.36}$$

This value for the leading terms on the right-hand side of (4.29) was used to plot the solid curve on Fig. 4.5b. Because we have adjusted the numerical value of this leading term to fit the data at $x = 0$, the solid curve goes exactly through the datum point there. The curve goes through the data at the ends of the fault, $x = \pm 192$ m, where the offset is zero by definition.

If we wanted to describe several different faults, we could measure offset markers for each and plot the offset as a function of distance along each fault. It would be difficult to compare the different faults, because each would be on a different graph. However, we can generalize the field data by dividing measurements of offset by the half-length of the fault. Carrying out the analogous operation for each side of the model equation we find the following dimensionless equation for the relative displacements:

$$\frac{\Delta u}{a} = 2(1 - \nu)\left(\frac{\Delta\sigma}{G}\right)\sqrt{1 - \frac{x^2}{a^2}} \tag{4.37}$$

The terms in this equation are numbers, dimensionless quantities, and dimensionless ratios. Using this dimensionless form we can plot field data from different faults on the same graph (Fig. 4.5c). When normalized in this way the abscissa values of all such data sets range from $x/a = -1.0$ to $x/a = +1.0$, but the ordinate values for a particular x/a may be quite different. The values at the center of the fault traces ($x = 0$) define a set of constants (C_1, C_2, C_3, etc.) equal to the quantity $2(1 - \nu)\Delta\sigma/G$ for each fault.

Although the dimensionless equation we have

just derived is useful, it is possible to represent the "generic" model fault on a single curve by moving the term $2(1 - \nu)\Delta\sigma/G$ to the left-hand side of (4.37):

$$\frac{\Delta u G}{2\Delta\sigma a(1 - \nu)} = \sqrt{1 - \frac{x^2}{a^2}} \qquad (4.38)$$

Plotting the left-hand side as a function of the right we generate the "generic" curve for dimensionless relative displacement versus dimensionless position (Fig. 4.5d). In this form one would refer to the relative displacement as having been *normalized* by the maximum relative displacement, $2(1 - \nu)\Delta\sigma/G$, the value of the displacement at the middle of the fault trace. The ends of the fault are given by $x/a = +1$ and $x/a = -1$.

In Figure 4.5d the curve for relative displacement is symmetric and goes to zero at the ends of the fault. At the middle of the fault, the offset of geologic markers would be greatest and, on this dimensionless graph, would have a magnitude of $+1$. All possible distributions of relative displacement for faults that approximate the behavior of this theoretical model would scatter about a single curve on this plot. The scatter would reflect errors in measurement and mechanical differences between the model and natural fault. All of the data sets for a set of faults could be plotted on this graph and thereby could be compared to each other and to the model.

Next we consider a model for heat conduction near an intrusion of magma to illustrate the dimensionless equation and graph for the continuous temperature variation in space and time (Carslaw and Jaeger, 1959; Cathles, 1977). In Fig. 4.6a the eroded remnants of an igneous dike are pictured and a glance at this photograph suggests that the shape of the dike is roughly tabular. The length along the outcrop and the height along the canyon face are much greater than the dike thickness. From observations on active volcanoes we know that the time scale for emplacement of some basaltic dikes can be small relative to the time scale for significant heat loss into the surrounding host rock (Delaney and Pollard, 1982). Although both the tabular shape and the relative time scales just mentioned must be reconsidered to understand the details of dike emplacement, these postulates serve to constrain an instructive model for the temperature field.

(a)

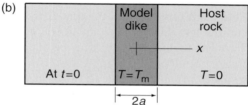

(b)

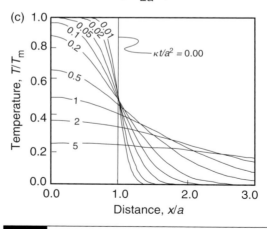

(c)

Fig 4.6 (a) Photograph of basaltic dike exposure from the San Rafael Swell, UT (Delaney *et al.*, 1986). (b) Thermal conduction model with initial conditions of elevated temperature in the dike and zero in the surroundings. (c) Graph of normalized temperature versus distance with curves representing successive normalized times (Carslaw and Jaeger, 1959). Photograph by D. D. Pollard. Graph reprinted from Carslaw and Jaeger (1959) by permission of Oxford University Press.

The model (Fig. 4.6b) is based on the solution for conduction of heat in one dimension, x, away from the tabular region $-a < x < +a$ in an infinite body with homogeneous thermal properties (Lovering, 1935, 1936; Jaeger, 1957). The tabular region is taken as a model for a dike of thickness $2a$. The only thermal property is the diffusivity, κ, which typically has values near $1 \times 10^{-6} \, \mathrm{m^2 s^{-1}}$ for rocks (Lee and Delaney, 1987). The initial conditions (IC) on the temperature, T, are defined at the arbitrary time, $t = 0$, and the boundary condition (BC) on the temperature is defined at an infinite distance from the model dike:

IC: for $t = 0$, $T = T_m$ for $-a < x < +a$

IC: for $t = 0$, $T = 0$ for $-a > x > +a$ (4.39)

BC: at $x = \pm\infty$, $T = 0$ for all t

Here T_m is the initial temperature throughout the model dike, the initial temperature is zero everywhere else, and very far from the model dike the temperature remains zero for all times. A constant ambient temperature, T_a, may be added to the solution for all positions and times.

The distribution of temperature in space, x, and time, t, normalized by the initial temperature, T_m, is (Carslaw and Jaeger, 1959):

$$\frac{T(x,t)}{T_m} = \frac{1}{2}\left[\mathrm{erf}\left(\frac{a-x}{2\sqrt{\kappa t}}\right) + \mathrm{erf}\left(\frac{a+x}{2\sqrt{\kappa t}}\right) \right],$$
$$-\infty < x < +\infty, \quad t \geq 0 \quad (4.40)$$

The function $\mathrm{erf}(\cdot)$ is the error function whose values are tabulated in reference books (Carslaw and Jaeger, 1959). Recalling from (4.26) that the dimensions of thermal diffusivity are $L^2 T^{-1}$, the terms in parentheses in (4.40) are dimensionless so the equation is dimensionally homogeneous.

In Figure 4.6c the normalized temperature distribution is plotted as a function of distance from the centerline of the dike using values of $\kappa t/a^2$ as a parameter that is a proxy for time. In this way, for a given diffusivity and dike thickness, each curve represents the distribution of temperature for a particular "snapshot" in time. Note that the initial temperature field is portrayed by the line labeled $\kappa t/a^2 = 0$, and the field for subsequent times has successively greater values of this parameter. In the first instant the temperature at the

contact, $x/a = 1$, changes to $T_m/2$. As time increases, temperatures in the model dike decrease and those in the immediate surroundings increase and then decrease. For $\kappa t/a^2 = 5$, corresponding to a time of about 58 days for a dike 1 m thick, the temperature has dropped to about 20% of its initial value and risen to a comparable temperature in the immediate surroundings.

4.3 | Dimensionless groups and the scaling of structural processes

Models of geologic structures provide insights about deformation in Earth's crust, some of which come from studying *dimensionless groups* of variables. In this section we explore examples of these dimensionless groups and show how they are used to understand the scaling of structural processes. The *direct method* to identify dimensionless groups considers the governing differential equations for the process and manipulates these to isolate the dimensionless groups (Bird *et al.*, 1960, pp. 107, 185, 338). While the direct method is preferred, it is not applicable if the governing equations are unknown or in doubt. In Chapter 12 we discuss the procedure for selecting the governing equations and general boundary conditions of a problem. We begin our discussion of the direct method with the bending of sedimentary layers over a laccolith and then consider the flow of magma through a sill.

Next we introduce the *Rayleigh method* of dimensional analysis (Brodkey and Hershey, 1988) with an example that addresses the buoyant rise of salt through a sedimentary basin in an intrusive form called a diapir. This method does not rely on knowledge of the governing equations for viscous flow, but does require a complete knowledge of all the variables relevant to the process. Underlying this method is a theorem introduced by Buckingham (1915) and based on the necessity for equations that describe physical processes to be dimensionally homogeneous. The Rayleigh method itself cannot assure one that the dimensionless groups so determined are correct, and an erroneous result will be found (with no warning) if the number of variables is too few or too many.

The choice of a method depends upon one's confidence in selecting the governing equations versus one's confidence in selecting all the variables (but no more) and properly grouping them.

4.3.1 Bending over a laccolith: the direct method

The first example is taken from the theory of bending of thin elastic plates under lateral loads (Timoshenko and Woinowsky-Krieger, 1959). This theory has been applied to the study of laccolithic intrusions (Johnson, 1970; Pollard and Johnson, 1973; Jackson and Pollard, 1990) in the Henry Mountains of southern Utah. Fig. 4.7a is a photograph of an outcrop on the flank of Trachyte Mesa, where the edge of a small laccolith, composed of diorite porphyry, is exposed and a few beds of Entrada Sandstone are bent over the laccolith. Only half of the laccolith model is illustrated here (Fig. 4.7b) because we postulate that it is symmetric about its center. Most of the overburden has been eroded from this site, but stratigraphic studies suggest that the depth, D, was a few kilometers at the time of magma intrusion. Note how the prominent Entrada sandstone layer is horizontal at the left side of the photograph, then bends concave upward against the diorite porphyry, and then bends concave downward and flattens out over the top of the laccolith.

The plate theory model represents a layer of sedimentary rock with height, H, and length, L, which overlies the laccolith (Fig. 4.7b). The strata are continuous beyond the periphery of the laccolith so L refers to that portion of a layer immediately above the intrusion. The x-axis is directed along the middle surface of the layer. Conceptually, the model supposes that magma is intruded upward through some unspecified conduit and then spreads laterally under the layer in question. The driving force for bending the layer is provided by the net upward pressure, p, which is taken to be constant. This pressure is given by the difference between the magma pressure and the pressure due to the weight of the overburden, $\rho g D$, where ρ is the average density and g is the acceleration of gravity. Bending is resisted by the elastic stiffness, B, a constant material property of the layer with the same

(a)

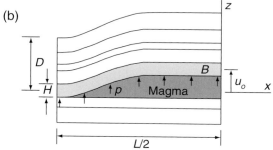

(b)

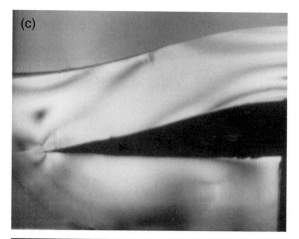

(c)

Fig 4.7 (a) Photograph of distal edge of a laccolith exposure from the Henry Mountains, UT (Pollard and Johnson, 1973). (b) Elastic plate model of bending strata over the laccolith. (c) Laboratory model with viscous fluid injected under elastic layer to simulate laccolith formation. Photograph by D. D. Pollard.

dimensions as pressure, that is $B\{=\}\,\mathrm{M\,L^{-1}\,T^{-2}}$. It is possible to consider a variable pressure due to magma flow, a variable resistance to bending, and resistance to bending provided by shear stress transmitted between adjacent layers (Pollard and

Johnson, 1973; Koch *et al.*, 1981), but these effects are ignored in order to introduce dimensional analysis using a simple model. These effects, in part, may account for the flatter top of the Trachyte Mesa laccolith (Fig. 4.7a) as compared to the laboratory model laccolith with a single layer (Fig. 4.7c).

The governing differential equation for the bending plate model is presented without derivation (Johnson, 1970), because our purpose is to demonstrate the direct method of dimensional analysis. This equation is based upon simplifying postulates about the kinematics of bending that are valid if the layer is thin compared to its length (Timoshenko and Woinowsky-Krieger, 1959). The differential equation for the vertical deflection, u_z, of the middle surface of the layer is:

$$\frac{d^4 u_z}{dx^4} = \frac{12p}{BH^3} \tag{4.41}$$

The first step in the analysis is to identify the variables, and to understand their roles in the physical process. Here, the spatial coordinate, x, is the only independent variable, and the vertical deflection, u_z, is the only dependent variable. A solution to (4.41) is $u_z = f(x)$, a function that describes the distribution of deflection with position along the layer.

The next step is to make the variables dimensionless (to normalize them) by dividing each by a *characteristic value* of a quantity with the same dimensions. The natural choice for normalizing x is L, the length of the layer in the x-direction. For a characteristic vertical deflection, we choose the value at the center of the plate, $u_o = u_z(x = 0)$. These choices are arbitrary, but are motivated by the geometry and the symmetry of the problem. The normalized variables are written with a superscript *:

$$x^* = \frac{x}{L}, \quad u_z^* = \frac{u_z}{u_o} \tag{4.42}$$

The differential operator in (4.41) also must be normalized. In this case $d^4/dx^4 \{=\}$ L^{-4}, and this operator is normalized using the length of the layer:

$$\frac{d^4}{d(x^*)^4} = L^4 \frac{d^4}{dx^4} \tag{4.43}$$

Next one substitutes the normalized variables and differential operator into the differential equation:

$$\frac{1}{L^4} \frac{d^4}{d(x^*)^4}(u_o u_z^*) = \frac{u_o}{L^4} \frac{d^4 u_z^*}{d(x^*)^4} = \frac{12p}{BH^3} \tag{4.44}$$

The final step is to rearrange the equation to group the constants into a single dimensionless group:

$$\frac{d^4 u_z^*}{d(x^*)^4} = \left[12 \frac{p}{B} \frac{L^4}{u_o H^3} \right] \tag{4.45}$$

The left-hand side of (4.45) is the dimensionless differential operator acting on the dimensionless dependent variable. The term in square brackets on the right-hand side is the dimensionless group we have identified for this differential equation.

In some contexts dimensionless groups are referred to as the *scale factors*. Note that the dimensionless group identified in (4.45) contains the elastic stiffness of the bent layer, B, the length, L, and height, H, of the layer, and the net upward pressure, p, acting on the layer. The powers to which these quantities are raised in the dimensionless group inform us about the relative sensitivity of the deflection, $u_z = u_z^* u_o$, to variations in these physical quantities. For example, the deflection scales directly with the fourth power of the length, L. Thus, all else being equal, two layers that differ in length by a factor of two would differ in deflection by a factor of sixteen. Changing the height also has a dramatic effect on the bending whereas changing the rock stiffness or the net upward pressure by a comparable factor has relatively little effect because the stiffness, B, and the net pressure, p, enter the dimensionless group to the first power. If the height is doubled, the deflection decreases by a factor of eight, but if the stiffness is doubled the deflection is decreased by a factor of two. Similarly, doubling the net pressure increases the deflection by a factor of two.

In this manner one can assess the importance of different physical quantities for the outcome of a tectonic process. Interestingly, this assessment does not require one to solve the differential equation (4.41). By determining the sensitivity of the dependent variable to the various parameters that affect that variable, one can design a strategy for field and laboratory investigations that focuses on measurement of the most sensitive parameters. For example, errors in the field measurement of length or height of the layer over the laccolith are of greater consequence than comparable errors in the laboratory measurement of rock stiffness. Of course, such assessments depend upon the correct selection of the governing equation. Recent analyses based on somewhat different governing equations, geometry, and boundary conditions for the deformation of strata over laccoliths have provided additional insights (Kerr and Pollard, 1998; Zenzri and Keer, 2001).

4.3.2 Magma flow in a conduit: the direct method

The direct method of dimensional analysis is illustrated using a problem from the theory of fluid dynamics for an isothermal viscous fluid (Bird *et al.*, 1960, p. 71). Viscous flow theory has been applied to a myriad of problems in structural geology including the folding of ductile strata, the development of salt domes, and rebound of the Earth's crust after glacial unloading (Johnson and Fletcher, 1994). The geological examples we refer to here are the sills of Shonkin Sag, Montana (Fig. 4.8a), thin horizontal conduits through which a viscous magma flowed (Hurlbut and Griggs, 1939; Pollard *et al.*, 1975). The governing equation for this flow is presented without detailed derivation, because our purpose, again, is to demonstrate the direct method of dimensional analysis.

The model is a parallel-sided conduit of width, W, filled with a viscous fluid (Fig. 4.8b). The Newtonian viscosity, η, measures the resistance to flow and is postulated to be constant in space and time. The viscosity has the same dimensions as pressure multiplied by time, that is $\eta \{=\}$ $M L^{-1} T^{-1}$. The mass density of the magma, ρ, also is taken as a constant. The length of the conduit, L, is very great compared to the width, as is the dimension out of the (x, z)-plane of view. Here the origin of coordinates is at the center of the conduit and the z-axis is parallel to the width of the conduit. We postulate that the only non-zero component of velocity, v_x, is directed along the length of the conduit, and the pressure decrease, $p_1 - p_2$, drives this flow.

(a)

(b)

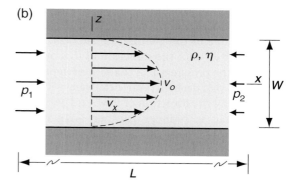

(c)

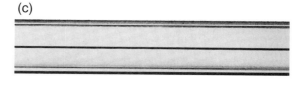

Fig 4.8 (a) Photograph of laccolith exposure (left) and a set of sills (right) from the Shonkin Sag, MT (Pollard *et al.*, 1975). (b) Viscous flow model between parallel plates. (c) Reynold's experiments of dye injected into viscous fluid flowing in a tube (Van Dyke, 1982): upper sketch shows laminar flow regime and lower sketches show turbulent flow regimes. Photograph of exposure by D. D. Pollard. Laboratory photographs by N. H. Johannesen and C. Lowe.

The governing equation for the flow of viscous magma in a sill is derived from two general principles, conservation of mass and conservation of momentum. The first of these dictates that v_x cannot vary in the direction of flow, but it can vary across the conduit in the z-direction, and it can vary in time. Thus, conditions on the velocity components are:

$$v_x = f(z, t) \text{ only}, \quad v_y = 0 = v_z \tag{4.46}$$

The velocity component, v_x, is one of the dependent variables of this problem.

The second principle, conservation of momentum, introduces the forces acting on volume elements of the magma. The decrease in pressure from one side of the element to the other introduces a net force in the direction of this pressure decrease. The pressure, p, is the second dependent variable in this problem and it can vary with position, x, along the direction of flow, and with time. Viscous drag introduces another force on the volume element and this is proportional to the viscosity, η. The gravitational force acts in the vertical direction, and therefore does not contribute to flow in the horizontal conduit, and is ignored. Under the restriction of constant density and viscosity, the pressure forces and viscous forces are capable of producing accelerations in the magma described by the equation:

$$\rho \frac{\partial v_x}{\partial t} = -\frac{\partial p}{\partial x} + \eta \frac{\partial^2 v_x}{\partial z^2} \tag{4.47}$$

This is a special case of the more general, three-dimensional equations of motion called the Navier–Stokes equations, developed by Navier in 1822 (Bird et al., 1960, p. 81). The left-hand side of this equation is the mass per unit volume times the acceleration (time derivative of the velocity). The right-hand side is the sum of the pressure and viscous forces per unit volume. In essence this equation is a specialized expression of Newton's Second Law of Motion written in the order $m\mathbf{a} = \mathbf{F}$, where m is the mass, $\mathbf{a}$ is the acceleration, and $\mathbf{F}$ is the net force acting on a fluid element.

There are two dependent variables, velocity and pressure, and three independent variables, the x- and z-coordinates and time in (4.47). In addition, there are two fluid constants, mass density and viscosity. Each of the variables must be normalized by a physical quantity that shares the same dimensions. It is customary in fluid dynamics to select a characteristic length and a characteristic velocity for this purpose. Here the only characteristic length is the width of the conduit, W. We select the velocity, v_o, at the center of the conduit to be characteristic. This is the maximum velocity, but the selection is arbitrary so we could have selected the average velocity. The normalized variables are defined as:

$$x^* = \frac{x}{W}, \quad z^* = \frac{z}{W}, \quad t^* = \frac{v_o}{W} t,$$

$$v_x^* = \frac{v_x}{v_o}, \quad p^* = \frac{p - p_o}{\rho v_o^2} \tag{4.48}$$

The characteristic velocity and distance are used in the ratio v_o/W to define a dimensionless time. Also, a reference pressure, p_o, is subtracted from the pressure and then the combination ρv_o^2 is used to normalize this reduced pressure. The reference pressure could be that at the entrance to the sill. The differential operators are normalized as follows:

$$\frac{\partial}{\partial t^*} = \frac{W}{v_o} \frac{\partial}{\partial t}, \qquad \frac{\partial}{\partial x^*} = W \frac{\partial}{\partial x},$$

$$\frac{\partial^2}{\partial (z^*)^2} = W^2 \frac{\partial^2}{\partial z^2} \tag{4.49}$$

The normalized variables (4.48) and differential operators (4.49) are substituted into the governing equation (4.47) to find:

$$\rho \frac{v_o}{W} \frac{\partial}{\partial t^*} (v_o v_x^*) = -\frac{1}{W} \frac{\partial}{\partial x^*} (\rho v_o^2 p^* + p_o)$$

$$+ \eta \frac{1}{W^2} \frac{\partial^2}{\partial (z^*)^2} (v_o v_x^*) \tag{4.50}$$

Bringing the constants outside the derivatives and eliminating the derivative of the constant reference pressure this equation becomes:

$$\frac{\rho v_o^2}{W} \frac{\partial v_x^*}{\partial t^*} = -\frac{\rho v_o^2}{W} \frac{\partial p^*}{\partial x^*} + \frac{\eta v_o}{W^2} \frac{\partial^2 v_x^*}{\partial (z^*)^2} \tag{4.51}$$

Note that the two combinations of physical constants in this equation are dimensional; they both have dimensions of force per unit volume; and each is associated with the magnitude of a different force acting in the flow system:

$$\frac{\rho v_o^2}{W} \propto \text{inertial force per unit volume} \tag{4.52}$$

$$\frac{\eta v_o}{W^2} \propto \text{viscous force per unit volume} \qquad (4.53)$$

Viscous forces are related to the product of the viscosity and velocity divided by the square of the characteristic length. If the viscosity is doubled, but the width and velocity remained unchanged, we would expect the viscous forces to double. Similarly, if the width of the conduit is cut in half, but the viscosity and velocity remained unchanged, we would expect the viscous forces to increase by a factor of four. Similarly, if the velocity were doubled, the inertial forces would increase by a factor of four, but the viscous forces would only double. In this way we understand that these combinations of quantities are the *scale factors* for the forces acting on the fluid.

Dividing all three terms of (4.51) by $\rho v_o^2/W$, a single dimensionless group is identified:

$$\frac{\partial v_x^*}{\partial t^*} = -\frac{\partial p^*}{\partial x^*} + \left[\frac{\eta v_o/W^2}{\rho v_o^2/W}\right]\frac{\partial^2 v_x^*}{\partial(z^*)^2} \qquad (4.54)$$

This group is a ratio of the viscous force (4.53) to the inertial force (4.52). This dimensionless group usually is written as the reciprocal of the form given here and called the *Reynolds Number*. It is associated with the name of a famous fluid mechanician, Osborne Reynolds, who studied the transition from laminar to turbulent flow in conduits (Reynolds, 1883):

$$\text{Reynolds Number} = \text{Re} \equiv \frac{W v_o \rho}{\eta},$$

$$\frac{\text{inertial force}}{\text{viscous force}} \qquad (4.55)$$

The magnitude of Reynolds Number can be used to characterize the transition in style of flow between two dramatically different flow regimes. This was demonstrated in the classic experiments by Reynolds in which he injected dye into the fluid flowing through a pipe (Fig. 4.8c) and observed how the flow changed as a function of the velocity, while the pipe diameter and the fluid density and viscosity remained constant (White, 1974). At relatively low velocity (upper illustration) the flow field is very regular, so the stream of dye is perfectly straight, regardless of the position of injection from near the wall to the center of the pipe. Clearly the path of any particle of fluid is straight and parallel to the walls of the pipe. This is

referred to as *laminar flow*. At a greater velocity (middle illustration) fluid particles follow circuitous paths, both along and across the axis of the pipe. Thus, the stream of dye mixes with the adjacent fluid and thereby spreads across the entire pipe with distance from the point of injection. Using special visualization techniques (lower illustration) this new flow regime can be seen as a complex set of eddies that vary rapidly with time. This is referred to as *turbulent flow*.

The transition from laminar to turbulent flow in a pipe occurs at Reynolds Numbers ranging from 2000 to 13 000, depending upon the roughness of the pipe and the geometry of the entrance. When the product of the diameter, velocity, and density, divided by the viscosity is less than 2000, viscous forces dominate over inertial forces and the flow is laminar. In the literature of fluid mechanics this is referred to as *low Reynolds Number flow*. The great viscosity of magma relative to typical products of conduit width, velocity, and density, usually places them in the laminar flow regime. There may be little direct evidence for flow laminae in igneous rock, although regular patterns of zenoliths or crystals may be suggestive. Observations of modern eruptions suggest that streams of lava approximate laminar flow. None-the-less, the inference that magma flow is in the laminar regime usually is based on estimates of Reynolds Number and analogies to laboratory experiments using other liquids.

4.3.3 Rise of a salt diapir: the Rayleigh method

One of the more interesting and challenging problems in structural geology is the rise of salt (or magma) from depth toward the surface (Fig. 4.9a), and the associated deformation of the host rock (Trusheim, 1960; Braunstein and O'Brien, 1968). The less dense salt responds to the forces of buoyancy and flows upward while the surrounding rock mass deforms in a fluid or ductile manner and flows out of the way. This conceptual model of salt intrusion is quite different from that proposed by G. K. Gilbert (1877) for the emplacement of magma in the Henry Mountains laccoliths (Fig. 4.7a). The laccoliths apparently formed at a relatively shallow level in the crust where the surrounding rock mass deformed largely as an elastic

(a)

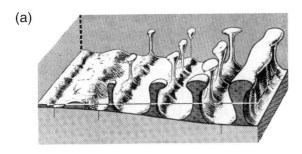

(b)

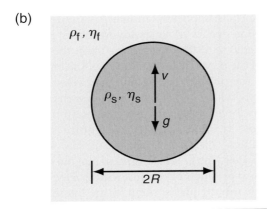

and brittle solid that bent and fractured in
response to the advancing magma. Masses of salt
(or magma) whose rise is largely accommodated
by ductile flow of the surrounding rock are called
diapirs. We illustrate the Rayleigh method of
dimensional analysis in the context of diapirs by
considering the slow rise of a buoyant viscous
sphere in another viscous fluid of greater density
(Fig. 4.9b). The solution by C. G. Stokes dates to the
middle of the nineteenth century and has found
innumerable applications in engineering and
science (White, 1974, p. 211). However, we analyze
this problem without the benefit of the governing
equations or their solution by employing dimensional analysis.

A postulate, born out by the Stokes solution, is
that the rising body of viscous fluid maintains a
spherical form. Therefore the size and shape of
this body is completely specified by its radius, R.
The viscosity of the sphere, η_s, and the viscosity of
the host fluid, η_f, are both considered constant, as

are the density of the sphere, ρ_s, and the density
of the host fluid, ρ_f. Since the sphere is rising
because of buoyancy, another parameter of this
problem must be the gravitational acceleration, g.
The velocity fields inside and outside the sphere
are complex, but here we focus only on the velocity of the sphere, v, relative to the static host at a
great distance from the sphere, and consider that
to be the dependent variable. For this conceptual
model we postulate that the flow is steady, so the
velocity is constant and time does not enter the
problem. Also we postulate that the flow is
isothermal, so heat transfer from the body to the
surroundings is ignored. We do not specify any
distance scale that would place boundaries on the
size of the surrounding fluid mass. Conceptually,
the body rises forever in a host fluid of infinite
extent. Finally, the direction of rise is tacitly
assumed to be in the opposite direction of the
gravitational acceleration, so no coordinate axes
are explicitly required to define this problem.

Despite all of the simplifying postulates made
in the previous paragraph, we have identified six
quantities that apparently affect the velocity of
the sphere. In an experimental approach to this
problem, each quantity would be systematically
varied, as all others are held constant, in order to
discover their relationships. The number of experiments would appear to be daunting; however,
dimensional analysis helps to reduce the number
of variables for experimentation. The first step is
to list all the physical quantities and identify their
dimensions:

$$\text{radius of sphere, } R\{=\}L \qquad (4.56)$$

$$\text{relative velocity of sphere, } v\{=\}L\,T^{-1} \qquad (4.57)$$

$$\text{density of host fluid, } \rho_f\{=\}M\,L^{-3} \qquad (4.58)$$

$$\text{density of sphere, } \rho_s\{=\}M\,L^{-3} \qquad (4.59)$$

$$\text{viscosity of host fluid, } \eta_f\{=\}M\,L^{-1}T^{-1} \qquad (4.60)$$

$$\text{viscosity of sphere, } \eta_s\{=\}M\,L^{-1}\,T^{-1} \qquad (4.61)$$

$$\text{acceleration of gravity, } g\{=\}L\,T^{-2} \qquad (4.62)$$

There are seven quantities in the three dimensions: length (L), mass (M), and time (T). We may
reduce this number by making the additional
assumption that the densities and the acceleration of gravity enter only through the difference
in specific weights of the two fluids:

difference in specific weights,

$$\Delta \rho g = (\rho_f - \rho_s)g \{=\} ML^{-2}T^{-2} \qquad (4.63)$$

Thus, the revised list includes only five independent quantities. Furthermore, the quantity mass density times gravitational acceleration is a measure of one of the forces acting in flow regimes such as the rising diapir:

$$\rho g \propto \text{gravitational force per unit volume} \qquad (4.64)$$

Recall that two other forces, inertial and viscous, were defined in (4.52) and (4.53).

The Rayleigh method takes each of the five independent quantities and raises it to an unknown integral or fractional exponent, here given by the symbols a through e. An objective of the analysis is to determine these exponents and use them to identify the dimensionless groups. The quantities, raised to these unknown powers, are multiplied together and it is asserted that their product is equal to a constant:

$$R^a v^b (\Delta \rho g)^c \eta_f^d \eta_s^e = \text{constant} \qquad (4.65)$$

The appropriate dimensional expressions are substituted for the physical quantities in (4.65):

$$L^a (LT^{-1})^b (ML^{-2}T^{-2})^c (ML^{-1}T^{-1})^d (ML^{-1}T^{-1})^e$$
$$= L^a (L^b T^{-b})(M^c L^{-2c} T^{-2c})(M^d L^{-d} T^{-d})(M^e L^{-e} T^{-e})$$
$$= 1 \qquad (4.66)$$

Because the product of the quantities raised to the unknown powers is a constant, the product of the dimensional terms raised to these powers must be dimensionless: the product must be equal to one. This implies that the product of each dimensional term raised to the given powers is equal to one:

$$L^a L^b L^{-2c} L^{-d} L^{-e} = L^{a+b-2c-d-e} = 1$$
$$M^c M^d M^e = M^{c+d+e} = 1 \qquad (4.67)$$
$$T^{-b} T^{-2c} T^{-d} T^{-e} = T^{-b-2c-d-e} = 1$$

From (4.67) we conclude that the sum of the exponents for each dimensional term is zero:

$$a + b - 2c - d - e = 0$$
$$c + d + e = 0 \qquad (4.68)$$
$$-b - 2c - d - e = 0$$

By this procedure we have reformulated the five unknown exponents into three equations. This suggests that there are only two dimensionless

groups and the exponents for these can be used to determine the other three exponents.

We choose the exponents c and e, and solve for the other exponents in terms of these:

$$d = -c - e$$
$$b = -2c - d - e$$
$$\quad = -2c - (-c - e) - e = -c \qquad (4.69)$$
$$a = -b + 2c + d + e$$
$$\quad = -(-c) + 2c + (-c - e) + e = 2c$$

The exponents a, b, and d are removed from (4.65) by substitution:

$$R^{2c} v^{-c} (\Delta \rho g)^c \eta_f^{(-c-e)} \eta_s^e = \left[\frac{R^2 (\Delta \rho g)}{v \eta_f} \right]^c \left[\frac{\eta_s}{\eta_f} \right]^e$$
$$= \text{constant} \qquad (4.70)$$

The terms in square brackets are the two dimensionless groups for this process. The dimensional analysis provides no additional information about the values of the exponents. That information is discovered through laboratory experimentation. However, we now have only two quantities to work with instead of the original five, so the design of the necessary experiments is greatly simplified.

The first term in square brackets in (4.70) contains two measures of force per unit volume of sphere. The gravitational force per unit volume (4.64) is proportional to the density difference between the host fluid and the sphere, and to the acceleration of gravity. The viscous force per unit volume (4.53) is proportional to the viscosity of the host fluid and the relative velocity, and inversely proportional to the square of the sphere radius. The rise of the sphere can thus be seen as dependent upon a competition between the gravitational and viscous forces. Considering the powers to which the variables are raised, we note that the relative velocity is most sensitive to changes in the radius of the sphere.

The second dimensionless group identified in (4.70) is the ratio of viscosities for the sphere and host. Because the viscosity of the sphere might be either zero (an open hole) or infinite (a rigid body), it is advisable to use the following dimensionless group:

$$\left[\frac{\eta_f - \eta_s}{\eta_f + \eta_s} \right]^e \qquad (4.71)$$

The quantity in square brackets ranges from -1 to $+1$ as the sphere changes from rigid ($\eta_s \to \infty$) to an open hole ($\eta_s \to 0$). This dimensionless group is eliminated from consideration if the viscosity of the sphere and the host fluid are the same.

The so-called *Buckingham Π Theorem* was published by E. Buckingham in 1915, and often is cited in discussions of dimensional analysis (Buckingham, 1915; Bird *et al.*, 1960; Brodkey and Hershey, 1988). This theorem is based upon the necessity for dimensional homogeneity of equations that describe physical phenomena. That is, every term in such an equation, when written in terms of the dimensions of the four fundamental quantities, must be made up of the same powers of each quantity. The theorem states:

The number of dimensionless groups for a particular physical process is equal to the number of variables less the number of dimensions represented in those variables.

Since there are five physical quantities in the rising sphere problem as conceptualized here, and there are three dimensions, there are only two independent dimensionless groups according to the Π theorem. The Rayleigh method determines two groups and that is consistent with the theorem.

4.3.4 Dimension analysis applied to the folding process

A fundamental question in structural geology concerns the length scale of structures comprising an array. A notable example is that of an array of folds (Fig. 4.10a), but the question pertains to many other structures. Convenient measures of length scales for folds include the distance along a particular surface from hinge to hinge and the thickness between adjacent surfaces (Fig. 4.10b). In a deformed terrain, folds will generally occur at many scales; from single layers a few millimeters in thickness, H, with arc lengths, L_a, of a few centimeters to composite rock layers several kilometers in thickness having arc lengths of ten or more kilometers.

The simpler example we address here is a folded layer embedded in deformed metamorphic rock (Fig. 4.10a). Hinge-to-hinge arc lengths for two

(a)

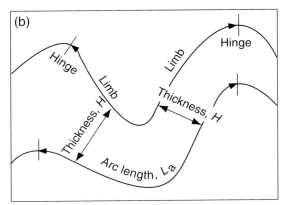

(b)

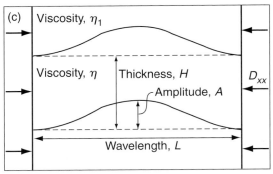

(c)

Fig 4.10 Fold styles, terminology, and modeling. (a) Photograph of folds in metamorphic rocks. (b) Sketch of a portion of a fold illustrating the hinges and limbs, and suggesting field measurements of arc length and thickness. (c) Model geometry and parameters described in the text. Photograph by R. C. Fletcher.

adjacent surface traces bounding a fold are likely to vary, as are thicknesses at different positions along the fold limbs. However, average values from multiple measurements along a train of folds provide quantitative estimates of the regularity of folding. The arc length is commonly, but incorrectly, called the fold wavelength (Fig. 4.10b). Our analysis considers the folded quartz vein to be "isolated." What we principally mean by this is that the folding is independent of that in nearby layers. That is, we do not see other nearby layers that are folded in concert with them.

Note that the original vein thickness was not uniform and that this has affected the regularity of the folding, but the arc length to thickness ratios fall within a modest range. What might this regularity mean? Clearly, it cannot easily be ascribed to something "built into" the rock prior to folding, since the regularity is present only in this layer. We must then ascribe it to some mechanism inherent in the process of folding itself. Before discovering an explanation, and, as an aid to this, we consider a perfectly regular, periodic structure of the same sort (Fig. 4.10c). This consists of a layer embedded in a uniform medium, with the upper and lower surfaces of the layer in the form of in-phase sinusoidal surfaces with *wavelength*, L, and amplitude, A. The infinite, perfectly periodic fold train is drawn with a low limb dip.

The truly periodic fold train is an idealization of the geometric form of a fold train and is used here to isolate a small volume of rock containing a single fold from the remainder of the layer. Because of the periodicity, the two vertical planes in Fig. 4.10c are mirror planes of symmetry. For such a plane, two conditions apply. First, in the deformation, which will be idealized to uniform layer-parallel shortening, except for the flow associated with the folding, a particle cannot pass through a mirror plane. Second, the shear stress must vanish at a mirror plane.

We model the case of a segment of the layer containing a single trough–crest–trough fold with a horizontal span given by the wavelength, L, and an arc length, $L_a > L$. To remind ourselves of the conditions that must apply at them, we replace the bounding mirror planes by rigid platens with smooth, frictionless, vertical surfaces. We suppose that these approach each other at a rate corresponding to a rate of deformation, D_{xx}. As a natural starting point, we shall be concerned only in the fields of velocity and stress

within this region at an instant of time, with the aim of analyzing the rate of change of quantities of interest.

The contrasting possibilities of interest are: (i) a negligible positive (or negative) value of the rate of change of fold amplitude, dA/dt, in which case the layer will undergo nearly uniform thickening; and (ii) a large positive value of dA/dt, corresponding to the marked folding or buckling of the layer. To think about that, we have to imagine, in a concrete fashion, what the properties of the rocks involved are under the conditions that the folds formed. Clearly, they have deformed in a more or less continuous fashion. Although it takes a rather large leap, we might assume, for simplicity, they behave like other stiff, but still deformable, fluid-like media with which we are familiar, and treat them as viscous fluids. We then suppose the layer and medium have viscosities η and η_1, respectively.

We now have a reasonably clear idea of a model that might address some aspect of the folding process so we turn to dimensional analysis. The quantities involved in the model, with their dimensions, are:

rate of change in fold amplitude,
$$dA/dt \{=\} LT^{-1} \tag{4.72}$$

bulk rate of shortening, $D_{xx} \{=\} T^{-1}$ (4.73)

fold amplitude, $A \{=\} L$ (4.74)

layer thickness, $H \{=\} L$ (4.75)

wavelength, $L \{=\} L$ (4.76)

layer viscosity, $\eta \{=\} M L^{-1} T^{-1}$ (4.77)

medium viscosity, $\eta_1 \{=\} M L^{-1} T^{-1}$ (4.78)

There are seven physical quantities involving three dimensions, M, L, and T, so the *Buckingham II Theorem* indicates that there are four dimensionless groups. Since M occurs only in the viscosities, one dimensionless group must be the viscosity ratio

$$R = \frac{\eta_1}{\eta} \tag{4.79}$$

It is useful to choose groups that are relatively simple and that have a concrete physical or geometrical interpretation. An appealing choice is the aspect ratio, layer thickness to wavelength, which we write in the form:

$$k = 2\pi\left(\frac{H}{L}\right) \qquad (4.80)$$

Since $\lambda = 2\pi/L$ is the wavenumber, we may call (4.80) a dimensionless or normalized wavenumber. The aspect ratio, H/L, is appealing because it immediately brings to mind the data on the ratio of thickness to arc length, H/L_a, which we obtained to express fold regularity. Including the wavenumber in (4.80) anticipates special results of folding theory.

As a third dimensionless group, we take the maximum slope of the folded surface, or the limb dip of the fold:

$$\tan\delta = \lambda A = 2\pi\left(\frac{A}{L}\right) \qquad (4.81)$$

Here δ is the maximum dip angle. With the aspect ratio, k, and the dip, δ, we may readily visualize the fold form. One might wonder why the *wavelength*, L, rather than the *arc length*, L_a, has been chosen. The implied reason is that we have tacitly assumed that in the process of folding the thickness/arc length ratios, which clearly involve a random element, are *selected* during the initial phase of folding, when the folds have low limb dip. In the geometric idealization of such a fold the arc length approximates the wavelength, $L_a \cong L$.

Only one dimensionless group remains to be set. This must involve the rate of change of amplitude, dA/dt, and the rate of deformation, D_{xx}, which have so far been left out. Excluding the viscosities, only two quantities contain the time, so the dimensionless group will have the form:

$$\frac{dA/dt}{X|D_{xx}|} \qquad (4.82)$$

Here X is a quantity with the dimension of length, and must be selected from the possibilities H, L, and A. Since the anticipated result is that $dA/dt > 0$, and shortening implies $D_{xx} < 0$, we take its absolute value to avoid *negative* dimensionless groups. We choose $X = A$, so the dimensionless group is:

$$\frac{dA/dt}{A|D_{xx}|} \qquad (4.83)$$

We term this ratio the dimensionless, or normalized, rate of growth.

We now write (4.83) as a function of the other dimensionless groups:

$$\frac{dA/dt}{A|D_{xx}|} = f(k, \lambda A, R) \qquad (4.84)$$

This states that the rate of growth, normalized by the rate of shortening, may be expressed, for any pair of viscous materials for which the viscosity ratio is given, as a function of the aspect ratio H/L or the dimensionless wavenumber, k, and the limb dip, λA. If we are correct in supposing that the folds, or the positions of fold hinges, are established when the deflections of the layer are still small, we may then limit ourselves to discovering something about the growth rate under the restriction $\lambda A \ll 1$. In that case this dimensionless group makes a negligible contribution to the relation and write (4.84):

$$\frac{dA/dt}{A|D_{xx}|} = q(k, R) \qquad (4.85)$$

Here q designates the unknown function.

If we further suppose that the relative rate of growth of the fold takes place rapidly, so that the aspect ratio remains the same, k may be treated as a constant. Hence, the function on the right-hand side will be a constant for a given pair of materials, R, and a given aspect ratio, k. As we will show later, k will vary according to $k(t) = k(0)\exp(-2D_{xx}t)$, where $k(0)$ is its initial value. But, if q is a constant, we may integrate the above equation to obtain the description of fold amplitude growth:

$$A(k, t) = A(k, 0)\exp(q|D_{xx}|t) \qquad (4.86)$$

Here, we are led to think about initial fold amplitude. Does this mean, somehow, that the regular length scale of folds in the fold train is "prefigured" in the form of the layer? The answer is yes, in the sense that we can hardly expect to get something, i.e. folding, if the layer is uniform in thickness and has perfectly planar surfaces to begin with. However, the answer is no, if we suppose that the initial layer form contains a kind of perfect although very greatly diminished template of the final fold train form. What is present initially is imperfection in the form of a gentle irregular, or random, waviness of the layer surfaces.

We know that such waviness can be broken up, mathematically, into its Fourier wavelength components. Here, we shall suppose merely for the sake of simplicity in visualization and analysis, that such waviness can be thought of as an infinite sum or superposition of *two-dimensional* cylindrical sinusoidal waves with axes normal to a single direction of layer shortening, each with a different wavelength, L. As with many other wave phenomena, we suppose, further, that each component behaves independent of all the others, at least in approximation. Then, the equation for $A(k, t)$ may be thought of as describing the growth or amplification, of each component, as a function of its k-value. If then, $q(k, R)$ varies in a suitable manner, and, in particular, if it has a single maximum at some value of $k = k_d$ corresponding to the ratio L_d/H, the amplification of the "fold components" will be *selective*. Here the subscript d refers to the dominant wavelength. That is, as time or layer shortening goes on, the component at L_d/H will receive the greatest amplification, and the shape of the layer will be dominated by a superposition of fold components with L/H at or near this value. In this manner, the regularity seen in the final configuration will be established.

When the folded form of the layer, which will inherit substantial irregularity from the randomness in amplitude and phase of the initial waviness, reaches some stage in its development, the independent growth of individual wavelength components will cease, and the form established at that point, as in the positions of fold hinges, will be "locked in." If folding or buckling accomplishes a shortening of the span of the layer with minor changes in its thickness, the spacing of hinges along the layer, in terms of arc length, will tend to be preserved. Thus, the data collected from our fold train may be referred back to the time of cessation of *selective amplification*.

It is reasonable to suggest that the mean value of L/H provides an estimate of the value L_d/H, or the so-called *dominant wavelength/thickness ratio*. If we knew the form of the function $q(k, R)$ we might then find L_d/H as a function of the viscosity ratio, R, and thus use the L/H data to estimate the ratio of the viscosities of the medium and the layer at the time the folding occurred. To anticipate results that we will obtain in a later chapter, this relation is

$$\frac{L_d}{H} \cong \frac{2\pi}{(6R)^{1/3}} \qquad (4.87)$$

A given value for $(L/H)_{mean}$, implies a particular viscosity ratio $R = \eta_1/\eta$. Issues arise in judging the validity of this result, including whether it is appropriate to treat rocks under the conditions of deformation as viscous fluids. However, it is satisfying to obtain information on the fundamental properties of rock by dimensional analysis. Such properties clearly cannot be inferred from field observations alone.

4.4 | Scaled laboratory models

It seems inevitable that model experiments coupled with theoretical analysis of the dynamics of tectonic processes will contribute greatly to a sound, coherent theory of structural geology and tectonics. By running scale models of tectonic events, one may ultimately hope to separate the physically possible from the physically impossible hypotheses, and the former may be studied in detail to illustrate tectonic processes to an extent not otherwise possible (Ramberg, 1967).

Both the length scale and the time scale for many tectonic processes make direct observation impossible. In terms of length, we have no difficulty observing the surface of the Earth at the necessary scale, but observations are extremely limited at depth. Mines and wells are few and far between, and modern imaging technologies (e.g. three-dimensional seismic reflection), while vastly improved, typically provide data only from locations of interest to the oil and gas industry. In terms of the time scale, some tectonic processes take millions of years to develop and their characteristic rates prevent most attempts to monitor or investigate the phenomena directly. If, as Hans Ramberg suggests, we can make models in the laboratory that reproduce these processes, we can directly observe the model structures as they develop and gain important insights. Ramberg's opinion was written at a time when numerical models of tectonic processes were still under development, and these now offer an alternative to laboratory models. In this section the constraints imposed by building a model with much smaller length scale and much shorter time scale are examined, and rules are described to ensure similarity between the natural process and the model process.

M. King Hubbert (1937) wrote one of the earliest papers that advocates a laboratory modeling approach to problems in structural geology and points out the requirements for scaling a model. These activities continue today and, indeed, the number, range, and sophistication of such experiments have increased greatly in the last few decades, with several multi-investigator laboratories active. For example, researchers at the Applied Geodynamics Laboratory of the Bureau of Economic Geology, University of Texas, have studied the rise of salt domes and salt withdrawal (Vendeville *et al.*, 1995; Ge and Jackson, 1998). Those at the Fault Dynamics Project at Royal Holloway, University of London, have studied a variety of structural styles and faulting mechanisms in extensional tectonic settings (McClay *et al.*, 1991; McClay and White, 1995). Researchers in France at Université Rennes are using laboratory models to study the development of growth fault systems (Manduit and Brun, 1998), while others at Université de Montpellier are investigating faulting in accretionary wedges (Gutscher *et al.*, 1998). Researchers in Canada at the Experimental Tectonics Laboratory at Queen's University are investigating fold–fault relationships and the influence of stratigraphic heterogeneities on faulting (Liu and Dixon, 1990, 1991). Despite the difficulty of mimicking the behavior of rock over geological time with sand and putty on a laboratory bench, laboratory model studies can provide important quantitative insight, and in most instances they record interesting relationships between the applied loading conditions and the development of structures that appear similar to those in the Earth. In some cases model experiments have been performed on actual rock samples at elevated pressures to investigate faulting (Patton *et al.*, 1998) or folding (Couples and Lewis, 1998).

Laboratory experiments are termed analog or *physical models* whereas computational or *numerical models* are performed usually on a computer

(a)

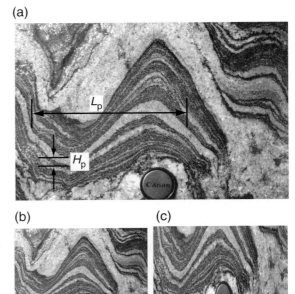

Fig 4.11 (a) Exposure photograph of banded metamorphic rock with small folds. (b) Same exposure reduced by a factor of two with geometric similarity maintained. (c) Same exposure but not geometrically similar. Photograph by D. D. Pollard.

and rarely on a piece of paper. These two types of experiments have something in common: both types obey the fundamental laws of mechanics. The theoretical models do this by design, whereas the laboratory models do this because they are part of the natural world from which those laws were derived. The same dimensionless groups of physical quantities that appear in the governing equations for a particular process in the Earth should be used to scale the laboratory models of this process.

4.4.1 Geometric and kinematic similarity

Figure 4.11a is a photograph of an exposure of a distinctly banded metamorphic rock that displays beautiful folds. The 50-mm lens cap (lower center) provides a length scale, so we know that the actual wavelength of the prominent gray band near the middle of the photo is about $L_p = 212$ mm and the height of this layer measured at its lowest point is about $H_p = 12$ mm. We refer to the outcrop with the banded fold as the *prototype*. It is simple to make a visual model of this outcrop that honors the geometry of the prototype using image processing software (Fig. 4.11b). Here the wavelength and height are halved in value, so $L_m = 106$ mm and $H_m = 6$ mm. The model ratio, L_r, for the lengths is:

$$\frac{L_m}{L_p} = L_r = \frac{1}{2} \qquad (4.88)$$

Any other length that we measure on this outcrop is related to the corresponding length in the model by this same ratio. For example, for the height of the gray band we have:

$$\frac{H_m}{H_p} = L_r = \frac{1}{2} \qquad (4.89)$$

The prototype and model are *geometrically similar*. The image of the outcrop shown in Fig. 4.11a is scaled down to a smaller size to fit on the page of this book. Thus, the lens cap displayed on the figure is not 50 mm in diameter, but it represents 50 mm on the actual exposure. The photographic image is, itself, a geometrically scaled model of the exposure and the process of reproduction of this image maintains geometric similarity.

Another "model" of the exposure is shown in Fig. 4.11c. Is this geometrically similar? The field of view has changed somewhat, but the image seems to have many similarities to the prototype shown in Fig. 4.11a. On the other hand, a careful inspection reveals that the fold shape is distorted relative to the prototype. We measure the wavelength in this model as $L_m = 106$ mm and the height as $H_m = 12$ mm. Comparing the model ratios we find:

$$\frac{L_m}{L_p} = \frac{1}{2} = L_r, \quad \frac{H_m}{H_p} = \frac{1}{1} \neq L_r \qquad (4.90)$$

The scaling in the horizontal direction is the same as that used to produce Fig. 4.11b, but lengths measured in the vertical direction are the same as those in the prototype. Thus, the height of the layer in the prototype and "model" are identical. This "model" does not preserve geometric similarity. Comparing the lens cap in the three figures confirms the scaling relations.

Tectonic processes may be very slow to develop, but they are not static. Thus, the relative time scales for the model, T_m, and the prototype, T_p, must be considered carefully when designing a model

experiment. The time is measured from some arbitrary moment, often at the initiation of the process, and the model ratio for time is defined as:

$$\frac{T_m}{T_p} = T_r \qquad (4.91)$$

Given this ratio, one can compare the prototype and a model at corresponding times during the development of the process. We say that the prototype and the model are *kinematically similar* if they are geometrically similar at every corresponding time over the duration of the process. By corresponding time we mean a time for the prototype process and a time for the model process that are related by the model ratio for time.

Kinematic similarity can be understood in terms of two motion pictures, one of the model and the other of the prototype. Let's say the model ratio for time is $T_r = 3.1 \times 10^{-11}$, so each model second represents one thousand prototype years. The camera recording the model process shoots at a speed of one frame per second and the camera recording the prototype process shoots at a speed of one frame per thousand years. If each successive pair of frames of the two motion pictures is geometrically similar, the two processes also are kinematically similar. The corresponding frames may have different length scales, but lengths throughout the prototype and model obey the model ratio for lengths.

Turning to a geological example, it is likely that the layers shown in Fig. 4.11a had lesser amplitudes and greater wavelengths at an earlier time in the folding process. In Fig. 4.12 three different stages in the hypothetical one million year development of the prototype fold are illustrated, assuming that the deformation conserved volume and that the shortening in the direction of the measured wavelength is simply the reciprocal of the elongation perpendicular to this direction. We start to record the process at an arbitrary time (0 s) shown in Fig. 4.12a. Five hundred thousand years into the process the prototype fold would look like the image in Fig. 4.12b, and at the end of the one million years the fold would have attained the shape observed in outcrop today (Fig. 4.12c).

For a kinematically similar model of this folding process using the model ratio proposed

(a) Time, t_0

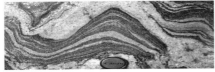

(b) Time, t_1

(c) Time, t_2

Fig 4.12 Snapshots of folding process with kinematic similarity. (a) Initial time. (b) After 500 000 years. (c) After 1 000 000 years. Photograph by D. D. Pollard.

above, $T_r = 3.1 \times 10^{-11}$, one model second is one thousand prototype years. At the beginning (0s) and at the ending (1000s) of the process, the model would look exactly like the images in Fig. 4.12a and c, respectively. At an intermediate stage, after 500s, an image of the model would look exactly like Fig. 4.12b. In order to achieve this kinematic similarity the motions of all particles in the model, when appropriately scaled for the model length and time ratios, must mimic the motions of corresponding particles in the prototype.

4.4.2 Dynamic similarity

Most of us are familiar with the concept of geometric similarity and can easily recognize intuitively when certain lengths are distorted relative to others. Most of us are less familiar with kinematic similarity, but we can recognize changes in time when a motion picture of everyday scenes is speeded up or slowed down.

On the other hand our intuition usually is not well developed when it comes to judging the similarity of a prototype and model with respect to forces. In this regard we must turn to calculations to test for *dynamic similarity* and these calculations

typically involve the dimensions of length, mass, and time. The model ratios for these fundamental quantities are:

$$\frac{L_m}{L_p} = L_r, \quad \frac{M_m}{M_p} = M_r, \quad \frac{T_m}{T_p} = T_r \quad (4.92)$$

To maintain strict similarity, all corresponding lengths, masses, and times in the model and the prototype must adhere to the given model ratios.

Model length scales typically are chosen for convenient experimentation on a laboratory bench, without the necessity of a microscope, so they vary from a decimeter to perhaps a meter. Prototype length scales can range from a meter to hundreds of kilometers. Model materials usually do not vary in mass density by more than a factor of two from the densities of common rocks, so the model ratio for density is of order one: $\rho_r = \rho_m/\rho_p \sim 10^0$. However, the model ratio for mass is the model ratio for density times the cube of the model ratio for length. Thus, the length ratio can impose very great differences between the mass of model and that of the prototype. The time scales for experiments are determined by convenience and necessity, and a few minutes to a few days duration is typical. Some tectonic processes (e.g. fracture propagation) may operate at these human time scales, but most are believed to develop over thousands to millions of years. Common ranges for the model ratios of the fundamental quantities are:

$$10^{-6} \leq L_r \leq 1, \quad 10^{-18} \leq M_r \leq 1,$$
$$10^{-10} \leq T_r \leq 1 \quad (4.93)$$

The model ratios for all three fundamental quantities vary from very small numbers to about unity.

The derived physical quantities can be evaluated in terms of their model ratios as well. Some important examples are:

$$\text{volume,} \quad \frac{V_m}{V_p} = \frac{L_m^3}{L_p^3} = L_r^3 \quad (4.94)$$

$$\text{acceleration,} \quad \frac{a_m}{a_p} = \frac{L_m T_m^{-2}}{L_p T_p^{-2}} = L_r T_r^{-2} \quad (4.95)$$

mass density, $\dfrac{\rho_m}{\rho_p} = \dfrac{M_m L_m^{-3}}{M_p L_p^{-3}} = M_r L_r^{-3}$ (4.96)

force, $\dfrac{F_m}{F_p} = \dfrac{M_m L_m T_m^{-2}}{M_p L_p T_p^{-2}} = M_r L_r T_r^{-2}$ (4.97)

stress, $\dfrac{\sigma_m}{\sigma_p} = \dfrac{M_m L_m^{-1} T_m^{-2}}{M_p L_p^{-1} T_p^{-2}} = M_r L_r^{-1} T_r^{-2}$ (4.98)

The derived quantities are reduced to their equivalent fundamental quantities and these are used to define the model ratios.

Notice that the model ratio for forces contains the ratios for length, time, and mass. Length and time are considered through their respective model ratios to assure geometric and kinematic similarity. Mass usually is not considered independently, but rather through the analysis of the force ratio, which is used to evaluate the dynamic similarity between a model and the prototype. To assure similarity one must identify all of the different forces acting in the tectonic process under investigation. For example, in our study of the dimensionless groups for flow of magma in a conduit (Fig. 4.8) and rise of a salt diapir (Fig. 4.9) we identified inertial forces (4.52) caused by the change in velocity with time, viscous forces (4.53) caused by the drag of magma against the side of the conduit, and gravitational forces (4.64) related to a density contrast. A model and prototype that are geometrically and kinematically similar, are said to be dynamically similar if the model ratios for all of the forces acting on any two corresponding particles are equal (Ramberg, 1967, p. 4):

$$\frac{F_{mi}}{F_{pi}} = \frac{F_{mv}}{F_{pv}} = \frac{F_{mg}}{F_{pg}} = \frac{F_{me}}{F_{pe}} = \cdots = F_r \quad (4.99)$$

Here the subscripts m and p refer to the model and prototype as before, and the subscripts i, v, g, and e refer to inertial, viscous, gravitational, and elastic forces, respectively. There may be other forces that should be considered.

It would be a daunting task to evaluate the forces acting on all corresponding particles for a prototype and a model, but fortunately a simpler procedure usually is adequate. Because the ratios of particular forces in the prototype and model all must be equal to a common model ratio, F_r, it

follows that any ratio of two different forces in the prototype must equal the corresponding ratio of those different forces in the model. For example, considering a process in which inertial, viscous and gravitational forces are present, we find:

$$\frac{F_{mi}}{F_{mv}} = \frac{F_{pi}}{F_{pv}}, \quad \text{or} \quad \text{Re}_m = \text{Re}_p \quad (4.100)$$

$$\frac{F_{mi}}{F_{mg}} = \frac{F_{pi}}{F_{pg}}, \quad \text{or} \quad \text{Fr}_m = \text{Fr}_p \quad (4.101)$$

Recall that Re is the dimensionless group called the Reynolds Number, defined in (4.55). Dynamic similarity requires that the Reynolds Numbers for the model and prototype be identical. These numbers can be evaluated using a characteristic length, w_o, a characteristic velocity, v_o, the density, ρ, and the viscosity, η, for both the model and prototype. The *Froude Number*, Fr, measures the relative importance of inertial and gravitational forces. From (4.52) and (4.64) we have:

$$\text{Froude Number} = \text{Fr} \equiv \frac{v_o^2}{g w_o},$$

$$\frac{\text{inertial force}}{\text{gravitational force}} \quad (4.102)$$

The Froude Numbers for the model and prototype can be evaluated in terms of characteristic velocities and lengths, and the acceleration of gravity, to assure dynamic similarity.

This example points out a second important role for dimensionless groups in structural geology. We have already shown how useful they are for understanding and interpreting the equations that govern mathematical models of tectonic processes. Now we see that they are useful in the design of scaled laboratory model experiments of these processes. Besides inertial, viscous, and gravitational forces, there are likely to be forces associated with spatial gradients in pressure or stress:

$$\frac{\Delta p}{w_o} \propto \text{pressure (stress) force per unit volume}$$

$$(4.103)$$

Here Δp refers to a characteristic change in pressure (or stress) from one location to another. These forces are used to define additional dimensionless groups that may be useful in model design (Ramberg, 1967, p. 40):

$$\text{Stokes Number} = \text{St} \equiv \frac{\Delta p / w_o}{\eta v_o / w_o^2},$$

$$\frac{\text{pressure force}}{\text{viscous force}} \qquad (4.104)$$

$$\text{"Ramberg" Number} = \text{Ra} \equiv \frac{\rho g}{\eta v_o / w_o^2},$$

$$\frac{\text{gravitational force}}{\text{viscous force}} \qquad (4.105)$$

$$\text{"Smoluchowski" Number} = \text{Sm} \equiv \frac{\rho g}{\Delta p / w_o},$$

$$\frac{\text{gravitational force}}{\text{pressure force}} \qquad (4.106)$$

Ramberg has referred to the ratio of gravitation to viscous forces as a "nameless ratio" but we suggest the *Ramberg Number* in recognition of the major contribution he made to tectonic modeling. Ramberg suggested the name for the *Smoluchowski Number* because of the two papers published by M. Smoluchowski in which a theory for buckling of elastic layers on a viscous foundation is developed along with associated model experiments (Smoluchowski, 1909). The *Stokes Number* is named for one of the pioneers in fluid dynamics who solved some of the classic problems for slow viscous flow. For strict dynamic similarity each of these numbers for the prototype must be equal to the corresponding number for the model.

The procedure for tectonic model design may be further simplified when some of the characteristic forces are much smaller than others. For example, inertial forces typically are much smaller than either the viscous or gravitational forces, so the Reynolds and Froude Numbers are very small. For example, in the rise of a salt dome the relevant parameters take on the following ranges (Ramberg, 1967, pp. 48–9):

$$1.5 \times 10^3 \,\text{m} \leq w_o \leq 3 \times 10^3 \,\text{m}$$

$$3 \times 10^{-10} \,\text{m s}^{-1} \leq v_o \leq 3 \times 10^{-7} \,\text{m s}^{-1}$$

$$1 \times 10^6 \,\text{N s m}^{-2} \leq \eta \leq 1 \times 10^{16} \,\text{N s m}^{-2} \qquad (4.107)$$

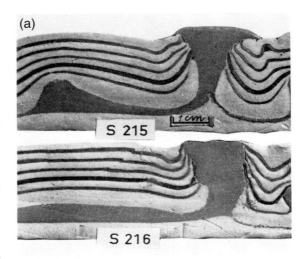

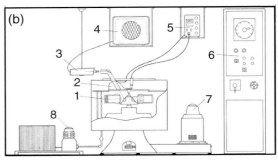

Fig 4.13 Centrifuge models and equipment (Ramberg, 1967). (a) Model of salt dome development. (b) Centrifuge used to increase the body force: 1, model in centrifuge cup; 2, stroboscopic light reflector; 3, camera; 4, camera electronics; 5, stroboscope; 6, temperature and speed control unit; 7, motor; 8, refrigerator.

$$\rho = 2.16 \times 10^3 \,\text{kg m}^{-3}$$

$$g = 9.8 \,\text{m s}^{-2}$$

The radius of the prototype salt dome ranges from 1.5 to 3 km, and the velocity ranges from 1 cm a^{-1} to 1 m a^{-1}. These values are inferred from field observations and interpretations of geological records. The density and viscosity are values estimated from laboratory measurements. Density is well known, but viscosity is poorly constrained because it can vary over many orders of magnitude depending upon temperature, pressure, and chemical environment. Based on the ranges of values given above, the Reynolds

Number for the rising salt dome would range from 1.9×10^{-6} to 9.7×10^{-20}, and the Froude Number from 6.1×10^{-18} to 3.1×10^{-24}. These very small ratios justify ignoring the effects of inertial forces when scaling models of salt dome development. A laboratory model of salt dome development is illustrated in Fig. 4.13a (Ramberg, 1967, p. 123).

Many experimental observations of viscous flow in conduits have demonstrated that the Reynolds Number must be greater than approximately 1×10^3 for the flow regime to become turbulent (Bird *et al.*, 1960, pp. 183–8). For Reynolds Numbers less than this value, flow in conduits is laminar (Fig. 4.8b). Because the range of Reynolds Numbers estimated for the rising salt dome (and many other tectonic processes involving flow) is many orders of magnitude less than this transition value, the flow regime is laminar. The precise scaling of inertial forces between the model and prototype is not necessary as long as the model is well within the laminar flow regime. The condition for strict dynamic similarity in terms of inertial forces between model and prototype can be relaxed without compromising the usefulness of the experimental results.

4.4.3 Gravitational forces: a problem for model similarity?

It was noted in the preceding section that all corresponding lengths, masses, and times in the model and the prototype must adhere to the given model ratios to maintain strict similarity. In general these are thought of as independent ratios, to be chosen at the convenience of the experimenter, or as constrained by the available materials. However, models of tectonic processes often are carried out on a lab bench where the acceleration of gravity is approximately 9.8 m s^{-2}, and this value is not significantly different for the prototype. Thus, the model ratio for accelerations is approximately one. Examining the model ratio for accelerations we find:

$$a_r = L_r T_r^{-2} = 1, \quad \text{so} \quad L_r = T_r^2 \qquad (4.108)$$

Thus, the model length and time ratios are not independent. Solving for the model time:

$$\frac{L_m}{L_p} = \left(\frac{T_m}{T_p}\right)^2, \quad \text{so} \quad T_m = T_p \sqrt{\frac{L_m}{L_p}} \qquad (4.109)$$

Using a reasonable range of model ratios for length ($10^{-6} < L_r < 1$) and for the time scales for tectonic processes ($10^2 \text{ s} < T_p < 10^{15} \text{ s}$), we calculate a range of model time scales from $T_m = 10^{-1}$ s to $T_m = 10^{15}$ s. At the lower end of this range the experimenter would have few problems, but clearly the upper end is unattainable. For example, a common model length scale is ten centimeters (0.1 m), corresponding to a prototype length scale of one kilometer (1000 m). A common time scale for the duration of tectonic processes is one million years (10^6 years). Given these values, the model time scale is ten thousand years (10^4 years), not a practical duration for experiments designed to be observed by humans!

The constraint on the model time scale imposed by similar accelerations of gravity acting on the prototype and the model is not fatal to all model experiments in tectonics because the inertial forces associated with accelerations in the prototype may be insignificant compared to other forces. Recall, for example, that flow of many geological materials is in the realm of low Reynolds Number and low Froude Number flow. With very small ratios of inertial to viscous forces (4.55) and inertial to gravitational forces (4.102), the inertial forces can be ignored.

There is, however, a constraint imposed on the strength of model materials that must deform under their own weight to simulate the deformation of very large masses of rock. Considering the model ratio for gravitational forces we have:

$$\frac{F_{mg}}{F_{pg}} = \frac{\rho_m g_m L_m^3}{\rho_p g_p L_p^3} \approx \frac{\rho_m L_m^3}{\rho_p L_p^3} \qquad (4.110)$$

Here the ratio of gravitational acceleration in the model and prototype is approximately one. Given this ratio of gravitational forces, the corresponding ratio of stresses and strengths is:

$$\frac{\sigma_{mg}}{\sigma_{pg}} = \frac{\rho_m L_m}{\rho_p L_p} \approx \frac{L_m}{L_p} \qquad (4.111)$$

Here the ratio of densities in the model and prototype is approximately one. This analysis leads to the conclusion that the strength ratio must scale as the length ratio. Using a reasonable range of model ratios for length ($10^{-6} < L_r < 1$) we conclude that the model ratios for strength must be in this same range ($10^{-6} < \sigma_r < 1$). The upper end of this range corresponds to laboratory experiments on meter-scale prototypes such as small folds and these can be effectively modeled with relatively strong materials (Ramberg, 1963). At the lower end of this range the experimenter must try to model processes with length scales of kilometers or tens of kilometers in the laboratory. If gravitational forces induce the deformation, very weak materials are required for the model to meet the constraint imposed by the model ratio for strengths.

M. King Hubbert (1945) brought this point to the attention of geologists in an article entitled "Strength of the Earth" that examined the apparent contradiction between the great strength of a hand sample of rock and the modest "strength" of a huge rock mass containing innumerable folds and faults that witness to its apparent weakness. To drive home this point Hubbert proposed the operation illustrated in the frontispiece to this chapter in which the state of Texas is lifted by a huge crane. Of course this would be impossible to implement, so he considered a laboratory model of such an operation. By considering the scaling of this model he concluded that it would be impossible under the existing force of gravity.

Consequently, if we tried to lift such a block in the manner indicated … the eyebolts would pull out; if we should support it on a pair of saw horses, its middle would collapse; were we to place it upon a horizontal table, its sides would fall off. In fact, to lift it at all would require the use of a scoop shovel … The inescapable conclusion, therefore, is that the good state of Texas is utterly incapable of self-support (Hubbert, 1945).

The scaling of model experiments has proven to be problematic because materials that flow and fracture under their own weight are rare, yet large masses of rock subject to gravitational forces do just that. A solution to this dilemma is to increase the body force in the model by placing it in a centrifuge (Fig. 4.13b) (Ramberg, 1967; Dixon and Summers, 1985). For example, if the dominant forces operating in the prototype are pressure, gravitational, and viscous forces, the Stokes (4.104), Ramberg (4.105), and Smoluchowski (4.106) Numbers must be examined and shown to be equivalent to the corresponding numbers for the model. Thus, comparing the Smoluchowski Numbers for the model and prototype, one must show that:

$$\left(\frac{\rho g w_o}{\Delta p} \right)_m = \left(\frac{\rho g w_o}{\Delta p} \right)_p \qquad (4.112)$$

If the gravitational force as measured by ρg is approximately the same in the prototype and model and the model ratio for lengths is 10^{-6}, then the model ratio for pressure (stress, strength) also must be 10^{-6} and this is not easily attained. On the other hand if the body force in the model can be artificially increased in a centrifuge, such that the model ratio for accelerations is 10^3, then the model ratio for strength need only be 10^{-3}. Materials with strengths required to meet this constraint are readily obtained for laboratory experiments. Similar conclusions about the appropriate viscosity for model materials are found by examining the Ramberg Number.

4.5 | Concluding remarks

In this chapter we introduced the material continuum, a construct that has produced astounding results in both fundamental physics and applied engineering, including solid deformation, fluid flow, and heat transport. Most human-made objects, from automobiles to spacecraft, from bridges to dams, from golf clubs to bicycles, are designed using continuum mechanical principles. Furthermore, many of these objects are built on or with machines that were, themselves, designed using these principles. The success of this way of thought should be beyond dispute, but curiously the application of continuum mechanics to structural geology lags considerably behind applications in other scientific and engineering disciplines. This textbook is designed to encourage students of structural geology to use the concept of the material continuum. We also reviewed some "bread and butter" techniques for the practicing structural geologist including dimensional analysis, dimensionless groups, and the scaling of tectonic processes. These should be readily available tools to take in the field as mapping progresses and questions arise, and to use at the desk when puzzling over the result of a computation.

Chapter 5

Deformation and flow

Nearly undeformed (upper left) and deformed (lower right) oöids with spherulitic cores viewed in thin section. Matrix is calcite with some mud and average ratios of long to short axes are 1.16 and 1.56 respectively. Samples from near Harrisonburg, VA. Reprinted from Cloos (1971, Plates 9 and 11) with permission of The John Hopkins University Press.

A clear separation between geometrical and dynamic considerations was maintained by Becker, the American geologist, at a very early date, and he referred to the English physicist Thomson (Lord Kelvin), who says very clearly: 'We can see, therefore, that there are many attributes of movement, displacement, and deformation which can be considered independently of force, mass, chemical composition, elasticity, heat, magnetism and electricity; and it is of greatest use to science for such properties to be considered as a first step' (Sander, 1970, p. 12).

M ost structural geologists think about deformation and flow in an *inverse problem* mode: from the final state back toward the initial state of the deformed body of rock. For example, the lower right photograph in the frontispiece for this chapter shows deformed oöids with elliptical shapes: ratios of long to short axes are about 1.56 (Cloos, 1947, 1971). The upper left photograph shows nearly undeformed oöids with approximately circular shapes: ratios of long to short axes are about 1.16. One can think of the deformed oöids being transformed back toward an initial state much like that of the nearly undeformed oöids. In other words the ellipsoidal particles become nearly spherical. This viewpoint is natural since the primary observational data of structural geologists are field observations of deformed rock.

The above admonition by the Swiss geologist Bruno Sander, written in 1948 (Sander, 1970), suggests that we set aside much of the physics in our initial study of rock deformation and focus exclusively on kinematics. Becker and Sander are prominent participants in the early history of structural geology. Their advice is followed to this date by an influential "school" of structural geologists, to which the present authors do not subscribe (Fletcher and Pollard, 1999; Pollard 2000). Instead, we take kinematics as an integral part of a complete mechanical analysis, including enough physics to formulate a well-posed problem. Therefore we devote this chapter to the subject of kinematics and succeeding chapters to the other elements of a complete mechanics.

Other types of observations enter a synthesis leading to understanding of a process of deformation and its products. For example, controlled laboratory experiments produce detailed information on the behavior of rock materials under load, ranging from brittle failure at modest temperature and pressure to slow creeping flow at high temperature and pressure. Moreover, theoretical study of deformation and failure of a wide range of materials and human-made structures over the last two centuries has provided a refined picture of the processes involved and the laws governing them. The considerable insight and information provided by these additional sources tend to favor the formulation of a *forward problem* for

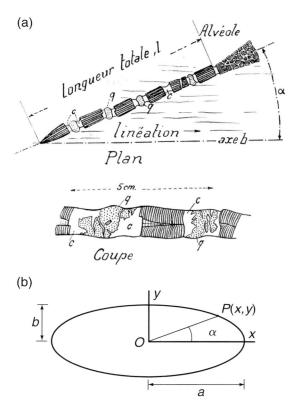

(a)

(b)

Fig 5.1 (a) Broken and extended fossil belemnite with quartz, q, and calcite, c, filling. (b) The deformed shape of an initial unit circle with radius of "one undeformed belemnite" is an ellipse with semi-axes a and b. The trace of cleavage (lineation) is parallel to the long axis of this strain ellipse and the orientation and stretch of the belemnite are represented by the radial line OP. Reprinted from Badoux (1963) with permission of Université de Lausanne.

such processes as faulting, folding, or mountain building at plate margins. Field observations of many sorts, including the deformed shapes of objects such as oöids may be selected to constrain a forward model built upon a synthesis of much previous information (Nur *et al.*, 1986; Pachell, *et al.*, 2003).

From the more traditional perspective the result of a process of deformation, such as one of the deformed objects shown in Fig. 5.1 and in the frontispiece to this chapter, is described, and the relationship between its present and initial forms is worked out. Applied to one or more such objects, this procedure may lead to an estimate of the strain of the rock containing them. The procedure chiefly involves considerations of geometry, although assumptions must be made as to the initial forms of the objects. However, as the above quotation suggests, no reference is made to the underlying physical process that resulted in the deformation. We begin this chapter by working through a few examples. Interpretation of the examples involves many simplifying assumptions that set aside complicating factors, which we return to after developing the other parts of a complete mechanics in subsequent chapters.

5.1 | Rock deformation: some observations and a simple description

5.1.1 Deformed belemnite

The closely lined segments of the stretched *belemnite* in Fig. 5.1a were initially connected to form an intact fossil (Badoux, 1963). First quartz and later calcite was precipitated into the gaps between the segments as stretching occurred. Measuring the final span occupied by the segments, l, and initial length, l_0, yields a measure of the elongation of a *material line*, the belemnite or its centerline. An assumption is that the segments did not stretch: the belemnite fractured into pieces that behaved as rigid objects embedded in a deformable medium, the rock containing it. The final length, measured from the figure, is $l = 153/60''$, measured with a scale marked off in 60ths of an inch, and the sum of the segment lengths is $l_0 = 103/60''$. The ratio l/l_0 $= 1.48$ termed the *stretch* of a material line is a dimensionless measure of the elongation. Thus, any units may be used for the measurements. The use of fossil belemnites to estimate strain goes back at least to the late-nineteenth century (Cloos, 1946; Hossain, 1979).

The motivation for study of the belemnite is not for its sake alone, but for what it might tell us about the deformation of the rock containing it. The belemnite lies in the bedding plane and is inclined at an angle α to *cleavage*, represented by the parallel line segments in the figure. Much research has shown that the plane of cleavage is normal to the direction in the rock that has undergone the greatest shortening, and contains the

direction in which the rock has undergone the greatest extension (Wood and Oertel, 1980). A belemnite oriented parallel to the cleavage would show the maximum value of the ratio l/l_0, providing a measure of the bulk rock deformation in that direction.

Estimation of the maximum stretch from the information available at the exposure, requires other assumptions. One is that the stretch of the belemnite was equal to that of any other linear material line in the rock with the same orientation, for example, one lying along the line "l" on the figure, or one much farther from the belemnite. This assumption implies *homogeneity of deformation* within some volume of rock containing the belemnite. In detail, the belemnite itself has not undergone a homogeneous deformation, but has broken into pieces that have separated by means of a process involving precipitation of material into the gaps. The belemnite might have been more resistant to extension than the surrounding rock, and thus its stretch would underestimate that of the rock.

We have introduced the notion of homogeneous deformation in a simple way. As we show later in this chapter the technical definition of a deformation is the transformation that relates the positions of particles in a body in one state to that in another. Here we speak of these two states as the initial state and the final state. A particle is an element of mass within the rock of small dimensions relative to the length scale of interest. Here, the only length scale is the length of the belemnite, so "small" is taken relative to that. The position of a particle is given by its position vector between a coordinate origin and the particle. In this more formal context homogeneity is defined as a *linear transformation* between positions in the initial and final states.

The intent here is to estimate, from the elongation of the belemnite and the angle between it and cleavage, the maximum elongation in the plane of cleavage. We also assume, for this example, that the plane of cleavage is normal to the bed containing the belemnite. The data given provide no basis for this assumption, but allow us to consider only the plane of particles making up the bedding surface and thereby reduce the problem to two dimensions.

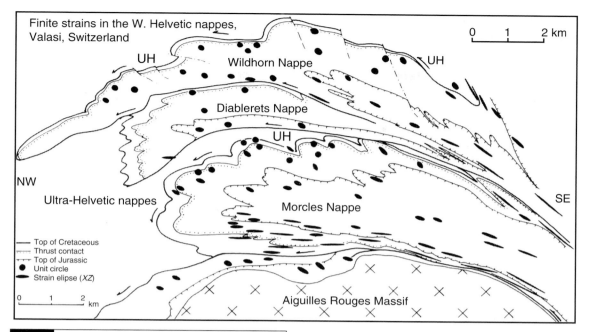

Fig 5.2 Strain distribution represented by strain ellipses in a down plunge section of folds through the western Helvetic nappes (Ramsay and Huber, 1983).

A linear transformation will take a circular locus on the bed surface and transform it into an ellipse. Since the long axis of the ellipse will lie parallel to the cleavage and we know the angle between the cleavage and the centerline of the belemnite, we may try to compute the maximum stretch from the stretch of the belemnite, $l/l_0 = 1.48$ and the angle α of $25°$. We write the parametric equations for an ellipse as:

$$x = a \cos \alpha$$
$$y = b \sin \alpha \qquad (5.1)$$

If the radius of the ellipse is 1.48 at $\alpha = 25°$, we have the relation:

$$a^2 \cos^2(25°) + b^2 \sin^2(25°) = (1.48)^2 \qquad (5.2)$$

Since this is only one equation in two unknowns, we need further information or assumptions in order to compute the maximum stretch. One approach would be to find another, differently oriented belemnite in the bedding plane, thus providing another equation of the above form. Another assumption is to suppose that an initial unit circle of radius "one undeformed belemnite,"

was deformed to an ellipse with the same area. The condition for this is that $ab = 1$. Using this, $a = 1.61$ and $b = 1/a = 0.62$. The ellipse, with lines representing the cleavage and belemnite, is shown in Fig. 5.1b. If the cleavage were normal to the plane of the drawing in Fig. 5.1a, the ellipse would be a principal section of the strain ellipsoid, the three-dimensional surface that would result from the homogeneous deformation of a spherical surface.

Interpretation of naturally deformed objects to yield the strain for some representative volume of rock has a large literature in structural geology. The volume of rock considered is kept sufficiently small so that the deformation may be approximated as homogeneous. Much systematic research has led to results of the type shown in Fig. 5.2, here for the ~10-km scale structures of the western Helvetic nappes of the Alpine orogen (Ramsay and Huber, 1987). Principal sections of strain ellipsoids that are approximately vertical are plotted in a vertical section through three stacked and folded sheets of sedimentary rock, called *nappes*, in the western Alps in Fig. 5.2. These give a synoptic picture of the deformation in the strongly deformed nappes. The distributions of their magnitude and orientation, simultaneously represented in this figure, may be used to think about the process of nappe emplacement. For example,

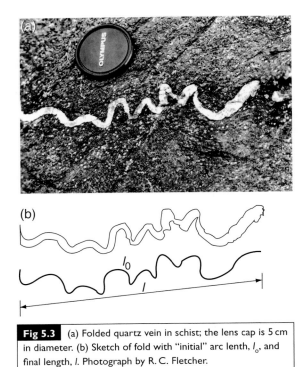

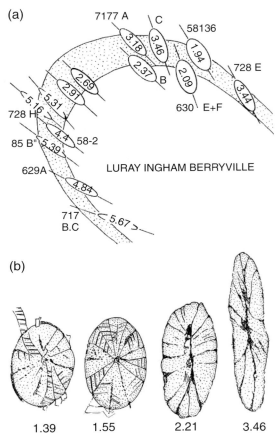

Fig 5.3 (a) Folded quartz vein in schist; the lens cap is 5 cm in diameter. (b) Sketch of fold with "initial" arc lenth, l_0, and final length, l. Photograph by R. C. Fletcher.

Fig 5.4 (a) Cross sections of the South Mountain Fold. Mean shapes of deformed oöids are given as the strike-normal section of the strain ellipsoid, its axial ratio, and its orientation. (b) Deformed oölite sections, with aspect ratios. Reprinted from Cloos (1971, Figs. 28 and 2) with permission of The Johns Hopkins University Press.

sliding or shearing of these vast rock masses, one upon the other, is indicated by the very large strains (large aspect ratio strain ellipses) present at the base of each nappe. Notice that the strain varies spatially. In the right-side-up strata at the upper part of the nappe, the strain is small to moderate, relative to the much larger strains near its base. The belemnite of Fig. 5.1 comes from a quarry at Leytron, Switzerland, just above the axial surface of the Morcles Nappe, at which the beds switch from overturned below to right-side-up above.

5.1.2 Other examples: folds and folded oölites

The quartz vein in Fig. 5.3 may be used to provide information on the strain in the rock containing it. The rock may have been deformed before the quartz vein formed, so the information pertains only to the subsequent deformation. If it is assumed the vein buckled into the folded form without changing its arc length, the final length l = 260/60" and the initial length l_0 = 370/60" give a ratio $l/l_0 = 0.70$. This ratio is less than one, and, also called a stretch, represents a contraction in the direction parallel to the line labeled l. If it is

maximum elongation occurred at right-angles to the contraction in the plane of the figure, and the area in the plane was unchanged in the deformation, the corresponding elongation would be the reciprocal of the above ratio, or 1.42, and this stretch refers to the material lines perpendicular to the line labeled l.

The horizontally flattened and vertically elongated oöids of Fig. 5.4b were initially approximately spherical in form. The folded layers in which the oöids occur, called oölites, were initially flat lying and uniformly thick. The vertical cross section of the fold illustrated in Fig. 5.4a (Cloos, 1947, 1971) shows the current traces of two layer interfaces. To change them to this form, a spatial distribution of relative motion between particles occurred. Each elliptical section in the figure represents the strain ellipse for some rock volume obtained by combining many oöid shape measurements, assuming homogeneous deformation over the sample area, and that these objects, as the belemnite in Fig. 5.1, underwent the same deformation as the rock. If oöids were stiffer than the matrix around them, they would have a strain less than that of the bulk rock. The numbers given are the long to short axial ratios, a quantitative measure of the strain. Since the initial ratio would have been unity for spherical oöids, a ratio of 4 represents an increase in the long diameter by a factor of 2 and a decrease in the short diameter by a factor of $\frac{1}{2}$.

Data on the distribution of the strain in the fold provide a constraint in addition to layer shape, on the deformation that took place. For example, we might suppose that the fold was formed when the rock layer was bent into a form of roughly a semi-circle with little change in thickness. The ratio of the diameter to the circumference of a semi-circle, $2/\pi$, would then correspond to the *bulk shortening* of the rock mass containing it. The square of the reciprocal of it, 2.46, might then correspond to an oöid axial ratio. This value falls within the range of ratios given. Since bending implies extension at the upper surface of the layer and contraction at the lower surface, and such a distribution is not indicated by the data, this model for the folding is not consistent with the deformation of the oölites.

The assumption that the oöids maintain constant volume allowed Cloos to determine that material lines normal to the plane of section kept their initial length (Cloos, 1947, 1971). The area of an ellipse is πab, where a and b are the lengths of the semi-axes, and $(4/3)\pi abc$ is the volume of an ellipsoid, where c is the length of the plane-normal semi-axis. Scale the dimensions so that $abc = a_0^3 = 1$, where $a_0 = 1$ is the radius of the initial sphere. Then, if $b = 1/a$, $c = 1$, and a material line in the normal direction has not changed its length.

5.1.3 Linear transformations

Consider the positions of particles, such as those that might lie in the bedding plane occupied by the belemnite of Fig. 5.1 in the initial and final states. We refer these positions to coordinate axes fixed in the bedding plane, with origin fixed to a particular particle, e.g. the tip of the belemnite. Under the postulate of homogeneous deformation, the final coordinates of a particle, x and y, may be related to its initial coordinates, denoted X and Y, by linear equations describing a linear transformation:

$$x = x(X, Y) = AX + BY$$
$$y = y(X, Y) = CX + DY \tag{5.3}$$

Here A, B, C, and D are constants. The mathematical statement $x = x(X, Y)$, where x occurs on both sides, is common in continuum mechanics and other branches of physics. The x on the left-hand side denotes the numerical value of the function x on the right-hand side for any pair of arguments X, Y. To use another letter means that our description will involve many additional letters and that we will have to keep track of what they refer to, e.g. if we had written $x = f(X, Y)$, we would have to remember that f went with x. This way, the expression is self-referential. The inverse transformation, between the final and initial positions, is:

$$X = X(x, y) = ax + by$$
$$Y = Y(x, y) = cx + dy \tag{5.4}$$

The constants a, b, c, and d may be expressed in terms of A, B, C, and D by solving (5.3) for X and Y and comparing coefficients. We obtain:

$$a = D/(AD - BC)$$
$$b = -B/(AD - BC)$$
$$c = -C/(AD - BC)$$
$$d = A/(AD - BC) \tag{5.5}$$

Likewise, we find:

$$A = d/(ad - bc)$$
$$B = -b/(ad - bc)$$
$$C = -c/(ad - bc)$$
$$D = a/(ad - bc) \tag{5.6}$$

The particle at the origin of coordinates stays there.

In a homogeneous transformation, a straight material line is transformed into another one with different position, length, and orientation. A unit circle in the undeformed state, $X^2 + Y^2 = 1$, is transformed into an ellipse. We used this result, with further assumptions, to draw a strain ellipse associated with the deformed belemnite. It should be clear, from the four constants required to obtain the full transformation, that the data afforded by this example is not sufficient to determine these and, hence, the initial positions of all particles that now lie on the strain ellipse. Later, we return to such transformations to study their properties in a more formal way.

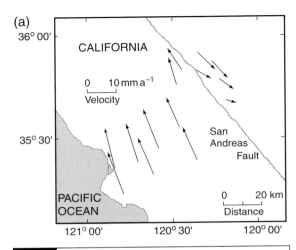

Fig 5.5 (a) Velocity vectors from geodetic measurements near the San Andreas Fault in central California (Harris and Segall, 1987).

5.2 | Evolving geometry of a structure: kinematic models, velocity models, and deformation

5.2.1 Geometric and kinematic models

We now consider forward models for the evolution of a structure in a deforming rock mass, such as the nappe structures in Fig. 5.2 or the folds in Figs. 5.3 or 5.4. We look at what sequence of steps this might involve, while continuing to avoid discussion of a complete physical description of the process. Instead, we focus on *geometric* and *kinematic* models, which include descriptions of the initial and current positions of particles, and of the motion of particles between the two states.

A first step in the study of a deformed or deforming structure is the geometric description of its form and internal structure. Topography is important in the description of an active mountain range or volcanic edifice because it both reflects and affects the dynamic process that created the structure and may continue to modify it. The description of the internal structure would include the configurations of surfaces such as layer or formation boundaries and fault surfaces or fault zones, the position, attitude, and form of minor folds, and so forth. A description of the belemnite of Fig. 5.1 would include details seen in the figure, but would involve a more precise and complete description as in a detailed map of the belemnite fragments, the intervening "veins," and the details of cleavage orientation in the surrounding rock. This is generally termed a description of the structure's geometry. It is more than that, because special significance is invariably attached to the features whose forms are documented, i.e. they are not merely abstract

geometric objects such as curved surfaces, triangles, or polyhedra. Without the significance attached to these objects, there would be little reason to painstakingly work out their forms and disposition in space. Only the final or current state of the body is described. We may imagine, or be able to reconstruct, an initial state.

A hypothetical picture of the continuous change in geometry between initial and final states might be conceived. Such a description would be termed a *geometric model* of the evolution of the form of the structure, as described, for example, by the changes in shape of the bed surfaces in Fig. 5.4a. In a *kinematic model*, the motions of all particles in the body between the initial and final states are described. If the observed final state and the imagined initial states are viewed as snapshots, a kinematic model may be compared to a movie showing all intervening states. Carrying the analogy a bit further, such a movie would not have a "sound track" that described the dynamics or causal elements of the process resulting in the motion and geometric evolution. To achieve a complete description of the process of formation of the structure, we must incorporate geometry and kinematics within a complete mechanical model.

5.2.2 Velocity fields

A description of the motion of particles, as in a kinematic model, at one instant of time is given

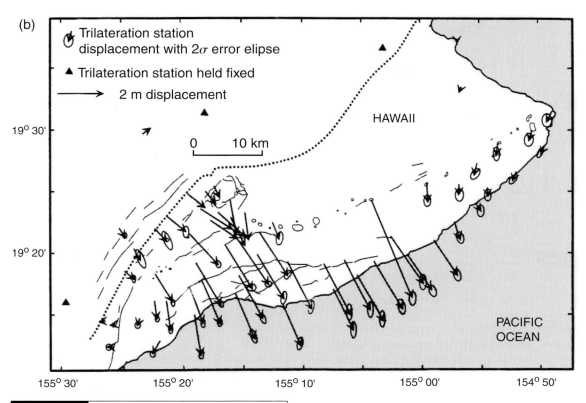

(b)

Trilateration station
displacement with 2σ error elipse

▲ **Trilateration station held fixed**

⟶ **2 m displacement**

0   10 km

HAWAII

19° 30'

19° 20'

PACIFIC
OCEAN

155° 30'   155° 20'   155° 10'   155° 00'   154° 50'

Fig 5.5 (cont.) (b) Horizontal displacement of monuments at the surface of Kilauea Volcano, HI (Delaney et al., 1998). The displacements, up to several meters, are small relative to the scale of the area. They represent motion over twenty years, so the greatest average velocity magnitude is about 20 cm a^{-1}.

by the velocity field. The velocity field is expressed in terms of the spatial distribution of the velocity vectors of particles currently occupying positions referred to a reference coordinate system.

Studies in *neotectonics* often start with the observation of such a velocity field. Precise repeated surveying of fixed monuments at the Earth's surface allows one to determine the current velocity distribution at Earth's surface (Segall and Harris, 1986). For example, the relative motion between two lithospheric plates (Fig. 5.5a) is determined from the relative changes in position of monuments on either plate over some interval of time (Harris and Segall, 1987; Murray et al., 2001; Murray and Segall, 2002). The motions of monuments distributed over the surface of a volcanic edifice (Fig. 5.5b) may be measured to monitor the influx of

magma from a deep source, motion of magma within the volcano, or other processes such as faulting (Delaney, 1990; Delaney et al., 1993, 1998).

Two lithospheric plates may move as nearly rigid bodies, the relative motion between them being taken up by adjustment at the plate boundary, generally over a zone of from tens to hundreds of kilometers in width. In the case of the volcanic edifice, the horizontal motions at the surface are seen to vary in a more or less continuous manner (Fig. 5.5b). To account for this, we may imagine a continuous distribution of motion within the edifice and its surroundings and this may lead to a detailed mechanical model of the edifice (Owen et al., 1995). Motions within the edifice are inferred, while those at the surface are measured, and serve to *constrain* the model. "Rigid plate" motions constrain models for the internal motions within the Earth and for the complex local motions in the plate boundary zones. They constrain, but do not determine such motions. In the geological literature, the word control is often used. The sense seems to be somewhere between

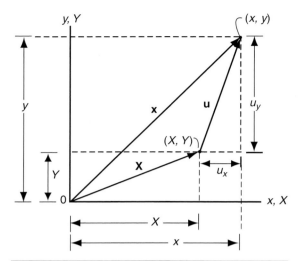

Fig 5.6 Initial and final position vectors, **X** and **x**, with components (X, Y) and (x, y). The displacement vector **u** has components $(u_x, u_y) = (x - X, y - Y)$.

constrain and determine, both of which, unlike control, have distinct and separate meanings.

The change in position of a monument over the time interval between two surveys is its *displacement*, the difference between the *final position* (during the final survey) and the *initial position* (during the first survey), as measured relative to some convenient reference frame. The components of displacement (Fig. 5.6) are:

$$u_x = x - X$$
$$u_y = y - Y \tag{5.7}$$

Dividing the displacement by the time interval yields an estimate for *velocity*. It is perhaps not suitable to do this if the motion was the result of a sudden seismogenic faulting event. Displacement and velocity are vectors. Since these quantities generally vary from monument to monument, and between them, they comprise *vector fields*. The study of these fields and of other derivative fields is called: "kinematics (1840): a branch of dynamics that deals with aspects of motion apart from considerations of mass and force" (*Webster's Ninth New Collegiate Dictionary*).

Discontinuous motion, as illustrated by plate motion, is familiar from observations of faulting, in which initially neighboring particles are displaced across the fault surface. When an entire fault surface, terminating within the rock mass is observed, it is seen that the discontinuous motion of particles along the surface is associated with a continuous distribution of motion within the surrounding rock.

In this chapter, we chiefly consider motion and deformation in two dimensions. This may be an adequate first approximation in structural geology and tectonics, as indicated by the geometry of the resulting structures. A mountain belt may span thousands of kilometers along strike, but only a few hundred kilometers in width. The approximation may work for the evolution of a single fold in a portion of a mountain belt, such as that in Fig. 5.7, or for a set of folds in an outcrop. Use of vertical cross sections or of down-plunge sections (Fig. 5.3 and 5.4) to illustrate roughly two-dimensional structure is based on this approximation.

Restriction to two dimensions results in simpler presentation of concepts and ease in obtaining results. Concepts are often more readily visualized and grasped. Fewer quantities are involved – two, rather than three, components of vectors, and four, rather than nine, components of second-rank tensors. Relations and graphical constructions can be carried out in two dimensions, so that, for example, true lengths and angles are represented, and we need only plane geometry. Many results can be obtained in closed form or by graphical construction.

On the other hand, to honor the geometry of structures, which may be determined to great accuracy and detail by modern surveying methods such as GPS, and to take the systematic study and interpretation of structures at all scales to a new level of refinement, it will be necessary to abandon the approximation of two dimensionality. In this book, we present and apply differential geometry as one step in this direction.

5.2.3 Deformation associated with the emplacement of an igneous pluton

An array of large batholiths, 50 to 100 km in diameter, intrude greenstone (metamorphosed volcanic and shallow intrusive rocks of intermediate to basic composition) and associated sediments (Fig. 5.8) in the Archean craton of Zimbabwe, southern Africa. Ramsay carried out a structural investigation of one of the smaller and more symmetrical structures, the Chindamora batholith

Fig 5.7 Map view of a segment of the South Mountain Anticline showing that the distribution of strain is roughly independent of position along strike, suggesting the validity of a two-dimensional approximation. Identical ellipses only indicate the trend of the long axis of the strain ellipse; the axial ratio in the cross section is plotted by each. Axial ratios are comparable in strike-parallel belts. Reprinted from Cloos (1971, Plate 1) with permission of The Johns Hopkins University Press.

(Ramsay, 1989). The *batholith* is zoned (Fig. 5.9a) in the order of intrusion, with the earliest intruded unit at its periphery. Ramsay determined the mean shapes of populations of *xenoliths* (Greek: foreign stones), consisting of fragments of the country rock, or of previously solidified intrusive units (cognate xenoliths). The distribution of xenolith shapes within the batholith is shown in Fig. 5.9b. More strongly flattened xenoliths are found in the earlier emplaced rocks and nearer the periphery. The exception, in both inward order of intrusion and presence of strongly flattened xenoliths, is the last-intruded western granite.

The initial forms of the xenoliths would have been irregular, but roughly equant, so we take the mean form as a sphere. The final form for a given local population of xenoliths averages out to a pancake-shaped ellipsoid with one short axis and two sub-equal long axes. Elliptical sections

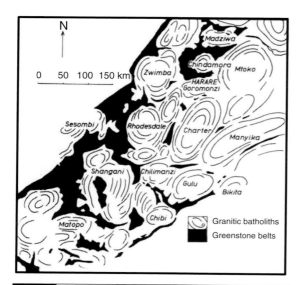

Fig 5.8 Array of batholiths in the Archean craton of Zimbabwe. Reprinted from Ramsay (1989) with permission from Elsevier.

showing the short and long axis are demonstrated for each population. All xenolith axial lengths are changed from their initial values.

Ramsay proposed an ingenious model to explain the shape variation of the xenoliths in the Chindamora batholith. The model addresses the radial increase of deformation outward and successive emplacement of magma at the batholith center. He supposed that the deformation of a xenolith begins when it is "captured" near the solidification front in mostly crystallized material that is strong, but still hot and plastic. The xenolith is then deformed with its host as further magma is injected into the center of the intrusion, inflating it. He presents a quantitative model of pluton inflation, which he treats as an expanding spherical or hemispherical body forcibly deforming the surrounding greenstone.

Inflation by means of magma supply from a dike-like or columnar conduit does not seem a plausible mechanism for the vast array of domical batholiths of the Zimbabwe greenstone belt. In an alternative model, an entire layer underlying the greenstone might have undergone melting or partial melting. Organized upwelling of domical masses of this layer might then have occurred (Fig. 5.8). Ramsay makes a suggestion along these lines

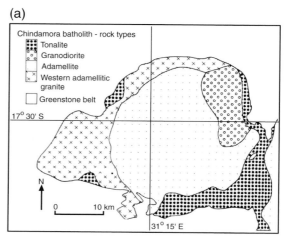

(a)

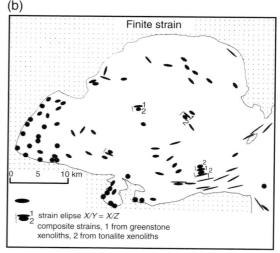

(b)

Fig 5.9 (a) Compositional zoning of the Chindamora batholith. (b) Distribution of representative elliptical sections for local populations of xenoliths. Where two sections are shown, the one with greater eccentricity is for country rock xenoliths embedded in xenoliths of the prior solidified magmatic phase, that with smaller eccentricity is for the cognate xenoliths. Reprinted from Ramsay (1989) with permission from Elsevier.

and the hemispherical inflation model then approximates the flow within the domes (Ramsay, 1989).

5.2.4 Inflation of a spherical shell: a kinematic model

Consider the inflation of a spherical shell, or hollow sphere. Inflation would be attributed to the action of an internal pressure, but we are not presently interested in the causal mechanism. By symmetry, the inflation, although of a three-dimensional object, is mathematically one dimensional, depending only on radius. The object is the volume contained between two concentric spherical surfaces. We may readily grasp the nature of the deformation from Fig. 5.10a. Focus on two bounding spherical surfaces, with initial radii R and R_1. Let R_1 be the radius of the surface occupied by the xenolith when it starts to deform and R be a nearby radius in the solid shell. The shell is assumed to have the same volume after deformation, when its inner and outer radii are r_1 and r, respectively. Then:

$$\frac{4}{3}\pi(r^3 - r_1^3) = \frac{4}{3}\pi(R^3 - R_1^3),$$
$$\text{or} \quad r^3 - r_1^3 = R^3 - R_1^3 \tag{5.8}$$

Since we are concerned with the deformation of the xenolith, a body of very small dimensions relative to the pluton, we let $R = R_1 + \Delta R$. Since $\Delta R \ll R$ and $\Delta r \ll r$, we can throw out terms in which ΔR or Δr are squared or cubed. For example:

$$r^3 - r_1^3 = (r_1 + \Delta r)^3 - r_1^3$$
$$= r_1^3 + 3r_1^2\Delta r + 3r_1(\Delta r)^2 + (\Delta r)^3 - r_1^3$$
$$\cong 3r_1^2\Delta r \tag{5.9}$$

With such approximation, substitution into (5.8) yields:

$$r_1^2\Delta r \cong R_1^2\Delta R, \quad \text{or} \quad \frac{\Delta r}{\Delta R} \cong \frac{R_1^2}{r_1^2} \tag{5.10}$$

Written in terms of infinitesimal quantities, the relation is exact:

$$\frac{dr}{dR} = \frac{R_1^2}{r_1^2} \tag{5.11}$$

To describe the deformation of the xenolith, consider the small elements shown in Fig. 5.10a. Since we have not described how to treat the deformation of a sphere to an ellipsoid we take a somewhat rougher approach. Suppose the initial spherical xenolith is just enclosed by the element. Then the ratio of the element's dimensions must be unity, or:

$$\frac{dR}{R_1 d\theta} = 1 \tag{5.12}$$

In the final state, we suppose the element just encloses an ellipsoid with long and short principal

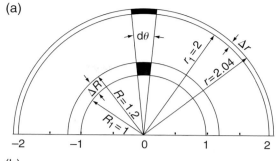

(a)

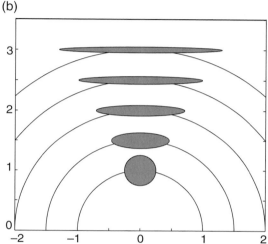

(b)

Fig 5.10 (a) Expanding sphere (or hemisphere) model for pluton emplacement (Ramsay, 1989). (b) Elliptical principal cross sections of initial spheres with ratio of final radius to radius at incorporation.

semi-axes, a and c:

$$\frac{dr}{r_1 d\theta} = \frac{2c}{2a} = \frac{c}{a} \tag{5.13}$$

Eliminating $d\theta$ between these:

$$\frac{c}{a} = \frac{dr}{dR}\frac{R_1}{r_1} \tag{5.14}$$

Substitution from (5.11) gives the desired result:

$$\left(\frac{c}{a}\right)^{1/3} = \frac{R_1}{r_1} \tag{5.15}$$

This states that the current position of the xenolith, r_1, and its shape, given by the ratio c/a, determine the initial position, R_1. Xenolith cross sections for values $r_1/R_1 = 1$, 1.5, 2, 2.5, and 3 are shown in Fig. 5.10b.

How may this description of a single xenolith be used to support or refute the notion that the

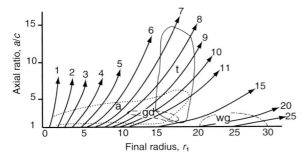

Fig 5.11 Plot of xenolith axial ratio, a/c, versus final radius, r_1, for the Chindamora pluton. Data symbols refer to t, tonalite; gd, granodiorite; a, adamellite; wg, western granite. Reprinted from Ramsay (1989) with permission from Elsevier.

mechanism of pluton emplacement is ballooning? Ramsay plots the axial ratio, a/c, versus the final radius of the corresponding xenolith population (Fig. 5.11). The points are scattered, but lie in relatively localized regions. If the capture radius, R_1, is used as a parameter, each value of it corresponds to a curve in r_1, a/c-space. Only certain of these curves will sweep through the regions for each intrusive rock type. The range in values of R_1 for these curves then corresponds to the position of the partial solidification front at which the xenolith is frozen into the expanding plastic shell.

The model of an inflating pluton with spherical symmetry is a *kinematic model* because it prescribes the motion of the particles within the body from the initial to final states. No information is required beyond the spherical symmetry during inflation, and the concept of a variable radius at which xenoliths are incorporated into the deforming shell. Given the fit between the strain data from the field and the model relation (Fig. 5.11), the model is a viable one. Can you propose further tests of it?

5.2.5 Internal deformation in a rising spherical diaper

A second model of *pluton* emplacement has been popular for over fifty years (Grout, 1945; Whitehead and Luther, 1975). Earlier studies used laboratory models and the principles of model scaling (Hubbert, 1937) discussed in Chapter 4. The model consists of the rise of an approximately spherical mass of viscous fluid, representing the pluton, in another viscous fluid, representing hot, plastic

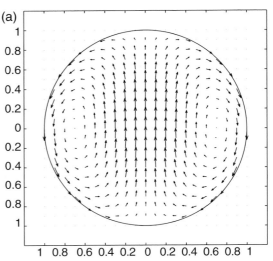

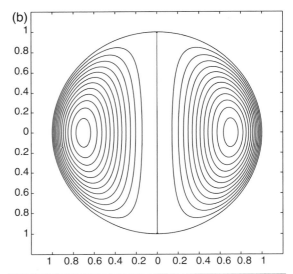

Fig 5.12 A buoyant viscous sphere rising in a viscous fluid (Lamb, 1945). (a) Velocity vectors. (b) Streamlines followed by particles. Surfaces across which particles do not move, and within which the fluid is confined during the rise, are toroidal, like the external surface of a donut; the traces of several such surfaces are shown.

country rock. The model has also been used to simulate the rise of hot, buoyant diapirs, or mantle plumes, through the mantle (Anderson, 1975; Whitehead and Luther, 1975; Ribe and Christensen, 1999).

This model is not simply a kinematic model, as the explicit involvement of materials of well-characterized behavior and properties, i.e. viscosity and density, η and ρ, and the acceleration of gravity, g, indicates. As we shall see, the velocity field, although expressed by (5.19), is not easy to conceive of in an ad hoc manner.

The remarkable solution of Stokes for a rigid sphere rising or sinking in a viscous fluid was modified by others to treat the rise of a *viscous sphere* (Lamb, 1945). A sphere of viscous fluid with density ρ_1, intrusion viscosity η_1, and radius R will rise in a viscous medium with density ρ and viscosity η if the density difference, $\rho - \rho_1$, is positive. Experiment and theory show that the sphere maintains its shape if the rate of rise is slow enough (Fig. 5.12). We use the results to illustrate the motion within the sphere, but specifically to determine the deformation within it and internal structures that might form between initial and final states, separated by an interval of rise.

The steady, or time-independent, rate of rise of the sphere is:

$$V = \frac{2}{3}\left[\frac{(\rho - \rho_1)gR^2}{\eta}\right]\left[\frac{(\eta + \eta_1)}{(2\eta + 3\eta_1)}\right] \quad (5.16)$$

You are likely to be familiar with the special case of a rigid sphere, $\eta_1 \to \infty$, sinking in a viscous fluid, which may be used to estimate the rate of settling of sediment particles in water:

$$V = \frac{2}{9}\left[\frac{(\rho - \rho_1)gR^2}{\eta}\right] \quad (5.17)$$

The other limiting case applies, for example, to the rise of a gas bubble, $\eta_1 \to 0$, in a viscous fluid such as a basaltic magma:

$$V = \frac{1}{3}\left[\frac{(\rho - \rho_1)gR^2}{\eta}\right] \quad (5.18)$$

The speed of rising or sinking only varies by a factor of 3/2 in going from a rigid sphere (5.17) to one that has low viscosity relative to its surroundings, $\eta_1/\eta \ll 1$, (5.18).

Position within the sphere is referred to Cartesian coordinates that are fixed at its center, with coordinate x in the vertical direction of motion, and y and z in the horizontal plane. As the flow continues, these positions will be occupied by different particles. We may continue to think of the spatial coordinates x, y, and z as giving the current position of a particle which occupied an initial position with coordinates X, Y, and Z. We may not be able to specify the initial coordinates usefully.

By symmetry, particles in the sphere move in vertical planes through its center, so that it will suffice to consider a description confined to one of these planes, the (x, y)-plane. Accordingly, the mathematical dependence of the solution is two dimensional. The velocity of a particle, referred to the spatial coordinates, is independent of time. The components of velocity, v_x and v_y, are:

$$v_x = -C\left[2\left(\frac{r}{R}\right)^2 - \left(\frac{x}{R}\right)^2 - 1\right], \quad v_y = C\left(\frac{xy}{r^2}\right) \quad (5.19)$$

where

$$r = \sqrt{(x^2 + y^2)}, \quad C = \frac{1}{3}\left[\frac{(\rho - \rho_1)gR^2}{2\eta + 3\eta_1}\right]$$

The velocity field can be represented by the *stream function*, a scalar quantity whose contours are the *streamlines* (Fig. 5.12b):

$$\Psi(x, y) = C\left[1 - \left(\frac{r}{R}\right)^2\right]r^2\sin^2\theta, \quad \sin\theta = \frac{y}{r} \quad (5.20)$$

Here θ is the angle in the section from the horizontal. In the figure, contours of the stream function at equal interval are plotted. The velocity vector (Fig. 5.12a) is tangent to the streamlines and the speed, or magnitude of the velocity vector, is inversely proportional to the contour spacing. Thus, the maximum speed, relative to an origin at the center of the sphere, occurs at the surface of the sphere at its "equator." Because the flow within the sphere is steady in a reference frame with origin at the sphere center, particles remain on the streamlines as the sphere rises. The steady internal motion is driven by the same steady rate of recovery of gravitational potential energy that drives the rise of the sphere. The external flow is also steady if referred to the coordinate system rising with the sphere.

To determine the final, or current, position of any particle in the sphere, for a given initial position, we must follow it over the course of the interval of rise using the relations (5.19). This is done numerically, since, while the velocity at any position is constant, particles move along paths through the sphere along which the velocity changes. If $x(t; X, Y)$ and $y(t; X, Y)$ are the coordinates of the current position of a particle that occupied position with coordinates X and Y at time $t = 0$:

$$x(0; X, Y) = X$$
$$y(0; X, Y) = Y$$ (5.21)

The position at a small increment of time Δt later is:

$$x(t + \Delta t; X, Y)$$
$$= x(t; X, Y) + v_x[x(t; X, Y), y(t; X, Y)]\Delta t$$
$$y(t + \Delta t; X, Y)$$ (5.22)
$$= y(t; X, Y) + v_y[x(t; X, Y), y(t; X, Y)]\Delta t$$

For certain motions, possibly even in the present case, this equation, or its equivalent, may be integrated in closed form. Here, however, we assign Δt a small but finite value, advance the particle to its new position, and repeat this process many times to achieve the desired result.

It is most convenient to refer the interval between initial and final states to the amount of rise of the sphere, expressed in units of its radius, R. The amount of rise is Vt, but from (5.16) and (5.19):

$$\frac{V}{C} = \frac{2(\eta + \eta_1)}{\eta} \cong 2$$ (5.23)

The intrusion viscosity, η_1, is much less than that of the country rock, η. Time will be expressed in units such that we may set $C = 1$ in (5.19). In unit time, the sphere will rise by an amount equal to its diameter, $2R$.

Figure 5.13 shows the deformed state of a grid whose intersection points correspond to the final positions of a set of particles that initially lay at the intersection points of the square grid in the figure after a rise of one sphere radius. The deformed grid lines are constructed by connecting grid points with straight segments. To a good approximation, the line segments in the final state correspond to the material lines connecting grid points in the initial state, because the grid elements are small enough.

As another example, Fig. 5.14b shows the final positions and forms of an array of material circles in the initial state (Fig. 5.14a) after rise of one sphere diameter. The circles may be interpreted as sections of initially spherical surfaces. Provided an initial circle is infinitesimally small,

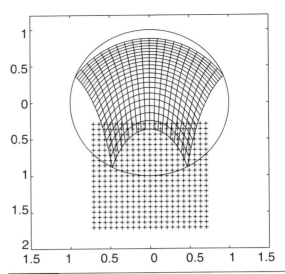

Fig 5.13 A buoyant viscous sphere rising in a viscous fluid (Lamb, 1945). Initial square grid of particles in vertical diametral plane of sphere and deformed grid after a sphere rise of one radius.

the three-dimensional surface in the deformed state is an ellipsoid. The sections look only approximately like ellipses because of their large size. The distribution of deformation, with more flattened forms outward and with long dimensions concentrically oriented is similar to that of deformed xenoliths in the Chindamora pluton (Fig. 5.9) or the model for it (Fig. 5.10b).

This result suggests that the rising sphere model might provide an alternative to the inflating intrusion model. However, this would not seem to be supported by the roughly concentric pattern of intrusive rock types in that pluton. In this model, a concentric pattern can be produced. Consider a set of equally spaced horizontal surfaces in the initial state (Fig. 5.15a). After a rise equal to the sphere diameter, these surfaces are deformed into those shown in Fig. 5.15b. The entire surfaces are formed by spinning this section around the vertical axis. If the magma body had developed a layered compositional sequence prior to its rise, then something resembling a concentric distribution of magma types might arise. The process of multiple injection proposed by Ramsay is supported by his observations. It is not clear, however, that multiple injection occurs by intrusion into the center of an expanding spherical or

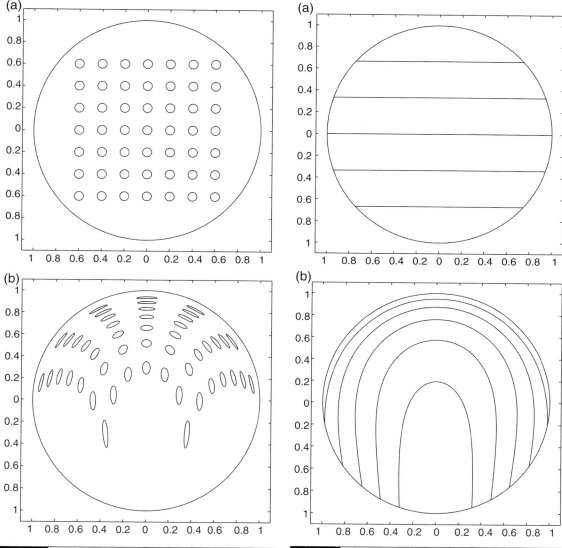

Fig 5.14 A buoyant viscous sphere rising in a viscous fluid (Lamb, 1945). (a) Initial array of circular material lines in vertical diametral plane of sphere. (b) Deformed final state array after rise of one sphere diameter.

Fig 5.15 A buoyant viscous sphere rising in a viscous fluid (Lamb, 1945). (a) Initial traces of equally spaced horizontal material planes. (b) Deformed traces after rise of sphere of one diameter.

hemispherical volume, and a scheme adapted to a rising sub-spherical intrusion might be worked out. In any case, the more elaborate model should follow Stokes' example and use a complete mechanics.

Thinning of the "wall rock" at the top of the sphere can be determined from the Stokes model. A *boundary condition* was imposed in the model that required the fluids to stick at their interface.

Thus, the stretching of a thin layer at the margin of the "intrusion" must be the same as that of a thin layer in the adjacent "wall rock." The thinning shown by the deformed initial spheres near the surface must substantially under-estimate the thinning at the contact with the overlying fluid medium, since a large fraction of this has been greatly thinned to make room for the material represented by the grid. To estimate the thinning at the contact, we use a method similar to that used to find the ratio of deformed ellipsoid axes in the spherical shell model.

Consider a pill-shaped element of material whose upper surface coincides with the surface of the sphere at its apex. The element is taken to be sufficiently small that the surface of the intrusion is approximated by the horizontal tangent plane. In the initial state, before any rise of the sphere, the radius of the pill is δY and its thickness is δX. The volume of the pill is $\delta V = \pi(\delta Y)^2 \delta X$. After some amount of rise, in the final state, the radius and thickness of the pill are δy and δx, and its volume is $\delta v = \pi(\delta y)^2 \delta x$. Since the volumes are equal, $\delta y / \delta Y = (\delta x / \delta X)^{1/2}$. The final form of the pill may be found by tracking the position of the particle with initial position $(R, \delta Y)$ on the tangent plane, or with initial position $(R - \delta X, 0)$ on the vertical axis of the sphere. For the former, the velocity away from the center point is:

$$v_y(R, \delta y) = \frac{d}{dt}(\delta y) = \frac{C\delta y}{R}, \quad \text{or} \quad \frac{d(\delta y)}{\delta y} = \frac{C}{R}dt \quad (5.24)$$

Integration from $t = 0$, and between the limits δY and δy corresponding to the initial and final positions of the particle at the end of the pill diameter, yields:

$$\ln\left(\frac{\delta y}{\delta Y}\right) = \left(\frac{C}{R}\right)t^*, \quad \text{so} \quad \frac{\delta y}{\delta Y} = \exp\left[\left(\frac{C}{R}\right)t^*\right] \quad (5.25)$$

Here t^* is the time of rise yielding the desired horizontal stretching of the pill-shaped element. A reduction in pill thickness by a factor of 0.1 corresponds to an increase in pill radius of $\sqrt{10} \cong 3.2$, or:

$$\left(\frac{C}{R}\right)t^* = \ln\left(\sqrt{10}\right) \cong 1.15 \quad (5.26)$$

The distance of rise of the sphere is:

$$\Delta x^* = Vt^* = V\left[1.15\left(\frac{R}{C}\right)\right] \quad (5.27)$$

Using (5.23), the amount of rise of the sphere is $\Delta x = 2.3R$, or slightly more that its entire diameter.

The Stokes model for the rise of a sphere in a ductily deforming (viscous) medium thus provides a rich source of potential interpretations of features of a pluton, such as included xenoliths, deformed internal contacts, and the stretching of the surrounding country rock. If these features conform to the predictions of the model, they serve to support it. If they do not, a markedly different model must then be formulated. Either outcome would advance our knowledge of the process of pluton emplacement.

5.3 | Relation between deformation and velocity fields

5.3.1 Chevron folds

The folds, seen in cross section in Fig. 5.16, are called *chevron folds* because of their straight limbs and narrow, sharp hinges (Ryan and Smith, 1998). A chevron is composed of two "stripes" that meet at a sharp angle with the apex generally up, as seen in insignia of rank on military uniforms. Prominent quartz veins, in the form of "saddle reefs" occur at the crests of the folds. Many more veins are present, including those along the limbs and parallel to bedding, and in fault zones whose location appears to be controlled in part by the prior presence of the fold structure. Important, also, is the remarkable dike that is emplaced along the hinge surface of the anticline. The quartz veins contain high-grade gold ore, so that the process that formed them and determined their distribution is of much commercial interest. Here we consider how the folds might have formed.

Evidence for slip between layers in the form of *slickenlines* is found in association with the bed-parallel quartz veins. Slipping layers generally consist of many individual beds and are ~10 m in thickness. The length of the fold limbs in the example from Bendigo, Australia (Ryan and Smith, 1998), is about 300 to 400 m or more, so that the ratio of the thickness of a slip-surface bounded layer to limb length is less than 1/100. The representative bedding traces shown in the cross sections do not show all interfaces on which slip has occurred; they are accurately drawn from data collected in the mine. Not all chevron folds show evidence for slip (Fig. 5.17), but it is commonly enough observed in this fold type to be viewed as characteristic.

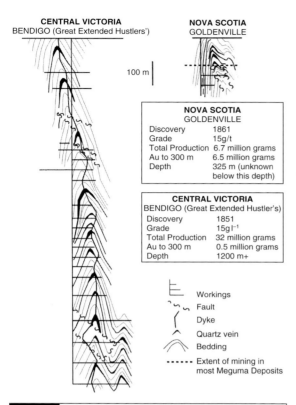

CENTRAL VICTORIA
BENDIGO (Great Extended Hustlers')

NOVA SCOTIA
GOLDENVILLE

100 m

NOVA SCOTIA GOLDENVILLE	
Discovery	1861
Grade	15g/t
Total Production	6.7 million grams
Au to 300 m	6.5 million grams
Depth	325 m (unknown below this depth)

CENTRAL VICTORIA BENDIGO (Great Extended Hustler's)	
Discovery	1851
Grade	15g l^{-1}
Total Production	32 million grams
Au to 300 m	0.5 million grams
Depth	1200 m+

Workings
Fault
Dyke
Quartz vein
Bedding
----- Extent of mining in most Meguma Deposits

Fig 5.16 Chevron folds as seen in mine sections from Bendigo, Victoria, Australia, and Goldenville, Nova Scotia. Reprinted from Ryan and Smith (1998) with permission from Elsevier.

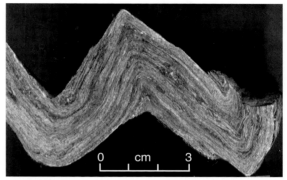

Fig 5.17 Chevron folds in phyllite–arenite layers, Poudre Canyon, Colorado. Photograph by R. C. Fletcher.

A second feature observed in the Bendigo fold is *cleavage* (Ryan and Smith, 1998). Cleavage is present in both the stiff graywacke sandstone layers and the interbedded softer metamorphosed pelitic rocks. Briefly, cleavage is a fine-scaled, structure – often called a fabric – that is pervasive, with features such as: (i) a strong planar alignment of platy mineral grains, such as micas; (ii) small-scale "crinkles," which may themselves have the aspect of chevron folds, formed in rocks possessing a prior strong orientation of the sort just mentioned, which may first form in the compaction of a clay-rich sediment (shale); or (iii) planar alignment of grains whose flattened shape is due to the deformation of the rock itself; or (iv) discrete, sub-parallel surfaces of dissolution, often indicated by build up of insoluble residue such as clay in limestone, referred to as *solution seams*.

The presence of these and other features results in a tendency for the rock to split more easily along surfaces parallel to the cleavage – hence, the name. Cleavage is inferred to lie normal to the direction of maximum shortening in the rock mass. In many cases, this inference is supported by direct evidence in the form of bodies of known initial shape now flattened in the plane of cleavage; an example is (iii).

Chevron folds are common in sequences of strata made up of thick "stiff" or "strong" sandstone layers separated by thin "soft" or "weak" shale layers, or their metamorphosed equivalents. In our discussion of postulated or actual rock properties, pairs of terms like stiff and soft, or strong and weak, are relative, and, often, as here, do not refer to an explicit type of material behavior, such as elasticity or viscous flow. Later, we do introduce this specificity and quantitative precision. Also, with regard to dimensions of rock bodies, we will often use the terms "large and small" or "thin and thick" in the same relative sense. That is, a dimension of the object under discussion, such as layer thickness, has two or more values, among which relations such as layer A is thick (thin, sub-equal) relative to layer B may be stated. They are also seen in folding at a much smaller scale (Fig. 5.17). The chevron fold form is so common and striking, apart from its association with gold deposits, that structural geologists have been inspired to develop models for the folding process and fold evolution from an initial state.

Because a structural geologist can observe the final structure, and can infer the initial form of the rock mass involved, kinematic models are popular. A suite of structures may be available from which stages in the development of the structure may be inferred. A kinematic model is formulated in three steps.

1. The geometry of the component elements of the structure, here the individual layers between slip surfaces, is idealized, providing a *geometric model*.
2. From the geometric model, a procedure for approximating the form of the structure throughout its evolution is devised: an *evolutionary model*.
3. Finally, consistent with the evolutionary model, a set of particle motions is devised to provide the motion and *deformation* of all individual rock elements within the structure. This is the *kinematic model* proper.

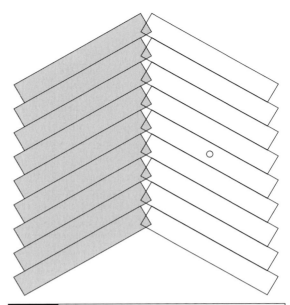

Fig 5.18 De Sitter (1964) model for chevron folding. The small circle on the right limb is the location of an imaginary "pin" that acts as the center of rotation for this layer.

5.3.2 Models for chevron folds

Most characteristic of chevron folds are long straight limbs in relation to narrow, tight hinges. An explanation for both features is required, though one might expect that the explanation for one might provide that for the other complementary feature. What we mean by explanation in this case is detailed answers to questions such as: "How do these features come about? What conditions and circumstances are involved? What must be the mechanical behavior of the rock layers and their interfaces?"

While natural chevron folds have variable layer thickness and form of individual limbs and hinges, those of Fig. 5.16 and 5.17 show regularity in layer thickness. Those in Fig. 5.16 also show a remarkable persistence in form in the vertical direction. In the geometric models for chevron folds that we consider, these two regularities are idealized: (i) fold limbs continue vertically without change in horizontal span or limb dip; and (ii) all layers making up a fold limb have the same thickness. A third idealization is that the fold limbs are straight and the hinge regions are narrow. In the evolutionary models for chevron folding considered here, this idealization, present in the folds observed in nature, is carried back to

all earlier, lower limb dip stages. This reflects a lack of any better understanding of how such a form might arise. The requirement of original "seed folds" present in the layered material is physically unrealistic, but in the evolutionary model, they are taken to be present.

We examine two kinematic models for chevron folds that are based on different *mechanisms of folding*. In a model first proposed by the structural geologist L. U. De Sitter (1964), the fold hinges are assumed to be broken, so the folding mechanism consists solely of the sliding and rotation of the rigid layers in each fold limb. A set of folds of very low limb dip, with broken hinges and straight limbs, is postulated as an initial state. A model fold produced in this manner is shown in Fig. 5.18. Following the geometric idealization, all layers have equal thickness. The fold is also taken to be symmetrical across the axial surface. The kinematics of a single fold limb of this type is also sometimes referred to as that of a *bookshelf model*, because it is similar to what ideally happens when support is taken away from a set of slightly tilted books on a flat surface, and the books slide in concert. In this version of the model, which differs somewhat from the original De Sitter model, the gaps opened up at the broken hinges are exactly compensated by interpenetrations between layers. If, instead of physically impossible interpenetration, the layer ends are dissolved and the material deposited in the gaps, both processes allowed by the presence of pore water and the slowness of the folding process, structures somewhat like the "saddle reefs" seen in the fold in Fig. 5.16 are produced. De Sitter's aim in "breaking" the layers was to produce gaps of this sort. However, he "backed the layers away," so that they only touched at single points, there was no interpenetration, and the gaps were larger.

In a second model, no slip between layers in the fold limbs occurs. An initial "seed" fold is flattened homogeneously to produce a fold with larger limb dips. An example of such flattening is shown in Fig. 5.19b, in which the "seed" fold is that in Fig. 5.19a. The shapes of some of the folds in Fig. 5.19b approximate those of the individual layers in the chevron fold in Fig. 5.16. Note, however, that these folds are not developed in a stack of layers. In this model, continuity of the layers through the hinges as seen in Fig. 5.16 is maintained. In Fig. 5.20, the model is used to tighten an initial chevron fold with lower limb dip.

We now analyze the particle motions in the two models. The first model accounts for the presence of slip surfaces seen in many, but not all, chevron folds. Since the layers are rigid, it does not account for the presence of cleavage in them. Conversely, the second model accounts for the presence of cleavage, and leads to an orientation of cleavage parallel to the axial plane of the fold, but it does not account for inter-layer slip. We may combine the two mechanisms to provide a kinematic model for chevron folds in which both observed features are present.

5.3.3 De Sitter model: rotation of and slip of rigid layers

The De Sitter model for chevron folding (De Sitter, 1964) is remarkably simple – but at the expense of whatever complication must really go on in the region of the fold hinges! This complication can be dealt with in several ways, one of which has been described. The fold limbs rotate as the span of the limb, S, normal to the axial plane of the fold, is reduced (Fig. 5.21a). Only a single limb is

(a)
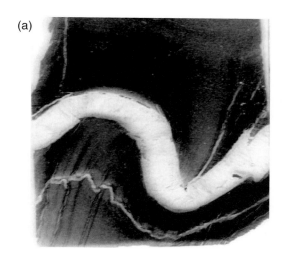

(b)
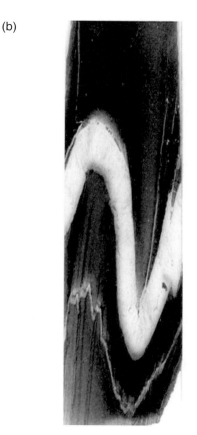

Fig 5.19 (a) Folded fibrous calcite veins in limey shale; sample width ~2 cm. (b) The image in (a) has been flattened in the horizontal direction by a factor of 1/2, and extended in a vertical direction by a factor of 2. This illustrates the "folding mechanism" of the second kinematic model. Photograph by R. C. Fletcher.

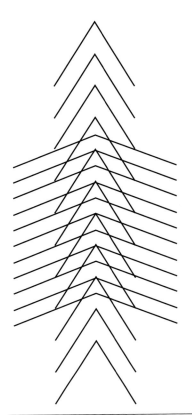

Fig 5.20 Chevron fold obtained by flattening a chevron fold of smaller limb dip; the amount of flattening is the same as that in Fig. 5.19b.

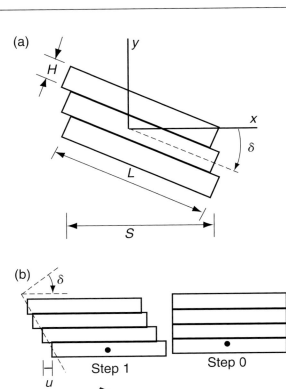

Fig 5.21 (a) Rotation of stack of layers of length, L, and thickness, H, through angle, δ. (b) Two-step procedure for forming a chevron fold limb by the De Sitter model (De Sitter, 1964).

shown here. Limb length, L, does not change; the layer thickness is H. The layer centered at the origin of coordinates is supposed to be "pinned" at this position. This artifice is necessary to provide a reference point from which the relative motions of other particles in the fold limb can be determined. The pinned particle stays where it is during folding. This definition of a reference point or coordinate origin is generally necessary in thinking about motion and deformation.

At limb dip δ:

$$S = L\cos\delta \qquad (5.28)$$

A measure of the progress of folding might be the limb dip itself, or the shortening of the span of the limb, S. The relation (5.28) yields an initial span S_0 for the initial value δ_0. With folding, S decreases from its initial value S_0, and a dimensionless measure of the change is:

$$\frac{S}{S_0} = \frac{\cos\delta}{\cos\delta_0} \qquad (5.29)$$

Since the absolute scale of the structure has no significance this measure seems a good choice. S/S_0 is a measure of *bulk strain*, since it gives the reduction in the horizontal dimension of the fold limb, and its inverse, the increase of an initial segment of the limb in its vertical dimension. But S/S_0 does not conform to a proper definition of strain in terms of initial and final lengths of a *material line*, because S and S_0 are not the final and initial lengths of the same material element.

Since the layers are rigid in the model, a material line element within an individual layer does not change its length and no such element undergoes strain. It will be useful to formulate a concept of bulk strain for the fold limb as a whole.

A rock mass cut by numerous faults may undergo a *bulk strain* for a set of displacements on the faults. The present model affords a simple example of such a situation, the "faults" being the layer-parallel or bed-parallel slip surfaces. Since rock bodies may deform by the relative motion of many approximately rigid elements, down to individual grains or grain fragments, this concept of bulk strain has many applications. In the present case, the slip across each interface is:

$$u = -H(\tan\delta - \tan\delta_0) \tag{5.30}$$

Here δ_0 is the initial dip of the "seed fold." The negative sign is adopted because the fold limb of Fig. 5.21a may be produced from the unfolded configuration by first sliding each layer above the pinned layer at the origin to the left by this amount and then rotating the whole limb by $-\delta$. The physics convention is that a positive rotation is counterclockwise (Fig. 5.21b).

We now seek a description of the two-dimensional deformation that corresponds to the De Sitter chevron fold model:

$$
\begin{aligned}
x &= x(X, Y)\\
y &= y(X, Y)
\end{aligned} \tag{5.31}
$$

The description (5.31) will be developed using the fixed coordinate axes of Fig. 5.21 to which initial and final coordinates will be referred. Since the layers rotate about axes parallel to z and particles move in cross-sectional planes of constant z we have $z = Z$. The particle at the origin remains there:

$$
\begin{aligned}
x(0, 0) &= 0\\
y(0, 0) &= 0
\end{aligned} \tag{5.32}
$$

If (5.31) is to be specified for all particles in the body for the rigid layer model, called the De Sitter model, they must be specified for each and every layer, since the slip between layers means that these functions cannot be continuous functions of initial position. This could be done in a compact form by identifying the pair of functions for each

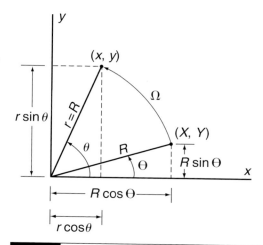

Fig 5.22 Rigid-body rotation about the origin through the positive, anticlockwise angle $\Omega = \theta - \Theta$.

layer with the Y-coordinate of its center point. For the nth layer upward, this would be nH, and downward, $-nH$. To avoid such complexity, at least initially, let us agree to find the functions (5.31) that apply only to the particles located on the centerlines of the layers. For these particles, the functions may be written as though the particle displacements were continuous. We thus obtain a description of the bulk deformation of the fold limb.

We write down continuous functions that capture exactly the initial and final positions of the particles on the mid-planes. These are most easily found by consulting Fig. 5.21b and combining the results for the two steps. Coordinates of the intermediate positions are:

$$x^{(1)} = X + \left(\frac{u}{H}\right)Y = X - (\tan\delta)Y \tag{5.33}$$

$$y^{(1)} = Y$$

A positive anticlockwise rotation about an axis through the origin by an angle Ω results in new particle coordinates (Fig. 5.22):

$$
\begin{aligned}
x &= X\cos\Omega - Y\sin\Omega\\
y &= X\sin\Omega + Y\cos\Omega
\end{aligned} \tag{5.34}
$$

Recall the expression of x and y in terms of the angle θ between the positive x-axis and the radius r or the distance between the origin and the position (x, y):

$$x = r\cos\theta, \quad y = r\sin\theta$$
$$X = R\cos\Theta, \quad Y = R\sin\Theta \tag{5.35}$$

But, from Fig. 5.22:

$$\theta = \Theta + \Omega, \quad r = R \text{ so}$$
$$x = R\cos(\Theta + \Omega)$$
$$= \cos\Omega(R\cos\Theta) - \sin\Omega(R\sin\Theta) \tag{5.36}$$
$$= X\cos\Omega - Y\sin\Omega$$

The expression for y is similarly derived. To carry out the second step, we substitute for the initial coordinates X and Y in (5.34) the intermediate coordinates $x^{(1)}$ and $y^{(1)}$ of (5.33) for the rotation $\Omega = -\delta$, yielding:

$$x = (X - Y\tan\delta)\cos\delta + Y\sin\delta = X\cos\delta$$

$$y = -(X - Y\tan\delta)\sin\delta + Y\cos\delta \tag{5.37}$$

$$= -X\sin\delta + Y\left(\frac{1}{\cos\delta}\right)$$

These continuous functions give the final positions of mid-plane particles but not the positions of particles off the mid-planes (Fig. 5.23). A material line of length L_0 is set out in the initial state. In the final state, this has been cut up into a series of segments that are inclined at the same angle to the layer surfaces and whose aggregate length is L_0. The continuous medium approximation to the deformed line is the straight line through the mid-points of length L. The ratio L/L_0 is a measure of the strain of this line. On the other hand, the measure of bulk shortening S/S_0 cannot be identified as the deformation of a material line in this manner.

The relations (5.37) may be written:

$$x = F_{xx}X + F_{xy}Y$$
$$y = F_{yx}X + F_{yy}Y$$
$$F_{xx} = \cos\delta, \quad F_{xy} = 0 \tag{5.38}$$
$$F_{yx} = -\sin\delta, \quad F_{yy} = \frac{1}{\cos\delta}$$

This *homogeneous linear transformation* describes the homogeneous deformation of the fold limb. Homogeneous refers to the fact that $F_{xx}, F_{yx}, \ldots,$ are independent of X and Y, and linear to the fact that the initial coordinates enter linearly. As is shown by the example, a homogeneous deformation

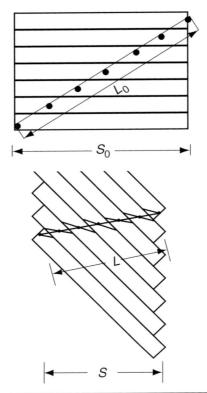

Fig 5.23 Continuous approximation to the deformation of the De Sitter model (De Sitter, 1964).

deforms any material line in the body to another material line with, in general, different length and orientation. The deformations (5.33) and (5.34) combined to achieve the final deformation are also homogeneous.

The simplicity of the De Sitter model is such that the change in fold shape as folding continues, or the evolutionary model, and the motions involved, or the kinematic model, are immediately apparent, although we still have to write these down in explicit form. However, a description of the deformation involves only the initial and a current or final state, and not the path between them. Before completing the kinematic model, we study a second model for chevron folding.

5.3.4 Homogeneous flattening model

The presence of cleavage in the Bendigo chevron folds (Fig. 5.16) means that they could not have formed solely by the rotation of rigid layers in the fold limbs with localized bending or breaking of the layers in the narrow hinges. Accordingly, we introduce another model for fold formation in which layers do not behave as rigid bodies. We begin with the limiting case in which inter-layer slip is excluded.

Start with the configuration shown in Fig. 5.20, which corresponds with perfect chevron folds of low limb dip. As above, consider a functional relationship that describes the final position of any particle in the body in terms of its initial position. We choose the simple relationship:

$$x = F_{xx}X$$

$$y = F_{yy}Y = \left(\frac{1}{F_{xx}}\right)Y \qquad (5.39)$$

Here F_{xx} and F_{yy} are constants. The initial and final fold forms are two-dimensional cylindrical forms with generator or axis parallel to the z-axis.

First consider what happens to a rectangular element of area in the (x,y)-plane whose initial corners are the points $(0,0)$, $(0,X)$, (X,Y), and $(0,Y)$. Its area is XY. In the deformed state, the element remains a rectangle, with corners at $(0,0)$, $(0,x)$, (x, y), and $(0,y)$ and area:

$$xy = (F_{xx}X)(F_{yy}Y) = (F_{xx}F_{yy})XY = XY \qquad (5.40)$$

Thus, by choosing $F_{yy} = 1/F_{xx}$ in (5.39) we prescribe that the cross-sectional area of the body, or any part of it, remains the same. Referring to a broad range of structure cross sections, structural geologists refer to this circumstance as one in which area is conserved. Keep in mind that *conservation of area* is NOT a law of nature, such as *conservation of mass*. Does the De Sitter model conserve area?

Application of the transformation (5.39) with $F_{xx} < 1$, to the configuration in Fig. 5.20, results in a tighter fold. An example is shown for $F_{xx} = 0.5$. Fig. 5.24 shows a model of this type for $F_{xx} = 0.5$, which starts with a chevron seed fold with a limb dip of 15°. Several circles in the initial configuration are deformed into ellipses. By our hypothesis for the relationship between deformation and cleavage, the model cleavage is oriented vertically, normal to the short axis of the ellipse. Application of (5.39) requires a computation for individual lines, circles, and other loci.

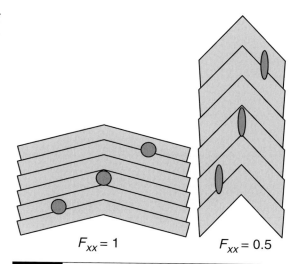

$F_{xx} = 1$ $F_{xx} = 0.5$

Fig 5.24 Initial chevrons ($F_{xx} = 1$) and "flattened" chevrons ($F_{xx} = 0.5$). Circular markers become strain ellipses.

We may compute a relationship between the initial and final dips, δ_0 and δ, or the ratio of the principal axes of the strain ellipse from the transformation (5.39). Without imposing the restriction of constant area:

$$\tan \delta = \left(\frac{F_{yy}}{F_{xx}}\right)\tan \delta_0$$

$$\frac{b}{a} = \frac{F_{yy}}{F_{xx}} \quad , \quad \frac{S}{S_0} = F_{xx} \qquad (5.41)$$

Here b and a are the vertical and horizontal semi-axes of the strain ellipse. In contrast to the ratio S/S_0 obtained in the rotating rigid layer model, this quantity does describe a strain: here the change in length of a horizontal material line between the initial and final states.

The type of folding, or the fold mechanism, of the homogeneous flattening model is often termed *passive folding* (Donath and Parker, 1974), since it corresponds to a situation in which the mechanical properties of layers or interfaces play no active role. It is as though the layers were composed of materials with the same isotropic mechanical properties, which allowed for a stiff fluid-like behavior, and surfaces of easy slip were not present. One may also apply this model to different "seed fold" forms, such as that defined by a set of sinusoidal surfaces (Fig. 5.25). Since the

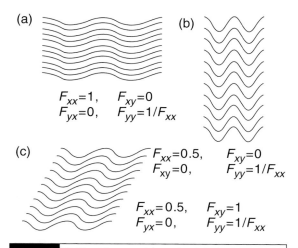

(a)

$$F_{xx}=1, \quad F_{xy}=0$$
$$F_{yx}=0, \quad F_{yy}=1/F_{xx}$$

(b)

(c)

$$F_{xx}=0.5, \quad F_{xy}=0$$
$$F_{xy}=0, \quad F_{yy}=1/F_{xx}$$

$$F_{xx}=0.5, \quad F_{xy}=1$$
$$F_{yx}=0, \quad F_{yy}=1/F_{xx}$$

Fig 5.25 Folds with sinusoidal initial and final surface forms produced by passive folding: (a) the seed fold, (b) flattening, (c) a combination of flattening and shearing. The coefficients defining the deformations are given.

variety is endless we should begin to think about what folds in rock actually look like and how they might have formed as constrained by the laws of physics and explicitly defined material properties. These considerations will be taken up in later chapters – for now we are limited to geometry and kinematics.

5.3.5 Inter-layer slip and homogeneous flattening

Since both the rigid layer slip model and the homogeneous deformation models of geometry and kinematics are quite simple, we may combine them to obtain a chevron fold model that shows both characteristic features: inter-layer slip and cleavage. One simple procedure for combining the models is to first apply one model, or mechanism, to achieve a fold form from an initial configuration, and then apply the other mechanism to the structure produced to achieve the final fold. This mirrors the two-part procedure of first slipping the layers in the fold limb, and then subjecting the whole to a rigid-body rotation, or vice versa (Fig. 5.21b). For example, beginning with the De Sitter model, the fold is obtained by first applying the transformation:

$$x^{(1)} = X \cos \delta^{(1)}$$

$$y^{(1)} = -X \sin \delta^{(1)} + Y\left(\frac{1}{\cos \delta^{(1)}}\right) \tag{5.42}$$

Here, we have assumed that the initial dip is vanishingly small. To obtain the final form, the transformation (5.39) is applied to (5.42):

$$x = F^{(2)}_{xx} x^{(1)}$$

$$y = \left(\frac{1}{F^{(2)}_{xx}}\right) y^{(1)} \tag{5.43}$$

Substituting from (5.42) we have:

$$x = (F^{(2)}_{xx} \cos \delta^{(1)}) X$$

$$y = \left(\frac{1}{F^{(2)}_{xx}}\right)\left[-X \sin \delta^{(1)} + \left(\frac{1}{\cos \delta^{(1)}}\right) Y\right] \tag{5.44}$$

Notice that the forms of the coefficients are:

$$x = F_{xx} X + F_{xy} Y$$
$$y = F_{yx} X + F_{yy} Y \tag{5.45}$$

In these equations the coefficients are:

$$F_{xx} = F^{(2)}_{xx} F^{(1)}_{xx} + F^{(2)}_{xy} F^{(1)}_{yx}$$

$$F_{xy} = F^{(2)}_{xx} F^{(1)}_{xy} + F^{(2)}_{xy} F^{(1)}_{yy}$$

$$F_{yx} = F^{(2)}_{yx} F^{(1)}_{xx} + F^{(2)}_{yy} F^{(1)}_{yx}$$

$$F_{yy} = F^{(2)}_{yx} F^{(1)}_{xy} + F^{(2)}_{yy} F^{(1)}_{yy} \tag{5.46}$$

The quantities $F^{(1)}_{xx}, \ldots$, are given in (5.42). Here, and throughout this section, we describe the De Sitter model in terms of its continuous medium approximation. We can appreciate that the algebraic complexity of such a description increases rapidly, although the operation itself is straightforward. Imagine applying each of the two mechanisms alternately over many steps!

The final dip δ is:

$$\tan \delta = \left(\frac{1}{F^{(2)}_{xx}}\right)^2 \tan \delta^{(1)} = \left(\frac{b}{a}\right) \tan \delta^{(1)} \tag{5.47}$$

The final limb dip δ may be measured, and if strain markers allowed b/a to be determined, (5.47) provides an estimate of the limb dip at which layer-parallel slip ceased – according to the model!

Because the circular sections are simply rotated during the layer-slip stage, and no slip occurs during the second stage, cleavage in the fold will be vertical. If we observe a chevron fold with such vertical cleavage, and with evidence for inter-layer slip, we might then conclude that our model is appropriate. If the cleavage were not vertical – except within the hinge region where symmetry requires it – another kinematic model must be concocted. We do not claim that geometric, evolutionary, and kinematic models are the final goal of our study, but they do provide a means of organizing observations and sorting out hypotheses as to folding mechanism.

5.4 | Velocity fields: the instantaneous state of motion

We have described the production of the limb of a chevron fold in terms of the homogeneous deformation, as described by the transformation from initial to final coordinates of the particles in the body through relations of the form (5.45). The quantities F_{xx}, F_{xy}, F_{yx}, and F_{yy} are the components of a second-order tensor, the deformation gradient tensor. In the models so far developed, the coefficients have been obtained for two simple kinds of deformation. Then, we obtained the coefficients for a sequence of two deformations in succession, one of each kind. This was consistent with two observed features of chevron folds: inter-layer slip and cleavage. However, this composite model seems artificial. It suggests a process in which slip surfaces are initiated between rigid layers and a fold forms in this manner up to a certain dip, at which point a completely different mechanism of folding sets in. The model describes neither the initiation of slip nor its cessation. The opposite sequence might also be considered. This composite process is plausible if the two mechanisms operated during episodes separated in time, in which the conditions were markedly different. For example, lower temperature and pressure and the presence of fluids might have been associated with an episode of inter-layer slip and higher temperature and pressure with an episode of homogeneous deformation.

Since a parameter such as δ changes continuously, the description obtained might be interpreted not only as the description of an initial and final state, but of the continuous progression of states between them. The term *progressive deformation* is often used by structural geologists to denote such a progression, whether or not it can be described in detail (Ramsay and Huber, 1983, 1987). That is, any rock mass may be viewed as having undergone a progressive deformation, the end result of which is the suite of structures and deformed objects that we see in the exposure. On the other hand, the term progressive deformation does not appear in the literature or texts of continuum mechanics, which also deal with the deformation of materials, including rocks. This term seems to be the special invention of structural geologists. In the context of our discussion, the description of a progressive deformation would appear to consist of a specification of the four coefficients $F_{xx}(t)$, $F_{xy}(t)$, $F_{yx}(t)$, and $F_{yy}(t)$ as functions of time.

Consider the rate of change in the positions of particles in the body. This description refers explicitly to the physical variable time t, and thus leads toward a consideration of the physical processes responsible for folding. Taking the derivatives of the expressions in (5.45) with respect to time:

$$\frac{dx}{dt} = \frac{dF_{xx}}{dt}X + \frac{dF_{xy}}{dt}Y$$
$$\frac{dy}{dt} = \frac{dF_{yx}}{dt}X + \frac{dF_{yy}}{dt}Y \tag{5.48}$$

Since X and Y are the initial coordinates of the particle, we do not operate on these. But the rates of change of the current coordinates of the particles are their velocity components, or:

$$\frac{dx}{dt} = v_x, \quad \frac{dy}{dt} = v_y \tag{5.49}$$

The velocity field at any time will depend on the current conditions, properties, and forces applied to the body. Such a description is generally developed in terms of position and time in the body, so that in the two-dimensional case under consideration:

$$v_x = v_x(x, y, t, \text{material properties, applied forces})$$
$$v_y = v_y(x, y, t, \text{material properties, applied forces})$$
$$\tag{5.50}$$

Here, x and y are used to describe the current coordinates of some particle in the body, but they are also used to describe position in space. The use of these quantities to describe current position of particular particles and position within the body creates no problem. For example, the velocity at a particular position is an attribute of the particle currently occupying this position. The mathematical description of the variation in velocity with position may be smoothly varying. While we may formally evaluate the function elsewhere than within the body, e.g. within a hole in the body, it is clear that the values of quantities there have no physical significance.

The velocity field within the body at a particular instant of time will depend upon the physical state of the body, its properties, and the forces applied to it. Thus, rather than the current state of deformation, with reference to some initial configuration, it is this that we must look to if we want to understand the process producing the structure of interest. We will examine this relationship in this textbook. An example given in this chapter is that of the Stokes solution. However, we also want to know how the history of the instantaneous state of motion, or the velocity field, gives rise to the current or final structure; and within the limited context of kinematics that is something we may accomplish in this chapter.

In the present case of a homogeneous deformation, as in a single limb of an idealized chevron fold, the deformation is given by the coefficients F_{xx}, F_{xy}, F_{yx}, and F_{yy}. Moreover, the velocity field within the fold limb – where we again consider the smooth equivalent of the rigid layer model – can be written:

$$v_x = L_{xx}x + L_{xy}y$$
$$v_y = L_{yx}x + L_{yy}y \tag{5.51}$$

Here the coefficients are uniform in the limb. Here, x and y denote both the spatial coordinates and the current positions of particles. Combining (5.45) and (5.48) through (5.51), we obtain relations for the rates of change of the components $F_{xx}, \ldots$:

$$v_x = \frac{dx}{dt} = \left(\frac{dF_{xx}}{dt}\right)X + \left(\frac{dF_{xy}}{dt}\right)Y$$
$$= L_{xx}x + L_{xy}y \tag{5.52}$$

$$= L_{xx}(F_{xx}X + F_{xy}Y) + L_{xy}(F_{yx}X + F_{yy}Y)$$

Collecting terms in X and Y and carrying out the same operation using v_y:

$$\frac{dF_{xx}}{dt} = L_{xx}F_{xx} + L_{xy}F_{yx}$$
$$\frac{dF_{xy}}{dt} = L_{xx}F_{xy} + L_{xy}F_{yy}$$
$$\frac{dF_{yx}}{dt} = L_{yx}F_{xx} + L_{yy}F_{yx} \tag{5.53}$$
$$\frac{dF_{yy}}{dt} = L_{yx}F_{xy} + L_{yy}F_{yy}$$

To illustrate how we think about velocity fields of the simple type (5.51) and how we incorporate them into (5.53) and solve for the state of deformation, we go back to our two chevron fold models. We show how we can combine the two models into one that allows the mechanisms of flattening and inter-layer slip and layer rotation to go on simultaneously. The key concept is that the separate velocity fields for the two mechanisms at any instant are additive.

Initial and final positions of particles for flattening are related by:

$$x = F_{xx}X, \quad y = F_{yy}Y \tag{5.54}$$

The set of differential equations (5.53) is incomplete without a set of initial conditions. Initially, the coordinates of particle position x and y are just equal to X and Y, so:

$$F_{xx}(0) = 1, \quad F_{xy}(0) = 0,$$
$$F_{yx}(0) = 0, \quad F_{yy}(0) = 1 \tag{5.55}$$

To have (5.54) at any time during the folding process, we must require that the coefficients F_{xy} and F_{yx} are always zero. Examination of (5.53) indicates that the quantities L_{xy} and L_{yx} must always be zero, and (5.53) reduces to:

$$\frac{dF_{xx}}{dt} = L_{xx}F_{xx}, \quad \frac{dF_{yy}}{dt} = L_{yy}F_{yy} \tag{5.56}$$

The equivalent velocity field is:

$$v_x = L_{xx}x, \quad v_y = L_{yy}y \tag{5.57}$$

To integrate (5.56) with the initial conditions (5.55), we need to know how L_{xx} and L_{yy} vary with time. In the simplest case they are constant. Integration then yields:

$$F_{xx}(t) = \exp(L_{xx}t)$$
$$F_{yy}(t) = \exp(L_{yy}t) \tag{5.58}$$

The condition of constant area requires $F_{yy}(t) = 1/F_{xx}(t)$, or, from (5.58):

$$L_{yy} = -L_{xx} \tag{5.59}$$

Indeed, constant area requires (5.59) whatever the time variation of these quantities. The time frame during which structures form is an interesting topic brought up by considerations of velocity. It is significant to questions such as that of the connection between folding and gold mineralization at Bendigo (Fig. 5.16). The velocity field (5.57) is illustrated by plotting velocity vectors on a square grid (Fig. 5.26).

Consider the second model, in which rigid layers rotate and slide relative to each other. Recall that our model for this is a smooth representation of the bulk deformation. The deformation is given by:

$$x = F_{xx}X = X\cos\delta$$

$$y = F_{yx}X + F_{yy}Y = -X\sin\delta + Y\left(\frac{1}{\cos\delta}\right) \tag{5.60}$$

If this applies throughout the folding process, we must require $F_{xy}(t) = 0$. Since examination of the form (5.53) indicates that this requires that L_{xy} vanish, (5.53) reduces to:

$$\frac{dF_{xx}}{dt} = L_{xx}F_{xx}$$

$$\frac{dF_{yx}}{dt} = L_{yx}F_{xx} + L_{yy}F_{yx} \tag{5.61}$$

$$\frac{dF_{yy}}{dt} = L_{yy}F_{yy}$$

In (5.60), $F_{yy} = 1/F_{xx}$, and the restriction $L_{yy} = -L_{xx}$ also holds. We may use (5.60) to compute the coefficients for the velocity field in (5.61):

$$L_{xx} = -L_{yy} = -\tan\delta\frac{d\delta}{dt}$$

$$L_{yx} = -(1 - \tan^2\delta)\frac{d\delta}{dt} \tag{5.62}$$

These expressions depend upon the rate of change of limb dip with time, and a question immediately

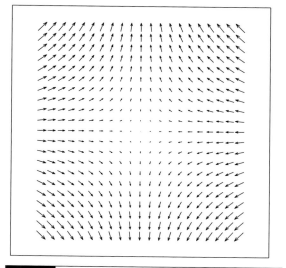

Fig 5.26 Velocity field (5.57) illustrated by plotting the velocity vectors for particles located on a square grid.

arises as to how to specify it. Further, the coefficients are functions of the current dip; in the first model this was not the case.

To get some feeling for (5.62) we evaluate the quantities:

$$v_x\left(\frac{d\delta}{dt}\right)^{-1} = -x\tan\delta$$

$$v_y\left(\frac{d\delta}{dt}\right)^{-1} = -x(1 - \tan^2\delta) + y\tan\delta \tag{5.63}$$

Velocity fields for $\delta = 0$ and $22.5°$ are shown in Fig. 5.27. The result for $\delta = 45°$ is the same as that shown in Fig. 5.26 for the flattening model! That this must be so is seen by substituting $\tan\delta = 1$ for $\delta = 45°$ in (5.63).

The velocity field must change as the dip changes, and you can perhaps visualize how these examples correspond to a combination of smoothed inter-layer slip and simultaneous rigid rotation of the entire limb. To aid visualization, we decompose the velocity field into these two component parts. The rigid-body rotation will always have the same form, but the part corresponding to the "sliding" will vary in magnitude with limb dip. For example, this decomposition is done for $\delta = 22.5°$ in Fig. 5.28. The decomposition of (5.63) is obtained by noting that the rigid-body rotation (Fig. 5.28b) is expressed as:

$$(v_x)_{\text{rotation}} \left(\frac{d\delta}{dt} \right)^{-1} = -y$$

$$(v_y)_{\text{rotation}} \left(\frac{d\delta}{dt} \right)^{-1} = x \tag{5.64}$$

The shear is expressed by the velocity field obtained by subtracting (5.64) from (5.63). The latter looks complicated, but yields a result like that in Fig. 5.28a for any choice of δ.

5.4.1 Combined model for chevron folding

We now formulate a kinematic model that combines the De Sitter model, model 1, and the homogeneous flattening model, model 2. The velocity field for the combined model is formed by summing the two velocity fields in some proportion:

$$v_x = f_1 v_x^{(1)} + f_2 v_x^{(2)}$$

$$v_y = f_1 v_y^{(1)} + f_2 v_y^{(2)} \tag{5.65}$$

$$f_1 + f_2 = 1$$

The fractions f_1 and f_2 might be taken to be functions of time or limb dip. This model is ad hoc, since we have advanced no physical principles that would allow us to fix f_1 and f_2. We present these models to illustrate results that might approximately simulate the development of chevron folds and to provide some experience in thinking about kinematics and deformation.

The fact that the velocity field of the De Sitter model (model 1) is expressed in terms of the rate of change in dip, $d\delta/dt$, creates difficulty. We might use the dip itself as a time-like variable, and assign some arbitrary constant value to $d\delta/dt$. However, the dip is also changed by homogeneous flattening (model 2). As one way of proceeding, we express the progress of folding by means of the rate of change in the span of the limb, normalized by the span itself. For model 1:

$$\left[\left(\frac{1}{S} \right) \frac{dS}{dt} \right]^{(1)} = \left(\frac{1}{S} \right) v_x^{(1)}(S,0)$$

$$= \left(\frac{1}{S} \right) L_{xx}^{(1)} S = -\tan\delta \left(\frac{d\delta}{dt} \right) \tag{5.66}$$

For model 2:

$$\left[\left(\frac{1}{S} \right) \frac{dS}{dt} \right]^{(2)} = L_{xx}^{(2)} \tag{5.67}$$

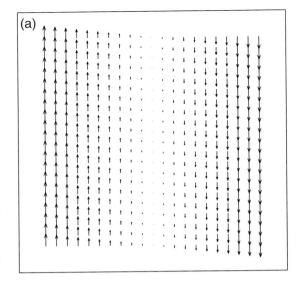

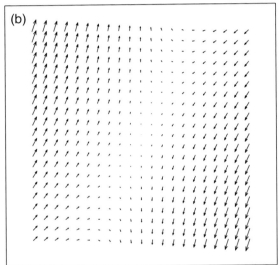

Fig 5.27 Velocity field for the rigid layer chevron fold model: (a) for $\delta = 0°$, (b) for $\delta = 22.5°$.

The total relative rate of change of S, as might have been anticipated, is:

$$\left(\frac{1}{S} \right) \frac{dS}{dt} = L_{xx}^{(1)} + L_{xx}^{(2)} = L_{xx} \tag{5.68}$$

A simple combined model is one in which the individual contributions are in constant ratio:

$$L_{xx}^{(1)} = \frac{L_{xx}}{1+R}, \quad L_{xx}^{(2)} = \frac{RL_{xx}}{1+R}, \quad R = \frac{L_{xx}^{(2)}}{L_{xx}^{(1)}} \tag{5.69}$$

(a)

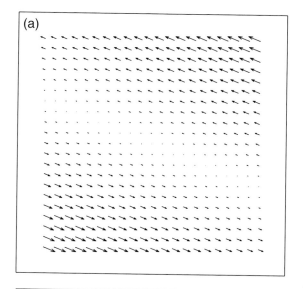

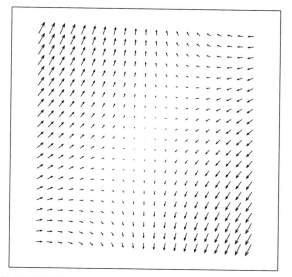

Fig 5.29 Velocity field for combined model at $\delta = 22.5°$ for $R = 1$. Compare with Figs. 5.28b and 5.27.

(b)

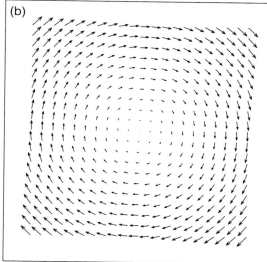

Fig 5.28 Decomposition of velocity field for model I for $\delta = 22.5°$: (a) layer-parallel "slip" or shear, (b) rigid-body rotation.

One might then ask which value of R best simulates a natural chevron fold in terms of amount of inter-layer slip and homogeneous layer deformation on the fold limb. With the choice of L_{xx} as defining the rate of the process, we may replace f_1 and f_2 in (5.65) using (5.69). The combined model is:

$$v_x = L_{xx}x$$

$$v_y = \left[\left(\frac{1}{1+R} \right) \left(\frac{1}{\tan \delta} - \tan \delta \right) x - y \right] L_{xx} \quad (5.70)$$

If both mechanisms contribute equally, $R = 1$; the velocity field at $\delta = 22.5°$ is shown in Fig. 5.29.

To follow the fold structure from an initial to a final state, we must first determine how δ varies with the relative change in limb span:

$$\frac{S}{S_0} = \exp(L_{xx}t) \quad (5.71)$$

Here L_{xx} is taken to be constant, for simplicity. From (5.66):

$$\frac{d\delta^{(1)}}{dt} = -\frac{L_{xx}^{(1)}}{\tan \delta} \quad (5.72)$$

Figure 5.30 shows how to compute the rate of change in dip associated with homogeneous flattening:

$$\tan(\delta + d\delta) \cong \frac{(\tan \delta + d\delta)}{(1 - d\delta \tan \delta)}$$

$$\cong \frac{[\tan \delta - v_y(1, -\tan \delta)dt]}{[1 + v_y(1, -\tan \delta)dt]} \quad (5.73)$$

Substituting for model 2, we obtain:

$$\frac{d\delta^{(2)}}{dt} = \frac{-2 \tan \delta L_{xx}^{(2)}}{(1 + \tan^2 \delta)} \quad (5.74)$$

Combining (5.73) and (5.74) with the expressions for $L_{xx}^{(1)}$ and $L_{xx}^{(2)}$:

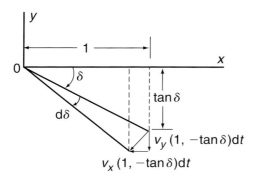

Fig 5.30 Trigonometric relations used to compute the rate of change in dip, δ, associated with homogeneous flattening.

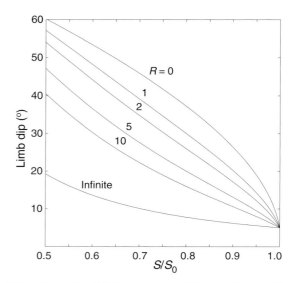

Fig 5.31 Limb dip as a function of S/S_0 for composite models with R as a parameter; initial dip of the "seed fold" was $5°$.

$$\frac{d\delta}{dt} = -\frac{L_{xx}^{(1)}}{\tan\delta} - \frac{2\tan\delta L_{xx}^{(2)}}{(1 + \tan^2\delta)}$$

$$= -\left(\frac{1}{1+R}\right)\left\{\frac{1}{\tan\delta} + \frac{2R\tan\delta}{(1+\tan^2\delta)}\right\}L_{xx} \quad (5.75)$$

Since, for constant L_{xx}, S/S_0 is given by (5.71), we may use (5.75) to obtain either $\delta(t)$ or $\delta(S/S_0)$. In either case, we must integrate (5.75) numerically. It is somewhat surprising that a relatively simple kinematic model produces such a complicated relation! Since:

$$\frac{d}{dt}\tan\delta = (1 + \tan^2\delta)\frac{d\delta}{dt} \quad (5.76)$$

The relation (5.75) may be recast into the somewhat simpler form:

$$\frac{d}{dt}\tan\delta = -\left(\frac{1}{1+R}\right)\left(\frac{1 + \tan^2\delta}{\tan\delta} + 2R\tan\delta\right)L_{xx}$$

$$(5.77)$$

A part of the description of chevron folding, according to the present kinematic model, would be the variation of limb dip with relative fold span. Integration of (5.75) for $R = 0$, 1, 2, 5, 10, and ∞ yields the curves shown in Fig. 5.31. Here, the ratio of final to initial fold span is given as $S/S_0 = e^{-t}$, where t is expressed in units of $1/L_{xx}$, and is used as a measure of deformation or time. Note that the progression of folding in the figure is from right to left. The results shown extend to $S/S_0 = 0.5$, a plausible typical amount of shortening for natural

examples of chevron folds, which have limb dips of 50 to 70°. Folding is initiated for seed folds with $\delta(0) = 5°$, meant to correspond to a dip that might be achieved by initial buckling before the chevron kinematics sets in. The limit $R \to \infty$ corresponds to passive, purely kinematic amplification; the limit $R = 0$ corresponds to deck-of-cards folding in which the limb length does not change. If this models natural chevron folds, attainment of adequate dip would imply that a model with $R \le 10$ is appropriate.

5.4.2 Forward integration of the motion: steady and non-steady velocity fields

Because we know what the velocity field is as a function of limb dip and can keep track of that, it is possible to follow the paths and current positions of particles in the fold limb by numerical integration. Given the current position of a particle and the limb dip, we compute its velocity. We then move the particle a small distance by the position increments Δx and Δy, so that the new positions are:

$$x(t + \Delta t) \cong x(t) + v_x[x(t), y(t); \delta(t)]\Delta t$$
$$y(t + \Delta t) \cong y(t) + v_y[x(t), y(t); \delta(t)]\Delta t$$

$$(5.78)$$

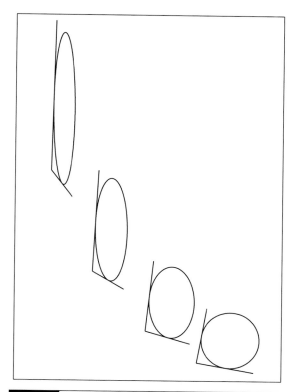

Fig 5.32 Initial and deformed material loci for homogeneous flattening model.

lines; for three-dimensional motions, they might be spherical surfaces, planes, or lines. These are *material loci*, made up of particles. Figure 5.32 shows initial loci consisting of two perpendicular lines of equal length and a circle at several stages during folding following the homogeneous flattening model. Also shown is the continuous path, or trajectory, taken by the intersection point of the two line segments. The more nearly horizontal line segment is taken to represent the initial tilted bed surface segment, and so its inclination equals the limb dip of the fold.

To determine the shape of a fold limb layer for the combined mechanism model the velocity field (5.70) is used, together with (5.75). Results for the De Sitter mechanism alone ($R = 0$) and equal contributions from each mechanism ($R = 1$) are shown in Fig. 5.33. The limbs end up with the same span, S. The fact that the De Sitter model produces a slightly larger strain, as measured by the deformation of the initial circular locus is puzzling. Recall that in this model, layers simply undergo rigid-body rotation. Recall, however, that the combined model is based on the continuous-deformation approximation to the De Sitter model, which does not represent discrete layers. The deformation shown is the bulk deformation. It would be observed if a large circle had been inscribed on a stack of "thin" layers such as a card deck.

The velocity field for the homogeneous flattening model is *steady state*: the velocity at any spatial position does not change with time. The velocity of a particle moving through the velocity field does change. This steady velocity field has been represented by vector "arrows" on a grid of positions in Fig. 5.26. The continuous-deformation variant of the De Sitter model, or the combined mechanism model do not yield steady velocity fields because the velocity distributions depend upon δ, as illustrated by the velocity fields shown in Figs. 5.27 through 5.29.

5.5 | General results

Our study of kinematic models for chevron folds involved general concepts in deformation and kinematics. These are basic tools in the study of

Here $\delta(t)$ is required to define the velocity field for the general model. This method uses quantities evaluated at the initial position of the particle. Since the velocity will generally change continuously between the initial and final positions, a gradual divergence between the computed trajectory of the particle and the true trajectory may develop. To minimize this, we use small time increments. Alternatively, the velocity may be computed at the new position, and the average velocity for the two positions used to re-compute the new position. This method involves a slightly lengthier computer program, but it provides more stable results. In the present examples this refined method is not used.

Following individual particles may be informative, such as convective motion in a magma chamber. We will often follow particle loci that allow us to visualize the velocity field or the current state of deformation. Such initial loci for two-dimensional motions might be circles or

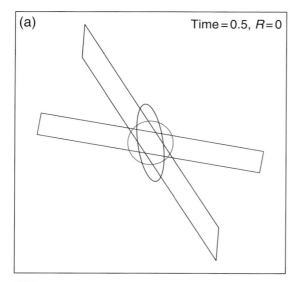

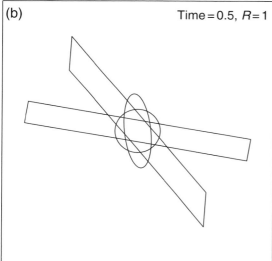

Fig 5.33 Fold limbs produced by the combined mechanism model; initial layer dip of 10°.

the processes and products of rock deformation. Here we introduce additional ideas and operations and refer the interested reader to standard references (Malvern, 1969). It seems appropriate at this point to take up a few formal topics and questions. Deformation and flow certainly can't be restricted to the homogeneous case over large volumes of rock: how would all the interesting structures that we observe in the field have formed? We should be suspicious from our strenuous, but not wholly satisfying, modeling of chevron folds. How do we

handle the non-homogeneous case? The secret here is to start by transforming our picture of homogeneous deformation down to the infinitesimal region known as the neighborhood of a particle. You may guess this from your experience with calculus.

5.5.1 Deformation in the neighborhood of a particle: two-dimensional case

In a two-dimensional plane or axisymmetric deformation the initial and final positions of particles remain in the same plane. A uniform additional displacement of all particles, or translation, an operation that maintains the initial orientation of the plane, would not affect this. An example is the uniform additional upward motion of the particles in the rising viscous sphere. A description relative to an external fixed coordinate would include this translation. For example, we might wish to describe the motion of particles in the sphere relative to a coordinate system fixed with respect to the stationary fluid medium far from it.

From our discussion of examples of deformation, such as the oölites of the South Mountain anticline (Fig. 5.4) or the deformed xenoliths of the Chindamora batholith (Fig. 5.9) you have likely noticed that a description of deformation is *local*. The range in variation between individual oölites within a hand sample may be large, but it represents a statistical or random variation attributed to the facts that the initial shapes of oölites deviate from perfect spheres, and that they are not homogeneous in their properties. One must sample a volume that is representative of a homogeneous deformation. On the other hand the ratios of the axial lengths of the ellipsoidal shapes of oölites or xenoliths vary between sample locations and these variations may be representative of a heterogeneous deformation.

Although they clearly and dramatically indicate that deformation has taken place, the axial ratios of oölites and their orientations do not fully quantify the deformation. As another example to introduce our present task, consider the deformed grid within the viscous sphere (Fig. 5.13). This shows a change in the shape, size, and orientation of initially square material elements after an interval of flow within the sphere. These

(a)

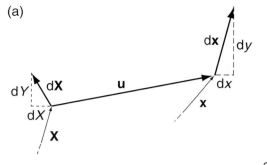

(b)

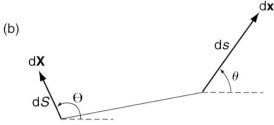

Fig 5.34 (a) Infinitesimal vectors d**X** and d**x** with components (dX, dY) and (dx, dy) lie along a material line segment in the initial and final states, respectively. The vectors emanate from the initial and final positions of the same particle. Only the end points of the position vectors, **X** and **x**, for that particle are indicated. The displacement vector **u** has components (u_x, u_y). (b) The vectors are represented in terms of polar coordinates (dS, Θ) and (ds, θ), respectively.

attributes of the elements vary smoothly within the body, and they are informative of the style and magnitude of deformation, but they do not provide a complete description. In the idealized continuous medium of this model, we may define the quantities describing deformation at a mathematical point in terms of tensors based upon gradients in deformation and displacement.

Consider a particle that occupies position (X, Y) in the initial state and position $(x, y) = (X + u_x, Y + u_y)$ in the final state (Fig. 5.34a). An arbitrarily oriented material line of particles that is infinitesimal in length is overlain by the vector d**X** with components (dX, dY) in the initial state. This material line is translated, stretched, and rotated and then is overlain by the vector d**x** with components (dx, dy) in the deformed state. Infinitesimal refers to the fact that, if the material line were not infinitesimal in length, it would generally show some curvature in the final state, and the vector

d**x** would no longer provide an adequate representation of the line element.

Writing quantities in component form, the infinitesimal material line in the deformed state is described by the vector components:

$$dx = \frac{\partial x}{\partial X}dX + \frac{\partial x}{\partial Y}dY$$
$$dy = \frac{\partial y}{\partial X}dX + \frac{\partial y}{\partial Y}dY \qquad (5.79)$$

The partial derivatives are referred to coordinates in the initial state and are called *deformation gradients*. For convenience, we write (5.79) in the form:

$$dx = F_{xx}dX + F_{xy}dY$$
$$dy = F_{yx}dX + F_{yy}dY \qquad (5.80)$$

We have encountered expressions of this form before in the case of homogeneous deformation in chevron fold models, (5.45). The array of quantities F_{xx}, F_{xy}, F_{yx}, and F_{yy} is a *second-order tensor*, since it satisfies the general definition:

A second-order tensor associates a vector with each direction in space by means of a relation that is linear and homogeneous in the direction cosines (Prager, 1961).

The vector components are (dx, dy), and the direction cosines of the direction in space are the quantities dX/dS, dY/dS (Fig. 5.34). Second-order tensors, relating pairs of vectors, have many physical applications (Malvern, 1969).

Another description of the vector d**x** is found using components of the displacement vector, **u**, by noting that:

$$x = X + u_x(X, Y)$$
$$y = Y + u_y(X, Y) \qquad (5.81)$$

The partial derivatives of these quantities are:

$$\frac{\partial x}{\partial X} = 1 + \frac{\partial u_x}{\partial X}, \quad \frac{\partial x}{\partial Y} = \frac{\partial u_x}{\partial Y}$$
$$\frac{\partial y}{\partial X} = \frac{\partial u_y}{\partial X}, \quad \frac{\partial y}{\partial Y} = 1 + \frac{\partial u_y}{\partial Y} \qquad (5.82)$$

The partial derivatives of u_x and u_y in (5.82) are the *displacement gradients*. The components of d**x** as functions of the displacement gradients are found by substituting (5.82) into (5.79).

The infinitesimal material line is represented by the vector d**X**, and therefore by its length $dS = [(dX)^2 + (dY)^2]^{1/2}$ and direction Θ, measured counterclockwise from the positive X-axis such that the components are (Fig. 5.34b):

$$dX = dS\cos\Theta, \quad dY = dS\sin\Theta \qquad (5.83)$$

The vector d**x** may be similarly expressed in terms of quantities ds and θ:

$$dx = ds\cos\theta, \quad dy = ds\sin\theta \qquad (5.84)$$

Here $ds = [(dx)^2 + (dy)^2]^{1/2}$ is the length of the material line in the deformed state.

Deformation, as we have seen examples of it, involves *strain* and *rotation*. A familiar aspect of strain is a change in the length of a material line which may be quantified using the square of the *stretch*, $(ds/dS)^2$, a dimensionless quantity referred to as the *quadratic elongation*. For an arbitrarily oriented material line segment of infinitesimal length we define the quadratic elongation using (5.80) and (5.83):

$$
\begin{aligned}
\left(\frac{ds}{dS}\right)^2 &= \frac{(dx)^2 + (dy)^2}{(dS)^2} \\
&= (F_{xx}\cos\Theta + F_{xy}\sin\Theta)^2 \\
&\quad + (F_{yx}\cos\Theta + F_{yy}\sin\Theta)^2 \\
&= \tfrac{1}{2}(F_{xx}^2 + F_{xy}^2 + F_{yx}^2 + F_{yy}^2) \\
&\quad + \tfrac{1}{2}(F_{xx}^2 - F_{xy}^2 + F_{yx}^2 - F_{yy}^2)\cos 2\Theta \\
&\quad + (F_{xx}F_{xy} + F_{yx}F_{yy})\sin 2\Theta
\end{aligned}
\qquad (5.85)
$$

The last two lines are found using the standard double angle formulae (Selby, 1975). This is an exact description of change in length in two dimensions at a point in terms of the deformation gradients and the orientation of the material line in the initial state.

Another useful measure of change in line length is the extension, defined as $\varepsilon_n = (ds - dS)/dS = (ds/dS) - 1$. The extension is related to the quadratic elongation as:

$$\left(\frac{ds}{dS}\right)^2 = (1 + \varepsilon_n)^2 = 1 + 2\varepsilon_n + \varepsilon_n^2 \approx 1 + 2\varepsilon_n \qquad (5.86)$$

In the last step we have utilized the approximation taken to define the so-called *infinitesimal strain*

which applies when the square of the extension is much less than the extension and much less than one. Because the infinitesimal strain is defined in terms of the displacement gradients we write the quadratic elongation (5.85) in terms of the displacement gradients using (5.82). For small strains we don't have to pay attention to the distinction between position (x, y) and position (X, Y). Then, the derivative operators with respect to initial coordinates, $\partial/\partial X$ and $\partial/\partial Y$, may be replaced by the operators $\partial/\partial x$ and $\partial/\partial y$. If the displacement gradients all are much less than one, we may approximate the quadratic elongation by discarding quantities in multiples of the gradients such as $(\partial u_x/\partial x)^2$ or $(\partial u_x/\partial y)(\partial u_y/\partial x)$ to find:

$$
\begin{aligned}
\varepsilon_n &= \frac{1}{2}\left(\frac{\partial u_x}{\partial x} + \frac{\partial u_y}{\partial y}\right) + \frac{1}{2}\left(\frac{\partial u_x}{\partial x} - \frac{\partial u_y}{\partial y}\right)\cos 2\Theta \\
&\quad + \frac{1}{2}\left(\frac{\partial u_y}{\partial x} + \frac{\partial u_x}{\partial y}\right)\sin 2\Theta
\end{aligned}
\qquad (5.87)
$$

The infinitesimal strain components in two dimensions are:

$$\varepsilon_{xx} = \frac{\partial u_x}{\partial x}, \quad \varepsilon_{yy} = \frac{\partial u_y}{\partial y}, \quad \varepsilon_{xy} = \frac{1}{2}\left(\frac{\partial u_y}{\partial x} + \frac{\partial u_x}{\partial y}\right) = \varepsilon_{yx} \qquad (5.88)$$

Then, the extension at a point in the direction Θ may be written in terms of these components by substitution into (5.87):

$$\varepsilon_n = \tfrac{1}{2}(\varepsilon_{xx} + \varepsilon_{yy}) + \tfrac{1}{2}(\varepsilon_{xx} - \varepsilon_{yy})\cos 2\Theta + \varepsilon_{xy}\sin 2\Theta \qquad (5.89)$$

The two-dimensional *infinitesimal strain tensor* components form a symmetric array because $\varepsilon_{xy} = \varepsilon_{yx}$:

$$\begin{bmatrix} \varepsilon_{xx} & \varepsilon_{xy} \\ \varepsilon_{yx} & \varepsilon_{yy} \end{bmatrix} \qquad (5.90)$$

If all its components vanish, no infinitesimal material line element at the point under consideration will undergo a change in length.

Turning now to the concept of rotation, a rigid-body rotation in the neighborhood of a particle is illustrated in Fig. 5.35. An arbitrarily oriented infinitesimal material line represented by the vector d**X** in the initial state is rotated through the angle ω, and there represented by

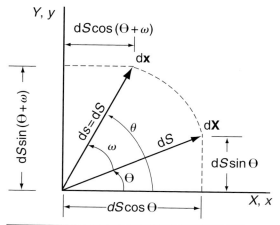

Fig 5.35 Pure rotation through the positive, counterclockwise, angle $\omega = \theta - \Theta$. Infinitesimal vectors d**X** and d**x** lie along a material line segment in the initial and final states, respectively. The vectors emanate from the same particle fixed at the origin. The vectors may be represented in terms of polar coordinates (dS, Θ) and (ds, θ), respectively, where $dS = ds$.

d**x**. The material line does not change length, so that $ds = dS$. If all such material lines behave this way, the local deformation is a *pure rotation*. From Fig. 5.35:

$$dx = dS \cos(\Theta + \omega)$$
$$= dS(\cos\Theta \cos\omega - \sin\Theta \sin\omega) \tag{5.91}$$

Repeating these steps for dy and associating the trigonometric functions of the angle of rotation, ω with the components of F_{ij} we have:

$$F_{xx} = \cos\omega, \quad F_{xy} = -\sin\omega$$
$$F_{yx} = \sin\omega, \quad F_{yy} = \cos\omega \tag{5.92}$$

Substitution of these expressions into (5.85) confirms the condition $ds/dS = 1$.

The displacement gradients for pure rotation are obtained by substituting (5.91) and (5.92) into (5.80) and (5.82):

$$\frac{\partial u_x}{\partial X} + 1 = \cos\omega, \quad \frac{\partial u_x}{\partial Y} = -\sin\omega$$

$$\frac{\partial u_y}{\partial X} = \sin\omega, \quad \frac{\partial u_y}{\partial Y} + 1 = \cos\omega \tag{5.93}$$

If the rotation is small, $\omega \ll 1$, then the series expansion of the trigonometric functions gives:

$$\sin\omega \cong \omega - \tfrac{1}{6}\omega^3 \cong \omega$$

$$\cos\omega \cong 1 - \tfrac{1}{2}\omega^2 \cong 1 \tag{5.94}$$

Under these conditions the derivative operators with respect to initial coordinates, $\partial/\partial X$ and $\partial/\partial Y$, in (5.93) may be replaced by $\partial/\partial x$ and $\partial/\partial y$, and the displacement gradients are related to the infinitesimal angle of pure rotation as:

$$\begin{bmatrix} \dfrac{\partial u_x}{\partial x} & \dfrac{\partial u_x}{\partial y} \\[2mm] \dfrac{\partial u_y}{\partial x} & \dfrac{\partial u_y}{\partial y} \end{bmatrix} = \begin{bmatrix} 0 & -\omega \\ \omega & 0 \end{bmatrix} \tag{5.95}$$

Combining (5.88) for the infinitesimal strain and (5.95) for the infinitesimal pure rotation, the displacement gradients may be expanded into symmetric and antisymmetric parts:

$$\begin{bmatrix} \dfrac{\partial u_x}{\partial x} & \dfrac{1}{2}\left(\dfrac{\partial u_y}{\partial x} + \dfrac{\partial u_x}{\partial y}\right) \\[3mm] \dfrac{1}{2}\left(\dfrac{\partial u_y}{\partial x} + \dfrac{\partial u_x}{\partial y}\right) & \dfrac{\partial u_y}{\partial y} \end{bmatrix}$$

$$+ \begin{bmatrix} 0 & -\dfrac{1}{2}\left(\dfrac{\partial u_y}{\partial x} - \dfrac{\partial u_x}{\partial y}\right) \\[3mm] \dfrac{1}{2}\left(\dfrac{\partial u_y}{\partial x} - \dfrac{\partial u_x}{\partial y}\right) & 0 \end{bmatrix}$$

$$= \begin{bmatrix} \varepsilon_{xx} & \varepsilon_{xy} \\ \varepsilon_{yx} & \varepsilon_{yy} \end{bmatrix} + \begin{bmatrix} 0 & -\omega \\ \omega & 0 \end{bmatrix} \tag{5.96}$$

Here the infinitesimal strain is symmetric and the infinitesimal rotation is antisymmetric.

When the strain and rotation are small, or infinitesimal in the sense that squares of quantities can be discarded, special results apply. The deformation can be broken up into a rotation and a strain, applied in either order, since the contributions are additive:

$$\begin{bmatrix} F_{xx} & F_{xy} \\ F_{yx} & F_{yy} \end{bmatrix} \cong \begin{bmatrix} 1 + \varepsilon_{xx} & \varepsilon_{xy} - \omega \\ \varepsilon_{yx} + \omega & 1 + \varepsilon_{yy} \end{bmatrix} \tag{5.97}$$

As we shall see in later chapters, small strains and rotations are significant in elasticity and its application in models for the formation of joints, dikes, faults, or other structures.

Notice that there are *two* applications of the "infinitesimal concept" in the preceding discussion. The first is introduced in calculus and concerns the treatment of a material line element of arbitrary orientation that is represented by the infinitesimal vector d**X** with components (dX, dY) in the initial state and d**x** with components (dx, dy) in the deformed state. These vectors are contained within a neighborhood of the particle or spatial point from which they emanate that is sufficiently small so one may ignore the non-linear terms in the Taylor series expansion about that particle or point. For example we have:

$$dx = \frac{\partial x}{\partial X}dX + \frac{\partial x}{\partial Y}dY + \frac{1}{2}\left[\frac{\partial^2 x}{\partial X^2}(dX)^2 \right.$$
$$\left. + 2\frac{\partial^2 x}{\partial X \partial Y}(dX)(dY) + \frac{\partial^2 x}{\partial Y^2}(dY)^2\right] + \cdots \quad (5.98)$$

For (5.79) only the first-derivative terms were kept. The resulting measures of strain at a point, such as the quadratic elongation (5.85), are exact and involve no approximations and therefore no errors of analysis. The second application is in the simplifying approximation of infinitesimal strain and rotation. If $\varepsilon_n \ll 1$ and $\omega \ll 1$, we discard terms higher than first-order in these quantities. This introduces errors of analysis which may or may not be tolerable (see Section 5.5.3).

An aspect of strain that is quite distinct from the change in length of material lines is *shear*. Shear is a measure of the change in angle between two initially perpendicular material line elements (Fig. 5.36). Consider *two* initial infinitesimal vectors directed at right-angles to each other: d**X**$_1$ with components (dX_1, dY_1) and d**X**$_2$ with components (dX_2, dY_2). The first infinitesimal vector is oriented at the arbitrary angle Θ. Since we are only interested in the angle between the material line elements in the deformed state, both vectors are given the same length dS. In the initial state the vectors have the components:

$$dX_1 = dS\cos\Theta, \quad dY_1 = dS\sin\Theta$$
$$dX_2 = -dS\sin\Theta, \quad dY_2 = dS\cos\Theta \quad (5.99)$$

In the deformed state the vectors have the components:

$$dx_1 = (F_{xx}\cos\Theta + F_{xy}\sin\Theta)dS$$
$$dy_1 = (F_{yx}\cos\Theta + F_{yy}\sin\Theta)dS$$
$$dx_2 = (-F_{xx}\sin\Theta + F_{xy}\cos\Theta)dS \quad (5.100)$$
$$dy_2 = (-F_{yx}\sin\Theta + F_{yy}\cos\Theta)dS$$

The cosine of the angle between these two vectors is obtained by forming their scalar product:

$$dx_1 \cdot dx_2 = (dx_1)(dx_2) + (dy_1)(dy_2)$$
$$= \sqrt{(dx_1)^2 + (dy_1)^2}\,\sqrt{(dx_2)^2 + (dy_2)^2}\,\cos\beta \quad (5.101)$$

In the second line β is the angle between the vectors. Substituting from (5.100) we have:

$$\cos\beta = \left[\frac{1}{2}\left(-F_{xx}^2 + F_{xy}^2 - F_{yx}^2 + F_{yy}^2\right)\sin 2\Theta \right.$$
$$\left. + (F_{xx}F_{xy} + F_{yx}F_{yy})\cos 2\Theta\right]$$
$$\times\left\{\left[\frac{1}{2}(F_{xx}^2 + F_{xy}^2 + F_{yx}^2 + F_{yy}^2)\right.\right.$$
$$+ \frac{1}{2}(F_{xx}^2 - F_{xy}^2 + F_{yx}^2 - F_{yy}^2)\cos 2\Theta$$
$$\left. + (F_{xx}F_{xy} + F_{yx}F_{yy})\sin 2\Theta\right]^{1/2}$$
$$\times\left[\frac{1}{2}(F_{xx}^2 + F_{xy}^2 + F_{yx}^2 + F_{yy}^2)\right.$$
$$- \frac{1}{2}(F_{xx}^2 - F_{xy}^2 + F_{yx}^2 - F_{yy}^2)\cos 2\Theta$$
$$\left.\left. - (F_{xx}F_{xy} + F_{yx}F_{yy})\sin 2\Theta\right]^{1/2}\right\}^{-1} \quad (5.102)$$

The change in angle between the two vectors is the angle of shear, or $\gamma = \pi/2 - \beta$, where:

$$\cos\beta = \cos\left(\frac{\pi}{2} - \gamma\right) = \sin\gamma \quad (5.103)$$

Considering only the angle change between the two orthogonal material lines for the case $\Theta = 0$, the components of the two representative vectors (5.99) reduce to:

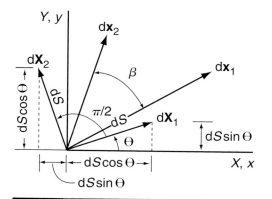

Fig 5.36 Shear is the angle change between two material line segments initially perpendicular to one another, here represented by the pair of infinitesimal vectors $d\mathbf{X}_1$ and $d\mathbf{X}_2$. In the final state these are $d\mathbf{x}_1$ and $d\mathbf{x}_2$.

$$dX_1 \cong dS, \quad dY_1 \cong 0,$$
$$dX_2 \cong 0, \quad dY_2 \cong dS \tag{5.104}$$

For this special case (5.102) reduces to:

$$\cos \beta = \sin \gamma = \frac{(F_{xx}F_{xy} + F_{yx}F_{yy})}{\sqrt{(F_{xx}^2 + F_{yx}^2)} \sqrt{(F_{xy}^2 + F_{yy}^2)}} \tag{5.105}$$

Since the results for the infinitesimal strain and rotation case are much simpler, we write (5.102) in terms of the displacement gradient using (5.82) and eliminate all products of these gradients. Then, using (5.88) for the strain components we have:

$$\cos \beta \cong [-(\varepsilon_{xx} - \varepsilon_{yy}) \sin 2\Theta + 2\varepsilon_{xy} \cos 2\Theta]$$
$$\times \{[(1 + \varepsilon_{xx} + \varepsilon_{yy}) + (\varepsilon_{xx} - \varepsilon_{yy}) \cos 2\Theta$$
$$+ 2\varepsilon_{xy} \sin 2\Theta]^{1/2} [(1 + \varepsilon_{xx} + \varepsilon_{yy})$$
$$- (\varepsilon_{xx} - \varepsilon_{yy}) \cos 2\Theta - 2\varepsilon_{xy} \sin 2\Theta]^{1/2}\}^{-1} \tag{5.106}$$

The numerator is first order in the small quantities already, so we have:

$$\cos \beta \cong -(\varepsilon_{xx} - \varepsilon_{yy}) \sin 2\Theta + 2\varepsilon_{xy} \cos 2\Theta \tag{5.107}$$

Since the quantity is small, $\cos \beta = \sin \gamma \cong \gamma$, so the angle of shear is related to the infinitesimal strain components as:

$$\gamma/2 \cong -\frac{1}{2}(\varepsilon_{xx} - \varepsilon_{yy}) \sin 2\Theta + \varepsilon_{xy} \cos 2\Theta \tag{5.108}$$

This relation also gives the value of the component ε'_{xy} of the infinitesimal strain tensor for the transformation of coordinates from axes (X, Y) to axes (X', Y') rotated by Θ. The geometric interpretation to ε'_{xy} is one-half the change in angle between material line elements parallel to the coordinate axes X' and Y' in the initial state.

In summary we note that *homogeneous deformation* consists of deformation within a *finite* region of a body for which the components of the deformation gradient tensor (5.80) are uniform. The finite region may extend to the entire body, but need not do so. It is always possible to express the deformation with respect to a coordinate system whose origin lies within this finite region. This is precisely the same logic as our use of a coordinate system fixed to the particle to describe the deformation in its neighborhood. Thus, for such a finite region, we may write as in the earlier sections the relations given in (5.45). Everything said above with reference to the neighborhood of a point applies to the homogeneous deformation throughout the finite region.

5.5.2 Deformation in the neighborhood of a particle: three-dimensional case

Here we summarize the three-dimensional case for deformation in the neighborhood of a particle and write down general expressions for the deformation tensor and the strain tensor in terms of deformation gradients and displacement gradients. Because there is little additional physical insight to be gained beyond the discussion of the two-dimensional case given in the previous section we rely more on indicial notation here. On the other hand, rock deformation is inherently three-dimensional so one needs to be acquainted with these forms of the basic kinematic equations. While far from being an exhaustive description of strain and deformation (see for example Malvern, 1969) we provide a basis consistent with the level of continuum mechanics used in this textbook. Means (1976) provides an explanatory review of strain and deformation in the context of structural geology.

Expanding the discussion of Fig. 5.34 to three dimensions, consider a particle located by position vector $\mathbf{X}$ with components $X_i = (X_1, X_2, X_3)$ in the initial state that is located by position vector $\mathbf{x}$ with components $x_i = (x_1, x_2, x_3)$ in the current state. An arbitrarily oriented material line extending from that particle in the initial state along the infinitesimal vector, $\mathbf{dX}$, with components (dX_1, dX_2, dX_3) is translated, rotated, and stretched to lie along the infinitesimal vector, $\mathbf{dx}$, with components (dx_1, dx_2, dx_3) in the current state. Infinitesimal refers to the fact that, if the vector were not infinitesimal in length, the material line element would be curved in the current state and the vector $\mathbf{dx}$ would not provide an adequate representation. In other words, the neighborhood of the particle is so defined that the deformation within it is reasonably taken as homogeneous.

The components of the vector $\mathbf{dx}$ in the current state may be calculated from the components of the corresponding vector $\mathbf{dX}$ in the initial state as:

$$dx_k = \frac{\partial x_k}{\partial X_M} dX_M = F_{kM} dX_M \tag{5.109}$$

Here and in what follows capital indices are used for coordinates in the initial state and lower case indices for coordinates in the current state, and these indices have the range 1, 2, 3. The F_{kM} are components of the three-dimensional deformation gradient tensor for which the partial derivatives are taken with respect to the initial coordinates. In other words this is the tensor that associates the vector, $\mathbf{dX}$, representing infinitesimal material lines of all possible orientations at the point $\mathbf{X}$ in the initial state with the vector, $\mathbf{dx}$, representing those material lines in the current state. This is referred to as the Lagrangian formulation of the deformation gradients in contrast to the Eulerian formulation in which the derivatives are taken with respect to the current coordinates (Malvern, 1969, Section 4.5).

The length of the material line in the initial state is the magnitude of the infinitesimal vector, $dS = |\mathbf{dX}|$, and the length in the current state is the magnitude $ds = |\mathbf{dx}|$. The square of the current length is related to the deformation gradients as:

$$(ds)^2 = dX_I \frac{\partial x_k}{\partial X_I} \frac{\partial x_k}{\partial X_J} dX_J \tag{5.110}$$

This result leads to the definition of the Green deformation tensor:

$$C_{IJ} = \frac{\partial x_k}{\partial X_I} \frac{\partial x_k}{\partial X_J} \tag{5.111}$$

A counterpart to this tensor, which is used to compute $(dS)^2$ using partial derivatives of the initial coordinates with respect to the current coordinates, is referred to as the Cauchy deformation tensor (Malvern, 1969).

In the Lagrangian formulation the change in the squared length of the material line is related to the deformation gradients as:

$$(ds)^2 - (dS)^2 = dX_I \left(\frac{\partial x_k}{\partial X_I} \frac{\partial x_k}{\partial X_J} - \delta_{IJ} \right) dX_J \tag{5.112}$$

This result leads to the definition of the Lagrangian strain tensor:

$$E_{IJ} = \frac{1}{2} \left(\frac{\partial x_k}{\partial X_I} \frac{\partial x_k}{\partial X_J} - \delta_{IJ} \right) \tag{5.113}$$

This is an exact description of the strain at a point in a continuum which involves no approximations, and there are no restrictions upon the magnitude of the components. The Lagrangian strain tensor (or its counterpart in the Eulerian formulation) often is referred to in the literature of structural geology as the *finite strain* in contrast to the infinitesimal strain, but it should be understood that these tensors are inclusive of all strain magnitudes whether small or large.

Comparing (5.111) and (5.113), the Lagrangian strain tensor is related to the Green deformation tensor as $2E_{IJ} = C_{IJ} - \delta_{IJ}$. These tensors are symmetric and both have three orthogonal principal axes at the point $\mathbf{X}$ in the initial state, the corresponding directions of which coincide (Malvern, 1969). The Green deformation tensor reduces to zero and the Lagrangian strain tensor reduces to one as the magnitudes of the deformation gradients all go to zero.

5.5.3 Errors associated with use of infinitesimal strains

One of the first questions that a structural geologist should ask when taking up a problem related to deformation in Earth's crust is: should the strains be approximated with the infinitesimal strain components? A positive answer opens the door to the possibility that linear elasticity may be employed to model the deformation. A negative answer means that the strain should be described using the Lagrangian strain tensor (5.113) or its Eulerian counterpart. To address this question one can, for example, compare the Lagrangian and infinitesimal strains for a given set of deformation or displacement gradients and calculate the error. Whether or not that error is acceptable depends upon the application. If one is looking for order of magnitude results from a calculation, large errors may be tolerable. If one is working under strict engineering guidelines, only very small errors may be tolerable.

To estimate the error we write the Lagrangian strain tensor as given in (5.113) in terms of the displacement gradients by noting that:

$$x_i = X_i + u_i(X_1, X_2, X_3, t) \tag{5.114}$$

In other words the displacement components, u_i, are functions of the coordinates in the initial state and of time. Here we have reverted to using only lower case indices in order to facilitate comparison with the infinitesimal strain components as conventionally written. Taking the partial derivatives of the x_i as described in (5.114) and substituting these into (5.113) we find the Lagrangian components of strain:

$$E_{ij} = \frac{1}{2}\left(\frac{\partial u_i}{\partial X_j} + \frac{\partial u_j}{\partial X_i} + \frac{\partial u_k}{\partial X_i}\frac{\partial u_k}{\partial X_j}\right) \tag{5.115}$$

The infinitesimal components of strain are defined using the first two terms on the right-hand side:

$$\varepsilon_{ij} = \frac{1}{2}\left(\frac{\partial u_i}{\partial X_j} + \frac{\partial u_j}{\partial X_i}\right) \tag{5.116}$$

The error introduced by using (5.116) instead of (5.115) may be defined as:

$$e_{ij} = \frac{E_{ij} - \varepsilon_{ij}}{E_{ij}} \times 100 \tag{5.117}$$

This evaluates the error, e_{ij}, on a component by component basis.

If squares and products of the displacement gradients are small enough compared with the gradients themselves to result in tolerable errors then the last term on the right-hand side of (5.115) may be dropped. What is left are the components of the infinitesimal strain written in terms of

displacement gradients referred to the initial coordinates. Under these conditions the differences between partial derivatives taken with respect to the initial coordinates and those taken with respect to the current coordinates are negligible, so the distinctions made here between the two sets of coordinates are ignored and the strain components are written:

$$\varepsilon_{ij} = \frac{1}{2}\left(\frac{\partial u_i}{\partial x_j} + \frac{\partial u_j}{\partial x_i}\right) \tag{5.118}$$

The two-dimensional forms of these equations referred to Cartesian coordinates are given in (5.88).

As an example of error analysis consider the photographs of oöids from the South Mountain fold shown in the frontispiece for this chapter. Recall that the average ratio of long to short axes for the less deformed sample (on the left) is 1.16, and that for the more deformed sample (on the right) is 1.56. For the sake of this example we consider plane deformation (zero displacement perpendicular to the photograph) and take the coordinate axes (X, Y) parallel to the average orientations of the long and short axes, respectively (no rotation of material lines that coincide with the principal directions in the deformed state). For the more deformed sample we take the displacement gradients in the plane as:

$$\frac{\partial u_x}{\partial X} = 0.25, \qquad \frac{\partial u_x}{\partial Y} = 0,$$
$$\frac{\partial u_y}{\partial X} = 0, \qquad \frac{\partial u_y}{\partial Y} = -0.20 \tag{5.119}$$

The components of the Lagrangian strain (5.115) are:

$$E_{xx} = 0.30, \quad E_{xy} = 0, \quad E_{yx} = 0, \quad E_{yy} = -0.18 \tag{5.120}$$

The components of the infinitesimal strain (5.116) are:

$$\varepsilon_{xx} = 0.25, \quad \varepsilon_{xy} = 0, \quad \varepsilon_{yx} = 0, \quad \varepsilon_{yy} = -0.20 \tag{5.121}$$

The errors in the two normal components of strain are found using (5.117):

$$e_{xx} \approx 17\%, \quad e_{yy} \approx -11\% \tag{5.122}$$

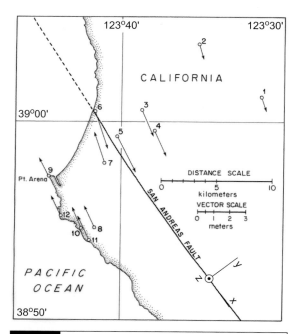

Fig 5.37 Map of the horizontal displacement of twelve monuments near Pt. Arena, CA, during the 1906 San Francisco earthquake (Lawson, 1908; Pollard and Segall, 1987).

In contrast the errors associated with the less deformed sample are 7% and −4%, respectively. Whether or not these errors are tolerable depends upon the magnitude of errors associated with data collection and the application of the analysis.

As a second example consider the displacement field associated with faulting during the great San Francisco earthquake of 1906 along the San Andreas Fault (Fig. 5.37). In the vicinity of Point Arena near the northern-most trace of the fault the relative horizontal displacements of monuments were calculated from triangulation surveys taken before and after the earthquake (Lawson, 1908). The displacement vectors on this map demonstrate that slip on the fault was right lateral, that the offset across the fault zone was about 4 m, and that Earth's surface displaced during the earthquake at least 15 km away from the fault by about 1 m. Can we use infinitesimal strains to characterize this deformation?

We choose a Cartesian coordinate system and reference frame on the trace of the fault with the x-axis horizontal and parallel to the trace, the y-

axis perpendicular to the vertical fault surface, and the z-axis vertical. Note that the displacement vectors are approximately parallel to the fault trace. Comparing the displacements of monuments 5, 4, and 1, the displacement is seen to decrease in magnitude with distance perpendicular from the fault. Furthermore, comparing monuments 1 and 2, or 3 and 4, or 9 and 10, it is apparent that the displacement does not vary significantly with distance parallel to the fault. We know from investigations of many subsequent earthquakes on the San Andreas Fault that ruptures typically extend to depths no greater that about 10 to 15 km, so the slip is likely to have varied from 4 m at the surface to zero at these depths.

Taking our observations of the displacement vectors on Fig. 5.37 as representative of the displacement field throughout this region we characterize the displacement components as:

$$u_x = u_x(y, z), \quad u_y \approx 0, \quad u_z \approx 0 \qquad (5.123)$$

The displacement of monument 5, adjacent to the fault zone, was about 2.5 m and the displacement of monument 1, at a distance of 13.5 km from the fault zone, was about 1 m. Using these values, and an estimated depth of faulting of 12.5 km, we estimate the displacement gradients as:

$$\frac{\partial u_x}{\partial y} \approx \frac{\Delta u_x}{\Delta y} = \frac{1.5\,\text{m}}{13.5 \times 10^3\,\text{m}} = 1.1 \times 10^{-4}$$

$$\frac{\partial u_x}{\partial z} \approx \frac{\Delta u_x}{\Delta z} = \frac{2.5\,\text{m}}{12.5 \times 10^3\,\text{m}} = 2.0 \times 10^{-4}$$

$$(5.124)$$

Although the slip on the fault was several meters, the displacement gradients are so small that squares and products of these gradients may be neglected. This conclusion admits use of infinitesimal strains and suggests that linear elasticity theory would be an appropriate tool to investigate the faulting process (Pollard and Segall, 1987).

5.6 | Concluding remarks

In this chapter, we examined deformed objects in rocks – belemnites, folded veins, concretions, and xenoliths – and indicated how a quantitative measure of strain might be obtained from measurements of them. Several examples demonstrate that strain typically has a continuous variation within structures, providing one constraint on the process of formation. More detailed treatment of practical methods of strain estimation from deformed geological objects are given in other textbooks of structural geology (Ramsay and Huber, 1983). Interpretation of deformed xenoliths in the Chindamora batholith by means of an appealing, but ad hoc, kinematic model illustrates a methodology aimed at constraining the mechanism of intrusion by means of strain measurements. In contrast, we showed how a simple steady-state distribution of velocity in a rising "diapir," provided by the complete mechanical model afforded by the Stokes solution, might be used to follow the positions of particles, thus generating a detailed picture of the evolution of the strain distribution in the body. As another bridge between observations of geometry and strain and detailed models of structural evolution, we considered geometric and ad hoc kinematic models of chevron folds. We study a mechanical model for their origin in a later chapter. The kinematic model presented here provides a simple example with which to illustrate the formal treatment of strain and rotation as integrals that follow a particle moving through a temporally and possibly spatially varying velocity field. In the rising viscous sphere example, strain ellipses were computed by following dense sets of particles by numerical means. The chapter concluded with a more formal treatment of plane deformation in two dimensions, and descriptions of deformation and strain in three dimensions. In this discussion we point out how to evaluate the errors expected when one chooses to employ the infinitesimal strain in the analysis of problems in structural geology.

Chapter 6

Force, traction, and stress

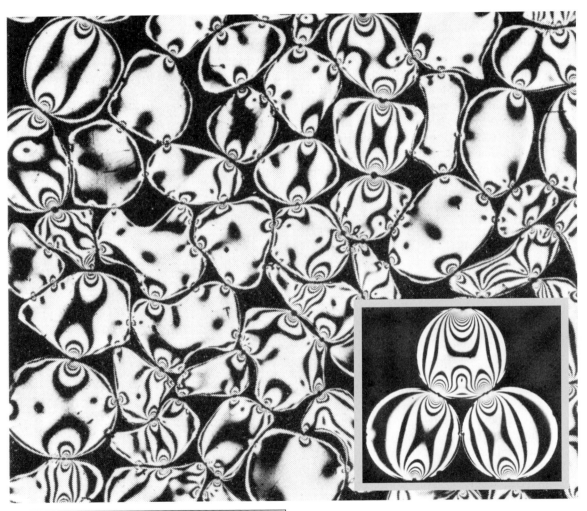

Photoelastic image of maximum shear stress contours in grains of model rock. Stress is concentrated at grain contacts. Inset: photoelastic image of three circular disks with point contact loads. Reprinted from Gallagher *et al.* (1974) with permission from Elsevier.

The concept of stress is the heart of our subject. It is the unique way continuum mechanics has for specifying the interaction between one part of a material body and another (Fung, 1969, p. 41).

n this chapter we define the relationships among forces, tractions, and stresses. One of the first concepts encountered in a physics class is that of the resultant force, F, acting on a particle with mass, m, and the associated linear acceleration, a, of that particle in the direction that the force acts (Fig. 6.1a). For a rigid body (Fig. 6.1b) one considers, for example, the resultant torque, τ, about the axis z, due to the force, f, acting at position, r, and the associated angular acceleration. For a deformable body the traction vector, t(n), is a measure of force per unit area acting on the surface of a body (Fig. 6.1c), where the surface has an orientation specified by the outward unit normal vector, n. This surface can be the exterior boundary of a rock mass or an imagined surface within the rock mass. The traction vector is defined at a point on such a surface in a limiting process as the area of a small element of this surface shrinks toward zero about the point. Similarly, if one imagines a small cubical element of a given orientation at a point within a body (Fig. 6.1d), one can define the tractions acting on all six sides as the volume shrinks toward zero. The components of the traction on each side define the components of the stress acting on the cubical element with reference to the chosen coordinate system, and this collection of forces per unit area is referred to as a tensor quantity. Normal and shear components of the stress tensor are directed perpendicular and parallel to the sides of the cubical element, respectively. In this hierarchy of concepts the force vector acts on a point mass; the torque vector acts about an axis; the force per unit area, or traction vector, acts on a surface element; and the set of forces per unit area, or stress tensor, acts on a volume element.

The traction and stress are of interest to the structural geologist because structures develop as the rocks of the Earth's crust strain and flow, and the distribution of this deformation is related to the stresses acting within the rock mass and the tractions acting on its surfaces. In this and later chapters we show how the concepts of traction and stress can be applied to understand the origin and evolution of geological structures. In most natural examples the traction and stress vary with position and time: they are field quan-

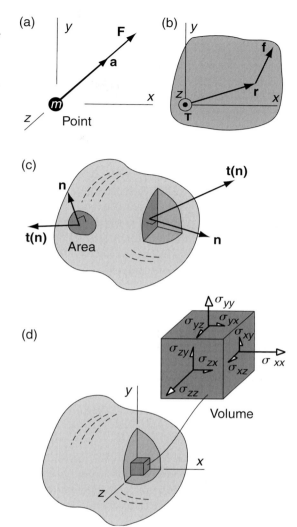

Fig 6.1 Force, torque, traction, and stress are illustrated as: (a) force vector, F, acting on a particle of mass, m with corresponding acceleration vector, a; (b) torque vector, τ, due to force, f, acting at position vector, r; (c) traction vector, t(n), acting on surface element with outward normal n; (d) stress tensor, σ_{ij}, acting on volume element with edges parallel to coordinate axes.

tities with spatial and temporal variations. For example, the frontispiece for this chapter is a photographic visualization of the distribution of shear stress in the grains of a model sandstone (Gallager *et al.*, 1974). An understanding of the possible variations of these fields in the Earth is of fundamental importance to structural geologists.

6.1 | Concepts of force and traction

In the context of rock masses that behave as deformable solids or fluids two classes of forces are recognized: *body forces* act on volume elements within the rock mass and *surface forces* act on surface elements, either the actual surface of the rock mass or imaginary surfaces within it. Common examples of body forces are those due to gravity and magnetic attraction, both of which act "at a distance" rather than through the direct contact to two objects. In contrast surface forces are those due to the direct contact of one object with another. For an imaginary surface within a rock mass one can think of the surface force due to the rock mass on one side of that surface in contact with the rock mass on the other side. Because rock is a porous material one has to consider the nature of such a contact and the definition of surface forces with some care. Body and surface forces are defined at arbitrary points in the continuous medium that we take as a model for the rock mass. In this section we consider body and surface forces and the traction vector; in the next section we take up the stress tensor.

6.1.1 Body force
If the vector **b** is the body force per unit mass acting on an infinitesimal volume element dV (Fig. 6.2a) then the resultant of all body forces acting on the finite volume, δV, is (Malvern, 1969):

$$\int_{\delta V} \rho \mathbf{b}\, dV = \mathbf{e}_x \int_{\delta V} \rho b_x\, dV + \mathbf{e}_y \int_{\delta V} \rho b_y\, dV + \mathbf{e}_z \int_{\delta V} \rho b_z\, dV$$

(6.1)

Here ρ is the mass density and (b_x, b_y, b_z) are the Cartesian components of **b**, and both the density and body force may vary with the spatial coordinates. The resultant body force is the vector sum of the body forces acting on all infinitesimal elements within the finite volume δV. The density and the body force per unit mass may vary in time, in which case (6.1) is considered to represent a given instant in time. In principle, if the spatial variations of $\rho \mathbf{b}$ are known as functions of the three coordinates, and if the shape of the finite volume is relatively simple (for example a rectangular

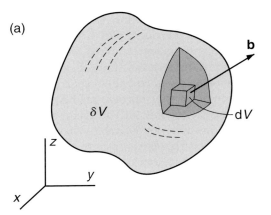

(a)

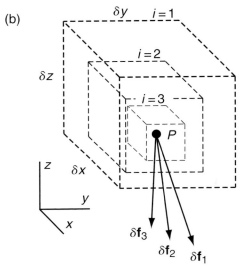

(b)

Fig 6.2 (a) Body force, **b**, per unit mass acting on infinitesimal volume element, dV, within a finite volume, δV. (b) Sequence of finite volumes, δV_i, with resultant body forces, $\delta \mathbf{f}_i$.

volume with sides aligned with the coordinate system as in Fig. 6.2b), the volume integral may be evaluated as a triple integral with appropriate ranges for the limits in the three coordinates:

$$\int_{z_1}^{z_2} \int_{y_1}^{y_2} \int_{x_1}^{x_2} \rho \mathbf{b}\, dx\, dy\, dz$$

(6.2)

As indicated in (6.1) each component may be written as a separate triple integral and these are added to compute the resultant body force.

In general we want to characterize the body force at any arbitrary point P in the deformable solid or flowing fluid and this requires an idealization of the rock mass as a material continuum. For this purpose we consider a sequence of finite volumes, δV_i, each with resultant body force, $\delta \mathbf{f}_i$, and average density, ρ_i, and each containing the point in question (Fig. 6.2b). The finite volumes are ordered from largest, $i = 1$, to smallest $i = n$, such that the volume approaches zero as $n \to \infty$. In this limit the largest dimension of the sample approaches zero, so the volume converges to the point P, not to a surface or a curve containing the point (Malvern, 1969). Furthermore, the resultant body force varies as one considers successive volumes in the sequence and approaches zero in the limit. The formal definition of the body force per unit mass at the point P in the material continuum is:

$$\mathbf{b} = \underset{n \to \infty}{\text{limit}} \left(\frac{\delta \mathbf{f}_n}{\rho_n \delta V_n} \right) \tag{6.3}$$

Although both the numerator and the denominator in (6.3) approach zero, a fundamental postulate is that the ratio approaches a definite value at each and every point in the continuum. The difficulty encountered when rationalizing definitions such as this with our knowledge of the properties of real materials is resolved as follows:

When we pass, however, to the infinitesimal limit dV (volume) or dS (surface), we are dealing with a hypothetical concept, a continuum or continuous medium, whose justification depends not on any study of actual materials in the small, but rather on the efficacy and utility of the concept in enabling us to describe and predict the behavior of actual materials in the large, i.e., the macroscopic behavior (Malvern, 1969).

For rock one must be aware that application of the material continuum may be problematic at the grain scale and at the intermolecular scale where sharp discontinuities break up an otherwise continuous body.

For most problems in structural geology gravity is the only significant body force, so the body force per unit mass is the gravitational acceleration, $\mathbf{b} = \mathbf{g}$. Furthermore, the magnitude of this body force, g, usually does not vary significantly over length scales from meters to kilometers, so it may be taken as uniform and equal to the standard value $g^* = 9.806\,65\,\text{m s}^{-2}$ (Mohr and

Taylor, 2003). For a Cartesian coordinate system with z-axis vertical and directed upward (Fig. 6.2b) the components of the body force per unit mass are:

$$b_x = 0, \quad b_y = 0, \quad b_z = -g^* \tag{6.4}$$

For the rectangular body of volume δV shown in Fig. 6.2b with side lengths $\delta x = x_2 - x_1$, $\delta y = y_2 - y_1$, and $\delta z = z_2 - z_1$ the resultant body force magnitude is:

$$\rho b_z \int_{z_1}^{z_2} \int_{y_1}^{y_2} \int_{x_1}^{x_2} \mathrm{d}x\,\mathrm{d}y\,\mathrm{d}z = -\rho g^* \delta x \delta y \delta z = -\rho g^* \delta V \tag{6.5}$$

Here density is taken as uniform so the calculation is greatly simplified.

The body force per unit volume is the vector quantity $\rho \mathbf{g}$. Under conditions where both mass density and the gravitational acceleration are taken as known values, constant in time and uniform in space, the components of the body force per unit volume with coordinates as in Fig. 6.2 are:

$$\rho b_x = 0, \quad \rho b_y = 0, \quad \rho b_z = -\rho g^* \tag{6.6}$$

The gravitational body force plays an important role in many tectonic processes from the buoyant rise of magma and salt through the crust to the loading and unloading of buried rock masses during mountain building and erosion.

6.1.2 Surface force: the traction vector

In order to discuss deformation in the Earth we need a way of talking about and quantifying the distribution of forces acting on an arbitrary surface within a rock mass. For example, we might ask what were the forces distributed on the surfaces of a fault that would cause it to slip? Or, what are the forces distributed on the surfaces of a dike that would cause it to open? Questions like these require us to understand and use the traction vector. The traction vector also is used to define the distribution of forces (or lack thereof) acting on any external surfaces of a rock mass. For example, the Earth's surface is characterized as being a *traction-free surface*. Of course large buildings, dams, and other engineering structures impose non-zero tractions and the filling of large reservoirs imposes sufficient traction to depress the surface over a broad region. The weight of the atmosphere provides a normal traction (1 atm = 0.1 MPa) and the wind imposes some shear traction, but all of these tractions acting on Earth's surface usually are ignored because the tractions involved in the tectonic processes leading to the development of geological structures are significantly greater in magnitude.

Consider a surface, S, arbitrarily located within the Earth and shown in cross section as the dashed curve in Fig. 6.3. This is not necessarily a physical boundary between rocks of different lithologies, nor does it have a particular scale. The surface could be located within a single rock unit or within a single mineral grain. The surface passes through the point P and the orientation of the surface at this point is given by the outward unit normal vector $\mathbf{n}$. We refer to the positive ($+$) side of the surface with reference to how $\mathbf{n}$ is directed. Given the orientation of $\mathbf{n}$, the surface S bounds that portion of the rock mass on the negative side, indicated by the gray swath on the cross section.

The forces acting on the surface S could have a complex distribution, varying from point to point in both magnitude and direction. This is schematically illustrated in an enlarged view (Fig. 6.3, inset) by a collection of arrows with their tails or heads on a small patch of the surface of area δA that contains the point P. These forces account for the mechanical action of the rock mass on the positive side of the patch and they may be represented by a resultant force, $\delta\mathbf{f}$, acting at the centroid, P, of the patch, and a resultant torque, $\delta\tau$, acting about an axis through the centroid. The resultant force and torque are not restricted as to direction. In some contexts the resultant torque is referred to as the resultant moment.

In a thought experiment the rock mass is idealized as a material continuum and we consider a sequence of patches of the designated surface, S, with finite areas, δA_i, each associated with a different resultant force, $\delta\mathbf{f}_i$, and each containing the point P. The patches are ordered from largest, $i = 1$, to smallest $i = n$, such that their surface areas approach zero as $n \to \infty$. In this limit the largest dimension of the patch approaches zero, so the patch converges to the point P and not to a curve

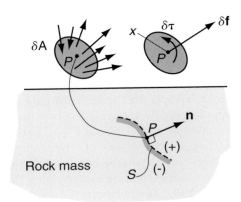

Fig 6.3 At point P on an arbitrary surface S within a rock mass the outward unit normal is $\mathbf{n}$. Inset shows force vectors acting on surface with area δA containing the point P. Resultant force is $\delta\mathbf{f}$ and resultant torque is $\delta\tau$.

through the point (Malvern, 1969). The resultant forces on each successive patch may vary in magnitude and direction, but they also approach zero in this limit. The ratio of resultant force to surface area is defined as the *traction vector*, $\mathbf{t}(\mathbf{n})$:

$$\mathbf{t}(\mathbf{n}) = \lim_{n \to \infty} \left[\frac{\delta\mathbf{f}_n}{\delta A_n} \right] \qquad (6.7)$$

The French mathematician Augustine-Louis Cauchy (1789–1857) apparently first contemplated this ratio and proposed that it approaches a definite value in this limit (Fung, 1969). The traction vector sometimes is referred to as the stress vector, but the stress is a different construct so this choice of words is confusing and should be avoided.

We have written the traction vector as $\mathbf{t}(\mathbf{n})$ in (6.7) to emphasize that this quantity is a function of the orientation of the surface upon which it acts. This orientation is specified by the vector $\mathbf{n}$ of unit magnitude, directed outward and normal to the surface (Fig. 6.4a). An infinite number of surfaces ($S_1, S_2, S_3, \ldots$) with different normal curvatures may be constructed through the point P, all having the same normal, $\mathbf{n}$, at that point. The traction vectors acting on all of these surfaces at P are identical in magnitude and direction. On the other hand two surfaces may be constructed through the same point P with different normals, $\mathbf{n}(1)$ and $\mathbf{n}(2)$ (Fig. 6.4b). The traction vectors, $\mathbf{t}[\mathbf{n}(1)]$

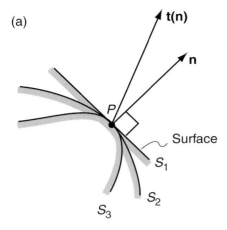

(a)

t(n)

n

P

Surface

S_1

S_2

S_3

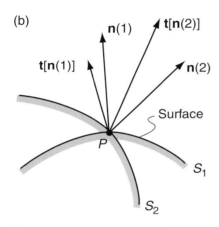

(b)

n(1)

t[n(2)]

t[n(1)]

n(2)

Surface

P

S_1

S_2

Fig 6.4 Relations among surfaces S_i through point P and traction vector at point P. (a) Surfaces with different curvatures but same outward unit normal, **n**, have the same traction. (b) Surfaces with different normals have different tractions regardless of their curvature.

tion vector for that force. The magnitude of this position vector is the distance from the centroid to the point of application of the force on the surface, and in the limit this distance goes to zero, so Cauchy's proposal has an intuitive appeal. Note that a resultant torque may exist on a surface of finite area. For example, as a layer of sedimentary rock is bent during folding most cross-sectional surfaces of the layer are loaded by forces that contribute to a net torque. This torque is called a bending moment and these moments play a prominent role in theories of bending and folding (Timoshenko, 1958; Timoshenko and Woinowsky-Krieger, 1959). The theory of coupled stresses, which will not be considered further in this textbook, admits the possibility of a continuous distribution of torques per unit area, with a limit at a point on a surface that is different from zero (Malvern, 1969).

The traction at a point on a surface is a measure of the force per unit area imparted by the material from one side of the surface to the material on the other side. This concept can be stated succinctly as (Fung, 1969, p. 51):

$$t[\mathbf{n}(2)] = -t[\mathbf{n}(1)] \tag{6.9}$$

Here it is understood that $\mathbf{n}(1)$ and $\mathbf{n}(2)$ are unit normals at the same point on a surface viewed from opposite sides, so $\mathbf{n}(1) = -\mathbf{n}(2)$. To interpret (6.9) consider Fig. 6.5a in which a rock mass is divided into two parts, 1 and 2, by the surface, S, illustrated here in cross section. The outward unit normal vector for part 1 is $\mathbf{n}(1)$, and that for part 2 is $\mathbf{n}(2)$: these are oppositely directed vectors. At the point P the rock of part 2 exerts a traction, $t[\mathbf{n}(1)]$, on part 1. As drawn, part 2 is pulling on part 1 at an angle that is somewhat oblique to $\mathbf{n}(1)$. Now, imagine removing part 2 and replacing the mechanical action of part 2 on part 1 with the appropriate distribution of tractions. If this operation were done accurately, according to Cauchy, nothing about the mechanical state of part 1 would change. Now consider the same surface with part 1 removed (Fig. 6.5b). What traction would have to be applied at point P to replace the mechanical action of part 1 on part 2? According to Cauchy's concept, we would have to apply a traction, here called $t[\mathbf{n}(2)]$, of magnitude equal to $t[\mathbf{n}(1)]$, but oppositely directed.

and $t[\mathbf{n}(2)]$, acting on these surfaces are different in magnitude and direction.

In a thought experiment similar to that leading to (6.7) the ratio of resultant torque to surface area is considered (Fig. 6.3). Cauchy apparently contemplated this ratio and proposed that the limiting value approaches zero:

$$\underset{n \to \infty}{\text{limit}} \left[\frac{\delta \boldsymbol{\tau}_n}{\delta A_n} \right] = 0 \tag{6.8}$$

Torque is the vector product of the force acting at a given distance from the centroid and the posi-

(a)

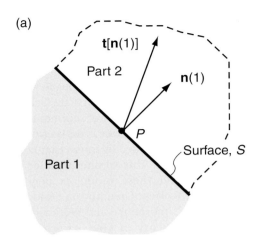

(b)

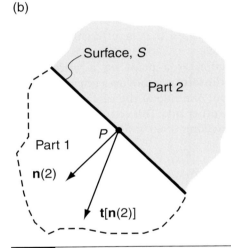

Fig 6.5 Surface, S, separates two parts of a body (Fung, 1969). (a) At point P part 2 exerts a traction $\mathbf{t}[\mathbf{n}(1)]$ on part 1. (b) At point P part 1 exerts a traction $\mathbf{t}[\mathbf{n}(2)]$ on part 2. These two tractions are equal in magnitude and oppositely directed.

The relationship expressed in (6.9) is an extension of *Newton's Third Law:* to every action there is always opposed an equal reaction; or, the mutual actions of two bodies upon each other are always equal, and directed to contrary parts (Resnick and Halliday, 1977, p. 79). Here action refers to force, so equal and opposite forces describe the mechanical response of one body upon another. By considering a small patch of a surface, and the resultant force acting on that patch, this law is extended to the traction vector.

To summarize, Cauchy apparently enunciated most of the following points concerning the traction vector in 1822 (Truesdell, 1961):

1. The traction is a vector quantity that acts at a point on an imaginary or real surface of arbitrary orientation (Fig. 6.3), specified by the outward unit normal vector, in the interior or on the exterior of a body.
2. The traction measures the limiting ratio of resultant force to surface area on a patch of the surface as this patch shrinks down about a point.
3. Different surfaces with the same orientation at a common point are acted upon by the same traction (Fig. 6.4a), but differently oriented surfaces through that same point are acted upon by different tractions (Fig. 6.4b).
4. The traction vector can vary in orientation from acting normal to the surface to acting tangential to the surface.
5. The traction at a point on a surface is equal and opposite to the traction that acts at that same point for the same surface with opposite outward unit normal vector (Fig. 6.5).
6. The physical dimensions of traction are force per unit area, $MLT^{-2}L^{-2} = ML^{-1}T^{-2}$.
7. The SI units for the traction are $Nm^{-2} = Pa$.

The conceptualization of the traction vector was a major accomplishment in the history of development of continuum mechanics.

6.1.3 Application of the traction vector to rock

The definition of the traction vector, $\mathbf{t}(\mathbf{n})$, at a point on a surface with outward unit normal, $\mathbf{n}$, depends upon the limit (6.7) in which a small patch shrinks toward the point and the ratio of resultant force acting on the patch to the area of the patch converges smoothly to a definite value. Such a definition is entirely appropriate for the idealized material continuum, but the application of this concept to rock requires careful consideration of scale and the constituent properties. As can be appreciated by glancing at Fig. 6.6a, rock viewed at the grain scale can be highly heterogeneous with a multitude of sharp discontinuities in material properties. This image of sandstone is a few hundred micrometers across and shows

Fig 6.6 Scale dependence of homogeneity in a rock mass. (a) Sandstone at 50 μm scale showing grains and pores: material is heterogeneous (photograph courtesy of Xavier du Barnard). (b) Sandstone at 50-mm scale: material is approximately homogeneous except for zone of deformation bands. Photograph by D. D. Pollard.

several sand grains, some grain fragments, cement, and pores. The grain-scale heterogeneity of rock leads to a very complex distribution of forces, tractions, and stress (see frontispiece of this chapter). On the other hand the image of sandstone in Fig. 6.6b is a few decimeters across and shows, with the exception of the prominent zone of deformation bands, a remarkably homogeneous and apparently continuous material. From these images important questions arise about mechanical behavior of rock. Can one ignore the grain-scale heterogeneity when considering the behavior of rock at the scale of an exposure? For what scale of problems must one explicitly include the geometry and differing material properties of individual mineral grains?

At the grain scale (Fig. 6.6a), the boundaries of each grain would be explicitly defined and tractions on these surfaces would serve as boundary conditions. For example, the grains might be idealized as continuous and homogeneous elastic spheres with traction-free surfaces, except on areas of contact where the non-zero normal and shear tractions would account for the distribution of forces transmitted across these areas of contact. The traction on any surface at points in the space between spheres would have no meaning in this context. The traction on any surface at points within each sphere would be determined by the boundary conditions. In contrast the sandstone at the exposure scale (Fig. 6.6b) could be idealized as a homogeneous elastic solid, perhaps infinite in extent with no internal or external boundaries, except around the zone of deformation bands. The traction on any surface at any point would ignore the grain-scale heterogeneity and would be interpreted as described below.

To appreciate the differences between the grain-scale and the exposure-scale interpretation of the traction in sandstone consider an imaginary surface that cuts across many grains and pores. On this surface the traction may vary from negligible (within a pore) to order 10 to 100 MPa (near a grain-to-grain contact). For exposure-scale problems we seek a patch size on the surface where a meaningful average of the grain-scale fluctuations is achieved. The size of such a patch may be estimated using a model in which a bed of springs (Fig. 6.7a) replaces the mechanical

(a)

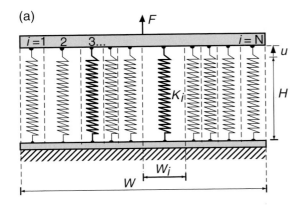

(b)

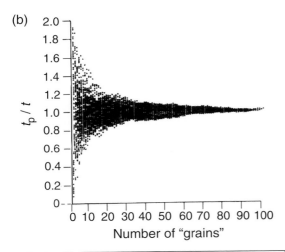

Number of "grains"

Fig 6.7 Model for grain-scale heterogeneity of rock. (a) Bed of springs with different stiffnesses accounts for grains and pores. (b) Partial traction normalized by total traction approaches a unit value as number of grains increases. Reprinted from Amadei and Stephansson (1997) with kind permission of Springer Science and Business Media.

behavior of the individual constituents of the sandstone at the grain scale (Amadei and Stephansson, 1997, p. 50). A row of N "grains" and "pores" is shown in two dimensions where the individual widths, W_i, combine to a total width, W. The height, H, before loading, and the depth out of this plane, D, are constants. The stiffness of each constituent is approximated with spring constant, K_i, and the force acting on each spring is F_i. The spring constant for "pores" would be very small compared with that for "grains." The loading system is a rigid platen that imposes the same displacement, u, on all the springs.

The relationship between the force, $\mathbf{F}$, and the displacement, $\mathbf{u}$, of a spring with constant, K, is $F = Ku$, so, for the one-dimensional loading system illustrated in Fig. 6.7a, we have:

$$F = Ku, \quad F_i = K_i u \tag{6.10}$$

Here F is the total force magnitude applied to the platen and K is the effective spring constant. By *effective spring constant* we mean the constant for a single spring that would have the same relationship between force and displacement as the entire bed of springs. The effective spring constant is the sum of all the individual constants, just as the total width of the array is the sum of individual widths:

$$K = \sum_{i=1}^{N} K_i, \quad W = \sum_{i=1}^{N} W_i \tag{6.11}$$

It is a characteristic of springs arranged in parallel that the spring constants are additive.

Because the platen that loads the bed of springs (Fig. 6.7a) applies the same displacement, u, to each constituent, the ratio of total force to effective spring constant, F/K, must be the same as the ratio of any individual force to the individual spring constant, F_i/K_i. For the purpose of understanding the definition of the traction vector, we substitute the appropriate traction, multiplied by the surface area on which it acts, for the forces acting on the constituents to find:

$$\frac{tDW}{K} = \frac{t_i DW_i}{K_i} = u \tag{6.12}$$

Here t is the total traction on the platen of area DW, and the t_i are the individual tractions that replace the mechanical action of the platen on each constituent of area DW_i. Because they have a negligible spring constant, those constituents representing "pores" carry a negligible traction regardless of their width. However, for a given displacement, this equation demonstrates that the traction acting on particular constituents increases in proportion to decreases in width. Also, the traction increases in proportion to increases in the spring constant. In other words, thinner constituents of the same stiffness carry greater traction, and stiffer constituents of the same width carry greater traction.

Consider an area that is only a part of the total area, and the partial traction, t_p, transmitted from the platen to the constituents under this partial area. The partial traction is defined as:

$$t_p = \frac{\sum\limits_{i=m}^{n} F_i}{D\sum\limits_{i=m}^{n} W_i} = \frac{u\sum\limits_{i=m}^{n} K_i}{D\sum\limits_{i=m}^{n} W_i}, \qquad \begin{cases} 1 \le m \le N \\ m \le n \le N \end{cases} \quad (6.13)$$

Note that the partial traction is found by summing the forces acting on the appropriate constituents, and then dividing by the partial area that this net force acts upon. The traction acting on the entire platen for the total of N constituents is:

$$t = \frac{F}{DW} = \frac{uK}{DW} = \frac{u\sum\limits_{i=1}^{N} K_i}{D\sum\limits_{i=1}^{N} W_i} \qquad (6.14)$$

We assume here that N is great enough so that a meaningful measure of the traction is assured.

To compare the partial and total tractions for different areas sampled consider their ratio:

$$\frac{t_p}{t} = \frac{\sum\limits_{i=m}^{n} K_i \sum\limits_{i=1}^{N} W_i}{\sum\limits_{i=m}^{n} W_i \sum\limits_{i=1}^{N} K_i}, \qquad \begin{cases} 1 \le m \le N \\ m \le n \le N \end{cases} \quad (6.15)$$

As the partial area approaches the total area in size, that is as m goes to 1 and n goes to N, the ratio t_p/t goes to 1. In other words, the partial traction approaches the value of the total traction, as expected. For partial areas less than the total area, the ratio may differ from one, and this difference is a measure of the variability in traction introduced by the heterogeneity in stiffness and width of the individual constituents.

An example of many calculations of the ratio t_p/t for different sample areas from a model rock is shown in Fig. 6.7b (Amadei and Stephansson, 1997, p. 50). For small numbers of constituents in the partial sample the scatter of the ratio about 1 is significant, but the inclusion of 50 constituents reduces the scatter to less than 10%. Since typical grains in medium sandstone are less than 0.50 mm in diameter, an area on the order of 10 mm² would be large enough to average out most of the variability in partial traction. Using this area the ratio of resultant force to surface

area would vary slowly and approximately continuously throughout the rock. The area defined by this procedure is referred to as the *representative elementary area*, because it includes enough constituents to be representative of the rock as a whole. In this way the concept of the traction vector, which presupposes a material continuum, is extended to rock that is both heterogeneous and discontinuous at the grain scale (Fig. 6.6a), but effectively homogeneous and continuous at the scale of a hand sample or exposure (Fig. 6.6b).

6.1.4 Variation of the traction with orientation of the surface

The traction vector at a point, P, varies with the orientation of the surface, S, upon which it acts (Fig. 6.4b). To understand how the traction varies consider a small tetrahedral element with three orthogonal sides that are parallel to the respective coordinate planes. The fourth side is a patch of the surface S with area δA that includes the point P and is arbitrarily inclined to the coordinate planes (Fig. 6.8a). This is referred to as the *Cauchy tetrahedron* because it was introduced in publications by Cauchy in 1823 and 1827 (Malvern, 1969). The orientation of the patch is determined by the outward-directed unit normal vector **n**, which makes direction angles $(\alpha_x, \alpha_y, \alpha_z)$ with the coordinate axes. Each angle is taken as the smaller of the two in the plane containing **n** and the respective coordinate axis. Because **n** is a unit vector, the components (n_x, n_y, n_z) are the direction cosines:

$$n_x = \cos\alpha_x, \quad n_y = \cos\alpha_y, \quad n_z = \cos\alpha_z \qquad (6.16)$$

Recalling the definition of the magnitude of a vector (2.9), these components are related as:

$$(n_x)^2 + (n_y)^2 + (n_z)^2 = 1 \qquad (6.17)$$

The areas of the three orthogonal sides of this element are found by projection of δA onto the coordinate planes such that:

$$\delta A_x = \delta A |n_x|, \qquad \delta A_y = \delta A |n_y|,$$
$$\delta A_z = \delta A |n_z| \qquad (6.18)$$

The direction cosines (6.16) range from $+1$ to -1, so their absolute values are taken in (6.18) to assure a non-negative projected area. These relationships are used below to derive equations that

(a)

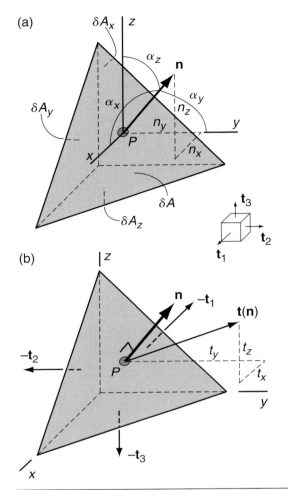

(b)

Fig 6.8 Cauchy tetrahedron used to define traction variation with orientation of plane. (a) Surface areas of sides parallel to coordinate planes are $(\delta A_x, \delta A_y, \delta A_z)$; direction angles for outward unit normal, $\mathbf{n}$, are $(\alpha_x, \alpha_y, \alpha_z)$; and components of the normal vector are (n_x, n_y, n_z). (b) Traction vectors acting on sides parallel to coordinate planes are $(-\mathbf{t}_1, -\mathbf{t}_2, -\mathbf{t}_3)$ and components of the traction vector $\mathbf{t(n)}$ are (t_x, t_y, t_z).

is possible to choose an orientation of Cartesian coordinates such that the tractions acting on the mutually orthogonal surfaces of a cubical element have zero tangential components (Fig. 6.8 inset). That is, the tractions are exactly perpendicular to the surfaces on which they act. On the three positive sides of this element (those with outward normals directed along the positive coordinate axes) we label these tractions $\mathbf{t}_1$, $\mathbf{t}_2$, and $\mathbf{t}_3$, and note that their components are $(t_1, 0, 0)$, $(0, t_2, 0)$, and $(0, 0, t_3)$. In keeping with convention the tractions are ordered such that $t_1 \geq t_2 \geq t_3$. In the limit as this element shrinks to the point P we use (6.9) to determine that the tractions on the negative sides are $-\mathbf{t}_1$, $-\mathbf{t}_2$, and $-\mathbf{t}_3$ and their components are $(-t_1, 0, 0)$, $(0, -t_2, 0)$, and $(0, 0, -t_3)$.

Now imagine that the tetrahedral element is cut free of the cubical element and the surrounding material and the mechanical action of this material on the element is replaced with the appropriate tractions (Fig. 6.8b). For the moment we ignore any body forces acting on the element. Although we understand that forces are distributed over the surfaces of the element, the tractions are drawn as single arrows with their heads or tails at the mid-points of the sides and each represents the appropriate ratio of resultant force to area as defined in (6.7). The tractions acting on the three mutually orthogonal sides are $-\mathbf{t}_1$, $-\mathbf{t}_2$, and $-\mathbf{t}_3$ and they are directed along the negative coordinate axes. The traction, $\mathbf{t(n)}$, acts on the patch with outward normal, $\mathbf{n}$, and has components $[t_x(\mathbf{n}), t_y(\mathbf{n}), t_z(\mathbf{n})]$ in the coordinate directions. In general there are no restrictions on the orientation of this traction vector: it may be parallel, inclined, or perpendicular to $\mathbf{n}$.

To find the relationship among the tractions acting on the tetrahedral element of Fig. 6.8b we use *Newton's Second Law*, $\mathbf{F} = m\mathbf{a}$, and postulate static equilibrium, $\mathbf{a} = 0$, so the net force in each coordinate direction is zero. Taking the x-coordinate direction as an example and computing the force components as the respective traction components times the areas of the surfaces on which these tractions act, the sum of the force components is written:

$$\sum f_x = [t_x(\mathbf{n})]\delta A + t_1 \delta A_x$$
$$= [t_x(\mathbf{n})]\delta A - t_1 \delta A_x = 0 \qquad (6.19)$$

describe the variation of the traction vector with $\mathbf{n}$.

In what follows we consider the limiting case in which the length of the longest edge of the tetrahedron (Fig. 6.8a) goes toward zero, so the sides converge toward the point P and the tractions acting on the four sides act at that point. The orientation of the coordinate planes that define the three orthogonal sides of the element is not arbitrary. In a later section we show that it always

Rearranging (6.19), we use (6.18) to eliminate the areas and write $t_x(\mathbf{n}) = t_1 n_x$. Here the absolute value sign in (6.18) has been dropped, so this relationship applies to the full range of orientations of $\mathbf{n}$. By similar arguments we have:

$$t_x(\mathbf{n}) = t_1 n_x, \quad t_y(\mathbf{n}) = t_2 n_y, \quad t_z(\mathbf{n}) = t_3 n_z \quad (6.20)$$

Note that the components of $\mathbf{t}(\mathbf{n})$ have opposite signs to the respective components of the tractions acting on the orthogonal sides of the element. Because, for example, the traction $-\mathbf{t}_1$ is directed in the negative x-direction, the component $t_x(\mathbf{n})$ must be positive for a balance of forces. As the inclined patch rotates toward parallelism with the (y, z)-plane such that $\mathbf{n}$ is directed along the positive x-axis, we have $n_x \to 1$, $n_y \to 0$, and $n_z \to 0$ so the y- and z-components of $\mathbf{t}(\mathbf{n})$ go to zero and $t_x(\mathbf{n}) \to t_1$, in keeping with (6.9). On the other hand, as $\mathbf{n}$ approaches the negative x-axis, we have $n_x \to -1$, so $t_x(\mathbf{n}) \to -t_1$. Although we derived (6.20) by ignoring body forces and postulating static equilibrium, we show in Chapter 7 that this relationship is more generally applicable to problems of both solid deformation and fluid flow that include body forces and admit accelerations in the equations of motion.

The relationships in (6.20) demonstrate that the traction vector $\mathbf{t}(\mathbf{n})$ is equal to the special tractions $\mathbf{t}_1$, $\mathbf{t}_2$, and $\mathbf{t}_3$ as $\mathbf{n}$ is successively directed in the positive x-, y-, and z-directions, and it is equal to $-\mathbf{t}_1$, $-\mathbf{t}_2$, and $-\mathbf{t}_3$ as $\mathbf{n}$ is successively directed in the negative x-, y-, and z-directions. But how does $\mathbf{t}(\mathbf{n})$ vary for intermediate orientations? Solving each of (6.20) for the respective component of the unit vector and substituting these into (6.17) we have:

$$\frac{[t_x(\mathbf{n})]^2}{[t_1]^2} + \frac{[t_y(\mathbf{n})]^2}{[t_2]^2} + \frac{[t_z(\mathbf{n})]^2}{[t_3]^2} = 1 \quad (6.21)$$

This equation is in the standard form for an ellipsoid drawn in "traction" space with coordinate axes $t_x(\mathbf{n})$, $t_y(\mathbf{n})$, and $t_z(\mathbf{n})$, (Fig. 6.9). The semi-major, semi-intermediate, and semi-minor axes of the ellipsoid have lengths t_1, t_2, and t_3, respectively. If the set of traction vectors for surfaces with all possible orientations through the point P are drawn with tails at the origin 0 in traction space, the traction ellipsoid (6.21) is the locus of points at the heads of these vectors. Special cases include the

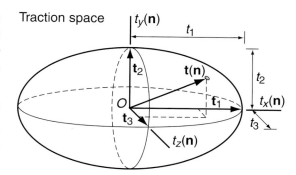

Fig 6.9 The traction ellipsoid is constructed with coordinate axes (t_x, t_y, t_z) in traction space. The semi-axes of the ellipsoid are coincident with the traction vectors ($\mathbf{t}_1$, $\mathbf{t}_2$, $\mathbf{t}_3$).

prolate ellipsoid $t_1 \geq t_2 = t_3$, the oblate ellipsoid $t_1 = t_2 \geq t_3$, and the sphere $t_1 = t_2 = t_3$.

The symmetry and continuity of all possible traction variations at a point are clarified by the traction ellipsoid, which apparently was described by Gabriel Lamé (1795–1870) between 1820 and 1830 (Fung, 1965, p. 76). This construction commonly is referred to as the "stress" ellipsoid, but the quantity being plotted is the traction vector. To emphasize the fact that traction and stress are distinct physical quantities we use the name traction ellipsoid. The traction vectors $\mathbf{t}_1$, $\mathbf{t}_2$, and $\mathbf{t}_3$ are shown in Fig. 6.9 aligned with the respective positive axes of the traction component coordinates. The traction vectors $-\mathbf{t}_1$, $-\mathbf{t}_2$, and $-\mathbf{t}_3$ would be aligned with the respective negative axes, and $\mathbf{t}(\mathbf{n})$ is drawn with all positive components, consistent with the balance of forces on the tetrahedral element of Fig. 6.8b.

The traction ellipsoid provides a useful visualization of the traction variation at a point, but does not by itself reveal the orientation of the surface on which a particular traction vector acts. The special tractions $\mathbf{t}_1$, $\mathbf{t}_2$, and $\mathbf{t}_3$ are exactly parallel to the unit normal vector for the surface on which they act, but for the general case the traction vector $\mathbf{t}(\mathbf{n})$ is not parallel to $\mathbf{n}$ (Fig. 6.8b). A second graphical construction, called the *traction-director surface*, provides a tool for the visualization of the surfaces on which the tractions act (Timoshenko and Goodier, 1970). We develop the relevant equations in three dimensions, but plot the special case $(n_z = 0)$ in two dimensions for

(a)

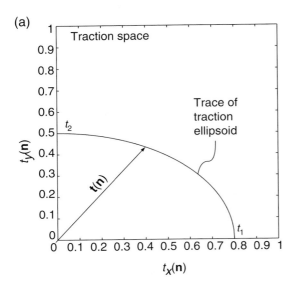

(b)

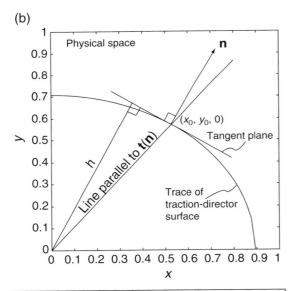

Fig 6.10 (a) Plot of the trace of a traction ellipsoid in first quadrant of the (t_x, t_y)-plane in traction space (MPa) with a particular traction vector, $\mathbf{t}(\mathbf{n})$. (b) Plot of the trace of the traction-director surface in the (x, y)-plane of physical space. The tangent plane at the point of intersection of a line parallel to $\mathbf{t}(\mathbf{n})$ is parallel to the plane on which this traction acts.

ease of representation. One quadrant of the $[t_x(\mathbf{n}), t_y(\mathbf{n})]$-plane in traction space is shown in Fig. 6.10a with a particular traction vector $\mathbf{t}(\mathbf{n})$ and the cross-sectional trace of the traction ellipsoid. For this example we take the following values (MPa):

$$t_1 = 0.8, \quad t_2 = 0.5, \quad t_3 = \text{arbitrary}$$
$$t_x(\mathbf{n}) = 0.4, \quad t_y(\mathbf{n}) = 0.433, \quad t_z(\mathbf{n}) = 0 \tag{6.22}$$

Note that t_3 may have any value, but (6.20) requires $t_z(\mathbf{n}) = 0$ for tractions in the plane $n_z = 0$. In other words the symmetry of the traction variation precludes any contribution from t_3 on surfaces that are parallel to the z-axis.

The three-dimensional surface in physical space called the traction-director surface is defined as (Timoshenko and Goodier, 1970, p. 222):

$$\frac{x^2}{t_1'} + \frac{y^2}{t_2'} + \frac{z^2}{t_3'} = 1 \tag{6.23}$$

For tractions scaled as $t' = t/1\text{MPa m}^{-2}$ this is an ellipsoid drawn in physical space with coordinate axes x, y, and z. The semi-major, semi-intermediate, and semi-minor axes of the ellipsoid (6.23) have lengths that are the positive square roots of t_1', t_2', and t_3', respectively. The trace of the traction-director surface for the two-dimensional example using (6.22) is illustrated in Fig. 6.10b. The tangent plane to the traction-director surface at an arbitrary point (x_0, y_0, z_0) is:

$$\frac{xx_0}{t_1'} + \frac{yy_0}{t_2'} + \frac{zz_0}{t_3'} = 1 \tag{6.24}$$

The so-called normal form of the equation for a plane at a perpendicular distance h from the origin and oriented by the unit normal vector $\mathbf{n}$ is (Selby, 1975):

$$\frac{xn_x}{h} + \frac{yn_y}{h} + \frac{zn_z}{h} = 1 \tag{6.25}$$

This plane is parallel to that on which the traction vector $\mathbf{t}(\mathbf{n})$ acts. The tangent plane (6.24) and the plane defined by (6.25) are identical if:

$$t_1' = \frac{hx_0}{n_x}, \quad t_2' = \frac{hy_0}{n_y}, \quad t_3' = \frac{hz_0}{n_z} \tag{6.26}$$

Substituting these expressions for the magnitudes of t_1, t_2, and t_3 into (6.20) we have:

$$t_x'(\mathbf{n}) = hx_0, \quad t_y'(\mathbf{n}) = hy_0, \quad t_z'(\mathbf{n}) = hz_0 \tag{6.27}$$

In other words the scaled components of the traction vector $\mathbf{t}(\mathbf{n})$ are proportional, respectively, to the coordinates of the point (x_0, y_0, z_0) on the traction-director surface, so the line drawn from the origin through the point (x_0, y_0, z_0) is parallel to this traction vector (Fig. 6.10b).

The unit normal vector, $\mathbf{n}$, determines the orientation of the tangent plane to the traction-director surface at the point (x_0, y_0, z_0) and this plane is parallel to the surface on which the traction vector $\mathbf{t(n)}$ acts. Given the magnitudes of the special tractions $\mathbf{t}_1$, $\mathbf{t}_2$, and $\mathbf{t}_3$ and the components of $\mathbf{t(n)}$, the components of $\mathbf{n}$ from (6.20) are:

$$n_x = \frac{t_x(\mathbf{n})}{t_1}, \quad n_y = \frac{t_y(\mathbf{n})}{t_2}, \quad n_z = \frac{t_z(\mathbf{n})}{t_3} \quad (6.28)$$

The following generalizations can be made about the traction vector at a point by studying the traction ellipsoid and the traction-director surface:

1. The traction vector $\mathbf{t(n)}$ varies continuously in magnitude and direction as the surface on which it acts changes orientation.
2. The special tractions $\mathbf{t}_1$, $\mathbf{t}_2$, and $\mathbf{t}_3$ act on three mutually orthogonal planes and have zero tangential components, so they are perpendicular to the respective plane on which they act.
3. The magnitudes of the tractions $\mathbf{t}_1$, $\mathbf{t}_2$, and $\mathbf{t}_3$ are represented by the lengths of the semi-axes of the traction ellipsoid: they are equivalent to the extreme values of the normal component of the traction at a point.
4. The traction $\mathbf{t(n)}$ is not parallel to the unit normal vector $\mathbf{n}$ except on surfaces where this traction is equal to either $\mathbf{t}_1$, $\mathbf{t}_2$, or $\mathbf{t}_3$.

Other facts about the traction vector are described after we introduce the stress tensor in the next section. The traction vector provides the link between the concept of a distributed surface force and the stress. It also provides the means to describe boundary conditions in terms of distributions of forces acting on the internal or external surfaces of the material continuum.

6.2 | Concept and analysis of stress

The shape of a deformed fossil (Fig. 5.1), the offset of a marker horizon across a fault (Fig. 2.14), and a multitude of other geological structures (Ramsay and Huber, 1983) provide direct evidence relevant to the kinematics of deformation; however, field evidence relevant to the state of stress is more enigmatic. This makes it challenging to develop an intuitive understanding for stress by simply observing or mapping geologic structures. However, certain structures can provide compelling data, because they have a simple geometrical relationship to some aspect of the stress field. Some of the best examples are vertical igneous dikes, formed as magma was injected into fractures that tend to be oriented perpendicular to the direction of least horizontal compressive stress. In such a case, a set of curves drawn parallel to the pattern of dikes provides a map of the orientation of the stress trajectories. Here we use a map pattern of dikes to introduce the concept of stress and to relate this to the traction vector.

Many vertical dikes crop out in the Raton Basin of southeastern Colorado. The photograph shown in Fig. 6.11 includes an outcrop of a large dike trending northward from near the base of West Spanish Peak. Many of the dikes of this region are more resistant to erosion than the sedimentary host rock and crop out as prominent vertical walls capping long ridges that form a radial pattern about the peak (Johnson, 1961, 1968). The radial dikes are classified based on their composition and Fig. 6.12a shows only those dikes of syenite and syenodiorite composition. The inference is that rocks of similar composition represent one period of magmatic activity and, perhaps, one regional stress field.

The sedimentary rocks of the Raton Basin (Fig. 6.12a) form the broad La Veta syncline with a steeply dipping western limb that abuts the older rocks of the Sangre de Cristo Mountains, and a gently dipping eastern limb that merges laterally with the sub-horizontal formations of the Great Plains. The sedimentary rocks folded into the Le Veta syncline are cut by the igneous rock and some deformed and metamorphosed sedimentary rock making up West and East Spanish Peaks. These impressive mountains rise almost 2 km above the topography of the surrounding plain and the pattern of igneous dikes seems to radiate from West Peak. It was this systematic map pattern that led Helmer Odé (1957) to propose a correspondence between the dike pattern and the stress distribution at the time of dike formation. He suggested that the dike pattern should correspond to the pattern of stress trajectories.

Fig 6.11 Photograph of East and West Spanish Peaks in southeastern Colorado with a large radial dike emanating from West Peak.

We infer that a magma chamber at depth below West Peak fed the igneous dikes making up the radial map pattern. The magma pressure acting in this chamber was apparently sufficient to fracture the host rock adjacent to the chamber (or at least to open pre-existing fractures) so the magma could invade these fractures and form the dikes. In Fig. 6.12b we show a schematic drawing of one-quarter of a vertical cylindrical magma chamber in a horizontal cross section below the current surface and an example of a potential dike path extending outward from the chamber wall. Other idealized chamber shapes are spherical (Anderson, 1936; Mogi, 1958) or sill-like (Johnson and Pollard, 1973; Pollard and Johnson, 1973; Fialko *et al.*, 2001). The magma pressure pushes outward on the chamber wall and induces a local stress field in the surrounding host rock. We use these geological structures to introduce the concept of stress and the physical quantity called the *stress tensor*.

6.2.1 The stress tensor

Consider a small cubical element, A, with one side oriented tangential to the wall of the magma chamber (shown in map view, Fig. 6.12b). A traction of magnitude $t(a)$ pushes on side a of this element with the same force per unit area as the magma pressure, p. The pressure in the chamber also induces a traction of magnitude $t(b)$ that pulls

against side b and thereby contributes to the stretching of the circumference of the chamber as it expands due to the magma pressure. Cauchy's relationship (6.9) states that the tractions acting on opposite sides of this element are equal in magnitude and oppositely directed in the limit as the element shrinks toward a point:

$$\mathbf{t}(c) = -\mathbf{t}(a) \quad \text{and} \quad \mathbf{t}(d) = -\mathbf{t}(b) \qquad (6.29)$$

Thus, the magma pressure induces a pair of tractions of magnitude $t(a)$ pushing inward and a pair of tractions of magnitude $t(b)$ pulling outward on element A. The former pair compresses the element in the radial direction and is used to define a component of *compressive stress*. The latter pair extends the element in a circumferential direction and is used to define a component of *tensile stress*. If the outward-directed pair of tractions is great enough, the rock will pull apart (fracture) along a line oriented perpendicular to these tractions and the magma may invade this fracture to initiate dike formation.

Along the potential dike path (Fig. 6.12b) a cubical element B has inward directed tractions acting parallel to the path and outward-directed tractions acting perpendicular to the path. The directions and magnitudes of these tractions change with the distance from the magma chamber. One special feature of the elements along the potential dike path as drawn in Fig. 6.12b is that the tractions act only normal to the element sides. Thus, the compressive and tensile stresses are referred to as *normal stress components*.

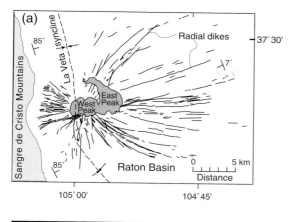

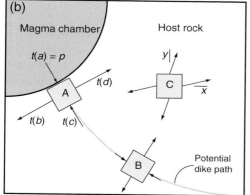

Fig 6.12 (a) Map of radial dike system focused on West Spanish Peak, CO (Johnson, 1961). Reprinted from Muller and Pollard (1977) with permission of Birkhanser-Verlag. (b) Schematic illustration of magma chamber below West Peak with trace of radial dike and elements with traction vectors.

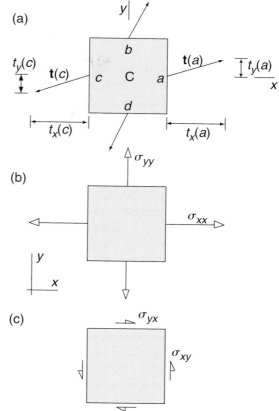

Fig 6.13 Relations among the traction vector components and stress tensor components. (a) Traction vectors acting on element. (b) Normal stress components. (c) Shear stress components.

If we were to consider an element C, not oriented with two sides parallel to a potential dike path, we would find that the tractions are oblique to the sides and have both normal and tangential components.

Viewing element C in two dimensions in Fig. 6.13a we set up a Cartesian coordinate system with x perpendicular to side a and y perpendicular to side b. The traction vector acting on side a resolves into components, $t_x(a)$ and $t_y(a)$, and the traction acting on side c resolves into components, $t_x(c)$ and $t_y(c)$. In the limit as the element shrinks to a point (6.9) requires these two tractions to be equal in magnitude and oppositely directed, so their respective components are:

$$t_x(c) = -t_x(a), \quad t_y(c) = -t_y(a) \tag{6.30}$$

Because of this special relationship between $t_x(a)$ and $t_x(c)$, a single quantity, σ_{xx}, is defined as the *normal component of stress* and is represented schematically as two open-headed arrows drawn perpendicular to sides a and c, with lengths and directions consistent with the respective traction components (Fig. 6.13b). The two subscripts signal that this stress component is acting *on* opposing planes with normal vectors that are parallel to the x-axis, and it is acting *in* an orientation parallel to the x-axis. This is referred to as the *on–in convention for subscripts*. We draw pairs of stress arrows with open heads to distinguish stress components from traction vectors and note that stress component arrows always are drawn in pairs. The normal stress component σ_{yy} is defined using a similar argument.

The combination of the two tangential traction components, $t_y(a)$ and $t_y(c)$, in Fig. 6.13a are used along with the condition (6.30) to define σ_{xy} as a *shear component of stress*. This quantity is represented schematically as two arrows drawn parallel to sides a and c, with lengths and directions consistent with the respective traction components (Fig. 6.13c). The two subscripts are chosen because this stress component is acting *on* two opposing planes with normals parallel to the x-axis and it is acting *in* an orientation parallel to the y-axis. The arrows have open heads, but only half of the head is drawn to distinguish the shear stress from the normal stress. The shear stress component σ_{yx} is defined using a similar argument.

There is an apparent contradiction in algebraic signs between traction components and stress components. For example, one of the arrows for σ_{xx} points in the positive x-direction and the other arrow points in the negative x-direction (Fig. 6.13b). This stress component is made up of two traction components that have opposite signs (Fig. 6.13a). On the other hand, we need to give a single algebraic sign to the stress component. The traditional choice, motivated by considering the sign conventions for the traction components pointing into the first quadrant on sides a and b (Fig. 6.13a), is to assign positive signs to stress components that correspond to these positive traction components. This makes a *tensile normal stress*, represented by outward directed arrows, a positive quantity, whereas a *compressive normal stress*, represented by inward directed arrows, is a negative quantity. Similarly, the two shear stresses are positive as drawn in Fig. 6.13c. This is the convention used in most of the physics and engineering literature. Because many of the concepts and analysis methods we use in structural geology are taken from that literature, this is an attractive choice and we will use it throughout this book, unless otherwise stated.

Most practitioners of soil and rock mechanics (Jaeger and Cook, 1979), as well as many structural geologists and geophysicists, use the opposite convention for signs of the stress components: com-

pression is positive and tension is negative. Shear stress components directed as shown in Fig. 6.13c are given negative signs. This choice is motivated by the fact that the normal stress typically is compressive at depth in the Earth, because it is related to the weight of the overlying rock. A disincentive for choosing this convention is the awkward result that components of the displacement vector, when related to the stress components, are found to be positive in the negative coordinate directions. This is at variance with standard practice for defining vector components. Students of structural geology should be able to work with both sign conventions, because both are used throughout the relevant literature.

A simple procedure for remembering how to draw all eight arrows representing the stress components in two dimensions is to consider the outward normal vector to the plane under consideration. If that normal points in the positive coordinate direction (as on sides a and b, Fig. 6.13), a positive stress component arrow should point in the positive coordinate direction. If that normal points in the negative coordinate direction (sides c and d), then a positive arrow should point in the negative coordinate direction. This produces a set of arrows consistent with the sign convention for positive stress components (Means, 1976).

By extension of the reasoning behind the definition of the Cartesian components of stress in two dimensions (Fig. 6.13), there are nine components of stress in three dimensions (Fig. 6.14), one normal component and two shear components acting on each of the three pairs of opposing sides of the cubical element. Arrows representing these nine components are shown acting on the visible sides of the element. These components are drawn in their positive orientations and it is understood that arrows drawn in the opposite directions on the opposing sides of the element make up the hidden member of each pair.

The nine components of stress are not independent. This is understood here by treating the cubical element in Fig. 6.14 as finite in size with side lengths δ_x, δ_y, and δ_z; considering the state of stress to be homogeneous throughout; and ignoring the effects of body forces. We imagine cutting the element free of the surroundings and

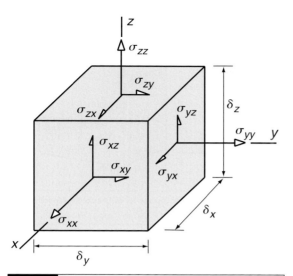

replacing the mechanical action of the surroundings by the appropriate stress components. Next we consider the proposition that the net force and net moment must be zero for static equilibrium (no linear or angular acceleration). For example, the stress components on the positive x-side of the element are associated with the following forces (stress multiplied by area) in the x-, y-, and z-directions:

$$\sigma_{xx}\delta y\delta z, \qquad \sigma_{xy}\delta y\delta z, \qquad \sigma_{xz}\delta y\delta z$$

$$\text{on } x = +\tfrac{1}{2}\delta x \qquad\qquad (6.31)$$

On the negative x-side the equivalent stress components give rise to negative forces of the same magnitudes in the x-, y-, and z-directions:

$$-\sigma_{xx}\delta y\delta z, \qquad -\sigma_{xy}\delta y\delta z, \qquad -\sigma_{xz}\delta y\delta z$$

$$\text{on } x = -\tfrac{1}{2}\delta x \qquad\qquad (6.32)$$

Similar arguments for the y- and z-sides demonstrate that the forces in the three coordinate directions exactly balance because, for a homogeneous stress state, the corresponding force components on opposing sides of the element are equal and opposite. The condition of force equilibrium places no constraints on the stress components.

However, consideration of moment equilibrium does constrain some of the stress

components. For example, the shear stress σ_{xy} on the positive x-side of the element is associated with a moment about the z-axis (stress multiplied by area and lever arm) that is $(\sigma_{xy}\delta_y\delta_z)(\delta_x/2)$. On the negative x-side, the shear stress σ_{xy} is associated with an exactly equivalent moment for a homogeneous stress state. On the positive and negative y-sides of the element the shear stress σ_{yx} is associated with moments about the z-axis and these are both equal to $-(\sigma_{yx}\delta_x\delta_z)(\delta_y/2)$. These are the only stress components that contribute to the moment about the z-axis. Therefore the sum of the moments about the z-axis is written:

$$\sum m_z = 2(\sigma_{xy}\delta y\delta z)(\tfrac{1}{2}\delta x) - 2(\sigma_{yx}\delta y\delta z)(\tfrac{1}{2}\delta x) = 0$$

$$(6.33)$$

Because the sides of the element are of finite length, the net moment is zero only if the two shear stresses are equal. Similar arguments lead to the conclusion that there are only six independent stress components in three dimensions because the shear stresses are related as:

$$\sigma_{xy} = \sigma_{yx}, \qquad \sigma_{yz} = \sigma_{zy}, \qquad \sigma_{zx} = \sigma_{xz} \qquad (6.34)$$

This constraint means that the following matrix representation of the state of stress is symmetric:

$$\begin{bmatrix} \sigma_{xx} & \sigma_{xy} & \sigma_{xz} \\ \sigma_{yx} & \sigma_{yy} & \sigma_{yz} \\ \sigma_{zx} & \sigma_{zy} & \sigma_{zz} \end{bmatrix} \qquad (6.35)$$

The normal stress components are placed along the main diagonal in this matrix and the equivalent shear stress components are placed in symmetric locations about this diagonal. The rows of this matrix contain, respectively, the stress components on the x-, y-, and z-sides of the cubical element pictured in Fig. 6.14.

Other notations for the stress components are found in the literature. For example, the symbol τ may replace σ for all shear stresses (e.g. τ_{xy}, τ_{yz}, τ_{zx}) to distinguish normal and shear stress components (Timoshenko and Goodier, 1970). Or, the normal stress components may have only one subscript (e.g. σ_x, σ_y, σ_z) because the subscripts are identical (Jaeger and Cook, 1979). To accommodate the use of indicial notation, the Cartesian coordinate axes (x, y, z) may be replaced by (x_1, x_2, x_3) and the stress components are referred to in aggregate as σ_{ij}, where it is understood that the ranges of the indices are $i = 1, 2, 3$ and $j = 1, 2, 3$. The constraint on the shear stress components (6.34) is expressed using indicial notation as:

$$\sigma_{ij} = \sigma_{ji} \tag{6.36}$$

This notation also facilitates the use of matrix algebra because the subscripts for the stress components correspond to the row and column numbers of the following matrix:

$$\begin{bmatrix} \sigma_{11} & \sigma_{12} & \sigma_{13} \\ \sigma_{21} & \sigma_{22} & \sigma_{23} \\ \sigma_{31} & \sigma_{32} & \sigma_{33} \end{bmatrix} \tag{6.37}$$

Recalling the "on-in" convention for subscripts the first row contains the stress components on the sides of the cubical element perpendicular to the x_1-axis and these components are directed, respectively, in the x_1-, x_2-, and x_3-directions.

Unlike the displacement, velocity, or acceleration the physical quantity we call the stress is not defined at a point in the continuum by a single vector with three components. In fact it takes six traction vectors, three of which are independent because of (6.9), acting on the orthogonal sides of the cubical element to determine the nine stress components. The *state of stress* at a point in the continuum is completely defined by the nine components of (6.35), six of which are independent because of (6.34). Stress is referred to as a *second-order tensor* to distinguish it from vectors, which are first-order tensors, and scalars, which are zero-order tensors. To complete the definition of stress at a point, one would include the appropriate unit of measure, along with the three coordinates of the point. If the stress state is a function of time then the definition would include the appropriate time.

We reduced the nine stress components to six by postulating static equilibrium for the finite cubical element, no body forces, and a homogeneous state of stress. In Chapter 7, after introducing the conservation laws, we show that (6.34) is not so restricted, but applies to problems of fluid dynamics in which elements experience both linear and angular accelerations, to deformation in the presence of body forces, and to heterogeneous stress states in solids and fluids. Here we

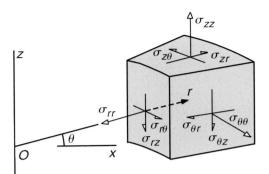

Fig 6.15 Cylindrical components of the stress tensor acting on a volume element.

also have ignored moments due to distributed body or surface couples because most problems in structural geology have found satisfactory correspondence to nature without invoking coupled stresses (Malvern, 1969). The constraint on the shear stress components (6.34) that leads to a symmetric matrix of stress components (6.35) is lost in the presence of coupled stresses.

Some problems in structural geology can be idealized using cylindrical symmetry about an axis in three dimensions. The map view of the dike pattern at Spanish Peaks is a possible example (Fig. 6.12a) because the dikes appear to radiate from a point near the center of West Spanish Peak. A practical example would be the cylindrical hole cut by a drilling rig to produce water or hydrocarbons from porous formations at depth. For these and other problems it is useful to define the stress components in terms of a cylindrical coordinate system (Fig. 6.15) which is composed of a cylindrical axis, Oz, a perpendicular axis, Ox, a radial distance, r, and a counterclockwise angle, θ, from the Ox-axis to the radial line.

The six independent stress components (σ_{rr}, $\sigma_{r\theta}$, σ_{rz}, $\sigma_{\theta\theta}$, $\sigma_{\theta z}$, σ_{zz}) are defined on a small element that has sides parallel to radial lines and concentric circles with centers at the origin. These are called the *cylindrical components of stress*. Shear components on adjacent faces must be of equal magnitude to prevent angular accelerations:

$$\sigma_{r\theta} = \sigma_{\theta r}, \qquad \sigma_{rz} = \sigma_{zr}, \qquad \sigma_{\theta z} = \sigma_{z\theta} \tag{6.38}$$

Note that the "on-in" convention for subscripts is followed: $\sigma_{r\theta}$ acts "on" the sides with normals

(a)

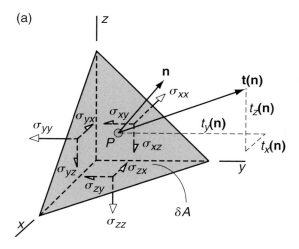

(b)

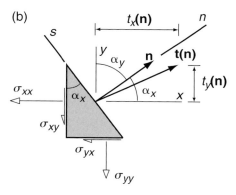

Fig 6.16 Relations among traction vector and stress tensor components. (a) Cauchy tetrahedron with traction **t(n)** acting on surface with outward unit normal **n** and stress components acting on coordinate planes. (b) Two-dimensional relations among traction vector and stress tensor components.

parallel to the radial, or r-direction, and "in" the circumferential, or θ-direction.

6.2.2 Cauchy's formula

We find important relationships among the traction and stress components by studying the Cauchy tetrahedron (Fig. 6.16a). Recall that the inclined side of this element is given an area δA and the areas of the orthogonal sides (δA_x, δA_y, δA_z) are found by projection of δA onto the coordinate planes (6.18). Unlike the case illustrated in Fig. 6.8b, here the traction vectors acting on the orthogonal sides are not constrained to be parallel to the respective normal vectors. In other

words we consider the most general case of loading. As a consequence, each traction vector may have three non-zero components, and each of these is equated to one of the nine stress components (Fig. 6.16a). Only one of the two arrows representing each stress component is shown because we have cut away half of the cubical element used to define the stress components (Fig. 6.14). On the inclined side of the tetrahedron the traction **t(n)** represents the mechanical action of that removed half and, in general, this vector has three non-zero components. We consider the limiting case in which the length of the longest edge of the tetrahedron goes to zero so the sides converge on the point P and investigate the relationship among the stress and traction components for surfaces through that point.

The force components acting on the sides of the tetrahedral element are the products of the stress or traction components and the respective areas of these sides. To find the relationship among these components we again invoke *Newton's Second Law*, $\mathbf{F} = m\mathbf{a}$, with the postulate of static equilibrium, $\mathbf{a} = 0$, so the net force in each coordinate direction is zero. Taking the x-coordinate direction as an example, the sum of the force components in x is written:

$$\sum f_x = [t_x(\mathbf{n})]\delta A - \sigma_{xx}\delta A_x - \sigma_{yx}\delta A_y - \sigma_{zx}\delta A_z = 0$$
(6.39)

Note that the component of force due to the traction component $t_x(\mathbf{n})$ is balanced by that due to the stress components acting in the x-direction on the x-, y-, and z-sides of the element. Rearranging (6.39) using (6.18), and following similar arguments for the balance of forces in the y- and z-directions, we find three equations that collectively are known as *Cauchy's Formula*:

$$t_x(\mathbf{n}) = \sigma_{xx}n_x + \sigma_{yx}n_y + \sigma_{zx}n_z$$
$$t_y(\mathbf{n}) = \sigma_{xy}n_x + \sigma_{yy}n_y + \sigma_{zy}n_z$$
$$t_z(\mathbf{n}) = \sigma_{xz}n_x + \sigma_{yz}n_y + \sigma_{zz}n_z$$
(6.40)

Cauchy's Formula instructs us that the traction vector, **t(n)**, on a surface of any orientation (defined by the outward unit normal vector **n**) through a given point, is completely determined by the nine (six independent) components of the stress tensor at that point. We derived Cauchy's Formula ignoring body forces and postulating static equilibrium, but these restrictions can be relaxed. After introducing the conservation of linear momentum in Chapter 7 we use this physical law alone to derive Cauchy's Formula, thereby showing that it is applicable to problems of solid deformation and fluid flow including body forces and accelerations.

Cauchy's Formula is expressed using indicial notation for the Cartesian coordinates x_i as:

$$t_i(\mathbf{n}) = \sigma_{ji}n_j \qquad (6.41)$$

Here it is understood that the repeated index on the right-hand side implies summation over the range of j. Given the range of i, (6.41) expands to three equations, one for each component of the traction vector. Using a matrix representation for the components of the traction vector, the stress tensor, and the unit normal vector, Cauchy's Formula may be expressed:

$$\begin{bmatrix} t_1(\mathbf{n}) \\ t_2(\mathbf{n}) \\ t_3(\mathbf{n}) \end{bmatrix} = \begin{bmatrix} \sigma_{11} & \sigma_{21} & \sigma_{31} \\ \sigma_{12} & \sigma_{22} & \sigma_{32} \\ \sigma_{13} & \sigma_{23} & \sigma_{33} \end{bmatrix} \begin{bmatrix} n_1 \\ n_2 \\ n_3 \end{bmatrix} \qquad (6.42)$$

Note that the matrix of stress components is the transpose of (6.37). The matrix representation (6.42) emphasizes the fact that the stress tensor can be thought of as a linear operator that gives the traction vector as a function of the unit normal vector. The components of stress are consistent with the definition of a *second-order tensor* quantity in that they associate a vector (the traction) with any direction in space as determined by the respective direction cosines (components of the unit normal vector).

Cauchy's Formula relates the tractions, acting as *boundary conditions* for models of geologic structures, to the stress components on a cubical element adjacent to that boundary. For example, consider the body shown in Fig. 6.17 and a small element that has one side coincident with the boundary of the body. For convenience we choose a coordinate system with the y-axis normal to that side, and the other two axes parallel to the edges of that side. The outward unit normal vector to the boundary of the body at that point, has components $n_x = 0$, $n_y = 1$, and $n_z = 0$, so the traction and stress components are related according to Cauchy's Formula:

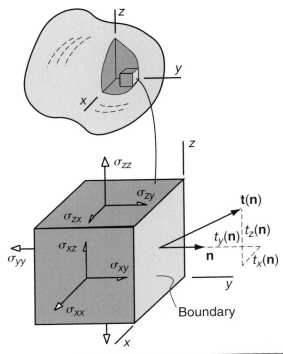

Fig 6.17 Volume element with one surface coincident with surface of a body. Components of the traction vector, $\mathbf{t}(\mathbf{n})$, acting on this surface are related to certain stress components acting on the element.

$$t_x(\mathbf{n}) = \sigma_{yx} = \sigma_{xy}, \qquad t_y(\mathbf{n}) = \sigma_{yy},$$
$$t_z(\mathbf{n}) = \sigma_{yz} = \sigma_{zy} \qquad (6.43)$$

The other components of the stress tensor, namely σ_{xx}, $\sigma_{xz} = \sigma_{zx}$, and σ_{zz}, are not determined by the traction acting on this boundary. These components may be calculated by solving a boundary value problem, but are not given by the boundary condition itself.

Cauchy's Formula given by (6.40) reduces to two dimensions for conditions of plane deformation. For example, taking the (x, y)-plane as the plane of interest (Fig. 6.16b) we have:

$$n_z = 0, \qquad \sigma_{xz} = 0 = \sigma_{zx}, \qquad \sigma_{yz} = 0 = \sigma_{zy} \qquad (6.44)$$

The two out-of-plane shear stresses must be zero by definition, and the out-of-plane normal stress which generally is not zero is eliminated from (6.40) because the direction cosine, n_z, is zero. The other two direction cosines are related to one another such that $n_x = \cos\alpha_x$ and $n_y = \cos[(\pi/2) - \alpha_x] = \sin\alpha_x$, so the two-dimensional form of Cauchy's Formula is:

$$t_x(\mathbf{n}) = \sigma_{xx}\cos\alpha_x + \sigma_{yx}\sin\alpha_x$$
$$t_y(\mathbf{n}) = \sigma_{xy}\cos\alpha_x + \sigma_{yy}\sin\alpha_x \tag{6.45}$$

Here α_x is the counterclockwise angle measured from the Ox-axis to the outward unit normal $\mathbf{n}$ for the plane on which $\mathbf{t}(\mathbf{n})$ acts.

6.2.3 Normal and shear tractions on a surface

For some problems in structural geology it is necessary to calculate the normal and tangential (shear) traction components acting on an arbitrarily oriented surface within the rock mass as a function of a homogeneous state of stress. For example, slip on a fault may be thought of as a frictional sliding process that is driven by the shear component of the traction vector acting on the fault surface (Wallace, 1951; Bott, 1959; Morris et al., 1996). To the extent that the rock mass on one side of a fault pushes against the adjacent fault surface the corresponding (negative) normal component of the traction deters frictional sliding. Thus, for a set of faults with the same frictional strength, those carrying the greatest shear traction and the least (negative) normal traction would be favored for slip. As a second example, opening of a joint may be thought of as driven by the pull of the adjacent rock mass on the prospective fracture surface (Pollard and Aydin, 1988). For a rock mass that is isotropic with respect to tensile strength the surface with the greatest (positive) normal traction would be favored for jointing.

The three-dimensional relationship between the traction vector, $\mathbf{t}(\mathbf{n})$, and the unit normal vector, $\mathbf{n}$, on an arbitrarily oriented surface is illustrated in Fig. 6.18. The angle θ is the smaller angle between these two vectors in the plane which they define (dashed rectangle) with their tails at the point P. The Cauchy tetrahedron is pictured with stress components acting on the coordinate planes representing a general state of stress. Any vector, $\mathbf{v}$, may be resolved into two vector components that are, respectively, parallel and perpendicular to an arbitrary unit normal vector, $\mathbf{n}$, with the relation-

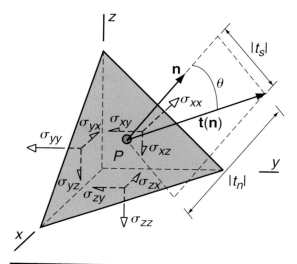

Fig 6.18 Cauchy tetrahedron with traction vector, $\mathbf{t}(\mathbf{n})$, decomposed into a normal and a shear component.

ship $\mathbf{v} = (\mathbf{v} \cdot \mathbf{n})\mathbf{n} + \mathbf{n} \times (\mathbf{v} \times \mathbf{n})$, (Malvern, 1969). This is used to resolve the traction vector, $\mathbf{t}$, into two vector components that are, respectively, normal and tangential to the surface:

$$\mathbf{t} = (\mathbf{t} \cdot \mathbf{n})\mathbf{n} + \mathbf{n} \times (\mathbf{t} \times \mathbf{n}) \tag{6.46}$$

In order to simplify the presentation in this section we write $\mathbf{t}(\mathbf{n})$ as $\mathbf{t}$ and understand that this and all other vectors act on the surface with outward unit normal $\mathbf{n}$.

In the first term on the right-hand side of (6.46) we use the fact that the component of any vector parallel to a unit vector is given by their scalar product to calculate the normal component of $\mathbf{t}$:

$$\mathbf{t} \cdot \mathbf{n} = |\mathbf{t}||\mathbf{n}|\cos\theta = |\mathbf{t}|\cos\theta = t_n \tag{6.47}$$

Because the range of the angle is $0 \leq \theta \leq \pi$, this scalar product may be positive or negative and, correspondingly, the vector $\mathbf{t}$ would pull or push on the surface. In other words, the direction of the vector component of $\mathbf{t}$ that is normal to the surface is given by $[\mathrm{sgn}(t_n)]\mathbf{n}$.

For the purpose of computing the normal component of $\mathbf{t}$ recall that a scalar product can be written as the sum of the products of the respective components:

$$\mathbf{t} \cdot \mathbf{n} = t_x n_x + t_y n_y + t_z n_z \tag{6.48}$$

Cauchy's Formula (6.40) is used to write (6.48) in terms of the stress components:

$$t_n = \sigma_{xx}n_x^2 + \sigma_{yy}n_y^2 + \sigma_{zz}n_z^2 + 2\sigma_{xy}n_xn_y + 2\sigma_{yz}n_yn_z$$
$$+ 2\sigma_{zx}n_zn_x \quad (6.49)$$

Given the state of stress and the orientation of a surface at a point, (6.49) is used to calculate the normal component of the traction vector.

We use the second term on the right-hand side of (6.46) to calculate the tangential (shear) component of t. The magnitude of the vector $t \times n$ is the magnitude of this component:

$$|t \times n| = |t||n|\sin\theta = |t|\sin\theta = |t_s| \quad (6.50)$$

Given the range $0 \le \theta \le \pi$, the quantity $|t|\sin\theta$ is always positive. Having specified only one reference direction, n, we cannot distinguish positive and negative signs for the tangential component of t. However, the vector $t \times n$ is directed perpendicular to the plane defined by t and n, and lies in the surface on which t acts because it is perpendicular to n. Recall that a vector product may be written in terms of the components as:

$$t \times n = (t_yn_z - t_zn_y)e_x + (t_zn_x - t_xn_z)e_y$$
$$+ (t_xn_y - t_yn_x)e_z \quad (6.51)$$

Similarly, the second vector product of (6.46) may be written using (6.51) as:

$$n \times (t \times n) = [(1 - n_x^2)t_x - n_xn_yt_y - n_xn_zt_z]e_x$$
$$+ [-n_xn_yt_x + (1 - n_y^2)t_y - n_yn_zt_z]e_y$$
$$+ [-n_zn_xt_x - n_zn_yt_y + (1 - n_z^2)t_z]e_z$$
$$(6.52)$$

This vector is the resolution of the traction t onto the surface with outward unit normal vector n. Cauchy's Formula (6.40) may be used to write (6.52) in terms of the stress components. The magnitude of the tangential (shear) component of t may be calculated as $|n \times (t \times n)|$ using (6.52) or, noting in Fig. 6.18 that $|t_n|$ and $|t_s|$ are the lengths of the sides of a right triangle and $|t|$ is the length of the hypotenuse, one may use the following (positive) square root:

$$|t_s| = \sqrt{|t|^2 - |t_n|^2} \quad (6.53)$$

The direction cosines of the vector component of t tangential to the surface are calculated from

(6.52) by dividing each component of $n \times (t \times n)$ by $|t_s|$.

The two-dimensional resolution in the (x, y)-plane of the x- and y-components of the traction t onto the n- and s-axes can be derived by inspection of Fig. 6.16b:

$$t_n = t_x\cos\alpha_x + t_y\sin\alpha_x$$
$$t_s = -t_x\sin\alpha_x + t_y\cos\alpha_x \quad (6.54)$$

Here the (n, s)-coordinate axes are arranged with n perpendicular and outward from the surface on which t acts and s tangential to this surface. Both n and s are in the (x, y)-plane and s is directed such that n is to the right when looking in positive s (a right-hand rule). Given these two reference directions, t_n and t_s may be either positive or negative. The two-dimensional forms of Cauchy's Formula, (6.45), are used to write (6.54) in terms of the stress components:

$$t_n = \sigma_{xx}\cos^2\alpha_x + \sigma_{yy}\sin^2\alpha_x + 2\sigma_{xy}\sin\alpha_x\cos\alpha_x$$
$$t_s = -(\sigma_{xx} - \sigma_{yy})\sin\alpha_x\cos\alpha_x$$
$$+ \sigma_{xy}(\cos^2\alpha_x - \sin^2\alpha_x) \quad (6.55)$$

Given a two-dimensional state of stress in the (y, z)- or the (z, x)-plane, (6.55) may be used with appropriate exchange of subscripts.

6.2.4 Principal values and principal axes of normal stress

In Section 6.1.4 we derived the equation for the traction ellipsoid (6.21) by postulating without derivation that three orthogonal surfaces at a point could be so oriented that the traction vector acting on each is directed parallel to the respective normal vector. In other words the tangential component of the traction on each orthogonal surface is identically zero. The tractions acting on these three surfaces (t_1, t_2, and t_3) correspond to the semi-axes of the traction ellipsoid (Fig. 6.9) and are ordered such that $t_1 \ge t_2 \ge t_3$. Here we derive these relationships in terms of the state of stress at a point by equating the normal component of the traction vector to the normal stress. We show that the normal stress takes on extreme values in three orthogonal directions and define each of these as a *principal normal stress*. The principal normal stresses play important roles in theories of failure, fracture, and faulting of rock, topics that we consider in later chapters.

We begin by considering an arbitrary state of stress at a point defined by six independent components and ask if a plane through this point exists upon which the shear component of the traction vector vanishes. Referring to Fig. 6.18, the traction vector, $\mathbf{t}$, would be parallel to the outward unit normal vector, $\mathbf{n}$, and the only stress component associated with this plane would be the normal stress, σ_{nn}. The components of the traction vector acting on this plane in the arbitrarily chosen Cartesian coordinate system would be:

$$t_x(\mathbf{n}) = \sigma_{nn} n_x, \qquad t_y(\mathbf{n}) = \sigma_{nn} n_y,$$

$$t_z(\mathbf{n}) = \sigma_{nn} n_z \qquad (6.56)$$

These same traction components are related to the stress components through Cauchy's Formula. Substituting the right-hand sides of (6.56) for the traction components in (6.40), and rearranging yields three linear equations for the unknown normal stress, σ_{nn}, and the three unknown components of the unit normal vector (n_x, n_y, n_z). We include (6.17) to make a set of four equations in four unknowns:

$$(\sigma_{xx} - \sigma_{nn})n_x + \sigma_{yx}n_y + \sigma_{zx}n_z = 0$$
$$\sigma_{xy}n_x + (\sigma_{yy} - \sigma_{nn})n_y + \sigma_{zy}n_z = 0$$
$$\sigma_{xz}n_x + \sigma_{yz}n_y + (\sigma_{zz} - \sigma_{nn})n_z = 0 \qquad (6.57)$$
$$(n_x)^2 + (n_y)^2 + (n_z)^2 = 1$$

Equations (6.57) have solutions for the components of the unit normal vector only if the determinant of the coefficients is equal to zero (Gere and Weaver, 1965):

$$\begin{vmatrix} \sigma_{xx} - \sigma_{nn} & \sigma_{yx} & \sigma_{zx} \\ \sigma_{xy} & \sigma_{yy} - \sigma_{nn} & \sigma_{zy} \\ \sigma_{xz} & \sigma_{yz} & \sigma_{xx} - \sigma_{nn} \end{vmatrix} = 0 \qquad (6.58)$$

Expanding the determinant and invoking the symmetry of the stress tensor (6.34) we have:

$$-\sigma_{nn}^3 + (\sigma_{xx} + \sigma_{yy} + \sigma_{zz})\sigma_{nn}^2 - (\sigma_{xx}\sigma_{yy} + \sigma_{yy}\sigma_{zz}$$
$$+ \sigma_{zz}\sigma_{xx} - \sigma_{xy}^2 - \sigma_{yz}^2 - \sigma_{zx}^2)\sigma_{nn}$$
$$+ (\sigma_{xx}\sigma_{yy}\sigma_{zz} + 2\sigma_{xy}\sigma_{yz}\sigma_{zx} - \sigma_{xx}\sigma_{yz}^2$$
$$- \sigma_{yy}\sigma_{zx}^2 - \sigma_{zz}\sigma_{xy}^2) = 0 \qquad (6.59)$$

This cubic equation for the unknown normal stress, σ_{nn}, has three real roots (Bell, 1920), and these are the three *principal stresses* $\sigma_1, \sigma_2, \sigma_3$ which are ordered such that $\sigma_1 \geq \sigma_2 \geq \sigma_3$. Standard algebraic techniques exist to solve such a cubic equation (Selby, 1975) and to show for all possible values of the stress components that the three roots are real.

Given the values of the principal stresses each may be substituted, successively, for the normal stress, σ_{nn}, in (6.57) and the three components of the unit normal vector for each principal stress axis may be determined (Fig. 6.19a). The three components of the unit normal vectors that are parallel to the principal axes are written:

$$(n_{x1}, n_{y1}, n_{z1}) \text{ components of } \mathbf{n}(1)$$
$$(n_{x2}, n_{y2}, n_{z2}) \text{ components of } \mathbf{n}(2) \qquad (6.60)$$
$$(n_{x3}, n_{y3}, n_{z3}) \text{ components of } \mathbf{n}(3)$$

Here, for example, the component n_{z1} is the direction cosine used to project the base vector for the z-axis onto the axis parallel to the direction of σ_1.

To show that the principal axes are orthogonal use $\sigma_{nn} = \sigma_1$ in (6.57) and multiply each equation by the respective components of $\mathbf{n}(2)$, (Jaeger and Cook, 1979, p. 20):

$$(\sigma_{xx} - \sigma_1)n_{x1}n_{x2} + \sigma_{yx}n_{y1}n_{x2} + \sigma_{zx}n_{z1}n_{x2} = 0$$
$$\sigma_{xy}n_{x1}n_{y2} + (\sigma_{yy} - \sigma_1)n_{y1}n_{y2} + \sigma_{zy}n_{z1}n_{y2} = 0 \quad (6.61)$$
$$\sigma_{xz}n_{x1}n_{z2} + \sigma_{yz}n_{y1}n_{z2} + (\sigma_{zz} - \sigma_1)n_{z1}n_{z2} = 0$$

Next use $\sigma_{nn} = \sigma_2$ in (6.57) and multiply each equation by the respective components of $\mathbf{n}(1)$:

$$(\sigma_{xx} - \sigma_2)n_{x2}n_{x1} + \sigma_{yx}n_{y2}n_{x1} + \sigma_{zx}n_{z2}n_{x1} = 0$$
$$\sigma_{xy}n_{x2}n_{y1} + (\sigma_{yy} - \sigma_2)n_{y2}n_{y1} + \sigma_{zy}n_{z2}n_{y1} = 0 \quad (6.62)$$
$$\sigma_{xz}n_{x2}n_{z1} + \sigma_{yz}n_{y2}n_{z1} + (\sigma_{zz} - \sigma_2)n_{z2}n_{z1} = 0$$

Adding the three equations (6.61); then adding the three equations (6.62); and finally subtracting the second sum from the first and invoking the symmetry condition (6.34) we find:

$$(\sigma_1 - \sigma_2)(n_{x1}n_{x2} + n_{y1}n_{y2} + n_{z1}n_{z2}) = 0 \qquad (6.63)$$

If these two principal stresses are not equal, then the second term in parentheses must be zero. Note that the second term is the scalar product of the two unit vectors, $\mathbf{n}(1)$ and $\mathbf{n}(2)$, and from the definition of the scalar product (2.19) we have

(a)

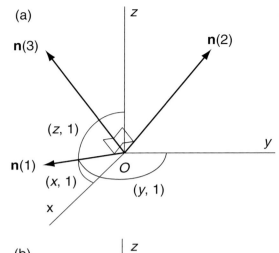

(b)

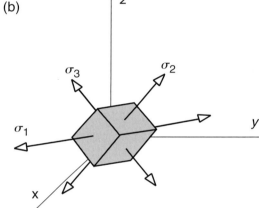

Fig 6.19 (a) Geometric relations among the Cartesian coordinates and the unit normal vectors directed parallel to the axes of principal stresses. (b) Volume element on which principal stresses act.

$\mathbf{n}(1) \cdot \mathbf{n}(2) = \cos \theta = 0$. Here θ is the angle between the two unit vectors which, in this case, must be $\pi/2$. A similar derivation for the other two pairs of principal stresses shows that they are mutually orthogonal.

If the Cartesian coordinate system is chosen to coincide with the axes of principal stress at a point then all the off-diagonal terms in the matrix of stress components (6.35) are zero and the diagonal terms are the principal stresses:

$$\begin{bmatrix} \sigma_1 & 0 & 0 \\ 0 & \sigma_2 & 0 \\ 0 & 0 & \sigma_3 \end{bmatrix} \tag{6.64}$$

(a)

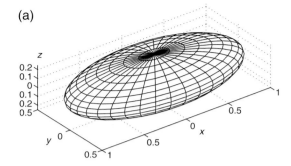

(b)

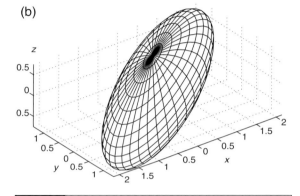

Fig 6.20 (a) Traction ellipsoid for state of stress with principal axes parallel to coordinate axes. (b) Traction ellipsoid for state of stress defined in (6.68) with principal axes not parallel to coordinate axes.

The stress state $\sigma_1 = 1$, $\sigma_2 = \frac{1}{2}$, $\sigma_3 = \frac{1}{4}$(MPa) is illustrated in Fig. 6.20a as a traction ellipsoid. In this illustration we have chosen $\sigma_{xy} = \sigma_{yz} = \sigma_{zx} = 0$, so the principal axes of stress are aligned with the coordinate axes, and $\sigma_{xx} = \sigma_1$, $\sigma_{yy} = \sigma_2$, $\sigma_{zz} = \sigma_3$. If the three principal stresses were equal $(\sigma_1 = \sigma_2 = \sigma_3)$ the state of stress would be isotropic and the traction ellipsoid would degenerate to a sphere. In this case any orthogonal set of axes may serve as the principal axes. If two of the principal stresses were equal the traction vectors would trace out an ellipsoid with the one unequal axis being the axis of revolution. In the plane perpendicular to the axis of revolution any two orthogonal axes may serve as the principal axes and only the principal axis parallel to the axis of revolution is unique. Because the three principal stresses are unequal in this example the traction vectors trace out an ellipsoid with three unequal axes which are coincident with the coordinate axes (Fig.

6.20a). The complete stress analysis, including principal stresses, trajectories, and all components, is shown in color on the textbook website.

Equations (6.57) may be solved using matrix algebra and this is a classic problem called an *eigenvalue problem*, which has many applications in the sciences and engineering (Gere and Weaver, 1965). Here we refer to this as a *principal value problem* since we are looking for the principal values of stress, and (6.57) is written:

$$\begin{bmatrix} \sigma_{xx} & \sigma_{yx} & \sigma_{zx} \\ \sigma_{xy} & \sigma_{yy} & \sigma_{zy} \\ \sigma_{xz} & \sigma_{yz} & \sigma_{zz} \end{bmatrix} \begin{bmatrix} n_x \\ n_y \\ n_z \end{bmatrix} = \sigma_{nn} \begin{bmatrix} n_x \\ n_y \\ n_z \end{bmatrix} \qquad (6.65)$$

A solution to (6.65) is the vector **n** with components (n_x, n_y, n_z), which determines the orientation of a principal plane with respect to the Cartesian coordinates (x, y, z). The product of the matrix of stress components and the unit normal components is equal to the product of a scalar, σ_{nn}, and the unit normal components, where this scalar is the unknown principal stress. Rearranging (6.65) we have the following *homogeneous equation*:

$$\left(\begin{bmatrix} \sigma_{xx} & \sigma_{yx} & \sigma_{zx} \\ \sigma_{xy} & \sigma_{yy} & \sigma_{zy} \\ \sigma_{xz} & \sigma_{yz} & \sigma_{zz} \end{bmatrix} - \sigma_{nn} \begin{bmatrix} 1 & 0 & 0 \\ 0 & 1 & 0 \\ 0 & 0 & 1 \end{bmatrix} \right) \begin{bmatrix} n_x \\ n_y \\ n_z \end{bmatrix} = \begin{bmatrix} 0 \\ 0 \\ 0 \end{bmatrix}$$
$$(6.66)$$

This equation is called homogeneous because the right-hand side is the *null vector*. The second matrix on the left-hand side is called the *identity matrix* because multiplication of a matrix of the same order by it results in the same matrix.

Carrying out the multiplication and subtraction indicated in (6.66) we have the set of equations (6.57) in matrix form:

$$\begin{bmatrix} \sigma_{xx} - \sigma_{nn} & \sigma_{yx} & \sigma_{zx} \\ \sigma_{xy} & \sigma_{yy} - \sigma_{nn} & \sigma_{zy} \\ \sigma_{xz} & \sigma_{yz} & \sigma_{zz} - \sigma_{nn} \end{bmatrix} \begin{bmatrix} n_x \\ n_y \\ n_z \end{bmatrix} = \begin{bmatrix} 0 \\ 0 \\ 0 \end{bmatrix}$$
$$(6.67)$$

One solution to (6.67) is the null vector **n**, referred to as a *trivial solution*, but this is of no interest for the physical problem we are considering. Nontrivial solutions exist only if the determinant of the coefficient matrix is zero, as stated in (6.58), and this leads to the cubic equation (6.59) in the unknown normal stress, σ_{nn}. This equation has three roots that are the so-called *eigenvalues* or, as we refer to them in this context, the principal values $\sigma_1, \sigma_2, \sigma_3$. The eigenvalues of an asymmetric matrix can be real or complex, but the special case of a symmetric matrix always yields real eigenvalues (Gere and Weaver, 1965), so the symmetric matrix of stress components always yields real principal stresses. Real eigenvalues may be positive, negative, or zero and likewise the principal stresses may be positive (tension), negative (compression), or zero subject only to the constraint that $\sigma_1 \geq \sigma_2 \geq \sigma_3$.

Each eigenvalue of a matrix is associated with a vector called the *eigenvector*. For the matrix of stress components the eigenvectors are the unit normal vectors for the planes on which the principal stresses act. Having determined the values of the three principal stresses from solving (6.59), these are substituted separately into (6.67) to obtain three simultaneous equations to be solved for the components of the normal vector **n**(1), **n**(2), or **n**(3), associated with each principal stress. In general, the eigenvectors for a symmetric matrix are orthogonal to one another (Gere and Weaver, 1965).

As an example, consider a point in a continuum where the following symmetric matrix provides the stress components referred to a specified Cartesian coordinate system (MPa):

$$\begin{bmatrix} \sigma_{xx} & \sigma_{xy} & \sigma_{xz} \\ \sigma_{yx} & \sigma_{yy} & \sigma_{yz} \\ \sigma_{zx} & \sigma_{zy} & \sigma_{zz} \end{bmatrix} = \begin{bmatrix} 2 & \frac{3}{4} & \frac{1}{4} \\ \frac{3}{4} & 1 & \frac{1}{2} \\ \frac{1}{4} & \frac{1}{2} & \frac{1}{2} \end{bmatrix} \qquad (6.68)$$

This state of stress is associated with a traction ellipsoid oriented such that none of the ellipsoidal axes correspond to the coordinate axes (Fig. 6.20b). The principal values of stress are (MPa):

$$\sigma_1 = 2.5080, \qquad \sigma_2 = 0.8261, \qquad \sigma_3 = 0.1659 \qquad (6.69)$$

The corresponding components of the principal vectors are:

$$\begin{bmatrix} n_{x1} \\ n_{y1} \\ n_{z1} \end{bmatrix} = \begin{bmatrix} -0.8398 \\ -0.4930 \\ -0.2273 \end{bmatrix}, \quad \begin{bmatrix} n_{x2} \\ n_{y2} \\ n_{z2} \end{bmatrix} = \begin{bmatrix} 0.5256 \\ -0.6333 \\ -0.5681 \end{bmatrix},$$

$$\begin{bmatrix} n_{x3} \\ n_{y3} \\ n_{z3} \end{bmatrix} = \begin{bmatrix} -0.1361 \\ 0.5965 \\ -0.7909 \end{bmatrix} \qquad (6.70)$$

At the point under consideration we may represent the state of stress with three lines, oriented parallel to the principal vectors (6.70) and scaled to the magnitudes of the principal stresses (6.69).

For a two-dimensional stress field, such as that associated with conditions of plane strain (Fig. 6.16), we take the plane of interest as the (x, y)-plane so the matrix of stress components is:

$$\begin{bmatrix} \sigma_{xx} & \sigma_{xy} & 0 \\ \sigma_{yx} & \sigma_{yy} & 0 \\ 0 & 0 & \sigma_{zz} \end{bmatrix} \tag{6.71}$$

The two in-plane principal stresses are (Timoshenko and Goodier, 1970):

$$\frac{1}{2}(\sigma_{xx} + \sigma_{yy}) + [\tfrac{1}{4}(\sigma_{xx} - \sigma_{yy})^2 + \sigma_{xy}^2]^{1/2}$$
$$\frac{1}{2}(\sigma_{xx} + \sigma_{yy}) - [\tfrac{1}{4}(\sigma_{xx} - \sigma_{yy})^2 + \sigma_{xy}^2]^{1/2} \tag{6.72}$$

The third principal stress is $\sigma_{zz} = v(\sigma_{xx} + \sigma_{yy})$. Because Poisson's ratio has a range $0 \le v \le \frac{1}{2}$, it is not possible to specify which will be the greatest, σ_1, intermediate, σ_2, and least principal stress, σ_3, before making these calculations.

The direction of greatest in-plane principal stresses is determined by:

$$\gamma_1 = \frac{1}{2}\tan^{-1}\left(\frac{2\sigma_{xy}}{\sigma_{xx} - \sigma_{yy}}\right) \tag{6.73}$$

The angle γ_1 is measured from Ox counterclockwise to the axis of maximum principal stress. Equation (6.73) enables one to calculate the orientation of the principal stresses at any point in a two-dimensional field of spatially varying stress, such as that around the model magma chamber beneath West Spanish Peak at the time the radial dikes formed (Fig. 6.21a). Because these orientations vary smoothly from point to point in the plane, it is possible to construct smoothly turning curves that are everywhere parallel to one of the local principal stresses. Similarly one can construct a set of curves everywhere parallel to the other local principal stress, and these two families of curves are orthogonal to one another. These curves are called *principal stress trajectories*.

One might suppose that the concept of stress trajectories could be extended to a three-dimensional stress field such that an orthogonal

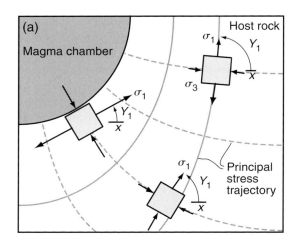

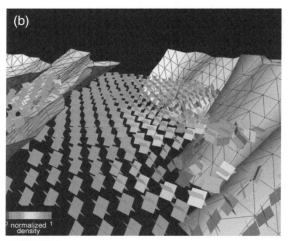

Fig 6.21 (a) Map of principal stress trajectories near the magma chamber under West Spanish Peak, CO.
(b) Visualization of three-dimensional stress field near normal faults in a North Sea hydrocarbon reservoir. Reprinted from Maerten *et al.* (2002) with permission of Elsevier.

system of "stress surfaces" would exist at every point being tangential to the three principal stress axes, but this is not generally true (Treagus and Lisle, 1997). None-the-less it is always possible to determine the principal stress magnitudes and orientations at a point and these may be visualized using three-dimensional graphical techniques (Fig. 6.21b). In this figure the pairs of small planes intersect along the direction of the intermediate principal stress, σ_2, and the smaller angle between these planes is bisected by the least principal stress, σ_3 (maximum compressive stress). The triangulated surfaces are model fault surfaces for a hydrocarbon reservoir in the North Sea and the principal stresses were used to predict the location and orientation of small faults in this reservoir (Maerten et al., 2002).

The orientation of the Cartesian coordinate system in the preceding discussion of principal stresses was arbitrary. Any orientation could be chosen and the resulting principal stresses and principal axes would be identical. In other words the three roots of the cubic equation (6.59) are the same, regardless of coordinate system, so the coefficients of this equation must not vary for a given state of stress. Rewriting this cubic equation by collecting the stress components into constant coefficients we have:

$$-\sigma_{nn}^3 + I_1\sigma_{nn}^2 - I_2\sigma_{nn} + I_3 = 0 \tag{6.74}$$

The invariant coefficients are:

$$I_1 = \sigma_{xx} + \sigma_{yy} + \sigma_{zz}$$
$$I_2 = \sigma_{xx}\sigma_{yy} + \sigma_{yy}\sigma_{zz} + \sigma_{zz}\sigma_{xx} - \sigma_{xy}^2 - \sigma_{yz}^2 - \sigma_{zx}^2$$
$$I_3 = \sigma_{xx}\sigma_{yy}\sigma_{zz} + 2\sigma_{xy}\sigma_{yz}\sigma_{zx} - \sigma_{xx}\sigma_{yz}^2 - \sigma_{yy}\sigma_{zx}^2 - \sigma_{zz}\sigma_{xy}^2$$
$$\tag{6.75}$$

These combinations of the Cartesian stress components are referred to as the *stress invariants*.

The definitions of the stress invariants in terms of the Cartesian components are reduced to definitions in terms of the principal stresses by rotating the coordinate system until it aligns with the principal axes. This is equivalent to setting the shear stress components to zero and equating the normal components to the principal stresses:

$$I_1 = \sigma_1 + \sigma_2 + \sigma_3$$
$$I_2 = \sigma_1\sigma_2 + \sigma_2\sigma_3 + \sigma_3\sigma_2 \tag{6.76}$$
$$I_3 = \sigma_1\sigma_2\sigma_3$$

Note in particular that the sum of the three normal stress components is invariant. This has a rather simple interpretation as three times the mean normal stress. The other invariants do not have such simple interpretations but all are employed in the development of constitutive laws for isotropic materials and in theories of failure because, it is argued, such laws and theories should not depend upon an arbitrary choice for the orientation of a coordinate system. Rather, the constitutive law and strength of a particular material should be a property of the material itself and the ambient conditions of temperature and pressure.

6.2.5 Maximum shear stresses

Given the principal normal stresses $(\sigma_1, \sigma_2, \sigma_3)$ and their orientations, one can calculate the variation in the shear traction magnitude, $|t_s|$, with the orientation, $\mathbf{n}$, of the plane on which it acts. We equate $|t_s|$ to the magnitude of the shear stress $|\sigma_{ns}|$ and seek orientations of the planes on which the shear stress attains extreme values because these quantities play important roles in rock deformation, particularly faulting. As shown in Fig. 6.18 and written in (6.53) the magnitudes of the traction vector, $\mathbf{t}$, and the stresses σ_{ns} and σ_{nn} are related such that:

$$\sigma_{ns}^2 = |\mathbf{t}|^2 - \sigma_{nn}^2 \tag{6.77}$$

Here we have equated the normal traction component, t_n, to the normal stress σ_{nn} acting on the plane of interest. To write the quantities on the right-hand side of (6.77) in terms of the principal stresses a Cartesian coordinate system is chosen with positive x-, y-, and z-axes in the directions of the unit vectors $\mathbf{n}(1)$, $\mathbf{n}(2)$, and $\mathbf{n}(3)$ respectively (Fig. 6.22a). Cauchy's Formula, (6.40), then reduces to $t_x = \sigma_1 n_x$, $t_y = \sigma_2 n_y$, $t_z = \sigma_3 n_z$ and the squared magnitude of the traction vector is the sum of the squared components:

$$|\mathbf{t}|^2 = \sigma_1^2 n_x^2 + \sigma_2^2 n_y^2 + \sigma_3^2 n_z^2 \tag{6.78}$$

The squared normal stress is taken from (6.49) with the shear stress components equal to zero and the normal stress components equal to the principal stresses:

$$\sigma_{nn}^2 = (\sigma_1 n_x^2 + \sigma_2 n_y^2 + \sigma_3 n_z^2)^2 \tag{6.79}$$

Substituting (6.78) and (6.79) into (6.77) we have:

$$\sigma_{ns}^2 = \sigma_1^2 n_x^2 + \sigma_2^2 n_y^2 + \sigma_3^2 n_z^2 - (\sigma_1 n_x^2 + \sigma_2 n_y^2 + \sigma_3 n_z^2)^2 \tag{6.80}$$

When this equation is expanded there are terms in each of the principal stresses that can be rearranged using (6.17) and the following example (Fung, 1965):

$$\sigma_1^2(n_x^2 - n_x^4) = \sigma_1^2 n_x^2(1 - n_x^2) = \sigma_1^2 n_x^2(n_y^2 + n_z^2) \quad (6.81)$$

Equation (6.80) then takes the form (Jaeger and Cook, 1979):

$$\sigma_{ns}^2 = (\sigma_1 - \sigma_2)^2 n_x^2 n_y^2 + (\sigma_2 - \sigma_3)^2 n_y^2 n_z^2$$
$$+ (\sigma_3 - \sigma_1)^2 n_z^2 n_x^2 \quad (6.82)$$

Note that the shear stress is a function of the principal stress differences.

The goal is to identify the extreme values of the shear stress as a function of the components of **n**. However, these three components are not independent, so we use (6.17) to eliminate n_z from (6.82) and write the shear stress as a function of the two independent variables, n_x and n_y:

$$\sigma_{ns}^2 = (\sigma_3 - \sigma_1)^2 n_x^2(1 - n_x^2) + (\sigma_2 - \sigma_3)^2 n_y^2(1 - n_y^2)$$
$$+ [(\sigma_1 - \sigma_2)^2 - (\sigma_2 - \sigma_3)^2 - (\sigma_3 - \sigma_1)^2]n_x^2 n_y^2 \quad (6.83)$$

The maximum and minimum, or stationary, values of the shear stress are found by taking the derivatives of (6.83) with respect to n_x and n_y:

$$2\sigma_{ns}\frac{d\sigma_{ns}}{dn_x} = (\sigma_3 - \sigma_1)^2 2n_x(1 - 2n_x^2) + [(\sigma_1 - \sigma_2)^2$$
$$- (\sigma_2 - \sigma_3)^2 - (\sigma_3 - \sigma_1)^2]2n_x n_y^2$$

$$2\sigma_{ns}\frac{d\sigma_{ns}}{dn_y} = (\sigma_2 - \sigma_3)^2 2n_y(1 - 2n_y^2) + [(\sigma_1 - \sigma_2)^2$$
$$- (\sigma_2 - \sigma_3)^2 - (\sigma_3 - \sigma_1)^2]n_x^2 2n_y \quad (6.84)$$

The right-hand sides of (6.84) are zero if $n_x = 0 = n_y$, but this refers to a principal plane on which the shear stress is zero (minimum).

Taking $n_x = 0$ the right-hand side of the first of (6.84) is zero and the second reduces to:

$$2\sigma_{ns}\frac{d\sigma_{ns}}{dn_y} = (\sigma_2 - \sigma_3)^2 2n_y(1 - 2n_y^2) = 0 \quad (6.85)$$

For $\sigma_2 - \sigma_3 \neq 0$, the second term in parentheses must be zero, and this requires $n_y^2 = \frac{1}{2}$. Using (6.17) we find $n_z^2 = \frac{1}{2}$ and conclude that the components of **n** for the planes carrying this shear stress are: $n_x = 0$, $n_y = \pm\sqrt{\frac{1}{2}}$, and $n_z = \pm\sqrt{\frac{1}{2}}$. These components define four planes that contain the x-axis (the direction of σ_1) and bisect the y- and z-axes (the directions of σ_2 and σ_3), (Fig. 6.22b). The magnitude of the shear stress acting on these planes is found by substituting the components into

(6.83) such that $|\sigma_{ns}| = \frac{1}{2}|(\sigma_2 - \sigma_3)|$. Substituting the components into (6.79) and equating the normal traction component to the normal stress, σ_{nn}, we find the magnitude of the normal stress acting on these planes is $|\sigma_{nn}| = \frac{1}{2}|(\sigma_2 + \sigma_3)|$. The steps of this paragraph are repeated taking $n_x = 0$ to find a second set of components for **n** and then the entire analysis is repeated after eliminating n_x or n_y from (6.82) to find a third set of components. All three sets are given in the Table 6.1 along with the magnitudes of the maximum shear stresses and the magnitudes of the normal stresses on these planes.

The shear stress we have identified as $\frac{1}{2}|\sigma_1 - \sigma_3|$ in Table 6.1 always is the greatest in magnitude, because $\sigma_1 \geq \sigma_2 \geq \sigma_3$, but the order of the other two depends upon the particular values of the principal normal stresses. The maximum shear stresses

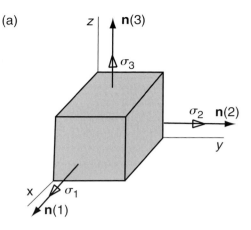

(a)

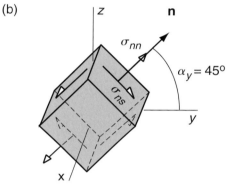

(b)

Fig 6.22 (a) Volume element oriented such that principal stresses act on sides. (b) Volume element rotated such that the maximum shear stress acts on sides.

Table 6.1. Components of **n** and magnitudes of maximum shear stress and normal stress.

n_x	n_y	n_z	$\|\sigma_{ns}\|$	$\|\sigma_{nn}\|$
0	$\pm\sqrt{\frac{1}{2}}$	$\pm\sqrt{\frac{1}{2}}$	$\frac{1}{2}\|\sigma_2 - \sigma_3\|$	$\frac{1}{2}\|\sigma_2 + \sigma_3\|$
$\pm\sqrt{\frac{1}{2}}$	0	$\pm\sqrt{\frac{1}{2}}$	$\frac{1}{2}\|\sigma_1 - \sigma_3\|$	$\frac{1}{2}\|\sigma_1 + \sigma_3\|$
$\pm\sqrt{\frac{1}{2}}$	$\pm\sqrt{\frac{1}{2}}$	0	$\frac{1}{2}\|\sigma_1 - \sigma_2\|$	$\frac{1}{2}\|\sigma_1 + \sigma_2\|$

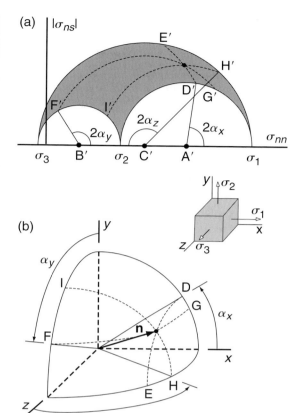

Fig 6.23 (a) Mohr space in which the magnitude of the shear stress is plotted versus the normal stress on surfaces with outward unit normal **n**. (b) Three-dimensional space with normal vector **n** related to angles and points in Mohr space. Reprinted from Jaeger and Cook (1979) with the kind permission of Mrs. Jennifer D. Cook.

act on planes that contain one of the principal normal stress directions and bisect the angle between the other two, so the normals to these planes make angles of $\pm45°$ with the principal axes of normal stress (Fig. 6.22). The magnitudes of the maximum shear stresses are one-half of the difference between the associated principal normal stresses. Recall that the principal normal stresses act on planes that carry zero shear stress. In contrast, the maximum shear stresses act on planes that have a normal stress equal in magnitude to the average of the associated principal normal stresses.

6.2.6 The Mohr diagram: visualizing stress variation for a given stress state

The variation of normal and shear stress with the orientation of the boundary on which they act in a region of homogeneous stress can be appreciated using a graphical construction called the *Mohr diagram*. Apparently the German civil engineer Otto Mohr first described this graphical construction in 1882 (Mohr, 1882; Timoshenko and Goodier, 1970). Since then it has been used in countless textbooks and journal articles, becoming a standard tool for stress analysis. The need for graphical constructions for the analysis of stress variation has largely been made obsolete by computers. The technique is reviewed here for historical reasons and to reinforce the intuitive understanding of these variations.

Detailed derivations of the equations behind the Mohr diagram are provided elsewhere (Malvern, 1969; Jaeger and Cook, 1979), so we only describe the graphical result. Consider a cubic element oriented in such a way that no shear trac-

tions act on the faces. These faces carry the maximum, intermediate, and minimum principal normal stresses (σ_1, σ_2, σ_3) and the principal directions **n**(1), **n**(2), **n**(3) are parallel to the x-, y-, and z-axes respectively (Fig. 6.23 inset). On an arbitrarily oriented plane with outward unit normal **n** the traction vector may be resolved into normal and shear components (Fig. 6.18) and we consider the associated normal and shear stress for this construction. In Mohr space (Fig. 6.23a) one plots the magnitude of the shear stress, $\|\sigma_{ns}\|$, on the ordinate and the normal stress, σ_{nn}, on the abscissa. Three half-circles are plotted with centers along the abscissa, and their intersections with the abscissa correspond to the principal stresses. The circle with a center at A′ traces out coordinate pairs $(\sigma_{nn}, |\sigma_{ns}|)$ from $(\sigma_1, 0)$ to $(\sigma_2, 0)$ as the angle $2\alpha_x$ varies from 0 to π for surfaces that contain the z-axis and the principal direction $\mathbf{n}(3)$ such that $\alpha_z = \pi/2$ (see Fig. 6.23b). Similar statements follow for the circles with centres at B′ and C′ that trace out coordinate pairs from $(\sigma_2, 0)$ to $(\sigma_3, 0)$ as $2\alpha_y$ varies from 0 to π and $\alpha_x = \pi/2$, and from $(\sigma_3, 0)$ to $(\sigma_1, 0)$ as $2\alpha_z$ varies from 0 to π and $\alpha_y = \pi/2$. The center of the circle at C′ corresponds to the normal stress $(\sigma_1 + \sigma_3)/2$ and the radius of that circle is the magnitude of maximum shear stress $(\sigma_1 - \sigma_3)/2$. The other stresses from Table 6.1 are related to the centers and radii of the circles centered at A′ and B′.

We now identify where, in Mohr space, coordinate pairs $(\sigma_{nn}, |\sigma_{ns}|)$ would plot that act on planes oblique to all three coordinate axes. The normal vector, $\mathbf{n}$, to the arbitrarily oriented plane in physical space (Fig. 6.23b) extends from the origin to the perimeter of a unit sphere. The direction angles for this vector are α_x, α_y, and α_z. The cone swept out by rotating about the Ox-axis with constant angle α_x intersects the unit sphere along the dashed circle D–E. The coordinate pairs $(\sigma_{nn}, |\sigma_{ns}|)$ acting on surfaces with these orientations are represented in Mohr space along the dashed circle D′–E′ with center at B′. Similarly, the cone about the Oy-axis with constant angle α_y traces the dashed circle F–G on the unit sphere and coordinate pairs $(\sigma_{nn}, |\sigma_{ns}|)$ acting on these surfaces are represented in Mohr space along the dashed circle F′–G′ with center at C′. Finally, the cone for constant angle α_z traces the dashed circle H–I on the unit sphere and coordinate pairs $(\sigma_{nn}, |\sigma_{ns}|)$ are represented in Mohr space along the dashed circle H′–I′ with center at A′. The common intersection of the three dashed circles in Mohr space provides the normal stress and the magnitude of the shear stress on the oblique plane with normal vector $\mathbf{n}$. All possible coordinate pairs fall in the gray region between the three half-circles.

From the Mohr diagram (Fig. 6.23a) we observe that the principal stresses act on orthogonal planes. For example, the point $(\sigma_1, 0)$ in Mohr space is associated with the double angle $2\alpha_z = \pi$, so in physical space we have $\alpha_z = \pi/2$. Because the principal stresses plot on the abscissa, the principal planes carry no shear stress. If the Mohr circles

are entirely to the right of the origin, the normal stresses on all possible planes are positive so they are tensions. If the circles are to the left of the origin, the normal stresses are negative so they are compressions. If the circles straddle the origin, then some planes carry tensile stresses and others carry compressive stresses. The greatest shear stress on a plane that contains the y-axis and $\mathbf{n}(2)$ is found on the circle with center at C′ where $2\alpha_z = 90°$. In other words, in physical space this shear stress acts on a plane oriented at 45° to the principal directions $\mathbf{n}(1)$ and $\mathbf{n}(3)$.

6.2.7 Variation of stress components with orientation of the coordinate system

Given the stress components referred to a Cartesian coordinate system with a particular orientation, it is useful to calculate the stress components referred to a Cartesian system with another orientation. In other words the two coordinate systems are related by a rotation about a common origin. This procedure is somewhat similar to the *transformation of coordinates* by rotation that was described in Chapter 2, but here the equations are different because the relative surface areas upon which the stress components act must be taken into consideration (Jaeger and Cook, 1979, pp. 24–5). It should come as no surprise that we employ Cauchy's Formula in the derivation.

The given stress components are referred to axes of the first coordinate system (x, y, z) and we seek the corresponding stress components referred to axes of a second coordinate system (x', y', z'). Basis vectors from the common origin, O, and directed along the positive axes Ox', Oy', and Oz' are used in the transformation equations and these are defined using the direction cosines of the angles between the respective coordinate axes (Fig. 6.24a):

$$\begin{aligned}
\mathbf{e}_{x'} &= m_{xx'}\mathbf{e}_x + m_{yx'}\mathbf{e}_y + m_{zx'}\mathbf{e}_z \\
\mathbf{e}_{y'} &= m_{xy'}\mathbf{e}_x + m_{yy'}\mathbf{e}_y + m_{zy'}\mathbf{e}_z \\
\mathbf{e}_{z'} &= m_{xz'}\mathbf{e}_x + m_{yz'}\mathbf{e}_y + m_{zz'}\mathbf{e}_z
\end{aligned} \tag{6.86}$$

The double subscripts on the direction cosines m_{ij} refer to the reference axis and the transformed axis, respectively. For example, $m_{yx'}$ is the cosine of the angle (y, x').

The normal stress component, $\sigma_{x'x'}$, acts on the plane with normal $\mathbf{e}_{x'}$ and in a direction parallel to

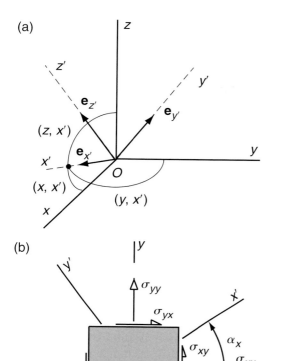

Fig 6.24 (a) Transformation of the stress components from the (x, y, z)-coordinate system to the (x', y', z')-coordinate system. Basis vectors and direction angles are shown. (b) Two-dimensional transformation.

$$\sigma_{x'x'} = \mathbf{t}(\mathbf{e}_{x'}) \cdot \mathbf{e}_{x'}$$
$$= \sigma_{xx}m_{xx'}^2 + \sigma_{yy}m_{yx'}^2 + \sigma_{zz}m_{zx'}^2 + 2\sigma_{xy}m_{xx'}m_{yx'}$$
$$+ 2\sigma_{yz}m_{yx'}m_{zx'} + 2\sigma_{zx}m_{zx'}m_{xx'} \quad (6.88)$$

The shear stress component acting on this plane and in a direction parallel to the y'-axis is found by resolving the traction vector $\mathbf{t}(\mathbf{e}_{x'})$ onto the Oy'-axis. In other words it is the scalar product of the traction vector and the unit normal vector $\mathbf{e}_{y'}$. The traction vector components are given in (6.87) and the components of $\mathbf{e}_{y'}$ are given in (6.86) so the shear stress is:

$$\sigma_{x'y'} = \mathbf{t}(\mathbf{e}_{x'}) \cdot \mathbf{e}_{y'}$$
$$= \sigma_{xx}m_{xx'}m_{xy'} + \sigma_{yy}m_{yx'}m_{yy'} + \sigma_{zz}m_{zx'}m_{zy'}$$
$$+ \sigma_{xy}(m_{xy'}m_{yx'} + m_{yy'}m_{xx'})$$
$$+ \sigma_{yz}(m_{yy'}m_{zx'} + m_{zy'}m_{yx'})$$
$$+ \sigma_{zx}(m_{zy'}m_{xx'} + m_{xy'}m_{zx'}) \quad (6.89)$$

Resolving the traction vector $\mathbf{t}(\mathbf{e}_{x'})$ onto the Oz'-axis determines the other shear stress component acting on this plane.

Following a similar procedure for planes with normal vectors $\mathbf{e}_{y'}$ and $\mathbf{e}_{z'}$, the other four transformation equations are (Jaeger and Cook, 1979, pp. 24–5):

$$\sigma_{y'y'} = \sigma_{xx}m_{xy'}^2 + \sigma_{yy}m_{yy'}^2 + \sigma_{zz}m_{zy'}^2$$
$$+ 2\sigma_{xy}m_{xy'}m_{yy'} + 2\sigma_{yz}m_{yy'}m_{zy'} + 2\sigma_{zx}m_{zy'}m_{xy'} \quad (6.90)$$

$$\sigma_{z'z'} = \sigma_{xx}m_{xz'}^2 + \sigma_{yy}m_{yz'}^2 + \sigma_{zz}m_{zz'}^2$$
$$+ 2\sigma_{xy}m_{xz'}m_{yz'} + 2\sigma_{yz}m_{yz'}m_{zz'} + 2\sigma_{zx}m_{zz'}m_{xz'} \quad (6.91)$$

$$\sigma_{y'z'} = \sigma_{xx}m_{xy'}m_{xz'} + \sigma_{yy}m_{yy'}m_{yz'} + \sigma_{zz}m_{zy'}m_{zz'}$$
$$+ \sigma_{xy}(m_{xy'}m_{yz'} + m_{xz'}m_{yy'})$$
$$+ \sigma_{yz}(m_{yy'}m_{zz'} + m_{yz'}m_{zy'})$$
$$+ \sigma_{zx}(m_{zy'}m_{xz'} + m_{zz'}m_{xy'}) \quad (6.92)$$

$$\sigma_{z'x'} = \sigma_{xx}m_{xz'}m_{xx'} + \sigma_{yy}m_{yz'}m_{yx'} + \sigma_{zz}m_{zz'}m_{zx'}$$
$$+ \sigma_{xy}(m_{xz'}m_{yx'} + m_{xx'}m_{yz'})$$
$$+ \sigma_{yz}(m_{yz'}m_{zx'} + m_{yx'}m_{zz'})$$
$$+ \sigma_{zx}(m_{zz'}m_{xx'} + m_{zx'}m_{xz'}) \quad (6.93)$$

this basis vector. This stress component is found by resolving the traction vector $\mathbf{t}(\mathbf{e}_{x'})$ acting on this plane onto the Ox' axis. In other words the normal stress is the scalar product of the traction vector and the basis vector $\mathbf{e}_{x'}$. The traction vector components are found from Cauchy's Formula, (6.40), by noting that the normal to the plane of interest is $\mathbf{e}_{x'}$:

$$t_x(\mathbf{e}_{x'}) = \sigma_{xx}m_{xx'} + \sigma_{yx}m_{yx'} + \sigma_{zx}m_{zx'}$$
$$t_y(\mathbf{e}_{x'}) = \sigma_{xy}m_{xx'} + \sigma_{yy}m_{yx'} + \sigma_{zy}m_{zx'} \quad (6.87)$$
$$t_z(\mathbf{e}_{x'}) = \sigma_{xz}m_{xx'} + \sigma_{yz}m_{yx'} + \sigma_{zz}m_{zx'}$$

Using these components of the traction vector and the components of $\mathbf{e}_{x'}$ from (6.86), the normal stress is:

Although these equations look complex, a few minutes study reveals patterns that reflect the fact that the three normal components transform in a similar fashion, as do the three shear components. Furthermore the sequence of subscripts is systematic and repetitive.

The transformation equations for stress components, (6.88) through (6.93), are more general than one might suppose. Equations of this same form are, for example, appropriate for the transformation of the infinitesimal strain components and other physical quantities (Fung, 1969, pp. 32–5). These quantities are collectively known as *tensors of rank two*. They are defined by two characteristics:

1. they are composed of nine components in the (x, y, z)-coordinate system; and
2. they transform to the (x', y', z')-coordinate system following equations of the form provided above.

The transformation of stress components in two dimensions follows from the three-dimensional expressions given above. For example consider the (x, y)-coordinate system transformed to the (x', y')-coordinate system by a rotation about the out-of-plane z-axis through an angle α_x, measured from Ox to Ox' (Fig. 6.24b). The following relationships are helpful:

$$\begin{bmatrix} m_{xx'} & m_{xy'} & m_{xz'} \\ m_{yx'} & m_{yy'} & m_{yz'} \\ m_{zx'} & m_{zy'} & m_{zz'} \end{bmatrix} = \begin{bmatrix} \cos\alpha_x & -\sin\alpha_x & 0 \\ \sin\alpha_x & \cos\alpha_x & 0 \\ 0 & 0 & 1 \end{bmatrix} \quad (6.94)$$

From these relationships the transformation equations for the normal and shear stress components are:

$$\sigma_{x'x'} = \sigma_{xx}\cos^2\alpha_x + \sigma_{yy}\sin^2\alpha_x + 2\sigma_{xy}\sin\alpha_x\cos\alpha_x$$
$$\sigma_{y'y'} = \sigma_{xx}\sin^2\alpha_x + \sigma_{yy}\cos^2\alpha_x - 2\sigma_{xy}\sin\alpha_x\cos\alpha_x$$
$$\sigma_{x'y'} = -(\sigma_{xx} - \sigma_{yy})\sin\alpha_x\cos\alpha_x$$
$$+ \sigma_{xy}(\cos^2\alpha_x - \sin^2\alpha_x) \quad (6.95)$$

Similar equations enable a two-dimensional transformation in the other coordinate planes.

The transformation equations from Cartesian to polar stress components, or vice versa, follow from those just derived. Consider the stress state at

a given point in the body determined by the polar coordinates r and θ (Fig. 6.15). One can imagine sliding the origin of coordinates to the point in question so the geometry is much like that in Fig. 6.24b where the coordinates (x', y') are oriented in the same direction as the coordinates (r, θ). If we take the angle α_x and the angle θ to be equal, the transformation from Cartesian stress components to polar stress components is identical to (6.95) after substituting θ for α_x and making the appropriate substitutions for the stress components:

$$\sigma_{rr} = \sigma_{xx}\cos^2\alpha_x + \sigma_{yy}\sin^2\alpha_x + 2\sigma_{xy}\sin\alpha_x\cos\alpha_x$$
$$\sigma_{\theta\theta} = \sigma_{xx}\sin^2\alpha_x + \sigma_{yy}\cos^2\alpha_x - 2\sigma_{xy}\sin\alpha_x\cos\alpha_x$$
$$\sigma_{r\theta} = -(\sigma_{xx} - \sigma_{yy})\sin\alpha_x\cos\alpha_x$$
$$+ \sigma_{xy}(\cos^2\alpha_x - \sin^2\alpha_x) \quad (6.96)$$

The inverse transformation, from polar to Cartesian stress components, is found by first exchanging the subscripts in (6.96) and then changing the sign of α_x. In this case only the sign of terms containing $\sin\alpha_x$ change.

6.2.8 An example: stress analysis at the grain scale

The individual sand grains of Fig. 6.6a are in contact over small areas between the pores, and the force that one grain exerts on another is entirely transmitted through that area of contact. The relatively great forces and small contact areas combine to produce significant concentrations and complex distributions of stress within individual grains. The spatial variation of the maximum shear stress within grains can be visualized using a technique called *photoelasticity* (Frocht, 1948). The frontispiece for this chapter is a photograph from a photoelastic model experiment that illustrates the shear stress distribution induced in simulated grains of a porous sandstone by the forces acting on the contacts (Price, 1966; Gallagher *et al.*, 1974). Each "grain" in this model is cut from a sheet of transparent and optically isotropic material, such as polycarbonate. The pattern of black bands in the photograph of these "grains" is equivalent to a contour map of the magnitude of the maximum shear stress at each point.

A somewhat simpler picture emerges if we consider only one "grain" loaded by opposed forces of

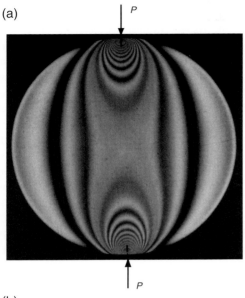

(a)

P

P

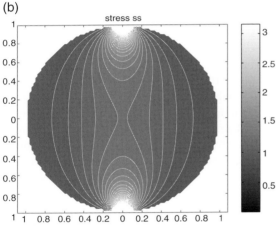

(b)

maximum shear stress ranges from zero along the sides of the disk, to greater values in the interior, to the greatest value near the points of application of the applied forces. Because the stress is concentrated near these two points, one would infer that fractures would initiate at these points if the stress were great enough. Indeed, microscopic examinations of deformed sandstone often reveal fractures emanating from grain contacts (Gallagher *et al.*, 1974) and examples can be seen in Fig. 6.6a.

Photoelasticity is a useful technique for direct visualization of part of the stress field in laboratory models of geologic structures. An alternative is to use mathematical models, based on elasticity theory (see Chapter 8). For example, Fig. 6.25b is a contour plot of the maximum shear stress (see Table 6.1) for a circular disk of thickness, t, and diameter, d, loaded by opposing point forces of magnitude P. The Cartesian stress components are (Frocht, 1948):

$$\sigma_{xx} = -\frac{2P}{\pi t}\left[\frac{(R-y)x^2}{r_1^4} + \frac{(R+y)x^2}{r_2^4} - \frac{1}{d}\right] \quad (6.97)$$

$$\sigma_{yy} = -\frac{2P}{\pi t}\left[\frac{(R-y)^3}{r_1^4} + \frac{(R+y)^3}{r_2^4} - \frac{1}{d}\right] \quad (6.98)$$

$$\sigma_{xy} = \frac{2P}{\pi t}\left[\frac{(R-y)^2x}{r_1^4} - \frac{(R+y)^2x}{r_2^4}\right] \quad (6.99)$$

Here the terms in the denominators are $r_1^2 = x^2 + (R-y)^2$ and $r_2^2 = x^2 + (R+y)^2$.

There is a remarkable similarity between the stress field calculated from the mathematical model (6.97) and the stress field visualized in the analogous laboratory experiment (Fig. 6.25a). Many such examples have demonstrated the efficacy of continuum mechanics for predicting stress variations in solid materials (Frocht, 1948). Given the remarkable computational power of modern computers and the availability of analytical and numerical methods to solve problems in elasticity, there is little need to turn to photoelastic experiments today.

Fig 6.25 Elastic models for the stress distribution in a single circular grain subject to point forces. (a) Photoelastic image of maximum shear stress contours (Frocht, 1948). (b) Maximum shear stress contours from the two-dimensional solution to the elastic boundary value problem.

6.3 | State of stress in the Earth

magnitude P (Fig. 6.25a). Again a laboratory experiment using photoelasticity provides an image of the maximum shear stress distribution (Frocht, 1948). This could be a model for a single grain of sand compressed between two other grains by the weight of the overlying rock. The geometry of the sand grain is idealized as circular and the mechanical actions of the neighboring grains on this grain are approximated as point forces. The

In the book *The Dynamics of Faulting and Dyke Formation with Applications to Britain*, E. M. Anderson described a state of stress that provides a good reference state for investigations of problems in structural geology:

It is possible to imagine a condition in which the lateral pressure from all sides increases steadily with depth, so as to be everywhere equal to the vertical. This will not often happen in nature, but it forms a convenient standard of reference, and may be defined as the "standard state" (Anderson, 1951, pp. 13, 148).

From this description we understand that the normal stress components ("pressure") are equal and the shear stress components are zero. In other words this is an *isotropic state of stress* and the magnitude is determined by the weight of overlying rocks. In this section we define a state of stress that is consistent with Anderson's concept and then describe data from field measurements that show typical variations from this state with depth. Two techniques for measuring the state of stress at shallow depths are described and the data from such tests are summarized. Finally, we provide examples at both the outcrop and the crustal scale that illustrate how tectonic states of stress act to supplement the standard state, and cause different styles of deformation.

Can stress be measured in the Earth? The measurement is not direct in the sense that one measures a distance directly with a ruler. Instead, calculations using measured values of other physical quantities and/or a model are required. Several techniques for so-called *in-situ stress measurement* have been developed and used at exposures and in boreholes and mines (Engelder, 1993). Amadei and Stephansson (1997) describe these techniques and also document much of the available data. These data have been used by mining engineers in the design of underground openings, and by civil engineers in the design of foundations for dams and other large construction projects. As structural geologists, our interest in the state of stress stems from the fact that the evolution of geologic structures depends upon the temporal and spatial variations of stress.

Because *in-situ* stress measurement techniques require direct access to the rock mass, stress measurements have only been made at shallow depths in the crust, typically less than a few kilometers.

Stress states at greater depths must be extrapolated from these data, inferred from studying data recorded on seismographs during earthquakes, or calculated from models. Seismic data indicate the orientations of the principal stresses in the vicinity of a significant earthquake (Engelder, 1993). Typically these events range from a few kilometers depth to a few tens of kilometers, so this method extends our knowledge of the stress state throughout much of the Earth's crust. The magnitudes of the stresses are not determined by this method, and there can be considerable uncertainty about the orientations (McKenzie, 1969). None-the-less, these so-called *fault-plane solutions* have proved to be very valuable in compiling maps of the principal stress orientations (Zoback, 1992).

In most *in-situ* stress measurement data sets the vertical normal stress ranges from zero at the surface to about 50 MPa at 2 km depth (Brown and Hoek, 1978), more or less following a linear distribution (Fig. 6.26a). This is consistent with the vertical normal stress being related simply to the weight of the overlying rock mass. On the other hand, the horizontal components of normal stress vary in a less systematic fashion with depth (Fig. 6.26b), possibly reflecting differing tectonic loading conditions. Here, the ratio of horizontal to vertical stress is shown to be widely scattered near the surface and converging toward values of one or less at depths greater than 2 km.

The direction of principal stress and its variation in map view across continents, plate boundaries, and other tectonic features may be compiled from the point measurements. Usually these data are presented in terms of the direction of the most compressive normal stress acting in the horizontal plane, near the Earth's surface (Fig. 6.27). In this particular figure the authors have focused on California and the orientation of this stress near the San Andreas Fault system (Zoback *et al.*, 1987). They find that the direction of the greatest compression is remarkably consistent across this region, being more or less from northeast to southwest. This direction varies from somewhat oblique to nearly perpendicular to the trace of the San Andreas Fault zone. Where the most compressive stress is oblique to the fault, one can think of this

(a)

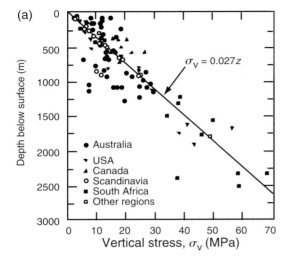

(b)

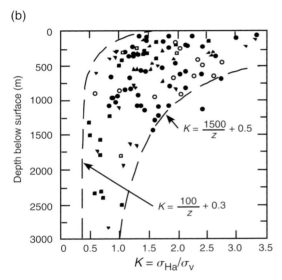

Fig 6.26 Variation of the stress components to depths of 3 km from *in-situ* measurements. (a) Vertical normal stress. (b) Horizontal normal stress normalized by vertical stress. Reprinted from Brown and Hoek (1978) with permission of Elsevier.

stress as promoting shearing. Where this stress is perpendicular to the fault, the cause of shearing is a puzzle that remains to be resolved.

6.3.1 Anderson's standard state and variations of stress with depth

For the coordinate system shown in Fig. 6.28, and the stress components and body force component

illustrated there, the state of stress envisioned by Anderson is defined as follows:

$$\sigma_{xx} = \sigma_{yy} = \sigma_{zz} = \rho g^* z$$
$$\sigma_{xy} = \sigma_{yx} = \sigma_{yz} = \sigma_{zy} = \sigma_{zx} = \sigma_{xz} = 0 \qquad (6.100)$$
$$F_x = F_y = 0, \quad F_z = -\rho g^*$$

Here ρg^* is the weight per unit volume of rock. Positive z is upward from the surface, so the normal stress components are negative (compressive) below the surface, and they increase in magnitude linearly with depth for a constant unit weight.

Values for the unit weight of rock vary from about 2.0×10^4 to 3.5×10^4 N m^{-3} with a pure quartzite having a unit weight of 2.65×10^4 N m^{-3} (Daly *et al.*, 1966). Summarizing many individual measurements of the vertical stress component, σ_{zz}, a value of 0.0265 MPa m^{-1} is reported for data from around the world at depths ranging from 100 to 3000 m (McGarr and Gay, 1978), a value of 0.0285 MPa m^{-1} over the depth range from 0 to 2300 m is reported for the Canadian Shield (Herget, 1993), and the data shown in Fig. 6.26 provide an average value of 0.027 MPa m^{-1}, again down to about 3000 m (Brown and Hoek, 1978). These data are roughly consistent with the rule of thumb: the vertical compressive stress gradient with depth is about 25 MPa km^{-1}. Anderson suggested that (6.100) may not be common, but it is a good place to start an investigation, and it has become known as *Anderson's standard state* (Hafner, 1951). Where measurements of the vertical stress depart from the standard state, there usually are obvious explanations in terms of the local topography, geological heterogeneities, or evidence for tectonic activity (Amadei and Stephansson, 1997).

In a body of water (or other viscous fluid) with constant density and at rest, the stress components are the same as Anderson's standard state (6.100). This is referred to as a *hydrostatic stress* or hydrostatic pressure. Hydrostatic is not a very good term to describe the stress state in a body of rock since the prefix "hydro" implies water. By analogy, however, a state of stress in the Earth that is isotropic and simply proportional to the average rock density, the local acceleration of gravity, and

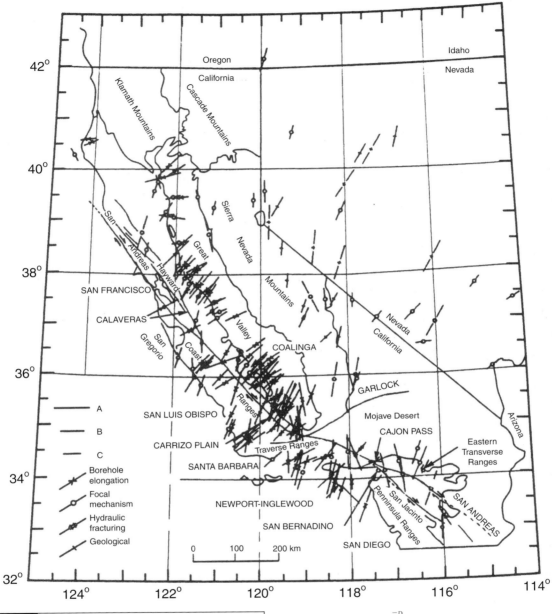

Fig 6.27 Directions of greatest compressive horizontal stress from various measurement techniques near the San Andreas Fault system in California. Reprinted with permission from Zoback et al. (1987), copyright 1987.

$$\sigma_{xx} = \sigma_{yy} = \sigma_{zz} = \int_0^{-D} \rho g \, dz$$

$$\sigma_{xy} = \sigma_{yx} = \sigma_{yz} = \sigma_{zy} = \sigma_{zx} = \sigma_{xz} = 0$$

(6.101)

depth is referred to as a *lithostatic state of stress*. For a variable density, ρ, and variable gravitational acceleration, g, with respect to depth, the stress components in a body of rock at depth, $z = -D$, may follow the relationship:

Jaeger and Cook refer to this as Heim's rule after the Swiss geologist Albert Heim (Jaeger and Cook, 1979, p. 371). For the investigation of many structural problems, it is not necessary to consider the continuous variations in these quantities. Rather, an average or representative unit weight can be adopted because the greatest variation of typical unit weights is only a factor of two. However, in some engineering applications, the level of detail suggested by (6.101) may be prudent (Amadei and Stephansson, 1997, pp. 41–5).

The following linear relationships summarize data on the variations in principal stresses with depths to 2300 m from the Canadian Shield (Herget, 1993):

$$\sigma_1 = -1.4 \text{ MPa} + (0.0225 \text{ MPa m}^{-1})z$$
$$\sigma_2 = -6.4 \text{ MPa} + (0.0293 \text{ MPa m}^{-1})z \qquad (6.102)$$
$$\sigma_3 = -12.1 \text{ MPa} + (0.0403 \text{ MPa m}^{-1})z$$

Based upon data from Sweden, over the depth range from 0 to 1000 m, the principal stress magnitudes vary with depth as (Stephansson, 1993):

$$\sigma_1 = -0.8 \text{ MPa} + (0.020 \text{ MPa m}^{-1})z$$
$$\sigma_2 = -5.1 \text{ MPa} + (0.029 \text{ MPa m}^{-1})z \qquad (6.103)$$
$$\sigma_3 = -10.8 \text{ MPa} + (0.037 \text{ MPa m}^{-1})z$$

These best-fitting linear relationships define gradients that range from 0.020 to 0.040 MPa m^{-1}. The stress magnitudes at the surface ($z = 0$) range from approximately 0 to greater than 12 MPa, and all the principal stresses are compressive over the range of depths. The conclusion that the state of stress is anisotropic (different principal stress magnitudes in different directions) should not come as a surprise to structural geologists, because the formation of most geologic structures requires an anisotropic stress state.

Because the surface of the Earth is essentially free of shear tractions (an exception being shear induced by wind), one of the principal stress directions must be normal to the surface, and this principal stress must be zero in magnitude. For the Canadian Shield data set the calculated value is −1.4 MPa and for the Sweden data set it is −0.8 MPa. This is probably indicative of the error introduced by fitting a linear relationship to scattered data. The two horizontal principal stresses are not constrained to be zero at the surface and, indeed, they can take on surprisingly great magnitudes in compression. For example, σ_3 at the surface for the Canadian data is −12 MPa, roughly equivalent to the compressive stress under a column of rock 500 m high.

The concept that the principal stress directions

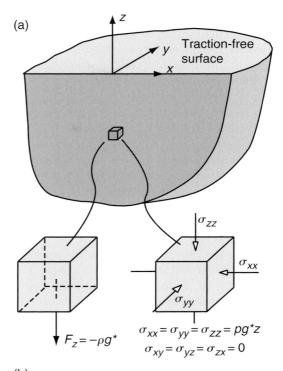

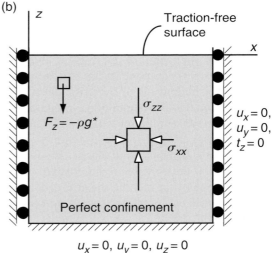

Fig 6.28 Models for the state of stress variation with depth. (a) Anderson's standard state (Anderson, 1951). (b) The state of perfect confinement.

are vertical and horizontal at shallow depths is supported by the results of many analyses of earthquake focal mechanisms from around the globe (Zoback et al., 1989; Engelder, 1993). Stress data from mines in Canada and South Africa indicate that the divergence in orientation of the most steeply inclined principal stress can be up to 30° from vertical (McGarr and Gay, 1978; Herget, 1993). The orientation data from the Canadian Shield are presented as contour plots of 165 observations on lower hemisphere stereonets (Fig. 6.29). There is a tight clustering of data for the greatest principal stress, σ_1, about the vertical axis (plunge of 90°), but some measurements plunge as shallowly as 60°. The other two principal stress orientations are widely scattered in azimuth, but the intermediate principal stress is approximately northwest–southeast and the minimum principal stress (greatest compression) is approximately northeast–southwest.

Despite the general tendency for the principal stresses to be vertical and horizontal, and for their magnitudes to increase linearly with depth, exceptions may occur, particularly near the surface of the Earth, and in the presence of significant topographic variations. Figure 6.30 illustrates the spatial variations in the magnitudes of the three stress components in the (x, y)-plane under a long symmetric (two-dimensional) ridge (Savage et al., 1985). Note that the y-axis is vertical and positive upward, and that both axes are scaled by the height of the ridge, b, above the origin. The stress components are scaled by $\rho g^* b$, the expected magnitude of the principal stresses at a depth equal to the height of the ridge, according to Anderson's standard state. In this model, the properties of the rock are assumed to be homogeneous, isotropic, and elastic. The loading of this ridge is entirely due to gravity, but others report examples that include the effects of a horizontal tectonic compression (Savage and Swolfs, 1986; Pan et al., 1995).

For Anderson's standard state and no topography, contours of the horizontal component of normal stress, $\sigma_{xx}/\rho g^* b$, would be equally spaced horizontal lines, with the 0-contour at the traction-free surface. Those contours under the symmetric ridge (Fig. 6.30a) are significantly perturbed from this simple pattern. At depths below the origin that are about equivalent to the ridge height the contour pattern simplifies to subhorizontal lines of approximately equal spacing. Contours of the vertical normal stress, $\sigma_{yy}/\rho g^* b$, mimic the shape of the topographic surface (Fig.

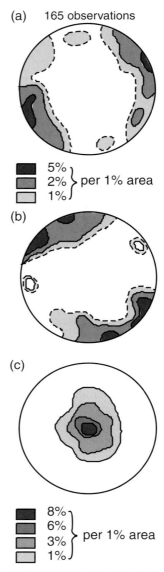

Fig 6.29 Orientations of principal stresses from the Canadian Shield. (a) Minimum principal stress (greatest compression). (b) Intermediate principal stress. (c) Maximum principal stress (least compression). Reprinted from Herget (1993) with permission of Elsevier.

6.30b) and are simpler than contours for the horizontal normal stress. At depths greater than the height of the ridge, the contours of vertical normal stress show only minor perturbations due to the topography. Note, however, that the magnitudes of the two normal stress components at these depths are significantly different, with the

(a)
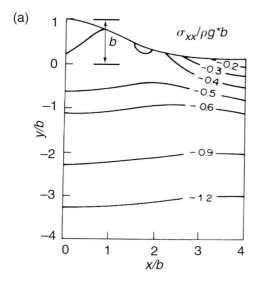

(b)
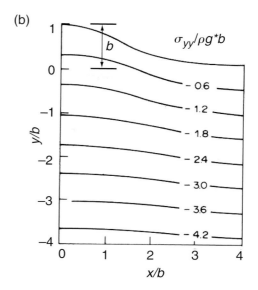

(c)
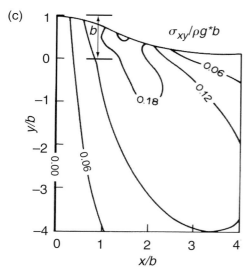

Fig 6.30 Elastic model for the variation in stress components due to gravity under a long symmetric ridge. Components are normalized by $\rho g^* b$, where b is the ridge height. (a) Horizontal normal stress. (b) Vertical normal stress. (c) Shear stress. Reprinted from Savage et al. (1985) with permission of Elsevier.

contours of shear stress are quite complex in pattern, but a 0-contour extends from the ridge top vertically downward, indicating that the principal stress directions are vertical and horizontal along that symmetry line. The small values of shear stress relative to the two normal stresses imply that the principal stress directions are approximately parallel to the coordinate axes.

The boundary conditions on the sides of the model (Fig. 6.30) are a zero horizontal displacement. This *horizontal constraint* results in compressive horizontal stresses throughout the model, with a magnitude that depends upon the nature of the constraint and the material properties. To quantify the stress state under conditions of a horizontal constraint, consider a model with a traction-free upper surface and no topography (Fig. 6.28b), and composed of an elastic material, loaded only by gravity. The lateral edges of this model are not constrained in the vertical direction, so $t_z = 0$ there. However, they are constrained to have zero horizontal displacements, so $u_x = 0 = u_y$. The cylindrical rollers between the rigid platen and the model are meant to imply traction-free vertical motion, but no horizontal displacements. A similar picture would illustrate the conditions in the (y, z)-plane. Under gravitational loading the model contracts vertically and the lateral constraints induce horizontal compressive stresses. The stress state at any depth

horizontal component being less than the vertical component. This is caused by the remote boundary conditions of no horizontal displacement. Contours of the shear stress, $\sigma_{xy}/\rho g^* b$, would not appear on a plot representing Anderson's standard state because that component would be zero everywhere. For the symmetric ridge (Fig. 6.30c) the

($z \leq 0$), along with the gravitational force components per unit volume, F_i, are given by:

$$\sigma_{xx} = \sigma_{yy} = \frac{v}{1-v}\sigma_{zz}; \qquad \sigma_{zz} = \rho g^* z$$

$$\sigma_{xy} = \sigma_{yx} = \sigma_{yz} = \sigma_{zy} = \sigma_{zx} = \sigma_{xz} = 0 \qquad (6.104)$$

$$F_x = F_y = 0, \qquad F_z = -\rho g^*$$

This state of stress is referred to as a state of *perfect confinement*.

The relationship between the vertical and horizontal components of stress (6.104) depends upon an elastic property called *Poisson's ratio*, v. For this discussion it is sufficient to understand that Poisson's ratio is a dimensionless number with values that range between 0 and 1/2. For $v = 0.25$, the value used for the models illustrated in Fig. 6.30, the horizontal stress is one-third of the vertical stress according to (6.104). For $v = 1/3$, the horizontal stress is one-half of the vertical stress, and as v goes to 1/2, the vertical and horizontal stress components become equal. Thus, Anderson's standard state is consistent with an elastic, perfectly constrained rock mass only if Poisson's ratio is equal to 1/2.

6.3.2 Measurement of *in-situ* stress: hydraulic fractures and wellbore breakouts

Two common methods for stress measurement at depth in the Earth's crust involve data taken from wellbores. The first method is based upon perturbing the local state of stress near a wellbore by increasing the internal fluid pressure until the wall of the wellbore fractures (Fig. 6.31). Because the fracture is induced by fluid pressure, this is referred to as the *hydraulic fracturing method*. The objective is to determine the magnitudes and orientations of the three principal stresses at the site of the measurement, so this is referred to as the *in-situ stress*. Here we introduce the elementary concepts and theory behind these tests. Amadei and Stephansson describe hydraulic methods for stress determination in more detail, and evaluate more general conditions for these tests (Amadei and Stephansson, 1997). Other techniques for estimating stress in the Earth's crust involve the interpretation of earthquake data (Hanks, 1977; Scholz, 1990) and the interpretation of geological structures (Zoback *et al*., 1989; Zoback, 1992).

Based on proximity of the Earth's traction-free

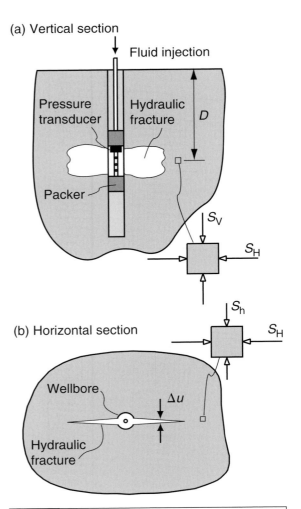

(a) Vertical section

Fluid injection

Pressure transducer

Hydraulic fracture

D

Packer

S_V

S_H

S_h

S_H

(b) Horizontal section

Wellbore

Δu

Hydraulic fracture

Fig 6.31 Schematic illustrations of hydraulic fracture generation from a wellbore. (a) Vertical cross section in the plane of the fracture and containing the wellbore. (b) Horizontal cross section through the fracture and wellbore. State of stress in absence of fracture and wellbore is (S_V, S_H, S_h).

surface, it is presumed that one principal stress is vertical. The magnitude of this compressive stress is called S_V, and it is aligned with the vertical axis of the wellbore (Fig. 6.31a). Furthermore, it is presumed that the magnitude of this stress is determined by the average unit weight, ρg^*, of the overlying rock and the depth, D:

$$S_V = \rho g^* D \qquad (6.105)$$

Given S_V, the problem is reduced to finding the magnitudes of the greater and lesser principal

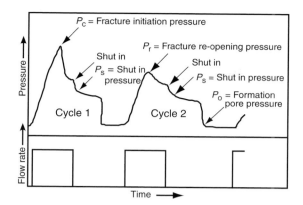

Fig 6.32 Plots of pressure versus time and flow rate versus time for hydraulic fracturing. Pressures used to infer the state of stress are indicated. Reprinted from Enever *et al.* (1992) with permission of Elsevier.

stresses in the horizontal plane, S_H and S_h, respectively, and their orientation (azimuth), (Fig. 6.31b). It is not known a priori whether S_V is the least, intermediate, or greatest principal stress. It is generally presumed that all of these stresses are compressive, so S_H is the greatest compressive stress and S_h is the least compressive stress in the horizontal plane. The pressure record from the hydraulic fracturing test is used to determine the magnitudes of these stresses. Their orientation is determined by assuming that the least compressive stress, S_h, is perpendicular to the fracture, and the fracture orientation is detected in the wellbore using devices called impression packers or borehole televiewers (Amadei and Stephansson, 1997).

To carry out the hydraulic fracturing procedure a short section of the well is sealed off from the fluid pressure above and below with so-called straddle packers, inflatable rubber tubes that press against the sides of the wellbore (Fig. 6.31a). The fluid pressure is monitored with an electronic pressure transducer, and it is controlled by pumping fluid into the section between the straddle packers at a constant rate. Schematic pressure versus time and fluid flow versus time records are shown in Fig. 6.32, with different characteristic pressures identified during two cycles of fluid injection (Enever *et al.*, 1992). The *breakdown pressure*, P_c, is the greatest pressure recorded on the first cycle of injection, and this is interpreted as the pressure at which the fracturing initiates. In

this record the subsequent gradually declining pressure occurs as the injected fluid flows into the fracture and the fracture tip propagates away from the wellbore. A sharp drop in pressure occurs when pumping ceases and further flow into or out of the section is prevented by closing the appropriate valves. This is the so-called shut-in phase, and the gradually declining pressure after shut-in is associated with leakage of fluid from the section or the fracture into the adjacent rock. The decrease in slope of the pressure versus time record, shortly after shut-in, is interpreted as the closing of the fracture, because this would curtail significant leakage from the fracture walls and thus tend to stabilize the pressure. This so-called *shut-in pressure*, P_s, may be difficult to detect, but it plays a crucial role in the determination of the stress state. On the next cycle of fluid injection into the packed off section of the wellbore, the *re-opening pressure*, P_r, is interpreted as that necessary to open the fracture at the wellbore. The decrease in slope of the pressure versus time record reflects the enhanced flow into the fracture. The second and subsequent injections provide additional measures of the shut-in pressure.

The various pressures recorded during the hydraulic fracturing procedure are used to estimate the stress state in the horizontal plane (Fig. 6.32b) by employing models that relate these physical quantities (Hubbert and Willis, 1957; Scheidegger, 1962; Fairhurst, 1964; Haimson and Fairhurst, 1967). The model reviewed here is based on elasticity theory. The rock surrounding the borehole is postulated to behave as a homogeneous and isotropic solid with respect to its elastic properties. More complete models would include the effects of fluids, present in the rock before the procedure and leaking into the pores of the surrounding rock from the wellbore and the fracture. The model presented here is based upon the solution for the two-dimensional stress state around a circular hole loaded by a uniform remote stress. This solution apparently was derived first by G. Kirsh and published in 1898, and it has been verified in numerous laboratory studies by direct strain measurement and photoelastic investigations (Timoshenko and Goodier, 1970, p. 90).

The geometry of the problem consists of a circular hole of radius R and a polar coordinate

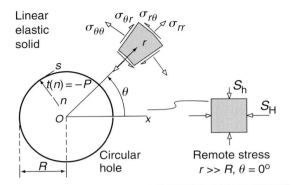

Fig 6.33 Geometry and stress components for the Kirsh solution to the elastic boundary value problem of a circular hole in an infinite body (Jaeger and Cook, 1979).

system with origin at the center of the hole (Fig. 6.33). For the sake of mathematical convenience the elastic body extends to an infinite distance from the hole, but the solution approximates finite bodies that extend to distances that are great compared to R. The internal boundary conditions for this problem are specified in terms of the traction acting on the edge of the hole:

$$\text{BC: on } r = R, \quad t_n = -P, \quad t_s = 0 \qquad (6.106)$$

This traction presses against the hole boundary with a magnitude equal to P, and has no shear component, so this is equivalent to a static fluid pressure. The remote boundary conditions are written in terms of the stress components decaying to some uniform values at infinite distances:

$$\text{BC: as } \frac{r}{R} \rightarrow \infty, \begin{cases} \sigma_{rr} \rightarrow -\frac{1}{2}(S_H + S_h) - \frac{1}{2}(S_H - S_h)\cos 2\theta \\ \sigma_{r\theta} \rightarrow +\frac{1}{2}(S_H - S_h)\sin 2\theta \\ \sigma_{\theta\theta} \rightarrow -\frac{1}{2}(S_H + S_h) + \frac{1}{2}(S_H - S_h)\cos 2\theta \end{cases}$$

$$(6.107)$$

For $\theta = 0°$ the stress components are $\sigma_{rr} = -S_H$, $\sigma_{r\theta} = 0$, and $\sigma_{\theta\theta} = -S_h$. In other words this is a biaxial state of compressive stress with the radial component being the greatest compression, S_H, and the circumferential component being the least compression, S_h. S_H and S_h are the magnitudes of the remote principal stresses, because the shear stress is zero for this orientation.

A solution to this elastic boundary value

problem consists of equations for the three polar stress components (Fig. 6.33) everywhere in the horizontal plane that match the conditions specified above at the edge of the hole and at great distances from the hole. The functions that solve this problem are:

$$\sigma_{rr} = -\frac{1}{2}(S_H + S_h)\left[1 - \left(\frac{R}{r}\right)^2\right] - P\left(\frac{R}{r}\right)^2$$
$$- \frac{1}{2}(S_H - S_h)\left[1 - 4\left(\frac{R}{r}\right)^2 + 3\left(\frac{R}{r}\right)^4\right]\cos 2\theta$$

$$(6.108)$$

$$\sigma_{r\theta} = \frac{1}{2}(S_H - S_h)\left[1 + 2\left(\frac{R}{r}\right)^2 - 3\left(\frac{R}{r}\right)^4\right]\sin 2\theta$$

$$(6.109)$$

$$\sigma_{\theta\theta} = -\frac{1}{2}(S_H + S_h)\left[1 + \left(\frac{R}{r}\right)^2\right] + P\left(\frac{R}{r}\right)^2$$
$$+ \frac{1}{2}(S_H - S_h)\left[1 + 3\left(\frac{R}{r}\right)^4\right]\cos 2\theta \qquad (6.110)$$

According to Jaeger and Cook this is, perhaps, the most important solution for the discipline of rock mechanics (Jaeger and Cook, 1979, p. 236), and it has been used for a number of important applications in structural geology as well. These rather complicated looking equations can be reduced to some simple relationships between the stress components and the pressure in the hole by analyzing how the stresses are distributed about the hole.

We learn from the Kirsh solution how the stresses are distributed with radial distance from the hole. For example, in Fig. 6.34a we plot the radial and circumferential stress components for the case of uniaxial remote compression. These stress components are normalized by the magnitude of the remote stress, S_H, and are plotted as they are distributed along the radial line, $\theta = 0°$, from the edge of the hole, $r/R = 1$, to a distance $r/R = 5$. The shear stress is zero along this line of symmetry. For uniaxial compression the radial stress is zero at the edge of the hole, it increases slightly to a tensile maximum, and then steadily decreases toward the remote compressive value $\sigma_{rr}/S_H = -1$. The circumferential stress at the edge of the hole is tensile and of the same magnitude as the remote stress, $\sigma_{\theta\theta}/S_H = +1$. The circumferential stress decreases rapidly away from the hole to a compressive minimum, and then increases slowly toward zero with greater distance from the hole.

The greatest stress perturbations occur at or near the edge of the hole. Based on theoretical models (Hubbert and Willis, 1957) and laboratory experiments (Haimson, 1968), researchers have argued that opening fractures, not shear fractures are the common result of increased fluid pressure in wellbores. These fractures typically trend along the axis of vertical wellbores, so it is the circumferential component of stress that would act to initiate and open the fracture. Therefore, we focus attention on the value of the circumferential stress at the edge of the hole in the elastic model. For the case of internal pressure, the circumferential stress is the same everywhere around the hole and is equal in magnitude to the applied pressure, $\sigma_{\theta\theta}/P = +1$. However, for the case of a uniaxial remote compression the circumferential stress varies systematically from a tension at $\theta = 0°$, where $\sigma_{\theta\theta}/S_H = +1$, to a compression at $\theta = 90°$, where $\sigma_{\theta\theta}/S_H = -3$ (Fig. 6.34b). That is, the remote compression induces a local tension along the edge of the hole that is oriented perpendicular to the applied stress, and it induces a local compression along the edge of the hole that is oriented parallel to the applied stress. Here we focus on the local tensile stress. The greatest tensile stress occurs at $r = R$ and $\theta = 0°$. From symmetry, this same stress is induced at $\theta = 180°$. Using these conditions in (6.108) through (6.110) we find the stress state at these points is:

$$\text{At } \frac{r}{R} = 1 \text{ and } \theta = 0, \pi: \begin{cases} \sigma_{rr} = -P \\ \sigma_{r\theta} = 0 \\ \sigma_{\theta\theta} = +P + S_H - 3S_h \end{cases}$$

$$(6.111)$$

For a given state of remote biaxial compression, the pressures necessary to induce a circumferential tension at these points are:

$$P > 3S_h - S_H \qquad (6.112)$$

To initiate an opening fracture in otherwise unfractured rock, the local tensile stress must equal the tensile strength, T, and the pressure nec-

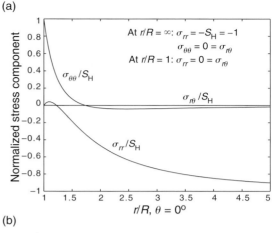

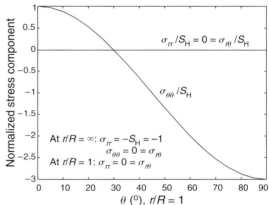

Fig 6.34 Plots of the polar stress components for the circular hole problem (Jaeger and Cook, 1979). (a) Components versus distance from the hole edge for uniaxial remote compression. (b) Components versus position on the hole edge for uniaxial remote compression.

essary to do this is referred to as the *breakdown pressure*, P_c:

$$\text{For } \sigma_{\theta\theta} = T, \qquad P = P_c = 3S_h - S_H + T \qquad (6.113)$$

By measuring the breakdown pressure during the hydraulic fracturing procedure, and by measuring the tensile strength in the laboratory for a sample of the formation being fractured, two of the four quantities in this equation can be determined (Scheidegger, 1962).

Because the appropriate tensile strength is that for the rock at the *in-situ* conditions of stress, temperature, etc., and because these conditions may be difficult to reproduce in the laboratory, an alternative method usually is employed (Brede-hoeft *et al.*, 1976). During the second (and subsequent) cycles of fluid injection, the pressure versus time record is monitored and then analyzed carefully to identify a change in slope of the rising pressure that signals the reopening of the fracture. The elastic model suggests that the *reopening pressure*, P_r, is that necessary to increase the circumferential stress just slightly above zero:

$$\text{For } \sigma_{\theta\theta} = 0, \quad P = P_r = 3S_h - S_H \quad (6.114)$$

This interpretation of the pressure versus time record implies that the *in-situ* tensile strength is:

$$T = P_c - P_r \quad (6.115)$$

The final measure of pressure used to estimate the *in-situ* stresses is that just sufficient to hold the developed fracture open against the least compressive horizontal stress, S_h. The relationship between this pressure and stress is found from a different solution to the elastic boundary value problem, because the geometry now is that of a crack, not a circular hole. The opening, Δu, of a crack in an elastic body is proportional to the difference between the internal pressure, P, that forces the walls apart, and the remote compressive stress, here taken as S_h, that pushes them together (Pollard and Segall, 1987):

$$\Delta u \propto P - S_h \quad (6.116)$$

Thus, the pressure and the stress must be just about equal as the crack starts to open, or as it closes. Just as the fracture surfaces come together, a second knee in the pressure record indicates the *shut-in pressure*, P_s, and this is interpreted as equal in magnitude to the least compressive stress:

$$\text{For } \Delta u = 0, \quad P = P_s = S_h \quad (6.117)$$

Given the depth of overburden, D, and its average unit weight, ρg^*, and the two pressures, P_s and P_r, read from the pressure versus time record, one can calculate all three *in-situ* principal stresses as:

$$\begin{aligned} S_V &= \rho g^* D \\ S_h &= P_s \\ S_H &= 3P_s - P_c + T = 3P_s - P_r \end{aligned} \quad (6.118)$$

This interpretation presumes that a vertical fracture has propagated in a plane that is perpendic-

ular to the direction of S_h, so the fracture orientation determines the orientation of S_H and S_h. The other principal stress is presumed to be vertical. Alternatively, one can use the breakdown pressure, P_c, and a measure of the tensile strength, T, in the determination of S_H.

The second wellbore procedure provides a direct determination of the orientation of the *in-situ* stresses, S_H and S_h. As with the hydraulic fracturing method, the simplest interpretations depend upon a vertical wellbore and the presumption that one of the principal stresses is vertical. A variety of instruments, including the borehole camera, dipmeter, acoustic televiewer, and electrical resistance microscanner are capable of measuring the shape of the wellbore (Amadei and Stephansson, 1997, p. 308). Although the drilling bit is designed to cut a cylindrical hole, the records from these instruments demonstrate that sections of some wellbores are not cylindrical, but instead have systematic increases in radii along two diametrically opposed zones (Fig. 6.35). These zones are referred to as *wellbore breakouts* because it is inferred that the hole was enlarged by the breakage of rock, due to a local stress concentration, and the subsequent spalling of the rock fragments into the wellbore.

The geometry of the zones of broken rock associated with a wellbore breakout suggest that these are not a result of a single fracture extending perpendicular to the wellbore, as in the hydraulic fracturing procedure (Fig. 6.31). Instead, it has been proposed that a set of shear fractures oriented oblique to the wellbore (Fig. 6.35), or a set of opening fractures oriented parallel to the wellbore, is responsible for the fragmentation of the rock (Zoback, 1985; Zheng *et al.*, 1989). In either case the stress concentration induced by drilling the hole is held responsible for the fracturing. Once the rock is fractured, flow of the drilling fluid carries the fragments away, leaving the open breakout.

The Kirsh solution for the elastic boundary value problem of a circular hole subject to internal pressure and remote biaxial compressive stresses provides the equations necessary for an elementary analysis of the stress concentration that may cause breakouts. To assure that hydraulic fractures have not initiated, and that

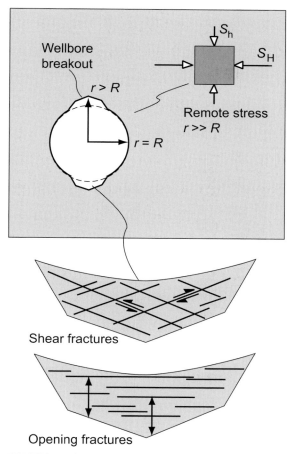

Wellbore breakout

$r > R$

$r = R$

S_h

S_H

Remote stress
$r \gg R$

Shear fractures

Opening fractures

Fig 6.35 Schematic illustration of wellbore breakouts. Inferred directions of greatest, S_H, and least, S_h, horizontal compressive stress remote from the wellbore are shown. Insets show breakouts generated from shear fractures and from opening fractures.

existing fractures have not opened due to the fluid pressure in the wellbore, consider cases where:

$$P < 3S_h - S_H \tag{6.119}$$

According to our previous analysis of the Kirsh solution, the greatest stress concentration is at the hole boundary where the boundary is oriented parallel to S_H. The stress state at these two points is:

$$\text{At } \frac{r}{R} = 1 \text{ and } \theta = \frac{\pi}{2}, \ \frac{3\pi}{2}: \begin{cases} \sigma_{rr} = -P \\ \sigma_{r\theta} = 0 \\ \sigma_{\theta\theta} = +P - 3S_H + S_h \end{cases} \tag{6.120}$$

For the sake of an example we choose the loading conditions $S_H/P = 2$ and $S_h/P = 1$, and note that the circumferential stress would be four times greater than the radial stress. This stress difference could be responsible for the fracturing that creates the breakout zone.

One of the more extensive demonstrations of the utility of wellbore breakouts for determining the orientation of the horizontal principal stresses came from a study in the Western Canadian Basin (Bell and Babcock, 1986). A map from this study (Fig. 6.36) shows the locations of 154 wells throughout the basin, and at each location the average direction of the wellbore breakouts is indicated by a short line. The solid lines indicate the average of the dominant population of breakouts whereas the dashed lines represent minor populations. Note the length scale on the map and the systematic nature of the breakout orientations. Given the interpretation described above, that the breakouts align with the direction of S_h, one would conclude that the greatest horizontal compressive stress, S_H, is dominantly oriented along a northeast–southwest trend, perpendicular to the boundary between the Rocky Mountains and the Canadian Basin. This systematic trend continues for over 1000 km along the range front.

6.3.3 Dike pattern at the Spanish Peaks

Ernest M. Anderson hypothesized a mechanical relationship between igneous dikes and the state of stress in Earth's crust: dikes are intruded perpendicular to the least compressive principal stress (Anderson, 1972). Anderson recognized that igneous dikes are a form of opening fracture driven by the competition between the internal fluid pressure and the remote compressive stress acting across the dike plane. He suggested that the most favorable orientation for the dike plane is perpendicular to σ_1, the least compressive stress. In a region of the crust subject to a homogeneous stress field one would expect dikes to be planar sub-parallel structures. On the other hand if the stress field exhibits spatial or temporal variations one would expect individual dikes to be curved, reflecting propagation along a curved stress trajectory. The radial dike set in the Spanish Peaks region (Fig. 6.12a) presumably reflects variations

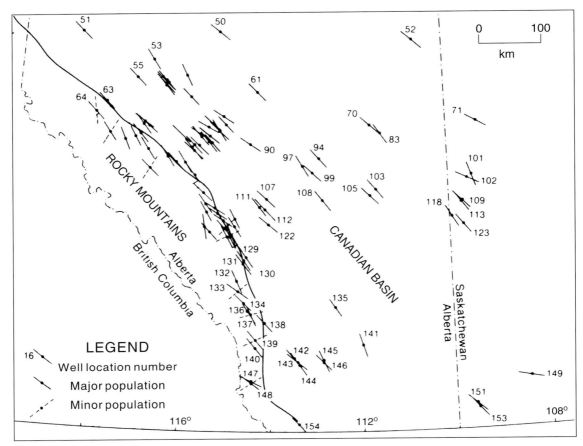

Fig 6.36 Map of western Canada with directions of least horizontal compressive stress inferred from wellbore breakouts. Reprinted from Bell and Babcock (1986) with permission of Elsevier.

in the orientation of the stress field, so these variations can be deduced from the pattern of dikes. The traces of dikes are correlated (Fig. 6.37) to the trajectories of maximum compressive stress determined from the solution to a boundary value problem of elasticity theory (Pollard and Muller, 1976; Muller and Pollard, 1977). For comparison purposes the trajectories and dike traces are presented in alternating vertical strips across the map. Here the correlation is surprisingly good and there is a unique relationship among the values for the remote principal horizontal stress components, S_H and S_h, the magma pressure, P, the radius of the magma chamber, r_o, and the distance from the magma chamber to the Sangre de Cristo Mountain front, d:

$$\frac{(S_H - S_h)d^2}{Pr_o^2} \approx 0.5 \tag{6.121}$$

For the model result shown in Fig. 6.37 the orientation of the greatest regional compression is $082°$ and the estimated difference between the principal values is $(S_H - S_h) = 0.03P$. Given an estimated upper bound for the magma pressure of $P \leq 100\,\text{MPa}$, based on the strength of rock surrounding the magma chamber, the regional stress difference is less than $5\,\text{MPa}$. For comparison an average value of $2.1\,\text{MPa}$ is reported for 26 measurements of horizontal principal stress difference from seven wells in the Piceance Basin of Colorado using the hydraulic fracturing technique (Bredehoeft et al., 1976).

The analysis used to estimate the regional stress difference is based upon the solution for an elastic body with a pressurized hole (the magma chamber), a rigid boundary (the Sangre de Cristo range), and a regional stress field. No account is made of the perturbation of the stress field by the

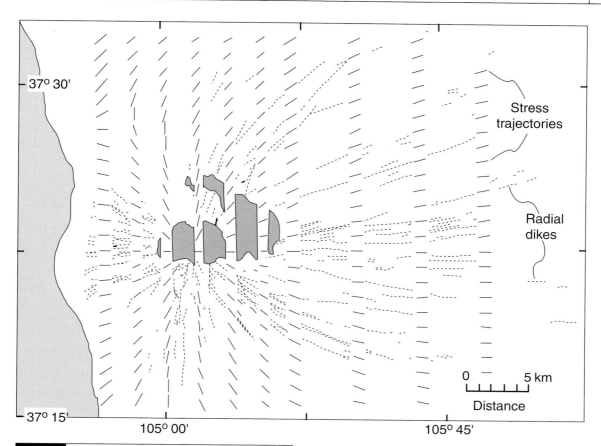

Fig 6.37 Map of Spanish Peaks region of southeastern Colorado with traces of dikes (dotted lines) and trajectories of greatest compressive horizontal stress (short solid lines) from an elastic solution. Reprinted from Muller and Pollard (1977) with permission of Birkhanser-Verlag.

emplacement of the dikes, yet each dike will perturb the local stress field and could thereby influence the propagation path of the next dike (Meriaux and Lister, 2002). Also, this analysis neglects the influence of pre-existing fractures, which may guide the propogating dike (Ziv and Rubin, 2000), and the effects of topography (Fialko and Rubin, 1999).

Anderson's concept has been applied to the injection of dikes under active volcanoes in the Aleutian Arc (Nakamura, 1977; Nakamura *et al.*, 1977). A direct relationship between chains of cinder cones on large volcanoes and the orientation of sub-surface dikes was inferred by suggesting that dikes provided the conduits for flow of magma to the surface of the volcano. With this relationship one can map the chains of cinder cones just like the exposures of dikes at the Spanish Peaks and use these data to estimate the horizontal principal stress orientations along volcanic arcs like the Aleutians (Fig. 6.38). Note that the estimated motion vectors for the Pacific plate relative to the North American plate are sub-parallel to the maximum horizontal compression inferred from the cinder cones. Apparently the convergence direction of the two plates is reflected in the compression direction within the volcanoes near the Earth's surface. This information is crucial to an understanding of the structural and volcanic history of such regions.

6.4 | Concluding remarks

In the Newtonian context of rigid-body dynamics it is understood that forces are associated with accelerations. On the other hand, in the context of a deformable solid the stress is associated with

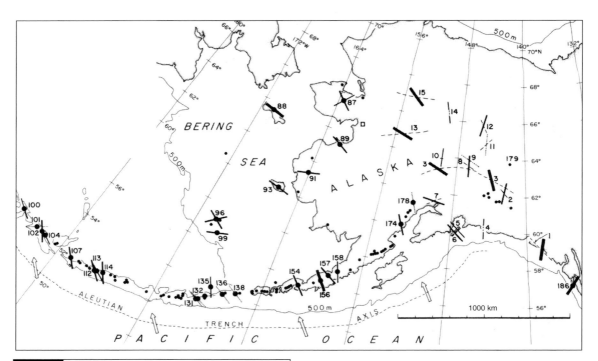

Fig 6.38 Map of Alaska and Aleutian Arc with directions of greatest compressive horizontal stress (short solid lines) from chains of cinder cones on volcanic centers and from active faults (Nakamura, 1977). Reprinted from Nakamura et al. (1977) with permission of Birkhanser-Verlag.

strain, and in the context of a flowing fluid the stress is associated with the rate of deformation. The boundary conditions on the solid and on the fluid may be described in terms of the tractions distributed over the bounding surfaces, both external and internal to the body under investigation. The structural geologist concerned with deformation of the brittle crust might ask: what stress drop across a fault produced a certain strain measured at Earth's surface using geodetic instruments? Or, the structural geologist concerned with flow in a ductile shear zone might ask: what stress state produced a certain rate of deformation? In this chapter we have described the attributes of the traction vector and the stress tensor and shown how to manipulate these quantities. Occasionally structural geologists have claimed that the kinematic quantities (displacement, velocity, acceleration, strain, rate of deformation, etc.) are more central to problem solving in structural geology and this has led others to claim that the dynamic quantities (force, traction, stress) are more central. Neither claim is defensible because both sets of quantities are required to solve problems. Both appear in the equations of motion described in Chapter 7 and they are inextricably linked to one another by constitutive laws described in Chapters 8, 10, and 11.

Chapter 7

Conservation of mass and momentum

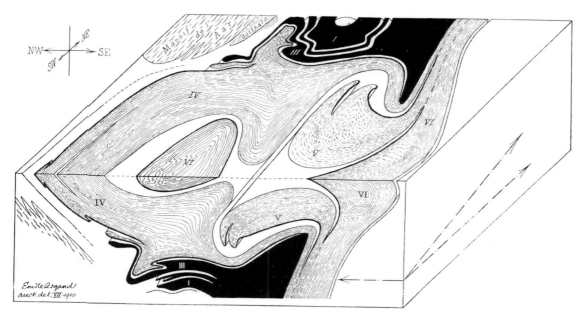

Stéréogramme tectonique des Alpes Pennines.

Structural block diagram of a part of the Penninic Alps, Switzerland (Argand, 1911).

At the heart of all this calculation lies the deeply held conviction that natural phenomena are, in essence, the consequence of just a small number of physical laws, and that these laws are best expressed in the language of mathematics. The goal is to construct a working model of the universe out of commonplace notions: ideas of number and order and measures of time and distance. With such a working model, we can leap ahead in time and predict what the otherwise opaque future has in store for us (Peterson, 1993).

In the context of structural geology we can construct a working model of mountain building from those small number of physical laws and then leap backward in time and understand the development of geological structures such as those depicted in the structural block diagram (Chapter 7, frontispiece) of a part of the Penninic Alps of Switzerland constructed by Emile Argand and published in 1911 (Argand, 1911). This is one of the earliest published block diagrams in the literature of structural geology (McIntyre and Weiss, 1956; Howarth, 1999) and it illustrates what was known in the early part of the twentieth century about one of the most interesting and complex regions of folding and faulting in that mountain chain.

Among the small number of physical laws that can be employed to understand tectonic processes and their structural products are those of mass, momentum, and energy conservation. Newton's Second Law of Motion, for example, relating force, mass, and linear acceleration is embodied in a generalized statement of momentum conservation. *Kinetics* is the branch of mechanics that considers the action of forces and torques on particles and rigid bodies, and their resulting accelerations. This should be familiar ground for students recently exposed to the mechanics section of a college physics course. However, we offer a short review for those who would benefit from a second encounter with these topics. This review serves another important purpose. Textbooks in structural geology typically fail to make a clear connection between the material taught in the mechanics section of an introductory college physics course and the mechanical concepts employed in analyzing geological structures. By making that connection explicit students are prepared to use the mechanics effectively and with a confidence that stems from understanding the fundamentals of the discipline.

We begin with the concepts of linear and angular momentum as treated in *particle dynamics* and generalize this to *rigid-body dynamics*. While the methods of classical dynamics have application in many familiar human endeavors (from tracking satellites to playing snooker) where accelerations are key to understanding, the rock masses that comprise Earth's crust do not experience appreciable accelerations, apart from those brief moments during rare events such as earthquakes. In the absence of appreciable accelerations, conservation of momentum requires that the resultant forces and torques acting on a rock mass are negligible. This condition ensures that the linear and angular momenta are nearly constant with respect to time. These requirements are fundamental and should be examined at an early stage of any program of modeling geologic structures.

Our review of concepts introduced in the typical college physics class leaves us short of having all of the necessary tools of mechanics to analyze tectonic processes. Given our human time scale and the poor resolution of our eyes for discerning small changes in the shapes of objects, rock does seem quite rigid. One might think that the dynamics of rigid bodies would be as far as we have to go to tackle problems of rock deformation in the Earth. Indeed, the early practitioners of plate tectonics conceptualized plates of the lithosphere as thin rigid masses slowing moving over a mobile aesthenosphere. Similarly, the typical mid-twentieth century structural geology textbook introduced students to faulting with diagrams showing rigid blocks moving relative to one another (Billings, 1972), and laboratory exercises utilized painted wooden blocks to illustrate the patterns of offset strata (Fig. 7.1). While these figures and blocks may be instructive guides to understanding the map patterns of faulted strata, the perceptive students might ask: what happens near the end of a fault? Clearly a rigid block model could not provide a satisfactory answer, because the "model fault" has no end.

Moving beyond the rigid block models, it is necessary to consider a continuous and deformable body of rock and to broaden our perspective to constrain explicitly how mass and momentum are conserved throughout such a body. Here we postulate that temperature changes and chemical changes within the body are negligible, so the model is *isothermal* and *isochemical*. If heat flow and chemical reactions play an important role, than conservation of energy and conservation of chemical species must be included. With these limitations in mind, conservation of mass leads to the *equation of continuity* and the conservation of momentum leads to the *equations of motion* for the material continuum. In turn, the equations of

(a)

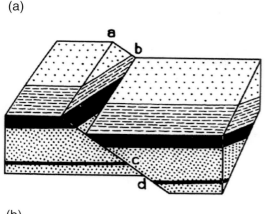

(b)

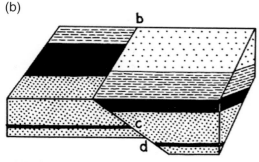

Fig 7.1 Rigid structural block diagrams of normal fault cutting inclined sedimentary strata (a) Faulted blocks. (b) Left-hand block eroded to remove fault scarp. Reprinted from Billings (1972) by permission of Peavson Education, Inc., Upper Saddle River, NJ.

(a)

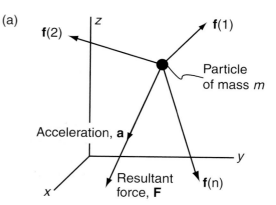

(b)

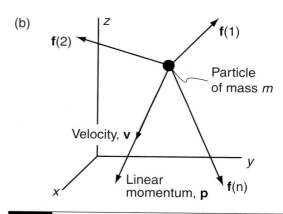

Fig 7.2 (a) Particle of mass, m, with set of forces, $\mathbf{f}(i)$, resultant force, $\mathbf{F}$, and acceleration, $\mathbf{a}$. (b) Particle of mass, m, with set of forces, $\mathbf{f}(i)$, linear momentum, $\mathbf{p}$, and velocity, $\mathbf{v}$.

motion are specialized for the linear elastic solid and the linear viscous fluid, two of the most useful material behaviors in studies of structural geology. Finally, we consider the equations of motion for a body that experiences negligible accelerations and derive the *equations of equilibrium*.

7.1 | Particle dynamics

7.1.1 Force and linear momentum

Consider the motion of a single particle under the action of applied forces (Resnick and Halliday, 1977, Chapter 5). In this idealized context a particle is considered to be an isolated quantity of mass residing at a point: it has neither a size nor a shape. Furthermore the mass is postulated to be constant with respect to time, so conservation of mass is satisfied by definition. The particle is positioned

with respect to a Cartesian coordinate system (x, y, z) and kinematic quantities, such as velocity and acceleration, are defined with respect to an inertial frame of reference (Fig. 7.2). An *inertial frame of reference* is fixed in space or moving with a constant velocity relative to the distant stars. Newton's Second Law describes the relationship between the acceleration of such a particle, relative to an inertial frame of reference, and the forces acting upon it:

$$\mathbf{F} = m\mathbf{a} \qquad (7.1)$$

Here the vector $\mathbf{a}$ is the *acceleration* of the particle, the vector $\mathbf{F}$ is the *resultant force* acting on the particle, and the scalar m is the *mass* of the particle.

What Newton meant by resultant force, $\mathbf{F}$, is the vector summation of all the forces – $\mathbf{f}(1)$, $\mathbf{f}(2)$, ..., $\mathbf{f}(n)$ – acting on the particle (Fig. 7.2a). Here the numbers in parentheses identify the different forces. The three components, F_x, F_y, and F_z of the resultant force are equal to the sum of the respective components of all forces acting on the particle. For example, the x-component is calculated as:

$$F_x = f_x(1) + f_x(2) + \cdots + f_x(n) = \sum_{i=1}^{n} f_x(i) = ma_x$$

$$(7.2)$$

Here n is the total number of different forces and a_x is the x-component of acceleration. The components F_y and F_z follow by changing subscripts. Note that the component of acceleration is directly proportional to the component of resultant force. Said another way, the acceleration components are in the same ratio as the resultant force components:

$$\frac{a_x}{a_y} = \frac{F_x}{F_y}, \quad \frac{a_y}{a_z} = \frac{F_y}{F_z}, \quad \frac{a_z}{a_x} = \frac{F_z}{F_x} \qquad (7.3)$$

Therefore, the acceleration takes place in exactly the same direction as the action of the resultant force. This phenomenon is referred to as a *linear acceleration* because it takes place in a line, the line of action of the resultant force.

The relationship among force, mass, and acceleration expressed as Newton's Second Law (7.1) can be rearranged to place either acceleration or force alone on the left-hand side of the equation. Thus, one can think of either the acceleration or the force as the dependent variable to be calculated given the mass and the other quantity. One might conclude from this mathematical manipulation that acceleration of a particle causes a force, or that application of a force on a particle causes acceleration. Newton's position on this question of causality is suggested in a recent translation of *The Principia* where the first and second laws are written as:

Every body preserves in its state of being at rest or of moving uniformly straight forward, except insofar as it is compelled to change its state by forces impressed.

A change in motion is proportional to the motive force impressed and takes place along the straight line in which that force is impressed (Newton, 1687, p. 416).

Apparently, for Newton (Fig. 7.3), forces cause accelerations and not the other way around. Modern physicists are more ambivalent about this question, probably because of the inherent symmetry in equations like $F = ma$ and because of philosophical concerns about the nature of causality. In

Fig 7.3 Portrait of Sir Isaac Newton by Sir James Thornhill in 1712. The original is at Woolsthorpe Manor, UK, birthplace and family home of Newton. Reproduced from a photographic image with the permission of the National Trust Photographic Library (NTPL/John Hammond).

calculations, physicists treat either **a** or **F** as dependent upon the other, based on the necessities of the problem at hand, and generally demure on questions of causality. In conversations, physicists usually follow Newton and speak of forces causing accelerations. This seems to be an effective way to proceed, despite the obvious duality of thought. Apparently, advances in physics do not depend upon a resolution of this question, so it is largely ignored. On the other hand the question of causality has attracted a good deal of attention from modern philosophers who discuss so-called causal asymmetries or the direction of causation in philosophical terms (Sosa and Tooley, 1993; Hausman, 1998; Pearl, 2000).

The *linear momentum*, **p**, of a particle is a vector quantity defined as the product of the particle mass and its velocity (Fig. 7.2b):

$$\mathbf{p} = m\mathbf{v} \qquad (7.4)$$

Just as the force and acceleration have the same direction, the linear momentum and velocity have the same direction because their respective components are in the same ratio, for example $p_x/p_y = v_x/v_y$.

Given constant resultant force acting on a particle of known mass, one can calculate its acceleration using (7.1). The *instantaneous velocity* of the particle is found using the fact that the time rate of change of velocity is the acceleration; so one can integrate a constant acceleration over time to calculate the changing velocity. In differential form $d\mathbf{v} = \mathbf{a}dt$, and integrating:

$$\int d\mathbf{v} = \mathbf{a}\int dt, \quad \text{so} \quad \mathbf{v} = \mathbf{a}t + \mathbf{v}(0) \qquad (7.5)$$

This constant, $\mathbf{v}(0)$, is the velocity at the initial time, $t = 0$. Although we tend to think of time as having no beginning or end in daily life, in idealizing these problems in mechanics we specify an arbitrary beginning of a process at the initial time. The velocity of a particle changes linearly with time, if the acceleration is constant, and from (7.4) we infer that the momentum changes linearly with time under these same conditions. Constant acceleration of a particle is, in turn, associated with a constant resultant force.

The time rate of change of linear momentum is equivalent to the resultant force acting on the particle. This is demonstrated using (7.1) and (7.4) as follows (Resnick and Halliday, 1977, p. 168):

$$\frac{d}{dt}\mathbf{p} = \frac{d}{dt}(m\mathbf{v}) = m\frac{d}{dt}\mathbf{v} = m\mathbf{a} = \mathbf{F} \qquad (7.6)$$

Here it is understood that the particle mass does not change with time.

7.1.2 Torque and angular momentum

The position of the particle with respect to the origin of coordinates and inertial frame of reference plays no role in relating force and linear momentum (7.6), but position is central in the relationship between torque and angular momentum. Therefore, consider a force vector, $\mathbf{f}$, acting on a particle of mass, m, located by the radial *position vector*, $\mathbf{r}$, drawn from the origin, O, of a coordinate system (x, y, z) and inertial frame of reference

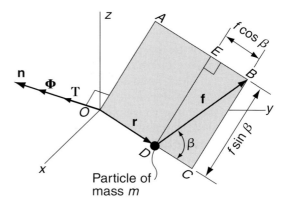

Fig 7.4 Schematic diagram to define the torque, τ, with respect to the origin, O, of a Cartesian coordinate system as the vector product of the radial position vector, $\mathbf{r}$, and the net force, $\mathbf{f}$, acting on a particle of mass, m.

(Fig. 7.4). The position and force vectors lie in the plane $OABC$ (shaded in the figure) that has a unit normal vector $\mathbf{n}$. The position of the mass and the direction of the force are arbitrary with respect to the coordinate origin and axes, but the normal emanates from the origin and it is perpendicular to the plane containing $\mathbf{f}$ and $\mathbf{r}$. The angle β is the *smaller* of the two angles measured in the plane $OABC$ between the lines of action of the radial vector, $\mathbf{r}$, and force vector, $\mathbf{f}$.

The torque is proportional to the distance from the origin to the point of application of the force, and also is proportional to the component of the force acting perpendicular to the position vector in the plane $OABC$ (Fig. 7.4). The torque is the vector product of the radial position vector, $\mathbf{r}$, and the force vector, $\mathbf{f}$:

$$\boldsymbol{\tau} = \mathbf{r} \times \mathbf{f} \qquad (7.7)$$

By definition this vector is directed perpendicular to the plane containing the two crossed vectors, so the torque is a vector parallel to $\mathbf{n}$ (Fig. 7.4). The direction of the torque vector is determined by aligning the thumb of your right hand with $\mathbf{n}$ such that your fingers curl from $\mathbf{r}$ toward $\mathbf{f}$. The direction of the torque is the direction in which your thumb points: a *right-hand convention*.

The magnitude of the torque is:

$$\tau = r(f\sin\beta), \quad \text{for } 0 \leq \beta \leq \pi \qquad (7.8)$$

Here r and f are the magnitudes of the radial and force vectors, respectively, and $f \sin \beta$ is the component of $\mathbf{f}$ along the line DE drawn perpendicular to the radial vector and in the plane containing $\mathbf{r}$ and $\mathbf{f}$ (Fig. 7.4). Thus, force acting parallel to the position vector produces no torque and force acting at right-angles to the position vector will contribute all of its magnitude to the torque.

The *angular momentum*, $\mathbf{\Phi}$, is defined in terms of the position vector of the particle, $\mathbf{r}$, and the linear momentum as:

$$\mathbf{\Phi} = \mathbf{r} \times m\mathbf{v} = \mathbf{r} \times \mathbf{p} \qquad (7.9)$$

Because the linear momentum acts in the same direction as the force, the angular momentum, $\mathbf{\Phi}$, acts in the same direction as the torque, $\boldsymbol{\tau}$ (Fig. 7.4). That is, $\mathbf{\Phi}$ acts along the normal $\mathbf{n}$ with a direction determined by the right-hand convention. The magnitude of the angular momentum is:

$$\Phi = r(p \sin \beta) = r(mv \sin \beta), \quad \text{for } 0 \leq \beta \leq \pi \qquad (7.10)$$

If the position vector and the linear momentum are parallel to one another, the magnitude of the angular momentum is zero. If the velocity of the particle is exactly perpendicular to $\mathbf{r}$, then the magnitude of the angular momentum is simply the product of the distance from the origin, the mass, and the magnitude of the velocity, rmv.

Recall that the time rate of change of the linear momentum is equivalent to the force acting on a particle (7.6). There is an analogous relationship for the time rate of change of the angular momentum and the torque, which is derived from (7.9) as follows (Resnick and Halliday, 1977, p. 234):

$$\frac{d}{dt} \mathbf{\Phi} = \frac{d}{dt} (\mathbf{r} \times \mathbf{p}) = \mathbf{r} \times \frac{d\mathbf{p}}{dt} + \frac{d\mathbf{r}}{dt} \times \mathbf{p}$$
$$= \mathbf{r} \times \mathbf{f} + \mathbf{v} \times m\mathbf{v} = \mathbf{r} \times \mathbf{f} = \boldsymbol{\tau} \qquad (7.11)$$

Here the standard form for the derivative of a product is used with the proviso that, for a cross product, the order of variables must be preserved. Also, note that the cross product of two parallel vectors, such as $\mathbf{v}$ and $m\mathbf{v}$, is always zero. The torque is equal to the time rate of change of the angular momentum.

It is important to recognize that the physical quantities we have defined in this section refer to the particular location of the origin of the coordinate system, O, and inertial frame of reference (Fig. 7.4). That is, we speak of the torque with respect to the origin, or the angular momentum with respect to the origin. If we were to move the location of the origin these quantities would change in magnitude and direction. Furthermore, the particle is not tied to the origin, so it will move along a path defined by the line of action of the applied force, $\mathbf{f}$, rather than spin about an axis of rotation parallel to $\mathbf{n}$. The line defined by $\mathbf{n}$ is not an axis of rotation for the particle per se, but rather it is the line along which the torque and angular momentum are directed.

7.2 | Rigid-body dynamics and statics

In this section we generalize the relationships of particle dynamics so they apply to an aggregate of particles making up a *rigid body*, one that does not change shape or size with time, and does not experience any gain or loss of mass. This rigid body, like the particle, satisfies conservation of mass by definition. The first step toward understanding the dynamics of a rigid body is to define the center of mass. Then we relate the forces acting on the body to its linear and angular momentum. Conservation of momentum is the underlying principle for rigid-body dynamics and provides the necessary conditions for static equilibrium of such a body.

7.2.1 Center of mass

To define the center of mass no restrictions need be placed on the size of the body: it may represent a few cubic meters or many cubic kilometers. Also, no restrictions are placed on the complexity of the geological structures within the body. For example, consider the structural block diagram (Chapter 7, frontispiece) of a part of the Penninic Alps (Argand, 1911). The distance across the front of the block is about 75 km and the distance from front to back is about 50 km, so this is a crustal-scale diagram. Note how the map pattern of the rocks is reflected in the cross section on the front of the block. This repetition of patterns occurs because the structures are plunging to the

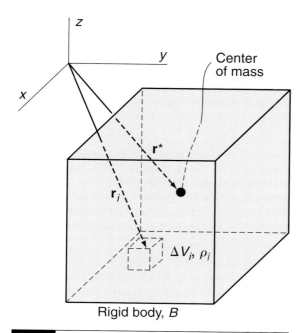

Fig 7.5 Schematic diagram to define the center of mass, r*, of a rigid body made up of m volume elements, ΔV_i, of mass density, ρ_i.

southwest and interpreted to be continuous. In Fig. 7.5 we schematically represent Argand's block diagram as a rigid body called B, which has an average density, $\bar{\rho}$, and total volume, V, neither of which change with time. You might wonder how the folds and faults could have formed if the block were rigid and, of course, the answer is that they could not. However, the center of mass can be calculated for an arbitrary instant in time during the deformation using the method introduced here. Furthermore, Argand's example serves to emphasize that this is not a vacuous exercise in mathematical physics, but rather a crucial step toward understanding the deformation of Earth's crust.

The rigid body of Fig. 7.5 is filled with m (not to be confused with the mass, m) small volume elements of rock, ΔV_i, each having a uniform density, ρ_i. Each volume element is located with a position vector, $\mathbf{r}_i$, radial to the origin, 0, of the (x, y, z)-coordinate system and inertial frame of reference. Fixing a coordinate system at some location in or on the Earth usually provides a suitable inertial frame of reference. The average density of the body is related to the individual densities and

volumes of the elements that make up its constituent parts as:

$$\bar{\rho} = \frac{1}{V}\sum_{i=1}^{m}\rho_i\Delta V_i \qquad (7.12)$$

Here it is understood that $\bar{\rho}V$ is the total mass of the body and $\rho_i\Delta V_i$ is the mass of each volume element. The total mass, $\bar{\rho}V$, contained in B does not change with time: it is conserved. The small volumes, ΔV_i, do not change with time because the body is rigid throughout. The individual densities, ρ_i, are uniform within each element but may vary spatially throughout the body. On the other hand, these individual densities do not vary in time: there is no mass transport from one volume element to another. In the limit as ΔV_i goes to zero this collection of volume elements is equivalent to a system of particles, and the motion of each element is governed by the relationships reviewed in the previous section.

Depending upon the forces that are applied to this rigid body an individual volume element may move in a complex manner that involves both translations and rotations with respect to the reference frame. Any two elements, however, do not move relative to one another, because the body is rigid by definition. There is one position in this body, called the *center of mass* (Fig. 7.5), that moves in the same manner as a single particle of concentrated mass, $\bar{\rho}V$, when subject to the resultant of all forces applied to the body. The center of mass is quite special in that it behaves like the particles we dealt with in the previous section, but there is only one such center of mass in any rigid body. The center of mass has a position vector, $\mathbf{r}^*$, that is (Resnick and Halliday, 1977, Chapter 9, p. 164):

$$\mathbf{r}^*\bar{\rho}V = \sum_{i=1}^{m}\mathbf{r}_i\rho_i\Delta V_i \qquad (7.13)$$

In other words, the product of the position vector for the center of mass of the body and the total mass is equal to the vector sum of the product of the position vectors for each volume element and their respective masses.

The coordinates of the center of mass of the body are the individual components of the position vector $\mathbf{r}^*$. For example, the x-coordinate of $\mathbf{r}^*$ is the component x^*:

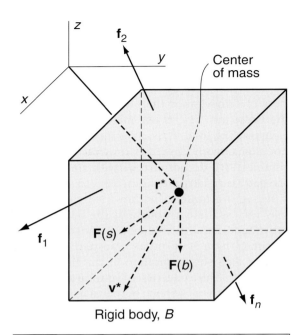

Fig 7.6 Schematic diagram to define linear momentum, **P**, of a rigid body acted upon by a set of surface forces, **f**(*i*), with a resultant surface force, **F**(*s*), and a resultant body force, **F**(*b*).

$$x^* = \frac{1}{\bar{\rho} V} \sum_{i=1}^{m} x_i \rho_i \Delta V_i \qquad (7.14)$$

The densities of the volume elements, ρ_i, are not necessarily the same, so these equations account for the spatial heterogeneity of density in deformed rock masses such as that depicted in Argand's block diagram from the Penninic Alps (Chapter 7, frontispiece). Given the structural architecture as worked out by Argand, and the densities of the individual rock units, as could be determined by a standard laboratory procedure, one could calculate the components of the center of mass using (7.14) and similar expressions for the y- and z-components.

7.2.2 Conservation of linear momentum

In Fig. 7.6 we represent the rock mass as a rigid body acted upon by arbitrary surface forces and body forces and use this to seek relationships among these forces and the linear momentum of the body. The resultant of the surface forces, **F**(*s*), is thought of as acting at the center of mass of the body. The resultant of the body forces, **F**(*b*), also may be thought of as acting at the

center of mass if they are uniformly distributed (see next section). We generalize the relationship between resultant force and linear momentum for an infinitesimal particle (7.6) to a form appropriate for a rigid body acted upon by internal and external forces by expanding the summation in (7.13):

$$\bar{\rho} V \mathbf{r}^* = \rho_1 \Delta V_1 \mathbf{r}_1 + \rho_2 \Delta V_2 \mathbf{r}_2 + \cdots + \rho_m \Delta V_m \mathbf{r}_m \qquad (7.15)$$

The left-hand side is the product of the mass of the entire body and the position vector for the center of mass, and the right-hand side is the sum of the products of the mass of each volume element and its position vector.

Next we take time derivatives of the terms on the right-hand side of (7.15). Because the volume and density of any element are constant in time we find:

$$\rho_1 \Delta V_1 \frac{d}{dt} \mathbf{r}_1 + \rho_2 \Delta V_2 \frac{d}{dt} \mathbf{r}_2 + \cdots + \rho_m \Delta V_m \frac{d}{dt} \mathbf{r}_m$$
$$= \rho_1 \Delta V_1 \mathbf{v}_1 + \rho_2 \Delta V_2 \mathbf{v}_2 + \cdots + \rho_m \Delta V_m \mathbf{v}_m \qquad (7.16)$$

Taking the time derivative again and using Newton's Second Law (7.1) we have:

$$\rho_1 \Delta V_1 \frac{d}{dt} \mathbf{v}_1 + \rho_2 \Delta V_2 \frac{d}{dt} \mathbf{v}_2 + \cdots + \rho_m \Delta V_m \frac{d}{dt} \mathbf{v}_m$$
$$= \rho_1 \Delta V_1 \mathbf{a}_1 + \rho_2 \Delta V_2 \mathbf{a}_2 + \cdots + \rho_m \Delta V_m \mathbf{a}_m = \mathbf{F} \qquad (7.17)$$

Each term is equivalent to the resultant force acting on a particular volume element, and their vector sum is the resultant force, **F**, acting on the body.

In *The Principia* Newton's Third Law is stated:

To any action there is always an opposite and equal reaction; in other words, the actions of two bodies upon each other are always equal and always opposite in direction (Newton, 1687, p. 417).

It follows that the internal forces acting between any two adjacent volume elements are equal in magnitude and oppositely directed. Thus, according to Newton's Third Law, the vector sum of these internal forces is zero. What remains on the right-hand side of (7.17) is the sum of the external surface forces and the body forces:

$$\rho_1 \Delta V_1 \frac{d^2}{dt^2}\mathbf{r}_1 + \rho_2 \Delta V_2 \frac{d^2}{dt^2}\mathbf{r}_2 + \cdots + \rho_m \Delta V_m \frac{d^2}{dt^2}\mathbf{r}_m$$

$$= \mathbf{F}(s) + \mathbf{F}(b) \qquad (7.18)$$

Note that the body force acts on all m elements of the body, but the n surface forces act at particular locations on the exterior surface of the body (Fig. 7.6).

Because neither the volume nor the average density is a function of time for the rigid body, the first time derivative of the left-hand side of (7.15) is:

$$\bar{\rho} V \frac{d}{dt}\mathbf{r}^* = \bar{\rho} V \mathbf{v}^* = \mathbf{P} \qquad (7.19)$$

This relationship defines the *linear momentum*, $\mathbf{P}$, of the entire rigid body with respect to the inertial reference frame. The velocity at any location other than the center of mass may be different, but the behavior of the body as a whole is characterized by $\mathbf{v}^*$. Analogous to (7.6), the time rate of change of the linear momentum, $\mathbf{P}$, from (7.19) is equal to the sum of the surface and body force resultants defined in (7.18):

$$\frac{d}{dt}\mathbf{P} = \bar{\rho} V \frac{d}{dt}\mathbf{v}^* = \mathbf{F}(s) + \mathbf{F}(b) \qquad (7.20)$$

This relationship expresses one of those "small number of physical laws" mentioned at the beginning of the chapter that summarize our understanding of natural phenomena. Here it is the law of *conservation of linear momentum*. For a rigid body, subject to given surface and body force resultants, linear momentum is neither created nor destroyed spontaneously, but changes with time in strict accordance to the action of these resultant forces.

For conditions where linear momentum does not change with time, the conservation of linear momentum (7.20) dictates that the resultant of all external forces must be zero:

$$\text{if } \frac{d}{dt}\mathbf{P} = 0, \quad \text{then } \mathbf{F}(s) + \mathbf{F}(b) = 0 \qquad (7.21)$$

This is one of two conditions required for *static equilibrium*. The linear momentum of individual volume elements of a rigid body may change with time, but the linear momentum of the body as a whole, with respect to an inertial frame of reference, must remain constant if the force resultants are zero. The second condition for static equilibrium depends upon a balance of the external

torques acting on the body and is derived in Section 7.2.4.

7.2.3 Evaluation of surface and body forces

We replace the mechanical action of the exterior rock mass on the body schematically in Fig. 7.6 with a set of surface forces, $\mathbf{f}_1, \mathbf{f}_2, \ldots, \mathbf{f}_n$, acting at discrete points. The resultant of these n surface forces is their vector sum which acts at the center of mass of the body:

$$\mathbf{F}(s) = \sum_{j=1}^{n} \mathbf{f}_j \qquad (7.22)$$

This concept will be generalized in Section 7.2.5 to account for a continuous distribution of forces per unit area, taken as the tractions acting on the surface of the body.

Evaluation of the body force focuses on the weight of the rock mass because this usually is the only significant contributor. Weight is the force exerted on a rock body by the gravitational attraction of the Earth. Consider the body shown in Fig. 7.6 subdivided into m volume elements each of mass $\rho_i \Delta V_i$. The weight of each element is:

$$\mathbf{w}_i = \rho_i \Delta V_i \mathbf{g}_i \qquad (7.23)$$

Here $\mathbf{g}_i$ is the local *acceleration of gravity* at the position of the element. The direction of the acceleration of gravity, $\mathbf{g}$, is downward by definition and therefore defines the local vertical. The acceleration of gravity is found by measurement to vary slightly from place to place over the Earth's surface and shallow interior due to local variations in rock density and distance from the Earth's center. In other words it is a *field quantity* that varies with position, so we specified that $\mathbf{g}_i$ is the local value at the position of the element. Because the Earth's crust deforms as faults slip and mountains grow, or as erosion brings down the height of mountains, the local acceleration of gravity can vary in time as well as space. These variations in $\mathbf{g}$ are studied by geophysicists and are used to infer density variations in the Earth (Turcotte and Schubert, 1982, Chapter 5).

Variations of $\mathbf{g}$ on and within the crust can account for body forces that are different from those one would calculate assuming a uniform $\mathbf{g}$, but these differences usually are insignificant for problems in structural geology. For example, density contrasts among typical rock types found in the Earth's crust could cause variations in $\mathbf{g}$, but common densities only range from about 2×10^3 to $3 \times 10^3 \, \text{kg m}^{-3}$ (Clark, 1966). Similarly, although $\mathbf{g}$ changes with distance from the center of the Earth, most of our attention in structural geology is focused on the outer shell of the Earth with a thickness less than 100 km, relative to the Earth's radius of over 6000 km. The difference between the equatorial radius (about 6378 km) and the polar radius (about 6357 km) is only 21 km, and the difference between the highest mountain peak (almost 9 km above sea level) and the deepest parts of the ocean floor (about 11 km below sea level) is only about 20 km. Neither of these differences is large compared to the radius of Earth. Thus, the variations in $\mathbf{g}$ within the crust are likely to be small, so we treat the magnitude and direction of the gravitational field as uniform in space and constant in time.

It is convenient from a computational point of view to replace the action of all the body forces, $\mathbf{w}_i$, with the resultant force acting at a *center of gravity*. The center of gravity and the center of mass are coincident if the gravity field over the body is uniform in magnitude. The resultant body force (weight) of the body is:

$$\mathbf{F}(b) = \sum_{i=1}^{m} \mathbf{w}_i = \bar{\rho} V \mathbf{g}^* \tag{7.24}$$

Here the acceleration of gravity is treated as a constant, $\mathbf{g}^*$, with a magnitude $g^* = 9.8 \, \text{m s}^{-2}$. This body force can be thought of as acting at the center of gravity, which is the center of mass. For a non-uniform acceleration of gravity the center of gravity and center of mass may not be coincident.

As a consequence of the discrete surface forces (7.22) and the uniform gravity field (7.24), the conservation of linear momentum (7.20) is written:

$$\frac{d}{dt}\mathbf{P} = \bar{\rho} V \frac{d}{dt}\mathbf{v}^* = \sum_{j=1}^{n} \mathbf{f}_j + \bar{\rho} V \mathbf{g}^* \tag{7.25}$$

If the sum of the surface forces and the weight in each coordinate direction is zero, the time rate of change of the linear momentum is zero. For the rigid body this means that the velocity of the center of mass does not change with time and the surface and body forces are related as:

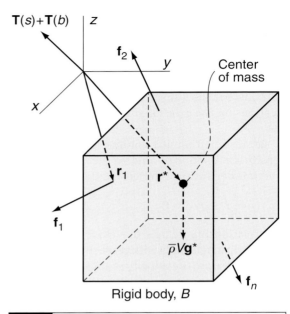

Fig 7.7 Schematic diagram to define angular momentum, $\mathbf{\Phi}$, of a rigid body acted upon by a set of forces, $\mathbf{f}(i)$, with a resultant torque, $\mathbf{T}(s)$, due to surface forces, and a resultant torque, $\mathbf{T}(b)$, due to the body forces.

$$\sum_{j=1}^{n} \mathbf{f}_j + \bar{\rho} V \mathbf{g}^* = 0 \tag{7.26}$$

This is a restatement of (7.21) and represents the first condition for static equilibrium of the rigid body subject to discrete surface forces and a uniform gravitational acceleration.

7.2.4 Conservation of angular momentum

When calculating the angular momentum for an isolated particle all forces act at the point where the particle resides (Fig. 7.4), but the points of application of the forces may differ for a body with finite shape and size (Fig. 7.7). To calculate the angular momentum the space occupied by this body is called B and it is filled with m distinct volume elements, ΔV_i, each having a uniform density, ρ_i. In keeping with the previous section we consider gravity to be the only body force and the gravitational acceleration to be uniform. Each element is located with a position vector, $\mathbf{r}_i$, radial to the origin of the coordinate system and inertial frame of reference. The body has an average density, $\bar{\rho}$, and total volume, V, and these quantities are related to the individual densities and volumes of its constituent elements using (7.15).

Taking the time derivative of the right-hand side of (7.15) with volume and density of each element considered constant gives (7.16), the vector sum of the linear momenta for the m elements. The cross products of the respective position vectors and linear momenta are the angular momenta of the elements, and the vector sum of these is:

$$\mathbf{r}_1 \times \rho_1 \Delta V_1 \mathbf{v}_1 + \mathbf{r}_2 \times \rho_2 \Delta V_2 \mathbf{v}_2 + \ldots + \mathbf{r}_m \times \rho_m \Delta V_m \mathbf{v}_m \tag{7.27}$$

From (7.11) the time derivative of the angular momentum is the torque, so the resultant torque, $\mathbf{T}$, acting on the rigid body is:

$$\frac{d}{dt}(\mathbf{r}_1 \times \rho_1 \Delta V_1 \mathbf{v}_1) + \frac{d}{dt}(\mathbf{r}_2 \times \rho_2 \Delta V_2 \mathbf{v}_2) + \cdots$$
$$+ \frac{d}{dt}(\mathbf{r}_m \times \rho_m \Delta V_m \mathbf{v}_m) = \mathbf{T} \tag{7.28}$$

This summation includes both the torques caused by external forces acting on the body and those caused by internal forces acting among the elements. Newton's Third Law is invoked to justify ignoring torques caused by internal forces (Resnick and Halliday, 1977).

What remains after eliminating the contributions of the internal forces are the torques caused by each of the n surface forces, $\mathbf{f}_j$, applied at positions, $\mathbf{r}_j$, and the torque caused by the uniform gravitational body force, $\bar{\rho} V \mathbf{g}^*$, acting at the center of mass, $\mathbf{r}^*$ (Fig. 7.7):

$$\sum_{j=1}^{n} [\mathbf{r}_j \times \mathbf{f}_j] + \mathbf{r}^* \times \bar{\rho} V \mathbf{g}^* = \mathbf{T}(s) + \mathbf{T}(b) \tag{7.29}$$

This is the resultant external torque with respect to the origin, O, and inertial frame of reference. From (7.11) the time rate of change of the angular momentum, $\mathbf{\Phi}$, of the body as a whole is equal to the resultant torque caused by all external forces acting on the body:

$$\frac{d}{dt} \mathbf{\Phi} = \sum_{j=1}^{n} [\mathbf{r}_j \times \mathbf{f}_j] + \mathbf{r}^* \times \bar{\rho} V \mathbf{g}^* \tag{7.30}$$

This equation expresses another of those "small number of physical laws" mentioned at the beginning of the chapter, in this case the law of *conservation of angular momentum*. For a rigid body, subject to given surface forces and gravity, angular

momentum is neither created nor destroyed spontaneously, but changes with time in strict accordance with the action of these forces.

If the angular momentum does not change appreciably with time one postulates that it is exactly zero for modeling purposes. The conservation of angular momentum then requires that the resultant of all external torques is zero:

$$\text{if } \frac{d}{dt} \mathbf{\Phi} = 0, \text{ then } \sum_{j=1}^{n} [\mathbf{r}_j \times \mathbf{f}_j] + \mathbf{r}^* \times \bar{\rho} V \mathbf{g}^* = 0 \tag{7.31}$$

This is the second condition used to establish the *static equilibrium* of a rigid body. The other condition is (7.21). Note that the angular momentum of individual elements of the body may change with time, but the angular momentum of the body as a whole, with respect to an inertial frame of reference, is constant in time if the resultant torque is zero.

7.2.5 Static equilibrium in integral form for the rigid continuum

When contemplating the equilibrium of a body of rock it would rarely be practical to think about a large number of volume elements, each with a particular density or momentum. While this device has clear pedagogical advantages for introducing the conservation laws for a rigid body, a more pragmatic approach is to invoke the continuum and let the physical quantities under discussion be defined at every point of the body. Then summation over the number of elements is replaced by integration. One of founders of structural geology in the nineteenth century, Grove Karl Gilbert (Fig. 7.8a), developed his mechanical model for laccolith formation (Fig. 1.18) using this approach to equilibrium. The concept of equilibrium, whether used in the consideration of mountain building or of erosion of the landscape was central to Gilbert's method of investigation (Pyne, 1980).

The concept of a center of mass is extended to the continuum by considering $\bar{\rho}$ and V to be the average density and total volume, neither of which change with time because the body is rigid. The mass of this body is conserved by definition. An integral over the volume of the body is derived from (7.13) by letting the element volumes, ΔV_i, shrink to an infinitesimal size, dV, so the position vector of the center of mass is:

$$\mathbf{r}^* = \frac{1}{\rho V} \int_V \mathbf{r} \rho \, dV \qquad (7.32)$$

Here the mass density is an integrable function of the spatial coordinates, $\rho(x, y, z)$.

Perhaps nowhere in the literature of structural geology (Pyne, 1980) is the concept of equilibrium used more decisively to guide the development of conceptual models than in the writing of G. K. Gilbert (Fig. 7.8a).

In Fig. 7.8b the rock mass is represented as a material continuum, bounded by the surface S, and points are located by position vectors, $\mathbf{r}$, associated with a coordinate system and inertial frame of reference. We consider the intensity of *distributed forces* acting over the surface S as described at a particular point by the traction vector, $\mathbf{t(n)}$, acting on the surface element, ΔS, with outward unit normal vector $\mathbf{n}$. Both the traction vector and the unit normal vector are functions of position on S and the resultant force acting on the area, ΔS, is approximated as $\mathbf{t(n)}\Delta S$. Letting the area element shrink toward zero, we write ΔS as the differential quantity dS, and take the integral of the force, $\mathbf{t(n)}dS$, over the entire surface:

$$\mathbf{F}(s) = \int_S \mathbf{t(n)} \, dS \qquad (7.33)$$

This integral is the resultant surface force, $\mathbf{F}(s)$, acting on the rigid body.

The body force is the weight and this can be described for a small volume, ΔV, within the body of rock (Fig. 7.8b) as the product of its average density, ρ, and the local acceleration of gravity, $\mathbf{g}^*$, treated as uniform. The quantity $\rho \mathbf{g}^*$ is the weight per unit volume. Letting the small volume shrink toward zero and writing ΔV as the differential quantity dV, we integrate the weight over the entire volume of the body:

$$\mathbf{F}(b) = \int_V \rho \mathbf{g}^* dV \qquad (7.34)$$

This integral expression represents the resultant body force due to gravity, $\mathbf{F}(b)$, and it may be thought of as acting at the center of mass of the body.

The surface and body forces may produce torques about the origin of the coordinate system.

(a)

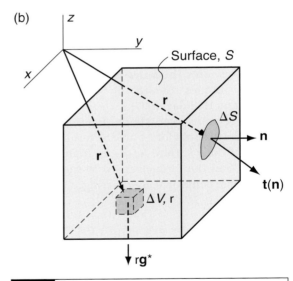

(b)

Fig 7.8 (a) Grove Karl Gilbert. Reprinted from Hunt (1988) with permission of The Geological Society of America. (b) Schematic diagram to define the static equilibrium of a continuous rigid body with a distribution of traction vectors, $\mathbf{t(n)}$, acting on surface elements, ΔS, and a distribution of weights per unit volume, $\rho \mathbf{g}^*$, acting on volume elements, ΔV.

In both cases the torque is found by considering the location of each surface and volume element in terms of the position vector, $\mathbf{r}$, and forming the cross product of the position vector with the force.

For the tractions acting on the surface of the body the resultant torque, $\mathbf{T}(s)$, is:

$$\mathbf{T}(s) = \int_S [\mathbf{r} \times \mathbf{t}(\mathbf{n})]\,\mathrm{d}S \qquad (7.35)$$

For the body force acting over the volume of the body the resultant torque, $\mathbf{T}(b)$, is:

$$\mathbf{T}(b) = \int_V [\mathbf{r} \times \rho \mathbf{g}^*]\,\mathrm{d}V \qquad (7.36)$$

The sum of these two integrals represents the resultant torque acting on the body, and this torque is thought of as a vector located at the origin of coordinates, O.

A restatement of conservation of linear and angular momentum for the continuous rigid body in equilibrium is that the resultant external force and torque due to surface tractions and gravity must be zero:

$$\int_S \mathbf{t}(\mathbf{n})\,\mathrm{d}S + \int_V \rho \mathbf{g}^*\,\mathrm{d}V = 0 \qquad (7.37)$$

$$\int_S [\mathbf{r} \times \mathbf{t}(\mathbf{n})]\,\mathrm{d}S + \int_V (\mathbf{r} \times \rho \mathbf{g}^*)\,\mathrm{d}V = 0 \qquad (7.38)$$

All of the physical quantities in these equations are defined at each and every point in the continuum. None of these quantities are functions of time, but the traction and density may vary spatially and must be integrable functions of the spatial coordinates. Gravitational acceleration is taken as uniform in space and constant in time.

7.2.6 An example: Appalachian fold and thrust mountain belt

In 1951 M. King Hubbert (Fig. 7.9a) published a paper in the Geological Society of America Bulletin entitled "Mechanical basis for certain familiar geologic structures." The abstract reads as follows:

A simple experiment with loose sand shows that this material exhibits faulting under deformational stress in a manner remarkably similar to rocks. Moreover, the sand experiment is amenable to theoretical analysis with good agreement between predicted and observed behavior. The same theoretical treatment, with slight modification, is also applicable to the behavior of rocks, and appears to afford a basis of

(a)

(b)

Fig 7.9 (a) M. King Hubbert: photograph reproduced with permission of the School of Earth Sciences, Stanford University. (b) Vertical cross section through idealized fold and thrust mountain belt. Reprinted from Hubbert (1951) with permission of The Geological Society of America.

understanding for a variety of empirically well-known geologic structures (Hubbert, 1951).

In this paper Hubbert provides the motivation for laboratory experiments using the *sandbox technique*. Similar techniques using model materials such as sand, clay, and plaster continue to provide insights concerning the development of crustal-scale structures to this day (Fossen and Gabrielsen, 1996; Wang and Davis, 1996; Guglielmo et al., 2000; Ackermann et al., 2001; Cobbold et al., 2001; McClay and Bonora, 2001). The sandbox used by Hubbert contained a rigid platen that produced a set of thrust faults when moved laterally (Fig. 7.10). The motion of the platen apparently increased the horizontal compressive stress while the vertical stress remained essentially that caused by gravity. These stress changes led to the development of the faults apparently analogous to those in fold and thrust mountain belts.

(a)

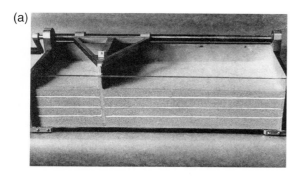

(b)

Fig 7.10 Photographs of sandbox model apparatus used to investigate the development of normal and thrust faults. (a) Sandbox with undeformed layers. (b) Platen has moved to the right generating a set of thrust faults. Reprinted from Hubbert (1951) with permission of The Geological Society of America.

Hubbert also demonstrated how an elementary analysis of homogeneous stress states in the sand could be combined with a criterion for shear failure, called the Coulomb criterion, to explain the relationship between the stress state and faulting (Hubbert, 1951). This method for analyzing faulting is in common use today and has been extended to the study of earthquake aftershocks and the triggering of smaller earthquakes by major earthquakes (King *et al.*, 1994; Stein *et al.*, 1996; Harris and Simpson, 1998; Cocco and Rice, 2002). These studies depend upon knowledge of the state of stress around the faults in question, and this usually comes from solutions to boundary value problems that obey conservation of mass and momentum. Here we show how the boundary conditions for such a model are constrained by the conditions of mechanical equilibrium. M. King Hubbert (Fig. 7.9a) was one of the

pioneers of modern structural geology in the twentieth century.

In Hubbert's paper a brief section called "Application of the Newtonian laws of motion" points out how popular concepts of fold and thrust faulted mountain belts, such as the Appalachians, suffered from an incomplete consideration of equilibrium (Hubbert, 1951). The fold and thrust mountain belts of the world were characterized as having a train of folded strata with increasing amplitude and degree of asymmetry in one direction, perpendicular to the belt (Fig. 7.9b). The most intense deformation is found on one side of the belt, the thrust faults characteristically dip toward the region of greater intensity of deformation, and the folds are overturned away from this region. The challenge for structural geologists at the time was to offer an explanation for the mechanical cause of the asymmetric style of mountain building. Hubbert describes a notion, apparently formulated and popularized by J.D. Dana (1847a, b), that the cause of fold and thrust mountain belts was a *one-sided, active thrust* from the side adjacent to the greatest deformation. According to this notion the thrusting force dissipated across the mountain belt and became insignificant on the side away from the intense deformation.

The one-sided thrust hypothesis is depicted in the context of a *free-body diagram* showing greater horizontal forces on one side than the other (Fig. 7.11a). The volume of rock has a long dimension, L, oriented across the mountain belt, a short dimension or width, W, and a height, H. The free body is a thin slice of rock across the belt that is meant to be representative of any other slice taken at other locations along the belt: all parallel slices would be similar in terms of geometry and loading conditions. The body is "free" in the sense that it is cut away from the rest of Earth's crust and the mechanical action of the exterior rock mass is replaced by a distribution of tractions acting on the surface and a distribution of gravitational forces acting on the body. According to the notion of an active thrust, the greater forces cause the intense deformation on the left-hand side, whereas the lesser forces are consistent with the lack of deformation on the right-hand side (Fig. 7.9b).

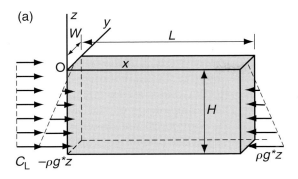

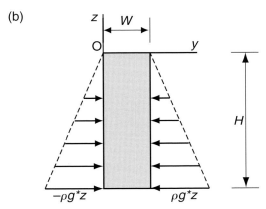

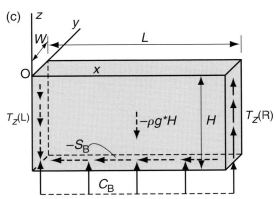

Fig 7.11 Free-body diagrams for fold and thrust mountain belt. (a) One-sided, active thrust concept with unbalanced tectonic traction, C_L, and lithostatic tractions, $\rho g^* z$. (b) Lithostatic tractions on cross sections in (y, z)-plane. (c) Additional loading necessary for static equilibrium includes shear tractions S_B on the base, and T_z on the sides, and normal traction C_B on the base.

The explanation based on an active thrust apparently was satisfactory for many structural geologists of the day; however, as Hubbert pointed out, the distribution of surface and body forces

does not satisfy conservation of linear momentum as embodied in the equilibrium equations (7.37) and (7.38). He proposed to correct the free body as drawn in Fig. 7.11a with a distribution of shear tractions on the bottom of the block acting to oppose the active thrust (Fig. 7.11c). In what follows we will examine the tectonic forces acting on a model for a fold and thrust mountain belt as conceived by Hubbert and determine the relative magnitudes of the tractions acting on the free body. Small changes in linear and angular momentum with respect to time are acknowledged for a mountain belt because we know that the deformation began at some time and later ended. Also as the thrust faults and folds accommodated shortening across the mountain belt, velocities certainly changed locally. None-the-less, at any given time throughout the history of mountain building the forces in any coordinate direction must (nearly) balance one another and the net torques about the origin in any coordinate direction must (nearly) balance one another.

We begin by evaluating the tractions acting in the x-coordinate direction on all six sides of the body (Fig. 7.11). On the left side the normal traction is composed of a tectonic part with a magnitude, C_L, and a lithostatic part related to the weight of the overlying rock, whereas the right side carries only the lithostatic tractions:

BC: on $x = 0$, $\quad 0 \leq y \leq W$,

$$-H \leq z \leq 0; \quad t_x = C_L - \rho g^* z$$

BC: on $x = L$, $\quad 0 \leq y \leq W$, $\qquad$ (7.39)

$$-H \leq z \leq 0; \quad t_x = +\rho g^* z$$

The tectonic traction is uniformly distributed over the left side whereas the lithostatic traction increases linearly with depth. Both parts of this traction push against the body and are positive in sign (note z is negative below the surface). The tractions are drawn as arrows pointed at the midsection of the body, but it should be recognized that the traction is uniformly distributed over the entire side of the free body. The traction on the right side pushes against the body in the negative x-direction, so its sign is negative.

The top surface of the free body is traction free and on the bottom surface the shear traction proposed by Hubbert is taken as uniform with a magnitude, S_B:

BC: on $0 \leq x \leq L$, $0 \leq y \leq W$, $z = 0$; $t_x = 0$

BC: on $0 \leq x \leq L$, $0 \leq y \leq W$, (7.40)
$z = -H$; $t_x = -S_B$

On the front and back sides of the free body we follow Hubbert's suggestion that there are no shear tractions:

BC: on $0 \leq x \leq L$, $y = 0$,
$-H \leq z \leq 0$; $t_x = 0$

(7.41)

BC: on $0 \leq x \leq L$, $y = W$,
$-H \leq z \leq 0$; $t_x = 0$

These conditions would apply for a linear mountain belt.

For equilibrium the integral of the x-components of the tractions over the surfaces on which they act must sum to zero (7.37):

$$\int_{-H}^{0}\int_{0}^{W}(C_L - \rho g^* z)\,dy\,dz + \int_{-H}^{0}\int_{0}^{W}(\rho g^* z)\,dy\,dz$$
$$+ \int_{0}^{W}\int_{0}^{L}(-S_B)\,dx\,dy = 0 \qquad (7.42)$$

Because the integrands are constant the inner definite integrals over the limits 0 to W with respect to y and 0 to L with respect to x produce the constants W and L, respectively. The remaining integrals are evaluated over their respective limits and the resulting expression is simplified as follows:

$$W(C_L z - \tfrac{1}{2}\rho g^* z^2)\Big|_{-H}^{0} + W\tfrac{1}{2}\rho g^* z^2\Big|_{-H}^{0} - LS_B y\Big|_{0}^{W} = 0$$
$$C_L WH = S_B WL \qquad (7.43)$$

The net force caused by the tectonic loading on the left side of the free body is exactly balanced by the net force caused by the resisting shear loading on the bottom of the body. The quantitative relationship between the magnitudes of the tectonic traction on the left side, C_L, and the resisting shear traction on the bottom, S_B, is:

$$S_B = C_L\left(\frac{H}{L}\right) \qquad (7.44)$$

The shear traction is equal to the tectonic traction times the ratio of the height to the length of the body.

The only y-components of the tractions acting on the free body (Fig. 7.11b) are those related to the lithostatic loading and these exactly balance one another. The z-components of the surface tractions and the body forces are shown on the free body in Fig. 7.11c. The presence of a shear traction on the bottom of the body raises a question about the possibility of a shear traction acting in the z-direction on the left and right sides. For the moment we do not explicitly define these tractions, because their distributions and magnitudes are best addressed in terms of the conservation of angular momentum, but account for them as follows:

BC: on $x = 0$, $0 \leq y \leq W$,
$-H \leq z \leq 0$; $T_z = T_z(L)$

(7.45)

BC: on $x = L$, $0 \leq y \leq W$,
$-H \leq z \leq 0$; $T_z = T_z(R)$

Here $T_z(L)$ and $T_z(R)$ are unspecified functions representing the traction components in the z-direction on the left- and right-hand sides of the body. The top surface is traction free, but the bottom surface is subject to a uniform traction in the z-direction of magnitude C_B:

BC: on $0 \leq x \leq L$, $0 \leq y \leq W$,
$z = 0$; $T_z = 0$

(7.46)

BC: on $0 \leq x \leq L$, $0 \leq y \leq W$,
$z = -H$; $T_z = C_B$

On the front and back sides of the body the symmetry of the loading dictates that there are no shear tractions in the z-direction:

BC: on $0 \leq x \leq L$, $y = 0$,
$-H \leq z \leq 0$; $T_z = 0$

BC: on $0 \leq x \leq L$, $y = W$,
$-H \leq z \leq 0$; $T_z = 0$ (7.47)

Referring to (7.37), we integrate the z-components of the tractions over the surfaces on which they act, integrate the body force over the volume, and set the sum to zero:

$$\int_{-H}^{0}\int_{0}^{W}T_z(L)\,dy\,dz + \int_{-H}^{0}\int_{0}^{W}T_z(R)\,dy\,dz + \int_{0}^{W}\int_{0}^{L}C_B\,dx\,dy$$

$$+ \int_{-H}^{0}\int_{0}^{W}\int_{0}^{L}(-\rho g^*)\,dx\,dy\,dz = 0 \qquad (7.48)$$

We postulate that $T_z(L)$ and $T_z(R)$ produce net surface forces that are equal in magnitude and oppositely directed, so they exactly balance and the first two integrals cancel one another. Carrying out the integration, we have:

$$C_B = \rho g^* H \qquad (7.49)$$

The normal traction on the bottom of the free body is the product of the density, the uniform acceleration of gravity, and the height of the body.

The distributions of shear tractions on the left and right sides of the free body are constrained using conservation of angular momentum (7.38). Because of the two-dimensional nature of the body we only consider the torques produced by forces acting in the (x, z)-plane (Fig. 7.12). The torques acting on the free body can be calculated with respect to any origin so it is helpful to choose an origin that simplifies the calculation. Choosing the lower left corner for the origin eliminates torques produced by the shear tractions on the left side and the bottom. Recall that the cross product of two vectors is the product of the magnitude of the first vector, the magnitude of the second vector, and the sine of the smaller angle between the lines of action of the two vectors. Thus, we evaluate the torque produced by the normal traction on the base of the free body, and that due to the weight acting at the center of gravity as (Fig. 7.12a):

On $0 \le x \le L$, $\quad 0 \le y \le W$, $\quad z = 0$,

or $r = x$; $\quad T_z = C_B$, $\quad \sin\beta = \sin(\pi/2)$

$$\qquad (7.50)$$

At $x = \frac{1}{2}L$, $\quad y = \frac{1}{2}W$, $\quad z = \frac{1}{2}H$,

or $r = r^* = \dfrac{L}{2\sin\beta^*}$; $\quad g = g^*$, $\quad \sin\beta = \sin\beta^*$

The torque caused by the bottom traction is negative (it acts out of the page in the negative y-

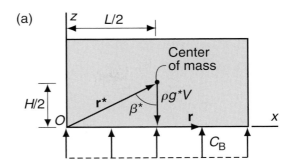

(a)

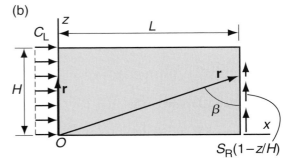

(b)

Fig 7.12 Free-body diagrams for fold and thrust mountain belt. (a) Torque due to weight and normal tractions on base. (b) Torque due to tractions on right and left side.

direction), and that caused by the weight is positive (it acts into the page in the positive y-direction). Combining the appropriate terms and integrating over the bottom surface and the volume we have:

$$-\int_{0}^{W}\int_{0}^{L} xC_B \sin(\pi/2)\,dx\,dy + \int_{0}^{H}\int_{0}^{W}\int_{0}^{L}\rho\left(\frac{L}{2\sin\beta^*}\right)$$

$$\times(g^*\sin\beta^*)\,dx\,dy\,dz = 0$$

$$-\tfrac{1}{2}C_B WL^2 + \tfrac{1}{2}\rho g^* L^2 WH = 0 \qquad (7.51)$$

From (7.49) we know that $C_B = \rho g^* H$, so these torques exactly balance.

Next consider the torques produced by the tectonic traction acting on the left side of the body and the shear traction acting on the right side (Fig. 7.12b). The shear traction on any vertical surface must be zero where that surface intersects the traction-free surface of the Earth. Thus, we postulate that the distribution of shear traction on the right side varies linearly from zero at the top to a value S_R at the bottom:

On $x = 0$, $0 \leq y \leq W$, $0 \leq z \leq H$,

or $r = z$; $T_x = C_L$, $\sin \beta = \sin(\pi/2)$

On $x = L$, $0 \leq y \leq W$, $0 \leq z = H$,

$$\text{or } r = \frac{L}{\sin \beta}; \quad T_z = S_R\left(1 - \frac{z}{H}\right), \quad \sin \beta = \frac{L}{r} \tag{7.52}$$

Combining the appropriate terms and integrating over the left and right sides of the body we have:

$$\int_0^W \int_0^H z C_L \sin(\pi/2) \, dy \, dz - \int_0^W \int_0^H \left(\frac{L}{\sin \beta}\right)$$

$$\times S_R\left(1 - \frac{z}{H}\right) \sin(\beta) \, dy \, dz = 0 \tag{7.53}$$

$$C_L W H - S_R L W = 0$$

Using (7.44) we find S_R is related to the magnitude of the basal shear traction as:

$$S_R = C_L\left(\frac{H}{L}\right) = S_B \tag{7.54}$$

The shear traction on the right side in the lower right corner ($x = L$, $z = 0$) is equal to the shear traction on the bottom, because the respective shear stresses must be equal. The shear tractions on the left- and right-hand sides are:

$$T_z(L) = -T_z(R) = -S_B\left(1 - \frac{z}{H}\right) \tag{7.55}$$

This completes the equilibrium analysis of Hubbert's Appalachian free body. This, or the analogous procedure using relationships that include the time rate of change of the linear and angular momentum, is a vital step in any modeling program to confirm that the prescribed tractions and body forces are consistent with the conservation of momentum. Without such confirmation, any discussion of the development of structures lacks the necessary foundation in mechanics to be credible, and it should be ignored.

7.3 | Conservation of mass and momentum in a deformable continuum

The previous sections of this chapter have developed the concept of momentum conservation within the context of particle dynamics and of rigid-body dynamics and statics. Despite the fact that equilibrium analysis of a rigid body is an important step to confirm the applicability of prescribed tectonic boundary conditions, this analysis does not consider the deformation of the body itself. For structural geologists the deformation of a rock mass is the central focus, so we turn now to conservation of mass and momentum in a deformable body of rock idealized as a material continuum. These relationships underlie the more specialized equations that we use later in the textbook to model rock deformation during folding, faulting, fabric development, and the formation of many other geological structures.

We note here that both of the conservation laws are developed without regard for particular material properties other than mass density, so they apply quite generally to the entire spectrum of rock deformation, from silicate magmas that flow like a fluid to rocks that deform like a malleable solid to rocks that deform like an elastic solid. We do restrict our attention to conditions where temperature fluctuations and the associated changes in density and flow of heat can be ignored. In addition, we ignore chemical reactions and the associated changes in density and concentration of chemical species. Thus, the relationships derived here apply, strictly speaking, to a material that is isothermal and isochemical. Although few tectonic processes would obey these restricted conditions in detail, we show by example that they do not preclude gaining considerable insight into those processes.

7.3.1 Referential and spatial descriptions of motion

Recall from the discussion of kinematics in Chapter 5 that two different sets of coordinates may be used to describe the positions of particles in a deforming rock mass: (X, Y, Z) are the coordinates of a particle in the *initial state*, and (x, y, z) are the coordinates of a particle in the *current state* (Fig. 5.6). The coordinates (X, Y, Z) are components of the position vector **X** and (x, y, z) are components of **x**. The two sets of coordinates usually are measured with respect to the same origin and axes. Each coordinate in the current state is given by the sum of the respective coordinate in the initial state and the corresponding component of the displacement vector, **u**:

$$\mathbf{x} = \mathbf{X} + \mathbf{u}, \quad \text{or} \begin{cases} x = X + u_x \\ y = Y + u_y \\ z = Z + u_z \end{cases} \quad (7.56)$$

In this and subsequent chapters we consider deformation primarily in the context of either an elastic solid or a viscous fluid. While the chosen coordinates are independent of material properties, the theories of elastic solid mechanics and viscous fluid mechanics have been developed from quite different points of view. In this section we consider how these different points of view impact the analytical descriptions of motion and develop concepts that are used in subsequent sections to apply the principles of conservation of mass and momentum to a material continuum.

The deformation of an elastic solid is viewed with the initial state taken as the reference. In an engineering context this state usually is associated with zero external loads. In other words there are no surface or body forces acting on the elastic solid. Then, a given loading is applied, and the particles displace to the current positions: it is understood that they return to the initial positions when all the loads are removed. Because the configuration of particles changes with time as the loading changes, but always returns to the initial state upon unloading, this unloaded condition is thought of as the *natural state* of the elastic body. In the geological context the initial state may be quite arbitrarily chosen and usually is associated with a pre-existing loading condition involving both surface and body forces. Displacements corresponding to this loading condition are undefined. One then considers some change of loading and the corresponding displacement of particles to their current positions. If the loading reverts to that of the initial state these

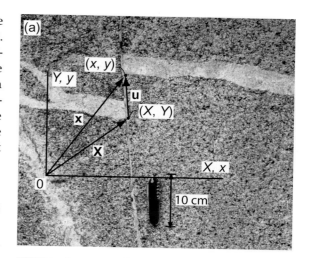

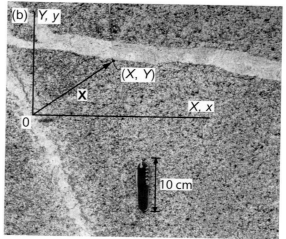

Fig 7.13 Illustration of the referential description of motion, $\mathbf{x} = \mathbf{x}(\mathbf{X}, t)$, using a small fault in granitic rock of the Sierra Nevada, CA (Segall and Pollard, 1983). The position vector **x** locates a particle in the current state that was located by the position vector **X** in the initial state. Photograph by D. D. Pollard.

displacements go to zero and the particles return to the initial positions.

For example, consider the exposure of granitic rock (Fig. 7.13a) from the Sierra Nevada of California where an aplite dike is offset about a decimeter by a fault with apparent left-lateral motion (Segall and Pollard, 1983a). The geological inference is that this structure can be restored from the current state to an initial state in which it was continuous across the fault (Fig. 7.13b). The mechanical inference is that the faulting can be described by elastic deformation, specifically the displacement field relating the initial and current states. We do not suppose that the offset aplite dike would return to its initial configuration if the rock mass were excised from the Sierra Nevada today and all external loads relaxed. This supposition ignores the loading that existed before faulting and the mechanical behavior of the rock mass over the ~80 million years since the faulting event. Rather, we suppose that the deformation at the time of faulting is adequately described as elastic. This supposition is supported by modern studies of deformation associated with active faulting and by laboratory studies of the constitutive properties of rock.

Taking the coordinates (X, Y, Z) and time, t, as the independent variables, we develop the so-called *referential description of motion* (Malvern, 1969). At the time just prior to $t = 0$ the particles of rock are in their initial configuration around the un-slipped fault (Fig. 7.13b), which is in mechanical equilibrium with respect to the pre-existing loads. Under the prescribed change in surface and/or body forces initiated at time $t = 0$, the particles displace to their current coordinates such that:

$$\mathbf{x} = \mathbf{x}(\mathbf{X}, t), \quad \text{or} \begin{cases} x = x(X, Y, Z, t) \\ y = y(X, Y, Z, t) \\ z = z(X, Y, Z, t) \end{cases} \quad (7.57)$$

Recall that the $\mathbf{x}$ (or x, y, and z) on the left-hand sides of these equations is the value of the function whereas the same symbols on the right-hand sides signify the function itself. After some unknown duration of time, slip ceased on the fault and the configuration of particles attained that seen in the exposure today (Fig. 7.13a). The position vector $\mathbf{x}$ locates the particle in the current state that was located by the position vector $\mathbf{X}$ in the initial state. This is called the referential description of motion because it refers back to the initial state. It also is called the Lagrangian description of motion after the Italian mathematician Joseph-Louis Lagrange (1736–1813), (Fig. 7.14). The coordinates (X, Y, Z) are called the *Lagrangian coordinates*, or sometimes the *material coordinates* because they describe the initial positions of material particles.

Fig 7.14 Portrait of the Italian mathematician Joseph-Louis Lagrange who was born in Turin in 1736 and baptised Giuseppe Lodovico Lagrangia. The coordinates (X, Y, Z) used in the referential description of motion are referred to as the Lagrangian coordinates. Reproduced with the permission of the Department of Special Collections, Stanford University Library.

A complete referential description of the motion of particles from the initial state would be a function $\mathbf{x}(\mathbf{X}, t)$ that describes the continuous change of position for every particle, each originally at a particular point $\mathbf{X}$, for all times from $t = 0$ to $t =$ the current time. In other words, the paths followed by the particles are traced out by the position vectors $\mathbf{x}$ according to (7.57). We do not know this functional relationship for the particles near the fault (Fig. 7.13), so must be content with a two-state description of the proposed elastic deformation. However, elastic models could be investigated that would track the particles as they accelerated from their initial positions, attained some peak velocity, and decelerated to their current positions. Given such a function that is differentiable with respect to time one may calculate the velocity, $\mathbf{v}$, of an arbitrary particle as the vector function $\mathbf{G}$:

$$\mathbf{v} = \left.\frac{\partial \mathbf{x}}{\partial t}\right|_{\mathbf{X}} = \mathbf{G}(\mathbf{X}, t) \quad (7.58)$$

Here the subscript after the vertical bar indicates **x** also is a function of the independent variable **X**, which is held constant during partial differentiation with respect to time. The material coordinates are held constant because we want to track the velocity of a particular particle. For this reason the partial derivative in (7.58) is referred to as the *material time derivative* and the resulting velocity is called the *particle velocity* (Malvern, 1969). To understand this viewpoint an analogy is drawn to an observer, stationed at the origin of the material coordinates (X, Y) in Fig. 7.13, who measures the time rate of change of the particle at every position along its path from **X** to **x** as the fault slips.

Given a function **x**(X, t) that is twice differentiable with respect to time, one may obtain the *particle acceleration*, **a**:

$$\mathbf{a} = \frac{\partial^2 \mathbf{x}}{\partial t^2}\bigg|_{\mathbf{X}} = \frac{\partial \mathbf{v}}{\partial t}\bigg|_{\mathbf{X}} = \frac{\partial}{\partial t}\mathbf{G}(\mathbf{X}, t) \qquad (7.59)$$

Again, we do not know the function **x**(X, t) for the particles near the fault (Fig. 7.13), but an elastic model would provide the particle accelerations according to (7.59). The particle velocity (7.58) and particle acceleration (7.59) are kinematic quantities employed in elastic solid mechanics.

We turn now to the flow of a viscous fluid, which is viewed with the current state taken as the reference. Under given loading conditions a particular rate of deformation is associated with the particle at each coordinate position in the current state and the initial configuration of those particles is not prescribed. Upon unloading each particle simply remains at rest at its current position. A special case is that in which the velocity field does not change with time and the rate of deformation is constant at any position in the flow. This is referred to as a *steady state* of flow for the viscous fluid. In the geological context, a nearly steady state may exist for some period of time, preceded and followed by periods of accelerating or decelerating flow. For the structural geologists standing on an exposure of igneous rock the "frozen" pattern of aligned xenoliths, phenocrysts, or vesicles may suggest how this material once flowed. Similarly, for an exposure of highly deformed metamorphic rock, although flow has long since ceased, the folds or boudinage may suggest directions and magnitudes of relative velocities. In this context "current" may be taken within the time frame of active deformation and certainly does not mean the present day.

As an example, consider another exposure from the Sierra Nevada of California where a mafic dike about 30 cm thick cuts the metamorphic host rock (Fig. 7.15a). The igneous rock is composed of a very fine-grained black groundmass interspersed with lath-shaped white phenocrysts (probably feldspar) that are arranged in an evocative pattern across the dike (Fig. 7.15b). Near the two contacts with the host rock the phenocrysts tend to have their long axes parallel to the contact, whereas near the mid-line of the dike the long axes are perpendicular to the contact. Furthermore, there appears to be a greater concentration of phenocrysts near the mid-line. The geological inference is that magma from an unknown source forced open this fracture and flowed through it for some period of time in the direction that the pencil is pointing. The phenocrysts were organized into a systematic pattern that eventually became "frozen" in place as enough heat was lost to solidify the magma. The mechanical inference is that the injection of magma into the dike can be described by the flow of a viscous fluid containing a number of lath-shaped solid objects.

We adopt a *spatial description of motion* which takes the coordinates (x, y, z), and time, t, as the independent variables (Malvern, 1969). These coordinates describe positions in space such that the point (x, y) in Fig. 7.15b is associated with a particle of a particular phenocryst at a given time, but would be associated with a particle of the ground mass or a different phenocryst at a later time as the magma flows through that fixed point. This viewpoint brings attention to given points in space rather then to given particles. With each successive instant in time the particle that was at a given position may move away and a new particle may move into the field of view, but the position in space remains fixed. This is called the spatial description of motion. It also is called the Eulerian description of motion after the Swiss mathematician Leonhard Euler (1707–83), (Fig. 7.16). The coordinates (x, y, z) are called the *Eulerian coordinates* and also the *spatial coordinates*.

Fig 7.15 Illustration of the spatial description of motion in which the velocity is a function of the current location and time, $\mathbf{v} = \mathbf{g}(\mathbf{x}, t)$. The igneous dike from the Sierra Nevada is about 30 cm thick and contains a pattern of phenocrysts that suggest the flow direction and relative magnitude. Photograph by D. D. Pollard.

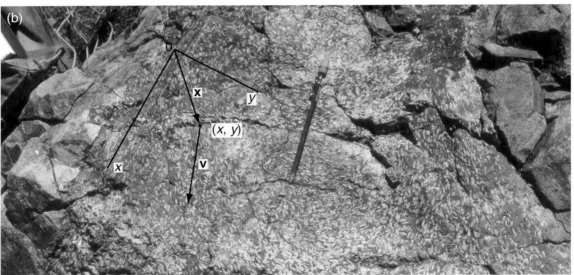

In contrast to the referential description of motion, particle paths are not a primary feature of the spatial description, and the initial positions of particles usually are not defined. For example, the initial positions of the phenocrysts in the mafic dike (Fig. 7.15) are unknown. A complete spatial description of motion would be a function that describes the velocity, $\mathbf{v}$, at every position, $\mathbf{x}$, for all times from $t = 0$ to $t =$ the current state. In our field example we might consider a steady velocity field of a viscous fluid containing lath-shaped solid objects within a conduit of fixed width equal to that of the dike. The velocity of the model magma would be described at every position as a function of time, providing the vector function:

$$\mathbf{v} = \mathbf{g}(\mathbf{x}, t) \qquad (7.60)$$

The quantity defined in (7.60) is called the *local velocity* because it refers to the velocity at a given location. Note that both (7.58) and (7.60) are equations for velocity, $\mathbf{v}$, so the particle velocity at a particular location and time is the same as the local velocity in that location at that time. However, the functions $\mathbf{G}(\mathbf{X}, t)$ and $\mathbf{g}(\mathbf{x}, t)$ are different because the former describes the velocity of

Fig 7.16 Portrait of the Swiss mathematician Leonhard Euler who was born in Basel, Switzerland in 1707. The coordinates (x, y, z) used in the spatial description of motion are referred to as the Eulerian coordinates. Reproduced with the permission of the Department of Special Collections, Stanford University Library.

a given particle along its path, while the latter describes the velocity of all particles that pass through a given location.

The time derivative of the local velocity (7.60) at a given current location is:

$$\frac{\partial \mathbf{v}}{\partial t}\bigg|_{\mathbf{x}} = \frac{\partial}{\partial t}\mathbf{g}(\mathbf{x}, t) \tag{7.61}$$

The quantity defined in (7.61) is referred to as the *local rate of change* of velocity (Malvern, 1969) and not as the acceleration because it does not necessarily define the particle acceleration (7.59) at the position $\mathbf{x}$ and time t. To appreciate this apparent contradiction recall the velocity distribution (5.19) within a rising viscous sphere (Fig. 5.12). This is an example of *steady flow*, which means that all of the kinematic quantities are constant in time at every point. Thus, at every current position $\mathbf{x}$ the time derivative of velocity as defined in (7.61) is identically zero. On the other hand the

velocity of a given particle that follows one of the stream lines illustrated in Fig. 5.12b changes with position, being greater where the stream lines are more closely spaced. This particle and every other particle, except those at the stagnation points at the top and bottom of the sphere, accelerate and decelerate as they circulate within the sphere. Clearly one cannot take the local rate of change of velocity (7.61) as the particle acceleration (7.59) in this particular case.

It is important to clarify the general relationship between the particle acceleration (7.59) and the local rate of change of velocity (7.61). We do this by showing how to calculate the material time derivative of a quantity given a spatial description of the kinematics of that quantity (Malvern, 1969). We start with the function $\mathbf{g}(\mathbf{x}, t)$ that describes the local velocity (7.60). The underlying premise is that particle motion may be defined by a function $\mathbf{x}(\mathbf{X}, t)$ for the referential description of motion (7.57). This relationship is substituted for the spatial coordinates, $\mathbf{x}$, in the function for the local velocity to transform it to a function of the material coordinates $\mathbf{X}$:

$$\mathbf{v} = \mathbf{g}[\mathbf{x}(\mathbf{X}, t), t] = \mathbf{G}(\mathbf{X}, t) \tag{7.62}$$

Because we have started with a spatial description of motion the referential description given by the function $\mathbf{x} = \mathbf{x}(\mathbf{X}, t)$ may not be known, but knowledge of this function is not necessary to define the material time derivative of (7.62). Recalling the Chain Rule of calculus, if $z = f(x, y)$ but $x = x(r, s)$ and $y = y(r, s)$ one takes the partial derivative of z with respect to s holding r constant as (Varberg and Purcell, 1992):

$$\frac{\partial z}{\partial s}\bigg|_r = \frac{\partial z}{\partial x}\bigg|_y \frac{\partial x}{\partial s}\bigg|_r + \frac{\partial z}{\partial y}\bigg|_x \frac{\partial y}{\partial s}\bigg|_r \tag{7.63}$$

Making the appropriate associations for the quantities in the vector function (7.62) we have:

$$\frac{\partial \mathbf{v}}{\partial t}\bigg|_{\mathbf{X}} = \frac{\partial \mathbf{v}}{\partial \mathbf{x}}\bigg|_t \frac{\partial \mathbf{x}}{\partial t}\bigg|_{\mathbf{X}} + \frac{\partial \mathbf{v}}{\partial t}\bigg|_{\mathbf{x}} \frac{\partial t}{\partial t}\bigg|_{\mathbf{X}} \tag{7.64}$$

The left-hand side is the material time derivative of the velocity which is, by (7.59), the particle acceleration, $\mathbf{a}$. The first partial derivative on the right-hand side may be calculated from the local velocity (7.60), which is given. The second partial derivative is the particle velocity (7.58), but that is equivalent to the local velocity, $\mathbf{v}$, defined in (7.60).

The third partial derivative is the local rate of change of velocity (7.61), which may be calculated from (7.60). The fourth partial derivative evaluates to one.

Using the above interpretations for the partial derivatives in (7.64) and rearranging them, we have an expression for the particle acceleration written in terms of the local velocity using a spatial description of motion:

$$\mathbf{a} = \frac{\partial \mathbf{v}}{\partial t}\bigg|_{\mathbf{X}} + \mathbf{v}\frac{\partial \mathbf{v}}{\partial \mathbf{x}}\bigg|_{t} \tag{7.65}$$

The first term on the right-hand side is the local rate of change of velocity at the current position $\mathbf{x}$. What distinguishes this term from the particle acceleration at that position is the second term, which is a product of the local velocity and the spatial derivative of velocity at the current time t. The second term may be interpreted as the rate of change of velocity due to the flow of material at velocity $\mathbf{v}$ through a spatially varying velocity field. For steady flow, such as that within the rising viscous sphere (Fig. 5.12), the first term on the right-hand side of (7.65) is zero, so particle accelerations are entire due to the spatial variations in velocity as described by the second term.

For example, the x-component of acceleration from (7.65) is written:

$$a_x = \frac{\partial v_x}{\partial t} + v_x\frac{\partial v_x}{\partial x} + v_y\frac{\partial v_x}{\partial y} + v_z\frac{\partial v_x}{\partial z} \tag{7.66}$$

The components a_y and a_z follow by change of subscripts. Here is it understood that the velocity components are known functions of the current position and time, $\mathbf{v} = \mathbf{g}(\mathbf{x}, t)$, so the partial derivatives are taken with the appropriate independent variables held constant as indicated in (7.65).

The operation characterized in (7.65) for calculating the particle acceleration from the local velocity may be generalized to calculate the *material time derivative* of any quantity associated with the material, given a spatial description of its kinematics:

$$\frac{D}{Dt} = \frac{\partial}{\partial t}\bigg|_{\mathbf{X}} = \frac{\partial}{\partial t}\bigg|_{\mathbf{X}} + \mathbf{v}\frac{\partial}{\partial \mathbf{x}}\bigg|_{t} \tag{7.67}$$

The operator D/Dt is also referred to as the *substantial derivative*, but material time derivative is more descriptive of its role. For example in the context

of fluid mechanics, as developed using the spatial description of motion, the operator (7.67) is used to calculate the rate of change of material properties that play roles in the fundamental principles of conservation of mass and momentum. Apparently the concepts embodied in (7.67) can be traced back to publications of Euler (Fig. 7.16) in 1770 and Lagrange (Fig. 7.14) in 1783 (Malvern, 1969).

The material time derivative operator (7.67) may be applied to scalar, vector (7.65), or tensor functions that describe a property of the material in terms of the spatial coordinates, $\mathbf{x}$, and time, t (Malvern, 1969). Suppose the mass density is known as $\rho = \rho(\mathbf{x}, t)$. The material time derivative of this scalar quantity is:

$$\frac{D\rho}{Dt} = \frac{\partial \rho}{\partial t}\bigg|_{\mathbf{X}} + \mathbf{v}\frac{\partial \rho}{\partial \mathbf{x}}\bigg|_{t} \tag{7.68}$$

The first term on the right-hand side of (7.68) describes the local rate of change of density at the current position $\mathbf{x}$. The second term describes the rate of change of density at the current time t due to the flow of material at velocity $\mathbf{v}$ with a spatially varying density field. In terms of the velocity components (7.68) is:

$$\frac{D\rho}{Dt} = \frac{\partial \rho}{\partial t} + v_x\frac{\partial \rho}{\partial x} + v_y\frac{\partial \rho}{\partial y} + v_z\frac{\partial \rho}{\partial z} \tag{7.69}$$

Here is it understood that the velocity components are known functions of the current position and time (7.60). Furthermore, the mass density is a known function of the current position and time, so the partial derivatives are taken with the appropriate independent variables held constant. Other scalar properties of the material are operated upon and interpreted similarly.

7.3.2 Conservation of mass: the equation of continuity

What constraints must be imposed to assure that the relative motions of particles in a deforming rock mass obey the fundamental law of mass conservation? To address this question we adopt the spatial description of motion and consider a fixed volume element within a deforming material continuum (Fig. 7.17). The center of the element is at the arbitrary point specified by the position vector $\mathbf{x}$ with components (x, y, z) which are the current coordinates. The sides of the element are parallel

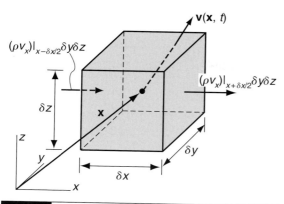

Fig 7.17 Schematic diagram to define the conservation of mass as material moves through a fixed volume element with velocity, $\mathbf{v}(\mathbf{x}, t)$. For example, the mass flux through the left-hand side of the element is the product of the mass density, ρ, and the velocity component, v_x, evaluated at that side times the surface area of the side.

to the coordinate axes and the lengths of the sides are δx, δy, and δz. As material moves through the volume element, the velocity at the center is a function of the current location and time, $\mathbf{v}(\mathbf{x}, t)$. Mass is accounted for in terms of the mass density, which also is a function of the current location and time, $\rho(\mathbf{x}, t)$. The conservation of mass for the volume element is prescribed as follows (Bird et al., 1960):

$$\begin{pmatrix} \text{rate of} \\ \text{mass} \\ \text{increase} \end{pmatrix} = \begin{pmatrix} \text{rate of} \\ \text{mass} \\ \text{in} \end{pmatrix} - \begin{pmatrix} \text{rate of} \\ \text{mass} \\ \text{out} \end{pmatrix} \quad (7.70)$$

In other words, mass may enter and leave the element and the total mass of the element may change with time, but mass is neither created nor destroyed within the element. We assume that mass is not converted to energy in the processes that generate geological structures (Wilezek, 2004).

The rate of accumulation of mass in the element, the left-hand side of (7.70), is measured by the temporal derivative of density evaluated at $\mathbf{x}$ and multiplied by the volume, $\delta x \delta y \delta z$:

$$\frac{\partial \rho}{\partial t} \delta x\, \delta y\, \delta z \quad (7.71)$$

The right-hand side of (7.70) is accounted for using the mass flux per unit volume. This vector quan-

tity is the product of mass density and the velocity, $\rho \mathbf{v}$, and so it is a function of the spatial coordinates and time. Because the element sides are parallel to the coordinate directions, the total mass flux through a particular side is proportional to the component of velocity acting perpendicular to that side, and to the surface area of that side. For example, through the left side of the element, as viewed in Fig. 7.17, the mass flux would be $\rho v_x \delta y \delta z$, where ρ and v_x are evaluated at $x - \delta x/2$. The arrows normal to the sides of the element are meant to represent the mass fluxes through the entire side, not just through a point at the middle. Similarly, the total mass flux through the right side would be $\rho v_x \delta y \delta z$, where ρ and v_x are evaluated at $x + \delta x/2$. The difference between the flux in through the left side and the flux out through the right-hand side is:

$$(\rho v_x)\big|_{x - \delta x/2} \delta y\, \delta z - (\rho v_x)\big|_{x + \delta x/2} \delta y\, \delta z \quad (7.72)$$

Because the velocity components v_y and v_z are parallel to these sides, they cannot contribute to this part of the mass flux.

Now consider a set of n elements, each containing $\mathbf{x}$, with successively smaller volumes such that the volume approaches zero in the limit as $n \to \infty$. In this limit the largest dimension of the element approaches zero, so the volume converges to the central point at $\mathbf{x}$ and not to a surface or line. The partial derivative of the x-component of the mass flux, ρv_x, with respect to x is defined in this limit as:

$$\frac{\partial}{\partial x}(\rho v_x) = \lim_{n \to \infty} \frac{(\rho v_x)\big|_{x + \delta x/2} - (\rho v_x)\big|_{x - \delta x/2}}{\delta x} \quad (7.73)$$

Equating (7.71) and (7.72), dividing through by the volume, and using (7.73) we have:

$$\frac{\partial \rho}{\partial t} = -\frac{\partial}{\partial x}(\rho v_x) \quad (7.74)$$

Both the rate of change of density and the spatial derivative of the component of mass flux are evaluated at the current location $\mathbf{x}$ in this one-dimensional description of mass conservation.

Conservation of mass during motion in one coordinate direction (7.74) is, perhaps, more interesting than one might surmise. Because both density and velocity may be functions of x, the derivative of their product is:

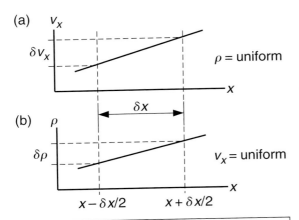

(a) v_x

δv_x

ρ = uniform

δx

(b) ρ

$\delta\rho$

v_x = uniform

$x - \delta x/2$ $x + \delta x/2$

Fig 7.18 Graphs to illustrate the two terms on the right-hand side of (7.75) that account for the mass conservation in one-dimensional flow. (a) Rate of change of density as a function of a spatial change in velocity with uniform density. (b) Rate of change of density as a function of a spatial change in density with uniform velocity.

$$\frac{\partial \rho}{\partial t} = -\left(\rho\frac{\partial v_x}{\partial x} + v_x\frac{\partial \rho}{\partial x}\right) \quad (7.75)$$

The first term in parentheses describes the rate of change of density if the density does not vary with x, but the velocity does vary with x (Fig. 7.18a). For example, where the velocity increases with x, the material in the vicinity of $\mathbf{x}$ is stretched, so the density there decreases with time in proportion to $\partial v_x/\partial x$. The second term in parentheses describes the rate of change of density if the velocity does not vary with x, but the density does vary with x (Fig. 7.18b). Where the density increases with x, motion in the x-direction carries material with lesser density into the vicinity of $\mathbf{x}$, so the density there decreases with time in proportion to v_x and $\partial \rho/\partial x$. Density at a fixed point in a material continuum can change by either one (or both) of these two independent mechanisms while mass is conserved.

The one-dimensional relationship (7.74) is generalized for mass fluxes through all six sides of the element using the differential operator, ∇, (called del) on the mass flux vector, $\rho\mathbf{v}$. When operating on a vector quantity ∇ is defined as the vector (Bird et al., 1960):

$$\nabla = \mathbf{e}_x\frac{\partial}{\partial x} + \mathbf{e}_y\frac{\partial}{\partial y} + \mathbf{e}_z\frac{\partial}{\partial z} \quad (7.76)$$

For the arbitrary vector, $\mathbf{u}$, we have:

$$\nabla \cdot \mathbf{u} = \left(\mathbf{e}_x\frac{\partial}{\partial x} + \mathbf{e}_y\frac{\partial}{\partial y} + \mathbf{e}_z\frac{\partial}{\partial z}\right) \cdot (u_x\mathbf{e}_x + u_y\mathbf{e}_y + u_z\mathbf{e}_z)$$

$$= \frac{\partial u_x}{\partial x} + \frac{\partial u_y}{\partial y} + \frac{\partial u_z}{\partial z} \quad (7.77)$$

Note that this operation is similar to the scalar product of two vectors: each partial derivative operates on the respective component of the vector and the resulting sum is a scalar quantity. Using the del operator, the rate of change of density may be written (Bird et al., 1960):

$$\frac{\partial \rho}{\partial t} = -\nabla \cdot (\rho\mathbf{v}) \quad (7.78)$$

This scalar equation is a spatial description of the conservation of mass because it describes changes at a fixed point in space and both the density and the velocity components are expressed as functions of the spatial coordinates. The relationship in (7.78) is called the *equation of continuity*.

In component form the continuity equation (7.78) is written:

$$\frac{\partial \rho}{\partial t} = -\left[\frac{\partial}{\partial x}(\rho v_x) + \frac{\partial}{\partial y}(\rho v_y) + \frac{\partial}{\partial z}(\rho v_z)\right] \quad (7.79)$$

Because both the density and the velocity components may be functions of the spatial coordinates, the partial derivatives in (7.79) expand as follows:

$$\frac{\partial \rho}{\partial t} = -\rho\left(\frac{\partial v_x}{\partial x} + \frac{\partial v_y}{\partial y} + \frac{\partial v_z}{\partial z}\right) - \left(v_x\frac{\partial \rho}{\partial x} + v_y\frac{\partial \rho}{\partial y} + v_z\frac{\partial \rho}{\partial z}\right)$$

$$(7.80)$$

Notice that the sum of the left-hand side and the terms in the second parentheses on the right-hand side are the material time derivative of density as defined in (7.69). Therefore we can write the continuity equation as (Malvern, 1969):

$$\frac{D\rho}{Dt} = -\rho\left(\frac{\partial v_x}{\partial x} + \frac{\partial v_y}{\partial y} + \frac{\partial v_z}{\partial z}\right) = -\rho\nabla\cdot\mathbf{v} \quad (7.81)$$

Here the operation $\nabla\cdot\mathbf{v}$ is called the *divergence* of the velocity vector field which sometimes is written div $\mathbf{v}$. The product of the density and the divergence of the velocity may be interpreted as the rate of change of density of the particle at the point **x** because the material in the vicinity of this particle is stretching in one or more of the coordinate directions, and this stretch is not exactly compensated for by a contraction in the other coordinate directions. Here it is understood that the spatial derivatives of the velocity components are evaluated at the current position and time.

Perhaps the most common postulate employed in setting up models in structural geology involving viscous fluid mechanics is that the rock is *incompressible*. This means that the density in the infinitesimal element surrounding any particle does not change with time, so the right-hand side of (7.81) is identically zero:

$$\frac{\partial v_x}{\partial x} + \frac{\partial v_y}{\partial y} + \frac{\partial v_z}{\partial z} = \nabla \cdot \mathbf{v} = 0 \tag{7.82}$$

In other words the divergence of the velocity vector field is zero. Near any particle in the material continuum and for all relevant times the velocity gradients are constrained such that a stretch in one coordinate direction is compensated exactly by contractions in the other coordinate directions. Equation (7.82) assures conservation of mass for the incompressible but deformable material continuum.

It follows from (7.81) and (7.82) that the material time derivative of density is zero for the incompressible material, $Dp/Dt = 0$. For a body that is homogeneous with respect to density and incompressible:

$$\frac{\partial \rho}{\partial x} = \frac{\partial \rho}{\partial y} = \frac{\partial \rho}{\partial z} = 0, \quad \text{and} \quad \frac{\partial \rho}{\partial t} = 0 \tag{7.83}$$

These are the most constrained conditions for the material continuum subject to conservation of mass: the mass density is uniform in space and constant in time.

7.3.3 Conservation of linear momentum: the equations of motion

Conservation of linear momentum for the rigid body is described by (7.20). Here we derive the

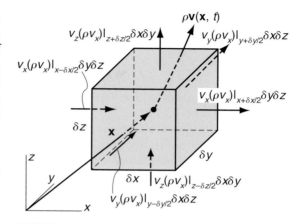

Fig 7.19 Schematic diagram to define the conservation of linear momentum as material moves through a fixed volume element with momentum, $\rho\mathbf{v}(\mathbf{x}, t)$. For example, the x-component of momentum flux through the left-hand side of the element is the product of the velocity component, v_x, and the momentum, ρv_x, evaluated at that side times the surface area of the side. The x-component of momentum flux includes terms from all other sides of the element.

analogous equation for a deformable material continuum by adopting the spatial description of motion and considering a volume element (Fig. 7.19) that is fixed in space with respect to the coordinate origin. In a word equation we have (Bird *et al.*, 1960):

$$
\begin{pmatrix} \text{rate of} \\ \text{momentum} \\ \text{increase} \end{pmatrix} = \begin{pmatrix} \text{rate of} \\ \text{momentum} \\ \text{in} \end{pmatrix}
$$

$$
- \begin{pmatrix} \text{rate of} \\ \text{momentum} \\ \text{out} \end{pmatrix} + \begin{pmatrix} \text{resultant} \\ \text{of all} \\ \text{forces} \end{pmatrix} \tag{7.84}
$$

Each term in (7.84) is taken per unit volume. The center of the element is at an arbitrary point specified by the position vector **x** with components (x, y, z) which are the current coordinates. The sides of the element are parallel to the coordinate axes, and the lengths of the sides are δx, δy, and δz. The momentum associated with the point at the center of the element is a vector function of the current location and time, $\rho\mathbf{v}(\mathbf{x}, t)$, with components in all three coordinate directions. The rate of increase of the momentum is:

$$\frac{\partial}{\partial t}(\rho \mathbf{v}) \tag{7.85}$$

This vector accounts for the left-hand side of (7.84).

As material moves through the fixed element (Fig. 7.19), momentum is carried in and out parallel to the three coordinate directions in proportion to the respective velocity components. This transport of momentum is measured by the *momentum flux per unit volume*, which is the product of the velocity and the momentum, $\mathbf{v}(\rho \mathbf{v})$. For example, on the left-hand side of the element we have $v_x(\rho v_x)$, where ρ and v_x are evaluated at $x - \delta x/2$. This quantity times the area, $\delta y \delta z$, is the momentum flux through the left-hand side, $v_x(\rho v_x)\delta y \delta z$. Similarly, the momentum flux through the right-hand side is $v_x(\rho v_x)\delta y \delta z$, where ρ and v_x are evaluated at $x + \delta x/2$. We account for the difference between the rate of momentum *in* through the left side and the rate *out* through the right-hand side as:

$$v_x(\rho v_x)\big|_{x-\delta x/2}\delta y \,\delta z - v_x(\rho v_x)\big|_{x+\delta x/2}\delta y \,\delta z \tag{7.86}$$

Because the velocity components v_y and v_z are parallel to these sides, they cannot contribute to this part of the rate of momentum change. On the other hand, v_y can carry x momentum, ρv_x through the front and back sides of the element, and v_z can carry x momentum, ρv_x through the bottom and top of the element. The pairs of arrows normal to the sides of the element in Fig. 7.19 are meant to represent these three fluxes of x momentum across the element. The order of the two velocity vector components is in keeping with an "on–in" subscript convention: e.g. $v_y(\rho v_z)\delta x \delta z$ is the momentum flux "on" a side with normal parallel to the y-coordinate of the momentum "in" the z-direction.

To convert the finite difference in (7.86) to a partial derivative a set of n elements (Fig. 7.19) is considered with successively smaller volumes that contain $\mathbf{x}$ and approach zero in the limit as $n \to \infty$ so the elements converge on the central point at $\mathbf{x}$. In this limit the partial derivative of the momentum flux, $v_x(\rho v_x)$, with respect to x is:

$$\frac{\partial}{\partial x}v_x(\rho v_x) = \lim_{n \to \infty} \frac{v_x(\rho v_x)\big|_{x+\delta x/2} - v_x(\rho v_x)\big|_{x-\delta x/2}}{\delta x} \tag{7.87}$$

Multiplying both sides of (7.87) by the volume and comparing this to (7.86), we see how the negative of the left-hand side of (7.87) accounts for one component of the rate of x-momentum change. The components of the rate of x-momentum change through the front and back of the element, and through the bottom and top of the element, are similarly defined so the net rate of change of x momentum is:

$$-\frac{\partial}{\partial x}v_x(\rho v_x)\delta y \,\delta z \,\delta x - \frac{\partial}{\partial y}v_y(\rho v_x)\delta x \,\delta z \,\delta y$$
$$-\frac{\partial}{\partial z}v_z(\rho v_x)\delta x \,\delta y \,\delta z \tag{7.88}$$

Here it is understood that the derivatives are evaluated at the point $\mathbf{x}$. The net rate of change of y and z momentum each have three components that are found using a similar procedure.

The one-dimensional relationship (7.88) for the rate of change of momentum is generalized to three dimensions using the differential operator ∇ on the momentum flux, $\mathbf{v}(\rho \mathbf{v})$. Because the momentum flux is a product of two vectors, referred to as a *dyadic product*, this operation is somewhat different from that defined in (7.77). The dyadic product is a special form of second-rank tensor with nine components. For example, the dyadic product of the two arbitrary vectors, $\mathbf{u}$ and $\mathbf{w}$ is (Bird *et al.*, 1960):

$$\mathbf{uw} = \begin{pmatrix} u_xw_x & u_xw_y & u_xw_z \\ u_yw_x & u_yw_y & u_yw_z \\ u_zw_x & u_zw_y & u_zw_z \end{pmatrix} \tag{7.89}$$

Using the del operator (7.76) on this dyadic product we have:

$$\nabla \cdot \mathbf{uw} = \left(\frac{\partial u_xw_x}{\partial x} + \frac{\partial u_yw_x}{\partial y} + \frac{\partial u_zw_x}{\partial z}\right)\mathbf{e}_x$$
$$+ \left(\frac{\partial u_xw_y}{\partial x} + \frac{\partial u_yw_y}{\partial y} + \frac{\partial u_zw_y}{\partial z}\right)\mathbf{e}_y \tag{7.90}$$
$$+ \left(\frac{\partial u_xw_z}{\partial x} + \frac{\partial u_yw_z}{\partial y} + \frac{\partial u_zw_z}{\partial z}\right)\mathbf{e}_z$$

The rate of change of momentum per unit volume is found by dividing (7.88) and its coun-

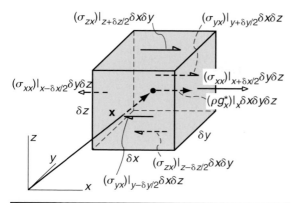

Fig 7.20 Schematic diagram to define the resultant force acting on fixed volume element. For example, the x-component of the resultant force on the left-hand side of the element is the product of the normal stress component, σ_{xx}, and the surface area of the side. The x-component of resultant force includes terms from all other sides of the element and involves both shear and normal stresses. The body force component per unit volume, ρg_x^*, times the volume also contributes to the resultant force.

terparts by the volume of the element and using the del operator:

$$\nabla \cdot [\mathbf{v}(\rho\mathbf{v})] = \left(\frac{\partial}{\partial x} v_x(\rho v_x) + \frac{\partial}{\partial y} v_y(\rho v_x) + \frac{\partial}{\partial z} v_z(\rho v_x) \right) \mathbf{e}_x$$
$$+ \left(\frac{\partial}{\partial x} v_x(\rho v_y) + \frac{\partial}{\partial y} v_y(\rho v_y) + \frac{\partial}{\partial z} v_z(\rho v_y) \right) \mathbf{e}_y$$
$$+ \left(\frac{\partial}{\partial x} v_x(\rho v_z) + \frac{\partial}{\partial y} v_y(\rho v_z) + \frac{\partial}{\partial z} v_z(\rho v_z) \right) \mathbf{e}_z$$

(7.91)

This vector accounts for the first and second terms on the right-hand side of (7.84).

The final term to evaluate in (7.84) is the resultant force. The resultant surface force in the x-coordinate direction is related to the x-components of the tractions acting on the sides of the fixed volume element (Fig. 7.20). It is conventional to use the equivalent stress components instead of the traction components to account for the surface forces. Thus, for example, the net surface force associated with the normal stress component, σ_{xx}, on the left- and right-hand sides of the element is:

$$-(\sigma_{xx})\big|_{x-\delta x/2} \delta y \, \delta z + (\sigma_{xx})\big|_{x+\delta x/2} \delta y \, \delta z$$

(7.92)

As the successively smaller elements converge on the point **x**, the partial derivative of the stress component, σ_{xx}, with respect to x is:

$$\frac{\partial \sigma_{xx}}{\partial x} = \lim_{n \to \infty} \frac{(\sigma_{xx})\big|_{x+\delta x/2} - (\sigma_{xx})\big|_{x-\delta x/2}}{\delta x}$$

(7.93)

Multiplying both sides of (7.93) by the volume and comparing this to (7.92) we see how the left-hand side of (7.93) accounts for part of the net force in the x-direction. The x-component of force due to shear stresses on the front and back of the element, and on the bottom and top of the element, are similarly defined with reference to Fig. 7.20 so the resultant of surface forces in the x-direction is:

$$\frac{\partial}{\partial x}(\sigma_{xx}) \, \delta y \, \delta z \, \delta x + \frac{\partial}{\partial y}(\sigma_{yx}) \, \delta x \, \delta z \, \delta y + \frac{\partial}{\partial z}(\sigma_{zx}) \, \delta x \, \delta y \, \delta z$$

(7.94)

Here it is understood that the derivatives are evaluated at the point **x**. The resultants of surface forces in the y- and z-directions are found by similar procedures.

The one-dimensional relationship for the surface force (7.94) is generalized to three dimensions using the differential operator ∇ (7.76) on the stress tensor, σ, following the procedure introduced in (7.91):

$$\nabla \cdot \sigma = \left(\frac{\partial \sigma_{xx}}{\partial x} + \frac{\partial \sigma_{yx}}{\partial y} + \frac{\partial \sigma_{zx}}{\partial z} \right) \mathbf{e}_x$$
$$+ \left(\frac{\partial \sigma_{xy}}{\partial x} + \frac{\partial \sigma_{yy}}{\partial y} + \frac{\partial \sigma_{zy}}{\partial z} \right) \mathbf{e}_y$$
$$+ \left(\frac{\partial \sigma_{xz}}{\partial x} + \frac{\partial \sigma_{yx}}{\partial y} + \frac{\partial \sigma_{zz}}{\partial z} \right) \mathbf{e}_z$$

(7.95)

This vector is the resultant surface force per unit volume. The body force per unit volume acting on the element is taken as:

$$\rho g^*$$

(7.96)

This vector accounts for the other part of the last term of (7.84).

Collecting terms from (7.85), (7.91), (7.95), and (7.96) we have a statement of the conservation of linear momentum (Bird et al., 1960, p. 78):

$$\frac{\partial}{\partial t}(\rho\mathbf{v}) = -\nabla\cdot[\mathbf{v}(\rho\mathbf{v})] + \nabla\cdot\sigma + \rho\mathbf{g}^* \tag{7.97}$$

This is a spatial description of the conservation of linear momentum because it describes changes at a fixed point in space where the density, velocity, stress, and acceleration of gravity are expressed as functions of the spatial coordinates. This is referred to as the *equation of motion* because it governs the motion of a deforming material subject to conservation of linear momentum. It is important to note that (7.97) does not depend upon particular properties of the material, such as elasticity or viscosity, so it applies to any body that can be suitably characterized as a material continuum.

Written out in component form, the first of the three equations of motion given by (7.97) is:

$$\frac{\partial}{\partial t}(\rho v_x) = -\frac{\partial}{\partial x}v_x(\rho v_x) - \frac{\partial}{\partial y}v_y(\rho v_x) - \frac{\partial}{\partial z}v_z(\rho v_x)$$

$$+ \frac{\partial\sigma_{xx}}{\partial x} + \frac{\partial\sigma_{yx}}{\partial y} + \frac{\partial\sigma_{zx}}{\partial z} + \rho g_x^* \tag{7.98}$$

The second and third equations follow by cyclic substitution of the subscripts. On the left-hand side of (7.98) is the time derivative of the x-components of momentum per unit volume. The first three terms on the right-hand side are spatial derivatives of the momentum flux per unit volume. The next three terms are the spatial derivatives of the stress components and the final term is the component of gravitational body force per unit volume. The equations of motion (7.97) may be written in a more general form by replacing the gravitational body force, $\rho\mathbf{g}^*$, with a generic body force, $\mathbf{F}(b)$, but applications to structural geology usually require only the gravitational body force, and this usually is taken as constant in time and uniform in space.

The equations of motion can be rewritten to refer to a particle traveling with the deforming material at the position $\mathbf{x}$ and current time t. For example, consider (7.98) and expand the partial derivative on the left-hand side:

$$\frac{\partial}{\partial t}(\rho v_x) = \rho\frac{\partial v_x}{\partial t} + v_x\frac{\partial\rho}{\partial t} \tag{7.99}$$

The first three terms on the right-hand side of (7.98) are expanded as:

$$-\rho v_x\frac{\partial v_x}{\partial x} - \rho v_x\frac{\partial v_y}{\partial y} - \rho v_x\frac{\partial v_z}{\partial z}$$

$$-v_x v_x\frac{\partial\rho}{\partial x} - v_x v_y\frac{\partial\rho}{\partial y} - v_x v_z\frac{\partial\rho}{\partial z} \tag{7.100}$$

$$-\rho v_x\frac{\partial v_x}{\partial x} - \rho v_y\frac{\partial v_x}{\partial y} - \rho v_z\frac{\partial v_x}{\partial z}$$

These terms are rearranged as follows:

$$-\rho\left(v_x\frac{\partial v_x}{\partial x} + v_y\frac{\partial v_x}{\partial y} + v_z\frac{\partial v_x}{\partial z}\right)$$

$$-v_x\left(\rho\frac{\partial v_x}{\partial x} + v_x\frac{\partial\rho}{\partial x} + \rho\frac{\partial v_y}{\partial y} + v_y\frac{\partial\rho}{\partial y} + \rho\frac{\partial v_z}{\partial z} + v_z\frac{\partial\rho}{\partial z}\right) \tag{7.101}$$

The equation of continuity (7.80) shows that the second term on the right-hand side of (7.99) is equal to the second term of (7.101), so these two terms are eliminated. What remains is the material time derivative of the velocity multiplied by the mass density. Similar results are obtained for the other two equations of motion such that (7.97) may be rewritten:

$$\rho\frac{D\mathbf{v}}{Dt} = \nabla\cdot\sigma + \rho\mathbf{g}^* \tag{7.102}$$

Using indicial notation the equations of motion in this form are:

$$\rho\frac{Dv_i}{Dt} = \frac{\partial\sigma_{ji}}{\partial x_j} + \rho g_i^* \tag{7.103}$$

Here it is understood that the indices i and j range over the three spatial coordinates (x, y, z). Written in component form we have:

$$\rho\frac{Dv_x}{Dt} = \frac{\partial\sigma_{xx}}{\partial x} + \frac{\partial\sigma_{yx}}{\partial y} + \frac{\partial\sigma_{zx}}{\partial z} + \rho g_x^* \tag{7.104}$$

$$\rho\frac{Dv_y}{Dt} = \frac{\partial\sigma_{xy}}{\partial x} + \frac{\partial\sigma_{yy}}{\partial y} + \frac{\partial\sigma_{zy}}{\partial z} + \rho g_y^* \tag{7.105}$$

$$\rho\frac{Dv_z}{Dt} = \frac{\partial\sigma_{xz}}{\partial x} + \frac{\partial\sigma_{yz}}{\partial y} + \frac{\partial\sigma_{zz}}{\partial z} + \rho g_z^* \tag{7.106}$$

This form of the equations of motion is credited to Augustine-Louis Cauchy (1789–1857) (Fig. 7.21) and is referred to as Cauchy's First Law of Motion (Malvern, 1969, p. 214). Recall from (7.65) that the material time derivative of velocity is the particle acceleration, $\mathbf{a}$, so the left-hand side of (7.102) is

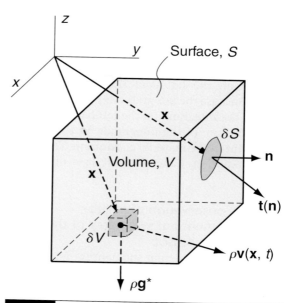

Fig 7.22 Schematic diagram to define the conservation of linear momentum for a fixed volume element based upon the integration of the tractions, $\mathbf{t(n)}$, acting on surface elements, δS, over the surface, S, and the integration of the unit weights, $\rho \mathbf{g}^*$, acting on volume elements δV, over the volume, V.

the mass per unit volume times the particle acceleration. The terms on the right-hand side are the resultant surface and body forces per unit volume. Therefore one can interpret (7.102) as a statement of Newton's Second Law, $m\mathbf{a} = \mathbf{F}$, set here in the context of a deformable continuum. Again it is important to emphasize that these equations of motion are independent of constitutive properties so they apply to any material that can be idealized as a continuum.

One of the basic postulates of continuum mechanics is the *momentum principle* (Malvern, 1969, p. 213):

the time rate of change of the total momentum of a given set of particles equals the vector sum of all the external forces acting on the particles of the set, provided Newton's Third Law of action and reaction governs the internal forces.

Recall that a similar statement, applied to a single particle, was expressed in (7.6) and again in (7.20) for the rigid body. In the context of a material continuum one imagines a set of particles of given total mass occupying a volume, V, with bounding surface, S, at a given instant in time, t (Fig. 7.22). The momentum is given using the spatial description of motion as $\rho \mathbf{v}(\mathbf{x}, t)$ and this is integrated over the volume. A distribution of surface forces per unit area is represented by the equivalent tractions, $\mathbf{t(n)}$, and this is integrated over the surface. A distribution of body forces per unit volume is taken as that due to the unit weight, $\rho \mathbf{g}^*$, and these are integrated over the volume. Then, the momentum principle is expressed as:

$$\frac{D}{Dt} \int_V \rho \mathbf{v} dV = \int_S \mathbf{t} \, dS + \int_V \rho \mathbf{g}^* dV \tag{7.107}$$

On the left-hand side the material time derivative is used because the momentum is given using the spatial description of motion.

Using the steps that we describe in the next section the stress tensor is substituted for the traction vector on the right-hand side of (7.107) and the surface integral is transformed to a volume integral using the divergence theorem (Malvern, 1969, p. 200). Reynolds transport theorem is used to move the material time derivative inside the integral on the left-hand side (Malvern, 1969, p. 210). Because the integrals refer to any arbitrary volume the integrand on the left-hand side must equal the sum of the integrands on the right at each point in the material continuum. The resulting equation is Cauchy's First Law of Motion (7.102).

7.3.4 Conservation of angular momentum: symmetry of the stress tensor

Conservation of angular momentum for the material continuum is described using the momentum principle, given in the previous quotation, with the word "angular" inserted before "momentum" and the words "all external torques" substituted for "all external forces." A similar statement, applied to a single particle, was expressed in (7.11) and again in (7.30) for the rigid body. One might suppose, based on what we have derived in the previous section for conservation of linear momentum that the conservation of angular momentum in a deforming continuum would lead to a set of equations relating density, velocity, stress, and gravitational acceleration in a form analogous to Cauchy's First Law of Motion (7.102). However, a derivation based on extending this concept to the continuum (Malvern, 1969, p. 215) leads to a remarkably simple set of equations, relating only the shear stress components to one another such that the stress tensor is symmetric. The derivation and its implications are described here.

In the context of a material continuum consider a set of particles of given total mass occupying a volume, V, with bounding surface, S, at a given instant in time, t (Fig. 7.22). For the particle at $\mathbf{x}$, the momentum per unit volume, $\rho\mathbf{v}$, is a function of the current coordinates and time, so the angular momentum per unit volume at that location, defined as $\mathbf{x} \times \rho\mathbf{v}$, also is a function of $\mathbf{x}$ and t. This quantity is integrated over the volume to obtain the total angular momentum. The body is acted upon by a distribution of surface forces per unit area represented by the equivalent trac-

tions, $\mathbf{t(n)}$, acting on the surface S. The cross product of the position vector and the traction, $\mathbf{x} \times \mathbf{t}$, is integrated over the surface as in (7.35) to find the resultant torque due to surface forces. A distribution of body forces per unit volume is represented by the unit weight, $\rho\mathbf{g}^*$, and the cross product $\mathbf{x} \times \rho\mathbf{g}^*$ is integrated over the volume as in (7.36) to find the resultant torque due to body forces. Newton's Third Law is invoked to argue that the forces due to internal interactions are equal, opposite, and collinear so they produce no resultant torque on the body.

The underlying postulate is that the material time derivative of the total angular momentum is equal to the vector sum of the resultant torques:

$$\frac{D}{Dt}\int_V (\mathbf{x} \times \rho\mathbf{v})\,dV = \int_S (\mathbf{x} \times \mathbf{t})\,dS + \int_V (\mathbf{x} \times \rho\mathbf{g}^*)\,dV$$

(7.108)

The material time derivative is used because the angular momentum must be that associated with particles.

The next step in the derivation involves writing the vector cross products in terms of the vector components. Recall from (3.27) that the vector product $\mathbf{u}$ of two arbitrary vectors, $\mathbf{v}$ and $\mathbf{w}$, is defined in terms of their Cartesian components as:

$$\mathbf{u} = \mathbf{v} \times \mathbf{w} = (v_y w_z - v_z w_y)\mathbf{e}_x + (v_z w_x - v_x w_z)\mathbf{e}_y$$
$$+ (v_x w_y - v_y w_x)\mathbf{e}_z$$

(7.109)

This expansion of (7.108) would involve a large number of terms, but is condensed using indicial notation and the permutation symbol e_{pqr}:

$$e_{pqr} = \begin{cases} 0, & \text{when any two indices are equal;} \\ +1, & \text{when indices are } (x, y, z), \\ & (y, z, x), \text{ or } (z, x, y); \\ -1, & \text{when indices are } (x, z, y), \\ & (y, x, z), \text{ or } (z, y, x). \end{cases}$$

(7.110)

Employing (7.110) the components of the vector product $\mathbf{u}$ are written:

$$u_p = e_{pqr} v_q w_r$$

(7.111)

Here it is understood that the indices p, q, and r range over x, y, and z and that repeated indices on the right-hand side imply summation over that range. Each component of **u** is composed of nine terms but eight of these are reduced to zero by (7.110) and the remaining terms are those found in (7.109).

The integral equation for the conservation of angular momentum (7.108) is rewritten using the vector components and the permutation symbol as:

$$\frac{D}{Dt}\int_V e_{pqr}x_q\rho v_r\,dV = \int_S e_{pqr}x_q t_r\,dS + \int_V e_{pqr}x_q\rho g_r^*\,dV$$

(7.112)

The left-hand side of (7.112) can be rearranged using *Reynold's transport theorem* (Malvern, 1969, p. 210) which applies to any scalar, vector, or tensor function. Given such a function, Q, of the current coordinates and time, the material time derivative of the volume integral may be rearranged according to this theorem as follows:

$$\frac{D}{Dt}\int_V \rho Q\,dV = \int_V \rho\frac{DQ}{Dt}\,dV$$

(7.113)

Therefore the left-hand side of (7.112) may be written:

$$\frac{D}{Dt}\int_V e_{pqr}x_q\rho v_r\,dV = \int_V e_{pqr}\rho\frac{D}{Dt}(x_q v_r)\,dV$$

$$= \int_V e_{pqr}\rho\left(x_q\frac{Dv_r}{Dt} + v_r\frac{Dx_q}{Dt}\right)dV$$

$$= \int_V e_{pqr}\rho x_q\frac{Dv_r}{Dt}\,dV$$

(7.114)

In the second step $Dx_q/Dt = v_q$ by definition and $e_{pqr}v_r v_q = 0$ using (7.110).

In the first term on the right-hand side of (7.112) Cauchy's Formula, $t_r = \sigma_{sr}n_s$, is used to replace the traction vector components with the stress tensor components, σ_{sr}, where n_s are components of the outward unit normal to the surface S:

$$\int_S e_{pqr}x_q t_r\,dS = \int_S e_{pqr}x_q\sigma_{sr}n_s\,dS$$

(7.115)

The surface integral of a vector quantity may be transformed to a volume integral using what is

referred to as the *divergence theorem* or *Gauss's theorem* (Malvern, 1969, p. 200). Written in terms of the components of an arbitrary vector, **u**, this theorem is:

$$\int_S u_i n_i\,dS = \int_V \frac{\partial u_i}{\partial x_i}\,dV$$

(7.116)

On the left-hand side the component of the vector **u** directed normal to the surface S is integrated over that surface. On the right-hand side the divergence of the vector **u** is integrated over the volume V bounded by that surface. Applying the divergence theorem to (7.115) we have:

$$\int_S e_{pqr}x_q\sigma_{sr}n_s\,dS = \int_V e_{pqr}\frac{\partial x_q\sigma_{sr}}{\partial x_s}\,dV$$

$$= \int_V e_{pqr}\left(x_q\frac{\partial\sigma_{sr}}{\partial x_s} + \sigma_{sr}\frac{\partial x_q}{\partial x_s}\right)dV$$

$$= \int_V e_{pqr}(x_q\frac{\partial\sigma_{sr}}{\partial x_s} + \delta_{qs}\sigma_{sr})\,dV$$

(7.117)

This transformation enables us to consider the right-hand side of (7.112) as a single volume integral:

$$\int_V e_{pqr}\left[x_q\left(\frac{\partial\sigma_{sr}}{\partial x_s} + \rho g_r^*\right) + \sigma_{qr}\right]dV$$

(7.118)

The last term in square brackets follows from the fact that $\delta_{qs}\sigma_{sr} = \sigma_{qr}$.

Using (7.114) and (7.118) the rearranged and transformed integral equation for the conservation of angular momentum (7.112) becomes:

$$\int_V e_{pqr}\rho x_q\frac{Dv_r}{Dt}\,dV = \int_V e_{pqr}\left[x_q\left(\frac{\partial\sigma_{sr}}{\partial x_s} + \rho g_r^*\right) + \sigma_{qr}\right]dV$$

(7.119)

Buried within this equation is Cauchy's First Law of Motion (7.103), such that the left-hand side of (7.119) exactly cancels the terms in parentheses on the right-hand side leaving:

$$\int_V e_{pqr}\sigma_{qr}\,dV = 0$$

(7.120)

This relation must hold for an arbitrary volume V and therefore the integrand must be zero. Employing (7.110) we have:

$$e_{pqr}\sigma_{qr} = 0, \quad \text{so for} \quad \begin{cases} p = x, \sigma_{yz} - \sigma_{zy} = 0 \\ p = y, \sigma_{zx} - \sigma_{xz} = 0 \ (7.121) \\ p = z, \sigma_{xy} - \sigma_{yx} = 0 \end{cases}$$

In general:

$$\sigma_{qr} = \sigma_{rq}, \quad q \neq r \tag{7.122}$$

This expression of conservation of angular momentum is credited to Augustine-Louis Cauchy (1789–857), (Fig. 7.21), and is referred to as Cauchy's Second Law of Motion (Malvern, 1969, p. 214).

It is noteworthy that the preceding derivation does not presume a homogeneous state of stress or static equilibrium, and it does not neglect body forces as we did in the Chapter 6 to first derive (7.122) and justify the symmetry of the stress tensor. The symmetry of the stress tensor applies to the material continuum with surface and body forces that induce heterogeneous stress states and both linear and angular accelerations. This conclusion is independent of the material properties so applies to elastic solids and viscous fluids. Perhaps because it is so broadly applicable, and because it does not contain the kinematic quantities, (7.122) is rarely mentioned as an integral part of the equations of motion. The symmetry of the stress tensor usually is tacitly presumed in applications of continuum mechanics to structural geology and that is the case throughout this textbook. In what follows, when referring to the equations of motion, we mean (7.102) and equations derived from it, but (7.122) is understood.

There are two caveats regarding the symmetry of the stress tensor. There must be no distributed surface and body couples that would lead to couple stresses and a non-symmetric stress tensor (Malvern, 1969, p. 217). Furthermore, for problems of elasticity one adopts the referential description of motion rather than the spatial description used here, and one supposes that equilibrium is established for the body in the undeformed state. For cases where the strains are taken as infinitesimal it may be plausible to argue that the initial coordinates and the current coordinates of particles are so little different that this supposition is reasonable. Examples of instability, such as buckling of thin beams and plates, demonstrate that this supposition is not always valid.

7.4 | Field equations for the elastic solid and viscous fluid

The equations of motion for the material continuum, (7.103) and (7.122), follow from conservation of linear and angular momentum and are independent of the constitutive properties of the material in motion. In the context of structural geology these equations account equally well for the dramatic motion associated with earthquake ruptures and the imperceptible motion of tectonic plates between major earthquake events. However, to apply these equations to a particular problem it is necessary to select an appropriate set of *constitutive equations* that relate the stress components to the strain or rate of deformation components and thereby explicitly define the mechanical behavior of the material. The constitutive equations are used to eliminate the stress components from the equations of motion, thereby reducing the number of dependent variables. In this way more specialized equations of motion are derived for elastic solids, viscous fluids, and other materials.

In some circumstances the constitutive properties can be measured directly in laboratory tests, so the appropriate behavior can be identified and used. In other cases one postulates the constitutive properties, based upon inferences from field observations. In Chapters 8 and 10 we describe the elastic solid and the viscous fluid in some detail, including testing methods designed for both the laboratory and the field. Here we derive the governing equations for the linear isotropic elastic solid and the linear isotropic viscous fluid from the more general equations of motion derived in the previous section. Those equations, you will recall, are already specialized to isothermal and isochemical conditions. In doing so we show how these equations are put into forms that have immediate practical applications in structural geology. Our focus is limited to these two most elementary constitutive laws because they provide an appropriate introduction to the subject and because they are adequate approximations for the deformation or flow accompanying the development of many geological structures.

7.4.1 Field equations for the linear isotropic elastic solid

The Lagrangian (material) coordinates **X** are taken as independent variables. Because there are only two states to compare, and it is the displacement that measures the change in position of any particle from the reference to the current state, the equations of motion (7.103) must be written in terms of the displacement **u** rather than the velocity **v**. Because the equations of motion (7.103) are written in terms of a spatial description of motion, conservation of momentum is satisfied in the current configuration of the deforming body. To evaluate the conditions under which conservation of momentum would be satisfied in the reference state, the stress tensor is written in a form other than that introduced by Cauchy. Consideration of this so-called Piola–Kirchhoff stress tensor is beyond the scope of this text so we refer the interested reader to other sources for the details of the evaluation (Fung, 1965; Malvern, 1969). In summary, equations of motion of the same form as (7.103) are written for the reference state using the Piola–Kirchhoff stress tensor. There equations may be transformed to those using the Cauchy stress tensor, but terms appear that may be approximated, for example, as:

$$1 + \frac{\partial u_x}{\partial X} + \frac{\partial u_y}{\partial Y} + \frac{\partial u_z}{\partial Z} + \text{higher-order terms} \approx 1$$

$$(7.123)$$

In other words, displacement gradients with respect to the material coordinates, X_i, must be small compared to unity. This is the same approximation that is made to reduce finite strains to the infinitesimal strains, and therefore it is in keeping with the well-understood postulates of linear elasticity theory. In addition, however, terms appear in the equations of motion that may be approximated, for example, as:

$$\left(1 + \frac{\partial u_x}{\partial x}\right)\sigma_{xx} + \frac{\partial u_x}{\partial y}\sigma_{yx} + \frac{\partial u_x}{\partial z}\sigma_{zx} \approx \sigma_{xx} \qquad (7.124)$$

Here products of displacement gradients with respect to the spatial coordinates, x_i, and stress components must be small compared to the stress components. This approximation is rarely acknowledged in applications of the linear theory and could prove to be problematic.

Further simplifications of the equations of motion (7.103) are achieved by considering the material derivatives of the kinematic quantities. For example, components of the particle velocity are linearized as:

$$v_x = \frac{Du_x}{Dt} = \frac{\partial u_x}{\partial t} + v_x\frac{\partial u_x}{\partial x} + v_y\frac{\partial u_x}{\partial y} + v_z\frac{\partial u_x}{\partial z} \approx \frac{\partial u_x}{\partial t}$$

$$(7.125)$$

Here products of the velocity components and the displacement gradients must be small compared to the time rate of change of displacement. Similarly, components of the particle acceleration are linearized as:

$$a_x = \frac{Dv_x}{Dt} = \frac{\partial v_x}{\partial t} + v_x\frac{\partial v_x}{\partial x} + v_y\frac{\partial v_x}{\partial y} + v_z\frac{\partial v_x}{\partial z} \approx \frac{\partial v_x}{\partial t} \approx \frac{\partial^2 u_x}{\partial t^2}$$

$$(7.126)$$

Here products of velocity components and the velocity gradients must be small compared to time rate of change of velocity.

Given the simplifications and linearizations described above, the equations of motion in the reference state are written:

$$\rho\frac{\partial^2 u_i}{\partial t^2} = \frac{\partial \sigma_{ji}}{\partial X_j} + \rho g_i^* \qquad (7.127)$$

It is understood that the density and acceleration of gravity are evaluated as functions of the material coordinates, and the partial derivatives of the displacement components with respect to time are taken with the material coordinates held constant. What may seem like inconsequential changes of notation between (7.127) and (7.103) involve the omission of terms as described above that could be significant in a given application. Each of these should be evaluated to understand the degree of accuracy of the solutions that are employed.

The right-hand side of (7.127) contains spatial gradients of the Cauchy stress components which are eliminated in favor of the displacements by first relating the displacement gradients to the strain components and then relating the strains to the stresses. These steps involve additional linearizations that are consistent with those mentioned above. The general equation for the finite strain tensor using the referential description of motion is (Malvern, 1969, p. 160):

$$E_{ij} = \frac{1}{2}\left(\frac{\partial u_i}{\partial X_j} + \frac{\partial u_j}{\partial X_i} + \frac{\partial u_k}{\partial X_i}\frac{\partial u_k}{\partial X_j}\right) \quad (7.128)$$

The E_{ij} are referred to as the Lagrangian finite strain components, because the partial derivatives are taken with respect to the Lagrangian (material) coordinates, X_i, and this description of motion is associated with Joseph-Louis Lagrange (Fig. 7.14). Particular longitudinal and shear components of the strain tensor are linearized to find the corresponding infinitesimal strain components, for example, as follows:

$$E_{xx} = \frac{\partial u_x}{\partial X} + \frac{1}{2}\left[\left(\frac{\partial u_x}{\partial X}\right)^2 + \left(\frac{\partial u_y}{\partial X}\right)^2 + \left(\frac{\partial u_z}{\partial X}\right)^2\right] \approx \frac{\partial u_x}{\partial X}$$

$$E_{xy} = \frac{1}{2}\left(\frac{\partial u_x}{\partial Y} + \frac{\partial u_y}{\partial X}\right) + \frac{1}{2}\left(\frac{\partial u_x}{\partial X}\frac{\partial u_x}{\partial Y} + \frac{\partial u_y}{\partial X}\frac{\partial u_y}{\partial Y} + \frac{\partial u_z}{\partial X}\frac{\partial u_z}{\partial Y}\right)$$

$$\approx \frac{1}{2}\left(\frac{\partial u_x}{\partial Y} + \frac{\partial u_y}{\partial X}\right) \quad (7.129)$$

Note that the non-linear terms are products of the displacement gradients and these must be small compared to the displacement gradients themselves. With approximations such as these the infinitesimal strain tensor, ε_{ij}, is related to the displacement gradients as:

$$\varepsilon_{ij} = \frac{1}{2}\left(\frac{\partial u_i}{\partial X_j} + \frac{\partial u_j}{\partial X_i}\right) \quad (7.130)$$

A finite strain tensor also may be written using the spatial description of motion and when a similar linearization is carried out an equation of the same form as (7.130) emerges in which the partial derivatives are taken with respect to the Eulerian (spatial) coordinates, x_i. Typically, the distinction between these two descriptions of the kinematics is overlooked in applications of linear elasticity.

For the linear elastic material the stress components are related to the infinitesimal strain components using constitutive equations called Hooke's Law after Robert Hooke (Fig. 7.23) the English polymath and contemporary of Isaac

Fig 7.23 Portrait of the English natural scientist Robert Hooke who was born in 1635 on the Isle of Wight, England (O'Connor and Robertson, 2004). The linear form of Hooke's Law for the isotropic elastic material is given in (7.131).

Newton. Chapter 8 is devoted to a discussion of the measurement of elastic material properties and various forms of Hooke's Law. The general linear form is simplified here for an isotropic material: one in which the elastic constants are not dependent upon direction. For such a material the stress–strain relationships are:

$$\sigma_{ij} = 2G\varepsilon_{ij} + \lambda\varepsilon_{kk}\delta_{ij} \quad (7.131)$$

Here G is the elastic *shear modulus* and λ is *Lamé's constant*. These are properties of the material and they have the same units and dimensions as stress. Expanding (7.131), typical normal and shear components of stress are related to the infinitesimal strains as:

$$\sigma_{xx} = 2G\varepsilon_{xx} + \lambda(\varepsilon_{xx} + \varepsilon_{yy} + \varepsilon_{zz})$$

$$\sigma_{xy} = 2G\varepsilon_{xy} \quad (7.132)$$

The three equations of motion (7.127), six kinematic equations (7.130), and six constitutive equations (7.131) form a complete set of field equations for the linearized isotropic and isothermal elastic material. The independent variables are the three material coordinates and time (X, Y, Z, t). The dependent variables (unknowns) are the three displacement components (u_x, u_y, u_z), the six infinitesimal strain components $(\varepsilon_{xx}, \varepsilon_{yy}, \varepsilon_{zz}, \varepsilon_{xy}, \varepsilon_{yz}, \varepsilon_{zx})$, and the six stress components $(\sigma_{xx}, \sigma_{yy}, \sigma_{zz}, \sigma_{xy}, \sigma_{yz}, \sigma_{zx})$. Usually, the mass density, ρ, the components of gravitational acceleration, g_i^*, and the two elastic constants, G and λ, are taken as given by laboratory or field data, and in most applications these quantities are postulated to be uniform in space and constant in time.

There are fifteen field equations and fifteen unknowns for the elastic boundary value problem as posed above. This problem is put in a more practical form by replacing the stress components in (7.127) with displacement components using the kinematic equations (7.130) and Hooke's Law (7.131), for example as:

$$\sigma_{xx} = 2G\frac{\partial u_x}{\partial X} + \lambda\left(\frac{\partial u_x}{\partial X} + \frac{\partial u_y}{\partial Y} + \frac{\partial u_z}{\partial Z}\right)$$

$$\sigma_{xy} = G\left(\frac{\partial u_x}{\partial Y} + \frac{\partial u_y}{\partial X}\right) \tag{7.133}$$

The other stress components follow by similar steps. Then (7.127) is written:

$$\rho\frac{\partial^2 u_i}{\partial t^2} = G\frac{\partial^2 u_i}{\partial X_k \partial X_k} + (G + \lambda)\frac{\partial^2 u_k}{\partial X_i \partial X_k} + \rho g_i^* \tag{7.134}$$

These are known as Navier's displacement equations of motion (Fung, 1969, p. 261) after the French mathematician and scholar of engineering science Claude Louis Marie Henri Navier (1785–1836), (Fig. 7.24). Apparently they were introduced by Navier in 1821 with only one elastic constant and corrected in 1822 by Cauchy (Malvern, 1969). It is understood that the partial derivatives of the displacement components with respect to time are taken with the material coordinates held constant.

In component form Navier's equations of motion (7.134) are:

Fig 7.24 Bust of the French mathematician and engineer Claude Louis Marie Henri Navier who was born in Dijon, France, in 1785 (O'Connor and Robertson, 2004). His name, along with that of Stokes, is associated with the velocity equations of motion for the viscous fluid (7.170).

$$\rho\frac{\partial^2 u_x}{\partial t^2} = G\left(\frac{\partial^2 u_x}{\partial X^2} + \frac{\partial^2 u_x}{\partial Y^2} + \frac{\partial^2 u_x}{\partial Z^2}\right) + (G + \lambda)$$
$$\times \left(\frac{\partial^2 u_x}{\partial X^2} + \frac{\partial^2 u_y}{\partial X \partial Y} + \frac{\partial^2 u_z}{\partial X \partial Z}\right) + \rho g_x^* \tag{7.135}$$

$$\rho\frac{\partial^2 u_y}{\partial t^2} = G\left(\frac{\partial^2 u_y}{\partial X^2} + \frac{\partial^2 u_y}{\partial Y^2} + \frac{\partial^2 u_y}{\partial Z^2}\right) + (G + \lambda)$$
$$\times \left(\frac{\partial^2 u_x}{\partial X \partial Y} + \frac{\partial^2 u_y}{\partial Y^2} + \frac{\partial^2 u_z}{\partial Y \partial Z}\right) + \rho g_y^* \tag{7.136}$$

$$\rho\frac{\partial^2 u_z}{\partial t^2} = G\left(\frac{\partial^2 u_z}{\partial X^2} + \frac{\partial^2 u_z}{\partial Y^2} + \frac{\partial^2 u_z}{\partial Z^2}\right) + (G + \lambda)$$
$$\times \left(\frac{\partial^2 u_x}{\partial X \partial Z} + \frac{\partial^2 u_y}{\partial Y \partial Z} + \frac{\partial^2 u_z}{\partial Z^2}\right) + \rho g_z^* \tag{7.137}$$

The independent variables are the three material coordinates and time (X, Y, Z, t) and the dependent variables (unknowns) are the three displacement components (u_x, u_y, u_z). A solution would be three equations for the displacement components as functions of the material coordinates and time. The three equations, (7.135)–(7.137), are solved for an elastic body of prescribed geometry subject to boundary conditions defined at every point on the exterior and interior boundaries in terms of the three displacement components. Derivatives of the displacement components with respect to time provide the particle velocity as in (7.125) and the particle acceleration as in (7.126). Derivatives of the displacement components with respect to the material coordinates (7.130) provide the infinitesimal strain components, and the isotropic forms of Hooke's Law (7.131) provide the stress components. In this way all of the relevant physical quantities are accounted for as functions of the material coordinates and time, and the fundamental laws of conservation of mass and momentum are obeyed.

The most familiar applications of solutions to the dynamic equations of elasticity (7.134) are to bodies set in motion by sudden loading or unloading, for example from an explosion or the impact of two bodies in motion, that generate waves within the elastic solid (Achenbach, 1973), or from the rapid propagation of a fracture (Freund, 1979). Well-known geological examples include the motion immediately following an explosive volcanic eruption, the impact of a meteor (Melosh, 1989), or the rupture of a fault (Li, 1987; Kostrov and Das, 1988; Scholz, 1990). In these cases rock particles close to the impulsive event are set in motion first, while the rest of the body is unaffected. Seismic waves propagate outward from the source with speeds on the order of a few kilometers per second and set the rest of the rock mass in motion (Aki and Richards, 1980).

7.4.2 Quasi-static equilibrium for the linear isotropic elastic solid

The equations of motion (7.134) for the isotropic and isothermal linear elastic material place no restrictions on the magnitudes of the velocity or acceleration of any particle in the continuum. They describe a material that may be accelerating or decelerating, but these changes are always related to the appropriate forces, so momentum is conserved. Typically, however, the structural geologist is not confronted with data in the field that directly constrain the particle velocity or acceleration. Rather it is the displacement from some inferred initial configuration to the current configuration, as in the opening of a dike or the slip on a fault. Therefore, the structural geologist generally approaches problems related to the development of structures from a point of view in which the left-hand sides of (7.134) are set to zero and Navier's displacement equations of motion become:

$$G\frac{\partial^2 u_i}{\partial X_k \partial X_k} + (G + \lambda)\frac{\partial^2 u_k}{\partial X_i \partial X_k} + \rho g_i^* = 0 \qquad (7.138)$$

The motion of particles is described by the displacement from the reference state to the current state, while the details of the path followed, velocities, and accelerations are ignored.

The restrictions imposed to derive (7.138) put the problem in the realm of *quasi-static equilibrium*. We use the prefix "quasi" because this is not a problem of a static rigid body, but rather one in which the body deforms and the relative displacement of particles is accounted for by the strain field. In component form the quasi-static versions of Navier's displacement equations are identical to (7.135)–(7.137) with the left-hand sides set to zero. A solution to these three equations would be three equations for the displacement components as functions of the material coordinates. The strains are computed from the displacements using the kinematic equations (7.130) and the stresses follow from Hooke's Law (7.131).

For some problems in structural geology it is more appropriate to formulate the elastic boundary value problem in terms of the stress components. Taking the equations of motion as (7.127) and supposing that the products of mass density and linearized accelerations are insignificant compared to the gradients in stress and the body forces per unit volume, we have:

$$\frac{\partial \sigma_{ji}}{\partial X_j} + \rho g_i^* = 0 \qquad (7.139)$$

These equations of quasi-static equilibrium are expanded in component form as:

$$\frac{\partial \sigma_{xx}}{\partial X} + \frac{\partial \sigma_{yx}}{\partial Y} + \frac{\partial \sigma_{zx}}{\partial Z} + \rho g_x^* = 0 \qquad (7.140)$$

$$\frac{\partial \sigma_{xy}}{\partial X} + \frac{\partial \sigma_{yy}}{\partial Y} + \frac{\partial \sigma_{zy}}{\partial Z} + \rho g_y^* = 0 \qquad (7.141)$$

$$\frac{\partial \sigma_{xz}}{\partial X} + \frac{\partial \sigma_{yz}}{\partial Y} + \frac{\partial \sigma_{zz}}{\partial Z} + \rho g_z^* = 0 \qquad (7.142)$$

These three equations are not sufficient to determine the six independent stress components. It is necessary to include the so-called equations of compatibility to solve problems of linear elasticity formulated in terms of the stress components.

The necessity of adding equations of compatibility may be appreciated by comparing the formulations of the elastic problem in terms of stresses or displacements. For the latter case, solution of Navier's three equations of motion (7.138) yields three displacement components; derivatives of these with respect to the material coordinates (7.130) provide the infinitesimal strains; and Hooke's Law (7.131) provides the stresses without ambiguity. On the other hand, given a stress state that satisfies the equilibrium conditions (7.139), Hooke's Law may be used to determine the strains without ambiguity, but the kinematic equations (7.130) for determining the displacements present the difficulty. There are six partial differential equations to determine three displacement components, so the solution is over-determined. In general, relationships must exist among the strain components that eliminate this ambiguity, and these are known as St. Venant's compatibility equations (Malvern, 1969, p. 183).

For a derivation of the compatibility equations we refer the interested reader to other sources (Fung, 1965; Malvern, 1969). St. Venant's compatibility equations for the infinitesimal strain components are:

$$\frac{\partial^2 \varepsilon_{xx}}{\partial Y^2} + \frac{\partial^2 \varepsilon_{yy}}{\partial X^2} + 2\frac{\partial^2 \varepsilon_{xy}}{\partial X \partial Y} = 0 \qquad (7.143)$$

$$\frac{\partial^2 \varepsilon_{yy}}{\partial Z^2} + \frac{\partial^2 \varepsilon_{zz}}{\partial Y^2} + 2\frac{\partial^2 \varepsilon_{yz}}{\partial Y \partial Z} = 0 \qquad (7.144)$$

$$\frac{\partial^2 \varepsilon_{zz}}{\partial X^2} + \frac{\partial^2 \varepsilon_{xx}}{\partial Z^2} + 2\frac{\partial^2 \varepsilon_{zx}}{\partial Z \partial X} = 0 \qquad (7.145)$$

$$-\frac{\partial^2 \varepsilon_{xx}}{\partial Y \partial Z} + \frac{\partial}{\partial X}\left(-\frac{\partial \varepsilon_{yz}}{\partial X} + \frac{\partial \varepsilon_{zx}}{\partial Y} + \frac{\partial \varepsilon_{xy}}{\partial Z}\right) = 0 \qquad (7.146)$$

$$-\frac{\partial^2 \varepsilon_{yy}}{\partial Z \partial X} + \frac{\partial}{\partial Y}\left(\frac{\partial \varepsilon_{yz}}{\partial X} - \frac{\partial \varepsilon_{zx}}{\partial Y} + \frac{\partial \varepsilon_{xy}}{\partial Z}\right) = 0 \qquad (7.147)$$

$$-\frac{\partial^2 \varepsilon_{zz}}{\partial X \partial Y} + \frac{\partial}{\partial Z}\left(\frac{\partial \varepsilon_{yz}}{\partial X} + \frac{\partial \varepsilon_{zx}}{\partial Y} - \frac{\partial \varepsilon_{xy}}{\partial Z}\right) = 0 \qquad (7.148)$$

These conditions are derived by assuming the existence of single-valued functions for the displacement components with continuous third partial derivatives (second partial derivatives of the strain components). It can be shown (Malvern, 1969, p. 187) that the six compatibility equations represent only three independent conditions. Also, it can be proved that the compatibility equations are necessary and sufficient conditions for the existence of single-valued displacements in a simply connected body. By ruling out a uniform translation or rigid rotation of the body these conditions ensure that a unique displacement distribution is derivable from the strain distribution.

To obtain a consistent set of governing equations in terms of the stress components, the compatibility equations are transformed from strains to stresses using Hooke's Law. In the form given in (7.131) we have the stress components as a function of the strain components and the two elastic constants, G and λ. For substitution into the compatibility equations, (7.131) must be solved algebraically for the strain components. This alternate form of Hooke's Law customarily is written using two different constants, Young's modulus E and Poisson's ratio ν, for the isotropic elastic material. For such a material the strain–stress relationships are:

$$\varepsilon_{ij} = \frac{1+\nu}{E}\sigma_{ij} - \frac{\nu}{E}\sigma_{kk}\delta_{ij} \qquad (7.149)$$

Young's modulus has the same units and dimensions as stress, and Poisson's ratio is dimensionless. Expanding typical normal and shear components of strain we have:

$$\varepsilon_{xx} = \frac{1}{E}\left[\sigma_{xx} - \nu(\sigma_{xx} + \sigma_{yy} + \sigma_{zz})\right]$$

$$\varepsilon_{xy} = \frac{1+\nu}{E}\sigma_{xy} \qquad (7.150)$$

Refer to Chapter 8 for a discussion of the measurement of E and ν, and for equations relating the isotropic elastic constants, only two of which are independent.

The derivation of the compatibility equations in terms of the stress components is given in detail elsewhere (Malvern, 1969, p. 502). In short, the stress components are substituted for the strain components using (7.149) and the equilibrium equations (7.139) are used to simplify the resulting equations and find the so-called Beltrami–Michell compatibility equations for the isothermal and isotropic linear elastic material. In the most general form of these equations there are partial derivatives of the body force per unit volume with respect to the material coordinates. To be consistent with our development thus far the body force is taken as mass density times gravitational acceleration, $\rho\mathbf{g}^*$, which is postulated to be uniform in space and constant in time. Under these conditions terms containing the body force drop out of the Beltrami–Michell compatibility equations which reduce to:

$$\nabla^2 \sigma_{ij} + \frac{1}{1+\nu} \frac{\partial^2 \sigma_{\kappa\kappa}}{\partial X_i \partial X_j} = 0 \qquad (7.151)$$

As mentioned above, these six equations represent only three independent conditions. These compatibility equations and the equilibrium equations (7.139) form a complete set for three-dimensional problems in elastic theory where the six stress components are the dependent variables.

Expanding typical members of (7.151) in component form we have, for example:

$$\left(\frac{\partial^2}{\partial X^2} + \frac{\partial^2}{\partial Y^2} + \frac{\partial^2}{\partial Z^2}\right)\sigma_{xx} + \frac{1}{1+\nu}\frac{\partial^2}{\partial X^2}(\sigma_{xx} + \sigma_{yy} + \sigma_{zz}) = 0$$

$$\left(\frac{\partial^2}{\partial X^2} + \frac{\partial^2}{\partial Y^2} + \frac{\partial^2}{\partial Z^2}\right)\sigma_{xy} + \frac{1}{1+\nu}\frac{\partial^2}{\partial X \partial Y}(\sigma_{xx} + \sigma_{xy} + \sigma_{zz}) = 0$$

$$(7.152)$$

Note that these relationships depend entirely upon second derivatives of stress components with respect to the material coordinates. Therefore functions for the stress components that are constant or linear in the material coordinates will automatically satisfy the compatibility conditions (Timoshenko and Goodier, 1970, Chapter 9). Such functions are solutions to the three-dimensional elastic problem if they satisfy the equilibrium conditions (7.139) and the prescribed boundary conditions. In these cases the boundary conditions are defined as traction distributions on the internal and external boundaries of the body. Because of the inherent difficulty of solving the compatibility equations in addition to those of equilibrium the number of analytical solutions for three-dimensional problems with stress components as the dependent variable is small. The more common approach is to take the three displacement components as the dependent variables and solve Navier's equations of motion (7.138). On the other hand many approaches and solutions exist for two-dimensional problems, examples of which are presented in Chapter 8.

7.4.3 Equations of motion for the linear isotropic viscous fluid

Fluid flow is investigated by focusing attention on the current state of the body and ignoring whatever might have been described as an initial or reference state. Therefore the spatial description of motion is adopted and we take the Eulerian (spatial) coordinates and time (x, y, z, t) as the independent variables. This is one of several ways in which the analysis of fluids differs from that of elastic solids, for which the referential description of motion is adopted. Instead of choosing the displacement components of particles, the velocity components at given positions are chosen as dependent variables. Rather than the infinitesimal strains, the fundamental kinematic quantities used to describe the deformation are the components of the rate of deformation tensor (Malvern, 1969, p. 145):

$$D_{ij} = \frac{1}{2}\left(\frac{\partial v_i}{\partial x_j} + \frac{\partial v_j}{\partial x_i}\right) \qquad (7.153)$$

Note both the similarity and the difference between this quantity and the strain as defined in (7.130). The infinitesimal strain, ε_{ij}, is proportional to partial derivatives of the displacement components, u_i, with respect to the material coordinates, X_i, whereas the rate of deformation, D_{ij}, is proportional to partial derivatives of the velocity components, v_i, with respect to the spatial coordinates, x_i. Furthermore, the rate of deformation is not limited to small velocity gradients in the manner that the infinitesimal strain is limited to small displacement gradients.

Perhaps the most fundamental mechanical distinction between a fluid and a solid is that the greatest shear stress is zero everywhere within a fluid at rest and within a fluid in a state of uniform velocity. This property sometimes is described by stating that a fluid at rest (or in uniform motion) is incapable of supporting a shear stress. Recall from Chapter 6, Table 6.1, that the maximum shear stresses are defined in terms of the principal normal stresses as:

$$\tfrac{1}{2}(\sigma_1 - \sigma_3), \quad \tfrac{1}{2}(\sigma_2 - \sigma_3), \quad \tfrac{1}{2}(\sigma_1 - \sigma_2) \qquad (7.154)$$

By definition $\sigma_1 \geq \sigma_2 \geq \sigma_3$, so all of the maximum shear stresses are positive or zero. If the greatest shear stress is zero, then all three shear stresses (7.154) must be zero, and the stress state must be isotropic. In this mechanical context the mean value of the principal normal stresses is defined as the *static pressure*, $\bar{p}_0$:

$$\bar{p}_0 = \tfrac{1}{3}(\sigma_1 + \sigma_2 + \sigma_3), \quad \sigma_1 = \sigma_2 = \sigma_3 \qquad (7.155)$$

If the fluid is in motion such that the velocity is not uniform, the mean value of the principal normal stresses is defined as the *mean normal pressure*, $\bar{p}$:

$$\bar{p} = \tfrac{1}{3}(\sigma_1 + \sigma_2 + \sigma_3), \quad \tfrac{1}{2}(\sigma_1 - \sigma_3) > 0 \qquad (7.156)$$

In this case the greatest shear stress must be greater than zero and the state of stress is not isotropic.

Pressure also is defined in a thermodynamic context. For a static fluid in thermodynamic equilibrium the pressure, absolute temperature, and mass density are related by an *equation of state* (Malvern, 1969, p. 295):

$$F(\bar{p}_0, T, \rho) = 0 \qquad (7.157)$$

For investigations of fluid flow it is assumed that the so-called *thermodynamic pressure*, p, is defined using this same relationship, even when the fluid is in motion:

$$F(p, T, \rho) = 0 \qquad (7.158)$$

Using (7.158) guarantees that the thermodynamic pressure, p, reduces to the static pressure, $\bar{p}_0$, when the fluid comes to rest or to a state of

Fig 7.25 Photograph of the Irish mathematician and fluid dynamicist George Gabriel Stokes who was born in Skreen, Ireland, in 1819 (O'Connor and Robertson, 2004). His name, along with that of Navier, is associated with the velocity equations of motion for the viscous fluid (7.160).

uniform velocity, but it may not be equal to the mean normal pressure (7.156) defined as a function of the normal stress components for a fluid in motion. In keeping with the postulates employed earlier in this chapter we limit our attention to *barotropic flows*, those in which the thermodynamic pressure is independent of temperature, so the equation of state is of the form:

$$f(p, \rho) = 0 \qquad (7.159)$$

These thermodynamic characterizations of pressure must be reconciled with the mechanical definitions of pressure from the preceding paragraph and this can be done by considering the constitutive law for the fluid.

The constitutive law for the viscous fluid continuum was developed by the Irish mathematician and hydrodynamicist George Gabriel Stokes (1819–1903), (Fig. 7.25). He proposed that the state of stress is determined by a combination of the thermodynamic pressure and a linear function of the rate of deformation tensor. Any fluid obeying this general linear form or simplifications of it is referred to as a *Newtonian viscous fluid* because of Newton's insightful investigations of viscous flow. The general linear form is simplified here for an isotropic fluid: one in which the viscous constants are not dependent upon direction. For such a fluid the stress–rate of deformation relationships are:

$$\sigma_{ij} = -p\delta_{ij} + 2\eta D_{ij} + \Lambda D_{kk}\delta_{ij} \tag{7.160}$$

Here η and Λ are the two material constants that characterize the viscosity of the fluid. Note both the similarity and the difference between this constitutive law and Hooke's Law for the elastic solid (7.131). The last two terms on the right-hand side are of the same form, but the rate of deformation replaces the infinitesimal strain and the constants have a different meaning. Here the additional term is that containing the thermodynamic pressure, p. For the fluid at rest the normal stress components are equal to the thermodynamic pressure.

Two further simplifications of the constitutive law for the Newtonian viscous fluid (7.160) lead to a reduction of the number of material constants to one. Both of these follow from the relationship between the mean normal pressure, $\bar{p}$ and the thermodynamic pressure, p (Malvern, 1969, p. 299):

$$\bar{p} = p + \left(\frac{2}{3}\eta + \Lambda\right)D_{kk} = p + \kappa D_{kk} \tag{7.161}$$

Here κ is a material property referred to as the *bulk viscosity* and D_{kk} is the rate of change of volume. The mean normal pressure is the sum of the thermodynamic pressure (present in the absence of volume change due to flow) and the pressure caused by the change in volume due to flow. Interpretation of (7.161) is facilitated by recalling that conservation of mass leads to the continuity equation (7.81) which is rewritten here as:

$$\frac{1}{\rho}\frac{D\rho}{Dt} = -\left(\frac{\partial v_x}{\partial x} + \frac{\partial v_y}{\partial y} + \frac{\partial v_z}{\partial z}\right) = -D_{kk} \tag{7.162}$$

One possibility is that the material time derivative of the density is identically zero:

$$\frac{D\rho}{Dt} = 0, \quad \text{so } D_{kk} = 0 \text{ and } \bar{p} = p \tag{7.163}$$

In other words the fluid is *incompressible*. Another possibility is that the bulk viscosity (7.161) is identically zero:

$$\kappa = 0, \quad \text{so } \Lambda = -\tfrac{2}{3}\eta \text{ and } \bar{p} = p \tag{7.164}$$

Apparently this was suggested by Stokes and so it is referred to as the *Stokes condition*. If either (7.164) or (7.163) is satisfied the constitutive law is reduced to one material constant, and coincidentally from (7.161) the mean normal pressure is equal to the thermodynamic pressure.

Employing the Stokes condition the constitutive law for the linear and isotropic viscous fluid is:

$$\sigma_{ij} = -p\delta_{ij} + 2\eta D_{ij} - \tfrac{2}{3}\eta D_{kk}\delta_{ij} \tag{7.165}$$

In the absence of any gradients in velocity the normal stress components are equal to the negative of the thermodynamic pressure and the stress state is isotropic. In the analysis of geologic structures it is commonly postulated that the rock mass is incompressible: in other words the mass density is constant. Using this constraint as described by (7.163) the constitutive law (7.165) becomes:

$$\sigma_{ij} = -p\delta_{ij} + 2\eta D_{ij} \tag{7.166}$$

Expanding (7.166) in component form, typical stress components are:

$$\sigma_{xx} = -p + 2\eta\frac{\partial v_x}{\partial x}, \quad \sigma_{xy} = \eta\left(\frac{\partial v_x}{\partial y} + \frac{\partial v_y}{\partial x}\right) = \sigma_{yx} \tag{7.167}$$

The stress components are linearly related to the rate of deformation components and the *Newtonian viscosity* is the proportionality constant.

Substituting for the stresses in one of Cauchy's First Laws of Motion (7.104) using the constitutive equations (7.166) we have, for example:

$$\rho\frac{Dv_x}{Dt} = -\frac{\partial p}{\partial x} + \eta\left(2\frac{\partial^2 v_x}{\partial x^2} + \frac{\partial^2 v_x}{\partial y^2} + \frac{\partial^2 v_y}{\partial x\partial y}\right.$$
$$\left. + \frac{\partial^2 v_z}{\partial x\partial z} + \frac{\partial^2 v_x}{\partial z^2}\right) + \rho g_x^* \tag{7.168}$$

Three of the partial derivatives in the parentheses can be eliminated as follows:

$$\frac{\partial^2 v_x}{\partial x^2} + \frac{\partial^2 v_y}{\partial x \partial y} + \frac{\partial^2 v_z}{\partial x \partial z} = \frac{\partial}{\partial x}\left(\frac{\partial v_x}{\partial x} + \frac{\partial v_y}{\partial y} + \frac{\partial v_z}{\partial z}\right) = 0 \quad (7.169)$$

Using (7.162) and (7.163) the term in parentheses is zero because the material is incompressible. Similar steps reduce the other equations of motion leaving:

$$\rho\frac{Dv_i}{Dt} = -\frac{\partial p}{\partial x_i} + \eta\frac{\partial^2 v_i}{\partial x_k \partial x_k} + \rho g_i^* \quad (7.170)$$

These are the Navier–Stokes equations for the flow of a linear, isotropic, and incompressible viscous fluid with constant mass density.

In summary, we have four equations in four unknowns. Conservation of mass for the incompressible fluid is taken from (7.162) in component form as:

$$\frac{\partial v_x}{\partial x} + \frac{\partial v_y}{\partial y} + \frac{\partial v_z}{\partial z} = 0 \quad (7.171)$$

Conservation of linear momentum is embodied in the Navier–Stokes equations (7.170), which in component form are:

$$\rho\frac{Dv_x}{Dt} = -\frac{\partial p}{\partial x} + \eta\left(\frac{\partial^2 v_x}{\partial x^2} + \frac{\partial^2 v_x}{\partial y^2} + \frac{\partial^2 v_x}{\partial z^2}\right) + \rho g_x^* \quad (7.172)$$

$$\rho\frac{Dv_y}{Dt} = -\frac{\partial p}{\partial y} + \eta\left(\frac{\partial^2 v_y}{\partial x^2} + \frac{\partial^2 v_y}{\partial y^2} + \frac{\partial^2 v_y}{\partial z^2}\right) + \rho g_y^* \quad (7.173)$$

$$\rho\frac{Dv_z}{Dt} = -\frac{\partial p}{\partial z} + \eta\left(\frac{\partial^2 v_z}{\partial x^2} + \frac{\partial^2 v_z}{\partial y^2} + \frac{\partial^2 v_z}{\partial z^2}\right) + \rho g_z^* \quad (7.174)$$

Conservation of angular momentum is implicit in Cauchy's Second Law of Motion and the symmetry of the stress tensor (7.122). In applications to structural geology the mass density, ρ, the acceleration of gravity, $\mathbf{g}^*$, and the viscosity, η, commonly are taken as given by laboratory or field data. Thus, the four dependent variables (unknowns) are the velocity components (v_x, v_y, v_z) and pressure, p, and these are sought as functions of the independent variables which are the three spatial coordinates and time (x, y, z, t). Given the velocity components the constitutive equations (7.167) are used to calculate the stress components. A solution to the Navier–Stokes equations provides three equations for the velocity components and one equation for the pressure as functions of the spatial coordinates and time. Spatial

derivatives of the velocity components give the rate of deformation components. The pressure and rate of deformation are used with the constitutive laws (7.167) to calculate the stress components.

The Navier–Stokes equations are the subject of classic textbooks in hydrodynamics (Lamb, 1945) and fluid mechanics (Landau and Lifshitz, 1960). Especially important in the context of structural geology is slow viscous flow, referred to as creeping flow or low Reynold's Number flow (Happel and Brenner, 1965), in which products of mass density and material time derivatives of the velocity components are considered negligible and the left-hand side of (7.170) is taken as zero. Applications to particular problems include folding of viscous layers (Johnson and Fletcher, 1994) and the geodynamics of Earth's crust (Turcotte and Schubert, 1982; Ranalli, 1987). Low Reynold's Number flow includes fully developed (steady-state) laminar flow in conduits, flow around immersed objects, flow in narrow but variable aperture conduits, and flow in porous materials (White, 1974, p. 202).

7.5 | Concluding remarks

In the title for a paper (Fletcher and Pollard, 1999) published in the twentieth anniversary special issue of the *Journal of Structural Geology* the authors of this textbook asked the question: "Can we understand tectonic processes and their structural products without appeal to a complete mechanics?" Our answer was, and is, "no." We argued that the majority of structural geologists in the twentieth century worked with isolated fragments of continuum mechanics (strain analysis, Mohr's circles, homogeneous stress states) which naturally led to the development of ad hoc "models." In particular the possibility that mechanical quantities such as displacement, velocity, and stress vary continuously in space and time was largely ignored. To address these variations in three-dimensional space and time requires the mathematical concept of partial differentiation with which one can formulate the governing equations of continuity and motion, and set up boundary value and initial value problems. It is these problems, and their solutions, that constitute the essential ingredients of model studies in structural geology. In this chapter we have provided the links between the concepts of calculus and physics as taught in typical undergraduate courses and the concepts of continuum mechanics as required to practice structural geology.

Chapter 8

Elastic deformation

Experiment　　　　Theory

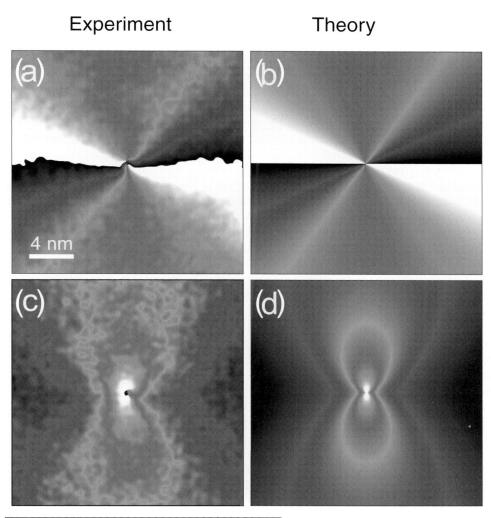

Comparison of displacement field components near an edge dislocation from phase images of experiments (left column) and from anisotropic elastic theory (right column). (a) and (b) displacement component u_x parallel to bottom edge of image. (c) and (d) displacement component u_y parallel to left edge of image. Photograph reproduced from (Hytch et al., 2003) with kind permission of Martin J. C. Hytch.

The conceptual success of the [infinitesimal theory of elasticity and the linear theory of viscosity] is perhaps the broadest we know in science: in terms of them we face, "explain", and in varying amount control, our daily environment: winds and tides, earthquakes and sounds, structures and mechanisms, sailing and flying, heat and light (Truesdell and Noll, 1965).

In this chapter we describe how the elastic properties of rock are measured in the laboratory and provide tables of numbers representing the range of values for different rock types. However, the need to understand and measure the resistance to deformation of rocks goes well beyond the simple accumulation of numbers in handbooks of rock properties. To paraphrase Truesdell and Noll (1965), the aim of structural geology is to construct mathematical models that enable us, from use of knowledge gathered in a few observations, to predict by logical processes the outcomes in many other circumstances. To analyze a geologic structure one must choose the appropriate boundary or initial value problem to serve as a mechanical model. To formulate such a problem one must postulate a particular mechanical behavior. That is, one must say exactly what the relationship is between the stress acting within a material and some measure of the deformation, usually strain or rate of deformation. These relationships are called *constitutive equations*. For example, researchers studying the displacement field around an edge dislocation in silicon as revealed by electron microscopy (Chapter 8, frontispiece) postulated an anisotropic linear elastic constitutive law and calculated model displacements that are remarkably similar to those observed.

We begin this chapter by describing the deformation of the Mancos Shale associated with the emplacement of a basaltic dike near Ship Rock, New Mexico, about 30 million years ago. In this example the shale was compressed as magma pressure forced the dike open, so the thickness of the dike gives us a measure of the resistance to deformation of the surrounding rock. Next we introduce the formal concept of linear elasticity as first envisioned by Robert Hooke in 1676, along with the constitutive equations that connect stress to strain for idealized elastic materials. These constitutive equations are central to the infinitesimal theory of an elastic continuum. As Truesdell and Noll (1965) suggest in the opening quotation for this chapter, elastic theory has played an enormous role in the development of science and engineering. Some examples are reviewed to illustrate the type of contributions

this theory has made to structural geology.

Next, the measurement techniques used to determine elastic properties in the laboratory and at engineering field sites are described. This leads to a discussion of how elastic properties vary with the size of the rock mass being tested. Considerations of scale effects are closely linked to those of heterogeneity with respect to elastic properties. To build intuition a solution to a boundary value problem is examined for a circular inclusion with different elastic stiffness and compressibility than the surrounding material. Finally, we consider how the elastic properties of rock may vary with orientation, in other words how anisotropic is rock with respect to elastic properties? After reviewing Hooke's Law for anisotropic materials in general, and providing some representative values of the elastic moduli from laboratory measurements, we describe a solution to a boundary value problem for an orthotropic elastic material. While it is well known that rock masses at the scale of Earth's crust can be heterogeneous and anisotropic to some degree, it is noteworthy how well isotropic and homogeneous elastic models correspond to measured deformation. This is illustrated using data on surface displacements during the 1999 Hector Mine earthquake.

8.1 | Estimating rock properties from geological field tests

To determine how rock masses resist deformation one must conceive an experiment and build or identify a testing apparatus that controls the applied loads and facilitates measurement of the resulting deformation. In the context of elastic solids the experiment is designed to determine a quantitative relationship between the stress and the strain. Here we focus on such experiments, conducted in the field rather than in a laboratory, because this enables one to estimate the elastic properties of rock at length scales of kilometers which are relevant to the geological structures under consideration.

8.1.1 A field test at Ship Rock, New Mexico

The "apparatus" for this field test is an igneous dike that crops out near the base of a volcanic edifice called Ship Rock in northwestern New Mexico (Fig. 8.1a). In this oblique aerial photograph Ship Rock is the most prominent feature, reaching about 600 m above the surrounding plain. This is the remnant of a volcanic conduit that fed surface eruptions and lava flows about 30 million years ago (Delaney and Pollard, 1981). It is one of the most spectacular geological features of the picturesque "four corners" region where the states of New Mexico, Arizona, Utah, and Colorado adjoin. The Navajo people who live in this region call this edifice Tse Bitai or "Winged Rock" and it plays a significant role in their creation story.

A geological map (Fig. 8.1b) reveals several dikes that form a crude radial pattern around the base of Ship Rock. These dikes, largely composed of a Tertiary volcanic rock called minette (Tmn), crop out in the nearly flat-lying upper part of the Cretaceous age Mancos Shale (Kmu) which is made up of thinly bedded shales, siltstones, and sandstones. An estimated 1 km of sedimentary rock has been eroded from this region since dike emplacement, so the top of the Ship Rock edifice (composed of Tertiary tuff breccia, Ttb) was probably within a few hundred meters of the old land surface at the time lava erupted from the central conduit of this volcano. Because the exposed dikes range up to 10 km in outcrop length it seems likely that some of them also erupted to feed lava flows. Today approximately 1 km of sedimentary rock lies below the ground surface and overlie a crystalline basement of Precambrian age. The limb dips on a gentle syncline that cuts across the northeastern dike are less than 5° and these dips are typical for the exposed sedimentary strata over much of the area.

The basic idea behind our use of dikes as natural testing machines is that magma pressure in dikes pushed against and elastically compressed the surrounding sedimentary rock mass. Our objective is to estimate the resistance of the sedimentary rock to this loading. For the sake of this example we idealize the dike walls as two rigid plates and the

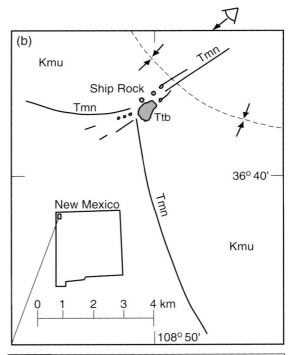

Fig 8.1 (a) Oblique aerial photograph of Ship Rock, NM (photograph by D. L. Baars). Height of edifice is about 600 m and length of the northeastern dike in the foreground is about 3 km. (b) Map of region near Ship Rock: Kmu, Cretaceous Mancos Shale; Tmn, Tertiary minette; Ttb, Tertiary tuff breccia (Delaney and Pollard, 1981).

Mancos Shale as four springs that resist the compression (Fig. 8.2a). The mechanical relationship between applied force, F, and the relative displacement, u, of the two ends of an elastic spring is:

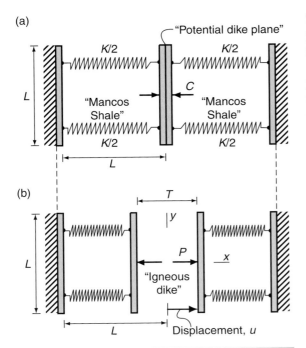

(a)

Fig 8.2 Spring and block model for dike. (a) Before dike emplacement compression, C, acts across the prospective dike plane; K/2 is the spring constant. (b) Pressure, P, compresses springs and model dike opens with displacement, u, in both directions.

$$F = Ku \qquad (8.1)$$

The *spring constant*, K, measures the stiffness, or resistance, to deformation. The springs are connected to two outer rigid plates, initially loaded by a compressive stress of magnitude, C, representing the tectonic loading at the time of dike emplacement. This compressive stress is transmitted through the springs (which have shortened accordingly), thereby holding the two inner plates tightly pressed together.

The plates have a length, L, the outcrop length of the dike, and a width (out of the plane of view) given by W, so their area is WL. Before dike emplacement, the distance, L, separates the inner and outer plates. At this point in our thought experiment the two outer plates are fixed in place and thereafter are not allowed to move, so we can measure the relative displacement of the spring ends as the plates are pushed apart. We refer to the distance between the inner plates as

T, equivalent to the thickness of the dike, and the plates move symmetrically apart, so the displacement is $u = T/2$.

We idealize the magma as a fluid under pressure, P, which is injected between the two inner plates (Fig. 8.2b). In order for this fluid to squeeze between the two plates and push them apart, the pressure must exceed the compressive tectonic stress holding the plates together. The displacement of the inner plates will be proportional to the amount by which P exceeds C, and this quantity, $P - C$, is called the *driving pressure*. Thus the force, F, associated with the plate separation is $F = (P - C)WL$. Note that the total force acting on the spring after injection of the fluid is PWL, but spring compression due to the tectonic force, CWL, took place before injection and is not related directly to the opening of the plates.

Substituting for the force and displacement in (8.1), we have:

$$(P - C)WL = K\left(\frac{T}{2}\right) \qquad (8.2)$$

The equivalent relationship between stress and strain is found by rearranging this equation:

$$(P - C) = \frac{K}{W}\left(\frac{T/2}{L}\right) = E\left(\frac{T/2}{L}\right) \qquad (8.3)$$

Here the left-hand side is the applied stress and the right-hand side is a constant, E, times the resultant strain associated with opening of the idealized dike. Recall that normal strain is a change in length divided by the original length of a line element. Here the change in the original spring length, L, is given by T/2, so the term in parentheses on the right-hand side is the normal strain. The constant, E, is called Young's modulus of elasticity. It measures the resistance of a material to change in length (strain) under an applied normal stress.

The northeastern dike at Ship Rock has an outcrop length $L = 2900$ m and an average thickness $T = 2.3$ m. Using (8.3) the ratio of driving pressure to Young's modulus is estimated as:

$$\frac{(P - C)}{E} \approx \frac{T}{2L} \approx 0.0004 \qquad (8.4)$$

By measuring dike length and thickness, and finding independent estimates for the magma pressure and compressive stress, we can use (8.4) to estimate Young's modulus for the rock mass deformed by the dike.

The geological evidence suggests that the current outcrop of the northeastern dike was about 1 km below the ground surface at the time of dike intrusion, and we assume that the dike erupted at that surface. We take $\rho_m = 2600 \ \mathrm{kg\,m^{-3}}$ and $\rho_r = 2400 \ \mathrm{kg\,m^{-3}}$ as the magma and host rock densities, $g^* = 9.8 \ \mathrm{m\,s^{-2}}$ as the acceleration of gravity, and $D = 10^3$ m as the height of the magma column and thickness of overburden. The magma pressure and compressive stress in the Mancos Shale at the depth of the current outcrop are calculated as $P \approx \rho_m gD \approx 25.5$ MPa and $C \approx \rho_r gD \approx 23.5$ MPa. Therefore, the driving pressure was $(P - C) \approx 2$ MPa and Young's modulus is estimated from (8.4) as $E \approx 5$ GPa. The southern dike has a length of about 9 km and an average thickness of about 10 m, and the small dike just to the south of the northeastern dike has a length of about 1 km and an average thickness of about 0.5 m. These data provide additional estimates of Young's modulus (see Table 8.1). We do not suggest that these values of Young's modulus necessarily are representative of other large rock masses, and they certainly are not known with the same precision expected for laboratory measurements. On the other hand, we believe that the method described here is important and should be applied to other igneous dikes.

The northeastern dike at Ship Rock is not continuous along the outcrop, but is divided into 35 echelon segments separated by Mancos Shale (Delaney and Pollard, 1981). Also, the thickness of the dike is partly attributable to erosion of the dike wall by the flowing magma. Apparently the hot magma caused thermal fracturing of the Mancos Shale at the contact and this fractured rock was locally removed by the magma. Clearly such a process is not included in the elastic model of fracture dilation, so thickness measurements should be corrected accordingly. Furthermore, one might want to make a small correction for shrinkage of the igneous rock as it cools from magmatic temperatures. Using a numerical solution to the elastic boundary value problem for

Table 8.1. Geologic field tests using Ship Rock dikes.

Dike name	Host rock	E (GPa)
Northeastern	Mancos Shale	5
Southern	Mancos Shale	4
Small	Mancos Shale	12

multiple dike segments yields a Young's modulus of about 2 GPa, not very different from the single fracture estimate (Table 8.1). If the dike did not propagate to the surface, the pressure would not necessarily be the hydrostatic value used above. Furthermore, the dike is unlikely to be two dimensional and the effect of the three-dimensional form on opening should be addressed using solutions to a three-dimensional boundary value problem of elasticity.

8.1.2 A generalized geological field method for estimating rock properties

Geological field methods for estimating rock properties are useful for two reasons. Most obvious is the fact that many geological structures are too large to submit to laboratory study; their size puts them beyond the capability of human engineering in terms of their length scale. Furthermore, if time is an important variable, then laboratory tests are incapable of duplicating geological time scales. Note that we are not referring here to scaled model experiments that seek to simulate geological processes (see Chapter 4), but rather to the measurement of the physical properties of rock. Second, the physical and chemical conditions under which many geological structures have formed is unknown, and even if these conditions could be deciphered, they may not be reproducible in the laboratory. Thus we are faced with a considerable challenge to determine the properties of rock masses at depth in the Earth at geological length and time scales.

One approach to this problem is to use tests under natural conditions and at natural length and time scales. That is, let nature do the experiment and look for an appropriate way to interpret what has been done. The method is summarized in six steps as follows:

1. Identify a natural experiment run under the conditions and at the scale of interest.
2. Use mapping techniques in the field to characterize the structures, identify the lithologies, and measure the relevant geometric parameters.
3. Infer the sequence of deformation and appropriate boundary conditions for loading and displacement (or other relevant physical quantities) from the field data.
4. Set up and solve, or borrow from the literature, the appropriate mechanical problem (usually a boundary or initial value problem from continuum mechanics).
5. Derive from the solution to this problem an equation for the physical property of interest in terms of the measured and/or inferred quantities.
6. Use the derived equation and available data to estimate the physical property.

This method is not limited to rocks with elastic properties, but is generally applicable to any material behavior described by a well-defined constitutive law. Nor is it limited to dikes, but is generally applicable to any geological structure that can be modeled using continuum mechanics.

8.2 | The idealized elastic material

The general concept of an elastic material is one in which the current configuration depends only on the initial (unstressed) configuration and the current state of stress, and not on the history of deformation from the initial to the current state (Truesdell and Noll, 1965). In most applications of elasticity theory one does not study the most general elastic material, but rather one in which the stress is linearly related to the infinitesimal strain. Because the infinitesimal strain is an approximation these elastic models must be considered an approximation. Never-the-less linear elastic theory has provided a wide variety of useful solutions for mechanical problems in structural geology.

8.2.1 The elastic solid

One common experience with the mechanical behavior of rock comes at the moment the geolo-gist's rock hammer hits an exposure. If the exposure is fresh granite, the hammer springs back quickly with a high-pitched ringing and vibrates vigorously for a second or two. The rock also gives off a sharp audible report. Perhaps a few small chips of rock or metal shoot out from the point of impact if the blow is particularly aggressive, but lighter blows permanently deform neither the hammer nor the rock. Both rock and hammer return nearly to their shapes just before the impact. If you held your hand on the exposure near the point of the hammer blow you would feel vibrations in the granite, a result of waves propagating out from the point of impact. Other types of rock respond in a similar fashion, but with some quantitative differences. For example, sandstone might respond with a duller sound and the hammer will not seem to jump back as quickly. When materials return essentially to their original shape after the applied loading is removed, we say they are *elastic*.

A linear relationship between force and extension is credited to the English natural philosopher Robert Hooke (1635–1703) who published a statement on the subject in 1676 in the following remarkable form (Gordon, 1976):

c e i i i n o s s s t t u u

Hooke apparently was intent on laying claim to this area of research, without providing the specifics, before the appearance of a lengthier treatise. The anagram has the following solution published in 1679 by Hooke:

ut tensio sic uis

J. E. Gordon provides the following translation (Gordon, 1976):

As the extension, so the force

In other words, the extension is proportional to the force.

Despite his obfuscation in presenting this discovery, Robert Hooke is honored by having this relationship, and a generalized version that extends the simple one-dimensional concept to three dimensions, referred to as *Hooke's Law* of linear elasticity. The book *The Abyss of Time* by Claude C. Albritton (1980) contains an informative account of Hooke's life and his scientific contributions to geology. The incomplete, one-dimensional form of the elasticity model introduced by Hooke was further developed in the 1700s by Bernoulli and Euler in order to describe the deformation of beams of materials used in construction. The development of a complete model was impossible at that time, because it depended on understanding the general concepts of stress and strain, which were not formulated until 1822 by Cauchy (Malvern, 1969).

We construct in our minds a perfectly elastic solid, one for which the extension is completely recoverable upon release of the stress. In order to focus on mechanical relationships, the temperature is postulated to be constant, so we consider *isothermal conditions*, and the bar is postulated to have *homogeneous material properties*. To quantify the behavior, consider a rectangular bar of this material with length B in the initial state (Fig. 8.3a). The length of the undeformed bar is parallel to the X-axis of the chosen coordinate system. The undeformed width and height of the bar are W and H, respectively, and the cross-sectional area is $A = WH$.

At some time, t, the bar is loaded by a force of magnitude, f, acting perpendicular to the ends and directed outward. The force arrows (Fig. 8.3b) are meant to be schematic; the actual force is uniformly distributed over the ends, so the stress within the bar is perfectly homogeneous. In response to the applied force the bar stretches to a deformed length b parallel to the x-axis of the coordinates for the current state. In earlier chapters you learned that the stress and the extension can be defined at every point within such a bar by taking limits on the local ratios of force to surface area and change in length to length. Here, because these quantities are postulated to be the same everywhere in the bar and act along the axis of the bar, we will refer to them as the *axial stress*, σ_a, and *axial extension*, e_a, at any point. The axial stress and axial extension are:

$$\sigma_a = \frac{f}{A}, \quad e_a = \frac{b - B}{B} \tag{8.5}$$

Values of axial stress, σ_a, are plotted versus axial extension, e_a, to represent the loading and unloading of the bar in graphical form (Fig. 8.4). Note that this graph includes both the tensile

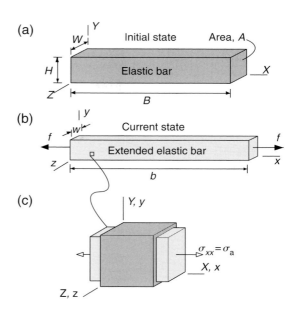

Fig 8.3 Idealized bar used to define elastic constants. (a) In the initial unloaded state the length of the bar is B. (b) In the current loaded state the bar has extended to a length b. (c) Element from the bar showing lateral contraction accompanying longitudinal extension.

stress (extensional strain) first quadrant and the compressive stress (contractional strain) third quadrant. The solid is *non-linear elastic* if the values follow a curved path, but return along the same curve to zero extension (the origin of the graph) upon complete unloading. If the values follow a straight-line segment and return to zero extension, the solid is *linear elastic*. If the loading and unloading paths are identical, the deformation is said to be *reversible*, and this is a necessary attribute of all elastic deformation whether it is linear or non-linear. In contrast, if the deformation is irreversible (does not follow the same curve upon unloading), it is *inelastic*. Notice that time has not appeared in our discussion of the elastic solid. The idealized elastic material will extend or shorten in proportion to the applied stress as this stress is increased and decreased on any time scale.

Now we place an additional restriction on the behavior of the elastic solid: namely we limit our discussion to elastic solids that are *isotropic* with respect to the material properties that relate stress and extension. For the elastic bar (Fig. 8.3)

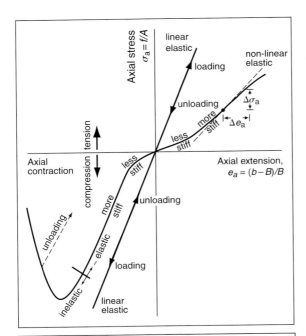

Fig 8.4 Plot of axial stress versus axial extension for linear elastic behavior (thick straight line), non-linear elastic behavior (curved line), and non-linear inelastic behavior.

$$E(\text{tangent}) = \frac{d\sigma_a}{de_a} = f(e_a) \qquad (8.7)$$

The local slope is the first derivative of the axial stress with respect to the axial extension and is a function of the extension.

Because extension is dimensionless, Young's modulus and the tangent modulus have the same dimensions as stress and carry the same units as stress:

Young's modulus, $E\{=\}$ ML^{-1}T^{-2}, and
$$E[=] \text{Nm}^{-2} = \text{Pa} \qquad (8.8)$$

Approximate values of Young's modulus for common materials are (Eshbach, 1961):

steel (spring),	$E \sim 200$ GPa
copper,	$E \sim 110$ GPa
aluminum,	$E \sim 70$ GPa
redwood (dry),	$E \sim 9$ GPa
plexiglas,	$E \sim 3$ GPa
rock,	$E \sim 1$ to 100 GPa

It is interesting to note that E for rocks covers most of the range of these familiar natural and synthetic solids. Rocks in the higher part of this range would ring when hit by a geologist's hammer, whereas those in the lower part would respond with a dull thud. Young's modulus is a property of a linear elastic solid which, in qualitative terms, characterizes how stiff it is in response to applied stress: *stiffer* elastic solids have steeper slopes on the stress versus extension graph (Fig. 8.4) and therefore greater Young's moduli. In contrast, *softer* elastic solids have less steep slopes.

Most of the direct evidence for the elasticity of rock comes from laboratory experiments conducted on small samples of rock. Figure 8.5 provides four examples of axial stress plotted versus axial contraction for uniaxial compression tests conducted in stiff testing machines (Jaeger and Cook, 1979, Fig. 4.2.3). Two of these rock types (Rand Quartzite and Solenhofen Limestone) display a nearly linear and apparently reversible behavior to axial compressions of about -200 MPa and axial contractions of -3 to -4×10^{-3}. We say apparently reversible because the data are not shown for unloading these samples, but the authors imply that the behavior was dominantly elastic. The Karroo Dolerite displays a nearly

this would mean that stretching along its length (in the *x*-coordinate direction) would produce exactly the same plot of stress versus extension as stretching the bar along its width (in the *z*-coordinate direction), or, for that matter, in any other direction. For a linear and isotropic elastic solid the proportionality constant in these one-dimensional stretching experiments is called *Young's modulus of elasticity* after the English scientist, Thomas Young. This modulus is customarily indicated with the symbol E and is defined as the ratio of the change in axial stress, $\Delta\sigma_a$, to the corresponding change in axial extension, Δe_a (Fig. 8.4). For the linear elastic solid the ratio of these changes is the same for any point along the loading path, so:

$$E = \frac{\Delta\sigma_a}{\Delta e_a} = \frac{\sigma_a}{e_a} = \text{constant} \qquad (8.6)$$

For non-linear elastic solids the slope changes continuously along the curve of stress versus extension. In this case a so-called *tangent elastic modulus* can be defined at every point as the slope of a tangent line (the dashed line segment on Fig. 8.4):

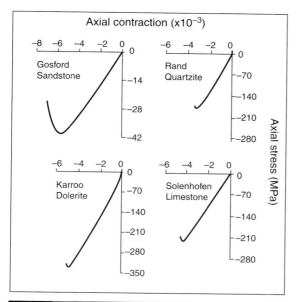

Fig 8.5 Uniaxial compression tests in a stiff testing machine for four different rock types. Reprinted from Jaeger and Cook (1979) with the kind permission of Mrs. Jennifer D. Cook.

linear and apparently reversible behavior to axial compression of about -300 MPa and axial contraction of about -4×10^{-3}. All of these samples have a distinct non-linear behavior near the peak axial stress and this was followed by brittle failure. Jaeger and Cook (1979, p. 79) conclude that these tests "show how unimportant the regions OA and BC [see Fig. 9.5] are in many practical cases and therefore that the assumption of linear elasticity up to failure really is a good one." The Gosford sandstone, in contrast, displays a non-linear behavior with increasing stiffness as the compression is increased. This rock is distinctly softer than the others and has a lower peak stress before loss of load-carrying capacity. Using linear elastic behavior to model this rock in the pre-failure stress–strain regime could be problematic.

When you stretch a rubber band it becomes thinner. The more you stretch the band, the thinner it becomes. The elastic bar (Fig. 8.3) is drawn to reflect this well-known property of elastic materials. The original width, W, is decreased to a final width, w, in a direction perpendicular to the applied force. Even though

there is no stress acting in this lateral direction, the bar is thinner. The perpendicular stress, σ_p, and the perpendicular extension, e_p, are respectively:

$$\sigma_p = 0, \quad e_p = \frac{w - W}{W} \qquad (8.9)$$

Usually when the axial stress is tensile, the perpendicular extension is a negative number because the width of the bar reduces, that is $W > w$. For an isotropic bar the extension in any direction, perpendicular to the specimen axis, would be the same. To characterize this behavior a second elastic property, called *Poisson's ratio* is defined:

$$\nu = -\frac{e_p}{e_a} \qquad (8.10)$$

Because the extension in the numerator and denominator of (8.10) usually are of opposite sign, a negative sign is used in the definition to make this quantity a positive number.

As a ratio of dimensionless quantities, Poisson's ratio is dimensionless itself, and carries no units.

$$\text{Poisson's ratio, } \nu \ \{=\} \ L^0 = 1 \qquad (8.11)$$

Different elastic materials have different values of Poisson's ratio and these fall in the range $0.0 \leq \nu \leq 0.5$, with those materials at the lower end of this range being *compressible* and those at the upper end being *incompressible*. For a given axial extension, a bar with a greater value of Poisson's ratio would thin more than a bar with a lesser value. Because Poisson's ratio does not depend on the sign of the extension, a greater value of ν also implies that a bar would thicken more for a given axial shortening. Values of Poisson's ratio for common materials include:

rubber,	$\nu \sim 0.5$
cork,	$\nu \sim 0.0$
rock,	$\nu \sim 0.1$ to 0.3

Rubber is a material that is nearly incompressible: it maintains a nearly constant volume by thickening just enough to compensate for a given shortening. In contrast, materials like cork or foam rubber, with a Poisson's ratio of nearly zero, are said to be compressible, because they can be shortened without getting thicker. This property of cork makes it possible to insert a cylindrical piece into the neck of a bottle by pressing on its end. In contrast, a rubber stopper must be tapered. Rocks are somewhat compressible.

8.2.2 Stress–strain relationships for the homogeneous, isotropic, linear elastic solid

For a homogeneous and isotropic linear elastic bar under isothermal conditions being stretched in the x-coordinate direction by an applied stress σ_{xx} (Fig. 8.3) the extension in x is proportional to the stress and the proportionality constant is the reciprocal of Young's modulus (8.6). The extensions in y or z are proportional to the stress and the proportionality constant is the Poisson's ratio divided by Young's modulus. That is $\varepsilon_{xx} = \sigma_{xx}/E$ and $v = -\varepsilon_{yy}/\varepsilon_{xx} = -\varepsilon_{zz}/\varepsilon_{xx}$ so $\varepsilon_{yy} = \varepsilon_{zz} = -(v/E)\sigma_{xx}$. Consider successively applying a normal stress in each coordinate direction and accounting for all of the possible normal strains. A consequence of the assumption of small strains and rotations is that the strain state is independent of the order in which the stresses are applied to the body. Therefore, these strain states can be superimposed and we have:

$$\varepsilon_{xx} = \frac{1}{E}\left[\sigma_{xx} - v(\sigma_{yy} + \sigma_{zz})\right]$$

$$\varepsilon_{yy} = \frac{1}{E}\left[\sigma_{yy} - v(\sigma_{zz} + \sigma_{xx})\right] \qquad (8.12)$$

$$\varepsilon_{zz} = \frac{1}{E}\left[\sigma_{zz} - v(\sigma_{xx} + \sigma_{yy})\right]$$

For the isotropic material these relationships do not depend upon the orientation of the coordinate system and hold, therefore, for any choice of orthogonal coordinate axes.

The relationships between the infinitesimal shear strains and the shear components of stress must be defined for a complete description of the strain–stress relationships (Timoshenko and Goodier, 1970, p. 9). Consider a cubic element with only normal stress components acting on the x- and y-faces of equal magnitude and opposite sign, such that $\sigma_{yy} = -\sigma_{xx}$ and $\sigma_{xy} = 0$ (Fig. 8.6a). From Cauchy's Formula the traction components acting

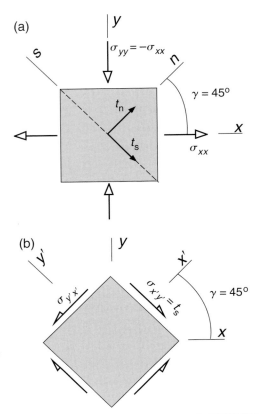

Fig 8.6 Element used to define relation between shear stress and shear strain for linear elastic material (Timoshenko and Goodier, 1970). (a) Tension and compression of equal magnitudes. (b) Shear stress on element oriented at 45° to that in (a).

on a diagonal boundary with outward unit normal, $\mathbf{n}$, oriented at $\gamma = 45°$ are:

$$t_n = \sigma_{xx}\cos^2 45° - \sigma_{xx}\sin^2 45° = 0$$

$$t_s = (\sigma_{yy} - \sigma_{xx})\sin 45° \cos 45° = -\sigma_{xx} \qquad (8.13)$$

These are the normal and shear traction components acting on the x'-face of an inclined cubic element, where the x'-axis makes an angle of 45° to the x-axis (Fig. 8.6b). The same result is found for the other faces of this inclined element, so the normal stress components both are zero, and the shear stress component is equal to the negative of σ_{xx}.

Using (8.12) the two normal strain components for the stress state shown in Fig. 8.6a are found to be equal in magnitude and opposite in sign, so

$\varepsilon_{yy} = -\varepsilon_{xx}$. In other words the extension in the x-direction is equal to the contraction in the y-direction. The element inclined at 45° experiences only a shear strain. This follows from the fact that the strains transform just as the stress components (Fung, 1969):

$$\varepsilon_{x'x'} = \varepsilon_{xx}\cos^2 45° - \varepsilon_{xx}\sin^2 45° = 0$$

$$\varepsilon_{x'y'} = (\varepsilon_{yy} - \varepsilon_{xx})\sin 45° \cos 45° = -\varepsilon_{xx} \quad (8.14)$$

The final step is to relate the shear stress and shear strain on the inclined element. From (8.12) where $\sigma_{yy} = -\sigma_{xx}$ and $\sigma_{zz} = 0$, we have:

$$\varepsilon_{xx} = \frac{1}{E}\left[\sigma_{xx} - \nu\sigma_{yy}\right] = \frac{1+\nu}{E}\sigma_{xx} \quad (8.15)$$

But we have just learned, from resolving stresses and strains on the inclined element, that $\sigma_{xx} = -\sigma_{x'y'}$ and $\varepsilon_{xx} = -\varepsilon_{x'y'}$, so:

$$\varepsilon_{x'y'} = \frac{1+\nu}{E}\sigma_{x'y'} \quad (8.16)$$

Thus, the shear strain is proportional to the shear stress acting on the inclined element and the constant of proportionality is $(1 + \nu)/E$.

The relationship between shear stress and infinitesimal shear strain (8.16) can be generalized for all of the components in three dimensions to give:

$$\varepsilon_{xy} = \frac{1+\nu}{E}\sigma_{xy}, \quad \varepsilon_{yz} = \frac{1+\nu}{E}\sigma_{yz}, \quad \varepsilon_{zx} = \frac{1+\nu}{E}\sigma_{zx} \quad (8.17)$$

Equations (8.12) and (8.17) are a statement of Hooke's Law for the isotropic elastic material. These six equations are written using indicial notation as:

$$\varepsilon_{ij} = \frac{1+\nu}{E}\sigma_{ij} - \frac{\nu}{E}\sigma_{kk}\delta_{ij} \quad (8.18)$$

Given the infinitesimal strain components, (8.18) can be rearranged as:

$$\sigma_{ij} = \left(\frac{E}{1+\nu}\right)\varepsilon_{ij} + \left[\frac{E\nu}{(1+\nu)(1-2\nu)}\right]\varepsilon_{kk}\delta_{ij} \quad (8.19)$$

It is clear from (8.18) that when all the stress components are identically zero, all the strain components are zero. This describes the initial, unloaded state of the elastic body.

The stress components appear as dependent variables in (8.19) to be calculated from the strain components (independent variables) and elastic moduli. In contrast, the strain components appear as dependent variables in (8.18) to be calculated from the stress components (independent variables) and elastic moduli. Some have suggested that the possibility of treating either stress or strain as the dependent variables implies that there is no cause and effect relationship between stress and strain (Marrett and Peacock, 1999). This notion is contrary to the concept of Newtonian mechanics in which force is described as the causative agent and acceleration is the resulting effect.

The natural extension of Newton's concept to the elastic continuum is to view stress or traction as the causative agent and strain or displacement as the resulting effect. Thus (8.18) and (8.19) simply show how stress components can be calculated from strain components, or vice versa, and nothing more profound is implied concerning the physical framework of Newtonian cause and effect.

The constitutive equations for the linear and isotropic elastic solid are used extensively in the analysis of geologic structures, often with little experimental justification. Ideally, the rocks would be sampled in the field area, brought back to the laboratory, and tested to reveal their mechanical properties. Usually, the facilities and funding for such testing is not available. Even if rock samples were tested rigorously, would the measured properties correspond to those millions of years ago when the geologic structures under investigation actually formed? Identifying those conditions is a challenging problem for structural geologists. More often than not, justification for using the elastic model comes a posteriori, after the solution to the boundary value problem provides a compelling correlation to field observations. Examples of such correlations are found throughout this book and in the cited literature.

8.2.3 Relations among elastic moduli for isotropic materials

To characterize further the isotropic and linear elastic material we derive the relation between volumetric strain and pressure. The infinitesimal volumetric strain is given by the change in volume of an element divided by the original volume, $\Delta V/V$. To understand how this quantity is related to the infinitesimal strain components consider a sphere of radius L in the initial state that deforms to an ellipsoid with half axial lengths L_1, L_2, and L_3 in the current state. Recall that the normal infinitesimal strain of a line element is equivalent to the extension of that line element. Thus, the normal strain of the line that becomes the major axis of the ellipsoid is $\varepsilon_1 = (L_1 - L)/L$, so $L_1 = (1 + \varepsilon_1)L$. The other axial lengths are similarly related to the principal strains. The volume of the sphere is $V_s = \frac{4}{3}\pi L^3$ and that of the ellipsoid is $V_e = \frac{4}{3}\pi(L_1 L_2 L_3)$ which may be approximated as:

$$V_e = \frac{4}{3}\pi(1 + \varepsilon_1)(1 + \varepsilon_2)(1 + \varepsilon_3)L^3$$
$$\approx \frac{4}{3}\pi(1 + \varepsilon_1 + \varepsilon_2 + \varepsilon_3)L^3 \qquad (8.20)$$

The approximation is obtained by neglecting products of the principal strains because they are very small compared to one or compared to the strains themselves.

It is one of the basic attributes of the infinitesimal strain tensor that the sum of the normal strains is invariant for any rotation of the orthogonal coordinate axes, so we can write the volume of the ellipsoid:

$$V_e \approx \frac{4}{3}\pi(1 + \varepsilon_{xx} + \varepsilon_{yy} + \varepsilon_{zz})L^3 \qquad (8.21)$$

Substituting for the volumes of the ellipsoid and sphere in the equation for the volumetric strain, we have:

$$\frac{\Delta V}{V} = \frac{V_e - V_s}{V_s} = \frac{\frac{4}{3}\pi(1 + \varepsilon_{xx} + \varepsilon_{yy} + \varepsilon_{zz}) - \frac{4}{3}\pi}{\frac{4}{3}\pi}$$
$$= \varepsilon_{xx} + \varepsilon_{yy} + \varepsilon_{zz} = \varepsilon_{kk} \qquad (8.22)$$

Note that the last term in (8.19) is proportional to the volumetric strain. Thus, each normal stress component is related to the corresponding normal strain component and the volumetric strain. Also, for the perfectly compressible material, $\nu = 0$, each normal stress is simply proportional to the corresponding normal strain, because the last term in (8.19) is zero.

Next we relate the volumetric strain to the *mean normal stress*, σ_m, defined as the average of the three normal stress components:

$$\sigma_m = \frac{1}{3}(\sigma_{xx} + \sigma_{yy} + \sigma_{zz}) = \frac{1}{3}\sigma_{kk} \qquad (8.23)$$

The sum of the normal stress components also is invariant for any rotation of the coordinate system. For an isotropic state of compressive stress the normal stress magnitude is the so-called pressure, $p = \sigma_{xx} = \sigma_{yy} = \sigma_{zz}$. Some use the phrase "hydrostatic pressure" or "hydrostatic compression" for this quantity, but this should be avoided, as the subject here is the deformation of elastic solids, not water. Because the volumetric strain (8.22) is the sum of the three normal strain components, we add these as defined in (8.12) and use (8.23) with $\sigma_m = -p$, to find:

$$\varepsilon_{kk} = -\frac{3(1 - 2\nu)}{E}p, \quad \text{or} \quad p = -K\varepsilon_{kk} \qquad (8.24)$$

Here K is called the *bulk modulus*, which relates the infinitesimal volumetric strain to the pressure for an isotropic state of stress.

Considering Young's modulus and Poisson's ratio as the two independent moduli of the isotropic elastic material, and using (8.24), the bulk modulus is written:

$$K = \frac{E}{3(1 - 2\nu)} \qquad (8.25)$$

Note that the bulk modulus, K, approaches an infinite value as Poisson's ratio approaches 0.5. This is consistent with the characterization of such materials as being incompressible. Most liquids are nearly incompressible, whereas gases are highly compressible. Very porous rocks are somewhat compressible, whereas rocks with low porosity tend to be less compressible. For the perfectly compressible material, $\nu = 0$, so the bulk modulus is $K = E/3$.

The elastic *shear modulus*, G, is used to relate shear stress to shear strain, as in (8.17), from which we have:

$$G = \frac{E}{2(1 + \nu)} \qquad (8.26)$$

The factor of one-half appears because we are using the tensor convention to define shear strain. This shear strain is one-half the magnitude of the so-called "engineering shear strain" and the shear modulus was originally defined using the engineering convention (Fung, 1969). For perfectly compressible material, $\nu = 0$, so $G = E/2$, and for incompressible material, $\nu = 1/2$, so $G = E/3$.

Gabriel Lamé (1795–1870) introduced another elastic constant, λ, in 1852 (Fung, 1969) and this is related to Young's modulus and Poisson's ratio as:

$$\lambda = \frac{Ev}{(1 + v)(1 - 2v)} \tag{8.27}$$

Poisson's ratio is related to Lamé's constant as:

$$v = \frac{\lambda}{2(G + \lambda)} \tag{8.28}$$

The constant λ characterizes the spectrum of behaviors from perfectly compressible materials, $v = 0$, for which $\lambda = 0$, to incompressible materials, $v = 1/2$, for which $\lambda = \infty$. Taken together, λ and G sometimes are called *Lamé's constants*. Equations (8.19) may be written in terms of Lamé's constants using (8.26) and (8.27) such that:

$$\sigma_{ij} = 2G\varepsilon_{ij} + \lambda\varepsilon_{kk}\delta_{ij} \tag{8.29}$$

The relatively simple behavior of the isotropic and linear elastic solid makes it ideally suited for analysis in continuum mechanical models. One can solve problems that involve quite complex geometries and boundary conditions by restricting the material behavior in this way, and the solutions provide important insights about the origins of some geologic structures.

8.3 | Quasi-static displacement boundary value problems

One may formulate a problem in elasticity theory in terms of the displacement components, or in terms of the stress components, as the dependent variables. In this section we take the equations of motion written in terms of the displacement components as the dependent variables. A specific example is provided using the two-dimensional solution for an edge dislocation which has surprisingly broad applications in structural geology, ranging from micrometer-scale defects in mineral grains to plate-bounding faults at continental margins (Weertman and Weertman, 1964; Weertman, 1996). Textbooks on elasticity theory provide many other useful solutions for displacement boundary value problems (Muskhelishvili, 1954;

Sokolnikoff, 1956; Timoshenko and Goodier, 1970; Barber, 1992).

The mathematical structure of the theory of elasticity makes it possible to solve boundary value problems of elasticity using displacement, traction, or mixed boundary conditions. This fact led to a debate about whether boundary displacements "cause" the elastic solid to deform (Marrett and Peacock, 1999; Tikoff and Wojtal, 1999; Peacock and Marrett, 2000; Pollard, 2000). In the authors' opinion the opportunity to employ displacement boundary conditions is no more than a consequence of the underlying mathematical relationships among traction and displacement components. In a Newtonian context one would seek an "explanation" for the specified displacements in terms of forces applied exterior to the model boundary, and these forces would be the ultimate causative agents for the resulting deformation in the interior. On the other hand, where tractions are the prescribed boundary conditions one may refer to the associated forces as the causative agents for the deformation.

8.3.1 Two-dimensional plane strain solutions for cylindrical structures

All structures in the Earth are three dimensional, but there are circumstances in which it is appropriate to ignore some of the components of stress, strain, and displacement. This has practical implications because the mathematical complexity of the boundary value problem is greatly reduced. One circumstance involves structures that are very long in one dimension relative to their size in the other two dimensions. If the geometry of such a structure does not change significantly along its length, it may be described as a *cylindrical structure*. A common geological example would be the surface of a sedimentary layer, folded into a shape that may be approximated by moving the fold axis through space without changing its orientation (Fig. 8.7a). Other common examples include the surfaces of blade-like dikes in volcanic rift zones and of vertical joints confined between two horizontal sedimentary layers (Fig. 8.7b).

The special case of deformation that applies to two-dimensional cylindrical structures is called *plane strain*. Here the (x, y)-plane is taken as the plane of interest (Fig. 8.7), and we postulate that

(a)

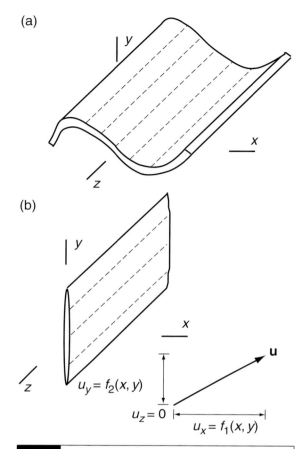

(b)

$u_y = f_2(x, y)$

$u_z = 0$

$u_x = f_1(x, y)$

Fig 8.7 Geological structures approximating plane strain conditions. (a) Cylindrical fold. (b) Blade-shaped dike or joint.

the out-of-plane displacement component, u_z, is identically zero, whereas the two in-plane components are functions of x and y only:

$$u_x = f_1(x,y), \quad u_y = f_2(x,y), \quad u_z = 0 \quad (8.30)$$

These conditions demand that neither the geometry nor the loading conditions change along the z-axis. Based upon these displacement conditions, and ignoring body forces, the quasi-static form of Navier's displacement equations of motion (7.137) reduce to:

$$(2G + \lambda)\frac{\partial^2 u_x}{\partial x^2} + G\frac{\partial^2 u_x}{\partial y^2} + (G + \lambda)\frac{\partial^2 u_y}{\partial x \partial y} = 0 \quad (8.31)$$

$$G\frac{\partial^2 u_y}{\partial x^2} + (2G + \lambda)\frac{\partial^2 u_y}{\partial y^2} + (G + \lambda)\frac{\partial^2 u_x}{\partial x \partial y} = 0 \quad (8.32)$$

These equations govern the spatial distribution of the two displacements in the (x, y)-plane. Note that here and in what follows we have replaced the

material coordinates (X, Y, Z) with the spatial coordinates (x, y, z) in keeping with the consequences of infinitesimal strains.

Using (8.30) as a constraint on the displacement vector, the kinematic relationships among spatial gradients in the displacement components and the infinitesimal strain components (7.129) simplify to the following:

$$\varepsilon_{xx} = \frac{\partial u_x}{\partial x}, \quad \varepsilon_{yy} = \frac{\partial u_y}{\partial y}, \quad \varepsilon_{xy} = \frac{1}{2}\left(\frac{\partial u_x}{\partial y} + \frac{\partial u_y}{\partial x}\right) \quad (8.33)$$

The normal strains in the x- and y-directions and the shear strain in the (x, y)-plane are only functions of the x- and y-coordinates. The out-of-plane strain components are identically zero: $\varepsilon_{zz} = 0$, $\varepsilon_{yz} = 0$, $\varepsilon_{zx} = 0$. The name "plane strain" follows directly from these two facts about the strain components.

The in-plane stress components are proportional to the strain components through Hooke's Law (8.29), which reduces to:

$$\sigma_{xx} = (2G + \lambda)\varepsilon_{xx} + \lambda\varepsilon_{yy},$$

$$\sigma_{yy} = \lambda\varepsilon_{xx} + (2G + \lambda)\varepsilon_{yy}, \quad \sigma_{xy} = 2G\varepsilon_{xy} \quad (8.34)$$

The three stress components in the (x, y)-plane are functions only of the x- and y-coordinates. The normal stress in the z-direction, σ_{zz}, is not generally zero despite the fact that the displacement and normal strain components in that direction are zero:

$$\sigma_{zz} = \lambda(\varepsilon_{xx} + \varepsilon_{yy}) = \frac{\lambda}{2(G + \lambda)}(\sigma_{xx} + \sigma_{yy})$$

$$= \nu(\sigma_{xx} + \sigma_{yy}) \quad (8.35)$$

The out-of-plane shear stress components are zero: $\sigma_{yz} = 0$ and $\sigma_{zx} = 0$.

8.3.2 A complete solution in two dimensions: the edge dislocation

The dislocation is an object worthy of study. Its existence permits metals to be plastically deformed with ease, a circumstance upon which our modern technology is so dependent. ... The dislocation also permits nonmetallic crystalline materials to be plastically deformed. ... Thus the dislocation plays a commanding role in those grandest of all deformations on earth: the upheavals that have produced the mountain ranges and the continents themselves (Weertman and Weertman, 1964, p. 1).

The *edge dislocation* provides an insightful example of a structure that can be modeled using the two-dimensional plane strain form of the equilibrium equations, (8.31)–(8.32), (Hirth and Lothe, 1982). Figure 8.8a shows dislocation loops (fine white lines) in a crystal of silicon observed at the 100-μm scale by chemical etching (Friedel, 1964, Fig. 1.19). Dislocations move through mineral grains during plastic deformation of rock as a result of the forces imposed during tectonic events (Poirier, 1985). Surprisingly, the quasi-static elastic solution for the displacement, strain, and stress in the vicinity of an edge dislocation at the micrometer-scale also can be used to model kilometer-scale geological structures, including those as diverse as igneous dikes and plate-bounding strike slip faults. In this broader context models utilizing dislocation solutions have provided a deeper understanding of the physical processes that shape mountain ranges and continents. In this section we describe the physical nature of the edge dislocation at the crystal-lattice scale and then examine the elastic solution and show how pairs of edge dislocations approximate the deformation near fractures and faults (Weertman and Weertman, 1964).

Figure 8.8b is a schematic two-dimensional illustration of a crystalline lattice that contains an edge dislocation. Note the extra column of atoms that appears to distort locally the otherwise regular lattice near the bottom atom in the column. The origin of the coordinate system (x, y, z) is chosen to be coincident with this atom. Although only a few atoms are illustrated, we imagine the lattice extending a very great distance in all coordinate directions. Furthermore we imagine that every lattice plane that is parallel to the (x, y)-plane is identical. Thus, the column of atoms is actually an extra half-plane of atoms in the (y, z)-plane, and the straight line parallel to the z-axis that marks the base of the half-plane is the *dislocation line*. In this sense the edge dislocation is a linear defect in the crystalline solid, but dislocation lines also may form loops as illustrated in Fig. 8.8a. A tangent vector, $\mathbf{t}$, parallel to the dislocation line, orients the dislocation in the crystal lattice. The direction of $\mathbf{t}$ is arbitrary, but here it is taken in the positive z-coordinate direction.

The magnitude and direction of the edge

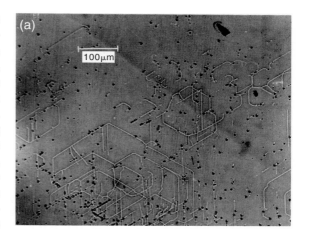

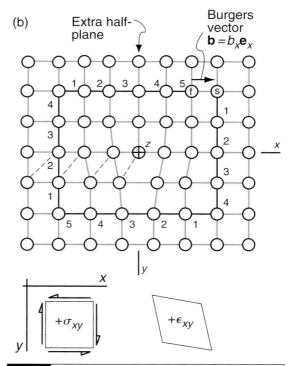

Fig 8.8 (a) Dislocation loops (fine white lines) in silicon (Friedel, 1964). (b) Two-dimensional illustration of crystalline lattice distorted by an edge dislocation with Burgers vector, **b** (Weertman and Weertman, 1964). Signs of shear stress and strain shown in inset.

dislocation are measured by completing a circuit along the rows and columns of atoms in a plane that is perpendicular to the dislocation line, in this case the (x, y)-plane (Fig. 8.8b). By convention the circuit is taken clockwise when the view is in the direction of the tangent vector, and the circuit is made with an equal number of steps (from atom to atom) along parallel paths. For example, starting at the arbitrarily chosen atom "s," one could take four steps down, five steps to the left, four steps up, and five steps to the right, finishing at atom "f." If the lattice were undistorted, "s" and "f" would be the same atom. The fact that the circuit does not close reveals the presence of the edge dislocation. The magnitude of the vector, $\mathbf{b} = b_x\mathbf{e}_x$, extending from atom "f" to atom "s" measures the distortion of the lattice and this vector is directed in the positive x-coordinate direction, i.e. $b_x > 0$. This is called the *Burgers vector* of the dislocation. For an edge dislocation the Burgers vector is always perpendicular to the dislocation line. For the so-called *screw dislocation* the Burgers vector is parallel to the dislocation line. Dislocation loops (Fig. 8.8a) are composed of segments of edge, screw, and mixed dislocations.

An edge dislocation line can move through a crystalline solid parallel to the plane containing the tangent vector and the Burgers vector. This plane is called the *glide plane*. A fundamental feature of the deformation associated with the edge dislocation is that the displacement field is discontinuous across that portion of the glide plane shown as shaded in Fig. 8.9. The edge dislocation is symbolized in this figure with an inverted "T" such that the cross-bar lies in the glide plane parallel to the Burgers vector, and the upright bar points in the direction of the extra half-plane of atoms. Note that the vector component b_x is positive when the extra half-plane extends in the negative y-coordinate direction. The extra half-plane of atoms is located 90° counterclockwise from the direction of the Burgers vector when looking in the direction of the tangent vector.

Dislocations exist at the atomic scale (Fig. 8.8) where the concept of a continuum is violated, yet the continuum concept is inherent to elastic theory. Furthermore, the distortions of the crystal lattice very near the dislocation are likely to be greater than the limiting strains imposed on the linear theory of elasticity. None-the-less, elastic solutions have proved invaluable for the investigation of these defects with the proviso that the mechanical fields so calculated are not applicable inside a small cylindrical volume that surrounds

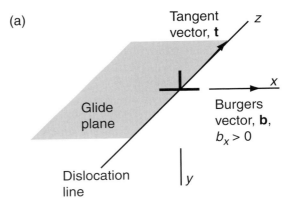

(a)

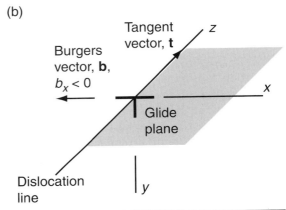

(b)

Fig 8.9 Geometric relationships among the glide plane, tangent vector, Burgers vector, and dislocation line (Weertman and Weertman, 1964). (a) Positive edge dislocation. (b) Negative edge dislocation.

the dislocation line (Fig. 8.10a). This small volume is called the *dislocation core*, and the radius of the core is estimated using the theoretical strength, S, of solids. For example, as we demonstrate below, the magnitude of the shear stress, σ_s, at a radial distance, r, from the edge dislocation is proportional to the elastic shear modulus, G, and to the magnitude of the Burgers vector, b, and inversely proportional to r, such that $|\sigma_s| \sim Gb/2\pi r$. The range of theoretical strengths, S, as a function of the elastic shear modulus is $G/30 \leqslant S \leqslant G/3$ (Weertman and Weertman, 1964, p. 35). Conservatively, taking the lower end of the range for strength and setting the radius of the core, r_c, to be that at which the stress equals the strength, we estimate $r_c \sim 5b$. Note that the shear stress, σ_s, from the elastic solution is singular at the dislocation where $r = 0$, suggesting that inelastic

(a)

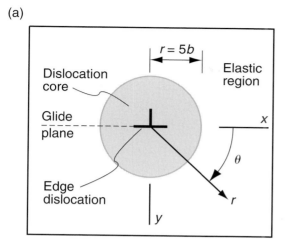

$$u_x = -\frac{b}{2\pi}\left[\tan^{-1}\left(\frac{y}{x}\right) + \left(\frac{G+\lambda}{2G+\lambda}\right)\left(\frac{xy}{x^2+y^2}\right)\right] \quad (8.36)$$

$$u_y = -\frac{b}{2\pi}\left[\left(\frac{G}{2(2G+\lambda)}\right)\ln\left(\frac{x^2+y^2}{C}\right)\right.$$
$$\left. + \left(\frac{G+\lambda}{2G+\lambda}\right)\left(\frac{y^2}{x^2+y^2}\right)\right] \quad (8.37)$$

Here the arbitrary constant C in the expression for u_y has dimensions of length squared, so the argument of the log term is dimensionless, and we assign C a value of one. This constant provides a uniform translation parallel to the y-axis that can be ignored in the displacement field and has no effect on the strain or stress fields which depend on spatial derivatives of the displacements.

Of the four terms in the displacement equations, (8.36)–(8.37), only the inverse tangent term is discontinuous for a circuit around the dislocation line (Fig. 8.10b, u_x term 1). Here the radius is taken as $r = 10b$, outside the dislocation core. Note how the contribution from this term to the normalized displacement, u_x/b, is zero at $\theta = 0$ and decreases linearly with θ to a minimum of -0.5 at $\theta = \pi$, the position of the glide plane. Then, the normalized displacement jumps discontinuously to $+0.5$ across the glide plane and thereafter decreases linearly to zero at $\theta = 2\pi$. The relative displacement, or displacement discontinuity, across the glide plane ($x \le 0$, $y = 0$) is equal to the magnitude of the Burgers vector, in this case a unit value. The other three terms in the displacement equations are necessary to satisfy the governing equilibrium equations, but do not contribute to the displacement discontinuity.

The kinematic equations (8.33) are used to determine the strain components:

(b)

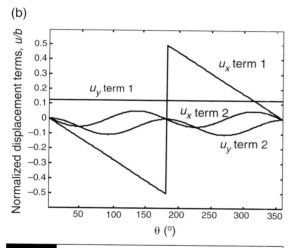

Fig 8.10 (a) Schematic illustration of edge dislocation and dislocation core inside of which the deformation is inelastic. (b) Plot of terms in the displacement equations, (8.36) and (8.37), versus angle θ defined in (a).

$$\varepsilon_{xx} = \left(\frac{by}{2\pi}\right)\left[\frac{(3G+2\lambda)x^2 + Gy^2}{(2G+\lambda)(x^2+y^2)^2}\right] \quad (8.38)$$

$$\varepsilon_{yy} = -\left(\frac{by}{2\pi}\right)\left[\frac{(G+2\lambda)x^2 - Gy^2}{(2G+\lambda)(x^2+y^2)^2}\right] \quad (8.39)$$

$$\varepsilon_{xy} = -\left(\frac{bx}{2\pi}\right)\left[\frac{2(G+\lambda)(x^2-y^2)}{(2G+\lambda)(x^2+y^2)^2}\right] \quad (8.40)$$

The denominators for each of the strain components is proportional to r^4 where $r = (x^2 + y^2)^{1/2}$ is the radial distance from the dislocation in the

deformation would occur there. Outside the core, and over length scales greater than the radius of the core, the continuum concept is valid and the assumptions of the linear theory are not violated. This has been verified by direct observation of the displacement field (see Chapter 8 frontispiece).

The elastic solution for the edge dislocation is premised on the conditions that the deformation may be taken as quasi-static and plain strain. The solution to the Navier's displacement equations of motion, (8.31) and (8.32), is (Weertman and Weertman, 1964, p. 36):

(x, y)-plane. Noting that $x = r\cos\theta$ and $y = r\sin\theta$, the numerators are proportional to br^3, so the strain components are proportional to b/r. Thus, as the distance to the dislocation line becomes very small, the strain becomes very large. In fact, there is a mathematical singularity in all of the strain components at the dislocation line (as $r \rightarrow 0$, $\varepsilon_{ij} \rightarrow \infty$). This is mathematically correct, but is non-physical, so we restrict attention to the region outside the dislocation core ($r > 5b$), where the strain components are finite.

Hooke's Law for plane strain conditions (8.34) is used to determine the stress components:

$$\sigma_{xx} = \left(\frac{by}{2\pi}\right)\left[\frac{2G(G+\lambda)(3x^2+y^2)}{(2G+\lambda)(x^2+y^2)^2}\right] \quad (8.41)$$

$$\sigma_{yy} = -\left(\frac{by}{2\pi}\right)\left[\frac{2G(G+\lambda)(x^2-y^2)}{(2G+\lambda)(x^2+y^2)^2}\right] \quad (8.42)$$

$$\sigma_{xy} = -\left(\frac{bx}{2\pi}\right)\left[\frac{2G(G+\lambda)(x^2-y^2)}{(2G+\lambda)(x^2+y^2)^2}\right] \quad (8.43)$$

Like the strain components, the stress components are proportional to b/r, so they also are singular at the dislocation line. As mentioned above we restrict attention to the region outside the dislocation core where the stress components are less than the strength of the material. Note that the presence of the edge dislocation alters the normal stress, σ_{zz}, parallel to the dislocation line according to (8.35).

The distributions of the stress components near a positive edge dislocation are illustrated in Fig. 8.11 as contour maps for a region that is $200b$ on a side, omitting the dislocation core where $r < 5b$, and using $G = \lambda = 3 \times 10^4$ MPa. The y-axis is positive downward, so the view is in the direction of the tangent vector and the extra half-plane extends upward from the origin along $y < 0$. All of the stress components decrease in magnitude away from the dislocation line (as $r \rightarrow \infty$, $\sigma_{ij} \rightarrow 0$). The normal stress, σ_{xx}, is tensile in the region $y > 0$, and compressive in the region $y < 0$ (Fig. 8.11a). That is, a compressive stress is induced on both sides of the extra half-plane of atoms, and a tensile stress is induced off the end of the half-plane. The main lobes of contours of the normal stress, σ_{yy}, are similarly distributed, with compression to both sides and tension off the end of the extra

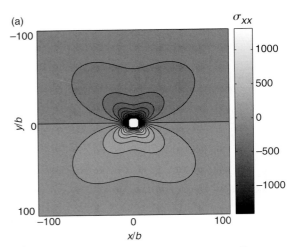

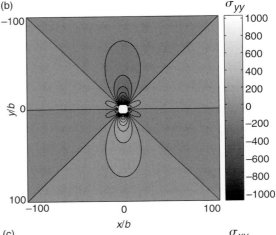

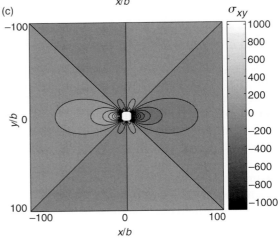

Fig 8.11 Contour maps of stress components near a positive edge dislocation omitting the dislocation core. (a) Normal stress, σ_{xx}. (b) Normal stress, σ_{yy}. (c) Shear stress, σ_{xy}.

half-plane of atoms (Fig. 8.11b). In a thought experiment one can cleave the crystal and insert the extra half-plane, thereby pushing the atoms aside and inducing this compressive stress. The wedging action of the inserted half-plane of atoms induces a tensile stress beyond the dislocation line. Of course this is not the way an edge dislocation is created, but the effect on the stress field is similar. Because of this similarity one can use the edge dislocation to model the wedging action of the fluid pressure in a dike or vein.

The main lobes of contours of the shear stress, σ_{xy} (Fig. 8.11c), are aligned with and symmetric about the glide plane (y-axis). The shear stress lobes are positive along the slipped portion ($x < 0$), and are negative along the un-slipped portion of the glide plane ($x > 0$). These signs are consistent with the shear strain along the glide plane. For example, note that distortion of the originally square lattice to the left of the dislocation line in Fig. 8.8b is bottom to the right. With the positive y-axis directed downward this distortion is a positive shear strain and is associated with a positive shear stress. To the right of the dislocation line the distortion is bottom to the left, so the shear strain and stress are negative. In a thought experiment to move the edge dislocation from its former location to its current location one can shear the columns of atoms in a negative sense (top to right) by application of a negative shear stress until the original bonds (dashed lines in Fig. 8.8b) break and new bonds (solid lines) are established on adjacent columns, thereby leaving the half-plane above the dislocation unconnected and appearing to be "extra." The displacement discontinuity across the glide plane of the edge dislocation is top to the right, similar to right-lateral slip across a fault or shear fracture. By analogy, slip on such a structure would be induced by a remotely applied negative shear stress and would induce a negative shear stress concentration off the end of the structure and a positive shear stress (drop) to the sides.

In two-dimensional analyses, dislocations are viewed as infinitely long straight lines oriented perpendicular to the field of view. Pairs of dislocations can be used to create defects in the crystal lattice where the extra plane segment of atoms is bounded in extent (Fig. 8.12). In this figure the

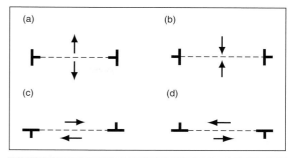

Fig 8.12 Pairs of edge dislocations used to model geological structures. (a) Opening fractures including joints, veins, dikes, and sills. (b) Closing fractures including solution surfaces and compaction bands. (c) Map view of right-lateral strike fault. (d) Map view of left-lateral strike slip fault.

tangent vectors for both dislocations in the pair are directed into the page. Two edge dislocations with parallel but offset glide planes and opposite signs constitute an "opening" or a "closing" defect in the lattice, depending upon their configuration. If the extra planar segment of atoms extends between the two dislocations (Fig. 8.12a), the surrounding lattice must spread apart to accommodate this defect, so this is described as an "opening" distortion. If the extra half-planes extend away from the two dislocations (Fig. 8.12b), the surrounding lattice distorts into the gap left between the dislocations, so this is described as "closing." The pair of edge dislocations that correspond to an opening displacement discontinuity serves as a model for joints, veins, dikes, and sills. The pair that corresponds to a closing displacement discontinuity serves as a model for solution surfaces and compaction bands.

If the two edge dislocations share the same glide plane and have opposite signs the planar segment between them is a "sliding" defect in the lattice. Columns of atoms that were originally continuous across this plane are offset by relative motion parallel to the glide plane and perpendicular to the dislocation lines. The sense of sliding depends upon the configuration of the dislocations such that the relative motion is always toward the adjacent extra half-plane of atoms. In map view, right-lateral (Fig. 8.12c) and left-lateral strike slip faults (Fig. 8.12d) may be modeled with appropriate pairs of edge dislocations. These figures may be viewed as arbitrary cross sections within the crust so these pairings of edge dislocations become models for thrust and normal faults as well.

8.3.3 A compelling example of elastic deformation: the Hector Mine earthquake

To provide a specific example at the kilometer-scale and to motivate the further application of linear elastic models to structural problems we describe the surface displacement field for the magnitude 7.1 Hector Mine earthquake that occurred on October 16, 1999, in southern California (Fig. 8.13). This earthquake is associated with the earlier Landers earthquake (Sieh *et al.*, 1993), a magnitude 7.5 event that occurred on June 28, 1992. Both earthquakes occurred in a desert region to the northeast of the San Andreas Fault. The desert terrain provided an excellent opportunity to observe and measure the rupture traces at the surface and to map the details of the shear zones and the crustal-scale deformation (Massonnet *et al.*, 1993). The Hector Mine earthquake was associated with surface rupture on several faults, including Lavic Lake, Bullion, and Mesquite Lake, which are arranged in a complex pattern trending from northerly to northwesterly over a distance of almost 50 km (Treiman *et al.*, 2002). The individual fault segments are arranged in parallel, intersecting, echelon, and curving patterns. The offset of natural and cultural features was dominantly right-lateral strike slip with a maximum of about 5 m. Here we focus on the broad pattern of displacements at the Earth's surface as revealed by *synthetic aperture radar* (SAR) interferometry (Zebker *et al.*, 1994; Price and Sandwell, 1998).

The use of SAR for the detection of ground displacements associated with tectonic events such as earthquakes was highlighted in an article appearing in *Nature* in July of 1993 (Prescott, 1993). The radar signal is transmitted from a satellite (in this case ERS-1 from an altitude of 785 km) to the ground surface where it is reflected back to the satellite and recorded as a set of pixels making up an image of the surface, each pixel representing an area of about 100 m² on the ground. Knowledge of the travel time and speed of the signal provides the information necessary

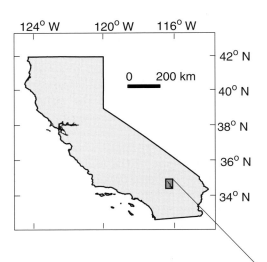

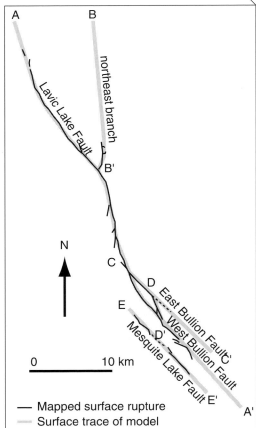

Fig 8.13 Location map for the Hector Mine earthquake, showing California with box indicating region of earthquake rupture, expanded in lower part of figure. Reprinted from Maerten *et al.* (2005) with permission of the Seismological Society of America.

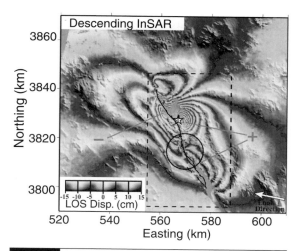

Fig 8.14 Synthetic aperture radar interferogram for time spanning Hector Mine earthquake. Reprinted from Jonsson *et al.* (2002) with permission of the Seismological Society of America.

to calculate the range, or distance, from the satellite to each reflective site on the surface. If the same region is imaged at two different times, and if the reflectivity of the surface has not changed significantly, the difference between the two images can be used to calculate the component of the surface displacement directed along the line between the satellite and the ground surface for each pixel. Because the satellite will not be in precisely the same position for the two images the effects of the topography must be removed. The resulting image is called an *interferogram*. Note that the data contained on the interferogram are not the displacement vector at each pixel, but one component of that vector.

To investigate deformation associated with the Hector Mine earthquake, SAR images for September 15, 1999, and October 20, 1999, were selected and compared (Jonsson *et al.*, 2002). The interferogram (Fig. 8.14) shows a pattern of white and black bands (called fringes) representing contours of the displacement component with each cycle representing an interval of 10 cm. The more prominent fault segments are shown as fine lines superimposed on this image. In this broad region, about 90×80 km in size, there is a distinct pattern of fringes with discreet lobes that extend outward to the northwest and southeast. This technology can resolve the displacement field

throughout this region, both tens of kilometers from the fault traces, and, in the very near field, within a few kilometers of the traces. The displacement field has been modeled using both vertical (Price and Burgmann, 2002) and steeply dipping (Jonsson *et al.*, 2002) rectangular fault segments. The latter investigation suggests that the segments dip about 83° to the east, but usage of dipping rectangular segments leads to gaps and overlaps in the fault geometry that may be unrealistic.

The model presented here (Maerten *et al.*, 2005) consists of a linear elastic half-space with a set of six fault surfaces that honor the details of the observed surface ruptures at a kilometer scale (Fig. 8.15). The half-space is bounded by a planar surface that extends out to infinite distances horizontally and is free of tractions. The model also extends to an infinite depth, but neither of these features is problematic because the faults are very small compared to the radius of curvature of the Earth. Each fault is composed of triangular elements, with an average side length of about 2.6 km that fit together in a continuous surface. Using the data from the interferogram (Fig. 8.14) and the given geometry of the faults, the slip distributions on the faults was determined using a linear inversion. The slip is partitioned among the six faults in a manner similar to that observed along the rupture traces. Most impressive, however, is the correspondence between the synthetic and the actual interferograms.

As you might imagine the success of this method of observation for monitoring and modeling displacement changes on the order of a few centimeters over regions on a crustal scale has stimulated a great deal of interest (Fialko *et al.*, 2003). It is clear that this technology has the potential for a wide variety of applications in structural geology. For our present purpose, however, the most compelling conclusion from this study is the applicability of models using linear elastic properties and infinitesimal strains to deformation in the Earth. Although the authors of the quote at the beginning of this chapter wrote about the efficacy of the linear theory of elasticity long before the Hector Mine earthquake they likely would find the correspondence between Figs. 8.14 and 8.15 very satisfying.

(a)

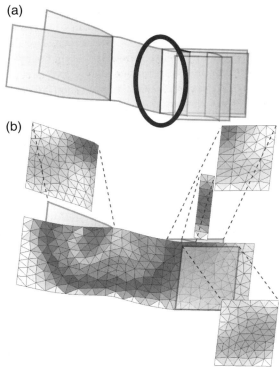

(b)

(c)

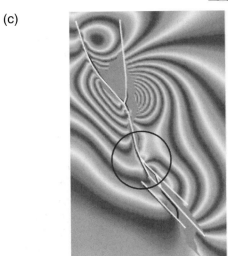

Fig 8.15 Elastic models used to investigate the Hector Mine earthquake. (a) Six fault surfaces. (b) Fault surfaces composed of triangular dislocation elements. (c) Model interferogram. Reprinted from Maerten *et al.* (2005) with permission of the Seismological Society of America.

8.4 | Quasi-static traction boundary value problems

In this section we take the equations of equilibrium, written in terms of the stresses, as the dependent variables. Constraints on the infinitesimal strain field that arise from the kinematic relations require that we incorporate conditions of compatibility, written in terms of the stress components, into the set of governing equations. Solving these equations for the stress components, the strains are calculated using Hooke's Law and the displacements are calculated by integration of the kinematic relations. The Airy stress function is introduced in Cartesian coordinates and used to solve a complete two-dimensional problem for a rectangular region of Earth's crust subject to simple tectonic and gravitational loading conditions. The generalized solution for two-dimensional problems in polar coordinates is introduced and used to model a cylindrical valley in an elastic half-space.

8.4.1 The Airy stress function in two-dimensional Cartesian coordinates

The six independent stress components (8.19) are reduced to three for two-dimensional problems (Timoshenko and Goodier, 1970, p. 15). One class of such problems, referred to as *plane stress*, applies to very thin plates with no tractions applied to either surface. Plane stress is widely used in engineering applications, but it has fewer applications in structural geology. Although the crust of the Earth can be approximated geometrically as a thin plate or spherical shell in the context of plate tectonics, only the upper surface is traction free (neglecting wind shear and atmospheric pressure). Sedimentary strata also can be approximated geometrically as thin plates, but they are bounded on both sides by layers that impose non-zero tractions. Therefore, the stress conditions in the interior of these thin plates are unlikely to be approximated by plane stress conditions.

A second class of two-dimensional problems, called plane strain, was defined in (8.30) and led to a pair of governing equations, (8.31) and (8.32), with the two in-plane displacement components as the dependent variables. Here, in contrast, the

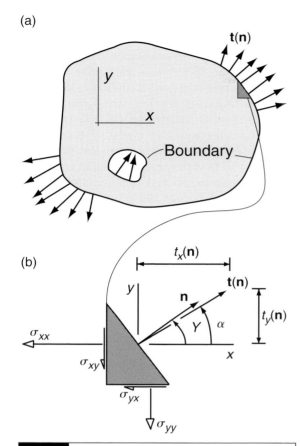

(a)

t(n)

y

x

Boundary

(b)

$t_x(\mathbf{n})$

y

$\mathbf{n}$

t(n)

Υ α

$t_y(\mathbf{n})$

x

σ_{xx}

σ_{xy}

σ_{yx}

σ_{yy}

Fig 8.16 Schematic illustration of traction boundary value problem. (a) Two-dimensional plane strain conditions with tractions, **t(n)**, distributed on internal and external boundaries. (b) Element used to define relations among the traction components and stress components.

dependent variables are the three in-plane stress components which only are functions of x and y:

$$\sigma_{xx} = f_1(x, y), \quad \sigma_{xy} = f_2(x, y), \quad \sigma_{yy} = f_3(x, y) \quad (8.44)$$

The out-of-plane-normal stress is given by (8.35), and the out-of-plane shear stresses are zero. Boundary conditions are specified in terms of the distribution of tractions, **t(n)**, acting on exterior and interior surfaces of the body (Fig. 8.16a). The outward unit normal, **n**, lies in the (x, y)-plane everywhere on these surfaces. These tractions induce a distribution of stresses throughout the body, and sufficiently close to a boundary the stresses must be in equilibrium with the tractions according to Cauchy's Formula (Fig. 8.16b):

$$t_x(\mathbf{n}) = \sigma_{xx} n_x + \sigma_{yx} n_y$$
$$t_y(\mathbf{n}) = \sigma_{xy} n_x + \sigma_{yy} n_y \quad (8.45)$$

The governing equations for the two-dimensional traction boundary value problem include the equations of static equilibrium written in terms of the stress components (7.139–7.141). Taking the (x, y)-plane as the plane of interest and using (8.44) these equations reduce to:

$$\frac{\partial \sigma_{xx}}{\partial x} + \frac{\partial \sigma_{yx}}{\partial y} = 0 \quad (8.46)$$

$$\frac{\partial \sigma_{xy}}{\partial x} + \frac{\partial \sigma_{yy}}{\partial y} - \rho g^* = 0 \quad (8.47)$$

Mass density, ρ, and gravitational acceleration, g^*, are presumed to be known constants. Also, the y-coordinate is taken as vertical and positive upward so the body force per unit volume acts in the negative y-direction with a magnitude ρg^*. These equilibrium equations assure that the spatial variation of the stress components in the (x, y)-plane are such that the net force is zero in both coordinate directions on every element in the body. The implicit condition, $\sigma_{xy} = \sigma_{yx}$, assures that the net torque about the z-axis is zero. These conditions apply to every infinitesimal element, as well as every macroscopic portion of the body, and to the entire body.

The infinitesimal strain components are calculated from the stress components using (8.18):

$$\varepsilon_{xx} = \frac{1}{E}[\sigma_{xx}(1 - \nu^2) - \sigma_{yy}\nu(1 + \nu)] \quad (8.48)$$

$$\varepsilon_{yy} = \frac{1}{E}[\sigma_{yy}(1 - \nu^2) - \sigma_{xx}\nu(1 + \nu)] \quad (8.49)$$

$$\varepsilon_{xy} = \frac{1 + \nu}{E}\sigma_{xy} \quad (8.50)$$

The out-of-plane strain components are zero. The final step in a complete solution is the determination of the in-plane displacement components. Using the kinematic equations for plane strain (8.33), one must determine two displacement components from three strain components. This problem is over-determined and the relationship among the strain components that appropriately restricts their spatial variations is the first of St. Venant's compatibility equations (7.142):

$$\frac{\partial^2 \varepsilon_{xx}}{\partial y^2} + \frac{\partial^2 \varepsilon_{yy}}{\partial x^2} - 2\frac{\partial^2 \varepsilon_{xy}}{\partial x \partial y} = 0 \qquad (8.51)$$

This is the two-dimensional *compatibility equation*, written in terms of the strain components.

Because we are taking the stress components as dependent variables, (8.48)–(8.50) are used to rewrite the compatibility equation in terms of the stress components:

$$\frac{\partial^2}{\partial y^2}[(1 - \nu)\sigma_{xx} - \nu\sigma_{yy}] + \frac{\partial^2}{\partial x^2}[(1 - \nu)\sigma_{yy} - \nu\sigma_{xx}]$$

$$- 2\frac{\partial^2 \sigma_{xy}}{\partial x \partial y} = 0 \qquad (8.52)$$

Differentiating (8.46) with respect to y, and (8.47) with respect to x with ρ and g^* constant, and adding we find:

$$\frac{\partial^2 \sigma_{yy}}{\partial y^2} + \frac{\partial^2 \sigma_{xx}}{\partial x^2} + 2\frac{\partial^2 \sigma_{xy}}{\partial x \partial y} = 0 \qquad (8.53)$$

Adding (8.52) and (8.53) we have:

$$\left(\frac{\partial^2}{\partial y^2} + \frac{\partial^2}{\partial x^2} \right)(\sigma_{xx} + \sigma_{yy}) = 0 \qquad (8.54)$$

The compatibility equation for plane strain and constant body forces reduces to this harmonic equation for the sum of the two in-plane normal stress components.

Solutions for the three in-plane-stress components must satisfy equilibrium (8.46)–(8.47) and compatibility (8.54). A method for solving these equations was proposed by G.B. Airy in 1862 (Timoshenko and Goodier, 1970, p.32) and the function used in this method, $\Phi(x, y)$, commonly is referred to as the *Airy stress function*. The stress components are written in terms of this stress function as:

$$\sigma_{xx} = \frac{\partial^2 \Phi}{\partial y^2} + \rho g^* y, \quad \sigma_{yy} = \frac{\partial^2 \Phi}{\partial x^2} + \rho g^* y,$$

$$\sigma_{xy} = -\frac{\partial^2 \Phi}{\partial x \partial y} \qquad (8.55)$$

Direct substitution demonstrates that these functions satisfy the equilibrium equations, (8.46)–(8.47), and substitution into the compatibility equation (8.54) yields the biharmonic partial differential equation:

$$\frac{\partial^4 \Phi}{\partial x^4} + 2\frac{\partial^4 \Phi}{\partial x^2 \partial y^2} + \frac{\partial^4 \Phi}{\partial y^4} = 0 \qquad (8.56)$$

This is the governing equation for plane strain problems of elasticity with constant gravitational body force and stress components as the dependent variables. Solutions to particular problems require a stress function that satisfies (8.56) and provides functions for the stress components using (8.55) that satisfy the traction boundary conditions. Textbooks in elasticity theory give numerous examples of Airy stress functions that apply to a wide variety of problems in structural geology (Timoshenko and Goodier, 1970; Jaeger and Cook, 1979; Barber, 1992).

Particular solutions for the biharmonic equation in the form of polynomials serve to illustrate simple states of stress. For example, choosing only terms up to first order and using C_0, C_1, and C_2 for constants, the Airy stress function is $\Phi(x, y) = C_0 + C_1 x + C_2 y$. Substituting this stress function into (8.55) we find:

$$\sigma_{xx} = \rho g^* y; \quad \sigma_{xy} = 0; \quad \sigma_{yy} = \rho g^* y \qquad (8.57)$$

Note that the shear stress is zero and the constants play no role in the functions for the stress components. A particular region in the (x, y)-plane (shaded rectangle in Fig. 8.17a) is illustrated with the traction boundary conditions (8.45) corresponding to this solution. The upper surface is traction free and therefore could represent Earth's surface. If the material is incompressible, $\nu = 0.5$, this Airy stress function gives the isotropic state of stress equivalent to Anderson's standard state: $\sigma_{xx} = \sigma_{yy} = \sigma_{zz} = \rho g^* y$. For values of Poisson's ratio less than 0.5, the out-of-plane-normal stress, $\sigma_{zz} = 2\nu\rho g^* y$, is somewhat less than the in-plane-normal stresses. For the perfectly compressible material, $\nu = 0$, the out-of-plane-normal stress is zero.

The region of interest in the (x, y)-plane is arbitrarily chosen, but the mathematical solution for the state of stress applies everywhere in the plane. This can lead to states of stress that satisfy the governing equation (8.56), but are not appropriate for the physical problem under consideration. For example, if the region of interest in Fig. 8.17a were to be extended upward to positive values of y, the resulting normal stresses would be tensile (positive), where y is positive. This would not represent stresses induced by the weight of the body and

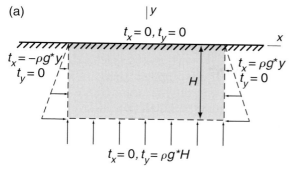

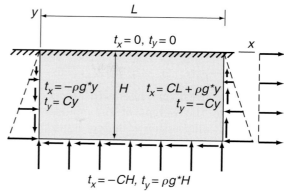

Fig 8.18 Schematic illustration of plane strain elastic problem used to investigate crustal-scale faulting (Hafner, 1951; Hubbert, 1951).

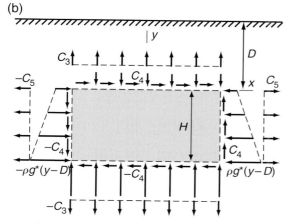

Fig 8.17 Schematic illustration of plane strain elastic problem with traction distributions on rectangular boundaries (Timoshenko and Goodier, 1970). (a) Free surface at top and lithostatic loading in the interior of a half-space. (b) Interior of half-space with lithostatic and tectonic loading.

therefore would be a physically inappropriate application of this solution.

If the region of interest is entirely below the traction-free surface, (8.55) can be modified to account for a translation of the origin to a depth, D, at the top of this region (Fig. 8.17b):

$$\sigma_{xx} = \frac{\partial^2 \Phi}{\partial y^2} + \rho g^*(y - D); \quad \sigma_{xy} = -\frac{\partial^2 \Phi}{\partial x \partial y};$$

$$\sigma_{yy} = \frac{\partial^2 \Phi}{\partial x^2} + \rho g^*(y - D) \tag{8.58}$$

We use this configuration to investigate higher-order terms in the stress function and thereby introduce stresses that may be attributed to tectonic forces. For example, consider the stress function $\Phi(x, y) = \frac{1}{2}C_3 x^2 - C_4 xy + \frac{1}{2}C_5 y^2$. Here, C_3, C_4, and

C_5 are constants with dimensions the same as stress. The in-plane stress components are:

$$\sigma_{xx} = C_5 + \rho g^*(y - D), \quad \sigma_{yy} = C_3 + \rho g^*(y - D),$$

$$\sigma_{xy} = C_4 \tag{8.59}$$

The two normal stresses include a linearly varying part that accounts for the gravitational body force and constant terms, C_3 and C_5, that represent a uniform tectonic loading (Fig. 8.17b). The tectonic tractions acting on the boundary of the rectangular region are drawn for positive values of these constants, and the normal stresses associated with these constant terms would be tensile. Changing the sign of the constants produces compressive tectonic stresses within the region. The sign of the tectonic shear stress depends on the sign of C_4.

8.4.2 From stress to strain to displacement fields in Cartesian coordinates

To illustrate the complete solution for a plane strain problem with traction boundary conditions, including stress, strain, and displacement fields, we consider the following stress function $\Phi(x, y) = \frac{1}{2}Cxy^2$. Here C is taken as a positive constant and the coordinate system and regions of interest are illustrated in Fig. 8.18. This stress function was used by M. King Hubbert to investigate the mechanical basis for crustal-scale faulting (Hubbert, 1951), and by Willy Hafner to investigate thrust faulting in fold and thrust mountain belts (Hafner, 1951). The in-plane stress components are found using (8.55):

$$\sigma_{xx} = Cx + \rho g^* y, \quad \sigma_{yy} = \rho g^* y, \quad \sigma_{xy} = -Cy \quad (8.60)$$

Both normal stress components include a contribution from the weight of the material that increases in compression with depth (negative y). The tectonic part of the horizontal normal stress varies linearly in the x-direction and is zero along the ($x = 0$)-coordinate axis. The tectonic shear stress varies linearly in the y-direction from zero along the ($y = 0$)-coordinate axis, taken here as the traction-free representation of the Earth's surface. The only regions of interest in the (x, y)-plane are in the third and fourth quadrants of the coordinate system, where $y \le 0$ and the gravitational normal stresses are compressive (negative). For a rectangular region in the fourth quadrant ($x \ge 0$), the tectonic normal stress is tensile and increases linearly with distance from the left-hand side of the region (Fig. 8.18). On the other hand, for a rectangular region in the third quadrant ($x \le 0$), the tectonic normal stress is compressive.

Hooke's Law (8.48)–(8.50) provides the in-plane strain components, but one should consider if the contribution from the weight of the material is relevant. This part of the strain field represents the deformation that would be experienced by the elastic material if gravity were turned off in the initial state and then turned on for the final state. For the Earth, the force of gravity is not turned on and off. Therefore, most problems in structural geology are better posed by comparing an initial state with gravitation loading, to a final state with gravitation loading plus the appropriate tectonic forces. In this context one should ignore the contributions of gravitational loading to the strain and displacement fields.

Substituting (8.60) for the stress components in Hooke's Law, without the term $\rho g^* y$, the in-plane tectonic strain components are:

$$\varepsilon_{xx} = \frac{1 - \nu^2}{E} Cx, \quad \varepsilon_{yy} = -\frac{\nu + \nu^2}{E} Cx,$$
$$\varepsilon_{xy} = -\frac{1 + \nu}{E} Cy \quad (8.61)$$

Note that the strains scale with the same constant, C, that scales the stresses. Also, the strains are inversely proportional to Young's modulus and directly proportional to a factor that includes Poisson's ratio. Although there is no tectonic normal stress in the y-direction, there is a tectonic normal strain in this direction, induced by the tectonic normal stress in the x-direction. The region $x \ge 0$ (Fig. 8.18) is one of horizontal tectonic extension ($\varepsilon_{xx} \ge 0$), so the vertical strain is a contraction ($\varepsilon_{yy} \le 0$). The region $x \le 0$ is one of horizontal tectonic contraction ($\varepsilon_{xx} \le 0$), so the vertical strain is an extension ($\varepsilon_{yy} \ge 0$). In both regions the strains increase in magnitude linearly from $x = 0$.

The tectonic displacement field is found by integrating the kinematic equations (8.33) after substituting (8.61):

$$u_x = \int \varepsilon_{xx} dx = \left(\frac{1 - \nu^2}{E}\right)\frac{1}{2}Cx^2 + f_1(y) + C_1 \quad (8.62)$$

$$u_y = \int \varepsilon_{yy} dy = -\left(\frac{\nu + \nu^2}{E}\right)Cxy + f_2(x) + C_2 \quad (8.63)$$

To evaluate the arbitrary functions and constants we use the kinematic equation for the shear strain (8.33) rearranged as follows:

$$\left(\frac{\partial u_x}{\partial y} + \frac{\partial u_y}{\partial x}\right) - 2\varepsilon_{xy} = 0 \quad (8.64)$$

Substituting for the displacement components from (8.62) and (8.63) and for the shear strain from (8.61) we find:

$$\frac{df_2(x)}{dx} + \frac{df_1(y)}{dy} - \left(\frac{\nu + \nu^2}{E}\right)Cy + 2\left(\frac{1 + \nu}{E}\right)Cy = 0$$
$$(8.65)$$

The first term is only a function of x and the last three terms are only functions of y so:

$$\frac{df_2(x)}{dx} = C_3 = -\left[\frac{df_1(y)}{dy} - \left(\frac{\nu + \nu^2}{E}\right)Cy + 2\left(\frac{1 + \nu}{E}\right)Cy\right]$$
$$(8.66)$$

Rearranging and integrating:

$$f_2(x) = \int C_3 dx = C_3 x + C_4 \quad (8.67)$$

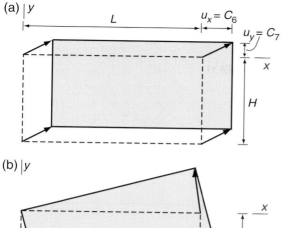

(a)

(b)

Fig 8.19 Schematic illustration of linear and constant terms in displacement equations (8.69) and (8.70). (a) Constant terms are rigid translation. (b) Linear terms are rigid rotation.

$$f_1(y) = \int \left[-\left(\frac{2 + \nu - \nu^2}{E} \right) Cy - C_3 \right] dy$$

$$= -\left(\frac{2 + \nu - \nu^2}{E} \right) \frac{1}{2} Cy^2 - C_3 y + C_5 \quad (8.68)$$

The functions $f_1(y)$ and $f_2(x)$ are substituted into (8.62) and (8.63), and the constants are combined to give the displacement components:

$$u_x = \left(\frac{1 - \nu^2}{E} \right) \frac{1}{2} Cx^2 - \left(\frac{2 + \nu - \nu^2}{E} \right) \frac{1}{2} Cy^2 - C_3 y + C_6$$

$$(8.69)$$

$$u_y = -\left(\frac{\nu + \nu^2}{E} \right) Cxy + C_3 x + C_7 \quad (8.70)$$

The last two terms in each displacement equation have a special interpretation. The constants, C_6 and C_7, represent a *rigid translation* of the region of interest (Fig. 8.19a). The two terms with the constant C_3 represent a *rigid rotation* of the region about the origin (Fig. 8.19b). These constants do

not appear in the expressions for the tectonic strain components (8.61) and stress components (8.60). This is consistent with the concept that rigid translations and rigid rotations do not contribute to the strain or stress fields. Therefore, these terms are of no relevance to studies that depend upon the strain or stress fields. In most applications the rigid motions are ignored.

8.4.3 Generalized solution for plane cylindrical (polar) coordinates

The natural coordinate system for some models of geological structures is made up of two in-plane coordinates, r and θ, and one out-of-plane coordinate, z (Fig. 8.20). If the structure is very long in the z-coordinate direction, it may be approximated using plane strain conditions where $u_z = 0$ everywhere and the in-plane displacements, u_r and u_θ are only functions of the two polar coordinates, r and θ. Under these conditions the three independent stress components are only functions of the polar coordinates:

$$\sigma_{rr} = g_1(r, \theta), \quad \sigma_{r\theta} = g_2(r, \theta), \quad \sigma_{\theta\theta} = g_3(r, \theta) \quad (8.71)$$

The out-of-plane normal stress is proportional to Poisson's ratio, and the out-of-plane shear stresses are zero: $\sigma_{zz} = \nu(\sigma_{rr} + \sigma_{\theta\theta})$, $\sigma_{rz} = 0$, $\sigma_{\theta z} = 0$. Taking the cylindrical z-axis and the reference axis Ox as horizontal, perpendicular to the direction of the gravitational body force, $\mathbf{F}$, near Earth's surface, the components of the body force are:

$$F_r = -\rho g^* \sin \theta, \quad F_\theta = -\rho g^* \cos \theta, \quad F_z = 0 \quad (8.72)$$

For these conditions the equilibrium equations are (Timoshenko and Goodier, 1970):

$$\frac{\partial \sigma_{rr}}{\partial r} + \frac{1}{r} \frac{\partial \sigma_{\theta r}}{\partial \theta} + \frac{\sigma_{rr} - \sigma_{\theta\theta}}{r} + F_r = 0 \quad (8.73)$$

$$\frac{\partial \sigma_{r\theta}}{\partial r} + \frac{1}{r} \frac{\partial \sigma_{\theta\theta}}{\partial \theta} + \frac{2\sigma_{r\theta}}{r} + F_\theta = 0 \quad (8.74)$$

The equilibrium equations are satisfied, as may be shown by substitution, with polar stress components related to an *Airy stress function*, $\Phi(r, \theta)$, as follows (Timoshenko and Goodier, 1970):

$$\sigma_{rr} = \frac{1}{r} \frac{\partial \Phi}{\partial r} + \frac{1}{r^2} \frac{\partial^2 \Phi}{\partial \theta^2} + \rho g^* r \sin \theta \quad (8.75)$$

$$\sigma_{r\theta} = -\frac{\partial}{\partial r}\left(\frac{1}{r}\frac{\partial \Phi}{\partial \theta}\right) \qquad (8.76)$$

$$\sigma_{\theta\theta} = \frac{\partial^2 \Phi}{\partial r^2} + \rho g^* r \sin \theta \qquad (8.77)$$

To solve a particular problem the stress components must satisfy the specified traction boundary conditions following Cauchy's Formula.

Hooke's Law is defined by noting that one may rotate the Cartesian coordinates (x, y) about the z-axis to coincide with the polar coordinates (r, θ). Then, the strain–stress relationships in polar coordinates are written by exchanging each Cartesian subscript in (8.48)–(8.50) with its polar counterpart:

$$\varepsilon_{rr} = \frac{1}{E}[\sigma_{rr}(1 - \nu^2) - \sigma_{\theta\theta}\nu(1 + \nu)] \qquad (8.78)$$

$$\varepsilon_{\theta\theta} = \frac{1}{E}[\sigma_{\theta\theta}(1 - \nu^2) - \sigma_{rr}\nu(1 + \nu)] \qquad (8.79)$$

$$\varepsilon_{r\theta} = \frac{1 + \nu}{E}\sigma_{\theta r} \qquad (8.80)$$

The kinematic equations in polar coordinates are (Malvern, 1969):

$$\varepsilon_{rr} = \frac{\partial u_r}{\partial r} \qquad (8.81)$$

$$\varepsilon_{\theta\theta} = \frac{1}{r}\left(u_r + \frac{\partial u_\theta}{\partial \theta}\right) \qquad (8.82)$$

$$\varepsilon_{r\theta} = \frac{1}{2r}\left(\frac{\partial u_r}{\partial \theta} + r\frac{\partial u_\theta}{\partial r} - u_\theta\right) \qquad (8.83)$$

The three strain components are used to determine two displacement components, so these strains must satisfy a compatibility condition which is written in terms of the Airy stress function, giving the biharmonic equation in polar coordinates (Malvern, 1969):

$$\left(\frac{\partial^2}{\partial r^2} + \frac{1}{r}\frac{\partial}{\partial r} + \frac{1}{r^2}\frac{\partial^2}{\partial \theta^2}\right)\left(\frac{\partial^2 \Phi}{\partial r^2} + \frac{1}{r}\frac{\partial \Phi}{\partial r} + \frac{1}{r^2}\frac{\partial^2 \Phi}{\partial \theta^2}\right) = 0 \qquad (8.84)$$

Solutions to this equation for stress states that satisfy particular boundary conditions are reviewed in textbooks on elasticity theory (Timoshenko and Goodier, 1970; Barber, 1992).

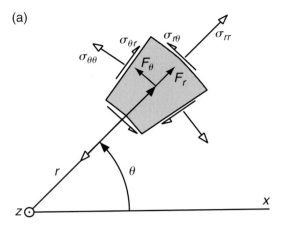

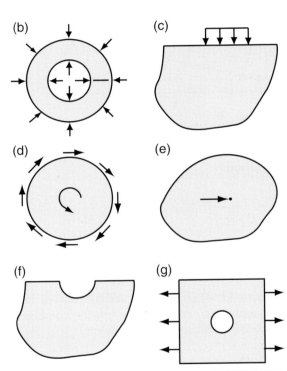

Fig 8.20 (a) Cylindrical coordinates (r, θ, z) and associated polar stress components. (b) Schematic illustrations of six different elastic boundary value problems solved by selected terms from Michell's general solution in polar coordinates (8.71) (Michell, 1899).

In 1899, J. H. Michell derived a generalized Airy stress function in polar coordinates, from which many particular solutions can be extracted (Michell, 1899; Timoshenko and Goodier, 1970):

$$\Phi(r,\theta) = a_0 \ln r + b_0 r^2 + c_0 r^2 \ln r + d_0 r^2 \theta + a'_0 \theta$$

$$+ \left(\frac{1}{2} a_1 r\theta\right)\sin\theta + (b_1 r^3 + a'_1 r^{-1} + b'_1 r \ln r)\cos\theta$$

$$- \left(\frac{1}{2} c_1 r\theta\right)\cos\theta + (d_1 r^3 + c'_1 r^{-1} + d'_1 r \ln r)\sin\theta$$

$$+ \sum_{n=2}^{\infty} (a_n r^n + b_n r^{n+2} + a'_n r^{-n} + b'_n r^{-n+2})\cos n\theta$$

$$+ \sum_{n=2}^{\infty} (c_n r^n + d_n r^{n+2} + c'_n r^{-n} + d'_n r^{-n+2})\sin n\theta$$

$$(8.85)$$

For example, the first three terms of (8.85) solve the problem of symmetric loading of a hollow cylinder (Fig. 8.20b), which is used for *in-situ* determination of elastic moduli in boreholes. The fourth term is used to solve the problem of an elastic half-space with a distributed constant normal traction (Fig. 8.20c). This finds many applications to loading of Earth's surface. The last term on the first line provides a pure shear stress as in a twisted rod (Fig. 8.20d). Terms on the second and third lines are used to solve the problem of a point force in an infinite body (Fig. 8.20e). Combinations of point forces have been applied as earthquake source mechanisms and the integration of the point force solution over a boundary is a standard technique for developing solutions to new problems. The first term on the third line is used below to solve the problem of a cylindrical valley loaded by gravity (Fig. 8.20f). The terms on the fourth line with $n = 2$ are the solution for a cylindrical hole in a body with a uniform normal stress at infinity (Fig. 8.20g). This has been called the most important problem in rock mechanics (Jaeger and Cook, 1979, p. 236) and apparently was first obtained by B. Kirsch (1898; Timoshenko and Goodier, 1970, p. 90). It has been applied to the stress distribution around boreholes and tunnels, and to a variety of *in-situ* stress measurement techniques.

8.4.4 The stress state induced by gravity near a valley

As an example of a particular solution taken from Michell's generalized solution (8.85), consider the state of stress near a valley excised into an otherwise featureless (planar) terrain (Fig. 8.21). The polar coordinate system (r, θ) is chosen such that the x- and z-axes are parallel to the planar surface

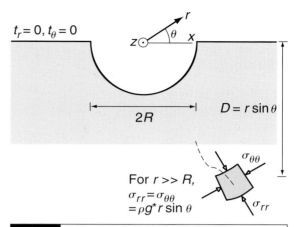

Fig 8.21 Schematic illustration of elastic half-space with half-cylindrical cut from traction-free surface used as model for a valley.

and the z-axis is parallel to the valley. The shape of the valley is idealized as a circular cylinder and it is very long in the z-direction compared to the radius, R. The geometry in the plane of interest is that of the half-space, $r \sin(\theta) \leq 0$, with a semi-circular cut that removes the elastic material where $r < R$.

The surface of the elastic half-space with the cut is traction free. Thus, the conditions on the three segments of the boundary are:

$$\text{BC: on} \begin{Bmatrix} r = R, \pi \leq \theta \leq 2\pi \\ r \geq R, \theta = \pi \\ r \geq R, \theta = 2\pi \end{Bmatrix}, \quad t_r = 0, \quad t_\theta = 0$$
$$(8.86)$$

Prior to the valley being incised the polar stress components are given by (8.75)–(8.77) without the terms containing the Airy stress function:

$$\sigma_{rr} = \rho g^* r \sin\theta = \sigma_{\theta\theta}, \quad \sigma_{r\theta} = 0 \quad (8.87)$$

Because the valley provides only a local perturbation of this stress state the boundary conditions in the remote field are:

$$\text{BC: as } r \to \infty \text{ and } \sin\theta \leq 0, \begin{cases} \sigma_{rr} \to \rho g^* r \sin\theta \\ \sigma_{\theta\theta} \to \rho g^* r \sin\theta \\ \sigma_{r\theta} \to 0 \end{cases}$$
$$(8.88)$$

The normal stress components are equal compressions that increase in magnitude linearly with depth, $D = r\sin\theta$.

To account for the stress perturbation of the valley, the first term in the third line of (8.85) is taken with the constant $c_1 = -\rho g^* R^2$, so the Airy stress function is:

$$\Phi(r, \theta) = \tfrac{1}{2}\rho g^* R^2 r\theta \cos\theta \qquad (8.89)$$

The polar stress components are found using (8.75)–(8.77):

$$\sigma_{rr} = -(\rho g^* r\sin\theta)\left(\frac{R}{r}\right)^2, \quad \sigma_{r\theta} = 0, \quad \sigma_{\theta\theta} = 0 \qquad (8.90)$$

Everywhere on the circular boundary, $r = R$, the perturbing radial stress is just sufficient to reduce the gravitational radial stress to zero. Both the gravitation and perturbing shear stress are zero. Therefore the boundary conditions on the valley wall are satisfied. Because the $\sin\theta$ terms are zero on the horizontal segments of the boundary, it is traction free. Because the perturbing stress scales with $(R/r)^2$, its contribution goes toward zero for radial distances that are large compared to the valley radius and the stress state approaches that due to gravity alone (8.88).

The distribution of the perturbing radial stress is illustrated in Fig. 8.22a for the particular case where $R = 10^3$ m and $\rho g^* = 0.025$ MPa m^{-1}. The perturbing stress is tensile and greatest at the valley bottom, decreasing toward zero at the upper edges of the valley. Contours of equal radial stress curve around the base of the valley and the distance between the contours increases with radial distance because of the $(R/r)^2$ distribution. These characteristics of the stress distribution indicate that there is a concentration of stress at the valley bottom. For this case the perturbing radial tensile stress there is 25 MPa. In other words the stress concentration is equal in magnitude to the gravitationally induced compressive stress at 1 km depth, but of opposite sign.

The total radial stress, found by adding (8.87) and (8.90), is illustrated in Fig. 8.22b. Note how the contours of equal radial stress are depressed under the valley, but return to nearly horizontal lines for depths greater than a few valley radii. Because the gravitational stress at the valley bottom is -25 MPa, the total radial stress is exactly zero there (and everywhere else on the boundary). The circumferential normal stress is

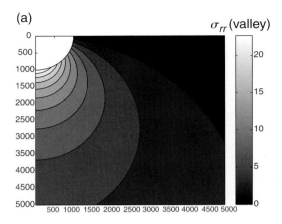

(a) σ_{rr} (valley)

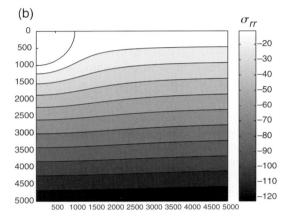

(b) σ_{rr}

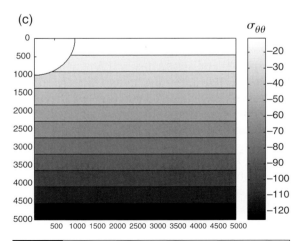

(c) $\sigma_{\theta\theta}$

Fig 8.22 Contour maps of stress components near an idealized valley. (a) Perturbing normal stress, σ_{rr}. (b) Total normal stress, σ_{rr}. (c) Normal stress, $\sigma_{\theta\theta}$.

not perturbed by the valley, so it remains compressive and increases in magnitude linearly with depth below the horizontal surface. Contours of the total circumferential stress are straight horizontal lines throughout the half-space including the vicinity of the valley (Fig. 8.22c). The total circumferential stress at the valley bottom is:

$$\sigma_{\theta\theta}(r = R, \theta = 3\pi/2) = -\rho g^* R \qquad (8.91)$$

In other words, the normal stress acting in the horizontal direction is compressive, and scales in magnitude with the average unit weight of the surrounding rock mass and with the vertical distance from the valley rim to the valley floor. Because the polar component of total shear stress is zero, the stress trajectories are radial lines (least compressive stress) and circumferential curves (greatest compressive stress).

One of the more interesting structures associated with deeply incised canyons are so-called *valley anticlines* (Potter and McGill, 1978). Potter and McGill identify two types of valley anticlines. The first type is characterized as broad upright folds that follow major drainages and, although the folding tends to die out upward, it may deflect strata all the way to the valley rim, up to 600 m above the valley floor. The second type is smaller, sometimes with straighter limbs and tighter hinges, and usually is confined to thin-bedded strata on the valley floor. The spatial association of landforms and structures often leads to an interpretation that the landform (drainage channel in this case) was superimposed on the structure because deformation related to the structure made the rock more susceptible to erosion. However, valley anticlines are interpreted in just the opposite way: the fluvial valley predated the anticline and the location of the fold was determined by the course of the river.

Superb outcrops of both types of valley anticlines are found in Canyonlands National Park, southeastern Utah (Potter and McGill, 1978; Huntoon, 1982). The major structure, called the Meander Anticline, follows the Colorado River for approximately 35 km and the trace of the fold hinge is almost perfectly coincident with the meandering course of the river (Fig. 8.23). Only where the river takes two very pronounced meanders at The Loops does the anticline cut across

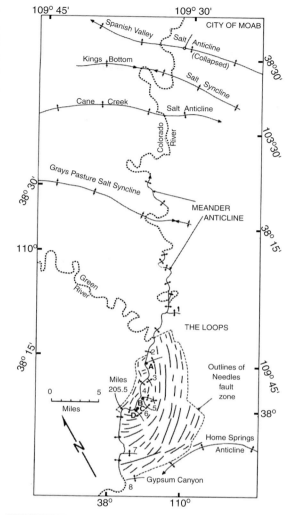

Fig 8.23 Map of Colorado River near Canyonlands National Park, UT, showing trace of the Meander Anticline. Reprinted from Huntoon (1982) with permission of The Geological Society of America.

the drainage, and even here a secondary anticline suggests that canyon incision in one of the loops did generate a fold. Viewed from the Colorado River (Fig. 8.24a), north of the confluence with the Green River, the Meander Anticline appears as a gentle symmetrical fold with a hinge line nearly coincident with the center of the river. At Mile 205.5, the limb dips have increased to 50°, and farther downstream the fold becomes asymmetric with limb dips of only a few degrees to the west and up to 30° to the east.

(a)

(b)

Fig 8.24 Photographs along the Colorado River. (a) The Meander Anticline viewed north of the confluence with the Green River. (b) Thrust faults striking approximately parallel to the fold axis near the Needles fault zone. Reprinted from Huntoon (1982) with permission of The Geological Society of America. Photographs by Peter Huntoon.

While most geologists who have written recently about the Meander Anticline agree that the meandering course of the Colorado River developed before the anticline, a number of hypotheses have been offered to explain the folding. For example, there is some debate about the role of evaporites (gypsum with minor limestone and shale) from the Paradox Member of the Pennsylvanian age Hermosa Formation that underlies much of this region. Some have suggested that the evaporites have flowed laterally and upward toward the canyon bottom because of stress changes caused by the rapid incision of the river (Potter and McGill, 1978). There is ample evidence for such flowage in the four salt plugs located along the southern portion of the anticline (Fig. 8.23, marked A, B, C, D) where evaporites have pierced through the overlying strata to the surface. Others have suggested that the plate of strata overlying the evaporites is sliding toward the canyon under the influence of gravity, while the evaporites remain essentially in place (Huntoon, 1982). This plate varies from about

700 m thick near the northern edge of the Needles fault zone (Fig. 8.23) to zero near the southern edge. There is ample evidence for gravitational sliding of the Needles fault zone, where normal faults bound a set of grabens that have extended toward the river (McGill and Stromquist, 1979; Cartwright *et al.*, 1995; Moore and Schultz, 1999).

Huntoon (1982, Fig. 5) suggests that models for the development of the Meander Anticline can be discriminated by comparing the stress states implied by the models to the stress states deduced from geological structures at two key locations, the Needles fault zone and the axis of the Meander Anticline. Specifically he deduces from the normal faults in the Needles fault zone that the greatest compressive stress is oriented vertically there. Along the axis of the anticline he documents thrust faults that strike approximately parallel to the fold axis and dip both eastward and westward at low angles (Fig. 8.24b). From these thrust faults he deduces that the greatest compressive stress is oriented horizontally and perpendicular to the fold axis. Huntoon concludes that only the sliding plate model is consistent with these two different stress states and suggests that the sliding plate produces compression in the rocks under the canyon and leads to the formation of the Meander Anticline. Potter and McGill (1978) conclude that excess horizontal compressive stress was responsible for the small valley anticlines.

The linear elastic solution for the stress distribution near a cylindrical valley is inappropriate for addressing questions about the flowage of the evaporite or about the sliding of the overlying plate on the evaporate because these processes involve inelastic deformation. However, the elastic solution does provide a useful tool for evaluating the stress distribution due to gravity acting on the valley alone. The stress perturbation due to formation of a cylindrical valley is a radial tension concentrated near the valley bottom (Fig. 8.22a). This radial tension reduces the lithostatic compression that acted perpendicular to the future valley walls and bottom to zero, thereby unloading the rock mass adjacent to the valley. This unloading occurs primarily below the valley and undoubtedly played an important role in the development of the Needles fault zone. The orientation of the stress trajectories to the side of the valley, with greatest compression approximately vertical and least compression approximately horizontal is consistent with the normal faulting.

8.5 | Elastic properties from laboratory and engineering field tests

The measurement of rock properties in the laboratory traditionally falls within the discipline called *rock mechanics*, although a broad variety of scientists and engineers, including geophysicists and structural geologists as well as mining and civil engineers, contribute to this activity. Structural geologists use the data from rock property testing, so we review the procedures and results while leaving aside many of the technical details. Some of the details of experiments to determine the elastic properties are described in textbooks on rock mechanics (Jaeger and Cook, 1979). Although we have referred to this activity as an "experiment" the procedure has become routine and is considered by some to be a standardized engineering test. We present selected values for Young's modulus and Poisson's ratio.

8.5.1 Measuring the elastic properties of laboratory samples

The most direct laboratory experiment to determine Young's modulus of elasticity for rock is the *uniaxial compression test*. In this test a machine applies a normal compressive force through a set of steel platens onto the circular ends of a cylindrical rock specimen (Fig. 8.25a). The machine, not shown in the figure, applies the force through a screw-driven or hydraulically driven piston. Because the force is applied only parallel to the axis of the specimen, this test is called *uniaxial*. Indeed, the intention is to induce only a normal stress, σ_a, of constant magnitude acting parallel to the axis of the specimen, and then to measure the axial extension, e_a. Young's modulus for a linear elastic material would be the ratio of these two quantities (8.6).

Although the test sounds simple enough, problems can lead to spurious data. For example, if the

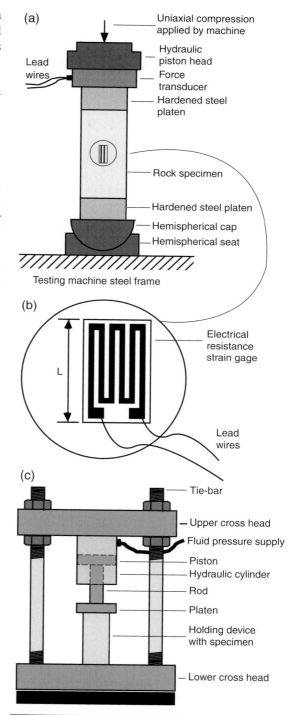

Fig 8.25 Equipment used for uniaxial compression testing of rock. (a) Sample with platens, hemispherical cap, and force transducer. (b) Electrical resistance strain gage. (c) Hydraulic testing machine.

specimen ends are not perfectly parallel, bending can be induced. Also, depending on differences in the elastic properties of the platen and specimen, and on the friction at their contacts, the specimen may be constrained by the platens or pushed radially outward as the platens expand under load. Both of these phenomena are accompanied by a non-uniform stress state on the scale of the entire specimen. To understand the possible severity and consequences of this non-uniformity, the state of stress can be calculated using a boundary value problem for a cylindrical body with the appropriate tractions or displacements on the ends (Peng, 1971). The hemispherical cap and seat (Fig. 8.25a), special platen material, and other standard testing procedures are designed to minimize the specimen-scale non-uniformities in the stress field. At the grain scale the stress and strain fields are likely to be very non-uniform. The presumption is that the stress and strain represent average values over the volume of the sample. Because of the difficulties inherent to the testing procedure we will refer to laboratory results as *apparent* Young's moduli.

An electronic *strain gage* can be glued onto the specimen to determine the axial extension (Fig. 8.25b). These gages are composed of thin wires that undergo a change in electrical resistance as they are stretched or shortened along with the specimen. This change in resistance is transformed into an electronic signal calibrated to the extension magnitude and read onto a digital display, chart recorder, or computer storage device. Thus electrical resistance change is measured and axial extension is estimated from this measurement via a calibration of the strain gage. The gage must be large compared to the grain size to measure an average extension. Alternatively, mechanical dial gages or electronic displacement transducers can be attached to the specimen or platens to measure the changes in length that, with the original length, are used to calculate the axial extension.

A *force transducer* placed between the piston and the specimen measures the normal force acting on the specimen (Fig. 8.25a). In fact, most force transducers use a strain gage to measure the extension of a small metal part within the transducer and then transform this into an electronic

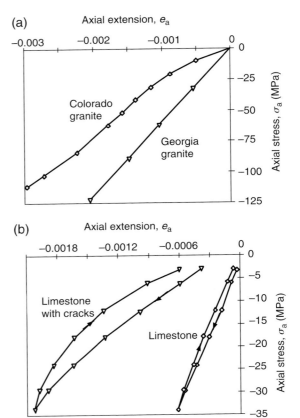

Fig 8.26 Uniaxial compression test results (Obert and Duvall, 1967). (a) Nearly linear behavior (Georgia granite) and non-linear behavior (Colorado granite). (b) Loading and unloading data for limestone with cracks and without cracks.

signal calibrated to the force magnitude. The cross-sectional area of the specimen is calculated from a measurement of the diameter and this is used to calculate the axial stress, which is assumed to represent the average stress throughout the specimen. Neither the stress nor the strain are measured directly.

Data from the uniaxial test include values of the average normal stress and extension acting along the cylindrical axis of the rock specimen. If extensions are very small, we assume the strain can be characterized as infinitesimal. From these data a graph of stress versus extension can be prepared and the slope of the curve used to estimate the apparent Young's modulus, or the tangent Young's modulus. The relationship between axial stress and extension for a specimen of Georgia

Table 8.2.	Rock mechanics laboratory tests for apparent Young's modulus (GPa).		
Rock type	From	To	Mean
Quartzite	70	105	90
Gneiss	16	103	68
Basalt	16	101	63
Granite	10	74	45
Limestone	1	92	48
Sandstone	10	46	22
Shale	10	44	28
Pittsburgh coal	1.5	3.7	3.2

Table 8.3.	Rock mechanics laboratory tests for apparent Poisson's ratio.		
Rock type	From	To	Mean
Quartzite	0.11	0.25	0.16
Gneiss	0.10	0.40	0.22
Basalt	0.13	0.38	0.22
Granite	0.10	0.39	0.23
Limestone	0.08	0.39	0.25
Sandstone	0.10	0.40	0.24
Shale	0.10	0.19	0.14
Witbank coal	0.33	0.37	0.35

granite is given in Fig. 8.26a (Obert and Duvall, 1967). The set of line segments drawn between successive data points on this graph form a nearly straight line. In contrast Colorado granite displays a distinctly non-linear behavior. The straight-line segments are not parallel, but these data could be used to calculate a tangent modulus.

Both granite specimens (Fig. 8.26a) failed by fracturing shortly after the most compressive stress shown on the graph was imposed. The results we have given do not include possible data on unloading to lesser compressive stresses, which would test whether the deformation of these granite specimens was reversible before fracturing began. Unloading data are shown in Fig. 8.26b for two limestone specimens (Obert and Duvall, 1967). One shows a nearly linear relationship between stress and extension, a relatively large modulus, and approximately reversible behavior. The other is distinctly non-linear, has lesser moduli, and does not follow the same path in loading and unloading. This non-linear behavior is attributed to the presence of abundant microcracks in the second of the limestone specimens.

8.5.2 Apparent Young's modulus and Poisson's ratio

Representative values of the *apparent Young's modulus* for selected metamorphic, igneous, and sedimentary rock types are given in Table 8.2 (Bieniawski, 1984). Young's modulus and the tangent modulus are not distinguished in these data. This table is not meant to be complete: one can turn to handbooks that have more extensive tabulations (Clark, 1966).

A few generalizations can be made from the apparent elastic moduli given in Table 8.2. A particular rock type is not associated with a particular modulus. This should come as no surprise because rock classification schemes are based on ranges of values of chemical composition, mineralogy, and texture. You have seen (Fig. 8.26b) that even samples from the same rock mass can exhibit different moduli. The metamorphic and igneous rocks typically have greater values than the clastic sedimentary rocks, although strongly weathered granite can be less stiff than well-indurated sandstone. Speaking qualitatively, we would describe rocks with values around 100 GPa as being very *stiff*, whereas rocks with values around 1 GPa would be termed very *soft*. From Table 8.2 we draw the following rule of thumb: *laboratory specimens of rock have Young's moduli that range from about 1 to 100 GPa with a "typical" value of about 50 GPa.* Rocks are very stiff relative to our experience with softer elastic materials like rubber, but they are elastic none-the-less.

When cylindrical specimens of rock are shortened axially in a uniaxial compression test (Fig. 8.25), they respond by expanding perpendicular to the applied load. The negative ratio of this perpendicular extension to the axial extension is Poisson's ratio (8.10). For most rock specimens Poisson's ratio is approximately constant only over restricted ranges of loading, time, and specimen size. None-the-less, representative values for the same suite of rock types selected for Table 8.2 are given in Table 8.3 (Bieniawski, 1984).

Unlike values of Young's modulus that vary over two orders of magnitude, values of Poisson's

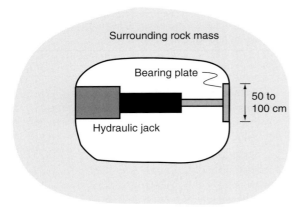

Fig 8.27 Schematic illustration of hydraulic jack used in tests for the elastic stiffness of rock surrounding an underground opening.

dependence of rock properties. One engineering field test is called a *plate-bearing* test (Fig. 8.27) because the applied load is transmitted to the rock surface by a circular bearing plate (Goodman, 1980). Hydraulic jacks load the plate while displacement gages measure the motion of the rock face. To calculate the applied stress and resulting strain, these quantities are substituted into an expression derived from the solution to a boundary value problem of elasticity. The characteristic length for these tests is the diameter of the bearing plate, which typically ranges from 50 to 100 cm. In contrast, the diameter of typical laboratory specimens ranges from 2.5 to 10 cm. Table 8.4 presents values for apparent Young's moduli at laboratory and engineering field scales, and the ratios of field modulus to laboratory modulus as selected from a more extensive data set (Bieniawski, 1984).

ratio for all of the rock types listed vary only from 0.08 to 0.40. We develop the following rule of thumb from these data: *laboratory specimens of rock have Poisson's ratios that range from about 0.1 to 0.4 with a "typical" value of about 0.25.*

8.5.3 Elastic properties of rock from engineering field tests

In light of the heterogeneous nature of rock masses as observed at laboratory, outcrop, and crustal scales, it seems natural to suspect that physical properties, such as the elastic moduli, would be length-scale dependent (Pinto da Cunha, 1990). Rock engineers have developed methods to estimate the *in-situ* properties of rock masses around underground openings and beneath large engineering structures like dams, and these tests provide valuable insight about the scale

The rock masses tested in the field usually are softer than laboratory samples of the same rock. Only one site, the mica project, of the fifteen given in the original data set, contradicts this generalization and data from that site show nearly the same Young's modulus at the two scales. We conclude that increasing the characteristic length for test specimens from centimeters to several meters may have little or no effect on stiffness, but usually it will decrease the stiffness by as much as two orders of magnitude. Because the conditions of the rock are likely to be quite different from site to site, similar rock types can behave very differently. For example crystalline rocks from the LG-2 site and the Tehachapi Tunnel site have practically identical laboratory moduli, yet their field

Table 8.4. Laboratory and engineering field tests for Young's modulus (GPa).				
Project site	Rock type	E (plate)	E (lab)	E (plate)
LG-2 project	Granite	50.0	80.0	0.62
Churchill Falls	Gneiss	41.5	55.0	0.75
Dworshak Dam	Granite/gneiss	23.5	51.7	0.45
Tumut 2	Gneiss/granite	6.9	59.1	0.12
Tehachapi Tunnel	Diorite gneiss	4.8	77.9	0.06
Mica project	Quartzite gneiss	27.6	27.0	1.04
Elandsberg	Graywacke	39.6	73.4	0.54
Waldeck II	Graywacke	5.0	20.0	0.25
York Canyon	Shaley sandstone	0.65	43.4	0.015

moduli differ by an order of magnitude. The granite from LG-2 was described as "massive," whereas the diorite gneiss from Tehachapi was described as "fractured." Apparently, the presence of fractures (and perhaps other heterogeneities) at the field scale produced a profound change in the rock stiffness. The three sedimentary rock types listed in Table 8.4 are consistent with the generalization that greater size correlates with lesser stiffness. They also illustrate the broad range of possible behaviors: for some graywackes the stiffness decreased by only a factor of two, whereas for some shaley sandstones the decrease was by a factor of more than sixty.

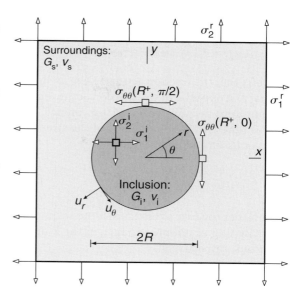

Fig 8.28 The plain strain elastic problem of a cylindrical inclusion with shear modulus and Poisson's ratio, G_i and ν_i, in surroundings with G_s and ν_s. Loading is by remote principal stresses, σ_1^r and σ_2^r (Jaeger and Cook, 1979).

8.6 | Elastic heterogeneity and anisotropy

A rock mass is *heterogeneous* with respect to an elastic property if the value of that property varies from place to place. A rock mass is *anisotropic* with respect to an elastic property if the value of that property varies with orientation at any given place. Thus heterogeneity refers to spatial variation and anisotropy refers to directional variation. These terms apply to any physical property so it is important to specify that property. A rock mass with no spatial variation in a particular property is said to be *homogeneous* with respect to that property, and one with no direction variation is said to be *isotropic* with respect to that property. In this section we describe heterogeneities and anisotropies with respect to elastic properties and show how these affect the solutions to certain elastic boundary value problems.

8.6.1 Deformation of a heterogeneous elastic material

Some heterogeneities serve to amplify locally a remote tension or compression, whereas others actually convert a remote compression into a local tension or vice versa. To keep the analysis simple and analytical we consider an *inclusion* of "foreign" material such as a fossil, clast, or xenolith in an otherwise homogeneous rock mass (Wiltschko and Sutton, 1982). Typically these foreign objects are composed of a different suite

of minerals than the surrounding rock, and they may have a different grain size and texture. As such, the elastic properties of the inclusion are likely to be different than those of the surroundings. A very instructive boundary value problem is the elastic solution for a circular inclusion (Jaeger and Cook, 1979, p. 248).

The inclusion has a radius, R, and the surrounding elastic material extends to an infinite distance from the origin of coordinates at the center of the inclusion (Fig. 8.28). Both a Cartesian (x, y)- and a polar (r, θ)-coordinate system are employed. The inclusion has a shear modulus, G_i, and Poisson's ratio, ν_i, and it is embedded in surroundings with shear modulus, G_s, and Poisson's ratio, ν_s. The following combinations of these constants are used for the plane strain conditions specified here:

$$\kappa_i = 3 - 4\nu_i, \quad \kappa_s = 3 - 4\nu_s, \quad k = G_i/G_s \quad (8.92)$$

The interface between the inclusion and the surroundings is *bonded*, so the inclusion remains fixed to the surroundings regardless of the applied loading. This boundary condition is specified by equating like components of the displacement vector on either side of the boundary:

BC: $u_r(r = R^-, \theta) = u_r(r = R^+, \theta)$,

$$u_\theta(r = R^-, \theta) = u_\theta(r = R^+, \theta) \qquad (8.93)$$

It follows that the traction acting on the inclusion is equal and opposite to the traction acting on the surroundings at every point of the contact. This implies that certain components of the stress are continuous across the interface:

$$\sigma_{rr}(r = R^-, \theta) = \sigma_{rr}(r = R^+, \theta),$$
$$\sigma_{r\theta}(r = R^-, \theta) = \sigma_{r\theta}(r = R^+, \theta) \qquad (8.94)$$

We consider the case of biaxial remote stresses, σ_1^r and σ_2^r, acting at infinite distance in the x- and y-directions, respectively:

BC: at $x = \infty, y = \infty$:

$$\sigma_{xx} = \sigma_1^r, \; \sigma_{xy} = 0 = \sigma_{yx}, \; \sigma_{yy} = \sigma_2^r \qquad (8.95)$$

Because the shear stress components are zero in the remote field the normal components are principal stresses.

A remarkable and non-intuitive result found by solving this boundary value problem is that the state of stress in the inclusion is homogeneous. The principal stresses within the inclusion, σ_1^i and σ_2^i, are (Jaeger and Cook, 1979, p. 249):

$$\sigma_{xx}^i = \sigma_1^i = \frac{[k(\kappa_s + 2) + \kappa_i]k(\kappa_s + 1)}{2(2k + \kappa_i - 1)(k\kappa_s + 1)}\sigma_1^r$$

$$+ \frac{[k(\kappa_s - 2) - \kappa_i + 2]k(\kappa_s + 1)}{2(2k + \kappa_i - 1)(k\kappa_s + 1)}\sigma_2^r \quad (8.96)$$

$$\sigma_{yy}^i = \sigma_2^i = \frac{[k(\kappa_s - 2) - \kappa_i + 2]k(\kappa_s + 1)}{2(2k + \kappa_i - 1)(k\kappa_s + 1)}\sigma_1^r$$

$$+ \frac{[k(\kappa_s + 2) + \kappa_i]k(\kappa_s + 1)}{2(2k + \kappa_i - 1)(k\kappa_s + 1)}\sigma_2^r \quad (8.97)$$

The homogeneity of stress and strain inside the inclusion is true for all possible values of the elastic moduli. The stress and strain also are homogeneous within an elliptical inclusion, and within a three-dimensional ellipsoidal inclusion (Muskhelishvili, 1954; Eshelby, 1957).

For the sake of easily interpretable results, consider the special case where $v_i = 0.25 = v_s$, so $\kappa_i = 2 = \kappa_s$. The stress everywhere inside the inclusion is:

$$\sigma_1^i = \frac{3k}{2k + 1}\sigma_1^r, \quad \sigma_2^i = \frac{3k}{2k + 1}\sigma_2^r \qquad (8.98)$$

Remarkably, the principal stresses within the inclusion are simply proportional to their respective values in the remote field and the proportionality constant is the same for each principal stress. The magnitude of the stress within the inclusion changes with the ratio of the shear moduli, k, but this quantity is always positive, so the sign of the internal stress is always the same as the sign of the respective remote stress. Thus, a remote tension induces tension within the inclusion, and a remote compression induces compression within the inclusion.

Recalling that $k = G_i/G_s$, the above equations can be used to determine how the stress state changes within the inclusion as a function of this ratio, again for the case where both Poisson's ratios are equal to $\frac{1}{4}$:

$$\sigma_1^i = \sigma_2^i \to 0, \quad \text{for } G_i \ll G_s \qquad (8.99)$$

$$\sigma_1^i = \tfrac{3}{2}\sigma_1^r \text{ and } \sigma_2^i = \tfrac{3}{2}\sigma_2^r, \quad \text{for } G_i \gg G_s$$

In general the stress in a softer inclusion is lesser in magnitude than that in the surroundings, and the stress in a stiffer inclusion is greater. In the limit as the stiffness of the inclusion goes to zero the behavior changes to that of a circular hole in elastic surroundings. The greatest stress that can be induced within a stiffer inclusion is an increase over the remotely applied stress by a factor of $\frac{3}{2}$.

Outside the inclusion the state of stress is heterogeneous but it changes with distance from the inclusion to approach the remote state of stress. The stress components in the surroundings are (Jaeger and Cook, 1979, p. 250):

$$\sigma_{rr} = \frac{1}{2}(\sigma_1^r + \sigma_2^r)\left(1 - \frac{BR^2}{r^2}\right)$$

$$+ \frac{1}{2}(\sigma_1^r - \sigma_2^r)\left(1 - \frac{2AR^2}{r^2} - \frac{3CR^4}{r^4}\right)\cos 2\theta$$

$$(8.100)$$

$$\sigma_{\theta\theta} = \frac{1}{2}(\sigma_1^r + \sigma_2^r)\left(1 + \frac{BR^2}{r^2}\right)$$

$$- \frac{1}{2}(\sigma_1^r - \sigma_2^r)\left(1 - \frac{3CR^4}{r^4}\right)\cos 2\theta \qquad (8.101)$$

$$\sigma_{r\theta} = -\frac{1}{2}(\sigma_1^r - \sigma_2^r)\left(1 + \frac{AR^2}{r^2} + \frac{3CR^4}{r^4}\right)\sin 2\theta \qquad (8.102)$$

The stress components are functions of the polar coordinates, r and θ, and the constants A, B, and C in these equations are related to the elastic constants as:

$$A = \frac{2(1-k)}{k\kappa_s + 1}; \quad B = \frac{\kappa_i - 1 - k(\kappa_s - 1)}{2k + \kappa_i - 1};$$
$$C = \frac{k-1}{k\kappa_s + 1} \qquad (8.103)$$

Consider the two points just outside the inclusion, where the $r = R^+$, and the polar angles are $\theta = 0$ and $\theta = \pi/2$. There we calculate the circumferential stress using (8.101). Again, consider the case where the two Poisson's ratios are equal to $\frac{1}{4}$, so the relevant constants are $A = 2(1-k)/(1+2k)$, $B = \frac{1}{2}A$, and $C = -\frac{1}{2}A$. Using these coordinates and constants we find:

$$\sigma_{\theta\theta}(r = R^+, \theta = 0) = -\left(\frac{1-k}{1+2k}\right)\sigma_1^r + \left(\frac{3}{1+2k}\right)\sigma_2^r$$
$$(8.104)$$

$$\sigma_{\theta\theta}(r = R^+, \theta = \pi/2) = \left(\frac{3}{1+2k}\right)\sigma_1^r - \left(\frac{1-k}{1+2k}\right)\sigma_2^r$$
$$(8.105)$$

Because the coefficients that multiply the remote stresses are just interchanged for the two points, consider only a uniaxial stress, σ_1, acting along the x-axis:

$$\sigma_{\theta\theta}(r = R^+, \theta = 0) \rightarrow \begin{cases} -\sigma_1^r, & \text{for } G_i \ll G_s \\ 0, & \text{for } G_i \rightarrow G_s \quad (8.106) \\ \frac{1}{2}\sigma_1^r, & \text{for } G_i \gg G_s \end{cases}$$

$$\sigma_{\theta\theta}\left(r = R^+, \theta = \frac{\pi}{2}\right) \rightarrow \begin{cases} 3\sigma_1^r, & \text{for } G_i \ll G_s \\ \sigma_1^r, & \text{for } G_i \rightarrow G_s \quad (8.107) \\ 0, & \text{for } G_i \gg G_s \end{cases}$$

If the inclusion is much softer than the surroundings, $G_i \ll G_s$, the circumferential stress component is similar to that for an open circular hole: on the interface that is perpendicular to the applied stress the local stress is equal in magnitude but opposite in sign, and there is a stress concentration factor of 3 on the interface that is parallel to the applied stress.

If the inclusion is much stiffer than the surroundings, $G_i \gg G_s$, there is a diminution factor of $1/2$ on the interface that is perpendicular to the applied stress, and the stress is zero on the interface that is parallel to the applied stress. In this sense the stiff inclusion creates a *stress shadow* in the surrounding softer material. The stiffer inclusion carries more of the applied load than adjacent regions by up to a factor of 3/2. The adjacent regions carry less of the applied load by up to a factor of 1/2. These results provide a useful benchmark for assessing the effect of stiffer or softer rock masses on the state of stress.

Distributions of the Cartesian stress components are illustrated in Fig. 8.29 for a uniaxial stress in the remote field $\sigma_1^r = 1$ and a softer inclusion with shear modulus $G_i = 10\,\text{GPa}$ and Poisson's ratio $\nu_i = \frac{1}{4}$ embedded in stiffer surroundings with shear modulus $G_s = 30\,\text{GPa}$ and Poisson's ratio $\nu_s = \frac{1}{4}$. Note that the stress components are uniform within the inclusion and that both the y-component of normal stress and the shear stress are zero. The x-component of normal stress within the softer inclusion is diminished in value relative to the remote stress. The contour patterns outside the inclusion are quite complex, but they clearly illustrate the facts that perturbations due to the inclusion are symmetric, they decrease with distance, and they are negligible at radial distances $r > 5R$.

8.6.2 Generalized Hooke's Law for anisotropic rocks and minerals

The most general linear relationship among the components of strain and stress is one in which each of the nine components of strain, ε_{ij}, is linearly related to the nine components of stress, σ_{ij}. For example, given a Cartesian coordinate system with orthogonal axes x, y, and z, the equation for the normal strain component, e_{xx}, may be written as (Nye, 1985, Chapter VIII):

$$\varepsilon_{xx} = s_{1111}\sigma_{xx} + s_{1112}\sigma_{xy} + s_{1113}\sigma_{xz}$$
$$+ s_{1121}\sigma_{yx} + s_{1122}\sigma_{yy} + s_{1123}\sigma_{yz}$$
$$+ s_{1131}\sigma_{zx} + s_{1132}\sigma_{zy} + s_{1133}\sigma_{zz} \qquad (8.108)$$

The s_{ijkl} are constants of proportionality and the four subscripts on each s correspond to the two subscripts of the strain component e, followed by the two subscripts of the stress component σ, with subscripts (1, 2, 3) corresponding to (x, y, z), respectively. There are eight more equations of this form, each one linearly relating a component of strain to

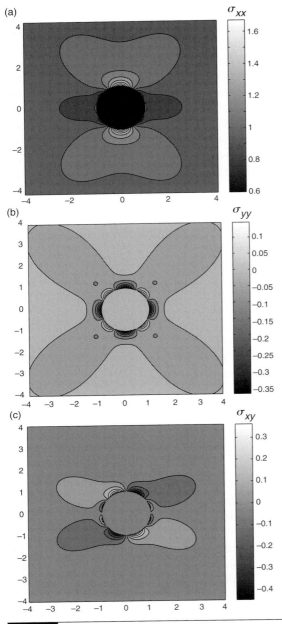

Fig 8.29 Contour maps of stress components near cylindrical inclusion. (a) Normal stress, σ_{xx}. (b) Normal stress, σ_{yy}. (c) Shear stress, σ_{xy}.

material is one in which relatively small stresses cause relatively large strains. In other words, the respective constants for a compliant material are greater than those for a stiff material.

The units and dimensions of compliance are the inverse of those for stress:

$$\text{compliance, } s[=] \, N^{-1}m^2 = Pa^{-1}$$
$$\text{compliance, } s\{=\} \, M^{-1}L \, T^2 \tag{8.109}$$

The symmetry of the infinitesimal strain components and of the stress components enables a reduction in the number of independent compliances to 36 according to:

$$s_{ijkl} = s_{jikl} \quad \text{and} \quad s_{ijkl} = s_{ijlk} \tag{8.110}$$

Therefore, the linear anisotropic elastic material is one in which each of the six independent components of strain is linearly related to the six independent components of stress (Lekhnitskii, 1963; Jaeger and Cook, 1979):

$$\varepsilon_{xx} = s_{11}\sigma_{xx} + s_{12}\sigma_{yy} + s_{13}\sigma_{zz} + s_{14}\sigma_{yz}$$
$$+ s_{15}\sigma_{zx} + s_{16}\sigma_{xy} \tag{8.111}$$

$$\varepsilon_{yy} = s_{21}\sigma_{xx} + s_{22}\sigma_{yy} + s_{23}\sigma_{zz} + s_{24}\sigma_{yz}$$
$$+ s_{25}\sigma_{zx} + s_{26}\sigma_{xy} \tag{8.112}$$

$$\varepsilon_{zz} = s_{31}\sigma_{xx} + s_{32}\sigma_{yy} + s_{33}\sigma_{zz} + s_{34}\sigma_{yz}$$
$$+ s_{35}\sigma_{zx} + s_{36}\sigma_{xy} \tag{8.113}$$

$$\varepsilon_{yz} = s_{41}\sigma_{xx} + s_{42}\sigma_{yy} + s_{43}\sigma_{zz} + s_{44}\sigma_{yz}$$
$$+ s_{45}\sigma_{zx} + s_{46}\sigma_{xy} \tag{8.114}$$

$$\varepsilon_{zx} = s_{51}\sigma_{xx} + s_{52}\sigma_{yy} + s_{53}\sigma_{zz} + s_{54}\sigma_{yz}$$
$$+ s_{55}\sigma_{zx} + s_{56}\sigma_{xy} \tag{8.115}$$

$$\varepsilon_{xy} = s_{61}\sigma_{xx} + s_{62}\sigma_{yy} + s_{63}\sigma_{zz} + s_{64}\sigma_{yz}$$
$$+ s_{65}\sigma_{zx} + s_{66}\sigma_{xy} \tag{8.116}$$

The s_{ij} form a matrix of constants of proportionality which also are referred to as compliances. Here the subscript notation for the compliances has been simplified, based on the order of listing the strain and stress components. The first subscript corresponds to the rank of the strain component in the column on the left-hand side. The second subscript corresponds to the rank of the stress component in each row on the right-hand side. For isothermal and

the nine components of stress, and each one having nine proportionality constants. Altogether there are 81 constants that are referred to as *compliances*. These constants make up a *fourth-rank tensor* quantity (Nye, 1985, p. 133). A compliant reversible deformation, considerations of the elastic strain energy (Nye, 1985, p. 136) prove that this matrix of compliances is symmetric:

$$s_{ij} = s_{ji} \qquad (8.117)$$

This symmetry further reduces the number of independent compliances to 21, so the matrix of compliances can be represented in the following manner:

$$\begin{bmatrix} s_{11} & s_{12} & s_{13} & s_{14} & s_{15} & s_{16} \\ & s_{22} & s_{23} & s_{24} & s_{25} & s_{26} \\ & & s_{33} & s_{34} & s_{35} & s_{36} \\ & & & s_{44} & s_{45} & s_{46} \\ & & & & s_{55} & s_{56} \\ & & & & & s_{66} \end{bmatrix} \qquad (8.118)$$

It is understood that the terms below the diagonal are equivalent to their counterparts above the diagonal.

It is intuitive that solids will extend in the direction of an applied tensile stress. Furthermore, we have experience with solids (e.g. a rubber band) that contract in the directions perpendicular to an applied tension. Earlier in this chapter we defined Poisson's ratio as the elastic property of an isotropic material that related such lateral contractions to the extension in the direction of the applied tensile stress. However, the general anisotropic elastic material exhibits behavior that is not so intuitive. For example, if a uniaxial tensile stress is applied along the z-axis, the only stress component is σ_{zz}, yet all six independent strain components would be non-zero:

$$\begin{aligned} \varepsilon_{xx} &= s_{13}\sigma_{zz}, & \varepsilon_{yy} &= s_{23}\sigma_{zz}, & \varepsilon_{zz} &= s_{33}\sigma_{zz}, \\ \varepsilon_{yz} &= s_{43}\sigma_{zz}, & \varepsilon_{zx} &= s_{53}\sigma_{zz}, & \varepsilon_{xy} &= s_{63}\sigma_{zz} \end{aligned} \qquad (8.119)$$

It is expected that a rectangular block of this material would extend parallel to the tension and contract perpendicular to this tension. However, there are shear strains induced by the tensile stress such that the block would have non-rectangular sides in the loaded state.

8.6.3 Compliances for anisotropic minerals and rocks

Minerals are natural examples of crystalline solids that are anisotropic with respect to elastic properties; however, the number of compliances for many

common minerals is less than 21 because of their symmetry. There are seven systems of crystal symmetry (triclinic, monoclinic, rhombic, tetragonal, trigonal, hexagonal, or cubic) and specific symmetry classes within each system (Lekhnitskii, 1963, pp. 26–32). Triclinic crystals have 21 different compliances, but as the symmetry increases the number of compliances, as referred to crystallographic reference axes, decreases. For example, some trigonal crystals have only six independent compliances (Nye, 1985, table 9):

$$\begin{aligned} & s_{11} = s_{22}, \quad s_{12}, \quad s_{44} = s_{55}, \quad s_{33}, \quad s_{13} = s_{23}, \\ & s_{14} = -s_{24} = 2s_{56}, \quad s_{66} = 2(s_{11} - s_{12}) \end{aligned} \qquad (8.120)$$

All hexagonal crystals have five independent compliances:

$$\begin{aligned} & s_{11} = s_{22}, \quad s_{12}, \quad s_{44} = s_{55}, \quad s_{33}, \\ & s_{13} = s_{23}, \quad s_{66} = 2(s_{11} - s_{12}) \end{aligned} \qquad (8.121)$$

Cubic crystals have three independent compliances:

$$s_{11} = s_{22} = s_{33}, \quad s_{12} = s_{13} = s_{23}, \quad s_{44} = s_{55} = s_{66} \qquad (8.122)$$

The compliances not listed in these relationships are identically zero.

Measured values for the compliances of a few well-known minerals from the trigonal, hexagonal, and cubic systems are given in Table 8.5 (Birch, 1966; Nye, 1985). The units are $10^{-11}\text{N}^{-1}/\text{m}^2$ (10^{-11}Pa^{-1}) and all refer to room temperature unless otherwise noted.

Recall that the range of Young's moduli for rock is from about 10^9 to 10^{11} Pa, so the inverse Young's moduli would range from 10^{-11} to 10^{-9} Pa^{-1}, roughly the same range as that of the values of compliance in this table. Note that the minerals from each crystal system span a similar range of compliances with the exception of ice, which is extraordinarily compliant. Also, minerals of the same composition, but different systems, such as α- and β-quartz, have different compliances. Usually, greater temperatures correspond to greater compliances, as in the case of halite. Finally, minerals known for their "hardness," such as diamond, have very low compliances.

Because rock is made up of many different minerals, and these minerals are anisotropic with respect to elastic properties, it is natural to suppose that rock would be anisotropic. However,

Table 8.5. Compliances of a few minerals ($\times 10^{-11} Pa^{-1}$).

Crystal	System	s_{11}	s_{12}	s_{44}	s_{33}	s_{13}	s_{14}
Calcite	trigonal	1.13	−0.37	4.03	1.75	−0.43	0.91
α-Quartz	trigonal	1.28	−0.15	2.00	0.96	−0.11	0.45
Hematite	trigonal	0.44	−0.10	1.19	0.44	−0.02	0.08
Ice (−10°C)	hexagonal	10.24	−4.22	33.00	8.37	−1.90	
β-Quartz (600°C)	hexagonal	0.94	−0.06	2.77	1.06	−0.26	
Apatite	hexagonal	0.75	0.10	1.51	1.09	−0.40	
Halite (900 K)	cubic	4.79	−1.34	9.47			
Halite (600 K)	cubic	3.19	−0.76	8.49			
Halite (300 K)	cubic	2.28	−0.45	7.81			
Galena	cubic	1.20	−0.30	4.00			
Diamond	cubic	0.14	−0.04	0.23			

in many examples the individual mineral grains are arranged with random orientations. Taking a sample of such a rock that is large compared to the grain size, the elastic properties would be approximately isotropic. Calculation procedures have been derived to estimate the average isotropic elastic constants for a rock from knowledge of the elastic properties and abundances of each mineral (Hearmon, 1961).

Some rocks at the hand-sample scale are anisotropic with respect to elastic properties because the constituent grains are not randomly oriented. For example, slates have a strong preferred orientation of the platy minerals. Such rocks are likely to have an axis of elastic symmetry perpendicular to the plane of the mineral fabric. Within the plane of the fabric the rock may be approximately isotropic. Such a material is described as having a plane of isotropy, or an axis (perpendicular to this plane) of rotational symmetry (Lekhnitskii, 1963, p. 24) and the linear strain–stress equations reduce to:

$$\varepsilon_{xx} = s_{11}\sigma_{xx} + s_{12}\sigma_{yy} + s_{13}\sigma_{zz} \tag{8.123}$$

$$\varepsilon_{yy} = s_{12}\sigma_{xx} + s_{11}\sigma_{yy} + s_{13}\sigma_{zz} \tag{8.124}$$

$$\varepsilon_{zz} = s_{13}\sigma_{xx} + s_{13}\sigma_{yy} + s_{33}\sigma_{zz} \tag{8.125}$$

$$\varepsilon_{yz} = s_{44}\sigma_{yz}, \ \varepsilon_{zx} = s_{44}\sigma_{zx}, \ \varepsilon_{xy} = 2(s_{11} - s_{12})\sigma_{xy} \tag{8.126}$$

Here the z-axis is the axis of rotational symmetry and the (x, y)-plane is the plane of isotropy. Notice

that there are five independent compliances for rocks with this form of symmetry and that the compliances have the same relationship to one another as in the hexagonal crystal class. Rocks with these elastic properties are referred to being *transversally isotropic.*

The strain–stress relations for the transversally isotropic rock can be written using variants of the more familiar elastic constants, Young's modulus and Poisson's ratio as follows:

$$\varepsilon_{xx} = \frac{1}{E}(\sigma_{xx} - \nu\sigma_{yy}) - \frac{\nu'}{E'}\sigma_{zz} \tag{8.127}$$

$$\varepsilon_{yy} = \frac{1}{E}(\sigma_{yy} - \nu\sigma_{xx}) - \frac{\nu'}{E'}\sigma_{zz} \tag{8.128}$$

$$\varepsilon_{zz} = \frac{1}{E'}\sigma_{zz} - \frac{\nu'}{E'}(\sigma_{xx} + \sigma_{yy}) \tag{8.129}$$

$$\varepsilon_{yz} = \frac{1}{G'}\sigma_{yz}, \ \varepsilon_{zx} = \frac{1}{G'}\sigma_{zx}, \ \varepsilon_{xy} = \frac{2(1 + \nu)}{E}\sigma_{xy} \tag{8.130}$$

Here E and ν are Young's modulus and Poisson's ratio for any direction of applied normal stress within the plane of isotropy. The constants E' and ν' are Young's modulus and Poisson's ratio for an applied normal stress along the axis of symmetry. The constant G' is the shear modulus for an applied shear stress in any plane that contains the axis of symmetry.

For plane strain deformation (8.30) with $u_z = 0$ consider the possibility that there are two orthogonal axes of elastic symmetry in the (x, y)-plane. These conditions require four compliances in contrast to the two elastic moduli for the isotropic material (8.48)–(8.50) and define the so-called *orthotropic solid*:

$$\varepsilon_{xx} = s_{11}\sigma_{xx} + s_{12}\sigma_{yy}, \quad \varepsilon_{yy} = s_{12}\sigma_{xx} + s_{22}\sigma_{yy},$$
$$\varepsilon_{xy} = s_{66}\sigma_{xy} \qquad (8.131)$$

In terms of Young's moduli and Poisson's ratios, these equations are written:

$$\varepsilon_{xx} = \frac{1}{E_1}\sigma_{xx} - \frac{\nu_{21}}{E_2}\sigma_{yy}, \quad \varepsilon_{yy} = -\frac{\nu_{12}}{E_1}\sigma_{xx} + \frac{1}{E_2}\sigma_{yy},$$
$$\varepsilon_{xy} = \frac{1}{G}\sigma_{xy} \qquad (8.132)$$

What appear to be five constants are only four because the two Poisson's ratios are related:

$$\frac{\nu_{21}}{E_2} = \frac{\nu_{12}}{E_1}, \quad \text{so} \quad \nu_{12} = \nu_{21}\frac{E_1}{E_2} \qquad (8.133)$$

E_1 and ν_{12} are Young's modulus and Poisson's ratio for an applied normal stress along the x-axis, whereas E_2 and ν_{21} are Young's modulus and Poisson's ratio for an applied normal stress along the y-axis. G is the shear modulus in the (x,y)-plane.

For isotropic materials, the number of independent compliances reduces to two because:

$$s_{11} = s_{22} = s_{33}, \ s_{12} = s_{13} = s_{23},$$
$$s_{44} = s_{55} = s_{66} = 2(s_{11} - s_{12}) \qquad (8.134)$$

How these compliances relate to the isotropic elastic constants introduced earlier can be deduced from the strain–stress relationships written using the compliances and (8.134), and comparing these to (8.18), (Nye, 1985, p. 143):

$$s_{11} = \frac{1}{E}, \ s_{12} = -\frac{\nu}{E}, \ 2(s_{11} - s_{12}) = \frac{1}{G} \qquad (8.135)$$

Data on anisotropic elastic properties for rock samples are presented in Table 8.6 for measurements of the modulus of elasticity (Young's modulus) perpendicular to bedding or foliation (if any) and in two orthogonal directions parallel to bedding or foliation (Obert and Duvall, 1967, p. 486).

8.6.4 Deformation of an anisotropic elastic body

To assess the importance of elastic anisotropy during deformation of a rock mass we consider a

Table 8.6. Young's modulus of a few rocks in orthogonal directions (GPa).

Rock type	Perpendicular	Parallel (A)	Parallel (B)
Gneiss	18.6	23.1	12.4
Marble	49.3	62.7	71.7
Granite	30.4	27.4	44.2
Limestone	33.4	41.0	37.2
Sandstone	6.0	6.7	8.8
Sandstone	7.1	10.6	11.2
Oil shale	12.4	21.4	
Oil shale	21.1	33.2	

circular hole (Fig. 8.30) in an orthotropic solid loaded by a remote uniaxial stress (Jaeger and Cook, 1979, pp. 284–5). This is a two-dimensional, plane strain solution, so the hole represents a long cylindrical opening perpendicular to the (x, y)-plane. The in-plane stress components are related to the Airy stress function by:

$$\sigma_{xx} = \frac{\partial^2\Phi}{\partial y^2}, \quad \sigma_{yy} = \frac{\partial^2\Phi}{\partial x^2}, \quad \sigma_{xy} = -\frac{\partial^2\Phi}{\partial x\partial y} \qquad (8.136)$$

Substituting these equations into the constitutive equations for the orthotropic elastic material (8.131):

$$\varepsilon_{xx} = s_{11}\frac{\partial^2\Phi}{\partial y^2} + s_{12}\frac{\partial^2\Phi}{\partial x^2}, \quad \varepsilon_{yy} = s_{12}\frac{\partial^2\Phi}{\partial y^2} + s_{22}\frac{\partial^2\Phi}{\partial x^2},$$
$$\varepsilon_{xy} = -s_{66}\frac{\partial^2\Phi}{\partial x\partial y} \qquad (8.137)$$

Substituting the constitutive equations into the compatibility equation written in terms of the strain components, we have:

$$s_{22}\frac{\partial^4\Phi}{\partial x^4} + (s_{66} + 2s_{12})\frac{\partial^4\Phi}{\partial x^2\partial y^2} + s_{11}\frac{\partial^4\Phi}{\partial y^4} = 0 \qquad (8.138)$$

Dividing through by s_{22} we define the following constants:

$$\frac{s_{11}}{s_{22}} = \alpha_1\alpha_2 = C_1, \quad \frac{s_{66} + 2s_{12}}{s_{22}} = \alpha_1 + \alpha_2 = C_2 \qquad (8.139)$$

The compatibility equation can be rearranged as follows:

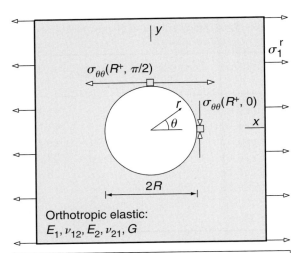

Fig 8.30 The plain strain elastic problem of a cylindrical hole in an orthotropic elastic material. Loading is by remote uniaxial principal stress, σ_1^r (Jaeger and Cook, 1979).

$$\left(\frac{\partial^2}{\partial x^2} + \alpha_1 \frac{\partial^2}{\partial y^2}\right)\left(\frac{\partial^2}{\partial x^2} + \alpha_2 \frac{\partial^2}{\partial y^2}\right)\Phi = 0 \qquad (8.140)$$

Note that the sum and the product of the constants α_1 and α_2 are related to the compliances (8.139), so one must solve these two equations simultaneously to find these relations. Multiplying the second of (8.139) by α_1 we have:

$$\alpha_1\alpha_2 = C_1, \qquad \alpha_1^2 + \alpha_1\alpha_2 = C_2 \qquad (8.141)$$

Subtracting the second equation from the first equation we find the following quadratic equation:

$$\alpha_1^2 - C_2\alpha_1 + C_1 = 0 \qquad (8.142)$$

The two solutions for this quadratic equation are:

$$\alpha_1 = \tfrac{1}{2}C_2 \pm \tfrac{1}{2}\sqrt{C_2^2 - 4C_1}, \quad \text{where } C_2^2 - 4C_1 \geq 0 \qquad (8.143)$$

The restriction on the values of C_1 and C_2 follows from the fact that the compliances are real numbers, so we are looking for solutions that are real values of α_1, given real values of C_1 and C_2. These constants are related to the familiar elastic constants as follows:

$$C_1 = \frac{s_{11}}{s_{22}} = \frac{E_2}{E_1}, \quad C_2 = \frac{E_2}{G} - 2\nu_{21} \qquad (8.144)$$

For the purpose of illustrating the effects of elastic anisotropy on the state of stress we consider the problem of the circular hole and select the following values for the elastic constants: $E_1 = 40\,\text{GPa}$, $E_2 = 20\,\text{GPa}$, $G = 10\,\text{GPa}$, $\nu_{12} = 0.2$, $\nu_{21} = 0.1$. This would be considered a very anisotropic rock, judging from Table 8.6: the ratio $E_1/E_2 = 2$ is greater than any of the examples given there. Only four constants are independent and these five constants are self-consistent according to (8.133). Using (8.144), we find $C_1 = 0.5$ and $C_2 = 1.8$, and solving the quadratic equation (8.143) we have $\alpha_1 = (1.457, 0.343)$. Using the first of (8.141), the second constant is $\alpha_2 = (0.343, 1.457)$. Note that there is only one pair of independent constants given by the solution to the quadratic equation. This follows from (8.140) where one can see that the constants α_1 and α_2 are interchangeable.

Stress states for the elastic boundary value problem are given in terms of yet more constants that are related to the constants α_1 and α_2 as follows:

$$\gamma_1 = \frac{\sqrt{\alpha_1} - 1}{\sqrt{\alpha_1} + 1} = 0.094, \quad \gamma_2 = \frac{\sqrt{\alpha_2} - 1}{\sqrt{\alpha_2} + 1} = -0.261 \qquad (8.145)$$

Now consider the circular hole in an infinite anisotropic body with uniaxial stress, σ_1, at an infinite distance acting in the Ox-direction (Fig. 8.30). The x- and y-axes are symmetry axes with respect to the anisotropy. At the edge of the hole, the circumferential normal stress is (Jaeger and Cook, 1979, p. 285):

$$\frac{\sigma_{\theta\theta}}{\sigma_1} = \frac{(1 + \gamma_1)(1 + \gamma_2)(1 + \gamma_1 + \gamma_2 - \gamma_1\gamma_2 - 2\cos 2\theta)}{(1 + \gamma_1^2 - 2\gamma_1\cos 2\theta)(1 + \gamma_2^2 - 2\gamma_2\cos 2\theta)} \qquad (8.146)$$

The stress distribution as a function of position, θ, around half the hole is illustrated in Fig. 8.31 where triangles mark the curve for the isotropic material, diamonds mark the curve for loading parallel to the direction of greater Young's modulus, E_1, and squares mark the curve for loading parallel to the direction of lesser Young's modulus, E_2.

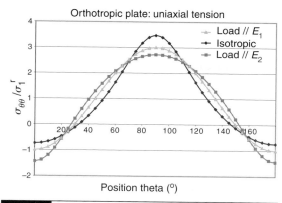

Fig 8.31 Plot of circumferential stress component, $\sigma_{\theta\theta}$, at edge of cylindrical hole in orthotropic elastic material with uniaxial remote stress, σ_1^r. Three different cases are: isotropic (triangles), loading parallel to E_1 (diamonds), and loading parallel to E_2 (squares).

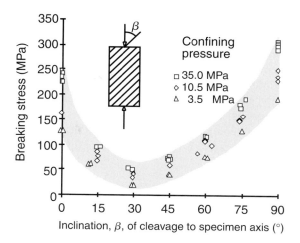

Fig 8.32 Plot of strength versus inclination of cleavage for triaxial tests of Martinsburg Shale for three different confining plessures: $\triangle$, 3.5 Mpa; $\diamond$, 10.5 Mpa; $\square$, 35 Mpa. Reprinted from Donath (1961) with permission of The Geological Society of America.

The normalized circumferential stress (Fig. 8.31) for the isotropic material varies from -1 at $\theta = 0$ to $+3$ at $\theta = \pi/2$. In comparison, the normalized circumferential stress for the anisotropic material defined above, and loaded parallel to the direction of greater Young's modulus, varies from -0.737 at $\theta = 0$ to $+3.475$ at $\theta = \pi/2$. Thus, the local stress acting perpendicular to the remotely applied stress is diminished somewhat less than that for the isotropic material, and the local stress acting parallel to the applied stress is concentrated somewhat more. If the remote loading is parallel to the lesser Young's modulus of this anisotropic material, the circumferential stress varies from -1.443 at $\theta = 0$ to $+2.722$ at $\theta = \pi/2$. Thus, the local stress is diminished somewhat more than that for the isotropic material, and concentrated somewhat less. For the degree of anisotropy used here, the differences in stress concentration and diminution relative to the isotropic material are modest. Using the isotropic solution to model this anisotropic rock does not change the qualitative nature of the stress distribution and the sign changes are preserved from one side of the hole to the other.

In assessing the effect of elastic anisotropy Jaeger and Cook conclude that the ratio $E_1/E_2 = 2$ as used in Fig. 8.31 is "rather extreme, so it is probably true that the effects of anistropy of strength of rocks are much more important in failure under inhomogeneous stresses than effects of anisotropy of elasticity" (Jaeger and Cook, 1979, p. 286). For example, data on the anisotropy of breaking strength under triaxial compression for samples of Martinsburg Shale are shown in Fig. 8.32 where values range over one order of magnitude depending upon the orientation of the cleavage (Donath, 1961). The greatest strength is measured when the cleavage is perpendicular to the compression and the least when the cleavage is at an angle of about 30° to the compression.

8.7 | Concluding remarks

Since the earliest investigations of geologic structures, geologists have used qualitative observations and everyday words to interpret how rocks behave as structures evolve. For example, two commonplace words, *competent* and *incompetent*, have been used to explain the style and relative magnitude of deformation. Being colloquial expressions, these words have been used quite freely to describe the mechanical behaviors of rock: competent implying less easily deformed and incompetent more readily deformed under a given set of forces. While these words are, perhaps, appropriate for ordinary conversations about structures, they lack the formal definition that might make them useful in a quantitative analysis. In this chapter we have introduced the concept of elasticity and the elastic properties of rock. These properties are useful in quantitative investigations of geologic structures because they provide precise measures of the relationship between stress and strain. To understand the tectonic processes that lead to the development of geological structures one must choose an appropriate boundary or initial value problem to serve as a mechanical model. To formulate such a problem one must postulate a particular mechanical behavior. Here we have chosen Hooke's Law for the linear elastic solid; in Chapter 10 we choose Newton's relation for the linear viscous fluid.

Chapter 9

Brittle behavior

Jointed limestone bed at Lilstock Beach on the southern coast of the Bristol Channel, England. Photograph by D. D. Pollard.

An admirer of Nature may be excused becoming enraptured when he takes a view from any of these noble terraces [in County Clare, Ireland]. Looking north, or south, his eyes are riveted on vast surfaces of gray limestone rocks, split up to an extent, and with a regularity of direction, truly wonderful ... The observer becomes so absorbed with the scene that he unconsciously begins to feel as if the rocks under and around him were in process of being illimitably cleft from north to south–as if the earth's crust were in course of splitting up from one pole to the other; and he only rids himself of the feeling to become bewildered with the question, as to what mysterious agent produced the singular phenomenon he is contemplating (King, 1875).

In the preceding chapter we learned that the mechanical behavior of rock under certain conditions can be approximated with a linear elastic material, a mathematical construct formulated using Hooke's Law to relate stress and infinitesimal strain. The elastic material is useful for describing both ancient and modern deformation in the Earth at a variety of length and time scales. However, the limestone described by King as "illimitably cleft from north to south" provides an evocative example of fracturing which is inelastic, non-recoverable deformation. Even if the fracture surfaces were pushed back together they would not heal. Similarly, the limestone bed pictured in the frontispiece for this chapter from Lilstock Beach on the southern margin of the Bristol Channel, England, is broken by numerous fractures, providing visual evidence of inelastic behavior (Rawnsley *et al.*, 1998; Engelder and Peacock, 2001). In this chapter we contemplate the singular phenomenon that bewildered King and describe the modern concepts, laboratory data, and fracture mechanics required to address his question.

A few fracture tips are visible on the bedding surface of the Lilstock exposure (Chapter 9, frontispiece). We infer that the stress state reached the rock strength near the tips of the fractures as they propagated through the limestone, so the local stress–strain behavior was non-linear and irrecoverable there. Presumably the tips now visible represent those points where the local stress dropped below the rock strength and propagation ceased. We also infer, based on experiments and theory to be described in this chapter, that the stress state remained within the elastic range in much of the rock between the fractures. This limited extent of inelastic deformation is characteristic of materials that have deformed in a *brittle state*. We seek to understand the consequences of brittle behavior for the state of stress and strain, the nature of the physical mechanisms that operate during such deformation, and the reasons why inelastic deformation may be localized into thin tabular zones.

9.1 | Brittle deformation in the laboratory and in the field

Laboratory experiments on rock samples loaded beyond their elastic limit under a variety of conditions help us to understand what happens with the onset of inelastic deformation in the Earth (Griggs and Handin, 1960b; Paterson, 1978; Carter *et al.*, 1981; Wong, 1982a,b; Reches, 1983; Reches and Dieterich, 1983; Duba *et al.*, 1990). Griggs and Handin (1960a) provide a useful summary in their illustration (Fig. 9.1) based upon decades of experience testing rock in the laboratory under conditions of triaxial compression and extension. In these experiments cylindrical specimens are subject to a uniform compressive radial stress called the *confining pressure* and an axial compressive stress. The experiments are referred to as *extension tests* (Fig. 9.1a) if the axial stress is the least compressive stress (designated σ_1 according to the sign conventions adopted here) or *compression tests* (Fig. 9.1b) if the axial stress is the greatest compressive stress (designated σ_3).

Rock specimens in extension tests (Fig. 9.1a) typically fail by the formation of an *extension fracture*, oriented perpendicular to the least compressive stress, at axial strains less than about 1%. The relative motion of the surfaces of extension fractures is dominantly opening. In compression tests at low confining pressures (Fig. 9.1b), *splitting fractures* form parallel to the greatest compressive stress at strains from about 1 to 5% (Fig. 9.2a). Splitting fractures also open although wedge-shaped fractures with dominantly shearing motion may develop near the ends of specimens. At modest confining pressures (Fig. 9.1c), *shear fractures* form at an acute angle to the greatest compressive stress at strains from about 2 to 8% (Fig. 9.2b). At greater confining pressures (Fig. 9.1d), the deformation is distributed across a *shear zone* at strains from about 5 to 10% (Fig. 9.2c). At high confining pressure (Fig. 9.1e), shearing is pervasive throughout the specimen, which deforms in what is called the *ductile state* and maintains its integrity to strains greater than 10%. Distributed flow is a characteristic feature of ductile deformation, a topic that we take up in a later chapter. Brittle deformation, in contrast, is localized into discrete fractures or tabular zones.

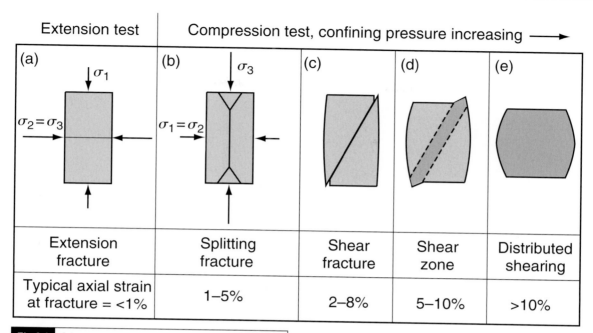

Extension test	Compression test, confining pressure increasing $\longrightarrow$			
(a)	(b)	(c)	(d)	(e)
Extension fracture	Splitting fracture	Shear fracture	Shear zone	Distributed shearing
Typical axial strain at fracture = <1%	1–5%	2–8%	5–10%	>10%

Fig 9.1 Schematic representation of brittle failure styles in triaxial tests. (a) Extension test. (b)–(e) Compression test with confining pressure increasing to the right. Reprinted from Griggs and Handin (1960a) with permission of The Geological Society of America.

Jaeger and Cook comment on the naming of inclined fractures in compression test specimens (Fig. 9.1c and 9.2b) as follows:

Griggs and Handin (1960) ... call it [the inclined fracture] a fault because of its correspondence with geological faulting, and they have been followed by many writers; however, it seems preferable to confine the term fault to the geological context and to retain the term shear fracture in the experimental context (Jaeger and Cook, 1979, p. 86).

Here we choose to follow the recommendation of Jaeger and Cook so the two phenomena, shear fractures in laboratory specimens and faults in Earth's crust, are clearly distinguished. Furthermore, we extend this recommendation to other styles of localized deformation. For example, extension fracture and splitting fracture are terms appropriate for laboratory fractures that open, whereas we confine the term joint to the geological context. What may seem like a semantic detail is important because it emphasizes the fact that laboratory tests rarely duplicate the length and time scales, the materials, or the conditions of

formation of faults or joints. On the other hand laboratory tests may produce useful values of material properties such as elastic stiffness, frictional strength, or fracture toughness over a range of confining pressures, temperatures, and strain rates. Although laboratory triaxial experiments may provide few insights about the processes of faulting or jointing, knowledge of the material properties obtained from them is vital for the development of models of faulting and jointing.

Ultimately the laboratory specimens depicted in the first three columns of Fig. 9.1 break apart into two or more fragments because extension or shear fractures propagate across the rock cylinders, which thereby loose their ability to support the applied compressive stresses. On the other hand, joints and faults are contained within Earth's crust, so any behavior of laboratory specimens that is dependent upon the cylindrical geometry or the properties of the testing apparatus in contact with the specimen is unlikely to be duplicated in nature. For example, consider the joints and faults in the inter-layered limestone and shale beds of the Blue Lias Formation at Lilstock Beach. These are exposed in cross section (Fig. 9.3) along the steep wave-cut cliff just inland from the exposure (Chapter 9, frontispiece) that reveals the joint traces on a single limestone bedding surface. In this cliff exposure vertical joints are seen to

(a)　　　　　　　　　　　(b)　　　　　　　　　　　(c)

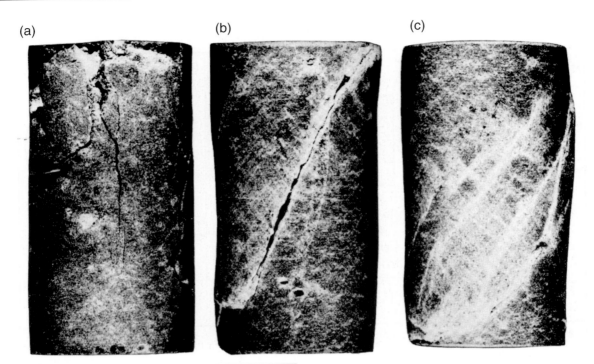

Fig 9.2 Examples of brittle failure in triaxial test specimens of Ohtawa basalt. (a) 0.1 MPa confining pressure. (b) 49 MPa confining pressure. (c) 98 MPa confining pressure. Reprinted from Hoshino et al. (1972) with permission of The Geological Survey of Japan.

fracture the limestone beds but terminate at or near interfaces with adjacent shale beds. Clearly a given limestone bed did not break along a single fracture: multiple parallel joints formed with a regular spacing and ultimately several differently oriented sets of joints developed. Two faults crop out in this exposure that cut across and locally disrupt the otherwise nearly horizontal bedding. Unlike a single open joint, each fault is composed of multiple closely spaced surfaces and each surface is in intimate contact with another surface. Members of this set of faults do not terminate within the exposure so their extent is unknown, but detailed knowledge of the stratigraphy has been used to estimate a few meters to a few tens of meters of slip (Engelder and Peacock, 2001). The juxtaposition of limestone and shale beds, the magnitude of the slip, the rotation of the fractured limestone blocks, and the flowage of the shale are some of the characteristics of these faults that are not duplicated in laboratory experiments.

Laboratory experiments other than the standard triaxial test are motivated by field observations of joints and faults. For example, exposures that reveal the tips of joints (Chapter 9, frontispiece) raise the question: what is the resistance to propagation of a single opening fracture in rock? To understand how the concentrated tensile stresses along the advancing fracture tip are resisted by rock strength one may conduct an experiment (Fig. 9.4a) where control of the oppositely directed displacement of the two pins enables one to monitor fracture propagation and measure the so-called *fracture toughness* of the rock specimen (Atkinson and Meredith, 1987). Specimens made up of layers of the same or different materials enable the researcher to investigate opening fractures that stop or propagate across layer interfaces (Renshaw and Pollard, 1995; McConaughy and Engelder, 2001). Exposures of faults such as those at Lilstock Beach (Fig. 9.3) raise the question: what is the resistance to sliding of one specimen in direct contact with another of the same or dissimilar rock type? Laboratory studies (Fig. 9.4b) of *frictional strength* help to address this question. While fracture toughness or friction experiments focus attention on mechanical aspects of opening fractures or

Fig 9.3 Joints and faults in inter-layered limestone and shale of the Blue Lias Formation at Lilstock Beach, Bristol Channel, England. Photograph by D. D. Pollard.

sliding surfaces that may be more relevant to the processes of jointing or faulting in the Earth than the triaxial experiment, the relevant material heterogeneities (sedimentary bedding, lithologic contacts, other joints or faults, etc.) that may play crucial roles in these processes typically are not included at laboratory scales. The challenge for the structural geologist is to understand these complex processes when direct laboratory simulations are not possible.

9.2 | Strength of laboratory samples

Rock samples tested in the laboratory under conditions that promote brittle behavior cannot be loaded to arbitrary values of stress, but are limited to values less than the *strength* of the sample. Because the strength of certain engineering materials, like steel, is greater than that of many rocks, it is possible to construct a laboratory

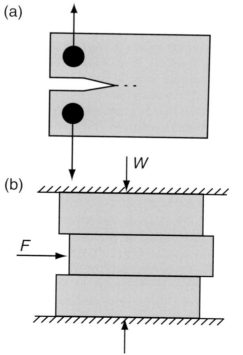

Fig 9.4 Alternative testing configurations to the triaxial test. (a) Crack propagation test. (b) Frictional sliding test.

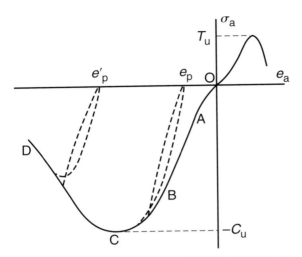

Fig 9.5 Generic axial stress versus axial extension curves for uniaxial tension and compression tests. Uniaxial tensile strength, T_u, and compressive strength, C_u.

Here f is the force recorded by the load cell, A is the measured cross-sectional area of the sample, L_i is the measured length of the undeformed sample, and $L - L_i$ is the displacement of the platen recorded by the displacement transducer. Alternatively, the strain may be measured by electrical resistance strain gages attached directly to the sample (Fig. 8.25). The axial stress should be adjusted for changes in the cross-sectional area, and non-uniformities in the state of stress caused by shear tractions imparted to the sample by differences in lateral extension of the platen and the sample should be considered in the design of the experiment (Peng, 1971). Furthermore, axial strain is not a component of the strain tensor as defined in Chapter 5, but is a measure of deformation commonly called the extension or the elongation. We refer to this quantity as the axial strain since that is the convention used in rock testing laboratories.

The "generic" stress–strain curve (Fig. 9.5) illustrates several important concepts and facilitates the definition of key terminology. For samples loaded in compression, the segment OA represents non-linear elastic adjustments (e.g. closing of cracks) and is followed by a nearly linear elastic segment AB with a slope that would be Young's modulus if the behavior were strictly linear. The segment BC is concave upward because inelastic deformation mechanisms within the sample act to decrease the stiffness. These mechanisms are irreversible, so unloading on the dashed path results in a permanent axial strain e_p. Upon reloading of the deformed sample, the stress–strain plot returns approximately to the original curve. The rock is said to be in a *ductile state* because it is accumulating permanent strain while subject to an increasing magnitude of compressive stress. The slope of the curve continues to decline as the sample shortens until the minimum stress (greatest compression) is reached at point C. For uniaxial tests, the stress at this point is the negative of the uniaxial compressive strength, C_u. The generic tensile test has a similar stress–strain curve (Fig. 9.5), here plotted in the first quadrant because both stress and strain are positive quantities. The tensile stress is limited by the uniaxial tensile strength, T_u.

The point C on Fig. 9.5 represents the beginning of the process of *failure*. The segment CD has

testing machine that can load rock samples to their limiting values of stress. Furthermore, the load-bearing members of the machine can be designed with greater cross-sectional area than the sample, so the net force induces a lesser stress in the machine than in the sample. An example of such a machine is shown in Fig. 8.25. The outer steel frame supports the load transmitted through the sample from a mobile platen to a fixed platen. A hydraulic pump provides pressure to move a piston that is attached to the mobile platen. A computer controls the flow of the hydraulic fluid (and thereby the motion of this platen) based upon electronic readings from a displacement transducer and load cell that monitor the deformation and loading of the sample.

Data from such tests on cylindrical samples of rock usually are recorded on graphs of axial stress, σ_a, plotted versus axial strain, e_a (Fig. 9.5), and the so-called *stress–strain curve* is used to understand and characterize the behavior of the sample (Jaeger and Cook, 1979). Note that tension and extension are taken as positive for this stress–strain graph. The *axial stress* and *axial strain* are calculated as follows:

$$\sigma_a = \frac{f}{A}, \quad e_a = \frac{L - L_i}{L_i} \tag{9.1}$$

a negative slope and the inelastic mechanisms operating there are responsible for a degradation of the load-carrying capacity as the sample continues to shorten and the failure process develops. The sample is said to be in a *brittle state* because it is accumulating permanent strain as the magnitude of the compressive stress decreases. Unloading during this brittle deformation along the dashed path results in a larger permanent strain, e'_p, and reloading returns approximately to the original curve. Tests typically end at a strain limited by the apparatus (e.g. point D) or complete failure of the sample.

9.2.1 Soft and stiff testing machines

Given a well-designed testing machine, the testing procedure to determine strength is straightforward: load the sample until it starts to lose its capacity to carry the load, and record the extreme value of stress. However, to understand the process of failure one must understand the mechanical interplay between the sample and the testing machine. It turns out that the machines can play a strong, and even dominant, role in the outcome of mechanical property tests and experiments. Indeed, the particular action of these machines has strongly influenced our understanding of how rock specimens behave when they are fracturing, so we need to understand this action and ask if it might duplicate the behavior of the Earth during natural deformation events. This action, as we learn in this section, depends upon whether the machine is soft or stiff relative to the rock sample.

For many discussions of extension and shear fracturing in the literature of rock mechanics the stress–strain curve after failure initiates is not shown because the testing machine was incapable of tracking these quantities accurately during the rapid failure event. Shortly after reaching the peak stress (Fig. 9.5, point C), the data stream was terminated because the specimen disintegrated into a pile of rock chips and dust with a loud bang. As early as 1943 it was clear that explosive disintegration was not necessarily a natural behavior, but rather "elastic energy is stored in the cylinder and in the machine … and the release of this energy causes the breakdown of the cylinder" (Whitney, 1943). Curiosity about the post-peak-stress part of the stress–strain curve led researchers to try to capture the *complete stress–strain curve* and to understand what influence the testing machine might have on the specimen behavior during failure (Hudson *et al.*, 1972; Jaeger and Cook, 1979, p. 177).

Consider the schematic illustration of a testing machine (Fig. 8.25) and note that it is composed of two basic components: an *hydraulic actuator* (including piston and cylinder, rod, and platen) for applying a force to the specimen and a *reaction frame* (tie-bars and cross-heads) for supporting this force. When fluid pressure is increased in the actuator the piston is driven downward applying a compression to the specimen and shortening it. The downward directed force is transmitted through the specimen to the lower cross-head. The actuator also applies an equivalent upward directed force to the upper cross-head so the tie-bars are placed in tension and elongate, while the cross-head bends. Both the actuator and the reaction frame deform and are capable of storing elastic energy. If the mechanical parts of the testing machine combine to be very much stiffer than the rock specimen, the machine would deform very little and we could ignore its role in the test. However, specimens are explosively disintegrated in some testing machines because the energy stored in the machine is released into the specimen even though no fluid is pumped into the actuator to do additional work. In other words, the *system* composed of the machine and the specimen self-destructs.

To understand this process the initial deformation of the specimen is idealized (Fig. 9.6a) with a spring of constant stiffness, C_s. The machine frame is idealized with two springs of stiffness $C_m/2$ in parallel and tied together with an upper and lower rigid bar. All of these springs are tied to a rigid basal support which is taken as the reference frame for measuring displacements. The vertical y-axis is positive downward so forces and displacement acting downward are positive. Two applied forces idealize the actuator: F_s acting downward on the specimen spring and F_m acting upward on the rigid bar joining the two machine springs (Fig. 9.6b). These forces are identical in magnitude and opposite in direction, so $F_s = -F_m$. Under the applied force, F_s, the specimen spring contracts and its upper end moves toward the

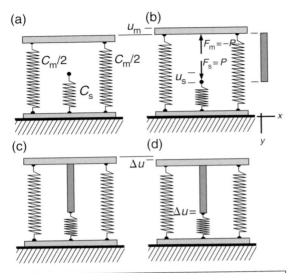

Fig 9.6 Idealized specimen and testing machine used to investigate stability of tests in soft and stiff testing machines.

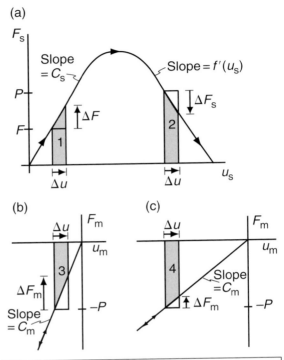

Fig 9.7 Force versus displacement plots for idealized specimen and machine of Figure 9.6. (a) Specimen. (b) Stiff testing machine. (c) Soft testing machine.

lower support with a displacement, u_s (Fig. 9.6b). On a force versus displacement graph (Fig. 9.7a) the linear relationship, $F_s = C_s u_s$, plots in the first quadrant because both quantities are positive. Meanwhile, under the action of the force, F_m, the machine springs extend and their upper ends move away from the lower support with a displacement, u_m (Fig. 9.6b). The linear relationship, $F_m = C_m u_m$, for the combined machine springs plots in the third quadrant (Fig. 9.7b, c) because both quantities are negative. We show stress–strain behaviors for a "stiff" machine (greater slope) and a "soft" machine (lesser slope).

For a rock specimen tested into the inelastic portion of the stress–strain curve the force, F_s, is not related linearly to the displacement, u_s, but takes on a relationship we characterize in a general way as $F_s = f(u_s)$. The slope of the stress–strain curve for the specimen is quantified by the first derivative of the function f with respect to u_s which we write as $f'(u_s)$. In the initial stage of the test $f'(u_s) = C_s$, so the slope is positive and constant (Fig. 9.7a), whereas after inelastic deformation begins $f'(u_s)$ is variable. At the peak value of stress the slope is zero and thereafter $f'(u_s)$ is negative. For the machine the linear relationship is retraced as the load decreases and the displacement fully recovers in the post-peak elastic regime (Fig. 9.7b, c).

The work done in this one-dimensional system by a constant applied force *on* an object is defined as the product of the force and displacement magnitudes, $W = Fu$. Work is positive if the force acts in the same direction as the displacement of the object, so a positive W implies that work is done *on* the object whereas a negative W implies work is done *by* the object. Because the force changes continuously with displacement we define work as the integral:

$$W_{12} = \int_{u_1}^{u_2} f(u)\, du \tag{9.2}$$

The work is equivalent to the area under the curve $f(u)$ on a force versus displacement graph between the two limiting displacements, u_1 and u_2. We do not specify a particular function, $f(u)$, and integrate it, but rather we geometrically determine the incremental work as one of the areas, 1 through 4 (Fig. 9.7) and compare them (Hudson *et al.*, 1972).

Consider a test in which loading has progressed along the elastic portion of the force–displacement curve until $F_s = F$ (Fig. 9.7a). For the next small increment of force, ΔF, the displacement increases by Δu and the increment of work done by the force on the specimen spring is:

$$\Delta W = F\Delta u + \tfrac{1}{2}\Delta F\Delta u \qquad (9.3)$$

ΔW is called the *virtual work* and Δu is called the *virtual displacement*. We use (9.3) to calculate the virtual work associated with the specimen and testing machine in the post-peak stress regime. In that regime, suppose the actuator applies forces $F_s = P$ and $F_m = -P$ so the system is in equilibrium. Imagine replacing the actuator with a perfectly rigid bar that transmits this force and couples the specimen and machine springs so they must displace by the same amount (Fig. 9.6c). If a downward virtual displacement, Δu, is imposed on the upper horizontal bar (Fig. 9.6d), the forces within the springs change as:

$$\Delta F_m = C_m\Delta u$$
$$\Delta F_s = f'(u_s)\Delta u = -|f'(u_s)|\Delta u, \ \text{post-peak stress} \qquad (9.4)$$

Using (9.3) the virtual work for the machine and specimen are:

$$\Delta W_m = -P\Delta u + \tfrac{1}{2}C_m(\Delta u)^2$$
$$\Delta W_s = P\Delta u - \tfrac{1}{2}|f'(u_s)|(\Delta u)^2 \qquad (9.5)$$

Note that Δu is small (less than unity), so $(\Delta u)^2$ is very small. Thus, the leading terms in (9.5) are larger than the second terms, so ΔW_m is a negative quantity and ΔW_s is positive. That is, work is done *by* the machine *on* the specimen.

The next step in the mechanical analysis is to determine if the system is stable by asking: what are the conditions under which the system will spontaneously evolve to a different state? Such a spontaneous response could represent catastrophic failure of the specimen. To address this question we apply the *principle of virtual work*: for any possible virtual displacement of an elastic body in equilibrium, the total virtual work done by the internal forces, the body forces, and the surface forces must vanish (Venkatraman and Patel, 1970, p. 120). Possible virtual displacements

are those that are not prevented by the boundary conditions, such as the fixed lower bar. Applying this principle to the system illustrated in Fig. 9.7 we add the two equations in (9.5) and set the results equal to zero:

$$\Delta W_m + \Delta W_s = \tfrac{1}{2}\Big[C_m - |f'(u_s)|\Big](\Delta u)^2 = 0 \qquad (9.6)$$

The system is in static equilibrium only if the machine stiffness, C_m, and the magnitude of the specimen stiffness, $|f'(u_s)|$, are identical.

To understand the implications of (9.6) we examine the two cases where equilibrium is not attained. First, consider the machine to be stiffer than the specimen, so $C_m > |f'(u_s)|$ and area 2 is greater than area 3 (Fig. 9.7a, b). For this condition, the work that the machine spring can do on the rest of the system is not sufficient to meet the requirements of the work done on the specimen spring. To achieve the downward displacement, Δu, work must be done by some external force, for example the hydraulic pump supplies more fluid to the actuator, thereby increasing the applied force. These testing conditions are described as *stable* because the system will remain in static equilibrium unless some external action is taken. If this external action is carefully controlled, the test can proceed under stable conditions and the complete stress–strain curve will be captured.

Now suppose the machine is softer than the specimen spring, so $C_m < |f'(u_s)|$ and area 2 is less than area 4 (Fig. 9.7a, c). The machine spring can do more work than the specimen spring requires; so if the distance between the upper bar and the specimen spring is not changed, the machine will drive the top of the specimen downward at an accelerating rate. For an actual testing machine, this could lead to a catastrophic result, and the stress–strain information for the remainder of the test would be lost. These testing conditions are described as *unstable* because the system self-destructs unless some external action is taken, for example the hydraulic pump drains fluid out of the actuator, thus decreasing the applied force. This must happen at a sufficient rate for the system to remain in equilibrium. Another solution is to control the test using the displacement of the specimen, u_s, instead of the force from the actuator. Modern testing machines use servo-control systems in which computers, connected to transducers monitoring force and displacement, are capable of feeding back the corrective action to sensitive hydraulic valves in order to stabilize the test.

Because C_m is always positive, instability requires that the derivative of the specimen force–displacement curve, $f'(u_s)$, be negative according to (9.6). Therefore we conclude that instability is only possible in the post-failure region of the typical stress–strain curve. Furthermore, instability requires that the magnitude of $f'(u_s)$ exceed that of C_m. Thus, unstable specimen behavior is defined as:

$$|f'(u_s)| > C_m \quad \text{and} \quad f'(u_s) < 0, \text{ unstable} \quad (9.7)$$

A soft testing machine is one in which the post-failure behavior is unstable. It should be clear that rock testing to failure and beyond is not a trivial endeavor, but these issues are, for the most part, addressed by modern servo-controlled testing machines.

9.2.2 Uniaxial tensile and compressive strength

Definitions of the *uniaxial tensile strength*, T_u, and *uniaxial compressive strength*, C_u, are written in terms of the extreme values of the axial stress, σ_a, and are conditional on the presumed homogeneous state of stress written here in terms of the principal values:

$$T_u \equiv \sigma_a(\text{max}), \quad \sigma_1 > 0, \quad \sigma_2 = 0 = \sigma_3 \quad (9.8)$$

$$C_u \equiv |\sigma_a(\text{min})|, \quad \sigma_1 = 0 = \sigma_2, \quad \sigma_3 < 0 \quad (9.9)$$

The tests usually are conducted at room (atmospheric) pressure, so the actual values of the two equal principal stresses are about -0.1 MPa. This is negligible compared to typical rock strengths in uniaxial tests which are of the order 10 to 100 MPa. The uniaxial tensile and compressive strengths have the same units and dimensions as stress:

$$\text{strength}, T_u \text{ or } C_u \ [=] \text{N m}^{-2} = \text{Pa} \quad (9.10)$$

$$T_u\{=\}\text{ML}^{-1}\text{T}^{-2}, C_u\{=\}\text{ML}^{-1}\text{T}^{-2} \quad (9.11)$$

Strength is a scalar quantity and does not carry a sign.

A schematic illustration of a uniaxial tensile strength apparatus is shown in Fig. 9.8 (Obert and

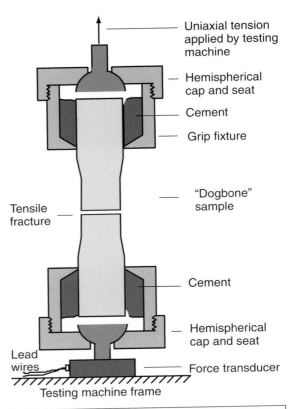

Fig 9.8 Specimen holder for uniaxial tensile strength test (Obert and Duvall, 1967). Dogbone sample is broken by a tensile fracture.

Duvall, 1967). The ends of the rock specimen are held by cementing them onto end pieces, attached to the testing machine through hemispherical caps and seats. The objective is to record the maximum value of the axial stress (9.8) and thereby measure the strength. These tests are designed to impart a uniform stress state throughout the sample; however, by cementing the specimen to the end pieces it is forced to contract radially and extend axially in concert with the end piece. This constraint can induce elevated and non-uniform stresses within the sample that can lead to premature failure. By machining the specimen to a smaller radius near its mid-section (Fig. 9.8) a "dogbone"-shaped sample is prepared that carries greater stress at the mid-section in proportion to the reduced cross-sectional area (Jaeger and Cook, 1979). With this shape, failure can be induced away from the end constraints, in a

Table 9.1. Rock mechanics laboratory tests for uniaxial tensile strength (MPa).			
Rock type	From	To	Mean
Quartzite	17	28	25
Gneiss	3	21	14
Basalt	2	28	13
Granite	3	39	12
Limestone	2	40	12
Sandstone	3	7	5
Shale	2	5	3
Pittsburgh coal	1.9	3.2	2.5

Table 9.2. Rock mechanics laboratory tests for uniaxial compressive strength (MPa).			
Rock type	From	To	Mean
Quartzite	200	304	252
Gneiss	73	340	159
Basalt	42	355	150
Granite	30	324	166
Limestone	48	210	102
Sandstone	40	179	96
Shale	36	172	95
Pittsburgh coal	14	30	22

region that has a more homogeneous state of stress.

A data set (Table 9.1) for uniaxial tensile strengths (Bieniawski, 1984) is given for the same suite of rocks used to tabulate elastic properties (refer to Tables 8.2 and 8.3).

The uniaxial tensile strengths range over about one order of magnitude among all rock types tabulated, and even among different samples of the same lithology. The tensile strengths for crystalline rocks can be as small as those for clastic sedimentary rocks, but typically they are somewhat greater. We conclude that laboratory specimens of rock have uniaxial tensile strengths that range from about 2 to 40 MPa with a "typical" value of about 10 MPa.

Comparing the apparent Young's moduli from Table 8.2 to the tensile strengths of Table 9.1, notice that the Young's moduli are several thousand times greater than the tensile strengths. Using 1:4000 as representative of the ratio of tensile strength to Young's modulus, the value of the axial extension at failure would be $e_a(max) = T_u/E \approx 2.5 \times 10^{-4}$. A practical consequence of this great difference between Young's modulus and the uniaxial tensile strength is that axial extensions in uniaxial test samples are very small. In most cases the deformation is approximately elastic for these small extensions. We conclude that rocks have an elastic stiffness on the order of 10^3 times the tensile strength under these conditions.

An apparatus for conducting uniaxial compressive tests is shown in Fig. 8.25. Again, the objective is to induce a uniform normal stress along the axis of the specimen and record the magnitude of its minimum (most compressive) value (9.9). Friction between the end platens and the sample may constrain the sample to expand laterally in concert with the platens. The resulting stress state near the ends can be non-uniform and not uniaxial. The effects of the end platens on the local stress state and the consequences for style and localization of deformation in uniaxial compression have been investigated (Peng, 1971; Peng and Johnson, 1972). Proposed methods to compensate for this effect include matching the elastic constants of the end platens to the sample and inserting materials between the ends and the platens to reduce the friction. These and other refinements of testing procedures have resulted in more accurate determinations of uniaxial compressive strengths (Bieniawski and Bernede, 1979).

Selected uniaxial compressive strengths are given in Table 9.2 (Bieniawski, 1984).

These uniaxial compressive strengths range over about one order of magnitude. Crystalline rocks tend to have greater compressive strengths than clastic sedimentary rocks, but some granites are weaker than some shales. We conclude that laboratory specimens of rock have uniaxial compressive strengths that range from about 30 to 350 MPa with a "typical" value of about 150 MPa. Comparing Tables 9.1 and 9.2 we draw another conclusion: typical laboratory samples of rock subject to uniaxial loading are weaker in tension than in compression by about one order of magnitude. This has profound implications for the development of brittle deformation in Earth's crust and its interpretation by structural geologists.

The minimum value of the axial strain (contraction) before failure is determined by comparing the Young's moduli and uniaxial compressive strengths taken from Tables 8.2 and 9.2, respectively. Using $1:300$ as a representative value for the ratio of compressive strength to Young's modulus, we have $e_a(\min) = -C_u/E \approx -3.3 \times 10^{-3}$. This and the preceding example should reinforce the important concept that stiffness and strength are different by three or four orders of magnitude, and that the magnitudes of the axial strains at the initiation of failure for these brittle materials are on the order of 10^{-3} to 10^{-4}.

Given the very small elastic strains that precede failure in uniaxial tests one might conclude that elastic deformation is unimportant for structural geologists. This would be a mistake. For one thing, it is common to have a "sample" length, L, measured in kilometers for structures in the Earth, so typical displacements would be on the order of decimeters to meters. For example, the dike at Ship Rock (Fig. 2.7) is about 3 km long and the adjacent rock was displaced about 1 m as the dike opened. Some of the fault segments that ruptured during the Hector Mine earthquake (Fig. 8.13) are more than 10 km long and slip up to several meters was recorded along their surface traces. Yet the surface displacement field clearly correlates with that of an elastic model. Thus, for structural geologists, the elastic strains that accompany brittle fracture play an important role in crustal deformation.

The most prominent macroscopic mechanism that acts to limit the stress under conditions of uniaxial testing is fracture. The word *macroscopic* is used here to refer to phenomena, observable with the unaided eye, such as extension fractures, splitting fractures, and shear fractures (Figs. 9.1 and 9.2). In contrast, the word *microscopic* refers to the grain-scale phenomena within the sample that individually are visible only with a microscope or hand lens. The details of the grain-scale deformation during these experiments, the ways in which this deformation proceeds to weaken the whole specimen over the course of the test, and the *strain localization* into discrete fractures along which the specimen breaks can be quite complex (Peng and Johnson, 1972). A great deal of research has been devoted to identifying the microscopic mecha-

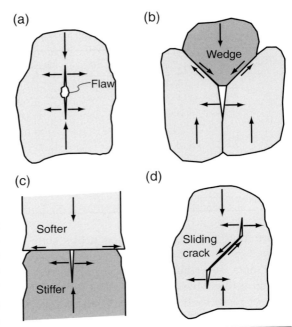

Fig 9.9 Schematic examples of microscopic mechanisms of deformation at the grain scale in rock during strength tests. (a) Microcrack growth from flaws within mineral grains. (b) Wedging of one grain between neighbors with grain boundary sliding. (c) Lateral extension of soft grain promotes crack growth in adjacent stiff grain. (d) Slip of inclined flaw induces wing cracks.

nisms of deformation during strength tests of rock, both in uniaxial and multi-axial compression (Tapponnier and Brace, 1976; Wong, 1982b; Kranz, 1983). The mechanisms of deformation include the nucleation, opening, and propagation of isolated microcracks from flaws within grains (Fig. 9.9a). Loads are concentrated at contacts between grains (Fig. 9.9b) and one grain may be driven into the other, opening a crack. The extension of a compliant (soft) grain parallel to the contact with a stiffer grain (Fig. 9.9c) can drive the growth of opening microcracks in the stiffer grain. Inclined grain boundaries, pre-existing cracks, or cleavages can slip during loading in compression, thereby creating tensile stress concentrations near the tips of the slipping surfaces from which opening (wing) cracks nucleate (Fig. 9.9d).

In conclusion, uniaxial tests measure the bulk strength of the collection of constituent mineral grains, cracks, pores, and other heterogeneities that make up particular samples. As such these samples may or may not be representative of the strength in the natural setting of that rock, or of the state that rock was in during the tectonic event of interest to the structural geologist. Both the uniformity of the stress and the homogeneity of the rock sample need to be evaluated when interpreting the results of laboratory strength tests. Finally, the strength criteria (9.8) and (9.9) do not explicitly address the physical mechanisms responsible for the loss of load-carrying capacity; they simply assert that this happens at a certain stress level.

9.2.3 Polyaxial strength, stress invariants, and stress deviation

Below the traction-free surface of the Earth the state of stress may be approximated by Anderson's standard state, introduced in Chapter 6, in which the principal stresses are equal in magnitude $(\sigma_1 = \sigma_2 = \sigma_3)$ and become more compressive linearly with depth. This isotropic state of stress is likely to be supplemented in regions of tectonic activity by stresses that result in a *polyaxial state of stress*: the principal stresses have different magnitudes, none of which is likely to be zero. In principal stress space (Fig. 9.10), the uniaxial tensile strength plots as a point $(T_u, 0, 0)$ on the positive σ_1-axis and the uniaxial compressive strength plots as a point $(0, 0, -C_u)$ on the negative σ_3-axis. The paths representing these tests are straight lines from the origin. A third path lies in the plane $(\sigma_1 = \sigma_2)$ and extends into the octant where all principal stresses are compressive along the straight line $\sigma_1 = \sigma_2 = \sigma_3$. This represents the isotropic compressive loading envisioned by Anderson and usually is followed initially in laboratory "triaxial" tests. Then, two of the principal stresses are held constant and equal to what is called the confining pressure, $-P_c$, while the third principal stress becomes more compressive until failure at the point $(-P_c, -P_c, -C_t)$, the "triaxial" compressive strength (see next section). Strength in the context of a polyaxial state of stress is represented by a surface, called the *failure surface,* that passes through these three points. The complete failure surface separates possible states of stress between the origin and the surface from impossible states of stress on and beyond the surface.

The combination of principal stresses $(\sigma_1, \sigma_2, \sigma_3)$ at any point on the failure surface represents

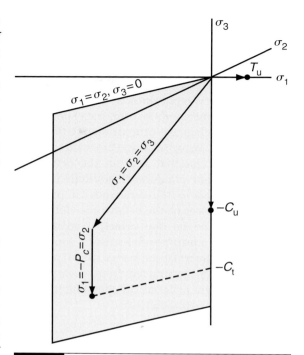

Fig 9.10 Plot in principal stress space with uniaxial tensile and compressive strengths, T_u and C_u, and triaxial compressive strength, C_t.

the strength. We define a *criterion for failure* as a function of the principal stresses that represents the failure surface and write this function in terms of the *stress invariants* as defined in Chapter 6. Recall that the invariants have the special property that they do not change magnitude with the orientation of the Cartesian coordinate system. Because physical properties of a material, such as strength, should not depend upon the arbitrary orientation of a coordinate system, it is natural to define such properties in terms of the stress invariants (Jaeger and Cook, 1979). Criteria for failure under uniaxial conditions are equivalent to placing limiting values on the first invariant of the stress tensor, $I_1 = \sigma_1 + \sigma_2 + \sigma_3$, when only one principal stress is non-zero:

$$I_1 = T_0, \quad \sigma_2 = 0 = \sigma_3 \tag{9.12}$$

$$I_1 = -C_0, \quad \sigma_1 = 0 = \sigma_2 \tag{9.13}$$

Note that this pre-supposes that the initiation of failure depends only upon the current homogeneous state of stress. That is, failure does not depend upon stress gradients or the history of loading.

For a polyaxial state of stress it is commonly assumed that failure is primarily related to the distortion of a material, whereas changes in volume are of secondary importance. Recall from our discussion of the bulk modulus of elasticity in Chapter 8 that volume change is proportional to the mean normal stress, $\sigma_m = \frac{1}{3}(\sigma_1 + \sigma_2 + \sigma_3) = \frac{1}{3}(I_1)$. This is the normal stress that acts on the octahedral planes, the eight planes with normals that are equally inclined to the directions of principal stress. The vertices of the octahedron defined by these planes lie on the principal stress axes. Therefore, the mean normal stress is sometimes referred to as the *octahedral normal stress*. The mean normal stress is subtracted from each normal stress component to define the components of the *stress deviation tensor* as follows:

$$s_{xx} = \sigma_{xx} - \sigma_m, \quad s_{yy} = \sigma_{yy} - \sigma_m, \quad s_{zz} = \sigma_{zz} - \sigma_m,$$
$$s_{yz} = \sigma_{yz}, \quad s_{zx} = \sigma_{zx}, \quad s_{xy} = \sigma_{xy} \quad (9.14)$$

Note that the shear stress components are identical to the shear stress deviation components.

The invariants of stress deviation are (Jaeger and Cook, 1979):

$$J_1 = s_{xx} + s_{yy} + s_{zz} = 0$$
$$J_2 = -(s_{xx}s_{yy} + s_{yy}s_{zz} + s_{zz}s_{xx}) + s_{xy}^2 + s_{yz}^2 + s_{zx}^2$$
$$J_3 = s_{xx}s_{yy}s_{zz} + 2s_{xy}s_{yz}s_{zx} - s_{xx}s_{yz}^2 \quad (9.15)$$
$$\quad - s_{yy}s_{zx}^2 - s_{zz}s_{xy}^2$$

The second invariant of stress deviation is related to the shear stress acting on the octahedral planes which is called the *octahedral shear stress*, σ_o:

$$\sigma_o = \frac{1}{3}[(\sigma_1 - \sigma_2)^2 + (\sigma_2 - \sigma_3)^2 + (\sigma_3 - \sigma_1)^2]^{1/2}$$
$$= \sqrt{\frac{2}{3}J_2} \quad (9.16)$$

For materials that failure due to shearing one possible criterion using stress deviation invariants is based on the octahedral shear stress attaining a critical value, O_o, taken as a constant (Jaeger and Cook, 1979):

$$O_o \equiv \sigma_o(\text{max}) \quad (9.17)$$

Here O_o is the *octahedral shear strength* of the material (Hobbs, 1962).

In practice, strength has been defined using many different combinations of the stress components as dictated by the many different kinds of testing machines and sample configurations that have been invented. Some of these are based on a mathematical premise, such as dependence upon invariants of stress or of stress deviation, whereas others are based on physical arguments for the causes and mechanisms of failure. Usually these strength criteria may be characterized as some functional relationship among the components of principal stress (Jaeger and Cook, 1979):

$$\sigma_1 = f(\sigma_2, \sigma_3) \quad (9.18)$$

Each of these functions defines a *failure surface* in principal stress space. These criteria do not take possible spatial gradients in the stress field into account, so they must be applied on a point-by-point basis in a heterogeneous field of stress.

9.2.4 Triaxial strength, confining pressure, and pore pressure

Largely because of the technical difficulties in the design of a true polyaxial apparatus, the most common procedure used in rock mechanics is the *triaxial test*. The conditions imposed are illustrated in principal stress space (Fig. 9.10) and the apparatus is shown in a schematic cross section (Fig. 9.11). More complete and precise engineering drawings are available (Griggs and Handin, 1960b). The apparatus itself is placed between the two platens of a testing machine (Fig. 8.25), which provides the axial load. A key feature of the apparatus is a port for supplying fluid, under pressure called the *confining pressure*, P_c, to the region between the inner wall of the pressure vessel and the cylindrical jacket surrounding the rock sample. The jacket, often rubber or malleable metal like copper, is impermeable to fluids and more easily deformed than the sample itself. A separate port can supply a different fluid, under pressure called the *pore pressure*, P_p, directly to the sample surface, and thence to the internal pores of the rock. Because $P_p < P_c$, the pore fluid does not inflate the jacket and stays within the rock pores. A furnace can be attached to the pressure vessel to heat the sample and the vessel to a designated temperature. Here we examine the role that

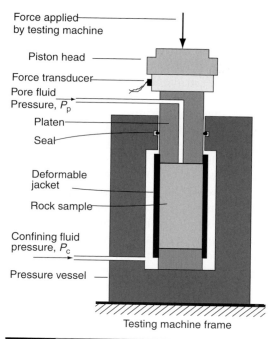

Force applied by testing machine

Piston head

Force transducer

Pore fluid Pressure, P_p

Platen

Seal

Deformable jacket

Rock sample

Confining fluid pressure, P_c

Pressure vessel

Testing machine frame

Fig 9.11 Schematic illustration of a triaxial testing apparatus.

confining pressure and pore pressure play in determining rock strength under conditions of brittle deformation.

The design objective for triaxial vessels (Fig. 9.11) is to achieve a uniform state of stress and pore pressure throughout the rock sample. The axial and radial stress components are presumed to be related to the applied force, f, and confining pressure, P_c, as:

$$\sigma_a = -f/A = \sigma_1 \text{ or } \sigma_3$$
$$\sigma_r = -P_c = \sigma_2 \text{ and } \sigma_3, \text{ or } \sigma_1 \text{ and } \sigma_2 \qquad (9.19)$$

The apparatus is called "triaxial," but it is not capable of imposing normal stresses of different magnitudes in three coordinate directions, only in the axial and radial directions. To record the results of a triaxial test graphically, some experimentalists plot the *differential stress*, $\Delta\sigma$, versus the axial strain, e_a (Clark, 1966), where:

$$\Delta\sigma = \sigma_a - \sigma_r \qquad (9.20)$$

The rationale is that rock samples only change in volume during loading to an isotropic state of

stress, $\sigma_a = \sigma_r$, but they change in shape for non-isotropic stress states, and these shape changes are believed to be related to failure. Recall, however, that an anisotropic elastic material will distort under isotropic loading (Chapter 8), so this presumption is appropriate, at best, for samples that are isotropic with respect to elastic properties.

Positive differential stress corresponds to *extension tests* and negative differential stress corresponds to *compression tests* (Fig. 9.1). Extreme values of the differential stress are recorded as the *differential strength* for extension, D_e, and compression, D_c, respectively:

$$D_e \equiv \Delta\sigma(\text{max}), \quad \sigma_1 > -P_c, \quad \sigma_2 = -P_c = \sigma_3 \qquad (9.21)$$

$$D_c \equiv |\Delta\sigma(\text{min})|, \quad \sigma_1 = -P_c = \sigma_2, \quad \sigma_3 < -P_c \qquad (9.22)$$

Some experimentalists use the extreme value of the axial stress as the measure of strength in triaxial tests (Jaeger and Cook, 1979):

$$C_t \equiv |\sigma_a(\text{min})|, \quad \sigma_1 = -P_c = \sigma_2, \quad \sigma_3 < -P_c \qquad (9.23)$$

For a compression test this is referred to as the *triaxial compressive strength* (Fig. 9.10).

As an example of results from triaxial testing consider data from a study of sedimentary rocks from the Tertiary basins of Japan (Hoshino et al., 1972). One hundred different rocks, ranging in age from Pliocene to Oligocene, were deformed in triaxial compression at room temperature, and the differential strengths, D_c, were recorded at confining pressures ranging from 0.1 MPa (atmospheric pressure) to 245 MPa (equivalent to about 10 km depth). The lithologies were primarily claystone, siltstone, shale, and sandstone, although a few volcanic rocks were included. All of the samples were dried (atmospheric pore pressure), and all were cored so the cylindrical axis was perpendicular to the sedimentary bedding. The triaxial compressive strengths (9.23) for three sandstones are used to plot the stress state at failure (Fig. 9.12) in the principal stress plane defined by the confining pressure and the axial compression.

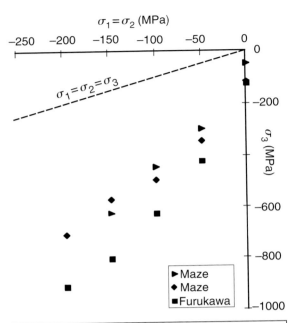

$\sigma_1 = \sigma_2$ (MPa)

$\sigma_1 = \sigma_2 = \sigma_3$

σ_3 (MPa)

► Maze
◆ Maze
■ Furukawa

Fig 9.12 Plot of triaxial strength data in principal stress space for three sandstones from Tertiary basins of Japan (Hoshino et al., 1972).

The uniaxial compressive strengths for the three sandstones range from 46 to 113 to 122 MPa, so there is considerable variability in strength even among samples representing the same lithology. The two samples of Maze sandstone, taken from the same formation, differ by almost a factor of three. Presumably these differences reflect subtle differences in the constituents of these rocks that are not reflected in their lithologic and formation names. The triaxial compressive strengths, $C_t = -\sigma_3$, increase as confining pressure, $P_c = -\sigma_1$, increases. Note that the general form of the experimental data for a particular suite of samples approximates a linear relationship between the principal stress components. Later in this chapter we introduce a failure criterion, called the Coulomb criterion that is consistent with a linear relationship between the principal stress components, σ_1 and σ_3, at failure.

In Figure 9.2 samples of Ohtawa basalt are shown after deformation in the same triaxial testing apparatus used in the previous example (Hoshino et al., 1972). These particular samples were deformed at confining pressures of 0.1, 49, and 98 MPa, respectively, while all other condi-

tions remained the same. Given an increase of compressive stress due to the weight of overlying rock of about 25 MPa km^{-1}, these tests could represent deformation of the Ohtawa basalt at the Earth's surface, at about 2 km depth, and at about 4 km depth. The macroscopic deformation mechanisms changed significantly in these tests from wedge fracture with axial splitting at the lowest confining pressure, to a localized shear fracture oblique to the sample axis at the intermediate confining pressure, to a broad network of oblique shear fractures at the highest confining pressure. Clearly the magnitude of the confining pressure plays an important role in determining the mechanisms that govern the strength of this rock.

An important concept concerning the strength of soils that are saturated with water or other fluid was introduced by Karl Terzaghi in 1923 and later found application in studies of rock, concrete, and other porous and permeable solids (Terzaghi, 1943). The concept depends upon the fluid filling all the pores of the material and these pores must be homogeneously and pervasively distributed throughout at a scale that is small compared to the scale of interest. Furthermore the pores must be interconnected in such a way that local changes in fluid pressure during deformation are rapidly equilibrated by flow through the network of pores. Finally, the concept is purely mechanical, so the fluid must not react chemically with the solid. Under these conditions, Terzaghi discovered that the deformation and failure of soil samples in the laboratory depended upon the so-called *effective stress state*, as opposed to the stress state as ordinarily defined (Nur and Byerlee, 1971).

The effective stress state is related to the stress state by adding the pore fluid pressure to the normal stress components:

$$\sigma'_{xx} = \sigma_{xx} + P_p, \quad \sigma'_{yy} = \sigma_{yy} + P_p, \quad \sigma'_{zz} = \sigma_{zz} + P_p,$$
$$\sigma'_{yz} = \sigma_{yz}, \quad \sigma'_{zx} = \sigma_{zx}, \quad \sigma'_{xy} = \sigma_{xy} \qquad (9.24)$$

Do not confuse the components of effective stress (9.24) with the components of stress deviation (9.14) defined by subtracting the mean normal stress from each of the normal stress components. One can visualize the role of pore pressure by considering the typical stress state to be compressive

Table 9.3. Triaxial test results on Berea Sandstone (MPa).

$P_c\,(P_p=0)$	D_c	$P_c=P_p$	D_c
0	72	0	72
50	159	50	82
100	242, 248	100	78
150		150	75
200	418, 432	200	60, 64
500		500	63

(negative) at depth. There, the normal stress components act inward on the boundaries of a representative element of porous rock, whereas the fluid pressure pushes outward in all directions from within the pores. In this way the pore pressure serves to counterbalance the compressive stress. Since the pore pressure acts equally in all directions it does not influence the shear stress components.

Two experimental observations, carried out using triaxial testing procedures, led Terzaghi to the concept of effective stress. When the axial and radial stress are of equal magnitude, the sample is subjected to an externally imposed isotropic state of stress, $\sigma_a = \sigma_r = -P_c$. As this isotropic state of stress changes, the volume of the sample changes. On the other hand if the pore pressure is increased in magnitude at the same rate as this isotropic stress so $P_c = P_p$, Terzaghi noted that the volume of the sample did not change appreciably. Thus, the volume change is related to the effective confining pressure, $P_c - P_p$.

The second observation of Terzaghi was that the strength of laboratory samples increased significantly with confining pressure, but did not increase appreciably if the pore pressure was increased in concert with the confining pressure. We use experimental data for Berea Sandstone in Table 9.3 to illustrate this phenomenon (Handin et al., 1963).

For this porous and permeable sandstone the differential strength, D_c, increased from 72 to over 400 MPa with increases in confining pressure from 0 to 200 MPa and zero pore pressure. With pore pressure equal to confining pressure the differential strength varied non-systematically over the range 60 to 82 MPa. These changes are probably within experimental error of being constant.

Taking the confining and pore pressures to 500 MPa resulted in a differential strength of 63 MPa, within the range of values for the tests at lower pressures. Clearly, the pore pressure serves to "neutralize" the role of confining pressure in increasing the differential strength of Berea Sandstone.

Consider the triaxial strength test data on Berea Sandstone plotted in principal stress space (Fig. 9.13a). Confining pressures were varied from 0 to 200 MPa, representative of depths to about 8 km. The tests were conducted at room temperature and pore pressures from 0 to 175 MPa. For each condition of confining and pore pressure, a data point represents the principal stress state at failure. For a given maximum principal stress ($\sigma_1 = -P_c$), say -200 MPa, the minimum principal stress ($\sigma_3 = \sigma_a$) at failure is less compressive as the pore pressure increases. This variation in strength is considerably greater than the variation between samples tested at the same pore pressure, so it is deemed to be significant. It is not possible to summarize these data with a single line or curve.

If Terzaghi's concept has merit, the strength of Berea Sandstone at a given effective confining pressure should be constant. The *effective confining pressure* is defined as the difference between the confining pressure and the pore pressure:

$$P_c' = P_c - P_p \tag{9.25}$$

In Figure 9.13b the data for Berea Sandstone are plotted in effective principal stress space. On the abscissa the maximum principal effective stress is plotted, and this is equivalent to the negative of the effective confining pressure, $\sigma_1' = -P_c'$. The minimum effective stress, σ_3', is plotted on the ordinate. All data points at a given effective confining pressure have essentially the same strength, thereby verifying Terzaghi's concept. Furthermore, the collection of data points representing effective stress states at failure collapse approximately (presumably within the experimental error) onto a straight line. This fact suggests that a single failure surface can be defined in terms of the effective principal stresses.

The pore pressure also effects the transition from brittle to ductile behavior (Handin et al., 1963). This is illustrated (Fig. 9.14) on axial stress versus axial strain curves for Indiana Limestone at

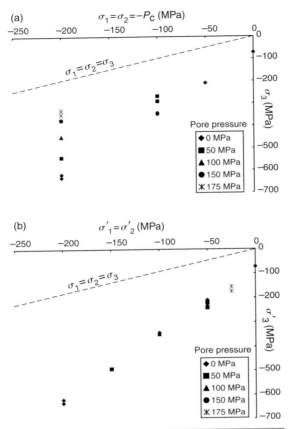

Fig 9.13 Plots of triaxial strength data for Berea Sandstone at a variety of pore pressures (Handin *et al.*, 1963). (a) Principal stress space. (b) Effective principal stress space.

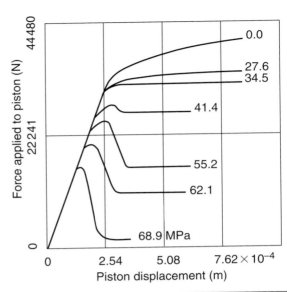

Fig 9.14 Plot of axial force versus piston displacement for triaxial test of Indiana Limestone at a constant confining pressure of 69 MPa and variable pore pressure from 0 to 69 MPa. Reprinted from Robinson (1959) with permission of the Colorado School of Mines Library.

9.2.5 Frictional strength

Though simply expressed, the laws of friction encapsulate a host of microscopic and nanoscopic phenomena whose elucidation has become one of the most fascinating pursuits in applied physics (Hähner and Spencer, 1998).

Leonardo da Vinci first addressed questions about friction through a series of experiments on sliding objects down an inclined plane (Resnick and Halliday, 1977). Since he lived from 1452 to 1519, long before force was clearly defined by Newton, his concepts were entirely empirical. These concepts are consistent with a simple proportionality between the magnitudes of two forces: F acting parallel to a horizontal plane at the moment motion begins, and W acting downward across the plane and being the weight of the object. The force F is said to initiate the motion while the weight W resists the motion. A somewhat more general relationship admits lesser values of the force F before the object moves, and retains the proportionality:

$$F < \mu_s W \text{ (static)};$$
$$F = \mu_s W \text{ (sliding initiates)} \qquad (9.26)$$

a fixed confining pressure $P_c = 69$ MPa and pore pressures varying from $P_p = 0$ to 69 MPa (Robinson, 1959). For all the tests the initial behavior is nearly linear and presumably elastic. For those tests conducted at pore pressures ranging from 0 to 34.5 MPa (effective confining pressures of 69 to 34.5 MPa) the axial stress becomes more compressive, or is approximately constant, as strain accumulates beyond the elastic limit. This corresponds to ductile behavior. In contrast, for greater pore pressures (lesser effective confining pressures), the axial stress becomes less compressive and the samples lose some load-carrying capacity as inelastic strain accumulates. This is characteristic of brittle behavior. In general, samples tested at low effective confining pressures exhibit brittle behavior; whereas those tested at high effective confining pressure are ductile (Heard, 1960).

The quantity μ_s is called the *static friction* and this proportionality is known as *Amonton's Law* after Guillaume Amonton who published his experimental results in 1699 (Bowden and Tabor, 1950). In this relationship the friction is independent of the apparent area of contact. There is no relative motion if the inequality is satisfied, because the force F is insufficient to overcome the frictional resistance between the object and the surface. Sliding initiates at the moment the force equals the product of the static friction and the weight. Today, the microscopic to macroscopic phenomena associated with frictional sliding on faults is one of the most fascinating pursuits of Earth scientists studying earthquakes (Dieterich, 1986, 1994; Linker and Dieterich, 1992; Lockner and Beeler, 2003).

On an inclined surface (Fig. 9.15a) the force that initiates sliding is the component of weight acting tangentially to the slope, W_x. The force resisting this motion is the component acting normal to the slope, W_y. For an angle of inclination specified by ϕ, the static friction is equal to the ratio of these forces and to the tangent of the angle at the moment sliding initiates:

$$\mu_s = \left| \frac{W_x}{W_y} \right| = \frac{\sin \phi}{\cos \phi} = \tan \phi, \quad 0° < \phi < 90° \quad (9.27)$$

The absolute value is taken to assure a positive sign. In this context the angle ϕ is referred to as the *angle of friction*.

A conceptual model for laboratory friction experiments includes a surface in contact with an object, sometimes called the slider, and a spring that represents the elastic behavior of the testing machine (Fig. 9.15b). As the right end of the spring moves with a steady velocity v imposed by the testing machine, the force F in the spring increases linearly with the displacement d of the point at the right-hand end of the spring, while the slider remains fixed, $d_s = 0$. When the equality in (9.26) is satisfied the slider begins to displace and the plot of force versus displacement becomes non-linear (Fig. 9.15c). The behavior of this system in the simplest cases can be described either as *stable sliding* or as *stick slip sliding* (Byerlee, 1978; Dieterich, 1981). In stable sliding, the slider accelerates gradually to a constant velocity equal to v and maintains this speed with a constant spring

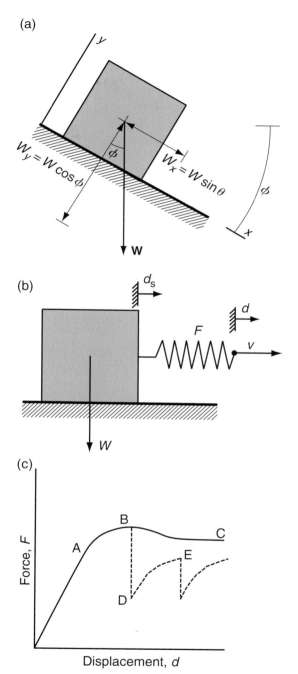

Fig 9.15 Schematic illustrations of concepts related to friction. (a) Block on inclined plane slides under the action of gravity. (b) Block on horizontal plane slides under action of force transmitted through a spring. (c) Plot of force versus displacement shows stable sliding (OABC) and stick slip (OABDE). Reprinted from Byerlee (1978) with permission of Birkhanser-Verlag.

Table 9.4. Static friction.

Rock type	From	To
Gabbro	0.48	0.67
Granite	0.18	0.66
Gneiss	0.61	0.71
Marble	0.62	0.75
Quartzite	0.48	0.67
Trachyte	0.56	0.68
Sandstone	0.51	0.68

force (path OABC). On the other hand, stick slip behavior involves the sudden acceleration of the slider with concurrent drop in the spring force. Eventually the force recovers and such events may be repeated many times during a single experiment (path OABDE, etc.). This behavior has been suggested as the laboratory counterpart of the mechanism responsible for earthquakes (Brace and Byerlee, 1966).

The actual configuration of specimen and testing machine for laboratory friction experiments is quite variable (Jaeger and Cook, 1979): some are not much more sophisticated than the conceptual model of a slider on a surface (Fig. 9.15b). A common design utilizes the standard triaxial test with a diagonal saw cut across cylindrical specimens (Fig. 9.11). Another design involves pushing a block of rock between two adjacent blocks (Fig. 9.4b), and still another (Tullis and Tullis, 1986; Tullis, 1988) employs the counter-rotation of two hollow cylinders. Reported values of the static friction do not vary widely. In Table 9.4 a few representative values are recorded (Jaeger and Cook, 1979).

The rule of thumb we take from these data is that values of the static friction for common rock types typically range from about 0.5 to 0.8, with 0.6 being a good general estimate. Apparently there is some ambiguity in the reported values of the static friction because some researchers use the force required to initiate sliding (point A, Fig. 9.15c), others use the greatest value (point B), and still others use the value after a stable sliding at a constant velocity is achieved (point C). For the case of sliding at a constant velocity a second value of friction usually is defined as:

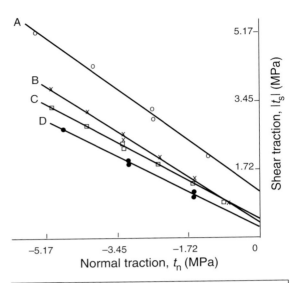

Fig 9.16 Plot of shear traction versus normal traction for laboratory friction tests on sliding surfaces in marble (A), trachyte (B), trachyte with smoother surfaces (C), and sandstone (D). Reprinted from Jaeger and Cook (1979) with the kind permission of Mrs. Jennifer D. Cook.

$$F = \mu_d W \text{ (constant sliding velocity)} \qquad (9.28)$$

Here μ_d is the *dynamic friction*. The dynamic friction typically is less than the static friction.

Although static friction, μ_s, is fundamentally defined in terms of the applied forces (9.26), one may divide through by the apparent contact area and write a comparable relationship for the static friction in terms of the shear traction, t_s, and normal traction, t_n, acting on the surfaces:

$$|t_s| = -\mu_s t_n, \quad t_n \leq 0 \text{ (sliding initiates)} \qquad (9.29)$$

The absolute value is used on the left-hand side because the relationship should not depend upon the arbitrary sign of the shear traction. Recall that a positive normal traction pulls on the surface, whereas a negative traction pushes against it. The normal traction must be zero or negative to insure that the two surfaces stay in contact.

Laboratory data using an apparatus similar in design to that shown in Fig. 9.4b approximate a linear relationship between the shear and normal tractions as sliding initiates for marble (A), trachyte (B), trachyte with smoother surfaces (C), and sandstone (D), (Fig. 9.16). The surfaces of the test specimens are described as "moderately rough" and the behavior is believed to be representative of many rock types (Jaeger and Cook, 1979). Note that the intercept on the shear traction axis is not zero for any of the data sets, so a more general linear relationship than (9.29) is required:

$$|t_s| = S_f - \mu_c t_n, \quad t_n \leq 0 \text{ (sliding initiates)} \quad (9.30)$$

The intercept on the ordinate, S_f, is the *frictional strength* in the absence of any normal traction and the slope μ_c is the *coefficient of friction*. This linear relationship is identical in form to *Coulomb's criterion* for the shear strength of intact solids which is described later in this chapter (9.38). The Coulomb criterion applies to the interior of a continuous solid rather than to discrete surfaces in frictional contact. The mathematical similarity of these equations should not obscure the fact that the former describes a friction experiment where sliding is induced along two surfaces in contact, whereas the latter describes the initiation of a shear fracture in an otherwise unbroken solid. Laboratory experiments also have demonstrated that friction is dependent upon the velocity of sliding and the time of contact (Dieterich, 1979a, b, 1981; Kilgore et al., 1993).

Given data that define the linear relationship (9.30), the static friction, μ_s, is derived from the frictional strength and coefficient of friction as follows:

$$\mu_s = \frac{|t_s|}{-t_n} = \frac{S_f}{-t_n} + \mu_c,$$
$$t_n \leq 0 \text{ (sliding initiates)} \quad (9.31)$$

For values of the normal traction less than or comparable to the frictional strength, the first term on the right-hand side makes a significant contribution to the static friction. Under these conditions it is not appropriate to equate the coefficient of friction and the static friction. If the normal traction is much greater than the frictional strength, the first term becomes insignificant and the coefficient of friction approaches the value of the static friction. Some laboratory values for the frictional strength and the coefficient of friction from (9.30) are reported in Table 9.5.

Laboratory data on the friction of rock surfaces may be categorized into three broad classes based

Table 9.5. Frictional strength and coefficient of friction.

Rock type	S_f (MPa)	μ_c
Marble	1.10	0.75
Trachyte	0.41	0.68
Gabbro	0.38	0.66
Granite	0.31	0.64
Sandstone	0.28	0.51

on the magnitude of the normal traction acting on the sliding surface (Byerlee, 1978). The first class includes normal traction conditions to −5 MPa and would therefore relate to very shallow conditions in the Earth, typically less than a few hundred meters depth. This is the environment of the engineering geologist and civil engineer (Barton, 1973). At moderate normal tractions, from −5 to −100 MPa, many laboratory results for maximum friction (point B on Fig. 9.15c) plot close to a line with zero intercept and a slope equal to a static friction of 0.85 (Fig. 9.17a). Rock types include sandstone, graywacke, limestone, quartzite, gneiss, granite, granodiorite, and gabbro. These results are applicable to underground excavations, well-bore problems, and sliding on faults down to about 4 km depth. Apparently the friction is not highly dependent on lithology (with a few exceptions), nor is it particularly dependent on the roughness of the sliding surfaces. The data set for maximum friction in the range from −100 MPa up to about −1500 MPa is applicable to sliding on faults at depths from 4 to perhaps 60 km (Fig. 9.17b). A linear relationship with an intercept of 50 MPa and a slope equal to a coefficient of friction of about 0.6 fits much of the data (excluding materials such as montmorillonite, vermiculite, and illite). For normal traction magnitudes greater than a few hundred MPa, the coefficient of friction is essentially equal to the static friction (9.31).

The frictional behavior of most rocks in the ranges of normal traction specified in Fig. 9.17a and b can be characterized as follows (Byerlee, 1978):

$$|t_s| = -0.85t_n, \quad -5 \geq t_n \geq -100 \text{ MPa}$$
$$|t_s| = 50 \text{ MPa} - 0.6t_n, \quad (9.32)$$
$$-100 \geq t_n \geq -2000 \text{ MPa}$$

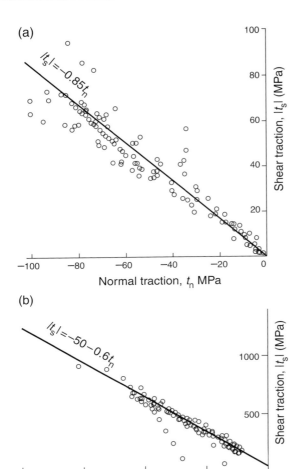

(a)

$|t_s| = -0.85 t_n$

Shear traction, $|t_s|$ (MPa)

Normal traction, t_n MPa

(b)

$|t_s| = -50 - 0.6 t_n$

Shear traction, $|t_s|$ (MPa)

Normal traction, t_n (MPa)

Fig 9.17 Plot of shear traction versus normal traction for laboratory friction tests. (a) Tests at normal tractions from -5 to -100 MPa. (b) Tests at normal tractions from -100 to -1500 MPa. Reprinted from Byerlee (1978) with permission of Birkhanser-Verlag.

These empirical equations, sometimes referred to as *Byerlee's Law*, have proven to be useful in many practical applications.

9.2.6 Fracture toughness

For the uniaxial tensile test configuration, a typical macroscopic event is that a single fracture nucleates somewhere within or on the surface of the specimen; this fracture propagates across the specimen; and the specimen is split into two parts (Fig. 9.8). The fracture surfaces are oriented roughly perpendicular to the uniaxial tensile stress within the specimen. The relative motion of the two fracture surfaces is approximately perpendicular to the fracture plane, so we refer to this structure as an *opening fracture*. In materials as heterogeneous at the grain scale as rock, it should not be surprising that the growth of a macroscopic opening fracture can involve many different microscopic deformation mechanisms. The double cantilever beam testing procedure (Fig. 9.18a) provides the necessary control on the rate of propagation to study these grain-scale mechanisms (Hoagland *et al.*, 1973). In these tests on specimens of Salem Limestone and Berea Sandstone a wedge was driven between two steel pins attached on either side of a pre-cut notch in the rock sample. As the notch was opened by this wedging action, a fracture initiated in the region of stress concentration at the notch tip and propagated through the specimen. The rate of fracture propagation was directly related to the rate of advance of the wedge. The load applied to the wedge and the opening displacement between the pins was recorded, along with observations of the microscopic deformation, acoustic emissions, and macroscopic fracture length.

A representative example of the load versus opening displacement records from these tests (Fig. 9.18a) is correlated to drawings of the samples at different stages of deformation (Fig. 9.18b). Examination of the samples before loading revealed minor microcrack damage near the notch, presumably associated with sample preparation. The initial loading produced a relationship between load and displacement that is approximately linear and reversible, consistent with elastic behavior, and only minor microcracking was detected. As loading increased the test record was characterized by some acoustic emissions, a distinct non-linearity in the load–displacement curve, and the development of abundant microcracks at the notch tip forming a so-called *damage zone*. When the advance of the wedge was stopped in this region the acoustic emissions continued, but at a decaying rate, and the load decreased somewhat with time. This demonstrated that there was a time dependence to microcrack growth and to the development of the damage zone.

Attainment of peak loading for the double can-tilever beam samples (Fig. 9.18a) roughly coincided with the initiation of a macroscopic opening frac-ture, propagating from the notch tip, and away from the advancing wedge. After some fracture growth a steady state was achieved, during con-stant advancement of the wedge, in which the fracture tip propagated through the sample accompanied by a zone of microcracking and other grain-scale damage. One moment in this steady-state process of fracture propagation is illustrated schematically in Fig. 9.18c. The damage zone (hachured region) develops in front of the fracture tip and is left behind as a "wake" along the side of the fracture surfaces. The spatial density of the microcracking is greater near the macroscopic fracture surfaces (double hachured region).

The phenomenon observed in these fracture propagation experiments is unlikely to occur in a material with homogeneous strength. Rather, the material would break at the point of greatest stress concentration (in this case the notch tip) and the fracture would propagate with little or no damage zone. Because most rocks are highly hetero-geneous at the grain scale, there are likely to be many weak points where inelastic deformation can proceed at local stress levels less than that at the point of greatest stress concentration. The microscopic deformation mechanisms active in these damage zones include the growth of existing microcracks within mineral grains (Fig. 9.19a), the nucleation of microcracks at flaws within grains (Fig. 9.19b), the opening of grain boundaries (Fig. 9.19c), and the shearing of grain boundaries (Fig. 9.19c) (Friedman *et al.*, 1972; Hoagland *et al.*, 1973; Peck *et al.*, 1985; Labuz *et al.*, 1987). The roughness of the fracture surfaces corresponds in part to the grain size, because the macroscopic fracture prop-agates both around and through individual grains, seeking the path of least resistance.

Consider an opening fracture (Fig. 9.20) that has not propagated through a laboratory speci-men. The specimen is subjected to an applied stress, σ_a, that is less than the uniaxial tensile strength, T_u. We would like to know the value of applied stress required to initiate and continue fracture propagation. Put another way, what is the resistance of a rock to fracture propagation?

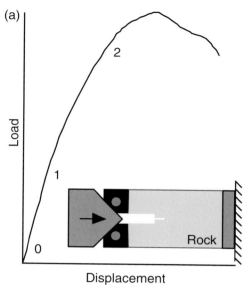

(a)

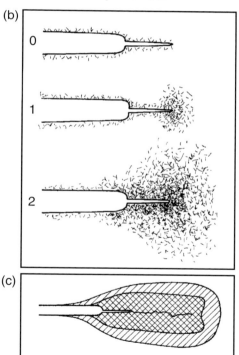

(b)

(c)

Fig 9.18 Double cantilever beam testing procedure for opening fracture propagation in Salem Limestone. (a) Plot of load versus displacement (inset illustrates testing apparatus). (b) Drawings of samples at different loads showing development of microcrack damage zone. (c) Schematic illustration of steady-state fracture propagation with damage zone. Reprinted from Hoagland *et al.* (1973) with permission of Springer-Verlag.

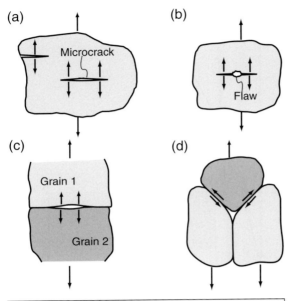

Fig 9.19 Schematic examples of microscopic deformation mechanisms in damage zone during opening fracture propagation. (a) Microcrack growth within mineral grains. (b) Growth of cracks from flaws. (c) Opening of grain boundaries. (d) Shearing of grain boundaries as grains pull apart.

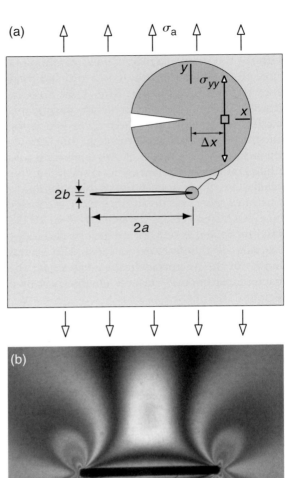

Fig 9.20 Opening crack and associated stress. (a) Crack subject to applied tensile stress, σ_a (inset shows crack tip stress σ_{yy}). (b) Photoelastic experimental image of maximum shear stress field near opening crack. Stress is concentrated in two lobes that converge on the crack tip.

The answer comes from the engineering discipline called *fracture mechanics* (Rice, 1968; Lawn and Wilshaw, 1975; Kanninen and Popelar, 1985; Anderson, 1995). By *fracture propagation* we mean that two new surfaces develop along an extension of the fracture plane that merge with and become part of the older fracture surfaces (Fig. 9.20 inset). Pulling the rock apart depends most directly on the local tensile stress, σ_{yy}, acting near the fracture tip. The founders of fracture mechanics discovered how to relate the remotely applied stress to the local stress near the fracture tip (Griffith, 1921, 1924; Irwin, 1958). They tackled this problem using elastic boundary value problems for the stress field around cracks subject to remote tension. The local stress near the crack tip is given approximately by:

$$\sigma_{yy} \cong \sigma_a \left[\frac{a}{2\Delta x} \right]^{1/2}, \quad \text{for } \Delta x \ll a, \quad y = 0 \quad (9.33)$$

Here, $2a$ is the fracture length and Δx is distance away from the tip in the plane of the fracture.

For many sample and fracture geometries, and for many loading configurations, the relationship between the local stress and the distance is the same: the local (crack tip) stress, σ_{yy}, varies approximately as one over the square root of the distance from the tip. This is referred to as the *near-tip stress distribution.* As the fracture tip is approached, Δx becomes smaller and smaller relative to $2a$, so σ_{yy} becomes larger and larger relative to σ_a. This indicates that the stress is highly concentrated near the fracture tip and it is this *stress concentration* (Fig. 9.20b) that promotes fracture propagation. Because the near-tip stress has the same dependence on distance for all opening fractures, we can redirect our attention to the other quantities in (9.33) and group them into a new parameter called the *stress intensity*, K_I:

$$K_I = \sigma_a \sqrt{\pi a} \qquad (9.34)$$

Here the subscript I stands for *mode I fracture* and indicates that the relative displacements of the fracture surfaces produce an opening motion. Later we consider the other two modes of fracture in which the relative displacements of the fracture surfaces produce a shearing motion. For other fracture geometries and other arrangements of the applied loads, equations comparable to (9.34) are tabulated in engineering handbooks (Tada *et al.*, 1973).

The stress intensity is a measure of the magnitude of the local stresses anywhere in the fracture tip region. Laboratory experiments have shown that fracture propagation depends on this local stress field and that one can write a propagation criterion in terms of the stress intensity reaching a critical value (Atkinson, 1987). The criterion is:

$$K_{IC} = K_I \text{ (at propagation)} \qquad (9.35)$$

Here, K_{IC} is called the critical stress intensity or *fracture toughness*. The units and dimensions of fracture toughness may be worked out from (9.34) and are:

$$\begin{aligned} &\text{fracture toughness}[=] \text{MPa m}^{-1/2} \\ &K_{IC}\{=\} M L^{-1/2} T^{-2} \end{aligned} \qquad (9.36)$$

Fracture toughness is a property that measures the resistance of a particular material to the propagation of a fracture. As such it should be independent of fracture size or geometry, but it may depend on such things as the temperature, confining pressure, and chemical environment.

A variety of laboratory procedures for measuring fracture toughness have been devised (Atkinson and Meredith, 1987), and representative values for selected rock types are given in Table 9.6. These

Table 9.6. Fracture toughness (MPa m$^{-1/2}$).

Rock type	From	To
Granite	1.66	3.52
Basalt	0.99	3.75
Quartzite	1.31	2.10
Marble	0.87	1.49
Limestone	0.86	1.65
Sandstone	0.34	2.66
Shale	0.17	2.61

values are for tests conducted at room temperature and atmospheric pressure.

The rule of thumb we take from this data set is: values of fracture toughness for common rock types tested at room temperature and atmospheric pressure range from about 0.1 to 4.0 with a representative value of 1.0 MPa m$^{-1/2}$. These concepts have found applications to hydraulic fracturing of wellbores (Rummel, 1987).

9.3 | Brittle failure in a field of homogeneous stress

Field observations and laboratory tests serve to motivate the development of a theory for the failure of rock samples subject to stress states that resolve both compression and shear across potential fracture surfaces. It is anticipated that a theory for shear strength will help to explain the development of shear fractures in laboratory specimens and, perhaps, be useful in extrapolating laboratory data to faults in Earth's crust. Given such a theory, and the appropriate data from field observations and laboratory experiments, the structural geologist should be in a position to estimate the magnitude of the stresses at the time of faulting. This would provide a sound physical basis for interpreting the geologic history of faulted rock masses.

9.3.1 Coulomb's concept of failure in shear

Conceptually one might postulate that shear fracturing is caused by shear stresses and that the sign of the shear stress is irrelevant to the strength. For an arbitrary polyaxial loading characterized by the principal stresses (σ_1, σ_2, and σ_3) we derived the magnitude of the *maximum shear stress* in Chapter 6 as $\sigma_s = \frac{1}{2}|\sigma_1 - \sigma_3|$. This shear stress is independent of the intermediate principal stress, σ_2. We define the *maximum shear strength*, S_m, as this shear stress at its limiting value:

$$S_m \equiv \sigma_s(\text{max}), \quad \sigma_1 > \sigma_3 \qquad (9.37)$$

The planes carrying the maximum shear stress form an orthogonal pair that intersect along the intermediate principal stress axis and are bisected by the σ_1- and σ_3-axes. That is, the normals to these planes lie in the (σ_1, σ_3)-plane and make angles of $\pm 45°$ with the σ_1-axis. At failure this criterion would predict the initiation of orthogonal *shear fractures* in these two orientations.

The concept of shear failure embodied in (9.37) is consistent with the uniaxial tensile and compressive strength criteria, (9.8) and (9.9), but it neglects the fundamental insight provided by Coulomb. Coulomb studied the frictional characteristics of materials in the eighteenth century and hypothesized that shear fracturing was driven by the applied shear stress and resisted by a combination of the cohesive strength (*adherence*) and the normal compressive stress acting across the predicted fracture surface (Coulomb, 1773; Jaeger and Cook, 1979). Accordingly, the compressive stress plays a role in shear fracture similar to the role of the normal traction in sliding friction (9.30): greater compression leads to greater resistance to shear fracture, just as greater inward directed normal traction leads to greater resistance to sliding.

To investigate Coulomb's criterion consider a rock mass subject to a homogeneous state of stress characterized by the principal stress components, σ_1, σ_2, and σ_3. The intermediate principal stress plays no role in the criterion, so we focus on the plane containing the maximum and minimum principal stresses and develop the theory in two dimensions (Fig. 9.21). In this figure the two principal stresses are compressive, but combinations of tension and compression are permitted if they do not lead to tensile failure. We refer to *potential shear fracture* when discussing the Coulomb criterion, because nothing in the criterion explicitly addresses what happens once the process of

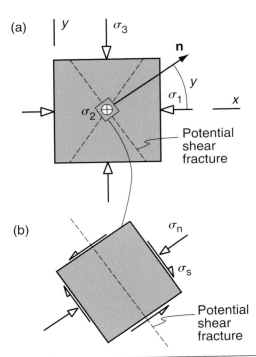

Fig 9.21 Schematic illustrations used to derive Coulomb criterion for shear failure. (a) Rock mass subject to homogeneous stress state with dashed lines representing potential shear fractures. (b) Element with side parallel to potential shear fracture subject to normal and shear stress, σ_n and σ_s.

failure begins. As the shear fracture initiates, the homogeneous stress field would change to a heterogeneous field with complex spatial variations near the shear fracture. The orientation of potential shear fractures (dashed lines in Fig. 9.21) is specified by an outward unit normal vector **n**. Because of the symmetry of the stress tensor two orientations of potential shear fracture exist. These orientations are symmetric with the principal stress axes but, as we show below, they are orthogonal only in the special case (9.37) where the normal stress plays no role in failure.

Coulomb's criterion may be stated as a linear relationship between the shear and normal stresses acting on the surfaces of a volume element that are parallel to the potential fracture plane (Fig. 9.21):

$$|\sigma_s| = S_0 - \mu_i \sigma_n,$$
$$\sigma_1 < T_u \text{ (shear fracture initiates)} \qquad (9.38)$$

The constant S_0 is referred to as the *inherent shear strength* because this is the resistance to shear fracture when the normal stress is zero. Because shear fractures develop independently of the sense of shearing, the absolute value of the shear stress is used. The effect of the normal stress is modified by a constant, μ_i, called the *coefficient of internal friction*. It should be understood that surfaces in frictional contact do not exist in the context of the Coulomb criterion, so the name is misleading. The linear relationship that relates shear and normal traction components on sliding surfaces is given by (9.30). The uniaxial tensile strength, T_u, is used in (9.38) to restrict the stress state to those that lead to shear fracture rather than tensile fracture. Because the actual stress state may be polyaxial, this restriction may have to include all principal stresses and depend upon a more generalized tensile strength criterion (Bourne and Willemse, 2001).

In (9.38) and what follows, the effective normal stress, $\sigma_n' = \sigma_n + P_p$, may be substituted for the normal stress to account for pore fluid pressure as in (9.24):

$$|\sigma_s| = S_0 - \mu_i(\sigma_n + P_p),$$
$$\sigma_1 < T_u \text{ (shear fracture initiates)} \qquad (9.39)$$

Because the normal stress usually is compressive (negative) and the pore pressure is a positive number, the addition of pore pressure mitigates the effect of the compression. In other words, the greater the pore pressure the lesser the shear stress required to induce shear fractures.

The Coulomb criterion (9.38) is used to define the *Coulomb stress*, σ_C:

$$\sigma_C = |\sigma_s| + \mu_i\sigma_n,$$
$$\sigma_1 < T_u \text{ and } \sigma_C \leq S_0 \qquad (9.40)$$

The Coulomb stress may be used to compare different potential shear fracture orientations in a deforming rock mass and assess which is closer to failure. These could be differently oriented planes at the same location subject to the same principal stress state, or two planes at different locations subject to different stress states. The potential fracture surfaces could be in different rock types with different coefficients of internal friction and different pore pressures. In all cases the Coulomb

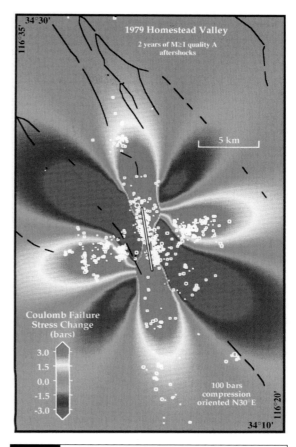

Fig 9.22 Map of aftershocks following the 1979 Homestead Valley earthquake and the Coulomb stress on planes parallel to the main fault at a depth of 3 km. Reprinted from Stein and Lisowski (1983) with permission of the Seismological Society of America.

stress is viewed as the dependent variable and would be calculated using the shear and normal stress acting on the potential shear fracture planes.

Two other important applications of the Coulomb stress (9.40) are to relate aftershock distributions to stress changes after major earthquakes, and to assess the likelihood of one earthquake event triggering another. For example, the spatial distribution of aftershocks following the 1979 Homestead Valley earthquake (Fig. 9.22) have been shown to correlate with the distribution of Coulomb stress change (Stein and Lisowski, 1983). Here the contours represent equal values of σ_C on planes parallel to the main fault at a depth of 3 km. The Coulomb stress was calculated by solving the boundary value problem for an elastic half-space with a fault that is 5.5 km long and 6 km high with a maximum slip of 0.5 m tapering to zero at the fault tip-lines. Two years of aftershock locations are plotted on the same map and show a distinct correlation to regions of elevated Coulomb stress change. The locations and fault plane solutions for earthquakes during the 1984 Morgan Hill seismic activity also show a correlation to Coulomb stress magnitudes and the orientations of planes on which the maximum Coulomb stress acts (Oppenheimer *et al.*, 1988). The locations of earthquakes that may have been triggered by the 1992 Landers earthquake also correlate with regions of elevated Coulomb stress (King *et al.*, 1994). These and other examples demonstrate the efficacy of this criterion for interpreting shear failure at crustal scales in regions of active faulting.

To carry out these analyses the Coulomb stress is evaluated in terms of the maximum and minimum principal stresses, σ_1 and σ_3, rather than the shear and normal components acting on the potential shear fracture. This is done employing Cauchy's Formula (6.55):

$$\sigma_n = t_n = \tfrac{1}{2}(\sigma_1 + \sigma_3) + \tfrac{1}{2}(\sigma_1 - \sigma_3)\cos 2\gamma$$

$$\sigma_s = t_s = -\tfrac{1}{2}(\sigma_1 - \sigma_3)\sin 2\gamma \qquad (9.41)$$

Here γ is the angle between the Ox-axis (here taken parallel to the direction in which σ_1 acts) and the normal, $\mathbf{n}$, to the potential shear fracture (Fig. 9.21). Substituting these expressions into (9.40) we have:

$$\sigma_C = \left| -\tfrac{1}{2}(\sigma_1 - \sigma_3)\sin 2\gamma \right|$$
$$+ \mu \left[\tfrac{1}{2}(\sigma_1 + \sigma_3) + \tfrac{1}{2}(\sigma_1 - \sigma_3)\cos 2\gamma \right] \qquad (9.42)$$

In order to proceed we exchange the absolute value sign and the negative sign in the first term on the right-hand side of this expression for a ± sign. Using these conditions (9.42) is written:

$$\sigma_C = \tfrac{1}{2}(\sigma_1 - \sigma_3)(\pm \sin 2\gamma + \mu_i \cos 2\gamma) + \tfrac{1}{2}(\sigma_1 + \sigma_3)\mu_i$$

$$\sigma_1 < T_u \text{ and } \sigma_C \leq S_0 \qquad (9.43)$$

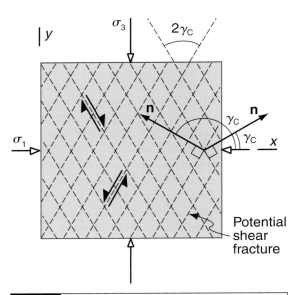

Fig 9.23 Potential shear fracture planes for the Coulomb criterion.

The positive sign is used for γ in the first and third quadrants and the negative sign is used for γ in the second and fourth quadrants. This expression is used to determine the Coulomb stress when one knows (or postulates) the orientation, γ, of the potential shear fracture (Fig. 9.21), the coefficient of internal friction, and the homogeneous stress state in terms of the principal stresses or the effective principal stresses, $\sigma_1' = \sigma_1 + P_p$, $\sigma_3' = \sigma_3 + P_p$, in the presence of pore fluids.

9.3.2 Predicting the orientation and initiation of potential shear fractures

In some applications it is useful to predict the orientation of potential shear fractures. This is accomplished by determining the orientation of the two planes on which the Coulomb stress is maximized for a given state of stress. The normals to these planes make angles, γ_C, to the axis of maximum principal stress (Fig. 9.23), and we refer to these as the *critical Coulomb angles*. Taking the derivative of σ_C with respect to the angle γ using (9.43), we find:

$$\frac{d\sigma_C}{d\gamma} = \frac{1}{2}(\sigma_1 - \sigma_3)(\pm 2\cos 2\gamma_C - 2\mu_i \sin 2\gamma_C) = 0$$

$$(9.44)$$

Rearranging to solve for the critical Coulomb angles:

$$\gamma_C = \frac{1}{2}\tan^{-1}\left(\frac{1}{\pm\mu_i}\right) \tag{9.45}$$

The principal stress planes ($\gamma_C = 0$, $\pi/2$, π, and $3\pi/2$) are excluded because no shear stress is resolved on these planes. Restricting attention to the first two quadrants, and noting that the coefficient of internal friction is positive by definition, the positive sign is associated with a critical angle in the range $0 < \gamma_C \leq \pi/4$ and the negative sign puts the angle in the range $3\pi/4 \leq \gamma_C < \pi$.

Based on (9.45) the potential shear fractures are oblique to the principal stress axes and at equal acute angles of 45° or less to the direction of least principal (most compressive) stress, σ_3 (Fig. 9.23). In other words the σ_3-axis is the acute bisector of the potential shear fracture planes. These are referred to as *conjugate shear fractures*. It should be understood that the criterion does not specify a particular location, only the orientation of these fractures. All of the parallel dashed lines drawn in this figure are equally likely to become shear fractures in a field of homogeneous stress. The two orientations of potential shear fractures shown in Fig. 9.23 have the opposite senses of shearing: one is right lateral, the other is left lateral.

The orientations of the potential shear fractures (9.45) are independent of the magnitudes of the principal stresses. In the context of the Coulomb theory these orientations are only dependent on the coefficient of internal friction. As $\mu_i \to 0$, $\gamma_C \to 45°$ and 135°, so potential shear fractures make angles of $\pm45°$ with the direction of σ_3 in this limit. This is the orientation predicted by the maximum shear stress criterion (9.37). As the coefficient of internal friction approaches zero, the contribution of the normal stress becomes insignificant, so the two criteria are consistent in this respect. For $\mu_i = 1$, the potential shear fractures make angles of $\pm22.5°$ with the direction of maximum compressive stress. In general, as μ_i increases the potential shear fracture orientations converge on the σ_3-axis.

Values of the coefficient of internal friction for seven different rocks are given in Table 9.7 along

Table 9.7. Rock mechanics laboratory tests for the coefficient of internal friction.

Rock Type	μ_i	γ_C (°)
Frederick Diabase	1.7	15
Westerly Granite	1.4	18
Witwatersrand Quartzite	1.0	23
Bowral Trachyte	1.0	23
Cheshire Quartzite	0.9	24
Carrara Marble	0.7	28
Gosford Sandstone	0.5	32

with the corresponding critical angle, γ_C, in the first quadrant (Brace, 1964; Hoek, 1965; Jaeger and Hoskins, 1966a, b).

The following rule of thumb is consistent with these laboratory results: the Coulomb criterion predicts shear fractures to form in rock specimens on planes that are oriented at acute angles between about 15° and 30° to the direction of maximum compressive stress.

Now that a relationship for the orientations of the potential shear fractures is established (9.45), we can determine the Coulomb stress acting on these particular planes. This is called the *critical Coulomb stress*, σ_{CC}, to emphasize that it is the Coulomb stress acting on planes oriented at the critical Coulomb angles, γ_C, for a given stress state and internal friction. Because this value is the same on both potential shear fractures we can, without loss of generality, consider only the first quadrant and write (9.43):

$$\sigma_{CC} = \tfrac{1}{2}(\sigma_1 - \sigma_3)(\sin 2\gamma_C + \mu_i \cos 2\gamma_C) + \tfrac{1}{2}(\sigma_1 + \sigma_3)\mu_i$$
$$\sigma_1 < T_u \text{ and } \sigma_{CC} \leq S_0 \tag{9.46}$$

This expression may be simplified using the following trigonometric relationships that are valid in the first quadrant (Selby, 1975):

$$\sin 2\gamma_C = \frac{(1/\mu_i)}{\sqrt{1 + (1/\mu_i)^2}} = \frac{1}{\sqrt{1 + \mu_i^2}}$$

$$\cos 2\gamma_C = \frac{1}{\sqrt{1 + (1/\mu_i)^2}} = \frac{\mu_i}{\sqrt{1 + \mu_i^2}} \tag{9.47}$$

Substituting these relationships into (9.46) and rearranging, we find:

$$\sigma_{CC} = \tfrac{1}{2}(\sigma_1 - \sigma_3)(1 + \mu_i^2)^{1/2} + \tfrac{1}{2}(\sigma_1 + \sigma_3)\mu_i \quad (9.48)$$

$$\sigma_1 < T_u \text{ and } \sigma_{CC} \leq S_0$$

Note that the critical Coulomb stress is a function of the coefficient of internal friction, half the principal stress difference (equivalent to the maximum shearing stress), and half the principal stress sum (equivalent to the mean normal stress in the plane of interest). As before one may use the effective principal stresses, $\sigma_1' = \sigma_1 + P_p$, $\sigma_3' = \sigma_3 + P_p$, to account for pore fluid pressure.

The inherent shear strength is defined as the critical Coulomb stress reaching a limiting value:

$$S_0 \equiv \sigma_{CC}(\text{max}), \quad (9.49)$$

This relationship is useful in analyses where the state of stress is computed using the solution to a boundary value problem. Given the principal stresses at these points, the coefficient of internal friction, and the inherent shear strength, one can use (9.48) to compute the normalized critical Coulomb stress, σ_{CC}/S_0, over the region of interest. Failure is predicted when this quantity equals one. By computing the orientations of the principal stresses and using (9.45), one can predict the orientations of the potential shear fractures. Then σ_{CC}/S_0 is contoured over the region of interest, thereby identifying the areas most prone to shear failure. This methodology was developed by Hubbert (1951) and Hafner (1951), and many others have followed their example for analyzing the state of stress in Earth's crust and the development of faults using the Coulomb criterion (Sanford, 1959; Couples, 1977; Segall and Pollard, 1980; Bourne and Willemse, 2001; Crider, 2001; Guiton et al., 2003).

It should be emphasized that the stress state will change as soon as the first fault initiates. To continue the analysis one must resort to numerical solutions of the boundary value problem in which the fault is explicitly included as a surface of displacement discontinuity. An example was described in Chapter 1 for normal faults from the Oseberg Field of the North Sea (Fig. 1.10) (Maerten, 2000; Maerten et al., 2002). Based on the Coulomb criterion one would interpret the major faults (broad lines, Fig. 9.24a) as forming in a regional stress field with the least compressive

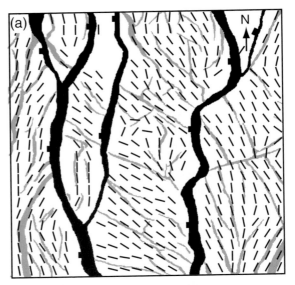

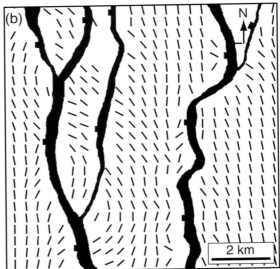

Fig 9.24 Comparison of fault orientations interpreted from a seismic reflection survey in the Oseberg Field, North Sea, and orientations predicted using the Coulomb criterion. (a) Major faults (black) and secondary faults (gray) with tick marks representing secondary fault orientations. (b) Tick marks representing predicted orientations. Reprinted from Maerten et al. (2002) with permission of Elsevier.

stress oriented east–west (direction of crustal extension), the intermediate compressive stress north–south, and the greatest compressive stress vertical. However, the three-dimensional seismic data reveal other faults with lesser throw (light gray lines, Fig. 9.24a) cutting the same part of the sedimentary sequence and trending oblique to the major faults. It was hypothesized that these faults developed in the same regional stress field, but slip on the major faults locally perturbed this field causing the smaller faults to form in oblique orientations. To test this hypothesis the geometry of the major faults was used as input for an elastic model. When subjected to an east–west extension the model faults slipped and the orientations of the principal stresses where computed. A comparison of the strikes of smaller faults interpreted from the seismic survey and the calculated directions of intermediate principal stress (Fig. 9.24b) suggests that the Coulomb criterion provides a good correlation at many locations.

9.3.3 The Coulomb criterion as a failure surface in stress space

Failure in tension and in shear may be defined using plots of a *failure surface* in principal stress space based on theoretical criteria and these may be compared to laboratory data. Consider a two-dimensional view of principal stress space that contains the maximum and minimum principal stresses (Fig. 9.25). By definition, $\sigma_1 \geq \sigma_3$, so the more darkly shaded portion of this figure is off limits. Also, the only restriction on the intermediate stress is $\sigma_1 \geq \sigma_2 \geq \sigma_3$, so this plane can be shifted along the σ_2-axis accordingly. To plot the failure surface we set the critical Coulomb stress equal to the inherent shear strength, $\sigma_{CC} = S_0$, using (9.48) and separate the principal stresses:

$$\sigma_3 = -2S_0[(1+\mu_i^2)^{1/2} + \mu_i] + \left[\frac{(1+\mu_i^2)^{1/2} + \mu_i}{(1+\mu_i^2)^{1/2} - \mu_i}\right]\sigma_1$$

$$= -C_u + [(1+\mu_i^2)^{1/2} + \mu_i]^2\sigma_1 \qquad (9.50)$$

In this linear relationship the first term on the right-hand side is the uniaxial compressive strength, C_u, the coefficient of the second term is the slope of the failure surface which is positive and greater than or equal to one. The region below this line (lightly shaded) is off limits because shear failure prevents the stress from attaining these values.

According to the Coulomb criterion (9.50) the uniaxial compressive strength, C_u, is related to the inherent shear strength, S_0, as:

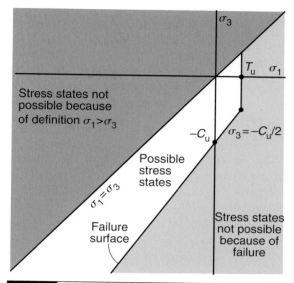

Fig 9.25 Principal stress space with two linear failure surfaces associated with the Coulomb criterion and the tensile strength criterion.

$$S_0 = \frac{C_u}{2[(1+\mu_i^2)^{1/2} + \mu_i]} \qquad (9.51)$$

Recall that S_0 is the strength of a potential shear fracture that has no normal traction acting upon it, a loading condition that is difficult to achieve. In principle, one can use the intercept and slope of the failure surface obtained from experimental data to determine C_u and μ_i, and then calculate S_0 using (9.51). In practice this can be problematic because the specimen might fail by axial splitting and the failure surface might not be linear. Nevertheless, values for the inherent shear strength sometimes are quoted in the literature. Before applying such values one should be aware how they were determined, and how well the laboratory tests conform to the basic postulates of the Coulomb criterion.

There are restrictions on the extension of the failure surface (Fig. 9.24) into the fourth quadrant. In particular, the intersection of this line with the σ_1-axis is not a measure of the uniaxial tensile strength, T_u, because the criterion is restricted to potential *shear* fracture surfaces. To understand how this restriction may limit the failure surface we substitute the second of (9.47) into the first of (9.41) and postulate that the normal stress across the potential shear fracture must not be tensile. Then, separating the principal stresses we find:

$$\sigma_1[(1 + \mu_i^2)^{1/2} + \mu_i] + \sigma_3[(1 + \mu_i^2)^{1/2} - \mu_i] \leq 0 \quad (9.52)$$

Rearranging (9.50) to put it in a similar form:

$$\sigma_1[(1 + \mu_i^2)^{1/2} + \mu_i] - \sigma_3[(1 + \mu_i^2)^{1/2} - \mu_i] = 2S_0 \quad (9.53)$$

These two expressions must coincide at the point in stress space where the failure surface and the restriction on the stress state are both satisfied. Eliminating σ_3 by adding (9.52) and (9.53), and then substituting for σ_1 in (9.52) we find:

$$\sigma_3 \leq -S_0[(1 + \mu_i^2)^{1/2} + \mu_i] \leq -\tfrac{1}{2}C_u \quad (9.54)$$

Thus, the restriction $\sigma_n \leq 0$ on the potential shear fracture truncates the failure surface where σ_3 is equal to the negative of half the uniaxial compressive strength (Fig. 9.25). For greater values of σ_3, it has been suggested that the uniaxial tensile strength would limit the stress state such that (Paul, 1961):

$$\sigma_1 = T_u, \quad \text{for } \sigma_1 \geq \sigma_3 \geq -\tfrac{1}{2}C_u \quad (9.55)$$

In this way the intersection of the failure surface with the (σ_1, σ_3)-plane is composed of two straight lines. The lightly shaded region (Fig. 9.25) below and to the right of these lines is off limits because of shear or tensile failure.

A number of laboratory studies have compared data on the stress state at failure during triaxial tests to the Coulomb criterion. These studies include those that focus on the effects of confining pressure, temperature, deformation rate, and pore pressure on the strength of a wide variety of rocks (Handin and Hager, 1957, 1958; Handin et al., 1963). As an example, we return to the data selected from a study of the mechanical properties of sedimentary rocks from Tertiary basins of Japan (Hoshino et al., 1972). Recall that in this study the rocks were deformed in triaxial compression tests at room temperature with no pore pressure. When plotted in principal stress space (Fig. 9.12) these data approximate a linear relationship of the form (9.50). Using the effective principal stresses, $\sigma_1' = \sigma_1 + P_p$, $\sigma_3' = \sigma_3 + P_p$, in

(9.50) to account for pore fluid pressure, the relationship remains linear and compares favorably to data (Fig. 9.13b) from triaxial compression tests on Berea Sandstone (Handin et al., 1963).

9.4 | Brittle failure in a field of heterogeneous stress

The Coulomb criterion, reviewed in the previous section, asserts that solids subject to a homogeneous stress state lose their load-carrying capacity when a certain combination of shear and normal stress acting on potential shear fractures reaches a critical value. The Coulomb criterion is calibrated using laboratory measurements of the uniaxial compressive strength and the coefficient of internal friction. Although this criterion provides a reasonable fit to some laboratory data and has been applied to numerous practical problems with some degree of success, it does not explicitly address development of the fractures themselves in the heterogeneous stress state induced by the fractures. Here we introduce methods for calculating the perturbed stress field around holes and cracks and use these to investigate brittle failure in a field of heterogeneous stress (Anderson, 1951; Hubbert, 1951; Chinnery, 1961, 1963, 1966; Cooke and Underwood, 2001; Bourne, 2003).

9.4.1 The boundary value problem of C. E. Inglis

One of the most cited articles in the literature of fracture mechanics was presented by C. E. Inglis in 1913 to the Royal Institute of Naval Architects in England (Inglis, 1913). The title of his article, "Stresses in a plate due to the presence of cracks and sharp corners," might seem somewhat abstract for a group of naval architects, but one of the principal causes of ship disasters in those days was the growth of fractures in plates making up the hulls of ships. To address this problem Inglis solved the elastic boundary value problem for an elliptical hole with major diameter, $2a$, and minor diameter, $2b$, in an elastic plate (Fig. 9.26).

At the time Inglis took up this problem, engineers knew that holes (e.g. those cut in deck plates to make hatches) would alter the local state of

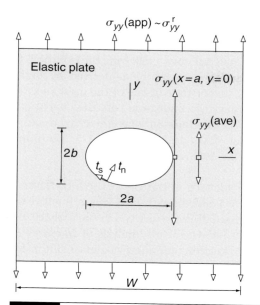

$\sigma_{yy}(\text{app}) \sim \sigma_{yy}^r$

Elastic plate

y $\quad \sigma_{yy}(x=a, y=0)$

$\sigma_{yy}(\text{ave})$

$2b$

$t_s \, \measuredangle \, t_n$

$2a$

x

W

stress, but they disregarded the shape of the hole and focused their attention on the cross-sectional area of material outside the hole (Gordon, 1976). For example, consider a uniformly applied stress, $\sigma_{yy}(\text{app})$, acting on the top and bottom edges of a square plate of side length, W, and thickness, D (Fig. 9.26). The total force acting on the plate would be the applied stress times the cross-sectional area of the plate, WD. At the mid-section of the plate, $y = 0$, the cross-sectional area is reduced to $(W - 2a)D$. The engineers did not know how to calculate the stress acting across the mid-section, so they simply dealt with the average value, $\sigma_{yy}(\text{ave})$. Equilibrium of forces requires that the same total force is transmitted across any section of the plate, so $\sigma_{yy}(\text{app})WD = \sigma_{yy}(\text{ave})(W - 2a)D$. Solving for the average stress:

$$\sigma_{yy}(\text{ave}) = \sigma_{yy}(\text{app})\left(\frac{W}{W - 2a}\right), \quad y = 0 \qquad (9.56)$$

The Latin phrase used by the engineers to describe this method, and perhaps to obscure their lack of an exact calculation, was *pro rata*. In other words the ratio of average stress to applied stress was the same as the ratio of plate width to reduced plate width. Inglis was able to show that

pro rata was not a good rule of thumb for these calculations.

Inglis solved this problem analytically and to help make the mathematical problem tractable he considered a plate that is infinite in extent. After solving the boundary value problem for the infinite plate it is possible to show that this solution closely approximates a finite plate that is only several times bigger than the major diameter of the hole. For a remote boundary condition on the plate, he specified that a uniform normal stress, σ_{yy}^r, acts perpendicular to the major diameter:

$$\text{BC: as } (x^2 + y^2)^{1/2} \to \infty, \quad \sigma_{xx} \to 0,$$
$$\sigma_{xy} \to 0, \quad \sigma_{yy} \to \sigma_{yy}^r \qquad (9.57)$$

For the internal boundary Inglis specified a traction-free condition:

$$\text{BC: on } \frac{x^2}{a^2} + \frac{y^2}{b^2} = 1, \quad t_n = 0 = t_s \qquad (9.58)$$

This condition ignores atmospheric pressure.

Inglis solved the governing equations of linear elasticity theory for the state of stress everywhere in the plate. The rather complex equations he derived can be reduced for special cases to gain physical insight. For example, the normal stress at the ends of the major diameter (Fig. 9.26) is:

$$\sigma_{yy}(x = \pm a, y = 0) = \sigma_{yy}^r\left(\frac{2a}{b} + 1\right) \qquad (9.59)$$

Note that the local stress is proportional to the remote stress, σ_{yy}^r, and is related to the shape of the hole through the ratio of major to minor diameters. Comparing (9.56) to (9.59) it is clear that the average stress can be a very poor estimate of the maximum stress. Inglis related this result to the fracture of ship hulls by noting:

When $a/b = 1{,}000$, the tension at $x = \pm a$, $y = 0$ is 2,001 times the mean tension. The ellipse in this latter case would appear as a fine crack, and a very small pull applied to the plate across the crack would set up a tension at the ends sufficient to start a tear in the material (Inglis, 1913).

This solution to the elastic boundary value problem provided, for the first time, a quantitative prediction of the great increase in stress at notches, corners, and crack tips and thereby led to an understanding of why such geometric features posed a great danger for engineering structures. According to (9.59) a remotely applied stress that is well within the normal safety factors for hull plates could be amplified locally by the presence of a crack to values well above that predicted by (9.56), and perhaps well above the strength of the material.

For practical purposes (9.59) suggests that the concentration of tensile stress near the ends of cracks in engineering structures can locally break the material apart and create a propagating fracture that might lead to catastrophic failure of the structure. A plausible propagation criterion would be that the stress at the fracture tip reaches the uniaxial tensile strength, T_u, of the material at that point: $\sigma_{yy}(x = \pm a, y = 0) = T_u$. Substituting this condition into (9.59) and rearranging to solve for the remote stress at propagation, we have

$$\sigma_{yy}^r \approx T_u \left(\frac{b}{2a} \right), \text{ for } b \ll a \qquad (9.60)$$

By measuring the uniaxial tensile strength of a material in the laboratory (Table 9.1) and knowing the geometry of any crack that might exist in the structure, an engineer could use (9.60) to place limits on the applied stress in order to prevent further fracture propagation. Although a vast improvement over the *pro rata* method, this approach is somewhat impractical because of the difficulty of measuring the minor axis of cracks. This difficulty may be addressed by characterizing the stress concentration in terms of the stress intensity factor (9.33), which is only a function of crack length.

Although the paper of Inglis contains a carefully constructed analysis and a thorough investigation of the results in practical terms, he met with considerable resistance to his new concepts. A prominent engineer wrote in the proceedings of the Royal Institute:

I regret to say that, although I have studied them with Professor Love's book on elasticity at my elbow, I find that the notations, which are doubtless very convenient for the discussion of vibrations and other complicated subjects, are so elaborate that I have not been able to do more than apply some simple tests to the results, and do not now feel satisfied that the mathematical deductions are fair representations of practical cases; in other words, the holes, corners, and cracks with which Mr. Inglis' paper deals are mathematical and not real ones (Inglis, 1913).

Despite such vacuous criticism, the solution to the boundary value problem derived by Inglis became a cornerstone of one of the most successful engineering endeavors of the twentieth century, the development of engineering fracture mechanics (Lawn and Wilshaw, 1975; Kanninen and Popelar, 1985; Anderson, 1995).

9.4.2 Fracture initiation at Griffith flaws

A. A. Griffith addressed the concept of fracture initiation in solids in two articles in the early 1920s. He is best known for his analysis of fractures in terms of a macroscopic energy balance, but in his second paper he addressed the local stress concentration near the ends of crack-like holes and related this to fracture initiation (Griffith, 1921, 1924). Perhaps the most important contribution of Griffith's research was his demonstration that solids contain sub-microscopic flaws that act to increase the tensile stress locally and thereby initiate tensile fracture growth. The presence of unseen flaws was a non-intuitive concept, considering that Griffith was working on laboratory glass specimens that appeared nearly flawless under the microscope.

Griffith began his research with the assertion that the analysis of C. E. Inglis (Inglis, 1913) for the state of stress around holes and notches in elastic plates could be used to estimate the *intrinsic tensile strength* of solids. By intrinsic strength Griffith meant the greatest stress that the solid could endure before rupture of the bonds between the atoms, ions, or molecules that hold the solid together. Apparently, he envisioned the bonds starting to break in the vicinity of a stress concentration created by a flaw, so the breaking bonds formed a more-or-less planar displacement discontinuity, perhaps along a lattice plane if the solid were crystalline. Griffith used the stress (9.59) at the end of a very eccentric elliptical hole ($b \ll a$) in an elastic plate (Fig. 9.26) to model the flaw and used the radius of curvature, $r_c = b^2/a$, to characterize the local shape of the flaw:

$$\sigma_{yy}(x = \pm a, y = 0) \approx 2\sigma_{yy}^r \left(\frac{a}{r_c} \right)^{1/2}, \text{ for } r_c \ll a \qquad (9.61)$$

Griffith suggested that the appropriate radius of curvature in (9.61) would be the intermolecular spacing for the solid, so $r_c \approx 5 \times 10^{-10}$ m, and he determined the value of the product $\sigma_{yy}^r a^{1/2}$ by experimentation in order to estimate the intrinsic tensile strength.

Griffith introduced a small scratch of known length, $2a$, onto the surface of cylindrical tubes or spherical bulbs of glass with a glass cutter. Then he pressurized the vessels with gas until they burst, and recorded the ultimate pressure. The relationship between the gas pressure and the remote stress component acting across the scratch, σ_{yy}^r, was determined from the boundary value problem for internal pressure in elastic tubes and spheres. Griffith discovered that the product, $\sigma_{yy}^r a^{1/2} \approx 2.63 \times 10^5 \, \text{N} \, \text{m}^{3/2}$ was nearly constant for the scratch lengths he tested, from 4 to 23 mm. Substituting into (9.61) Griffith evaluated the stress at the tip of the incipient fracture as 2.3×10^4 MPa and suggested this was an estimate for the intrinsic strength, T_i. However, this estimate is very great relative to measured uniaxial tensile strengths which typically are of the order 10^1 to 10^2 MPa (Table 9.1).

To understand this puzzling result, Griffith divided the estimated intrinsic strength by Young's modulus for glass, $E = 6.2 \times 10^4$ MPa, to estimate a strain of 0.37 at failure. He realized that Hooke's Law probably would not hold at these levels of strain and he knew that the concepts of an elastic continuum were on shaky ground at the molecular scale. Therefore he inferred that the intrinsic tensile strength would be somewhat less than the value calculated above. Griffith suggested that a reasonable order-of-magnitude value was:

$$\sigma_{yy}(x = \pm a, y = 0) \equiv T_i \approx \frac{E}{10} \approx 6 \times 10^3 \, \text{MPa} \quad (9.62)$$

This value is greater than the uniaxial tensile strengths for glass specimens, the strongest of which Griffith measured at $T_u = 1.7 \times 10^2$ MPa, and many specimens had uniaxial tensile strengths as much as two orders of magnitude less than the intrinsic strength. These results inspired the conclusion mentioned above: brittle solids such as glass must contain a myriad of flaws, too small to be detected by the optical microscope, but very large compared to molecular dimensions. These *Griffith flaws* serve to concentrate the stress and thereby weaken the material so that the macroscopic measures of strength are much less than the intrinsic strength. Fossils, clasts of different lithologies, pore cavities, grain boundaries, and microcracks are some of the many possible flaws that can provide the stress concentration necessary to initiate fractures in rock.

9.4.3 Griffith's criteria for brittle failure

In the second of his two classic papers on fracture Griffith explored the problem of fracture initiation and failure under a biaxial remote stress, using the solution of Inglis for an elliptical cavity in an elastic material (Inglis, 1913; Griffith, 1924). Here we review Griffith's analysis, but, to make it more relevant to geological applications, we include fluid pressure acting on the cavity walls. The limiting case of an elliptical cavity with very great aspect ratio, $a/b \gg 1$, is used to model a crack-like flaw. Flaws of all possible orientations relative to the remote principal stress axes are examined, and the one with the greatest induced tensile stress is identified as the "most dangerous." When this tensile stress equals the uniaxial tensile strength the initiation of a tensile fracture is predicted and this condition is assumed to be coincident with failure of the material. This procedure is used to define a failure surface in principal stress space and that surface is compared to laboratory data.

The boundary conditions at an infinite distance from the elliptical hole (Fig. 9.27) consist of uniformly distributed normal stresses that are the principal stresses, σ_1 and σ_3, directed along the x- and y-axes, respectively:

$$\text{BC: at } \sqrt{x^2 + y^2} = \infty, \quad \sigma_{xx} = \sigma_1,$$
$$\sigma_{xy} = 0, \quad \sigma_{yy} = \sigma_3 \quad (9.63)$$

Recall from the discussion of elliptical coordinates in Chapter 2 that $\xi = $ constant defines a family of confocal ellipses with ξ_0 being the particular ellipse designated as the surface of the hole. The boundary conditions there consist of a uniform normal traction of magnitude P and no shear traction:

$$\text{BC: on } \xi = \xi_0, t_n = -P, t_s = 0 \quad (9.64)$$

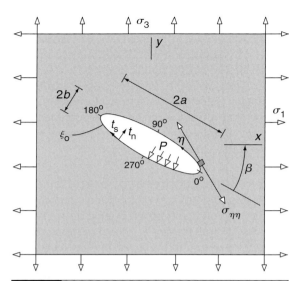

Fig 9.27 Schematic illustration of elastic boundary value problem for an inclined elliptical hole subject to biaxial applied stress (Jaeger and Cook, 1979).

The angle η is the elliptical coordinate that determines the position on the hole boundary and η varies from 0 to 2π counterclockwise from the right-hand tip. The hole may be inclined to the remote principal stress directions and this inclination is specified by the angle β measured from the major diameter to the Ox-axis.

Griffith postulated that fracture initiation would occur somewhere along the hole boundary and that the incipient opening fracture would be oriented perpendicular to the boundary. Thus he focused attention on the normal stress component, $\sigma_{\eta\eta}(\xi=\xi_0)$, acting tangential to the hole boundary (Fig. 9.27). To simplify the notation we refer to this stress as σ_t (Jaeger and Cook, 1979):

$$\sigma_t = -P + \frac{(\sigma_1 + \sigma_3 + 2P)2ab}{(a^2 + b^2) - (a^2 - b^2)\cos 2\eta}$$
$$- \frac{(\sigma_1 - \sigma_3)[(a + b)^2 \cos 2(\beta - \eta) - (a^2 - b^2)\cos 2\beta]}{(a^2 + b^2) - (a^2 - b^2)\cos 2\eta}$$

(9.65)

Some familiar results are contained in (9.65). For example, the tangential stress at the tip of an elliptical hole, $\eta = 0°$, oriented with long axis parallel to the x-axis, $\beta = 0°$, and loaded by internal pressure, P, and remote compressive stress, $\sigma_3 = -C$, is:

$$\sigma_t = P\left(\frac{2a}{b} - 1\right) - C\left(\frac{2a}{b} + 1\right)$$

(9.66)

The remote compression is concentrated by a factor that is proportional to the axial ratio, a/b, as Inglis discovered (9.59). The internal pressure results in a tensile stress concentration also proportional to the axial ratio.

The elliptical hole induces tangential stresses that can be of the same sign as the remotely applied stress, or of the opposite sign. This result particularly intrigued Griffith because he was interested in local tensile fracture under a compressive remote stress. To develop a criterion for failure Griffith approximated (9.65) for a crack-like flaw, $b/a \ll 1$, and determined the maximum tangential stress, $\sigma_t(\max)$, as a function of position, η, using $\partial\sigma_t/\partial\eta = 0$. Then he determined the extreme value of $\sigma_t(\max)$, as a function of the orientation of the flaw, β, using $\partial\sigma_t(\max)/\partial\beta = 0$. The flaw with this orientation, β_c, was designated the most dangerous flaw because $\sigma_t(\max)$ would be the greatest for a given loading condition. Griffith found two solutions for the most dangerous flaw. Under some biaxial loading conditions the most dangerous flaw is inclined to the principal stress axes, $0° < \beta_c < 90°$; under other conditions the most dangerous flaw is symmetric to the principal stresses, $\beta_c = 90°$, with long dimension perpendicular to the greatest principal stress, σ_1. The following relationships define these two cases. If $3\sigma_1 + \sigma_3 + 4P < 0$, then:

$$\sigma_t(\max) \approx -\frac{(\sigma_1 - \sigma_3)^2}{4\xi_0(\sigma_1 + \sigma_3 + 2P)}, \text{ inclined flaw}$$

(9.67)

If $3\sigma_1 + \sigma_3 + 4P > 0$, then:

$$\sigma_t(\max) \approx \frac{2(\sigma_1 + P)}{\xi_0}, \text{ symmetric flaw}$$ (9.68)

Because these equations contain the shape of the most dangerous flaw, ξ_0, Griffith realized that the theory could not be related to the strength of materials under various loading conditions unless the shapes of all crack-like flaws were known. Without knowing these shapes, his result had little practical value.

To solve the dilemma Griffith proposed to eliminate ξ_0 from these equations by relating it to the uniaxial tensile strength, T_u. Considering the symmetric case, $\beta_c = 90°$, he suggested that a laboratory specimen would fail if $\sigma_1 + P = T_u$ (here we added the internal pressure). Substituting this relationship into (9.68) we have $\sigma_t(\text{max}) \approx 2T_u/\xi_0$. This is the predicted stress at the tip of the most dangerous symmetric flaw just as a fracture initiates. Substituting this relationship into (9.67) and (9.68), the unwanted term ξ_0 is eliminated, leaving the *Griffith criteria* for failure. If $3\sigma_1 + \sigma_3 + 4P < 0$ then:

$$(\sigma_1 - \sigma_3)^2 + 8T_u(\sigma_1 + \sigma_3 + 2P) = 0, \text{ inclined flaw} \tag{9.69}$$

In this case a crack would propagate away from the inclined flaw oblique to its long axis, forming a so-called *wing crack* (Segall and Pollard, 1983; Cruikshank and Aydin, 1995; Cooke, 1997; Willemse and Pollard, 1998). Experimental investigations using plexiglass and glass (Fig. 9.28) show that the newly created cracks propagate along curved paths until they are approximately parallel to σ_3, and then stop (Brace and Bombolakis, 1963; Hoek and Bieniawski, 1965). On the other hand if $3\sigma_1 + \sigma_3 + 4P > 0$ then:

$$\sigma_1 + P - T_u = 0, \text{ symmetric flaw} \tag{9.70}$$

In this case a crack would propagate away from the tip of the symmetric flaw parallel to its long axis.

9.4.4 The Griffith criteria as a failure surface in stress space

The two conditions (9.69) and (9.70) can be plotted on a graph of σ_1/T_u versus σ_3/T_u, where we neglect the effects of fluid pressure. To construct this failure surface (9.69) is rearranged into the standard quadratic form and solved for σ_1:

$$\sigma_1 = \tfrac{1}{2}\Big\{ -(8T_u - 2\sigma_3) \\ \pm [(8T_u - 2\sigma_3)^2 - 4(8T_u\sigma_3 + \sigma_3^2)]^{1/2} \Big\} \tag{9.71}$$

This equation is divided by T_u, and plotted in Fig. 9.29a as the curved part of the failure surface. The other part is the straight line, $\sigma_1/T_u = 1$.

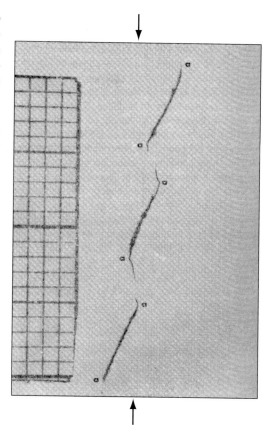

Fig 9.28 Photograph of laboratory experiment with three echelon cracks subject to compression. Wing cracks propagated from near the ends of these into a direction approximately parallel to the applied compression (Brace and Bombolakis, 1963).

Because $\sigma_1 \geq \sigma_3$, legitimate values of the stress state plot below the isotropic stress line, $\sigma_1 = \sigma_3$, thus eliminating the shaded region of Fig. 9.29a from consideration. Griffith supposed that fracture initiation would limit possible states of stress to values above the solid curve. By solving (9.69) for the special case of a uniaxial compressive stress, where $\sigma_1 = 0$ and $\sigma_3 = -C_u$, we find $C_u = 8T_u$: the uniaxial compressive strength is predicted to be eight times the uniaxial tensile strength. This prediction is within a factor of two or three for most rocks (refer to Tables 9.1 and 9.2), but the discrepancy suggests that the Griffith theory fails to address some important aspects of failure in compression.

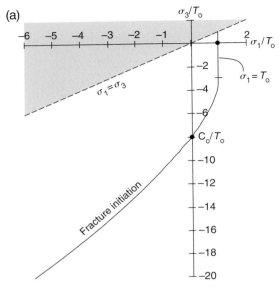

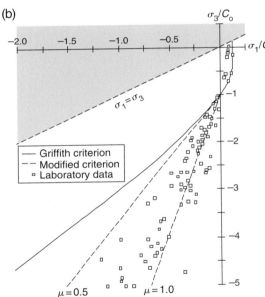

If the initial state of stress changed such that its representation as a point on Fig. 9.29a moved to the curved portion of the solid curve, Griffith's criterion predicts that a crack would initiate on the surface of an inclined flaw. Griffith supposed that this crack would continue to propagate and eventually break the body into two parts, thereby limiting the state of stress. In fact (Fig. 9.28), additional compression is necessary for continued propagation, so this phenomenon will not necessarily lead to failure of the entire body. Experiments on sets of flaws oriented oblique to the direction of maximum compression show how shearing induces growth of tensile fractures that may link to adjacent flaws and create a through-going structure (Nemat-Nasser and Horii, 1982).

Laboratory experiments have been carried out in triaxial testing vessels and compared to various strength criteria (Hoek and Bieniawski, 1965). In Fig. 9.29b the stress state at failure is normalized by the uniaxial compressive strength for 32 different rocks, including sandstones, limestones, shales, marbles, quartzites, gneisses, basalt, and granite. The solid line on this graph is the original Griffith criterion, (9.69) and (9.70), which underestimates the strength of most rocks at large compressive stresses. In part, this discrepancy is related to a boundary condition that Griffith overlooked. Under compressive stress, crack-like flaws are likely to close, so their walls will be in frictional contact. A *modified* Griffith criterion depends on the coefficient of friction, μ_c, and predicts a somewhat greater strength (McClintock and Walsh, 1962). Comparing the modified criterion to the strength data one finds that most fall within the bounds of the criterion for a range of friction, $0.5 \leq \mu_c \leq 1.0$ (Fig. 9.29b).

In summary, we have shown that the criterion of strength based on fracture initiation at flaws, as proposed by Griffith, and suitably modified to account for closing of flaws, is a reasonably good predictor of laboratory triaxial test data. It gives an explicit value of strength under any biaxial loading condition when calibrated by the uniaxial tensile strength. It also predicts the orientation of fracture, perpendicular to the greatest principal stress, for the cases where this fracture initiates at the end of the flaw. Most importantly it provides an explicit *mechanism* for failure, growth of tensile fractures from stress concentrations near preexisting flaws. Griffith provided an important building block for our understanding of strength and brittle deformation in Earth's crust.

9.5 | Fracture propagation and fault growth

Criteria for failure in a homogeneous stress state, such as the Coulomb criterion (9.50), inform us about the limiting stress conditions that are obtained at failure, but do not explicitly include the structure (e.g. a shear fracture) that is associated with the process of failure. Criteria for failure in a heterogeneous stress state, such as the Griffith criteria, (9.69) and (9.70), include the stress concentrating structure and describe the initiation of cracking, but do not address the propagation of the crack or other possible events and mechanisms that may be involved in the evolution of structures such as joints and faults. By combining solutions to elastic boundary value problems with principles of fracture mechanics one can explore the processes of fracturing and faulting in rock from the initiation stage through a stage of propagation or development to the eventual cessation of tectonic activity as the structure attains the size and configuration we observe in exposure today.

The evolution of structures in brittle rock is a large topic with interesting examples that are too numerous to be described in detail here. Instead we focus on a few examples that are meant to provide a summary of the methodology of investigation and some insight concerning the kinds of results one might expect. The first example is the propagation of opening fractures such as joints, veins, and dikes. Earlier in this chapter we described the loading conditions necessary for propagation in terms of the stress intensity at the fracture tip reaching the fracture toughness of the rock (9.35). Here we show how the loading conditions determine the path that the fracture follows as it propagates. The second example is the growth of faults in granite and in sandstone. In the granite it is the propagation of opening fractures to link adjacent sheared joints that enables the faults to grow in length. In the sandstone it is the clustering of deformation bands that enables the fault to grow in thickness. Through these examples of fault growth we make the point that faulting is a process that can involve several different physical mechanisms.

9.5.1 Propagation of joints, veins, and dikes

Fractures are idealized as two surfaces with mirror image geometry that are in contact in the initial unloaded state and are bounded in extent by a common curve called the tipline. Sufficiently close to the tipline the shape of this curve is approximately straight and the surfaces are approximately planar. We adopt a Cartesian coordinate system with the y-axis normal to the plane of the surfaces and the z-axis parallel to the tipline (Fig. 9.30). Upon loading of the elastic body the fracture surfaces move relative to one another and this motion may be classified according to the coordinate directions we have chosen (Kanninen and Popelar, 1985). Relative motion in the y-coordinate direction is referred to as Mode I or the *opening mode*; relative motion in the x-coordinate direction is mode II or the *sliding mode*; and relative motion in the z-coordinate direction is mode III or the *tearing mode*. Mode I is associated with geologic structures such as joints, veins, and dikes, whereas modes II and III are associated with shear fractures and faults. Modes II and III both involve a shearing motion of the surfaces with the former being perpendicular to the tipline and the latter being parallel to the tipline. This classification may appear arbitrary, but because of the symmetry of the fracture tip the elastic stress fields near the tip are uniquely distinguished by these modes, and each mode is associated with a different style of propagation.

There are many solutions in the literature for linear elastic problems that involve fractures (Sih, 1973; Tada *et al.*, 1973). A common feature of these is that the stress components in the vicinity of the fracture tip are distributed in a way that depends largely upon the fracture mode (Irwin, 1957; Williams, 1957). In contrast, the magnitudes of the stress components depend upon the fracture geometry away from the tipline and the loading conditions. This interesting and perhaps non-intuitive fact comes about because the near-tip stress distributions are dominated by the local geometry of the fracture tips, which are taken as identical for all modes, and by the relative motion of the fracture surfaces, which are uniquely distinguished by the modes (Fig. 9.30).

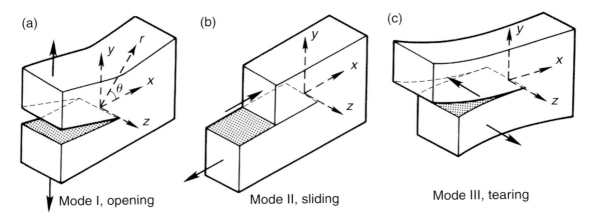

(a)

(b)

(c)

Mode I, opening

Mode II, sliding

Mode III, tearing

Fig 9.30 Three modes of fracture. (a) Opening mode I. (b) Sliding mode II. (c) Tearing mode III. Reprinted from Kanninen and Popelar (1985) with permission of Oxford University Press.

To examine the stress distributions in the vicinity of the fracture tip it is convenient to use a polar coordinate system (r, θ) with origin at the tip (Fig. 9.30). What we mean by "the vicinity of the fracture tip" (Fig. 9.20) is a distance $r < 0.01a$, where $2a$ is a characteristic length of the fracture (Pollard and Segall, 1987). When analytical solutions for the plane strain stress components are expanded about the fracture tip and higher-order terms in powers of r are eliminated, what remains is proportional to $r^{-1/2}$ and contains trigonometric functions of θ of order unity. For pure mode I fracture tips, the stress components in the (x, y)-plane are approximated as:

$$\begin{Bmatrix} \sigma_{xx} \\ \sigma_{yy} \\ \sigma_{xy} \end{Bmatrix} \cong \frac{K_I}{(2\pi r)^{1/2}} \begin{Bmatrix} \cos(\theta/2)[1 - \sin(\theta/2)\sin(3\theta/2)] \\ \cos(\theta/2)[1 + \sin(\theta/2)\sin(3\theta/2)] \\ \sin(\theta/2)\cos(\theta/2)\cos(3\theta/2) \end{Bmatrix}$$
(9.72)

K_I is the mode I *stress intensity*, which has units and dimensions given in (9.36) and has a value that depends upon the fracture geometry and loading conditions. Stress intensity factors are tabulated in engineering handbooks (Tada *et al.*, 1973).

For pure mode II fracture tips, the components are approximated as:

$$\begin{Bmatrix} \sigma_{xx} \\ \sigma_{yy} \\ \sigma_{xy} \end{Bmatrix} \cong \frac{K_{II}}{(2\pi r)^{1/2}} \begin{Bmatrix} -\sin(\theta/2)[2 + \cos(\theta/2)\cos(3\theta/2)] \\ \sin(\theta/2)[\cos(\theta/2)\cos(3\theta/2)] \\ \cos(\theta/2)[1 - \sin(\theta/2)\sin(3\theta/2)] \end{Bmatrix}$$
(9.73)

The term K_{II} is the mode II stress intensity factor. For pure mode III fracture tips, the stress components are approximated as:

$$\begin{Bmatrix} \sigma_{xz} \\ \sigma_{yz} \end{Bmatrix} \cong \frac{K_{III}}{(2\pi r)^{1/2}} \begin{Bmatrix} -\sin(\theta/2) \\ \cos(\theta/2) \end{Bmatrix}$$
(9.74)

The term K_{III} is the mode III stress intensity factor. One may summarize the equations for the near-tip stress components as follows:

$$\sigma_{ij} \cong [K_I f_{ij}(\theta) + K_{II} g_{ij}(\theta) + K_{III} h_{ij}(\theta)]/(2\pi r)^{1/2} \quad (9.75)$$

Here the indices i and j range over x, y, and z. This clearly demonstrates the separation of stress magnitude (intensity) from stress distribution. Note that several of the trigonometric functions in (9.75) are zero.

Because the stress intensity and the inverse square root of the radial distance are common to all stress components (9.75), the components are most easily compared by plotting the trigonometric functions over the range $-\pi < \theta < +\pi$, from one fracture surface around to the other (Fig. 9.31). Positive values are associated with tensile normal stresses. Some instructive results concerning geologic structures are found in these plots. For mode I the function f_{yy} is proportional to the normal stress component, σ_{yy}, acting perpendicular to the plane of the opening fracture. One might expect this stress component to have a maximum value just ahead of the fracture tip in the plane of the fracture, $\theta = 0°$. Instead, σ_{yy} has two equal maxima to either side of the fracture plane (Fig. 9.31a). These maxima may, in part, explain the cloud of microcracks that develop around the opening fracture tip in the laboratory experiments on Salem Limestone and Berea Sandstone illustrated schematically in Fig. 9.18.

The dual maxima for f_{yy} (Fig. 9.31a) provide an explanation for the secondary deformation observed where igneous dikes have propagated to within a few tens of meters of the ground surface in volcanic rift zones (Fig. 9.32). This map records open vertical cracks and normal faults in the Keanakakoi ash deposit of the Kau Desert in the southwest rift zone of Kilauea Volcano caused by the eruptive event of December 31, 1974 (Pollard et al., 1983). Lava erupted from 85 echelon fissures forming a set that extend about 4.5 km along the rift. The map shows the northeast end of one fissure with the lava that issued from it and flowed primarily to the south. Lava from the next fissure to the northeast also flowed to the south and merged with the lava from this fissure but did not cover the adjacent Keanakakoi ash. In the ash deposit a set of open vertical cracks formed at the time of the eruption, which are approximately parallel to the fissure and cluster into two groups, one to either side of the projection of the fissure to the northeast. We interpret these two clusters of cracks as forming because of the dual maxima in the normal stress component, σ_{yy} (Fig. 9.31a). Here the upward propagating dike is the mode I fracture and this normal stress component would be parallel to the ground surface and perpendicular to the cracks.

The distribution of g_{xx} (Fig. 9.31b) for the mode II fracture provides an explanation for the secondary structures mapped in association with small left-lateral faults in limestone from the Languedoc region of southern France (Fletcher and Pollard, 1981; Rispoli, 1981). We described these structures in Chapter 1 (Figs. 1.13, 1.14) where it was pointed out that opening veins and closing solution surfaces form on opposite sides of the faults near their tips. For mode II fracture, the function g_{xx} is proportional to the normal stress component, σ_{xx}, acting parallel to the plane of the sliding fracture. This stress component has a maximum (greatest tension) on one surface of the fracture, $\theta = -\pi$, and a minimum (greatest compression) on the other surface, $\theta = +\pi$. Considering the small left-lateral faults to be approximated by mode II fractures, extreme values of the normal stress with opposite signs on the adjacent

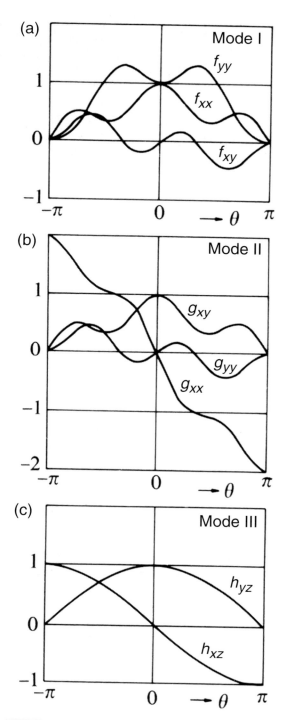

Fig 9.31 Plots of spatial variation with angle θ of near fracture tip Cartesian stress components. (a) Mode I. (b) Mode II. (c) Mode III. Reprinted from Lawn and Wilshaw (1975) with permission of Cambridge University Press.

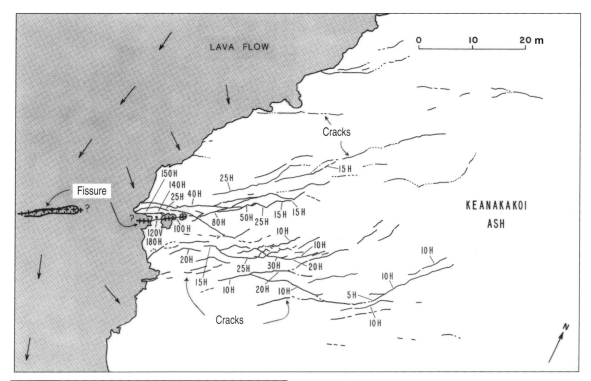

Fig 9.32 Map of open fissures and normal faults in Keanakakoi ash deposit associated with the 1974 fissure eruption on the southwestern rift of Kilauea Volcano. Reprinted from Pollard *et al.* (1983) with permission of Elsevier.

surfaces is consistent with the formations of veins and solution surfaces there. Because the graph in Fig. 9.31b is for right-lateral slip, one must change the sign of g_{xx} to apply the result to the Languedoc faults.

The traces of many joints, veins, and dikes in outcrop are remarkably straight (Fig. 2.12) or gently curved (Chapter 9, frontispiece). In a rock mass that is isotropic with respect to fracture toughness, the direction of propagation for these mode I fractures is determined by the stress field, and the systematic traces suggest that the principal stress axes were uniformly oriented or smoothly varying on the length scale of the fractures. Here we distinguish two regions, one far from the fracture and the other very near the fracture tip relative to the in-plane fracture length. We describe these as the remote stress field and the near-tip stress field, respectively. The remote stress field is thought of as uniform, except in the

vicinity of the fracture where it is perturbed, and this perturbation is greatest in the near-tip stress field as defined in (9.75). Before the fracture develops, the stress field is uniform throughout the body and equal to the remote stress. The symmetry of the opening displacements for straight joints and dikes suggests that these fractures form symmetrically with respect to the remote principal stress axes. The greatest mode I stress intensity is achieved if the fracture is perpendicular to the least compressive (most tensile) remote principal stress, so that is the preferred orientation. Furthermore, the near-tip stress field tends to guide the fracture tip into an orientation that is symmetric with the remote principal stress axes (Cotterell and Rice, 1980).

For the pure opening fracture (Fig. 9.33a) there is no resolved remote shear stress on the plane of the fracture. For the near-tip stress field (9.72), we have $K_I > 0$, but $f_{yx} = 0$ at $\theta = 0°$ (Fig. 9.31a) so the near-tip shear stress $\sigma_{yx} = 0$ on the next increment of growth in the plane of the fracture. Under these conditions the mode I fracture is predicted to propagate along a straight path. However, if this fracture propagates straight into a region with differently oriented remote principal stress axes,

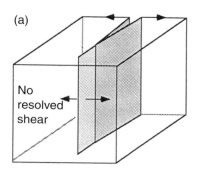
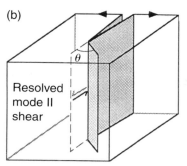
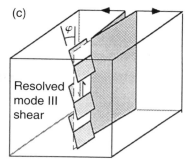

Fig 9.33 Schematic illustrations of fracture propagation path for dominantly opening mode fractures. (a) Pure mode I. (b) Mixed modes I and II. (c) Mixed modes I and III. Reprinted from Pollard and Aydin (1988) with permission of The Geological Society of America.

some shear stress, σ_{yx} and/or σ_{yz}, would be resolved on the fracture plane. Here we consider the case where a remote shear stress, σ_{yx}, induces a non-zero shearing mode stress intensity, K_{II}. For the near-tip stress field (9.73), we have $K_{II} \neq 0$ and $g_{yx} = 1$ at $\theta = 0°$ (Fig. 9.31b) so the near-tip shear stress $\sigma_{yx} \neq 0$ on the extension of the fracture plane (the patch bounded by dashed lines in Fig. 9.33b).

We postulate that the next increment of fracture propagation is parallel to the radial plane carrying the greatest local circumferential stress, $\sigma_{\theta\theta}(\text{max})$, (Erdogan and Sih, 1963). The circumferential stress in the near-tip field for mixed mode I–II loading is found by transforming (9.72) and (9.73):

$$\sigma_{\theta\theta} = (2\pi r)^{-1/2} \cos\left(\tfrac{1}{2}\theta\right)\left[K_I \cos^2\left(\tfrac{1}{2}\theta\right) - \tfrac{3}{2}K_{II}\sin(\theta)\right]$$
(9.76)

The extreme values of this stress component are found by differentiating (9.76) with respect to θ and setting the result to zero:

$$\cos\left(\tfrac{1}{2}\theta\right)\{K_I \sin(\theta) + K_{II}[3\cos(\theta) - 1]\} = 0 \quad (9.77)$$

This equation has two solutions where $\theta = \pm\pi$, but these correspond to zero values on the stress-free fracture surfaces which are of no interest. The relevant solution for fracture propagation is found where the terms in braces sum to zero (Erdogan and Sih, 1963):

$$K_I \sin(\theta_0) + K_{II}[3\cos(\theta_0) - 1] = 0 \quad (9.78)$$

The angle θ_0 is the predicted orientation of the next increment of fracture propagation.

For pure mode I loading ($K_{II} = 0$), the fracture is predicted to propagate in its established plane, $\theta_0 = 0$, according to (9.78). Right-lateral shearing of the fracture is associated with a positive K_{II} which corresponds to a negative θ_0 and a clockwise turning of the fracture. If the introduction of mode II loading is associated with propagation through a smoothly varying stress field, the fracture may follow a curved path. On the other hand if the fracture does not propagate while significant mode II loading is added, eventual propagation may occur at a sharp angle to the former fracture plane. For example, under pure mode II loading ($K_I = 0$), the fracture path is predicted to take a sharp kink and propagate at angles of $\theta_0 = \pm 70.5°$. Here the negative sign corresponds to a positive K_{II}. In this way the geometry of fracture traces at exposure may be used to infer the loading conditions during fracture propagation (Pollard and Aydin, 1988; Olson and Pollard, 1989; Olsen, 1993; Willemse and Pollard, 1998; Kattenhorn et al.,2000).

The postulates leading to the prediction of fracture paths in mixed mode I–II loading using (9.78) have been tested in controlled laboratory experiments, some of which focus on kinked paths (Erdogan and Sih, 1963) and others on curved paths (Thomas and Pollard, 1993). Here we describe biaxial tests of curved paths in thin sheets of polymethyl methacrylate (PMMA), a transparent and nominally isotropic plastic called plexiglass. Two narrow, parallel slots were milled into the PMMA with echelon geometry, a constant parallel separation of 19 cm, and a variable perpendicular spacing of 1.0, 3.0, and 6.0 cm (Fig. 9.34). The biaxial remote loading was a tension acting perpendicular to the slots, and a stress acting parallel to the slots that was an equal tension (all around tension, ATT), or zero stress (uniaxial loading, UNI), or a compression of equal magnitude (crack parallel compression, CPC). A small crack was notched into the proximal tips of the slots to initiate fracture propagation. Typically the fracture paths (dashed curves, Fig. 9.34) are nearly straight and perpendicular to the remotely applied tensile stress (parallel to the starter slot) until the fracture tip entered the stress field perturbed by the second slot. For the smallest spacing the mechanical interaction between the fracture and slot is greatest and the paths have the greatest curvature. The mechanical interaction is most pronounced for the AAT loading and least for the CPC loading so the paths for a given spacing have the greatest curvature for the AAT loading. When mechanical interaction dominates (lesser spacing and AAT loading) the fracture path first turns away from the slot and then turns toward it. When the remote loading dominates (greater spacing and CPC loading) the paths are nearly straight and perpendicular to the applied tensile stress.

The laboratory experiments were modeled (Thomas and Pollard, 1993) using a numerical computer code and the Boundary Element Method (Crouch and Starfield, 1983) which is based on linear elastic theory. The sample boundary was subject to displacement and/or traction boundary conditions to match those applied by the testing machine. The slots were modeled as a set of boundary elements with traction-free conditions. The biaxial remote loading on the sample was prescribed according to one of the ratios (ATT, UNI, or CPC) and the elastic boundary value problem was solved. The loading was increased until the stress intensity factors, K_I and K_{II}, satisfied the fracture criterion. Then a new boundary element was added to the current end of the fracture in the orientation θ_0 determined by (9.78). That element perturbs the local stress field so the boundary value problem was solved again and the next increment of fracture path determined. The numerical fracture paths (solid curves, Fig. 9.34) are remarkably similar to the

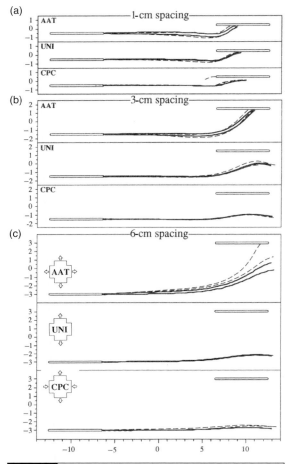

Fig 9.34 Comparison of fracture propagation paths in laboratory experiments using PMMA (dashed curves) and paths predicted by solutions to elastic boundary value problems (solid curves). Loading conditions indicated by inset. (a) 1-cm initial spacing. (b) 3-cm initial spacing. (c) 6-cm initial spacing. Reprinted from Thomas and Pollard (1993) with permission of Elsevier.

experimental curves, suggesting that the maximum circumferential stress provides a reasonable criterion for the direction of continuous opening fracture propagation in mixed mode I–II loading conditions.

Examples of fracture paths that are similar to those from the laboratory experiments in PMMA (Fig. 9.34) are found for a variety of length scales and structures (Fig. 9.35). Traces of cracks in glass at a 25-μm scale, hydrothermal veins in granitic rock at a 25-cm scale, basaltic dikes in shale at a 250-m scale, and oceanic ridges along the East

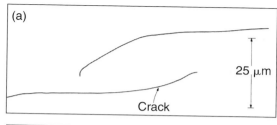

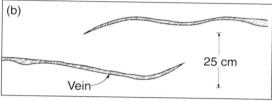

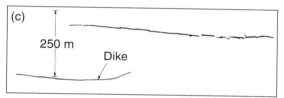

Fig 9.35 Examples of paths of dominantly opening fractures showing mechanical interaction in different materials at different scales (Pollard et al., 1982). (a) Glass at 25 μm. (b) Granite at 25 cm. (c) Shale at 250 m. (d) Basalt at 2.5 km.

field (9.74), we have $K_{III} \neq 0$ and $h_{yz} = 1$ at $\theta = 0°$ (Fig. 9.31c), so the near-tip shear stress $\sigma_{yz} \neq 0$ on the extension of the fracture plane (the patch bounded by dashed lines in Fig. 9.33c). We postulate that the next increment of fracture propagation is perpendicular to the direction of greatest local tensile stress for mixed mode I–III loading (Pollard et al., 1982; Olson and Pollard, 1991). This direction defines a set of planes that contain the y-axis and are rotated about this axis through an angle ϕ_0. With continued propagation the fracture breaks down into a set of echelon fractures that extend from the tipline where the mode III loading was introduced (Fig. 3.20, 3.22). Natural examples include echelon dike segments, echelon vein segments, and hackle on joints (Woodworth, 1896; Nicholson and Ejiofor, 1987; Pollard and Aydin, 1988; Cooke and Pollard, 1996).

We have focused on the propagation of a single opening mode fracture and the resulting geometry and surface textures. However, there are systematic relationships among the members of an opening mode fracture set (Renshaw and Pollard, 1994; Wu and Pollard, 1995; Renshaw and Park, 1997; Renshaw, 2000). For example, many studies have shown that joints in sedimentary rocks may have a regular spacing that is linearly related to the thickness of the jointed unit (Narr and Suppe, 1991; Gross, 1993; Gross et al., 1995). Linear elasticity has provided important insights about this phenomenon through the investigation of the stress distribution between two adjacent opening mode fractures in the middle layer of a three-layer elastic model subject to extension (Bai and Pollard, 2000; Bai et al., 2000). These models reveal that the stress changes from tensile to compression when the ratio of fracture spacing to layer thickness falls below a critical value of about one. This stress transition defines the condition of fracture saturation: continued extension of the layers is accommodated by fracture opening rather than the initiation of new fractures.

We conclude that the propagation of opening fractures in brittle rock is a process that can be conceptualized in terms of the increase in area of the two fracture surfaces as the fracture tipline advances. Particles on these surfaces that once were bonded together are separated by a displacement discontinuity and each increment of new

Pacific Rise at a 2.5-km scale all appear to have followed curving, hook-shaped paths that are characteristic of opening fracture propagation under conditions of significant mechanical interaction in a material that is nominally isotropic with respect to fracture toughness and elastic properties (Pollard and Aydin, 1984). Some of these even display such subtle effects as the paths first turning away from the neighboring fracture.

As implied by Fig. 9.33c the propagation of an opening fracture is perturbed in a more complex way if a remote shear stress, σ_{yz}, is resolved on the fracture plane and induces a non-zero tearing mode stress intensity, K_{III}. For the near-tip stress

(a)

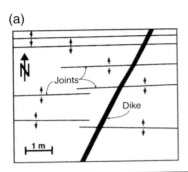

(b)

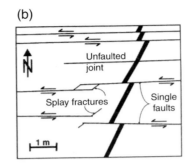

(c)

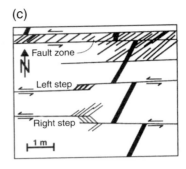

Fig 9.36 Schematic illustration of development of faults in granitic rocks of the Sierra Nevada (Segall and Pollard, 1983; Martel et al., 1988). (a) Joints propagate to form one set of opening fractures. (b) Some joints slip to form left-lateral faults with wing cracks near tips linking to neighboring faults. (c) Adjacent left-lateral faults form boundaries of fault zones. Reprinted from Bürgmann et al. (1994) with permission of Elsevier.

surface area is oriented approximately perpendicular to the local maximum tensile stress. This simple conceptual model may require modification to explain features of some opening fractures such as a process zone of microcracks (Fig. 9.18), or the development of plastic deformation beyond the near-tip region, or the propagation of fractures in non-elastic materials, but tools exist in the literature of fracture mechanics to investigate these phenomena (Kanninen and Popelar, 1985; Renshaw and Harvey, 1994; Anderson, 1995).

9.5.2 Growth of faults in granite and sandstone

In contrast to opening fractures, the development of faults apparently is a more complicated process that can involve several different physical mechanisms which are not readily conceptualized in terms of the propagation of a fracture tipline and the increase in area of two surfaces that formerly were bonded together. As an example we consider the growth of faults in granitic rock of the Sierra Nevada, California, in the Late Cretaceous (Segall et al., 1990). The oldest fracturing event, probably related to cooling of the Lake Edison Granodiorite, was the formation of a set of nearly vertical east-northeast-striking joints (Fig. 9.36a), which are filled primarily with epidote and chlorite and quartz deposited from a hydrothermal fluid (Segall and Pollard, 1983; Bergbauer and Martel,

1999). These joints are organized into domains with horizontal dimensions of several tens to a few hundreds of meters within which the strikes vary by only a few degrees, but between which the strikes can differ by as much as 20°. Over glaciated outcrops and cliff exposures tens of meters in extent the traces of individual joint segments are nearly straight, indicating that they are approximately planar in three dimensions. The joint segments are arranged in echelon patterns (Fig. 9.37a) and trains of segments interpreted as a single joint may be several tens of meters in length. Individual joints are up to a centimeter in thickness and spacing between adjacent joints ranges from a few decimeters to a few tens of meters.

The filled joints cross-cut older aplite dikes, the margins of which were separated in a direction perpendicular to the plane of the joint. These small normal separations are clearly distinguished from left-lateral offsets (Fig. 9.37b), ranging from a few millimeters to 2 m, that document the next event in the development of the faults. The hydrothermal minerals within the faults have acquired a mylonitic fabric (Fig. 9.37c), whereas those mineral grains within nearby unsheared joints are not deformed (Segall and Pollard, 1983; Segall and Simpson, 1986). The presence of these two parallel structures, joints and faults, containing the same mineral assemblage in the same exposure suggests that the faults once were members of the joint set. This interpretation is further supported by the fact that joints exist in some exposures without faults, but exposures containing faults always include joints. We interpret the faults as sheared joints rather than shear fractures. Sheared joints develop when a slip event nucleates and

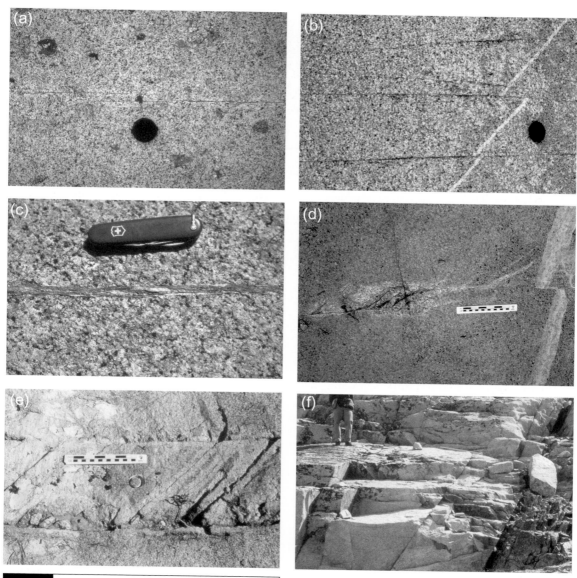

Fig 9.37 Photographs at exposures depicting stages in growth of faults in granitic rock. (a) Joints sealed with epidote, chlorite, and quartz. (b) Sheared joints become left-lateral faults and offset older aplite dike. (c) Hydrothermal minerals in sheared joints have a mylonitic fabric. (d) Extensional step between two fault segments. (e) Fault zone between adjacent left-lateral faults with one set of inclined fractures linking boundaries. (f) Compound fault zone with about 100 m of left-lateral offset. Photograph by D. D. Pollard.

propagates along a pre-existing joint, separating particles with a shearing displacement discontinuity that were separated originally with an opening displacement discontinuity.

Apparently, the slip events that propagated along the former joints were unable to nucleate a shear fracture in the unbroken granite when the slip reached the tip of a joint segment. Instead, an opening fracture, called a splay fracture, nucleated on one side of the sheared joint near the tip and propagated in an oblique direction counterclockwise from the trace of the fault (Fig. 9.36b). These splay fractures are explained using the stress distribution near the tip of a mode II fracture (Fig. 9.31b). The normal stress, σ_{xx}, acting parallel to the fracture is greatest in magnitude on the fracture surface where $\theta = \pm \pi$ and is tensile

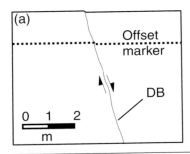 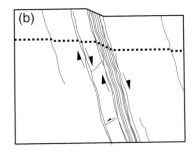 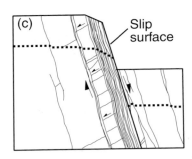

Fig 9.38 Schematic illustration of development of faults in porous sandstones of the San Rafael Desert (Aydin, 1978; Aydin and Johnson, 1978). (a) Single shearing deformation band (DB) offsets marker horizon by a few millimeters. (b) Deformation bands cluster into a zone with offset of several centimeters. (c) A slip surface develops on one margin of a zone with offset of several meters. Reprinted from Davatzes and Aydin (2003) with permission of Elsevier.

on one surface and compressive on the other. The splay fractures extend no more than a few meters from the fault surfaces and near their ends strike from 15 to 60° counterclockwise from the trend of the faults.

Where two echelon fault segments are arranged with a left step (looking toward the tip, the next segment is to the left), splay fractures emanating from both segments may link to the adjacent segment and some may open to form rhomb-shaped cavities up to 10 cm wide (Fig. 9.37d). These extensional steps range from a few centimeters to approximately 1 m in width (normal distance between the segments) and are up to 2 m in length (overlap of the segments). The slip on fault segments may be transferred to adjacent segments in a succession along strike by this linkage mechanism such that faults more than 100 m in trace length are formed. The length of faults apparently increased not by shear fracture propagation, but rather by the end-to-end linkage of echelon segments through opening splay fractures in extensional steps. At some locations near the contact with the younger Mono Creek Granite, right steps display well-developed ductile fabrics with a foliation oriented oblique to the fault segments and these also may serve to transfer slip (Bürgmann and Pollard, 1992, 1994).

The next stage in the development of faults in the Lake Edison Granodiorite (Fig. 9.36c) involved the side-to-side linkage of parallel and adjacent

faults with oblique fractures (Martel et al., 1988; Martel and Pollard, 1989). These fault zones typically are 0.5 to 3 m in width, reflecting the spacing inherited from the original joint set. The most prominent and earliest formed fractures within the zone strike at an acute counterclockwise angle to the two bounding surfaces of the zone and do not cross-cut those boundaries (Fig. 9.37e). Left-lateral offset of older structures is localized on the former faults that bound these zones and can be as great as 10 m. In contrast to the mylonitic textures found in the faults (Fig. 9.37c), the same epidote, chlorite, and quartz assemblage in the boundary faults is characterized by cataclastic textures. The fault zones can be up to 1 km in length and are composed of segments a few tens of meters in length joined end-to-end at steps and bends. This segmentation reflects the geometry of the earlier formed joint set and its domains. The granitic rock outside the two bounding surfaces of the fault zone is fractured near the steps and bends, but elsewhere the fracturing is strictly confined to the zone. Many of the internal fractures show evidence only for opening but some also are sheared. Right-lateral deformation was accommodated on kink bands (Davies and Pollard, 1986). The final stage identified in the development of the faults is the side-to-side linkage of adjacent fault zones and faults with oblique fractures to form a compound fault zone (Fig. 9.37f) about 10 m in width and several kilometers long (Martel, 1990). These zones offset older structures by as much as 100 m in a left-lateral sense.

The second example considers fault development in porous sandstone (Aydin, 1978; Aydin and Johnson, 1978). These faults were identified, mapped, and described from outcrops of Entrada and Navajo Sandstones in the San Rafael Desert of

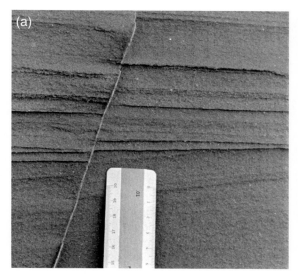

Fig 9.39 Photographs of exposures depicting stages in growth of faults in sandstone (Aydin, 1977). (a) Single deformation band in Entrada Sandstone. (b) Zone of deformation bands with sub-parallel bands in vertical section and anastamosing bands in horizontal section. (c) Zone of deformation bands with slip surface on the left margin that offsets Entrada Sandstone beds by about 7 m. Photographs reprinted with permission of A. Adyin.

southeastern Utah (Aydin, 1977). There are three structural elements found in the exposures: individual shearing deformation bands, zones of these bands, and slip surfaces (Fig. 9.38). The spatial relationships among these elements provide the evidence necessary to interpret their sequential development. Slip surfaces only exist in association with zones of deformation bands yet some zones lack a slip surface. Similarly, zones are always composed of individual deformation bands, but individual bands are commonly found isolated from any neighboring bands. From these systematic occurrences it was deduced that individual bands formed first; these occasionally clustered into zones; and some zones became the locus of slip surfaces.

The first stage in the process is the growth of shearing deformation bands (Fig. 9.38a) across which there are relative displacements parallel to the band of a few millimeters to a few centimeters (Fig. 9.39a). There is no evidence of discrete sliding surfaces within the bands, nor is there evidence of pre-existing structures such as joints that could have served to localize the deformation. Perhaps these structures propagate as mode II fractures (Petit and Barquins, 1988). The deformation within the bands includes both the relative motion of sand grains and the fracturing of grains accompanied by a pronounced decrease (60 to 75%) in porosity. A typical deformation band is tabular in shape, up to a few millimeters in thickness and tens of meters in outcrop length. Single bands are organized into sub-parallel sets.

The second stage in the development of faults in these sandstones is the clustering of two or more individual deformation bands into a zone (Fig. 9.38b). The deformation bands within a zone have approximately the same orientation as the zone itself but locally vary in orientation (Fig. 9.39b). The traces of bands are nearly straight on cross sections parallel to the direction of offset, but form a wavy pattern on cross sections perpendicular to the offset. Lenses of sandstone may be preserved between wavy bands but the bands rarely appear to cross one another. The thickness of a zone increases simply by the addition of deformation bands. The relative shearing displacement across a zone is the sum of that across the members and may be as great as 25 to 30 cm for a zone containing 100 bands.

The third stage in the development of these faults is the localization of discrete surfaces (Fig. 9.38c) with slickenlines and striations indicating slip. These slip surfaces are found on the margins of thick zones of deformation bands (Fig. 9.39c) and they accommodate several decimeters to several meters of offset. There is a reduction in grain size and porosity within a few millimeters of the slip surfaces and the surfaces themselves may be highly polished relative to the sandstone. Investigations at other localities suggest that slip surfaces nucleate in small patches which link to form an anastomosing network (Shipton and Cowie, 2001).

This review of the physical mechanisms involved in faulting of granitic rock in the Sierra Nevada (Fig. 9.36) and of sandstone in the San Rafael Desert (Fig. 9.38) serves to make the point that faulting is a more complicated process than the development of opening fractures such as the veins or dikes described in the previous section. Multiple physical mechanisms are involved and these may differ depending upon the rock type and tectonic setting (Bürgmann et al., 1994). The fault zones in granite begin to form with relatively little internal deformation except for a single set of oblique fractures. The fault zones in sandstone only form by the accumulation of bands accounting for considerable internal deformation. The thickness of zones in granite is determined by the original spacing of joints whereas the thickness of zones in sandstone is determined by how many deformation bands cluster together. In neither case is the growth of these faults readily conceptualized in terms of the propagation of a fracture tipline and the increase in area of two surfaces that formerly were bonded

together. It is conceivable that the slip surfaces in sandstone propagate in this way, but they require the previous development of the zone of deformation bands in order to nucleate.

The development of faults in granitic rock is not expected to conform to the example presented here unless a pre-existing set of weak surfaces is present. If such anisotropy is absent, or if more than one set exists, we would anticipate a different outcome. For porous sandstone the sequence from deformation band to slip surface described above is not the only possibility. For example, in the presence of a set of pre-existing joints the mechanisms involved in the evolution of faults in sandstone is quite different (Flodin and Aydin, 2004; Meyers and Aydin, 2004). Furthermore, for a different lithology, such as interbedded limestone and shale, the mechanisms are different than those described for granite or sandstone (Peacock, 1991; Peacock and Sanderson, 1991, 1994; Willemse et al., 1997; Cooke, 1997). Some phenomena described here may be explained using quasi-static elastic models; others may require solutions for dynamic elastic problems (Rice, 1980; Poliakov et al., 2002).

9.6 | Concluding remarks

The dominant behavior of rock in Earth's upper crust is elastic and brittle at scales that range from that of mineral grains to the crust itself. Brittle deformation is manifest in rock structures including microcracks, joints, veins, dikes, deformation bands, compaction bands, and faults. In the laboratory, extension and shear fractures form as loading conditions reach the strength of samples. While these laboratory experiments do not necessarily reproduce the mechanisms responsible for outcrop-scale structures, they do provide important data regarding strength, friction, and fracture toughness. The strength of rock samples typically increases with increasing confining pressure and decreases with increasing pore pressure. The fact that tensile strength is about one order of magnitude less than compressive strength helps to rationalize the abundance of opening fractures in the crust despite the nominal compressive stress regime due to the overburden weight. Griffith's concept of stress concentration at flaws and the tools of linear elastic fracture mechanics are usefully employed to understand the initiation, propagation, and pattern development of opening fractures. The Coulomb criterion for shear fracture initiation has found many insightful applications to faulting and earthquake phenomena. On the other hand, exposure studies of faults reveal that stress and material heterogeneity not incorporated into the Coulomb criterion play important roles in the development of faults. These and other contributions represent a considerable achievement in understanding the phenomena of faulting (Sibson, 1986, 1987, 1989), and a comparable body of literature has advanced our understanding of the mechanics of faulting (Rudnicki, 1977, 1979, 1980; Rice, 1980, 1992), but the research to integrate these different views of faulting stands before us.

Chapter 10

Viscous flow

Straight-limbed chevron-like folds in Cretaceous strata in the footwall of the Lewis Thrust, Canadian Rockies, from the Kananaskis Highway between Banff and Blairmore, looking south. Photograph by D. Wiltschko.

This bulletin is the second contribution to the general investigation of the physical constants of rocks, the experiments concerning which follow a general plan devised by Mr. Clarence King. Questions bearing directly on the viscosity of rock masses make up so large a part of Mr. King's geological observations, that the duty of enquiring into the physics of this enormously complicated subject devolved seriously upon me. Above all things some form of reliable working hypothesis was to be discovered; and this is what the present bulletin endeavors to accomplish. I believe the physical hypothesis has been found and that the data afford substantial corroboration of Maxwell's theory of the viscosity of solids (Barus, 1891).

10.1 Rock deformation by viscous flow

As the above quotation indicates, over one hundred years ago, the first director of the United States Geological Survey, Clarence King, hired a scientist to determine the *viscosity of rock*. Searching through King's account of the survey of the fortieth parallel, we find no mention of "Questions bearing directly on the viscosity of rock masses..." King did not write much, and so it appears his thoughts on this subject and the observations that motivated them may have been lost. King undoubtedly looked at rock masses that contained fold structures like those shown on the frontispiece for this chapter and in Fig. 10.1a, which would have suggested to him that rocks underwent continuous flow. Barus worked at elevated temperature with steel and other substances, but not, to our knowledge, with rock. The first experimental studies in which rock was deformed in a continuous manner were those of Adams and Nicholson (Adams and Nicholson, 1901). Although interesting results were obtained, research on the rheological behavior of rocks apparently stopped until Griggs took it up in the 1930s, working with technology developed by Bridgman, the 1946 Nobel Prize winner in physics for his studies of the behavior of materials at high pressure (Griggs, 1939). Examples of ordinary viscous fluid include cooking oils, lubricating oils, molasses and honey, asphalt, molten glass, and magmas with modest volume fractions of crystals and bubbles. Direct experience with some of these materials reveals the large temperature dependence of their viscosity.

The use of the constitutive relations for an isotropic Newtonian viscous fluid, defined below, as a model for the rheological behavior of rock in mathematical models of rock deformation has a long history. Haskell (1937) used it for homogeneous crust and mantle in a model used to interpret measurements of glacial rebound. Cathles (1975) treats the same phenomenon by representing the crust and mantle as a series of layers with different viscosity, thus dealing approximately with the large effects of temperature and composition on rheological behavior. The slow flow of

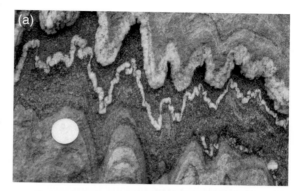

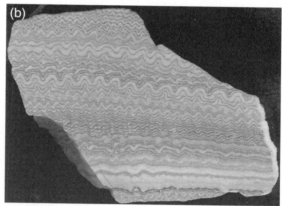

Fig 10.1 (a) Multi-layer folds (Moine Formation, Scotland). (b) Multi-layer folds in alternating dark carbonate–light anhydrite, now gypsum, annual layer pairs (Castile Formation, Permian Basin, near Carlsbad, New Mexico). Photographs by D. V. Wiltschko and K. Cruickshank.

ice, as in glaciers, and of salt, has been treated as though these materials behave as viscous fluids, and numerous researchers have modeled mantle convection as flow in a viscous fluid. The first detailed models of rock folding treat the buckling of a viscous layer (Ramberg, 1960; Biot, 1961; Chapple, 1968; Dietrich, 1969; Dieterich and Carter, 1969; Dieterich and Onat, 1969).

Newton (1687) addressed the definition of a viscous fluid in *The Principia*: "The resistance which arises from the lack of lubricity in the parts of a fluid – other things being equal – is proportional to the velocity by which the parts of the fluid are being separated from each other." The statement is a bit hard to interpret, but we imagine Newton may have had two parallel plates containing a fluid in mind, and the velocity is that of one plate relative to the other in the direction of their plane. Lack of lubricity is viscosity. Resistance is shear stress and separation velocity must be the velocity gradient perpendicular to the plane of the plates. We study Newton's fluid in this chapter, although much experimental work has demonstrated that glacier ice and other rocks at high homologous temperatures (temperature/ temperature of melting) and slow rates of deformation behave as *non-Newtonian* fluids. By slow we mean rates of order $D_{xx} = -10^{-14}\,\mathrm{s}^{-1}$, which would for example account for a shortening to 50% in 2.2 Ma. None-the-less, many viscous boundary value problems used by engineers have application to questions motivated by geological field observations. Several are discussed in the classic text *Elasticity, Fracture, and Flow* ... (Jaeger, 1964a), including the flow of a viscous fluid between approaching or separating rigid plates (Robin and Cruden, 1994), which we discuss later in this chapter.

The aim this chapter is to establish familiarity with the formulation and analysis of models involving slow, creeping flow that have application in structural geology. Models are developed analytically, although some require numerical implementation to evaluate expressions or contour quantities. Current research in this area often uses numerical codes based on the finite-element, the finite-difference, or other methods for solving the field equations subject to boundary conditions. The models or boundary value problems examined here provide preparatory experience and insight necessary for further study using these numerical methods, and a better fundamental understanding of these phenomena.

10.2 | Constitutive relations for isotropic viscous fluids

10.2.1 Newtonian viscous fluid

Consider an interpretation of Newton's thought "experiment" shown in cross section in Fig. 10.2. We could imagine performing an experiment like this, but it would create a mess because the fluid is not wholly contained. A slab of a fluid, such as warm asphalt, of suitably large viscosity, thick-

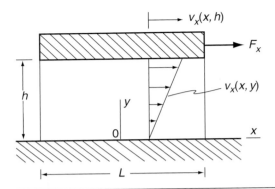

Fig 10.2 An interpretation of Newton's thought experiment.

ness h, length L, and depth W is placed on the planar horizontal surface of a rigid substrate roughened to prevent slippage so $v_x(x,0) = 0$. Although not drawn that way, L and W are supposed to be much greater than h, so that conditions at the periphery of the sheet will not have a major effect on the interior flow. A rigid plate is placed on top of the fluid and a horizontal force, F_x, is applied to it. The plate is rough so that the fluid adheres to it and attains the same velocity. Because the plate spreads out the application of the force in a uniform manner over the surface of the fluid, once a bit of motion takes place, the horizontal traction is:

$$t_x \cong F_x/LW \tag{10.1}$$

Recall from Cauchy's formula (Chapter 6) that this traction component is related to the stress components as $t_x = \sigma_{xx}n_x + \sigma_{yx}n_y + \sigma_{zx}n_z$. Since the outward normal to the surface has components $n_x = 0$, $n_y = 1$, and $n_z = 0$, the shear stress at the surface is:

$$\sigma_{yx} \cong F_x/LW \tag{10.2}$$

Gravity would cause the fluid to ooze out of the sides of the apparatus in Fig. 10.2, but to a substantial extent, the rigid plates prevent that from happening. We shall suppose that the upper plate is not so thick and of such a large density that its presence would contribute to outward flow at the edges. We hypothesize that the fluid a few thicknesses, h, away from the edge will not sense its presence, so there will be no dependence of velocity or stress on x. Ignoring the weight of the fluid itself and that of the rigid plate, only the stress component σ_{xy} is non-zero. Then, in the absence of accelerations and gravity, Cauchy's Laws of Motion (Chapter 7) reduce to the single stress equilibrium equation:

$$\frac{\partial \sigma_{yx}}{\partial y} = \frac{\partial \sigma_{xy}}{\partial y} = 0 \qquad (10.3)$$

In other words, the shear stress in the (x, y)-plane is constant within the layer of fluid.

For a layer composed of an isotropic Newtonian viscous fluid, experiments show that the velocity of the plate is proportional to the shear stress σ_{xy} or:

$$v_x(h) = C\sigma_{xy} \qquad (10.4)$$

Here C is a constant with dimensions $M^{-1}L^2T$. Only the rate of deformation component D_{xy} is non-zero (Chapter 5), and because $v_y = 0$:

$$D_{xy} = \frac{1}{2}\frac{\partial v_x}{\partial y} \qquad (10.5)$$

For a given stress, experiments show that C is proportional to the thickness of the fluid, h, so the velocity profile is linear and:

$$v_x(h) = 2D_{xy}h = C\sigma_{xy} \qquad (10.6)$$

Taking the constants $C/h = \eta$, we write:

$$D_{xy} = \sigma_{xy}/2\eta \qquad (10.7)$$

Here η is a material constant, the viscosity, with dimensions of $ML^{-1}T^{-1}$. Other things being equal, the shear stress is proportional to the velocity gradient and the proportionality constant is twice the Newtonian viscosity.

This experimental result is a special case of the full set of constitutive relations for an isotropic fluid. A general linear relation between the infinitesimal strain tensor and the stress tensor for an isotropic elastic solid was given in Chapter 8. The relations desired here may be obtained from these by replacing the components of infinitesimal strain with the components of the rate of deformation tensor, and writing G' and ν' for the shear modulus, G, and Poisson's ratio, ν:

$$D_{xx} = [\sigma_{xx} - \nu'(\sigma_{yy} + \sigma_{zz})]/[2G'(1 + \nu')]$$
$$D_{yy} = [\sigma_{yy} - \nu'(\sigma_{zz} + \sigma_{xx})]/[2G'(1 + \nu')]$$
$$D_{zz} = [\sigma_{zz} - \nu'(\sigma_{xx} + \sigma_{yy})]/[2G'(1 + \nu')]$$
$$D_{yz} = \sigma_{yz}/2G' \qquad (10.8)$$
$$D_{zx} = \sigma_{zx}/2G'$$
$$D_{xy} = \sigma_{xy}/2G'$$

If the fluid is incompressible, the instantaneous rate of change in volume is zero:

$$\frac{1}{V}\frac{dV}{dt} = D_{xx} + D_{yy} + D_{zz} = 0 \qquad (10.9)$$

Substituting from (10.8), this requires $\nu' = 1/2$. Using this in (10.8) and replacing G' with the viscosity, η, as indicated by the experiment of Fig. 10.2, we have:

$$D_{xx} = [\sigma_{xx} - (1/3)(\sigma_{xx} + \sigma_{yy} + \sigma_{zz})]/2\eta$$
$$D_{yy} = [\sigma_{yy} - (1/3)(\sigma_{xx} + \sigma_{yy} + \sigma_{zz})]/2\eta$$
$$D_{zz} = [\sigma_{zz} - (1/3)(\sigma_{xx} + \sigma_{yy} + \sigma_{zz})]/2\eta$$
$$D_{yz} = \sigma_{yz}/2\eta \qquad (10.10)$$
$$D_{zx} = \sigma_{zx}/2\eta$$
$$D_{xy} = \sigma_{xy}/2\eta$$

The constitutive relations for a viscous fluid have the same form as those for an incompressible elastic solid, and the kinematic equations for the rate of deformation in terms of velocity gradients have the same form as the kinematic equations for infinitesimal strain in terms of displacement gradients. Thus, there is a complete formal equivalence between the equations governing the deformation of an elastic solid and those governing the flow of a viscous fluid. A solution to a problem for the deformation of an elastic body is associated with an equivalent solution to a problem for flow of a viscous body. This equivalence is described through the *Correspondence Principle* of Maurice Biot, and it extends to all viscoelastic substances, whose behavior combines elastic and viscous responses (Biot, 1965).

10.3 | Plane and antiplane flow

10.3.1 Governing equations

The flows considered in this chapter depend only on coordinates x and y. Two sorts of flow satisfy this restriction, and interesting cases have both going on simultaneously. For *plane flow*:

$$v_x = v_x(x,y), \quad v_y = v_y(x,y), \quad v_z = 0 \tag{10.11}$$

Non-zero components of the rate of deformation tensor are:

$$D_{xx} = \frac{\partial v_x}{\partial x}, \quad D_{yy} = \frac{\partial v_y}{\partial y}, \quad D_{xy} = \frac{1}{2}\left(\frac{\partial v_y}{\partial x} + \frac{\partial v_x}{\partial y}\right) \tag{10.12}$$

For $D_{zz} = 0$, (10.10) gives:

$$\sigma_{zz} = (\sigma_{xx} + \sigma_{yy})/2 \tag{10.13}$$

The constitutive relations for plane flow in an isotropic fluid are:

$$D_{xx} = -D_{yy} = (\sigma_{xx} - \sigma_{yy})/4\eta$$
$$D_{xy} = \sigma_{xy}/2\eta \tag{10.14}$$

The equilibrium equations for plane flow are:

$$\frac{\partial \sigma_{xx}}{\partial x} + \frac{\partial \sigma_{yx}}{\partial y} = -f_x$$
$$\frac{\partial \sigma_{xy}}{\partial x} + \frac{\partial \sigma_{yy}}{\partial y} = -f_y \tag{10.15}$$

Here f_x and f_y are the body force components per unit volume. Here, and in what follows, it is understood that $\sigma_{xy} = \sigma_{yx}$. With the y-axis vertical and upward, and gravity as the only body force, the components would evaluate as $-f_x = 0$ and $-f_y = \rho g$. Equations (10.12)–(10.15) are the governing equations for plane flow of an isotropic viscous fluid.

A second flow independent of the coordinate z is the *antiplane* flow where the velocity components are constrained as:

$$v_x = 0, \quad v_y = 0, \quad v_z = v_z(x,y) \tag{10.16}$$

There are only two non-zero components of the rate of deformation tensor:

$$D_{xz} = \frac{1}{2}\frac{\partial v_z}{\partial x}, \quad D_{yz} = \frac{1}{2}\frac{\partial v_z}{\partial y} \tag{10.17}$$

The two constitutive relations are:

$$D_{xz} = \sigma_{xz}/2\eta$$
$$D_{yz} = \sigma_{yz}/2\eta \tag{10.18}$$

The single equilibrium equation is:

$$\frac{\partial \sigma_{xz}}{\partial x} + \frac{\partial \sigma_{yz}}{\partial y} = -f_z \tag{10.19}$$

Here f_z is the body force component per unit volume acting in the z-direction. Equations (10.17)–(10.19) are a complete set of governing equations for antiplane flow in an isotropic incompressible viscous fluid. Antiplane flows are not treated further in this chapter.

10.3.2 Flow down an inclined plane

Consider an infinite sheet of viscous fluid of uniform thickness h supported by the planar surface of a rigid substrate sloping at an angle α (Fig. 10.3), to which it adheres. Gravity is turned on, so the fluid flows downhill like a glacier and we take x parallel to the slope and y normal to it. The boundary conditions for adherence to the substrate are:

$$v_x(x,0) = 0, \quad v_y(x,0) = 0 \tag{10.20}$$

At the upper surface, the normal and shear tractions vanish, yielding:

$$\sigma_{yy}(x,h) = 0, \quad \sigma_{xy}(x,h) = 0 \tag{10.21}$$

The equilibrium equations are:

$$\frac{\partial \sigma_{xx}}{\partial x} + \frac{\partial \sigma_{xy}}{\partial y} = -\rho g \sin \alpha$$
$$\frac{\partial \sigma_{xy}}{\partial x} + \frac{\partial \sigma_{yy}}{\partial y} = \rho g \cos \alpha \tag{10.22}$$

Here the body force components are those shown in Fig. 10.3.

Supposing that neither density nor viscosity vary in the x-direction, and if the density ρ is uniform, we may set the first terms in (10.22) equal to zero, integrate, and apply the boundary conditions (10.21), obtaining:

$$\sigma_{xy} = -\rho g \sin \alpha \, (y - h)$$
$$\sigma_{yy} = \rho g \cos \alpha \, (y - h) \tag{10.23}$$

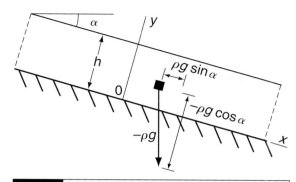

Fig 10.3 Section through the model for glacier-like gravitational flow.

The stress distribution is *statically determinate* in this case. That is, it only depends on the stress boundary conditions and the equilibrium equations. This means that we might consider any kind of fluid flowing downhill provided its properties only vary in the y-direction. Only D_{xy} is non-zero, and for the uniform viscous fluid:

$$\frac{\partial v_x}{\partial y} = \frac{\sigma_{xy}}{\eta} = -(\rho g/\eta)\sin\alpha\,(y-h) \qquad (10.24)$$

Integrating and applying the velocity boundary condition (10.20) yields:

$$v_x(y) = -(\rho g/\eta)\sin\alpha\left(\tfrac{1}{2}y^2 - hy\right) \qquad (10.25)$$

Glacier-like flow has been viewed as a possible mode of emplacement of large thrust sheets and fold nappes in which gravity is interpreted as the dominant factor (Hudleston, 1992). For example, the northeasterly flow of supracrustal rocks of the southern Canadian Rockies is envisioned as a result of gravitational spreading from a region of buoyant upwelling of metamorphic and plutonic rocks in the core of the fold belt (Price, 1973). In another example, thrusting and folding of rock of the Pyrenees Mountains (Fig. 10.4a) is envisioned as a result of the upwelling of lower crust or mantle, here called the asthenolith (Choukroune and Seguret, 1973). If the lower crust is much less viscous because of its composition than the underlying mantle, downslope motion of the crust off such a high might be accomplished chiefly by a glacier-like flow. If we apply the velocity field (10.25) to an initially upright fold form,

the recumbent form of a fold nappe is developed (Fig. 10.4b). Actual fold nappes are shown in Fig. 5.2 and in the frontispiece for Chapter 7.

The flow law of ice under conditions in many glaciers is *non-Newtonian*. Ice is incompressible and, for simplicity, we may treat it as isotropic, although most glacier ice is strongly anisotropic. The complete constitutive relations for a non-linear isotropic and incompressible fluid are more complicated than the linear relations (Chapter 11), but the one-dimensional relation between the rate of shearing and the shear stress is:

$$D_{xy} = B(\sigma_{xy}^2)^{[(n-1)/2]}\sigma_{xy} \qquad (10.26)$$

All other deviatoric stress components are zero. The form of (10.26) takes care of signs, since D_{xy} and σ_{xy} must have the same sign whatever the value of $n \geq 1$. If, as here, both are positive, we may write, more simply:

$$D_{xy} = B\sigma_{xy}^n \qquad (10.27)$$

B is a material constant, expressed in SI units as $(\text{MPa})^{-n}\text{s}$, and n is the *stress exponent*. The isotropic Newtonian viscous fluid (10.7) is a special case of this so-called *power-law fluid* for which $n=1$ and $B = 1/2\eta$. The rheological behavior of ice under glacier flow conditions and of many rock-forming minerals such as quartz and olivine are approximated by such a law with $n \approx 3$ (Kirby and Kronenberg, 1987; Evans and Kohlstedt, 1995).

Since (10.27) may be applied to the flow on an inclined plane, we substitute from the first of (10.23) and obtain:

$$\frac{\partial v_x}{\partial y} = 2B\left[\rho g h \sin\alpha\right]^n\left(1-\frac{y}{h}\right)^n \qquad (10.28)$$

This may be integrated to give:

$$v_x = c - \left\{\frac{2Bh}{n+1}\left[\rho g h \sin\alpha\right]^n\right\}\left(1-\frac{y}{h}\right)^{n+1} \qquad (10.29)$$

Here c is a constant of integration. Ignoring the possibility of the fluid sliding on its supporting plane, we take the velocity to vanish at the base, $y=0$, so c equals the term in braces, and the final result is:

$$v_x = \left\{\frac{2Bh}{n+1}\left[\rho g h \sin\alpha\right]^n\right\}\left\{1-\left(1-\frac{y}{h}\right)^{n+1}\right\} \qquad (10.30)$$

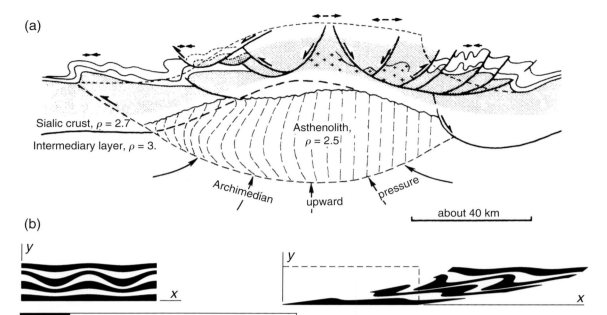

(a)

Sialic crust, $\rho = 2.7$

Intermediary layer, $\rho = 3$.

Asthenolith, $\rho = 2.5$

Archimedian

upward

pressure

about 40 km

(b)

Fig 10.4 (a) Schematic diagram suggesting the mechanism for thrusting and folding in the Pyrenees Mountains. (b) Deformation of initial upright folds by glacier-like gravitational flow. Reprinted from Choukroune and Seguret (1973) with permission of John Wiley & Sons.

The term in braces is the velocity at the surface of the layer, $y = h$, since the second term equals 1 when $y = h$. For given material properties, n and B, one may evaluate this velocity. Alternatively, we may measure glacier thicknesses, slopes, and surface velocities to estimate these properties, in the spirit of a field experiment. Notice that the surface velocity is proportional to h^{n+1}.

An effect of the stress exponent, n, may be seen by plotting the dimensionless ratio $v_x/v_x(h)$ against y/h for various n (Fig. 10.5a). As n increases, shearing becomes strongly concentrated downward with increasing shear stress. For example, velocity profiles through the thickness of a glacier may be measured by melting a vertical borehole and placing a cable in it (Raymond, 1971; Meier et al., 1974). After an interval of time, the cable may be "re-occupied" by sliding a melting device along it. Measurement of the inclination of the cable as a function of inextensible wire length from the surface then allows the profile to be determined by integration from the surface position.

If a mass of rock did flow in approximately this fashion, and was cut by erosion, measurement of the shear strain distribution would allow one to estimate n. Given the velocity field, which in this case is steady, we may determine the distribution of strain in the body for a given amount of surface displacement (Fig. 10.5b). Total displacement is different for each profile in order to separate them. The deformed shapes of small circles initially situated along the y/h-axis were computed from a series of initial particle positions. Because of the gradient in shear rate, the resulting loci only approximate ellipses. For example, see the strongly deformed circle at the base of the sheet for $n = 10$. Procedures in Chapter 5 provide exact results: since the velocity gradient tensor for a particle is constant as it moves along a line at constant height y, the displacement gradient tensor may be computed by direct integration.

10.3.3 Flow between approaching or separating rigid plates

The flow of fluid outward from approaching rigid plates has been in the literature of structural geology for several decades (Jaeger, 1964a). It has been applied to deformation in an orogenic belt between lithospheric plates whose relative motion

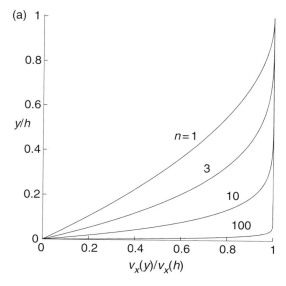

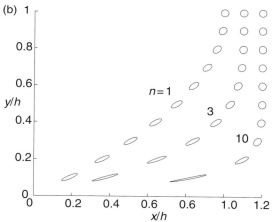

Fig 10.5 (a) Normalized velocity profiles for $n = 1, 3, 10,$ and 100. (b) Strain ellipses after surface displacements $x/h \sim 1$ for $n = 1, 3,$ and 10.

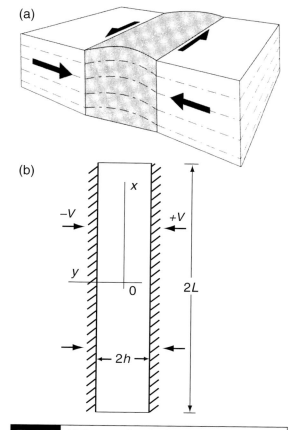

Fig 10.6 (a) Conceptual model for deformation in an orogenic belt between lithospheric plates with normal and tangential relative motion; reprinted from Robin and Cruden (1994) with permission of Elsevier. (b) Axes and parameters for flow between approaching parallel plates (Jaeger, 1964).

is both normal to and tangent to their boundary (Fig. 10.6a): the case of transpression (Robin and Cruden, 1994). The problem may be done either in plane flow or in radially symmetric flow in (r, z)-coordinates; the former is the case of interest here. This boundary value problem is historically interesting because it demonstrated to structural geologists that a flow of some complexity in terms of velocity and stress fields could be worked out by elementary means.

The configuration and coordinate axes are shown in Fig. 10.6b. The plates are of width $2L$, so that the slit in which the viscous fluid flows is open to the outside at $x = \pm L$. To satisfy the end conditions exactly greatly increases the difficulty of the problem, and we almost ignore them. The idea used is that these conditions will only significantly affect the flow within a few slit widths from the end. We thus restrict attention to the case $L/h \gg 1$, so that these regions will be small relative to the total length.

If the fluid sticks to the surfaces of the plates, the boundary conditions there are:

$$v_x(x, -h) = 0 = v_x(x, +h)$$
$$v_y(x, -h) = V = -v_y(x, +h) \tag{10.31}$$

The magnitude of the velocity of each plate is V. We select the coordinate axes so that the flow will have maximum symmetry:

$$v_x(x, -y) = v_x(x, y)$$
$$v_y(x, -y) = -v_y(x, y) \qquad (10.32)$$
$$v_x(-x, y) = -v_x(x, y)$$

That is, v_x is an even function of y and an odd function of x, and v_y is an odd function of y. The second restriction implies that $v_x(0, y) = 0$. A vertical mirror plane of symmetry is present at $x = 0$. Such a plane behaves like the frictionless surface of a rigid medium, preventing horizontal flow. Symmetry also requires that the shear traction on the $(x = 0)$-plane be zero.

Fluid flows in opposite directions from the central mirror plane of symmetry. The fluid flux at some distance $|x|$ from the mirror plane must be equal to the volume per unit depth swept out by the approaching plates per unit time, or $2V|x|$. Both conditions can be met by setting $v_x \sim x$. The simplest function satisfying this condition and (10.31) is:

$$v_x = A(y - h)(y + h)x = A(y^2 - h^2)x \qquad (10.33)$$

From incompressibility the velocity gradients are related as:

$$\frac{\partial v_y}{\partial y} = -\frac{\partial v_x}{\partial x} = -A(y^2 - h^2) \qquad (10.34)$$

Integrating (10.34) we find:

$$v_y = -A\left(\tfrac{1}{3}y^3 - h^2 y\right) \qquad (10.35)$$

This velocity distribution satisfies the conditions (10.31) if:

$$A = -3V/2h^3 \qquad (10.36)$$

The velocity field over a distance of $4h$ from the mid-plane is illustrated by streamlines and vectors in Fig. 10.7.

From the constitutive relations (10.14) and kinematic relations (10.12) we have:

$$\sigma_{xy} = \eta\left(\frac{\partial v_y}{\partial x} + \frac{\partial v_x}{\partial y}\right) = 2\eta Axy$$
$$\sigma_{xx} - \sigma_{yy} = 4\eta\frac{\partial v_x}{\partial x} = 4\eta A(y^2 - h^2) \qquad (10.37)$$

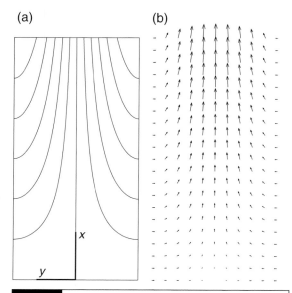

Substituting the first of these into each of the equilibrium equations (10.15) without gravity yields:

$$\frac{\partial \sigma_{xx}}{\partial x} = -2\eta Ax, \qquad \frac{\partial \sigma_{yy}}{\partial y} = -2\eta Ay \qquad (10.38)$$

Integrating each of (10.38) we find:

$$\sigma_{xx} = -\eta Ax^2 + f_1(y)$$
$$\sigma_{yy} = -\eta Ay^2 + f_2(x) \qquad (10.39)$$

By combining the second relation in (10.37) with (10.39), we obtain:

$$4\eta A(y^2 - h^2) = -\eta Ax^2 + f_1(y) + C_1 + \eta Ay^2 - f_2(x) \qquad (10.40)$$

The arbitrary functions $f_1(y)$ and $f_2(x)$ are:

$$f_1(y) = \eta A(3y^2 - 2h^2) + C$$
$$f_2(x) = \eta A(-x^2 + 2h^2) + C \qquad (10.41)$$

Then the two normal stress components from (10.39) are:

$$\sigma_{xx} = \eta A(-x^2 + 3y^2 - 2h^2) + C$$
$$\sigma_{yy} = \eta A(-x^2 - y^2 + 2h^2) + C \qquad (10.42)$$

The constant C may be determined by specifying boundary conditions at the ends of the plates. For example, suppose that the mean normal pressure, $\bar{p} = \frac{1}{3}(\sigma_1 + \sigma_2 + \sigma_3) = \frac{1}{2}(\sigma_{xx} + \sigma_{yy})$, is zero there. Specifically we take:

$$\text{BC: } \sigma_{xx} + \sigma_{yy} = 0 \text{ at } x = \pm L, y = 0 \qquad (10.43)$$

Since $h/L \ll 1$, ignore the terms in h^2 in comparison with those in L^2 and take:

$$C = \eta A L^2 \qquad (10.44)$$

The two normal stress components for these boundary conditions are:

$$\sigma_{xx} = \eta A(-x^2 + L^2 + 3y^2 - 2h^2)$$
$$\sigma_{yy} = \eta A(-x^2 + L^2 - y^2 + 2h^2) \qquad (10.45)$$

The average normal stress acting on the plates to produce an approach velocity of $2V$ is:

$$\sigma_{yy}(\text{ave}) = \frac{1}{L} \int_0^L \sigma_{yy}(x, \pm h)\,dx \qquad (10.46)$$

Substituting from the second of (10.45) we find:

$$\sigma_{yy}(\text{ave}) = \tfrac{2}{3}\eta A L^2 = -\eta V L^2/h^3 \qquad (10.47)$$

We note that the approach velocity, V, of the plates scales with the applied stress and h^3, whereas it is inversely proportional to the viscosity and L^2.

Robin and Cruden (1994) use this flow field to simulate the deformation in a slab of material lying between two lithospheric plates (Fig. 10.7a) that have a component of normal motion as well as tangential relative motion, i.e. the deformation termed transpression. In this case, the region shown in Fig. 10.7b is imagined as vertical, with material in it extruding out from the top to form a kind of mountain belt. The "trans-" part of the motion is shearing across the region, but in and out of the plane. The shearing motion may be superposed on the "-pression" motion derived here, since the governing equations are linear. Although the resulting velocity field is easy to visualize, the distribution of strain and rotation in the fluid slab is complicated; the results must be computed and puzzled out.

10.3.4 Lubrication theory: steady-state solution for an accretionary wedge

An accretionary wedge (Fig. 10.8) is built up at the edge of a plate under which another subducts (Chapple, 1978; Davis et al., 1983; Batt et al., 2001; Brandon, 2004). Such accretionary wedges have been treated as though the material involved exhibited sand-like, or plastic, behavior (Dahlen et al., 1984; Hilley and Strecker, 2004; Hilley et al., 2004). Here we develop a simple model that assumes the material behaves as a viscous fluid. This assumption has been used by Emerman and Turcotte (1983), who first worked out the model presented here. As they did, we could also obtain a solution for the non-linear power-law fluid discussed in Section 10.3.2. In contrast to the boundary value problem for the flow down an inclined plane, the analysis set up here has many more steps, and involves more approximations than the problem for flow between approaching parallel plates.

A schematic illustration of the model configuration (Fig. 10.8) has a feature termed a *backstop*. We do not wish to motivate and justify this peculiar feature exhaustively here, but some discussion seems necessary. An accretionary wedge is composed of sediments and other materials scraping off a subducting plate, and the analogy has been drawn between this process and pushing a mass of material across a horizontal or tilting surface as between a snowplow mounted at the front of a truck and the road surface. The relative motion is inverted here so the subducting plate moves, while the plow stays fixed. The wedge of material on the subducting plate moves in a direction opposite to that of subduction. The backstop is identified with the plow and taken to be vertical. No plow is present towards the rear of a natural accretionary wedge, so this must stand in as an approximation for some other feature.

Progressing from the toe (Fig. 10.8), an accretionary wedge has a topographic culmination, to the rear of which it loses topography. The reason for this is that the subducting plate piles up material as long as it exerts a shearing motion at the base of the wedge, but once the plate surface contacts lower, hotter material of negligible strength,

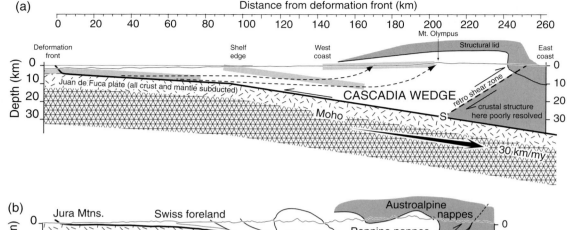

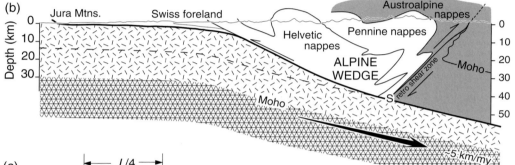

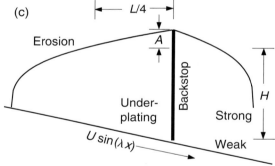

Fig 10.8 Comparison of the structure of (a) the Cascadia margin, Washington State, and (b) the European Alps, Switzerland (Brandon, 2004). (c) Schematic diagram of an accretionary wedge model.

this ceases to occur. The topographic culmination occurs approximately above this position. In the present case, at least, we take the backstop to represent the position of the topographic culmination and, by making it vertical and frictionless, we approximate the accretionary wedge as having mirror symmetry. An accretionary wedge does continue beyond the topographic culmination, but it tends to possess a strong asymmetry. Here,

we focus on the prominent seaward side of the wedge. We speak of the backstop and occasionally of plowing as in these physical analogies.

To solve for the steady-state shape of the wedge, $h(x)$, and the flow and stresses within it, we will employ the approximations of *lubrication theory* (Batchelor, 1967; Schlichting, 1979). The idea behind lubrication theory as applied here is that the wedge is slender: the maximum thickness is much smaller than its width, so $h(0)/L \ll 1$, where $h(0)$ is the maximum height at the backstop. We suppose that the velocity of plowing is sufficiently small for this to be so. For such a body, it is natural to suppose that quantities vary much more rapidly in the vertical direction than in the horizontal direction. Thus, horizontal derivatives of quantities of the same sort, e. g. stress components, may be neglected relative to vertical derivatives. In the analysis, we postulate that the unit weight, ρg, and viscosity, η, are uniform while recognizing these quantities would vary spatially in an actual accretionary wedge.

The first step is to drop the x-derivative in the second equation in (10.15) and write:

$$\partial \sigma_{yy}/y \cong \rho g \qquad (10.48)$$

Integrating this equation with the condition that the normal stress vanish at the top of the wedge, approximated as $\sigma_{yy}(x,h) \cong 0$, yields:

$$\sigma_{yy} \cong \rho g(y - h), \quad h = h(x,t) \qquad (10.49)$$

In the kinematic relations (10.12), derivatives of v_x occur in D_{xy} and D_{xx}, and that in D_{xy} is larger, by hypothesis, so $D_{xy} \gg D_{xx}$. Discarding the derivative $\partial v_y/\partial x$ in D_{xy}, we have:

$$D_{xy} \cong \tfrac{1}{2}(\partial v_x/\partial y) \qquad (10.50)$$

From (10.14) we conclude that $\sigma_{xy} \gg |\sigma_{xx} - \sigma_{yy}|$. Using these approximations in the first equilibrium equation (10.15), the result (10.49) yields:

$$\frac{\partial \sigma_{xy}}{\partial y} = -\frac{\partial \sigma_{xx}}{\partial x} \cong -\frac{\partial \sigma_{yy}}{\partial x} \cong \rho g \frac{\partial h}{\partial x} \qquad (10.51)$$

Integrating, and using the requirement that the shear traction vanish at the upper surface, approximated by $\sigma_{xy}(h) \cong 0$, we obtain:

$$\sigma_{xy} \cong \rho g \frac{\partial h}{\partial x}(y - h) \qquad (10.52)$$

We may now use (10.14), (10.50), and (10.52) to write:

$$\frac{\partial v_x}{\partial z} \cong \frac{\rho g}{\eta} \frac{\partial h}{\partial x}(y - h) \qquad (10.53)$$

Integration gives:

$$v_x \cong \frac{\rho g}{\eta} \frac{\partial h}{\partial x}\left(\frac{y^2}{2} - hy\right) + v_x(0) \qquad (10.54)$$

If the viscous wedge does not slip at its base, $v_x(0) = -V$. You may wonder how we are able to move the wedge along with our plow with this no-slip condition. The notion is that the fluid is "scraped off" right at the backstop, but the mass of fluid is not sliding over the surface as a whole.

As in the analysis of the flow between approaching rigid plates (Section 10.3.3), end conditions on the wedge are ignored. Thus, the details as to how the material is scraped off the

subducting plate at the backstop are not provided. Indeed, no conditions at a backstop are specified in the formulation of this problem! Rigorously, we cannot even speak of its presence because it has not entered the formulation and analysis.

At this point, a complete approximate solution for stress and velocity in the wedge is expressed in terms of the unknown profile $h(x,t)$. To obtain this, we write the relation for conservation of mass between vertical surfaces at x and $x + dx$ for wedge material of uniform and constant density:

$$\frac{\partial h}{\partial t} dx = J_x(x) - J_x(x + dx) = -\frac{\partial J_x}{\partial x} dx \qquad (10.55)$$

Here J_x is the volume flux across a vertical surface per unit strike length, or:

$$J_x(x) = \int_0^h v_x(x, y)dy \qquad (10.56)$$

Substituting (10.54) with the condition $v_x(0) = -V$ into (10.56) and integrating:

$$J_x = -\frac{\rho g h^3}{3\eta} \frac{\partial h}{\partial x} - Vh \qquad (10.57)$$

Because the wedge slopes toward its toe, $\partial h/\partial x < 0$, the first term is positive, signifying a flux toward the toe. The second negative term represents the motion of the subducting plate relative to a fixed backstop.

Substituting (10.57) into (10.55), yields a partial differential equation in h:

$$\frac{\partial h}{\partial t} = \frac{\partial}{\partial x}\left(\frac{\rho g h^3}{3\eta} \frac{\partial h}{\partial x} + Vh\right) \qquad (10.58)$$

We look for a steady-state solution, in which the form of the wedge is unchanged, and set $\partial h/\partial t = 0$. Integrating the resulting ordinary differential equation yields:

$$\frac{\rho g h^3}{3\eta} \frac{\partial h}{\partial x} + Vh = C \qquad (10.59)$$

This equation satisfies the condition that the wedge has a finite width, L, that is $h(L) = 0$, if $C = 0$. Factoring out an h, integrating again, and re-applying this condition gives (Emerman and Turcotte, 1983):

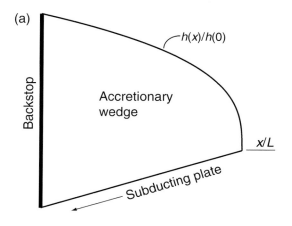

(a)

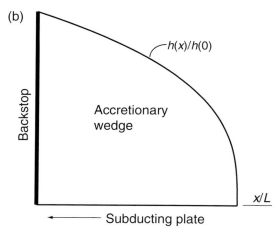

(b)

Fig 10.9 Schematic diagrams of accretionary wedges forward of a backstop. (a) Inclined boundary between wedge and subducting plate. (b) Horizontal boundary.

$$h = \left[\frac{9\eta VL}{\rho g} \left(1 - \frac{x}{L}\right) \right]^{1/3} \tag{10.60}$$

The profiles of the wedges in Fig. 10.9 have the form specified by (10.60), where h in both cases is taken as the total vertical height above the planar base. The solution applies to a finite wedge of any cross-sectional area A, where:

$$A = \int_0^L h(x)dx = \left(\frac{243\eta VL^4}{64\rho g} \right)^{1/3} \tag{10.61}$$

The maximum wedge thickness at $x = 0$ from (10.60) is:

$$h_0 = \left(\frac{9\eta VL}{\rho g} \right)^{1/3} \tag{10.62}$$

Typical values for an accretionary wedge are $h_0 = 20$ km, $L = 200$ km, $\rho = 2600$ kg m^{-3} and a subduction velocity $U = 5$ cm a^{-1} (Emerman and Turcotte, 1983; Batt *et al.*, 2001). The relation (10.62) yields a wedge viscosity $\eta \approx 0.7 \times 10^{20}$ Pa s^{-1}. This is a plausible estimate for rock viscosity in an accretionary wedge (Emerman and Turcotte, 1983). An estimate of 10^{21} Pa s^{-1} has been obtained for the weak upper mantle (Haskell, 1937). The lubrication theory model for a viscous accretionary wedge may be used to assess the effect of factors such as rate of supply of material, rate of erosion, and viscosity on wedge dynamics.

10.4 | Viscous flow in layers: mullions and folds

The great variety of structures produced by rock deformation and their variation in form and association may be usefully grouped into a few categories. One category contains structures produced by the deformation of *layers*. Examples in this chapter include the folds seen in the frontispiece and in Fig. 10.1; additional examples follow. Other categories are the *crack-like* structures described in Chapter 9 such as faults, joints, dikes, veins, and anticracks, and *inclusions* of one material embedded in another. Models for structures in each category are commonly formulated using special sets of mathematical tools. Here we focus on the deformation of layers.

10.4.1 Biharmonic equation and its solution

In Chapter 8 we introduced the three components of stress in the (x, y)-plane written as partial derivatives of the Airy stress function, $\phi(x, y)$:

$$\sigma_{xx} = \frac{\partial^2 \phi}{\partial y^2}, \quad \sigma_{xy} = \frac{\partial^2 \phi}{\partial x \partial y}, \quad \sigma_{yy} = \frac{\partial^2 \phi}{\partial x^2} \tag{10.63}$$

These expressions satisfy the two-dimensional stress equilibrium equations (10.15) and thus replace three unknown stress components in a problem of plane flow with a single unknown function from which they may be derived.

The plane flow kinematic relations (10.12) are three equations in two unknowns, v_x and v_y.

Eliminating the two components of velocity between them yields the rate of deformation compatibility relation:

$$\frac{\partial^2 D_{xx}}{\partial y^2} - 2\frac{\partial^2 D_{xy}}{\partial x \partial y} + \frac{\partial^2 D_{yy}}{\partial x^2} = 0 \qquad (10.64)$$

In order to obtain this equation by taking partial derivatives, and even before that to write the rate of deformation components in terms of partial derivatives of the velocity components, the velocity components must be continuous and have continuous partial derivatives to third order. This continuity is a prior necessary condition for deriving (10.64). Structural geologists often refer to the compatibility condition as a condition required to insure that the velocity field (or displacement field) is smooth, so that pieces of the body described are not slipping or separating relative to each other. This interpretation has things backwards: continuity is required to write down (10.64).

From (10.14) and (10.63) the rate of deformation components in terms of the stress function are:

$$D_{xx} = -D_{yy} = \frac{1}{4\eta}\left(\frac{\partial^2 \phi}{\partial y^2} - \frac{\partial^2 \phi}{\partial x^2}\right), \quad D_{xy} = \frac{1}{2\eta}\frac{\partial^2 \phi}{\partial x \partial y}$$

$$(10.65)$$

Substituting into (10.64), we find:

$$\left(\frac{\partial^2}{\partial y^2} - \frac{\partial^2}{\partial x^2}\right)\left[\frac{1}{4\eta}\left(\frac{\partial^2 \phi}{\partial y^2} - \frac{\partial^2 \phi}{\partial x^2}\right)\right]$$
$$- 2\frac{\partial^2}{\partial x \partial y}\left(-\frac{1}{2\eta}\frac{\partial^2 \phi}{\partial x \partial y}\right) = 0 \qquad (10.66)$$

In the present case, we suppose that the viscosity, η, is not a function of position so we obtain:

$$\frac{\partial^4 \phi}{\partial y^4} + 2\frac{\partial^4 \phi}{\partial y^2 \partial x^2} + \frac{\partial^4 \phi}{\partial x^4} = 0 \qquad (10.67)$$

This is the *biharmonic equation*, often written in the condensed form:

$$\nabla^4 \phi = \nabla^2(\nabla^2 \phi) = 0 \qquad (10.68)$$

Having reduced the general set of equations for plane flow, (10.12)–(10.15), to a single equation in one unknown function, $\phi(x, y)$, the next step is to set up some boundary value problems of interest and solve them.

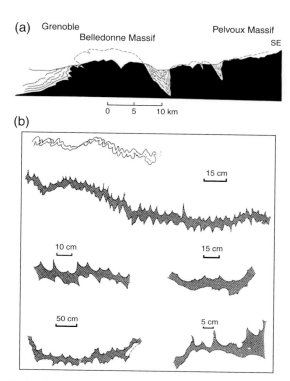

(a) Grenoble
Belledonne Massif
Pelvoux Massif
SE

0   5   10 km

(b)

15 cm

10 cm   15 cm

50 cm   5 cm

Fig 10.10 Mullion structures: (a) large scale (Ramsay, 1967); (b) small scale (reprinted from Sokoutis (1987) with permission of Elsevier).

10.4.2 Mullions

Mullion structure was the first geological structure to be investigated using the finite-element method (Dieterich and Onat, 1969). Here, we will learn something about its formation from a simple analytical study. This structure, illustrated at scales of centimeters and kilometers in Fig. 10.10, consists of a lobe-and-cusp morphology of interfaces between different rock types and is interpreted to have formed during interface-parallel shortening of large magnitude. Lobate forms are developed in the stiffer rock with the softer, or less viscous, rock-filling cusps. One might suppose that the surfaces of the more viscous rock layers were puckered, so as to undergo little surface-parallel shortening. If so, one could lay out the surface trace in a straight line and use this to estimate the original length of the interface. Then, as done for the folded vein in Fig. 5.3, one could estimate the amount of bulk shortening.

The mullion structures in Fig. 10.10a have a variable cusp-to-cusp span that is much smaller than the vertical dimensions, not indicated in the figure, of the bodies at whose interface they lie. Both are probably layer-like or sheet-like in form. Large mullions in this figure have spans of about 10 km, but many smaller "parasitic" mullions have dimensions of a kilometer, so mullions apparently form at multiple scales. These observations lead us to infer that mullion initiation in this case may not depend on a characteristic dimension of the initial configuration, such as a layer thickness. We thus consider a configuration consisting of two viscous half-spaces. In contrast, the mullions in Fig. 10.10b show a regular span on the decimeter scale with cusp-to-cusp arc lengths comparable to the thickness of the layer separating them. The model developed here will not give insight into this aspect of their deformation.

Suppose two materials undergo uniform shortening parallel to a *planar* interface without the formation of mullion structure. Quantities in the upper half-space are identified with the superscript (1), and those in the lower half-space with (2). Assuming plane flow, (10.12)–(10.15), the homogeneous shortening is described by:

$$\overline{D}_{xx}^{(1)} = \overline{D}_{xx}^{(2)} = \overline{D}_{xx}$$
$$\overline{D}_{yy}^{(1)} = \overline{D}_{yy}^{(2)} = \overline{D}_{yy} = -\overline{D}_{xx}$$
$$\overline{D}_{xy}^{(1)} = 0 = \overline{D}_{xy}^{(2)}$$

(10.69)

From (10.69) and the constitutive relations (10.14) we have:

$$(\overline{\sigma}_{xx}^{(1)} - \overline{\sigma}_{yy})/4\eta_1 = (\overline{\sigma}_{xx}^{(2)} - \overline{\sigma}_{yy})/4\eta_2 = \overline{D}_{xx}$$
$$\overline{\sigma}_{xy}^{(1)} = \overline{\sigma}_{xy}^{(2)} = \overline{\sigma}_{xy} = 0$$

(10.70)

The stress components $\overline{\sigma}_{yy}$ and $\overline{\sigma}_{xy}$ are the same in both half-spaces, as required by the continuity of traction at the planar interface. The surface-parallel normal stress must be different unless the viscosities are the same.

Taking the coordinate origin at the interface, the velocity components, with the origin fixed, are:

$$\overline{v}_x^{(1)} = \overline{v}_x^{(2)} = \overline{D}_{xx} x$$
$$\overline{v}_y^{(1)} = \overline{v}_y^{(2)} = \overline{D}_{yy} y = -\overline{D}_{xx} y$$

(10.71)

These satisfy the condition that adjacent particles in the two viscous fluids remain neighbors as

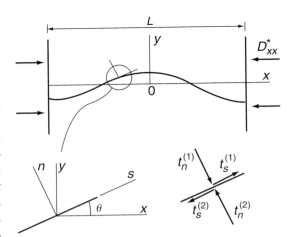

Fig 10.11 Portion of interface for the mullion model, with axes and tractions locally tangent and normal to the interface.

deformation continues. This completes the solution for the case of a perfectly planar interface, which we term the *basic state*.

Now suppose that mullion structure is formed by the amplification of an irregular waviness present on the interface before shortening. We treat the interface as a *cylindrical* surface of sinusoidal form (Fig. 10.11) with axis normal to the (x, y)-plane of flow, amplitude A, wavenumber λ, and wavelength $L = 2\pi/\lambda$:

$$y = \zeta(x, t) = A(t)\cos\lambda(t)x$$

(10.72)

Both the amplitude and wavenumber are functions of time, t. The interface in the case of mullions shown in Fig. 10.10a is not periodic, nor does (10.72) describe the lobe-and-cusp asymmetry of the mullion interface. However, a sum of wavelength components provides the possibility of extending the solution to cover these variations. By considering a periodic interface form, we isolate a region of interest that is a single wavelength wide. The vertical planes at $x = \pm L/2$ may be treated as though they were the frictionless planar surfaces of two rigid platens, between which the two media with their sinusoidal interface shorten. Because the shear stress must vanish on a mirror plane of symmetry, these planes have the property of a frictionless surface.

The local slope with maximum at $x = \pm L/4$ of magnitude λA is:

$$\tan\theta = \partial\zeta/\partial x = -(\lambda A)\sin\lambda x \qquad (10.73)$$

Taking $\lambda A \ll 1$, we use the approximations:

$$\tan\theta \cong \theta + \theta^3/3 \cong \theta \cong -(\lambda A)\sin\lambda x$$
$$\sin\theta \cong \theta - \theta^3/6 \cong \theta \cong -(\lambda A)\sin\lambda x \qquad (10.74)$$
$$\cos\theta \cong 1 - \theta^2/2 \cong 1$$

We seek a solution accurate to terms proportional to λA. In the derivation, if terms proportional to $(\lambda A)^2$ or higher are encountered, they are deleted. We cannot hope to simulate the development of a large-amplitude mullion (Fig. 10.10a) with this approximation. Instead, we study mullion initiation and the inception of an asymmetric lobe-and-cusp structure.

For the wavy interface, the basic-state solution no longer satisfies all boundary conditions at the interface to the desired accuracy, as we now demonstrate by introduction of a correction term in the form of additional sets of velocity, stress, and rate of deformation components. The velocity components in the two media are the sum of the respective components from the basic state and from this corrective state, so they have the form:

$$v_x^{(1)} = \bar{v}_x^{(1)} + \tilde{v}_x^{(1)}, \quad v_y^{(1)} = \bar{v}_y^{(1)} + \tilde{v}_y^{(1)}$$
$$v_x^{(2)} = \bar{v}_x^{(2)} + \tilde{v}_x^{(2)}, \quad v_y^{(2)} = \bar{v}_y^{(2)} + \tilde{v}_y^{(2)} \qquad (10.75)$$

The stress and rate of deformation components are composed of similar sums. Suppose that the interface is welded, so velocity components of adjacent particles across it are equal:

$$v_x^{(1)}(x,\zeta) = v_x^{(2)}(x,\zeta)$$
$$v_y^{(1)}(x,\zeta) = v_y^{(2)}(x,\zeta) \qquad (10.76)$$

Since the basic-state velocity components already satisfy these conditions, (10.76) reduce to:

$$\tilde{v}_x^{(1)}(x,\zeta) = \tilde{v}_x^{(2)}(x,\zeta)$$
$$\tilde{v}_y^{(1)}(x,\zeta) = \tilde{v}_y^{(2)}(x,\zeta) \qquad (10.77)$$

The boundary conditions on the normal and shear components of the traction on the interface are:

$$t_s^{(1)}(x,\zeta) = -t_s^{(2)}(x,\zeta)$$
$$t_n^{(1)}(x,\zeta) = -t_n^{(2)}(x,\zeta) \qquad (10.78)$$

The tractions will be evaluated for each medium in terms of the interface geometry and the components of stress (Fig. 10.11). We might also have used the components with respect to the coordinate axes x and y. The present choice is more generally useful; for example, if the interface were frictionless, the shear component of the traction would be required to vanish. It would then be necessary to write the velocity boundary conditions in terms of normal and tangential components also, since slip on a frictionless interface would exclude a condition being set on the tangential component of velocity.

Expressing the tractions in terms of the stress components referred to the local coordinate axes, n and s:

$$t_n^{(1)} = \sigma_{nn}^{(1)}, \quad t_n^{(2)} = -\sigma_{nn}^{(2)}$$
$$t_s^{(1)} = \sigma_{ns}^{(1)}, \quad t_s^{(2)} = -\sigma_{ns}^{(2)} \qquad (10.79)$$

In terms of the stress components, the boundary conditions are:

$$\sigma_{nn}^{(1)}(x,\zeta) = \sigma_{nn}^{(2)}(x,\zeta)$$
$$\sigma_{ns}^{(1)}(x,\zeta) = \sigma_{ns}^{(2)}(x,\zeta) \qquad (10.80)$$

These conditions must be written in terms of the components of stress referred to the (x, y)-coordinates used in the field equations, in which the solution will be expressed. Using the transformation law we have:

$$\sigma_{nn} = \sigma_{xx}\sin^2\theta - 2\sigma_{xy}\sin\theta\cos\theta + \sigma_{yy}\cos^2\theta$$
$$\sigma_{ns} = -(\sigma_{xx} - \sigma_{yy})\sin\theta\cos\theta + \sigma_{xy}(\cos^2\theta - \sin^2\theta) \qquad (10.81)$$

Using (10.74), and retaining only terms up to those proportional to λA, we have:

$$\sigma_{nn} \cong -2\sigma_{xy}\theta + \sigma_{yy}$$
$$\sigma_{ns} \cong -(\sigma_{xx} - \sigma_{yy})\theta + \sigma_{xy} \qquad (10.82)$$

No correction to the basic-state solution is necessary if the interface is perfectly planar ($\lambda A = 0$); that is, the perturbing solution is identically zero. Therefore we postulate that the components of stress and velocity in the perturbing solution are themselves proportional to λA. Since $\bar{\sigma}_{xy} = 0$, we have $\sigma_{xy} = \tilde{\sigma}_{xy}$ and the term $\sigma_{xy}\theta$ in the first of (10.82) can be discarded because it is a product of two terms, both of which are proportional to λA. Applying these conditions, and the forms (10.74), the stress boundary conditions (10.82) become:

$$\tilde{\sigma}_{yy}^{(1)}(x, \zeta) \cong \tilde{\sigma}_{yy}^{(2)}(x, \zeta)$$

$$\tilde{\sigma}_{xy}^{(1)}(x, \zeta) - (\overline{\sigma}_{xx}^{(1)} - \overline{\sigma}_{yy})[-(\lambda A)\sin\lambda x] \quad (10.83)$$

$$\cong \tilde{\sigma}_{xy}^{(2)}(x, \zeta) - (\overline{\sigma}_{xx}^{(2)} - \overline{\sigma}_{yy})[-(\lambda A)\sin\lambda x]$$

The second relation in (10.83) is consistent with the hypothesis that the perturbing flow is proportional to λA. Indeed, any information that the interface is not planar, and, hence, that a perturbing flow must be present, comes only from this condition.

The second boundary condition in (10.83) determines the x-dependence of the required solution of the biharmonic equation (10.67). Two pieces of information are supplied. First, the condition must be satisfied for all values of x on the *nearly* planar interface $y = \zeta(x)$. This suggests the possibility that the function $\phi(x,y)$ and, from it, the components of stress and velocity, might be written in a separable form:

$$\phi(x,y) = F(y)G(x) \quad (10.84)$$

Since $\tilde{\sigma}_{xy} = -\partial^2\phi/\partial x\partial y$, the second condition in (10.83) could be satisfied if $G(x) = \cos\lambda x$, giving:

$$\tilde{\sigma}_{xy}(x, \zeta) = -(dF/dy)_{y=\zeta}\sin\lambda x \cong -(dF/dy)_{y=0}\sin\lambda x \quad (10.85)$$

To the present approximation, this condition becomes:

$$-(dF^{(1)}/dy)_{y=0}\sin\lambda x + (\lambda A)(\overline{\sigma}_{xx}^{(1)} - \overline{\sigma}_{yy})\sin\lambda x$$
$$= -(dF^{(2)}/dy)_{y=0}\sin\lambda x + (\lambda A)(\overline{\sigma}_{xx}^{(2)} - \overline{\sigma}_{yy})\sin\lambda x \quad (10.86)$$

The common factor $\sin\lambda x$ may be cancelled in (10.86).

The stress function is taken as:

$$\phi(x,y) = -(1/\lambda^2)F(y)\cos\lambda x \quad (10.87)$$

Here the factor $-1/\lambda^2$ leads to simpler expressions for the stress components. Substituting (10.87) into the biharmonic equation (10.67) we obtain the ordinary differential equation:

$$\frac{d^4F}{dy^4} - 2\lambda^2\frac{d^2F}{dy^2} + \lambda^4F = 0 \quad (10.88)$$

The solution to (10.88) may be written:

$$F(y) = 2\eta\lambda\{[a + b(\lambda y-1)]e^{\lambda y} + [c + d(\lambda y + 1)]e^{-\lambda y}\} \quad (10.89)$$

Here a, b, c, and d are arbitrary coefficients whose values are fixed by the boundary conditions. The term $e^{\lambda y}$ is multiplied by $a - b$ to give the resulting stress components a symmetric form. The factor $2\eta\lambda$ is added to make the expressions for the velocity components simpler in form. The stress components associated with the perturbing flow are found from (10.63):

$$\tilde{\sigma}_{xx} = -2\eta\lambda\{[a + b(\lambda y + 1)]e^{\lambda y} + [c + d(\lambda y-1)]e^{-\lambda y}\}\cos\lambda x$$

$$\tilde{\sigma}_{yy} = +2\eta\lambda\{[a + b(\lambda y-1)]e^{\lambda y} + [c + d(\lambda y + 1)]e^{-\lambda y}\}\cos\lambda x \quad (10.90)$$

$$\tilde{\sigma}_{xy} = -2\eta\lambda[(a + b\lambda y)e^{\lambda y}-(c + d\lambda y)e^{-\lambda y}]\sin\lambda x$$

From the constitutive relations (10.14) and the kinematic relations (10.12) for plane flow we have:

$$\frac{\partial\tilde{v}_x}{\partial x} = \frac{\tilde{\sigma}_{xx} - \tilde{\sigma}_{yy}}{4\eta} = -\lambda[(a + b\lambda y)e^{\lambda y}$$
$$+ (c + d\lambda y)e^{-\lambda y}]\cos\lambda x \quad (10.91)$$

Integrating (10.91) the x-component of velocity is:

$$\tilde{v}_x = -[(a + b\lambda y)e^{\lambda y} + (c + d\lambda y)e^{-\lambda y}]\sin\lambda x \quad (10.92)$$

The y-component of velocity is found from the condition of incompressibility written as $\partial\tilde{v}_y/\partial y = -\partial\tilde{v}_x/\partial x$ and (10.92):

$$\tilde{v}_y = \{[a + b(\lambda y - 1)]e^{\lambda y} - [c + d(\lambda y + 1)]e^{-\lambda y}\}\cos\lambda x \quad (10.93)$$

Using this solution for the components of stress and velocity, we are able to solve a great many interesting problems for layers. Our first application is in the analysis of the mullion. Later, we use this solution to study the buckling of viscous layers (Fig. 10.1a and Fig. 10.14). Other examples are discussed elsewhere (Johnson and Fletcher, 1994).

In the present case, the solutions for the perturbing flows in the upper and lower half-spaces are special cases of the more general forms just obtained. Since the flows in the two half-spaces must be distinct, there are eight arbitrary constants to be fixed using boundary conditions. These constants are: $a_1, b_1, c_1, d_1, a_2, b_2, c_2, d_2$, where subscripts 1 and 2 refer to the upper and lower half-spaces, respectively. At the interface there are only four boundary conditions, (10.77) and (10.83), thus indicating that we have not yet specified four boundary conditions elsewhere. Considering the y-component of velocity (10.93) in the upper half-space, $y > 0$, notice that the coefficients a_1 and b_1 multiply terms proportional to $e^{\lambda y}$, which grow in magnitude without limit as y increases. Since a relatively gentle waviness at the interface cannot be expected to produce an ever-increasing flow away from the interface, we take $a_1 = b_1 = 0$. Considering the same situation in the lower half-space, we conclude that $c_2 = d_2 = 0$.

The remaining four coefficients are fixed by application of the four boundary conditions at the interface. Begin with the condition on the continuity of the shear stress, (10.86). Using (10.90), and substituting $y = \zeta$ in the functions contained in the expressions $\tilde{\sigma}_{xy}^{(1)}$ and $\tilde{\sigma}_{xy}^{(2)}$, we obtain:

$$2\eta_1\lambda(c_1 + d_1\lambda\zeta)e^{-\lambda\zeta} + (\lambda A)4\eta_1\bar{D}_{xx}$$
$$= -2\eta_2\lambda(a_2 + b_2\lambda\zeta)e^{\lambda\zeta} + (\lambda A)4\eta_2\bar{D}_{xx} \quad (10.94)$$

Recall our hypothesis that the perturbing flow is proportional to λA. This can be the case only if the coefficients themselves are proportional to this quantity. Since $\lambda\zeta = (\lambda A)\cos\lambda x \sim \lambda A$, we expand the exponential functions to first order in this quantity: $e^{\lambda\zeta} \cong 1 + \lambda\zeta$ and $e^{-\lambda\zeta} \cong 1 - \lambda\zeta$. Retaining only terms linearly proportional to λA we find $\eta_1 c_1 + \eta_2 a_2 = 2(\eta_2 - \eta_1)\bar{D}_{xx}(A)$. The condition on continuity of v_x, (10.77), treated in the same way, yields $c_1 = a_2$. Combining these equations we have:

$$c_1 = a_2 = -2[(\eta_1 - \eta_2)/(\eta_1 + \eta_2)]\bar{D}_{xx}A \quad (10.95)$$

The remaining two boundary conditions on the normal component of stress and the vertical component of velocity yield:

$$c_1 + d_1 = 0 = a_2 - b_2 \quad (10.96)$$

From (10.95), if the viscosities of the two media are equal, the perturbing flow vanishes.

We consider the deformation of the interface by following particles on it. We postulate that

such particles are not dissolved away or eroded, nor is new material added to the interface. Using the solution for the coefficients, (10.95) and (10.96), and the expressions for the velocity components, (10.92) and (10.93), we may evaluate the velocity vectors for a large number of particles on the interface, $y = A\cos\lambda x$, and increment their positions by multiplying the velocity vectors by a small quantity Δt. The velocity components in the lower layer are:

$$v_x^{(2)} = \bar{D}_{xx}x - a_2(1 + \lambda y)e^{\lambda y}\sin\lambda x$$
$$v_y^{(2)} = -\bar{D}_{xx}y + a_2\lambda y e^{\lambda y}\cos\lambda x \quad (10.97)$$

This includes the basic state and the perturbing flows. If the viscosity of the lower medium is greater than that of the upper, $\eta_2 > \eta_1$, then $a_2 > 0$ for shortening, $\bar{D}_{xx} < 0$. It is useful to re-cast the expressions (10.97) with (10.95) and (10.96) into a dimensionless form, using $|\bar{D}_{xx}|L$ as the characteristic velocity:

$$\frac{v_x^{(2)}}{|\bar{D}_{xx}|L} = \mathrm{Sgn}(\bar{D}_{xx})\left[\frac{x}{L} - \frac{1}{\pi}\left(\frac{1-R}{1+R}\right)\left(\frac{2\pi A}{L}\right)\right.$$
$$\left. \times (1 + \lambda y)e^{\lambda y}\sin\lambda x \right]$$

$$(10.98)$$

$$\frac{v_y^{(2)}}{|\bar{D}_{xx}|L} = \mathrm{Sgn}(\bar{D}_{xx})\left[-\frac{y}{L} - \frac{1}{\pi}\left(\frac{1-R}{1+R}\right)\left(\frac{2\pi A}{L}\right)\right.$$
$$\left. \times \lambda y e^{\lambda y}\cos\lambda x \right]$$

Here the dimensionless quantities are $2\pi A/L = \lambda A$ and $R = \eta_2/\eta_1$. If the half-spaces are undergoing shortening, $\mathrm{Sgn}(\bar{D}_{xx}) = -1$, but for interface-parallel extension, $\mathrm{Sgn}(\bar{D}_{xx}) = +1$.

Figure 10.12a shows the perturbing part of the velocity field in the lower, more viscous half-space for $R = 10$. Notice how the perturbing flow is concentrated near the surface and has zero vertical velocity there. The horizontal flow away from the crest of the sinusoidal perturbation in surface shape broadens the lobes and tightens the cusps in the interface form. This is kinematically amplified in the basic state of uniform shortening. Figure 10.12b shows contours of the perturbing part of the horizontal normal stress. A horizontal zero contour lies at $y = -L/\pi$, below which this stress component changes sign, from tensile to

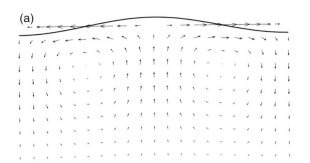

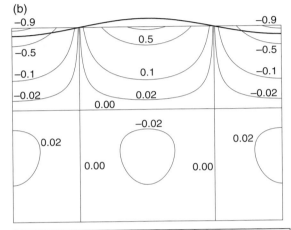

Fig 10.12 (a) Velocity vectors for the mullion perturbing flow. (b) Contours of the perturbing horizontal normal stress, normalized by its maximum value.

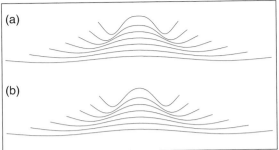

Fig 10.13 (a) Profiles from mullion model computed by incrementing positions of particles. (b) Profiles computed using the interface evolution equations.

compressive under the crest of the structure. The contours shown below the zero contour are only ±0.02 of the maximum; these contours are also represented above the zero contour.

Figure 10.13a shows a sinusoidal surface with an initial maximum slope of 0.02 radians and new surfaces obtained by evaluating the velocity vector at points on the surface and using them to move particles for small dimensionless increments of $|\bar{D}_{xx}|\Delta t$ for $R = 10$. The profiles are shifted vertically to separate them. The change in horizontal span of the surfaces indicates the finite homogeneous shortening. The surface begins to assume a lobe-and-cusp form with broader anticline and tighter flanking synclines. The last two profiles have slopes too large for a good approximation by the first-order solution, but are shown here to clarify the mullion-like forms.

Another means of following the evolution of an interface or surface requires the use of the *material time derivative*, derived in Chapter 7. If f is a scalar property of a material element the material time derivative is:

$$\frac{Df}{Dt} = \frac{\partial f}{\partial t} + v_x\frac{\partial f}{\partial x} + v_y\frac{\partial f}{\partial y} + v_z\frac{\partial f}{\partial z} \qquad (10.99)$$

A special property of a particle on the interface is that it stays on the interface. For the two-dimensional case considered here there is no dependence on the coordinate z. We then take as the property:

$$f(x, y, t) = y - \zeta(x, t) = 0 \qquad (10.100)$$

While other particles may be free to take arbitrary positions, or x- and y-coordinates, the position of a particle on the interface is constrained to have a special relationship between its x- and y-coordinates:

$$\frac{D}{Dt}[y - \zeta(x, t)] = 0 \qquad (10.101)$$

Using (10.99) with x, y, and t as the independent variables we find:

$$\frac{\partial \zeta}{\partial t} = v_y(x, \zeta) - v_x(x, \zeta)\frac{\partial \zeta}{\partial x} \qquad (10.102)$$

This is the interface evolution equation.

Recall that we have obtained an approximate solution for the sinusoidal shape perturbation, $\zeta = A\cos \lambda x$. Such a solution applies to an arbitrary two-dimensional, or cylindrical, shape perturbation because: (1) this may be treated as a sum of Fourier components with form allowing for variation in phase; and (2) to the approximation of the present solution, such components are linearly independent, i.e. non-interacting. However, for a periodic perturbation, we may analyze how the incipient mullion structure evolves at larger amplitude and interface slope while keeping the mathematics manageable. A step in this direction is to substitute the solution into the interface evolution equation (10.102).

Imagine that the initially sinusoidal interface develops into a form better approximated by:

$$\zeta(x, t) = A \cos \lambda x + A' \cos 2\lambda x \qquad (10.103)$$

Here the initial amplitudes are $A(0) = A_0$ and $A'(0) = 0$. The asymmetric lobe-and-cusp modification to the sinusoidal form is represented by the second term. When velocity components are substituted in (10.102), we retain contributions proportional to $\cos 2\lambda x$. In the expansion of $v_y^{(2)}(x, \zeta)$, we retain terms in $a_2 \lambda \zeta$, that is those proportional to $(\lambda A)^2$. Substituting (10.103) and (10.98) into (10.102):

$$\frac{dA}{dt} \cos \lambda x - A \sin \lambda x \left(x \frac{d\lambda}{dt} \right) + \frac{dA'}{dt} \cos 2\lambda x$$

$$- A' \sin 2\lambda x \left(2x \frac{d\lambda}{dt} \right)$$

$$= -\overline{D}_{xx}(A \cos \lambda x + A' \cos 2\lambda x) + a_2(\lambda A \cos \lambda x) \cos \lambda x$$

$$- (\overline{D}_{xx} x - a_2 \sin \lambda x)(-\lambda A \sin \lambda x - 2\lambda A' \sin 2\lambda x)$$

$$(1.104)$$

We find, according to this computation, that A' is proportional to $(\lambda A)^2$. The product $a_2(\lambda A)$ also is proportional to $(\lambda A)^2$. Since $d\lambda/dt = \overline{D}_{xx}\lambda$, the terms proportional to x on both sides cancel. Then, since this relation must be satisfied at all x, the terms in $\cos \lambda x$ and $\cos 2\lambda x$ on each side must be equal, requiring:

$$dA/dt \cong -\overline{D}_{xx} A$$

$$dA'/dt \cong -\overline{D}_{xx} A' - 2[(1 - R)/(1 + R)]\overline{D}_{xx} A(\lambda A)$$

$$(10.105)$$

Here we use the relation $\cos 2\lambda x = \cos^2 \lambda x - \sin^2 \lambda x$ and have substituted for a_2. These are a coupled set of two equations in the shape of the interface expressed in terms of a primary sinusoidal form and a first-harmonic form with one-half the wavelength. Because we have not obtained a complete solution accurate to terms proportional to $(\lambda A)^2$, there will generally be terms missing in the re-

lation for dA'/dt. In fact, if the missing term is included, the 2 in the second equation must be cancelled so (10.105) over-estimates the rate at which the lobe-and-cusp structure develops. The more accurate result is shown in Fig. 10.13b, which is computed using this method.

To improve upon the analysis of stress, velocity, morphological development, and strain within mullion structures, one may appeal to numerical codes (Dieterich and Onat, 1969), or obtain more accurate results by extending the analysis used here to higher orders of approximation (Johnson and Fletcher, 1994). The relatively simple method of analysis and results provided here offers insight that helps us to understand how the lobe-and-cusp morphology develops. In essence, the cusps occur due to a small compressive stress concentration offset by a stress reduction in the material that extends outward into the less viscous fluid (Fig. 10.12b). We may follow the strain distribution as well as the interface morphology using the present results, or to see to what extent a tendency to preserve arc length along the interface exists. Both the kinematics and the stress distribution suggest that a variety of minor structures might be formed close to the interface in a region of marked strain variation.

10.4.3 Folding of a single viscous layer

The method of analysis developed in the preceding section may be applied to the folding of a more viscous layer isolated in a less viscous medium, giving insight into how folds such as those in Fig. 10.1a and 10.14 are initiated. The latter shows a train of folds in a single layer of coarse K-feldspar/quartz "leucosome" sandwiched between two layers of quartz–plagioclase–biotite gneiss of somewhat different composition. The layer is irregular, because either it formed that way, in part, or because it was possibly stretched in an irregular fashion before it was then folded in layer-parallel shortening. Of particular interest is the rough regularity in the arc lengths between fold hinges. Other features, such as the tendency to find quartz filling in the tightly appressed hinges and the fold forms are also of interest. The lobe-and-cusp forms seen in the mullion structures are also approximately seen in the forms of

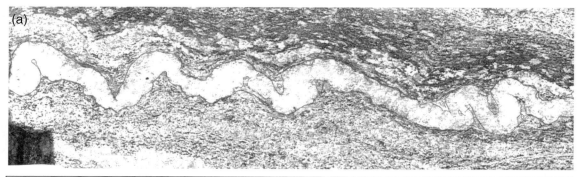

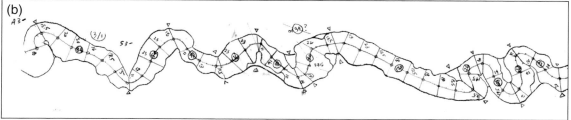

Fig 10.14 (a) Single-layer fold in a leucosome layer embedded in a fine-grained quartz–plagioclase–biotite gneiss. (b) "Working drawing" from which values of L_{arc} and layer thickness were measured. Photograph by R. C. Fletcher.

each layer surface; this morphology gives nearly uniform thickness, ignoring the irregularities. An interpretation of the quartz fillings is that the layer pulled away from the gneiss, with the separation accompanied by precipitation of quartz, so an open cavity never formed. Longer arc length folds on the left show less quartz infilling than the tight group of smaller arc length/thickness ratio folds on the right. The lower "working drawing" indicates measures of the hinge-to-hinge arc lengths and local layer thickness that were made in order to quantify the regularity in this and other profiles from this fold train giving the data shown in Fig. 10.20.

A regular but not periodic train of folds is initiated by a process of selective amplification acting on the slight initial irregularity present in the surfaces of a layer. The multi-layer folds of Fig. 10.1b are remarkably regular. The present analysis will allow us to understand how such regularity comes about.

Irregularity on the two surfaces may be mathematically decomposed into a set of waveforms at different wavelength, L, which is a continuous variable. At each wavelength, the component in the perturbation to the upper and lower surfaces may be written:

$$y = +h + B'\cos(\lambda x + \delta') = +h + B'\cos\delta'\cos\lambda x$$
$$- B'\sin\delta'\sin\lambda x$$

$$y = -h + B''\cos(\lambda x + \delta'') = -h + B''\cos\delta''\cos\lambda x$$
$$- B''\sin\delta''\sin\lambda x \qquad (10.106)$$

The parts of the perturbation at $L = 2\pi/\lambda$ that are proportional to $\cos\lambda x$ and $\sin\lambda x$ do not interact in the case of folding in layer-parallel shortening, which we study here. Hence, we examine only the case of a pair of in-phase surface forms, those proportional to $\cos\lambda x$. We then re-write (10.106) in the form:

$$y = +h + (B_b + B_s)\cos\lambda x$$
$$y = -h + (B_b - B_s)\cos\lambda x$$

$$B_b = \tfrac{1}{2}(B'\cos\delta' + B''\cos\delta'') \qquad (10.107)$$

$$B_s = \tfrac{1}{2}(B'\cos\delta' - B''\cos\delta'')$$

Any pair of in-phase surface perturbations at a given L may be decomposed into a buckle fold form and a pinch-and-swell form with amplitudes B_b and B_s ("buckle" and "swell"), respectively (Fig. 10.15). These waveforms are selectively amplified when the slopes along the layer surfaces are small. Each

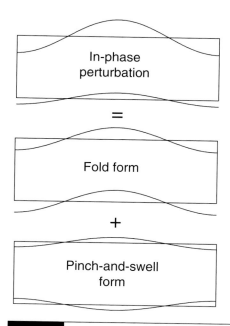

Fig 10.15 Decomposition of in-phase perturbation into fold and pinch-and-swell parts.

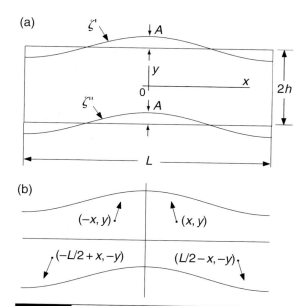

Fig 10.16 (a) Axes and parameters used in analysis of low-slope folding. (b) Symmetry of the velocity vector.

pair of component waveforms, on the two layer surfaces, at a particular wavelength, L, gives rise to an independent perturbing flow within the layer and surrounding medium, i.e. the components are non-interacting. The perturbing flow associated with it causes the amplitude of each pair of component waveforms to grow or decay. In layer-parallel shortening, growth always occurs, and is most rapid at the dominant wavelength, L_d, better represented as the ratio L_d/H, where H is the layer thickness. The rate of growth decreases for wavelengths that are longer or shorter than L_d. We might guess that fold arc lengths from one anticlinal or synclinal hinge to the next divided by the local layer thickness would approximately equal L_d/H.

We now set up and solve the problem of cylindrical folding in plane flow in layer-parallel shortening. To go from the results to an interpretation of the fold arc length/thickness statistics derived from fold trains or fold train segments such as that shown in Fig. 10.14 requires additional steps that will be discussed later. This interpretation will yield an estimate of the ratio of the viscosity of the host to that of the layer. Here, we postulate that these materials may be adequately represented as linear viscous fluids.

Consider a layer of thickness $H = 2h$ of viscous fluid of viscosity η embedded in a viscous fluid of viscosity η_1 (Fig. 10.16). As in the mullion analysis, we prescribe a basic state that exactly describes the flow if the layer surfaces are perfectly plane and parallel. We then consider the approximate solution for the perturbing flow when the two surfaces of the layer are sinusoidal, with the same amplitude and phase. The two surfaces are:

$$\zeta' = +h + A\cos\lambda x$$
$$\zeta'' = -h + A\cos\lambda x \tag{10.108}$$

The basic-state flow is taken to be uniform layer-parallel shortening, the same as that for the mullion problem. The rates of deformation and stress in the lower and upper half-spaces of the embedding medium are equal. These are given in (10.71) and (10.70). In the present case, we retain superscript or subscript 1 to denote the upper half-space and use no superscripts or subscripts for layer quantities. The symmetry of the problem will be exploited, so that it will not be necessary to deal with the lower half-space and the boundary conditions at the lower layer/medium interface. In a demonstration of this the superscript 2 will be used for quantities in the lower half-space.

To exploit the symmetry seen in Fig. 10.16b, take the coordinate origin for the layer at its midplane. The velocity vector is shown for four particles in symmetric relation to each other. Vertical mirror planes of symmetry are present at at $x = 0$, $+L/2$, and $-L/2$, with centers of symmetry at $x = \pm L/4$ and $y = 0$. The y-component of the velocity vector for the perturbing flow in the layer then satisfies $\tilde{v}_y(x, y) = \tilde{v}_y(-x, y)$, so $\tilde{v}_y$ is an even function of x. We accordingly use the general form (10.93). The center of symmetry requires $\tilde{v}_y(L/2 - x, -y) = -\tilde{v}_y(x, y)$. Using these conditions we obtain:

$$\{[a + b(-\lambda y - 1)]e^{-\lambda y} - [c + d(-\lambda y + 1)]e^{\lambda y}\}$$
$$\times \cos[(2\pi/L)(L/2 - x)]$$
$$= -\{[a + b(-\lambda y - 1)]e^{-\lambda y} - [c + d(-\lambda y + 1)]e^{\lambda y}\}$$
$$\times \cos \lambda x$$
$$= -\{[a + b(\lambda y - 1)]e^{-\lambda y} - [c + d(\lambda y + 1)]e^{\lambda y}\}$$
$$\times \cos \lambda x \tag{10.109}$$

For this to hold at all x and y, the coefficients of $e^{\lambda y}$, $e^{-\lambda y}$, $\lambda y e^{\lambda y}$, and $\lambda y e^{-\lambda y}$ must be equal, requiring $c = -a$ and $d = b$. Substituting into (10.93), the y-component of perturbing velocity is:

$$\tilde{v}_y = \{a(e^{\lambda y} + e^{-\lambda y}) + b[\lambda y(e^{\lambda y} - e^{-\lambda y})$$
$$- (e^{\lambda y} + e^{-\lambda y})]\}\cos \lambda x \tag{10.110}$$

Thus, $\tilde{v}_y$ is an even function of y, and symmetry reduces the number of arbitrary coefficients from four to two. The x-component of perturbing velocity is:

$$\tilde{v}_x = -[a(e^{\lambda y} - e^{-\lambda y}) + b\lambda y(e^{\lambda y} + e^{-\lambda y})]\sin \lambda x \tag{10.111}$$

The perturbing stress components in the layer are:

$$\tilde{\sigma}_{xx} = -2\eta\lambda\{a(e^{\lambda y} - e^{-\lambda y}) + b[\lambda y(e^{\lambda y} + e^{-\lambda y})$$
$$+ (e^{\lambda y} - e^{-\lambda y})]\}\cos \lambda x$$
$$\tilde{\sigma}_{yy} = 2\eta\lambda\{a(e^{\lambda y} - e^{-\lambda y}) + b[\lambda y(e^{\lambda y} + e^{-\lambda y}) \tag{10.112}$$
$$- (e^{\lambda y} - e^{-\lambda y})]\}\cos \lambda x$$
$$\tilde{\sigma}_{xy} = -2\eta\lambda[a(e^{\lambda y} + e^{-\lambda y}) + b\lambda y(e^{\lambda y} - e^{-\lambda y})]\sin \lambda x$$

In the upper half-space, the perturbing velocity and stress components are the same as those in the mullion problem. However, we refer them to a coordinate system in which the x-coordinate is the same as that for the layer, but the origin is moved up an amount $+h$ to the mean interface position. Then, the velocity components in the upper half-space are:

$$\tilde{v}_x^{(1)} = -(c_1 + d_1\lambda y)e^{-\lambda y}\sin \lambda x$$
$$\tilde{v}_y^{(1)} = -[c_1 + d_1(\lambda y + 1)]e^{-\lambda y}\cos \lambda x \tag{10.113}$$

The stress components in the upper half-space are:

$$\tilde{\sigma}_{xx}^{(1)} = -2\eta_1\lambda[c_1 + d_1(\lambda y + 1)]e^{-\lambda y}\cos \lambda x$$
$$\tilde{\sigma}_{yy}^{(1)} = +2\eta_1\lambda[c_1 + d_1(\lambda y - 1)]e^{-\lambda y}\cos \lambda x \tag{10.114}$$
$$\tilde{\sigma}_{xy}^{(1)} = 2\eta_1\lambda(c_1 + d_1\lambda y)e^{-\lambda y}\sin \lambda x$$

The coefficients in the solution are determined from the four boundary conditions at the upper surface; these suffice to determine the coefficients a, b, c_1, and d_1. The additional two constants for the lower half-space, a_2 and b_2, are related to c_1 and d_1 by symmetry conditions. Approximations used in the mullion problem are used here, and the detailed computations are not repeated. For example, in a term of the form $ae^{\lambda\zeta'}$, we take $e^{\lambda\zeta'} \cong e^{\lambda h}(1 + \lambda A\cos \lambda x) \cong e^{\lambda h}$. If no slip occurs at the interface:

$$\tilde{v}_x(x, h) \cong \tilde{v}_x^{(1)}(x, 0)$$
$$\tilde{v}_y(x, h) \cong \tilde{v}_y^{(1)}(x, 0) \tag{10.115}$$

Recalling that the origin for the upper half-space is taken at the mean base of this medium to simplify algebraic expressions, these conditions yield:

$$a(e^{\lambda h} - e^{-\lambda h}) + b\lambda h(e^{\lambda h} + e^{-\lambda h}) = c_1$$
$$a(e^{\lambda h} + e^{-\lambda h}) + b[\lambda h(e^{\lambda h} - e^{-\lambda h}) - (e^{\lambda h} + e^{-\lambda h})]$$
$$= -(c_1 + d_1) \tag{10.116}$$

Continuity of the normal and shear tractions requires:

$$\tilde{\sigma}_{yy}(x, h) \cong \tilde{\sigma}_{yy}^{(1)}(x, 0)$$
$$\tilde{\sigma}_{xy}(x, h) + 4\eta\bar{D}_{xx}(\lambda A)\sin \lambda x$$
$$\cong \tilde{\sigma}_{xy}^{(1)}(x, 0) + 4\eta_1\bar{D}_{xx}(\lambda A)\sin \lambda x \tag{10.117}$$

These yield:

$$2\eta\lambda\{a(e^{\lambda h} - e^{-\lambda h}) + b[\lambda h(e^{\lambda h} + e^{-\lambda h}) - (e^{\lambda h} - e^{-\lambda h})]\}$$
$$= 2\eta_1\lambda(c_1 + d_1) - 2\eta\lambda[a(e^{\lambda h} + e^{-\lambda h})$$
$$+ b\lambda h(e^{\lambda h} - e^{-\lambda h})] - 4\eta\bar{D}_{xx}\lambda A \tag{10.118}$$
$$= 2\eta_1\lambda c_1 - 4\eta_1\bar{D}_{xx}\lambda A$$

Coefficients c_1 and $c_1 + d_1$ may be eliminated between these pairs of relations to give

$$(a-b)(\sinh \lambda h + R \cosh \lambda h) + b\lambda h(\cosh \lambda h$$
$$+ R \sinh \lambda h) = 0$$

$$a(\cosh \lambda h + R \sinh \lambda h) + b\lambda h(\sinh \lambda h \qquad (10.119)$$
$$+ R \cosh \lambda h) = (1-R)\bar{D}_{xx}A$$

Here $R = \eta_1/\eta$. Solving for the constants we find:

$$a = -(1/M)[\lambda h(\cosh \lambda h + R \sinh \lambda h)$$
$$-(\sinh \lambda h + R \cosh \lambda h)]2(1-R)\bar{D}_{xx}A$$

$$b = (1/M)(\sinh \lambda h + R \cosh \lambda h)2(1-R)\bar{D}_{xx}A \quad (10.120)$$

$$M = k(1-R^2) - (1/2k)[(1+R^2)\sinh k + 2R \cosh k]$$

Here $k = 2\lambda h = \lambda H$, where H is the full layer thickness.

The rate of growth of perturbation amplitude, from (10.102) and (10.110) is:

$$\frac{dA}{dt} = -\bar{D}_{xx}A + 2\{a \cosh(\lambda h)$$
$$+ b[\lambda h \sinh \lambda h - \cosh \lambda h]\} \quad (10.121)$$

Upon further substitution:

$$\frac{dA}{dt} = \left\{-1 + \frac{2k(1-R)}{(1-R^2)-[(1+R^2)\sinh k + 2R \cosh k]}\right\}$$
$$\times \operatorname{Sgn}(\bar{D}_{xx})|\bar{D}_{xx}|A \quad (10.122)$$

The description of the evolution of layer shape for the single sinusoidal perturbation is completed by the relations $dL/dt = \bar{D}_{xx}L$ and $dH/dt = -\bar{D}_{xx}H$ from which:

$$dk/dt = -2\bar{D}_{xx}k \quad (10.123)$$

It may be more useful to think in terms of the growth rate in the maximum slope, λA, because this is a dimensionless quantity and we perceive a fold chiefly by its maximum limb dip or slope. Since $d\lambda/dt = -\bar{D}_{xx}\lambda$, we have:

$$\frac{d(\lambda A)}{dt} = -(2+q)\operatorname{Sgn}(\bar{D}_{xx})|\bar{D}_{xx}|(\lambda A) \quad (10.124)$$

Here the quantity q is defined from (10.122) as:

$$q = -\frac{2k(1-R)}{(1-R^2)-[(1+R^2)\sinh k + 2R \cosh k]} \quad (10.125)$$

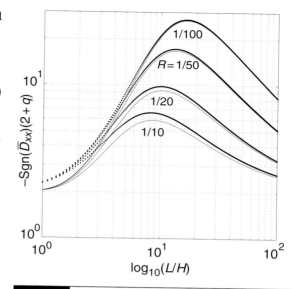

Fig 10.17 $-\operatorname{Sgn}(\bar{D}_{xx})(2+q)$ versus $\log_{10}(L/H)$ showing maxima, for $R = 0.01, 0.02, 0.05$, and 0.1.

A plot of $-\operatorname{Sgn}(\bar{D}_{xx})(2+q)$ versus $\log_{10}(L/H)$ is shown in Fig. 10.17 for $R = 1/100, 1/50, 1/20$, and $1/10$. Maximum growth rate occurs for a component at the dominant wavelength (Biot, 1961), L_d/H, for which $q = q_d$. Since growth is exponential for each component and the components do not interact as long as $\lambda A \ll 1$, L_d/H provides an estimate of the fold arc length/thickness ratio that might be seen in a natural or experimentally produced fold train. When maximum slopes in the folding layer reach 10° to 15°, the linear independence of wavelength components breaks down, current positions of fold hinges are "locked-in," and folding continues at approximately constant layer thickness.

Amplification for a 10% thickening of the layer, or for $D_{xx}\Delta t \cong -0.1$, is $\exp[-0.1(-2+q)]$. For amplification by a factor of 10, $0.1(q+2) = 2.3$, or $q = 21$. This corresponds to a strong folding instability, since a perturbation at the dominant wavelength with initial dip of 0.01 radian ($\approx 0.5°$) would reach a dip of 15° in about 15% layer thickening. This requires a viscosity ratio $R \cong 1/50$. Folding instability is weaker for a viscosity ratio $R = 1/20$, and 25% layer thickening is required to yield amplification by a factor of 10. For $R = 1/10$ a thickening of 46% is required.

If $R \ll 1$, (10.125) may be expanded to leading terms in k to obtain:

(a)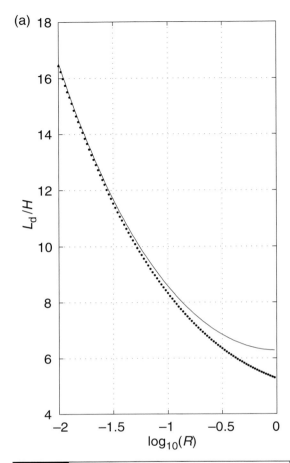

(b)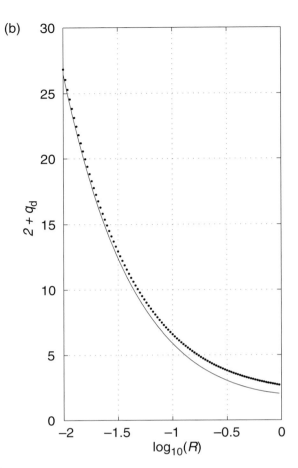

Fig 10.18 (a) L_d/H versus R; dotted curve is thin-plate approximation. (b) $2 + q_d$ versus R.

$$q \cong 2 \left| \left(\frac{k^2}{6} + \frac{2R}{k} + Rk \right) \right|$$ (10.126)

Typically, only the first two terms are given in the so-called "thin-plate approximation" (Biot, 1961), but the third term improves the approximation (Fig. 10.17). The expression (10.126) sums two effects. The part of the curve descending as L/H decreases is dominated by the term $k^2/6$ in the denominator, and is tied to the bending resistance of the layer; the part of the curve descending as L/H increases is dominated by the terms $\sim R$ and is associated with resistance of the medium to layer deflection. At the dominant wavelength, the two effects are balanced to give a maximum growth rate.

Using only the two terms of (10.126) we have:

$$k_d = 2\pi/(L_d/H) \cong (6R)^{1/3}$$
$$q_d \cong (16/9)^{1/3}R^{-2/3}$$ (10.127)

L_d/H and q_d are plotted in Fig. 10.18 from a numerical evaluation of (10.125) and the approximations (10.127). The solutions for L_d/H and q_d do not admit of values less than 2π for L_d/H, or of more than moderately strong folding instability with $q_d \gtrsim 10$ for L_d/H less than about 10. Thus, the folds in Fig. 10.14 cannot be interpreted from these relations. It is necessary to follow amplification of fold components as layer thickening continues, and the value of L/H of a component decreases. This is done by numerically integrating (10.124) using:

$$\frac{1}{\lambda A} d \ln(\lambda A) = -\text{Sgn}(\bar{D}_{xx})(2 + q) dt$$ (10.128)

with an initial value $\lambda(0)A(0)$. The result for $R = 1/20$ at several values of layer thickening is shown

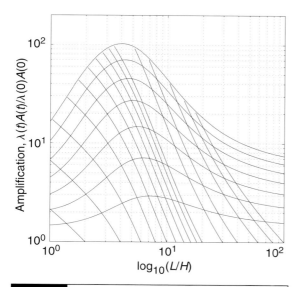

Fig 10.19 Amplification of λA as a function of L/H with layer thickening H/H_0 from 1.2 to 2.4 in increments of 0.2. Trajectories of individual components are for initial values $L/H = 2, 4, 6, \ldots, 18, 20, 30, 40, 60, 80,$ and 100.

in Fig. 10.19. The value L_{max}/H of the component with the maximum amplification is $\approx L_d/H$ at $H/H_0 = 1.1$ and ≈ 6.5 at $H/H_0 = 2$. Curves of amplification versus L/H for individual fold components are the lines rising to the left.

The above relations allow interpretation of data collected from fold trains of the sort shown in Fig. 10.14, if the layer and surrounding medium may be approximated as uniform viscous fluids. The data set for this profile and others from the same fold train is presented as a histogram of fold arc length to thickness ratio and also a cumulative frequency distribution in Fig. 10.20. An interpretation of the data to estimate the viscosity ratio and in this case the amount of uniform layer thickening H/H_0 may be based on the variations of maximum amplification and values L_{max}/H at which it occurs, as given in Fig. 10.21. Details of the argument are given elsewhere (Sherwin and Chapple, 1968). Simulations of fold train formed by combining wavelength components of specified amplitude derived from an initial white roughness amplitude spectrum (all components have the same initial slope) showed that the mean of the fold arc length thickness ratio, L_{arc}/H, is a good estimate of the value at maximum amplification,

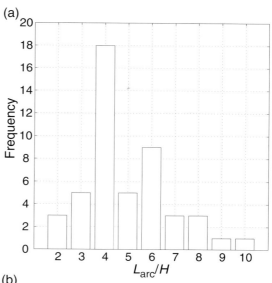

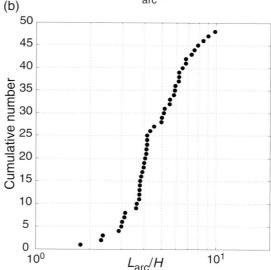

Fig 10.20 Frequency distribution of L_{arc}/H for fold train, an example of which is shown in Fig. 10.14: (a) histogram, (b) cumulative frequency.

L_{max}/H. Despite the notation, L_{arc} is not a wavelength but simply, in this case, twice the hinge-to-hinge arc length in a fold train, a quantity that has a random distribution. For the fold train from which Fig. 10.14 comes, the average value is $\langle L_{arc}/H \rangle = 4.92$. Thus, values of R and H/H_0 will lie along a contour close to that for the 5 contour in Fig. 10.21. From an assessment of the degree of regularity of folding in terms of the dispersion (standard deviation/mean) of the distribution shown in

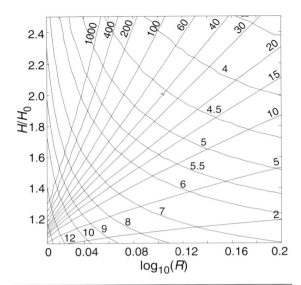

Fig 10.21 Summary model results from which R and H/H_0 may be estimated.

Fig. 10.20, the maximum amplification may be estimated, and a value in the range from 15 to 40 is indicated. The method is not given here. The corresponding arc of the contour $L_{arc}/H = 4.9$ then gives a range in R from 1/11.5 to 1/8.3 and a corresponding range in H/H_0 from 1.7 to 1.9. Thus, in modeling rock masses containing coarse K-feldspar-rich pegmatite, granite, or gneiss in finer-grained quartz–plagioclase–biotite gneiss, the former may be given a viscosity approximately ten times that of the latter. Evidently, a more extensive and detailed study along these lines would provide estimates that are more reliable and their uncertainty.

10.4.4 Circulating cell model for a steady-state accretionary wedge

The lubrication theory model for a viscous accretionary wedge presented in Section 10.3.4, from which only the simplest steady-state example was extracted, provides a basis for assessing the influence of factors such as rate of supply of material, rate of erosion, or viscosity on wedge dynamics. This model is less useful in providing details of internal deformation and trajectories of rock volumes within the wedge. Such information is essential for interpreting field observations of deformation in the rocks exposed by erosion in

currently active accretionary wedges like those of Taiwan and the Himalaya (Hilley and Strecker, 2004) and the Olympic Mountains of Washington State (Batt *et al.*, 2001; Brandon, 2004), or in extinct wedges. Here, we formulate and analyze a model for flow, deformation, and stress in the region of the backstop of an accretionary wedge, using another solution for a viscous layer.

A model for an accretionary *wedge* based on a *layer of uniform thickness* requires a substantial approximation that dispenses with the tapered form of the entire wedge. Thus, it cannot model the toe region. Our goal here is to visualize the processes occurring near the rear of an accretionary wedge, where exhumation of rock passing through the wedge takes place by a combination of horizontal thickening and concomitant uplift and erosion, with or without near-surface extension. Figure 10.8c illustrates features that the model will attempt to capture and we have earlier used it to discuss the central concept of a *backstop*. Near the backstop, particle motion approaches vertical. Vertical velocity at the surface acts to increase the height of the wedge, but is offset by erosion and tectonic denudation that produces thinning by flow or normal faulting. Material may be added to or removed from the wedge by underplating or basal erosion.

The present model seeks to address the details of wedge behavior in the region of exhumation that cannot be modeled by lubrication theory, since what is involved is chiefly sub-horizontal compression or extension, not sub-horizontal shear. Treatment of the backstop as a vertical mirror plane suggests that we treat the wedge as a layer segment bounded by two such symmetry planes (Fig. 10.22), one of which must then be a "frontstop." This is an unrealistic feature, but we only apply the rear half of the model to flow near the backstop, the segment of width $L/4$.

A cylindrical topographic surface with amplitude A slopes to the right, opposite to the direction of basal motion due to subduction drag. The model is composed of a homogeneous viscous fluid of viscosity η and density ρ. To complete its specification, we need to set the boundary conditions that determine the internal flow. The conditions at the lateral bounding surfaces are the symmetry conditions:

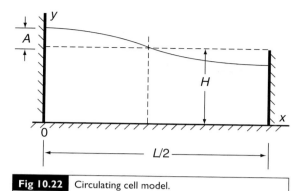

Fig 10.22 Circulating cell model.

$$v_x(0, y) = v_x(L/2, y) = 0$$
$$\sigma_{xy}(0, y) = \sigma_{xy}(L/2, y) = 0 \tag{10.129}$$

The conditions at the base of the model are those that "drive" the flow, since any topography would decay under the action of gravity alone. We adopt conditions that lead to a simple solution and flow pattern. We earlier considered a condition in which the base of the wedge adheres to the subducting plate. However, estimated horizontal motions within a natural wedge are generally much smaller than the subduction velocity. Here, we specify the basal velocity without relation to subduction velocity as:

$$v_x(x, 0) = -U \sin \lambda x \tag{10.130}$$

Thus, coupling between subducting plate and wedge is taken to be greatest at the mid-point of the cell, $x = L/4$, from which it tapers off toward the backstop and the frontstop. We specify a distribution of underplating:

$$v_y(x, 0) = W \cos \lambda x \tag{10.131}$$

This is maximum at the backstop and, forward of the mid-point $x = L/4$, corresponds instead to basal erosion.

At the upper surface, $y = H + A \cos \lambda x$, and the normal and shear traction vanish. These conditions are approximated by a boundary condition on the plane $y = H$ where:

$$\sigma_{xz}(x, H) \cong 0$$
$$\sigma_{zz}(x, H) \cong -\rho g A \cos \lambda x \tag{10.132}$$

Note that in the present model the basic state is one of lithostatic stress and no flow. Thus, the

boundary conditions are expressed in terms of the total flow. The normal stress components σ_{xx} and σ_{yy} in fact include the lithostatic basic state, but to simplify notation, this is not written out. The appropriate forms of the velocity components, (10.92) and (10.93), and the stress components, (10.90), are those used for the perturbing flows in the previous models for mullions and folds. The x-dependences of these are appropriate, with v_y proportional to $\cos \lambda x$. Indeed, the boundary conditions on subduction drag and underplating were chosen to conform to this sinusoidal dependence. Again, by imposing conditions that are somewhat artificial, we obtain a description of wedge dynamics that is remarkably simple, and thus capable of providing sharp, if restricted, physical insight into accretionary wedge dynamics.

Development of the boundary conditions (10.130), (10.131), and (10.132) leads to the relations:

$$a' + c' = U$$
$$a' - b' - c' - d' = W \tag{10.133}$$
$$(a' + b'k)e^k - (c' + d'k)e^{-k} = 0$$
$$[a' + b'(k-1)]e^k + [c' + d'(k+1)]e^{-k} = -\rho g H A / 2 \eta k$$

Here, we have re-named the coefficients using a prime. The dimensions of the coefficients are those of velocity, as indicated by the first pair of relations in (10.133). Using the magnitude of subduction drag, U, as the reference velocity, we divide (10.133) through by it to obtain:

$$a + c = 1$$
$$a - b - c - d = \alpha$$
$$(a + bk)e^k - (c + dk)e^{-k} = 0 \tag{10.134}$$
$$[a + b(k-1)]e^k + [c + d(k+1)]e^{-k}$$
$$= -(\rho g H / 2 \eta U)(A/k)$$

Here a, b, c, and d are dimensionless.

Recall that accretionary wedges gain material by frontal accretion and by underplating. In this case, frontal accretion corresponds in a rough sense to the flux of material across the vertical plane at $x = L/4$ (Fig. 10.22), where the flow is horizontal. Wedges loose material by erosion. In nature, wedges do not have a vertical backstop, and material can flow within the wedge past the point of highest surface relief and erosion may take place on both sides of this. A very simple modification of the present model may be made to account for this, but we avoid the temptation to introduce it in order to achieve the simplest approximation to wedge dynamics. Moreover, the effect of any such modification to a model is best appreciated by first studying the behavior before it is introduced.

Prior to solving (10.134), we consider the special restriction to the case of a *steady-state* wedge, in which the amount of material lost by erosion and outward flow is just balanced by the inward flow, and the balance is achieved by time-independent regimens of influx, underplating, and erosion. For the present model, this requires that the vertical flux of material in the interval of interest, $0 \leq x \leq L/4$, and at the upper surface, is just balanced by erosion. We use a rate of erosion proportional to the local topographic relief which, in view of the sinusoidal variation of topography, is described by:

$$(\mathrm{d}A/\mathrm{d}t)_{\mathrm{erosion}} = -KA \qquad (10.135)$$

In the steady state, this loss is just balanced by the flux associated with $v_y(x, H)$ over the same interval in x. This gives the condition:

$$-KA_{\mathrm{ss}} + U\{[a + b(k-1)]e^k - [c + d(k+1)]e^{-k}\} = 0 \qquad (10.136)$$

Here A_{ss} is the amplitude of the steady-state topographic relief.

Substitution of (10.136) into the fourth equation in (10.134) yields the set of equations:

$$\begin{aligned} &a + c = 1 \\ &a - b - c - d = \alpha \\ &(a + bk)e^k - (c + dk)e^{-k} = 0 \\ &(1 - \Omega/k)[a + b(k-1)]e^k + (1 + \Omega/k) \\ &\qquad \times [c + d(k+1)]e^{-k} = 0 \end{aligned} \qquad (10.137)$$

This indicates that the flow and stress distribution in the steady-state accretionary wedge is a function of only three dimensionless parameters:

$$k = 2\pi/(L/H), \quad \alpha = W/U, \quad \Omega = \rho g H/(2\eta K) \qquad (10.138)$$

The first dimensionless group contains the aspect ratio of the wedge, $(L/2)/H$, which may be identified roughly with the backstop-to-toe width of the

wedge divided by its mean or maximum thickness. The second dimensionless group is the ratio of the magnitude of underplating to that of subduction drag. The third dimensionless group is the ratio of the lithostatic stress to a quantity with the dimensions of stress that is proportional to the viscosity and K. The parameter K is associated with thinning of the wedge by erosion: it is not a rate of deformation, but has the same dimensions as one (time)$^{-1}$. The third dimensionless group may be interpreted as the ratio of the relative outward flux of material by gravity-driven "glacier flow" within the wedge to that by erosion. Note that $\rho g H/2\eta$ is a rate of deformation. Each of these dimensionless groups, then, has a clear and concrete connection with major aspects of wedge form and dynamics, and a connection with measurable quantities such as wedge form, the amplitude of topographic relief, and rate of erosion or exhumation, or erosional flux. These parameters also establish the deformation within the wedge and the strain observed in rocks exposed at the surface.

Before solving for the coefficients, we obtain one other result that emphasizes the simplicity of the model and, by inference, that of the dynamics of a natural accretionary wedge when viewed at a suitably large length scale and increment of time. The velocity and stress distributions may be obtained if we know the stream function, Ψ, where $v_x = -\partial\Psi/\partial y$ and $v_y = \partial\Psi/\partial x$. For this case:

$$\begin{aligned} \Psi = -UH(1/\lambda H)\{[a + b(\lambda y - 1)]e^{\lambda y} \\ - [c + d(\lambda y + 1)]e^{-\lambda y}\}\sin\lambda x \end{aligned} \qquad (10.139)$$

We want to obtain a self-consistent set of velocity and stress components, or an equivalent expression of the stream function, that contain the dimensionless groups. Further, since accretionary wedges are slender, in the sense that $H/(L/2) \ll 1$, or $k \ll 1$, we seek polynomial expressions in λz that contain only leading terms in k or $\lambda z \leq k$. This requires that we obtain a suitable approximate solution to the boundary conditions (10.137) and a corresponding expansion of the stream function Ψ in (10.139).

When all expressions are expanded *uniformly* to terms proportional to $(\lambda z)^3$, the results are not self-consistent in the sense that the velocity components do not exactly satisfy the condition of incompressibility, and the stress components do not satisfy the equations of stress equilibrium. For these conditions to be satisfied by the polynomial approximations, several terms must then be dropped; the result is:

$$\Psi \cong -(U/\lambda)[(a-b-c-d) + y(a+c) + (y^2/2)$$
$$\times (a+b-c+d) + (y^3/6)$$
$$\times (a+2b+c-2d)]\sin \lambda x \qquad (10.140)$$

The displacement components are:

$$v_x \cong -U[(a+c) + y(a+b-c+d)$$
$$+ (y^2/2)(a+2b+c-2d)]\sin \lambda x$$
$$v_y \cong -U[(a-b-c-d) + y(a+c)$$
$$+ (y^2/2)(a+b-c+d)$$
$$+ (y^3/6)(a+2b+c-2d)]\cos \lambda x \qquad (10.141)$$

The stress components are:

$$\sigma_{xy} \cong -2\eta\lambda U[(a-c) + y(a+b+c-d)$$
$$+ (y^2/2)(a+2b-c+2d)]\sin \lambda x$$
$$\sigma_{yy} \cong -2\eta\lambda U[(a-b+c+d) + y(a-c)$$
$$+ (y^2/2)(a+b+c-d)$$
$$+ (y^3/6)(a+2b-c+2d)]\cos \lambda x$$
$$\sigma_{xx} \cong -2\eta\lambda U[(a+b+c-d)$$
$$+ y(a+2b-c+2d)]\cos \lambda x \qquad (10.142)$$

It is somewhat easier to solve for the coefficients in the approximate solution by using the $k \ll 1$ expansions in the boundary conditions (10.134). The result is:

$$a \cong 1/2 - SA/2 - k$$
$$c \cong 1/2 + SA/2 + k$$
$$b \cong SA/2k - SA/2 - \alpha/2 + 1/2 - k \qquad (10.143)$$
$$d \cong -SA/2k - SA/2 - \alpha/2 - 1/2 - k$$

These satisfy the boundary conditions to within residuals that are a small factor k^2 times the remaining terms. From the condition (10.136):

$$A_{ss} \cong (1/k^2)(3\eta U/\rho g H)(\alpha + k)/(1 + \Delta)$$
$$= (W + kU)/(K + k^2 \rho g H/3\eta) \qquad (10.144)$$
$$\Delta = (1/k^2)(3\eta K/\rho g H) = 3/(2k^2\Omega)$$

The dimensionless parameter Δ is preferred over Ω because it is zero, rather than infinite, when the rate of erosion goes to zero. The approximate form of the stream function is:

$$\Psi \cong -\frac{UH}{k}\left[\alpha + y - \frac{3y^2}{2k^2}\left(\frac{\alpha+k}{1+\Delta}\right)\left(1 - \frac{y}{3k}\right)\right]\sin \lambda x \qquad (10.145)$$

While this approximation may be used to compute the pattern of streamlines and other quantities, its chief utility is in indicating the relative simplicity of the model dynamics and in obtaining closed-form solutions for quantities of interest. In the computations whose results are given below, the exact relations, with coefficients derived from (10.137) are used.

Again, insofar as the model simulates the dynamics of a natural accretionary wedge in the region in which exhumation takes place, only three dimensionless parameters are involved, either (10.138) or k, α, and Δ. In addition, the topography scales with the height $3\eta U/\rho g H$, from (10.144). It is of interest, then, to estimate these parameters from field observations.

A further conclusion concerns the role of finite strain in the mechanics of this large-scale tectonic structure. The finite deformation may be computed, but it plays no role in the underlying physics. Rheological properties are invariably altered during deformation, but any model for this transformation would be described by a set of evolution equations for their rates of change, and strain itself would enter as neither dependent nor independent variables. The computation of finite strain, especially its distribution in outcrop, does provide a powerful means of constraining any model for wedge dynamics.

Figure 10.23 compares streamlines computed from the approximation and the exact solution for the case $\alpha = 0.1$, $\Delta = 0.2$, and $k = \pi/10$. The exact solution is obtained for a wedge of maximum thickness $H = 20$ km and a topographic-culmination-to-toe distance $L/2 = 200$ km. The approximation is excellent; for other values of α and Δ it may not be so good. The change in slope of the streamlines indicates a transition from motion toward the backstop below about one-third of the wedge thickness and flow away from it above that depth. This implies a component of horizontal extension superposed on earlier shortening for rock volumes traveling along the streamlines. Because the flow is steady, the streamlines are particle trajectories.

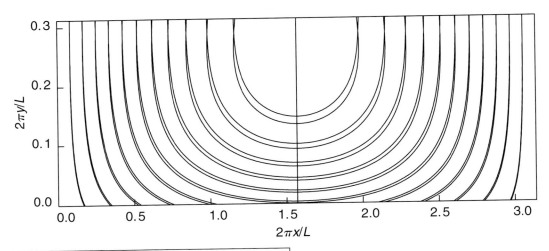

Fig 10.23 Exact and approximate (higher in each pair) streamlines for a circulating cell model.

Using the Olympic accretionary wedge as an example (Fig. 10.8a), we may roughly estimate the model parameters (Batt *et al.*, 2001; Brandon, 2004). A rate of erosion ≈ 1 km Ma^{-1} is associated with a topographic amplitude $A \approx 1.5$ km, giving an erosion constant $K \approx 2/3$ Ma^{-1}. Using a density $\rho \approx 2700$ kg m^{-3}, acceleration of gravity $g = 9.8$ m s^{-2}, and $H \approx 20$ km, we obtain $\Delta \approx 1.2$, much larger than the value used in Fig. 10.23. The ratio $\alpha = W/U$ can be estimated from interpretation of observations. Strain measured from rock at exposure gives no indication of extension, which is favored by larger values of α, i.e. of underplating. This provides an upper limit on α. While this estimate may be established by examining model streamlines, it is simpler to examine the rate of deformation and strain of a particle underplated at the backstop. The approximate solution for the velocity components provides convenient closed-form results:

$$\frac{D_{xx}(0,y)}{\lambda U} = -1 + \left(\frac{3}{2k^2}\right)\left(\frac{\alpha + k}{1 + \Delta}\right)\left(2y - \frac{y^2}{k}\right) \quad (10.146)$$

Using $L = 400$ km, or twice the width of the backstop-to-toe distance, the magnitude of the rate of deformation, λU, is 0.5×10^{-14} s^{-1} times the value of U expressed in cm a^{-1}. The horizontal rate of deformation is a minimum (greatest *negative* value) at the base of the wedge, and increases upwards. Near-surface extension occurs for any α greater than a value which gives zero at $y = k$, or

for $\alpha \geq (k/3)(2\Delta - 1)$. In the present case, $k = \pi/10$ and $\Delta = 1.2$, and $\alpha = 0.15$.

In Fig. 10.24, streamlines are plotted for four pairs of α and Δ with $k = \pi/10$. In these figures, the small $A/H \ll 1$ surface amplitude is not shown and the upper surface is taken as nominally plane. Figure 10.24a with $\alpha = 0.1$ and $\Delta = 1$ is a possible approximation for the Olympic accretionary wedge. If $\alpha = \Delta \cong 0$, strong horizontal extension occurs at the upper surface, with large magnitude shearing of opposite sign corresponding to the inward and outward fluxes of material in the wedge flow. Vigorous underplating (Fig. 10.24c) eliminates much of the shearing associated with basal drag. Vigorous erosion (Fig. 10.24d) eliminates the near-surface extension.

The finite deformation may be computed by integration to determine the displacement gradient tensor F_{ij} along particle trajectories. In plane flow the evolution equations reduce to:

$$\begin{aligned}
DF_{xx}/Dt &= D_{xx}F_{xx} + (D_{xy} - \omega_z)F_{yx} \\
DF_{xy}/Dt &= D_{xx}F_{xy} + (D_{xy} - \omega_z)F_{yy} \\
DF_{yx}/Dt &= (D_{yx} + \omega_z)F_{xx} + D_{yy}F_{yx} \\
DF_{yy}/Dt &= (D_{yx} + \omega_z)F_{xy} + D_{yy}F_{yy}
\end{aligned} \quad (10.147)$$

Here $\omega_z = 1/2(\partial v_y/\partial x - \partial v_x/\partial y)$. Since the velocity components are known, integration may be carried out numerically. A simpler means of obtaining an *illustration* of the strain ellipses is to follow the deformation of an initial circle of particles by incrementing their positions for a succession of small time steps, but this operation does

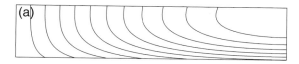

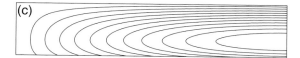

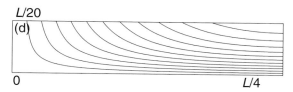

L/20

0   *L*/4

Fig 10.24   Streamlines for four sets of model parameters: (a) $\alpha = 0.1$, $\Delta = 1$; (b) $\alpha = 0$, $\Delta = 0$; (c) $\alpha = 0.1$, $\Delta = 0$; (d) $\alpha = 0$, $\Delta = 1$.

not directly supply the tensor F of the center point. A result for $\alpha = 0.1$, $\Delta = 1$, and $k = \pi/4$ is shown in Fig. 10.25. In preparing the figure, a dense set of particles lying on a circle of very small radius was followed to assure an adequate approximation to homogeneity; the resulting strain ellipse was then enlarged by a factor of about 10. Only the deformation after the element has been underplated can be evaluated, as indicated by the circular locus at the base of the wedge. Although we do not expect that near-surface ductile flow as in this model will be present in natural accretionary wedges, pressure solution may result in ductile deformation to within a few kilometers of the surface. If material is then not strongly deformed as it moves upward, as indicated by the streamlines of Fig. 10.24a, the model strain distribution will still be comparable to a natural outcrop pattern.

An impression of strain magnitude near the backstop and its dependence on the dimensionless parameters may be obtained from a closed-form expression for the strain of a particle underplated at the backstop and rising vertically along it. At the backstop, the only non-zero

components of the displacement gradient tensor are $F_{yy} = 1/F_{xx}$. We then have:

$$\frac{DF_{yy}}{Dt} = \frac{\partial F_{yy}}{\partial t} + v_y \frac{\partial F_{yy}}{\partial y} = D_{yy} F_{yy} \tag{10.148}$$

This is a special case of the general relations given in (10.147). Since the flow is steady, $\partial F_{yy}/\partial t = 0$ and since $v_y(0,y)$ and $F_{yy}(0,y)$ are only functions of y, (10.148) reduces to:

$$v_y \frac{dF_{yy}}{dy} = D_{yy} F_{yy} = \frac{dv_y}{dy} F_{yy}, \quad \text{or} \quad \frac{1}{F_{yy}} dF_{yy} = \frac{1}{v_y} dv_y \tag{10.149}$$

Integrating between y_1 and y_2, we have:

$$\frac{F_{yy}(y_2)}{F_{yy}(y_1)} = \frac{v_y(y_2)}{v_y(y_1)} \tag{10.150}$$

The total strain of a particle rising from the base of the wedge as a function of its height is:

$$F_{yy}(0,y) = v_y(0,y)/W$$
$$= \frac{1}{\alpha}\left[\alpha + y - \left(\frac{3}{2k^2}\right)\left(\frac{\alpha + k}{1 + \Delta}\right)\left(y^2 - \frac{y^3}{3k}\right)\right] \tag{10.151}$$

The ratio of vertical to horizontal axes of the strain ellipse, or the quadratic elongation, is $(F_{yy})^2$. This is plotted versus the dimensionless height from the base of the wedge, $y/H = y/k$ in Fig. 10.26 for $k = \pi/10$, $\Delta = 1$, and $\alpha = 0.1$ 0.15, 0.2, 0.4, and 1. The maximum on the curve indicates the height at which the *horizontal* rate of deformation is zero, and goes from shortening to extension. The quadratic elongation is then a maximum. If the curve crosses the line $(F_{yy})^2 = 1$, the initial *vertical* elongation is cancelled out, and the strain thereafter is vertical shortening.

In the simple circulating cell model for the region of an accretionary wedge about one-third to one-half its length from its culmination a complete picture of wedge dynamics may be established. This depends on only a few dimensionless groups: k, α, and Δ, plus the scaling quantities U for velocity, λU for rate of deformation, and $3\eta U/\rho gH$ for topographic amplitude. Semi-quantitative fits may likely be obtained between model parameters and observed and estimated quantities from a natural accretionary wedge.

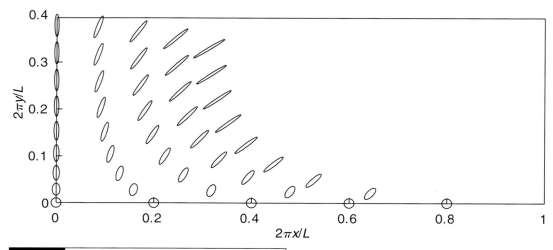

Fig 10.25 Strain ellipses for particles rising along trajectories at 0, 0.2, 0.4, 0.6, and 0.8 of the half-cell width for the case $\alpha = 0.1$, $\Delta = 1$.

10.5 | Flow of anisotropic viscous fluids

Rocks composed of layers, such as sedimentary and metasedimentary rocks, those made up of less-continuous layers or of lenticular bodies, such as gneisses and some sedimentary rocks, and those with a strong foliation, compositional banding, and alignment of mineral grains, will exhibit anisotropic rheological behavior. Such rocks often contain structures, such as folds, at several scales. The dimensions of the smallest structures scale with the thickness of individual layers, lenses, or even mineral grains, as in mica schists. The dimensions of larger scale structures may be tens to hundreds of times the thickness of components, as are the chevron folds described in Chapter 5. We now formulate constitutive relations for an anisotropic viscous fluid. This will then be used in a mechanical model for chevron folds.

10.5.1 Constitutive relations for anisotropic viscous fluids

As in the case of an anisotropic elastic solid (Chapter 8), formal derivation of general relations may start with the postulate that the components of the rate of deformation are linear and homo-geneous functions of the components of stress. We then write:

$$D_{xx} = a_{11}\sigma_{xx} + a_{12}\sigma_{yy} + a_{13}\sigma_{zz} + a_{14}\sigma_{yz}$$
$$+ a_{15}\sigma_{zx} + a_{16}\sigma_{xy}$$

$$D_{yy} = a_{12}\sigma_{xx} + a_{22}\sigma_{yy} + a_{23}\sigma_{zz} + a_{24}\sigma_{yz}$$
$$+ a_{25}\sigma_{zx} + a_{26}\sigma_{xy}$$

$$D_{zz} = a_{13}\sigma_{xx} + a_{23}\sigma_{yy} + a_{33}\sigma_{zz} + a_{34}\sigma_{yz}$$
$$+ a_{35}\sigma_{zx} + a_{36}\sigma_{xy}$$

$$2D_{yz} = a_{14}\sigma_{xx} + a_{24}\sigma_{yy} + a_{34}\sigma_{zz} + a_{44}\sigma_{yz}$$
$$+ a_{45}\sigma_{zx} + a_{46}\sigma_{xy}$$

$$2D_{zx} = a_{15}\sigma_{xx} + a_{25}\sigma_{yy} + a_{35}\sigma_{zz} + a_{45}\sigma_{yz}$$
$$+ a_{55}\sigma_{zx} + a_{56}\sigma_{xy}$$

$$2D_{xy} = a_{16}\sigma_{xx} + a_{26}\sigma_{yy} + a_{36}\sigma_{zz} + a_{46}\sigma_{yz}$$
$$+ a_{56}\sigma_{zx} + a_{66}\sigma_{xy}$$

(10.152)

This notation follows that in Lehknitskii (1963), who has written a useful treatise on the deformation of anisotropic elastic bodies. The relations (10.152) are equivalent to those for the elastic solid, but with the strain components, ε_{ij}, replaced by the rate of deformation components, D_{ij}. The form of the coefficients is based on the identifications: 1 with xx, 2 with yy, 3 with zz, 4 with yz, 5 with zx, and 6 with xy.

The symmetric a_{ij} matrix from (10.152) has $(6 \times 6)/2 + 3 = 21$ distinct elements. Since the material is incompressible, (10.9) applies, requiring the six conditions:

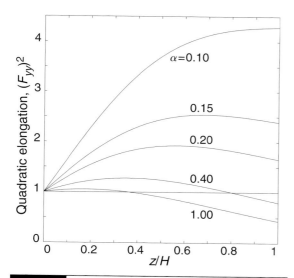

Fig 10.26 Quadratic elongation (a/b) for particles rising along the backstop, for $\Delta = 1$ and $\alpha = 0.1, 0.15, 0.2, 0.4,$ and 1.

$$a_{i1} + a_{i2} + a_{i3} = 0, \quad i = 1, 2, 3, 4, 5, 6 \qquad (10.153)$$

The number of independent coefficients for a general anisotropic viscous fluid is reduced from 21 to 15.

Following the discussion of anisotropic elastic materials with certain symmetry restrictions, we write for an orthorhombic material with three mutually perpendicular mirror planes of symmetry, initially setting aside the conditions (10.153):

$$D_{xx} = a_{11}\sigma_{xx} + a_{12}\sigma_{yy} + a_{13}\sigma_{zz}$$
$$D_{yy} = a_{12}\sigma_{xx} + a_{22}\sigma_{yy} + a_{23}\sigma_{zz}$$
$$D_{zz} = a_{13}\sigma_{xx} + a_{23}\sigma_{yy} + a_{33}\sigma_{zz}$$
$$2D_{yz} = a_{44}\sigma_{yz} \qquad (10.154)$$
$$2D_{zx} = a_{55}\sigma_{zx}$$
$$2D_{xy} = a_{66}\sigma_{xy}$$

This simpler form of the constitutive relations only applies when the axes $x, y,$ and z are principal axes of anisotropy, fixed in material directions coinciding with the intersections of pairs of mirror planes in this case.

We will investigate a plane flow problem for an incompressible anisotropic viscous fluid. One requirement for plane flow is that the plane of

flow is a mirror plane of symmetry. Let plane flow take place in the (x, y)-plane for the orthorhombic material of (10.154). We may then eliminate the normal component of stress σ_{zz} by the condition that $D_{zz} = 0$, or from (10.154):

$$\sigma_{zz} = -\frac{a_{13}}{a_{33}}\sigma_{xx} - \frac{a_{23}}{a_{33}}\sigma_{yy} \qquad (10.155)$$

Using this in the equations from (10.154) for D_{xx} and D_{yy}, and retaining the relation for D_{xy}, we have:

$$D_{xx} = b_{11}\sigma_{xx} + b_{12}\sigma_{yy}$$
$$D_{yy} = b_{12}\sigma_{xx} + b_{22}\sigma_{yy} \qquad (10.156)$$
$$2D_{xy} = a_{66}\sigma_{xy}$$

Here $b_{11} = a_{11} - a_{13}^2/a_{33}$ and $b_{12} = a_{12} - a_{13}a_{23}/a_{33}$. Evoking incompressibility, we obtain $b_{11} + b_{12} = 0$ and $b_{12} + b_{22} = 0$, so $b_{22} = b_{12} = b_{11}$. Substituting for the two independent constants in (10.156) the constitutive relations for plane flow are:

$$D_{xx} = (\sigma_{xx} - \sigma_{yy})/4\eta_n$$
$$D_{yy} = -(\sigma_{xx} - \sigma_{yy})/4\eta_n \qquad (10.157)$$
$$D_{xy} = \sigma_{xy}/2\eta_s$$

Here η_n and η_s are the principal viscosities for plane flow in the (x, y)-plane (10.154). For plane flow in other symmetry planes, the numerical values of these quantities would change.

We may further suppose that the material of interest is transversely isotropic, with equivalent directions x and z, so that only the y-axis is a unique direction within the material. The coefficients in (10.154) then have the additional restrictions:

$$a_{23} = a_{12}, \quad a_{33} = a_{11}, \quad a_{44} = a_{66}, \quad a_{55} = 2(a_{11} - a_{13}) \qquad (10.158)$$

The last condition arises from isotropy in the (x, z)-plane, i.e. that the constants do not change for such a material when the coordinate axes are changed by an arbitrary rotation about the y-axis. An incompressible, transversely isotropic aniso-tropic viscous fluid is then described by only two parameters, the principal viscosities η_n and η_s of (10.157).

Such a material may be thought of as an

approximation to a layered medium made up of alternating layers of stiff and soft isotropic viscous fluid when the scale of the flow of interest is much greater than the layer thickness, as in the case of chevron folds. Suppose the layers have thicknesses h_1 and h_2 and viscosities η_1 and η_2, and take the axes x and z parallel to layering so the y-axis is normal to the layering. The bulk properties of this composite material are obtained as follows. In layer-parallel extension, the rates of extension in the two layer types must be equal. In the two in-plane directions:

$$D_{xx}^{(1)} = D_{xx}^{(2)} = D_{xx}, \quad D_{zz}^{(1)} = D_{zz}^{(2)} = D_{zz} \qquad (10.159)$$

For simplicity, consider plane flow in the (x, y)-plane, so that for example:

$$D_{zz}^{(1)} = \left[\sigma_{zz}^{(1)} - \tfrac{1}{3}\left(\sigma_{xx}^{(1)} + \sigma_{yy} + \sigma_{zz}^{(1)} \right) \right] / 2\eta_1 = 0$$

$$\sigma_{zz}^{(1)} = \left(\sigma_{xx}^{(1)} + \sigma_{yy} \right)/2 \qquad (10.160)$$

Then, developing the first of (10.159):

$$\left(\sigma_{xx}^{(1)} - \sigma_{yy} \right)/4\eta_1 = \left(\sigma_{xx}^{(2)} - \sigma_{yy} \right)/4\eta_2 = \left(\sigma_{xx} - \sigma_{yy} \right)/4\eta_n \qquad (10.161)$$

The components of normal stress acting normal to the interface are equal. The last expression in (10.161) identifies a bulk layer-parallel normal stress σ_{xx} and a bulk viscosity in layer-parallel shortening or extension η_n. The bulk normal stress component parallel to the layering is:

$$\sigma_{xx} = \frac{h_1 \sigma_{xx}^{(1)} + h_2 \sigma_{xx}^{(2)}}{h_1 + h_2} \qquad (10.162)$$

Combining (10.161) and (10.162):

$$\eta_n = \frac{h_1 \eta_1 + h_2 \eta_2}{h_1 + h_2} = f_1 \eta_1 + f_2 \eta_2 \qquad (10.163)$$

Here f_1 and f_2 are the thickness (volume) fractions of the alternating layer types. The bulk viscosity in layer-parallel shear is obtained by taking the average of the rate of shear:

$$D_{xy} = f_1 D_{xy}^{(1)} + f_2 D_{xy}^{(2)} = f_1 \left(\frac{\sigma_{xy}}{2\eta_1} \right) + f_2 \left(\frac{\sigma_{xy}}{2\eta_2} \right) = \frac{\sigma_{xy}}{2\eta_s} \qquad (10.164)$$

Rearranging, the bulk viscosity in layer-parallel shear is:

$$\eta_s = \left(\frac{f_1}{\eta_1} + \frac{f_2}{\eta_2} \right)^{-1} \qquad (10.165)$$

The ratio of the principal viscosities is:

$$m = \frac{\eta_n}{\eta_s} = \left(f_1 \eta_1 + f_2 \eta_2 \right) \left(\frac{f_1}{\eta_1} + \frac{f_2}{\eta_2} \right) \qquad (10.166)$$

This is a measure of the degree of anisotropy. Inspection shows that $m \geq 1$. It may be shown that the maximum of m occurs at $f_1 = f_2 = 0.5$.

The full constitutive relations for the transversely isotropic anisotropic fluid, in principal coordinates, are:

$$D_{xx} = \left[\sigma_{xx} - \tfrac{1}{3}(\sigma_{xx} + \sigma_{yy} + \sigma_{zz}) \right] / 2\eta_n$$
$$D_{yy} = \left[\sigma_{yy} - \tfrac{1}{3}(\sigma_{xx} + \sigma_{yy} + \sigma_{zz}) \right] / 2\eta_n$$
$$D_{zz} = \left[\sigma_{zz} - \tfrac{1}{3}(\sigma_{xx} + \sigma_{yy} + \sigma_{zz}) \right] / 2\eta_n$$
$$D_{yz} = \sigma_{yz}/2\eta_s, \quad D_{zx} = \sigma_{zx}/2\eta_n, \quad D_{xy} = \sigma_{xy}/2\eta_s \qquad (10.167)$$

10.5.2 Chevron folding of an anisotropic viscous fluid

In Chapter 5, we studied several kinematic models for chevron folding in a stack of layers of equal thickness between which slip could take place. Here, we consider a simple but complete mechanical model that makes use of the continuum approximation of a finely layered medium by an anisotropic viscous fluid. We will be able to extract, by a separate procedure, the amount of inter-layer slip as a function of limb dip as well as the deformation of the layers. In the continuum approximation of this material it is not possible to treat in detail the deformation in the region of a fold hinge, whose dimension will be a few times the thickness of an individual layer. The approximation to chevron folding is supported by the large fraction of the rock volume occupied by the straight fold limbs. Recall that the continuum approximation only applies to flow at a scale that is much greater than the individual layer thickness. However, for the homogeneously deforming fold limbs, an exact interpretation of the macroscopic solution may be made to give the quantities for component layers or surfaces.

As in Chapter 5, consider the evolution of symmetric, periodic chevron folds formed by shortening normal to their axial planes (Fig. 10.27). The

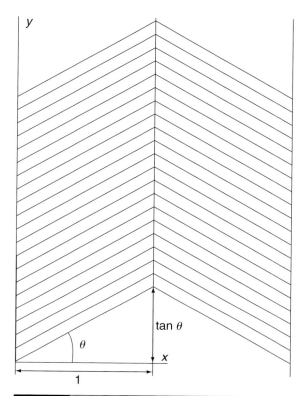

Fig 10.27 Portion of a set of periodic chevron folds for a stack of layers with inter-layer slip; shown are 1/2 the spans of the right-dipping and left-dipping limbs and the fixed (x, y)-coordinate axes, and the limb dip θ.

constitutive equations for a transversely isotropic anisotropic viscous fluid are given in (10.157). We also showed how these could be identified as the bulk constitutive relations for a layered material consisting of alternating stiff and soft isotropic viscous layers. Now let x' and y' denote the principal axes of anisotropy as in (10.157) and take the x-axis fixed in the direction of bulk shortening normal to the fold axial plane. The constitutive relations for the homogeneous material in the left-dipping fold limb are then, by transformation of coordinates:

$$4\eta_n D_{xx} = [(1+m) + (1-m)\cos 4\theta]s_{xx}$$
$$+ (1-m)\sin 4\theta s_{xy}$$
$$4\eta_n D_{xy} = (1-m)\sin 4\theta s_{xx}$$
$$+ [(1+m) - (1-m)\cos 4\theta]s_{xy} \qquad (10.168)$$

Here the stress components are the deviatoric stress components defined as:

$$s_{xx} = (\sigma_{xx} - \sigma_{yy})/2, \quad s_{xy} = \sigma_{xy} \qquad (10.169)$$

Consider the deformation of a segment of the trace of a folded surface on the left-dipping limb of the fold (Fig. 10.27) whose projection onto the x-axis is taken to be 1 in arbitrary units. The rate of change in limb dip as well as in the length of the fold limb may be obtained by considering the velocity of the particle on its end:

$$v_x(1, \tan\theta) = D_{xx}$$
$$v_y(1, \tan\theta) = -D_{xx}\tan\theta + 2D_{xy} \qquad (10.170)$$

From Fig. 10.28, the new limb dip, $\theta + d\theta$, after an infinitesimal time dt is given by:

$$\tan(\theta + d\theta) = \frac{\tan\theta + v_y(1, \tan\theta)dt}{1 + v_x(1, \tan\theta)dt} \qquad (10.171)$$

Combining (1.170) and (1.171) we have:

$$\frac{d}{dt}\tan\theta = (1 + \tan^2\theta)\frac{d\theta}{dt} = 2(D_{xy} - D_{xx}\tan\theta) \qquad (10.172)$$

Symmetry requires that the shear component of the deviatoric stress s_{xy} equals zero. Thus, the relations in (10.168) reduce to:

$$4\eta_n D_{xx} = [(1+m) + (1-m)\cos 4\theta]s_{xx}$$
$$4\eta_n D_{xy} = (1-m)\sin 4\theta s_{xx} \qquad (10.173)$$

The first of (10.173) is used to eliminate s_{xx} from the expression for D_{xy}, and substitution of the result into (10.172) yields:

$$\frac{d}{dt}\tan\theta = (1 + \tan^2\theta)\frac{d\theta}{dt}$$
$$= 2\left\{\frac{(1-m)\sin 4\theta}{[(1+m) + (1-m)\cos 4\theta]} - \tan\theta\right\}D_{xx} \qquad (10.174)$$

This relation may be integrated numerically to follow the evolution in limb dip with shortening. As in Chapter 5, it is necessary to introduce a periodic set of seed folds with initial limb dip θ_0.

Examples of fold evolution in terms of limb dip, θ, for several values of the viscosity ratio, $m = \eta_n/\eta_s$, are given in Fig. 10.29 for $m = 1, 1.5, 2, 3, 4, 10$, and ∞. Note that fold growth corresponds to a decrease in fold span and so progress is from right to left on this figure. For the isotropic fluid, $m = 1$, fold growth is the "passive" kinematic amplification of

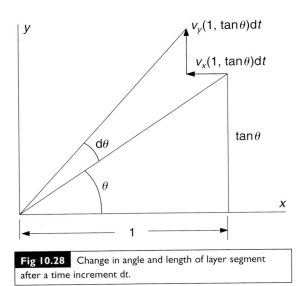

Fig 10.28 Change in angle and length of layer segment after a time increment dt.

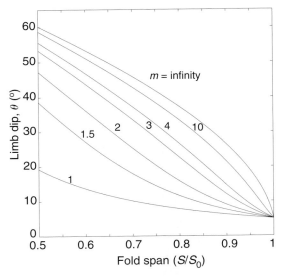

Fig 10.29 Limb dip of chevron folds as a function of current to initial fold span S/S_0 for $m = 1$, 1.5, 2, 3, 4, 10, and ∞.

a surface in homogeneous shortening. In the "deck of cards" limit, $m \to \infty$, where the normal viscosity greatly exceeds the shear viscosity, the component layers do not change their thickness. A modest value of $m = 1.5$ leads to significant fold amplification, and a value $m = 10$ behaves nearly like the limiting case of rigid layers. Since the notion that natural chevron folds begin with limb dips as low as 5° is not firmly established (Fletcher and Pollard, 1999), the relation between limb dip and fold span is not necessarily that characteristic of the natural folds. None-the-less, the methodology described here illustrates the application of anisotropic viscous flow and suggests a fruitful path for research on the behavior of layered geological materials.

10.6 | Concluding remarks

In this chapter, we have used the constitutive relations for a linear (Newtonian) viscous fluid to complete a mechanical description for the large, permanent ductile deformation of rock, both isotropic and anisotropic. Models have been restricted to plane flow, for which solutions are readily obtained and the results can be understood from illustrations of a cross section. Another set of solutions may be obtained for antiplane flow, the equations for which are only introduced here. Solutions for plane flow are

derived and applied to natural examples: glacier-like flow driven by gravity; the -pression part of transpression; the gross dynamics of accretionary wedges; and deformation of layers that have roughly planar surfaces as in mullion structure, folding, and flow within the exhumation region of an accretionary wedge. Other models for flow in a viscous fluid may be obtained by taking advantage of the correspondence principle to convert elastic solutions presented in this text.

An important conclusion is that finite strain, while it plays a prominent role in modern structural investigations, does not directly enter the formulation or development of forward models of ductile rock deformation, which are centered on the velocity and stress fields. Evidently, finite strain plays a significant role, as in the interpretation of natural single-layer folds, in constraining such models. However, the many attempts to forge models implicitly or explicitly involving causal aspects in terms of finite strain or other attributes of the deformed state, as embodied in the words "the strain was partitioned..." or in the common misconception surrounding "strain compatibility," must prove to be essentially vacuous. Experience with forward models of rock deformation may result in a re-examination of this issue.

Chapter 11

Rheological behavior

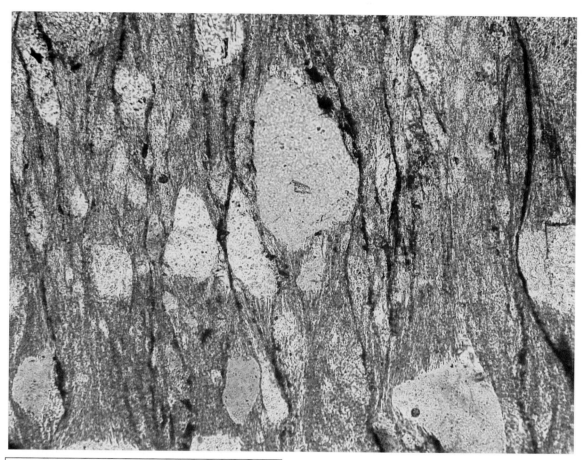

Pressure solution in sandstone from the Olympic accretionary wedge, Olympic Mountains, NW Washington State, USA. The horizontal dimension is ~10 mm. Photograph by J. M. Rahl.

No mathematical theory can completely describe the complex world around us. Every theory is aimed at a certain class of phenomena, formulates their essential features, and disregards what is of minor importance. The theory meets its limits of applicability where a disregarded influence becomes important (Flugge, 1967).

11.1 Departures from linear viscous flow

Laboratory determinations of steady-state rock creep and field observations indicate that ductile rocks may not be well-approximated by homogeneous, isotropic, incompressible, and linear viscous fluids of uniform viscosity. In this chapter, we consider other constitutive relations that broaden the range in rock behavior described and provide a basis for understanding some of the differences arising. Because the linear Newtonian viscous fluid is the simplest material that undergoes large permanent deformation, the formulation and analysis of models using it and their application to interpret a set of field observations is always a useful first step (see Chapter 10). The results obtained establish a benchmark from which to understand differences in behavior associated with other constitutive relations. Whether the new model results in a large or subtle contrast in behavior relative to an already well-understood viscous model, we will achieve a better understanding of the reasons for the differences and a greater confidence in data interpretation.

For example, initiation of a regular train of folds by selective amplification was studied for the Newtonian viscous layer in Chapter 10. Data from natural fold populations yield a limited range in mean fold arc length/thickness ratios of about 4 to 6. Interpretation of the data in terms of the folding of a Newtonian layer implies: (i) a modest layer to host viscosity ratio, $1/R$, of about 10 to 20; (ii) a weak folding instability, so that a large layer-parallel shortening is required to establish a regular fold train, e.g. a doubling of layer thickness. On the other hand, laboratory studies of steady-state rock creep suggest that much larger contrasts in effective viscosity should be common (Table 11.1), with equivalent $1/R$ values of about 100 to 1000 or more, and that constitutive relations for rock creep should generally be non-linear. Do the laboratory results extrapolate to natural rock behavior at much smaller rates of deformation and lower temperatures? Answers to this question not only affect conclusions as to small-scale folding, but also the modeling of large-scale crustal deformation.

In one instance (Groshong, 1975), layer thickening associated with a well-developed set of folds in a limestone layer embedded in shale was only ~10%. Interpretation of data for these folds (Fletcher, 1974) is consistent with the type of non-linear relation observed in the laboratory for creep of carbonate rock. It has been suggested that the limited range in fold arc length/thickness ratios ~4 to 6 is a manifestation of highly non-linear behavior (Smith, 1977, 1979). Further evidence for markedly non-linear behavior is offered by examples of necking in layer-parallel extension, which cannot occur in a Newtonian layer. Alternatively, interpretation of the relative viscosities of component rocks in a deformed conglomerate has been offered as evidence of linear viscous behavior (Treagus and Treagus, 2002). Motivated by these questions, we study necking and folding of layers of non-linear power-law fluid in this chapter.

Inhomogeneity in rock masses occurs at a wide range in scale, from less than a grain diameter to the tens or hundreds of kilometers appropriate to the first-order dynamics of crustal deformation. A useful postulate is that at the scale of interest the rock may be treated as a continuum whose behavior is approximated by constitutive relations containing only a few rheological parameters. The question then arises as to how these parameters might be estimated from the three major determinants of the bulk behavior: the volume fractions of the significant mechanically distinct components, their individual constitutive relations, and the phase geometry of the composite material. Answers to this question would provide a better understanding of the degree of complexity of rocks and a basis for accepting or maintaining doubts about the approximation of a locally homogeneous continuum with spatially varying properties. In this chapter, we use elementary methods to analyze composites made up of two isotropic viscous components. Composite materials must generally exhibit anisotropy in their rheological behavior, with isotropic behavior being only a special case. We therefore include consideration of anisotropy.

Anisotropic materials such as foliated or layered rock may have nearly uniform properties with respect to their principal axes of anisotropy.

Table 11.1. Rheological constants for a few quartzites and carbonates.

Material	n	$\log_{10}A_0$ $(MPa^n s^{-1})$	Q' $(kJ\,mol^{-1})$	$\log_{10}B$ $(MPa^n s^{-1})$	$\log_{10}\eta_{eff}$ $(Pa\,s^{-1})$
Quartzite (d)	2.8	−5.463	184	−19.1	23.0
Quartzite (d)	2.9	−5.30	170	−17.9	21.7
Quartzite (w)	2.6	−1.35	230	−18.6	22.7
Quartzite (w)	1.8	−2.54	151	−13.9	18.8
Quartzite (w)	4.0	−9.4	135	−19.0	21.7
Marble	8.3	−3.9	260	−22.2	20.6
Limestone	3.4	3.4	298	−18.9	20.7

Deformation of a rock mass containing small random perturbations in the orientation of the principal axes may give rise to their strong selective amplification leading to folding, internal boudinage, or other structures (Cobbold *et al.*, 1971). Here, we examine the internal instability in plane flow of an anisotropic viscous fluid.

A third deviation from the Newtonian fluid is through compressibility that is mediated by the transport by intergranular diffusion or by Darcy flow of a mobile component – one that is soluble in an intergranular pore fluid or acts as a weak fluid in a much stiffer "solid" framework, as in a partly melted rock. In this chapter, we consider the former alternative, and model some of the effects that arise from it in folding and necking when the medium containing a stiff layer exhibits this kind of behavior in combination with Newtonian viscosity.

All deviations from the homogeneous Newtonian viscous fluid lead to effects that produce observable features in the structures and internal fabrics of deformed rocks, and they are of substantial interest in application to the interpretation of field data.

11.2 | Boudinage and the non-linear power-law fluid

Confusion with regards to the significance of the term boudin has undoubtedly arisen in some countries because of the different ways in which sausages are displayed in shops. On the continent of Europe, large boudins are found lying side-by-side on grocers' slabs;

in Britain and America, the smaller type of sausage is more common, and these are seen hanging in strings, end to end. Transverse sections of non-equidimensional boudins remind the unwary of the latter. This misinterpretation of Lohest's original description has unfortunately been made in at least two papers (Wilson and Cosgrove, 1982).

Necking as exhibited in pinch-and-swell structures in stiff layers (Fig. 11.1a) is an example indicating rheological non-linearity in natural rock deformation. The ability to work molten glass to produce sheets of uniform thickness depends on the absence of a necking instability in a linear viscous fluid. In structural geology, boudinage includes the continuous necking that produces pinch-and-swell structures (Fig. 11.1a) and the processes that produce discretely segmented boudins (Fig. 11.1b, c). While discretely segmented in cross section, they may coalesce in the axial direction. Discrete boudins may often have undergone an initial episode of continuous necking. Two mechanisms of segmentation occur: mode I cracks that contemporaneously fill with precipitated minerals (Fig. 11.1b), and mode II faults or shear bands (Fig 11.1c). After separation, boudins tend to undergo further deformation that results in a variety of striking forms. The modeling of boudinage presented here is restricted to continuous necking.

It is not clear whether examples of necking of rock layers are chiefly a consequence of non-linearity derived from *strain rate thinning*, in which the rate of deformation increases more rapidly than linearly with the deviatoric stress, or that derived from *strain softening*, in which an element weakens as it deforms, since both contribute to necking (Neurath and Smith, 1982). We first give a

Fig 11.1 (a) Continuous necking in a gneiss layer $\sim$6 cm in thickness. (b) Discrete boudins separated by deformed quartz precipitated into the boudin gaps; hammer length $\sim$40 cm. (c) Boudins deformed and partially separated by right-dipping normal faults; horizontal span $\sim$10 m. Photograph by R. C. Fletcher.

simple analysis of necking of a free plate, or unconfined layer. We then show how selective amplification occurs in layer extension, giving necking, and, in layer-parallel shortening, giving folding, in a layer of homogeneous and isotropic power-law fluid embedded in a weaker medium.

A model for large-scale crustal necking is presented to illustrate the roles of gravity and surficial processes acting on topography.

11.2.1 Plane-sections-remain-plane analysis for a free plate

Let the material be the isotropic incompressible power-law fluid already treated in the glacier-like flow of Chapter 10. Consider a free plate of cylindrical form whose thickness varies as in Fig. 11.2. It is not necessary to assume such a restricted form, but we do suppose in the present case that layer thickness varies slowly with length and that the thickness variation is small relative to the mean thickness. For this periodic shape, these requirements are:

$$\lambda A \ll 1 \text{ and } A/h \ll 1 \tag{11.1}$$

Here $\lambda = 2\pi/L$ is the wavenumber and A is the amplitude of the sinusoidal perturbation. We later use this configuration to study initiation of necking in an embedded layer. Here, though, we more generally consider the deformation of a layer of thickness $H(x, t)$ that satisfies the equivalent conditions:

$$H(x, t) = \bar{H}(t) + \tilde{H}(x, t)$$
$$\frac{\partial(\tilde{H})}{\partial x} \ll 1 \text{ and } \frac{\tilde{H}}{\bar{H}} \ll 1 \tag{11.2}$$

Here $\bar{H}$ is the mean thickness and $\tilde{H}$ is the deviation from it. The thickness variation of the plate is also cylindrical with a constant profile in the layer direction normal to x. The plate undergoes plane deformation when subjected to an axial force per unit depth of constant magnitude $F_x > 0$. As here, the use of H for the full thickness of a layer, but also h for the half-thickness, is done to avoid having to write $H/2$ in boundary conditions when the coordinate origin is taken at the center of a layer to exploit symmetry.

The mean axial normal stress on a vertical surface through the plate is:

$$\sigma_{xx}(x, t) = \frac{F_x}{H(x, t)} \tag{11.3}$$

This stress is taken to be uniform on a vertical surface across the plate. We only treat the case of a free plate with zero traction on its surface.

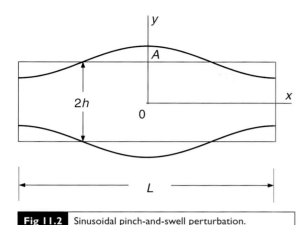

Fig 11.2 Sinusoidal pinch-and-swell perturbation.

As a second related approximation, we adopt the familiar plane-sections-remain-plane approximation used in engineering (Timoshenko and Young, 1968) – or perhaps formerly used when numerical codes were not readily available. Each vertical section of the plate thus is treated as undergoing homogeneous extension:

$$D_{xx} \cong -\frac{1}{H}\frac{\partial H}{\partial t} \tag{11.4}$$

The applicable single-component relation for a power-law fluid relates D_{xx} and the deviatoric stress component, s_{xx}, which for plane flow is:

$$s_{xx} = \frac{1}{2}\sigma_{xx} = \frac{1}{2}\frac{F_x}{H} \tag{11.5}$$

The constitutive relation is:

$$D_{xx} = B'(s_{xx}^2)^{(n-1)/2}s_{xx} \tag{11.6}$$

Substituting (11.4) and (11.5) into (11.6) we have:

$$D_{xx} = -\frac{1}{H}\frac{dH}{dt} = B'\left[\left(\frac{1}{2}\frac{F_x}{H}\right)\right]^n = \frac{C}{H^n}$$
$$\text{so, } -H^{n-1}\frac{dH}{dt} = C \tag{11.7}$$

This is the relation for change in vertical dimension of an infinitesimal material element of cross-sectional area $dA = Hdx$ and thus the derivative is a material time derivative. We could use the constancy of area dA, expressing conservation of mass for an incompressible material in plane flow, to establish the relative positions of sections along the layer, but this problem is set aside.

Linearizing the relation (11.7) for a perturbation in thickness $\tilde{H}$ about a mean value $\bar{H}$ yields:

$$-[\bar{H}^{n-1} + (n-1)\bar{H}^{n-2}\tilde{H}]\left(\frac{d\bar{H}}{dt} + \frac{d\tilde{H}}{dt}\right) \cong C \tag{11.8}$$

Expansion and separation of mean and perturbing parts gives:

$$-\bar{H}^{n-1}\frac{d\bar{H}}{dt} = C$$
$$-(n-1)\tilde{H}\left(\frac{1}{\bar{H}}\frac{d\bar{H}}{dt}\right) - \frac{d\tilde{H}}{dt} \cong 0 \tag{11.9}$$
$$\frac{d\tilde{H}}{dt} \cong (n-1)\bar{D}_{xx}\tilde{H}$$

The last relation indeed shows that the perturbation $\tilde{H}$ does not grow for a viscous layer, $n = 1$, and grows only slowly unless n is large. Values of n obtained in the laboratory for high-temperature steady-state creep of rock tend to be modest, typically ranging from 3 to 5 (Table 11.1), so that only a weak necking instability arises from the non-linear relation between the rate of deformation and the deviatoric stress. For the sinusoidal perturbation (Fig. 11.2) comparison with (11.9), with $\bar{H} = 2h$ and $\tilde{H} = A\cos\lambda x$, yields:

$$\frac{dA}{dt} \cong (n-1)\bar{D}_{xx}A \tag{11.10}$$

We may use this approximation to follow the change in shape of the layer segment (Fig. 11.2) by completing (11.10) with relations for the changes in wavelength L and mean thickness $2h$. These are:

$$\frac{dL}{dt} = D_{xx}L$$
$$\frac{dh}{dt} = D_{xx}h \tag{11.11}$$

The relations (11.10) and (11.11) are only appropriate under the conditions (11.1). The initial and final shapes for a stretch of 1.29 for a material with $n = 5$ and an initial configuration with $h(0) = 1$ and $A(0) = 0.1$ is given in Fig. 11.3. This example looks good, but amplitude growth from (11.10) may exceed layer thinning, so that the maximum thickness of the final form ends up larger than initially! If $n = 10$ is used in this example, such a result is obtained. One has to be careful with approximations.

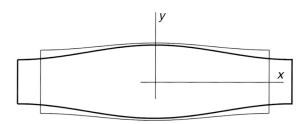

Fig 11.3 Evolution of an initial pinch-and-swell perturbation in a free plate after a stretch of 1.29.

The expectation for a layer embedded in a medium is that the degree or strength of instability will be less than that for the mechanically unconstrained layer. In part to study this aspect, we formulate a complete tensor characterization of a power-law fluid and use it to analyze necking and folding in the manner of the treatment given in Chapter 10.

11.2.2 Constitutive relations for an isotropic power-law fluid and a plastic solid

A general tensor relationship between the components of the rate of deformation and those of the deviatoric stress is needed to treat arbitrary deformations of the power-law fluid. In experiments (Evans and Kohlstedt, 1995) on right-circular cylinders of rock under axial stress, σ_1, generally compressive, and uniform radial or circumferential stress, σ_3, acting on the surface of the cylinder, results are usually given in the form:

$$\frac{d\varepsilon_1}{dt} = A_0 \exp\left(-\frac{Q'}{R'T'}\right)(\sigma_1 - \sigma_3)^n \qquad (11.12)$$

Here $d\varepsilon_1/dt = \dot{\varepsilon}_1$ is the axial strain rate. Because experiments are conducted in compression, the experimentalists treat a rate of shortening and a compressive stress as positive. The constant preceding the power of the difference between axial and circumferential normal stress components is written as the product of a pre-exponential constant, A_0, and a term expressing temperature dependence, where Q' is an activation energy, R' is the gas constant, and T' is the absolute temperature. Primes are introduced since the symbols Q, R, and T will be used for other quantities. In our development, we retain the convention of taking compressive stress as negative.

A convenient isotropic non-linear form for the constitutive relations (Nye, 1953; Calladine and Drucker, 1962) is:

$$D_{ij} = B J_2^{(n-1)/2} s_{ij}, \qquad J_2 = \tfrac{1}{2} s_{kl} s_{kl},$$
$$s_{ij} = \sigma_{ij} - \tfrac{1}{3}\sigma_{kk}\delta_{ij} \qquad (11.13)$$

Here the scalar J_2 is the second isotropic invariant of the deviatoric stress. Thus, all quantities in (11.13) are independent of the orientation of the coordinate axes with respect to the material, and the relations are those for an isotropic material. We may write, in analogy with a Newtonian viscous fluid:

$$D_{ij} = \frac{1}{2\eta_{\text{eff}}} s_{ij} \qquad (11.14)$$
$$2\eta_{\text{eff}} = [B J_2^{(n-1)/2}]^{-1}$$

Here η_{eff} is an effective viscosity that is generally position dependent through the local value of the stress. A comparison of the form (11.13) with the experimental relationship (11.12), reversing the usual sign convention used for experiments, is obtained as follows. Taking x_1 for the direction along the cylindrical sample axis, we have:

$$s_1 = \sigma_1 - \tfrac{1}{3}(\sigma_1 + \sigma_2 + \sigma_3) = \tfrac{2}{3}(\sigma_1 - \sigma_3)$$
$$s_2 = s_3 = -\tfrac{1}{3}(\sigma_1 - \sigma_3) \qquad (11.15)$$
$$J_2 = \tfrac{1}{2}(s_1^2 + s_2^2 + s_3^2) = \tfrac{1}{3}(\sigma_1 - \sigma_3)^2$$

Then:

$$D_1 = B\left[\tfrac{1}{3}(\sigma_1 - \sigma_3)^2\right]^{(n-1)/2} \tfrac{2}{3}(\sigma_1 - \sigma_3)$$
$$= A_0 \exp(-Q'/R'T')(\sigma_1 - \sigma_3)^n$$
$$B = [(3)^{(n-1)/2}(3/2)]A_0 \exp(-Q'/R'T') \qquad (11.16)$$

The coefficient B is expressed in units $(\text{MPa})^{-n}\,\text{s}^{-1}$ in terms of constants given in the literature. Constants for several polycrystalline quartzites and marbles are given in Table 11.1 (Evans and Kohlstedt, 1995). Values of effective viscosity (11.14) at a temperature of 400° C and a maximum shear stress of 10 MPa were computed from these quantities and are also given.

In later analysis, the inverse of (11.13) is used. To derive this, first we form:

$$I_2 = \tfrac{1}{2}D_{ij}D_{ij} = B^2 J_2^{(n-1)} \tfrac{1}{2} s_{ij}s_{ij} = B^2 J_2^n \qquad (11.17)$$
$$J_2 = (I_2/B^2)^{1/n}$$

Using (11.17) in (11.13) we have:

$$s_{ij} = B^{-1/n}I_2^{-(n-1)/2n}D_{ij} \qquad (11.18)$$

It is useful to make a comparison between the relations for the Newtonian viscous fluid, the power-law fluid, and a third material, the rigid, perfectly plastic solid. For simplicity, the results for plane flow are given, for which $s_{xx} = -s_{yy} = \tfrac{1}{2}(\sigma_{xx} - \sigma_{yy})$, $s_{xy} = \sigma_{xy}$. All materials are incompressible so the rates of deformation are related as:

$$D_{xx} + D_{yy} = 0 \qquad (11.19)$$

The constitutive relations for the viscous fluid are:

$$D_{xx} = (\sigma_{xx} - \sigma_{yy})/4\eta$$
$$D_{xy} = \sigma_{xy}/4\eta \qquad (11.20)$$

The constitutive relations for the power-law fluid are:

$$D_{xx} = BJ_2^{(n-1)/2} \tfrac{1}{2}(\sigma_{xx} - \sigma_{yy}), \quad D_{xy} = BJ_2^{(n-1)/2}\sigma_{xy}$$

where $J_2 = \tfrac{1}{4}(\sigma_{xx} - \sigma_{yy})^2 + \sigma_{xy}^2 \qquad (11.21)$

The constitutive relations for the rigid, perfectly plastic solid at yield are:

$$D_{xx} = \Lambda\tfrac{1}{2}(\sigma_{xx} - \sigma_{yy}), \quad D_{xy} = \Lambda\sigma_{xy}$$

where $J_2 = \tfrac{1}{4}(\sigma_{xx} - \sigma_{yy})^2 + \sigma_{xy}^2 = K^2 \qquad (11.22)$

K is the maximum shear stress attained at yielding of the material. Here $\Lambda = \Lambda(x, y)$ is not a material constant but is a function of position. The first pair of conditions in (11.22) is a statement of isotropy alone: the principal axes of the rate of deformation tensor coincide with the principal axes of the stress tensor or the deviatoric stress tensor. To complement the addition of a new unknown, an additional equation in the stress components, the yield condition is specified. For stresses below this condition, the material is rigid and, further, the stress state cannot lie outside the yield condition, which is a circle in $(\tfrac{1}{2}(\sigma_{xx} - \sigma_{yy}), \sigma_{xy})$-space. All three materials satisfy the governing equations of stress equilibrium and the kinematic relations.

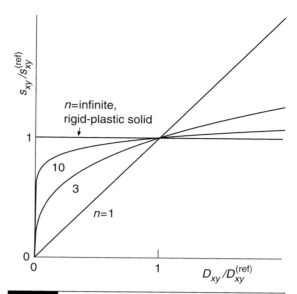

Fig 11.4 Normalized one-dimensional relations between rate of deformation and deviatoric stress for power-law fluids with different stress exponents n.

If the deviatoric stress component $\tfrac{1}{2}(\sigma_{xx} - \sigma_{yy})$ is zero, we may write the normalized relation for the power-law material:

$$\frac{\sigma_{xy}}{\sigma_{xy}^{(\mathrm{ref})}} = \left(\frac{D_{xy}}{D_{xy}^{(\mathrm{ref})}}\right)^{1/n} \qquad (11.23)$$

Here the value $D_{xy}^{(\mathrm{ref})}$ occurs at $\sigma_{xy}^{(\mathrm{ref})}$. The relation is shown in Fig. 11.4 for the viscous fluid, $n = 1$, and non-linear power-law fluids with $n = 3$, 10, and ∞. The last may be readily identified with the rigid-plastic solid where $\sigma_{xy}^{(\mathrm{ref})}$ for it is the yield stress K. The rate of deformation is zero below the yield stress; at the yield stress, the rate of deformation is indeterminate from the relation (11.23) alone; and the stress cannot exceed the yield value.

11.2.3 Linearization of the constitutive relations and solution for low-slope necking and folding of a power-law layer

The fact that necking of an embedded layer or inter-layer sequence produces pinch-and-swell structures with regularity in neck-to-neck span to mean layer thickness implies selective amplification of an initial random waviness in layer surfaces. This behavior depends upon the linear independence of wavelength components in the random waviness. Selective amplification may then only occur when the constitutive relations of a non-linear material can be linearized about a basic state of flow, since only then do the wavelength components in the perturbing flow not interact. Linear independence also requires that *linearization* of the boundary conditions, when only terms proportional to λA are retained, is accurate, as in our analysis of viscous folding.

Here, the basic state is taken as uniform layer-parallel extension or shortening, which simply changes the sign of $\overline{D}_{xx}$. To emphasize this, we write:

$$\overline{D}_{xx} = \text{Sgn}(\overline{D}_{xx})|\overline{D}_{xx}| \tag{11.24}$$

Since we have not studied folding in layer-parallel shortening for a non-linear fluid layer, we also consider that here. We shall see that other types of instability in the shortening or extension of a layer occur; for example shortening of a soft layer between stiff media produces mullions (Smith, 1975).

To add interest to the analysis, consider a basic-state flow in which the principal rates of deformation, $\overline{D}_{xx}, \overline{D}_{yy}, \overline{D}_{zz}$, are all non-zero, with axes x and z in the plane of the layer and y normal to it. The perturbing flow is restricted to a plane flow associated with a cylindrical component in the shape perturbation whose axis lies parallel to the principal axis of the basic state, ζ.

To linearize the constitutive relations, it is convenient initially to carry out the computation using indicial notation:

$$\overline{D}_{ij} + \tilde{D}_{ij} \cong B\left[\frac{1}{2}(\bar{s}_{kl}\bar{s}_{kl} + 2\bar{s}_{kl}\tilde{s}_{kl})\right]^{(n-1)/2}(\bar{s}_{ij} + \tilde{s}_{ij})$$

$$\cong B\bar{J}_2^{(n-1)/2}\left[1 + \frac{(n-1)\bar{s}_{kl}\tilde{s}_{kl}}{2\bar{J}_2}\right](\bar{s}_{ij} + \tilde{s}_{ij}) \tag{11.25}$$

From the second line of (11.25) we find:

$$\overline{D}_{ij} = B\bar{J}_2^{(n-1)/2}\bar{s}_{ij}$$

$$\tilde{D}_{ij} \cong B\bar{J}_2^{(n-1)/2}\left\{\tilde{s}_{ij} + \left[\frac{(n-1)}{2\bar{J}_2}\right]\bar{s}_{ij}\bar{s}_{kl}\tilde{s}_{kl}\right\} \tag{11.26}$$

We now reduce the second set of six equations, where indices i and j take values 1, 2, and 3, for the restrictions of interest: the perturbing flow is

plane and only the normal, principal components of $\bar{s}_{ij}$ are non-zero, yielding:

$$2\bar{\eta}\tilde{D}_{xx} \cong \tilde{s}_{xx} + \left[(n-1)/2n\bar{J}_2\right]\bar{s}_{xx}(\bar{s}_{xx}\tilde{s}_{xx} + \bar{s}_{yy}\tilde{s}_{yy} + \bar{s}_{zz}\tilde{s}_{zz})$$

$$2\bar{\eta}\tilde{D}_{yy} \cong \tilde{s}_{yy} + \left[(n-1)/2n\bar{J}_2\right]\bar{s}_{yy}(\bar{s}_{xx}\tilde{s}_{xx} + \bar{s}_{yy}\tilde{s}_{yy} + \bar{s}_{zz}\tilde{s}_{zz})$$

$$2\bar{\eta}\tilde{D}_{xy} \cong \tilde{s}_{xy} \tag{11.27}$$

Here $\tilde{D}_{xx} + \tilde{D}_{yy} = 0$. Because of the proportionality of components of the rate of deformation and deviatoric stress in the isotropic relations for the basic state in (11.26), the basic-state deviatoric stress components and $\bar{J}_2$ may be replaced by basic-state rate of deformation components and $\bar{I}_2 = \frac{1}{2}\overline{D}_{kl}\overline{D}_{kl}$ such that:

$$\bar{I}_2 = \frac{1}{2}(\overline{D}_{xx}^2 + \overline{D}_{yy}^2 + \overline{D}_{zz}^2) = \overline{D}_{xx}^2(1 + \xi + \xi^2) \tag{11.28}$$

The quantity $\xi = \overline{D}_{zz}/\overline{D}_{xx}$ is the ratio of the basic-state rate of deformation component parallel to the axis of the shape perturbation to that acting in the plane of the layer and normal to the axis. The plane flow case is then $\xi = 0$.

Because restrictions are placed on the components of the rate of deformation, it is more convenient to use the inverse relations (11.18). The linearized form is obtained in indicial notation:

$$\bar{s}_{ij} + \tilde{s}_{ij} \cong B^{-1/n}\bar{I}_2^{-(n-1)/2n}\left[1 - \frac{(n-1)}{2n\bar{I}_2}\overline{D}_{kl}\tilde{D}_{kl}\right](\overline{D}_{ij} + \tilde{D}_{ij}) \tag{11.29}$$

From (11.29) we extract the basic-state and perturbation relations:

$$\bar{s}_{ij} = B^{-1/n}\bar{I}_2^{-(n-1)/2n}\overline{D}_{ij}$$

$$\tilde{s}_{ij} \cong B^{-1/n}\bar{I}_2^{-(n-1)/2n}\left[\tilde{D}_{ij} - \frac{(n-1)}{2n\bar{I}_2}\overline{D}_{ij}\overline{D}_{kl}\tilde{D}_{kl}\right] \tag{11.30}$$

In the present case, we introduce two restrictions: (i) the only non-zero components are the principal components $\overline{D}_{xx}, \overline{D}_{yy},$ and $\overline{D}_{zz}$; and (ii) the perturbing flow is plane, with non-zero components $\tilde{D}_{xx} = -\tilde{D}_{yy}, \tilde{D}_{xy}$. The relations (11.30) give for the perturbing flow:

$$\tilde{s}_{xx} \cong 2\bar{\eta}\left[1 - \frac{(n-1)}{2n\bar{I}_2}\overline{D}_{xx}(\overline{D}_{xx} - \overline{D}_{yy})\right]\tilde{D}_{xx}$$

$$\tilde{s}_{yy} \cong 2\bar{\eta}\left[1 - \frac{(n-1)}{2n\bar{I}_2}\overline{D}_{yy}(\overline{D}_{yy} - \overline{D}_{xx})\right]\tilde{D}_{yy} \tag{11.31}$$

$$\tilde{s}_{xy} \cong 2\bar{\eta}\,\tilde{D}_{xy}$$

Here $2\bar{\eta} = B^{-1/n}\bar{I}_2^{-(n-1)/2n}$ and $\bar{\eta}$ is the effective viscosity (11.14) in the basic state, which is uniform within the layer. These may be further condensed to:

$$\tilde{s}_{xx} \cong 2\bar{\eta}\left(\frac{1}{n_x}\right)\tilde{D}_{xx}$$

$$\tilde{s}_{yy} \cong 2\bar{\eta}\left(\frac{1}{n_y}\right)\tilde{D}_{yy} \qquad (11.32)$$

$$\tilde{s}_{xy} \cong 2\bar{\eta}\,\tilde{D}_{xy}$$

Here the inverse of n_x and n_y are defined:

$$\frac{1}{n_x} \cong 1 - \frac{(n-1)}{2n\bar{I}_2}\bar{D}_{xx}(\bar{D}_{xx} - \bar{D}_{yy})$$

$$\frac{1}{n_y} = 1 + \frac{(n-1)}{2n\bar{I}_2}\bar{D}_{yy}(\bar{D}_{xx} - \bar{D}_{yy}) \qquad (11.33)$$

The stress and deviatoric stress components are related by:

$$\tilde{\sigma}_{xx} \cong 2\bar{\eta}\left(\frac{1}{n_x}\right)\tilde{D}_{xx} - \tilde{p}$$

$$\tilde{\sigma}_{yy} \cong 2\bar{\eta}\left(\frac{1}{n_y}\right)\tilde{D}_{yy} - \tilde{p} \qquad (11.34)$$

$$\tilde{\sigma}_{xy} \cong 2\bar{\eta}\,\tilde{D}_{xy}$$

Here $\tilde{p} = -\frac{1}{3}(\tilde{\sigma}_{xx} + \tilde{\sigma}_{yy} + \tilde{\sigma}_{zz})$ is the perturbing part of the pressure, or the negative of the mean normal perturbing stress. For plane flow, the condition of incompressibility is:

$$\tilde{D}_{xx} + \tilde{D}_{yy} = \frac{\partial\tilde{v}_x}{\partial x} + \frac{\partial\tilde{v}_y}{\partial x} = 0 \qquad (11.35)$$

This is automatically satisfied by the separable expressions:

$$\tilde{v}_x = -\frac{1}{\lambda}\frac{dV}{dy}\sin\lambda x \qquad (11.36)$$

$$\tilde{v}_x = V\cos\lambda x$$

Substituting (11.36) and (11.32), using (11.34), into the stress equilibrium equations (10.15):

$$\frac{\partial\tilde{\sigma}_{xx}}{\partial x} + \frac{\partial\tilde{\sigma}_{xy}}{\partial y} = 0$$

$$\frac{\partial\tilde{\sigma}_{xy}}{\partial x} + \frac{\partial\tilde{\sigma}_{yy}}{\partial y} = 0 \qquad (11.37)$$

Eliminating $\tilde{p}$ between the two equilibrium equations, we obtain an ordinary differential equation in $V = V(y)$:

$$\frac{d^4V}{dy^4} - 2\left(\frac{1}{n_x} + \frac{1}{n_y} - 1\right)\lambda^2\frac{d^2V}{dy^2} + \lambda^4V = 0 \qquad (11.38)$$

The solution may be written:

$$V = (a\cos\beta\lambda y + b\sin\beta\lambda y)e^{\alpha\lambda y}$$
$$+ (c\cos\beta\lambda y + d\sin\beta\lambda y)e^{\alpha\lambda y} \qquad (11.39)$$

Here:

$$\alpha = \sqrt{\frac{1}{\hat{n}}}, \quad \beta = \sqrt{1 - \frac{1}{\hat{n}}}$$

$$\hat{n} = n\left[1 + \frac{3(n-1)\xi^2}{4(1 + \xi + \xi^2)}\right]^{-1} \qquad (11.40)$$

To obtain the expression for $\hat{n}$ in (11.40) we used the relations (11.28) and the following:

$$\frac{2}{\hat{n}} = \frac{1}{n_x} + \frac{1}{n_y} \qquad (11.41)$$

From (11.36) and (11.40), the expressions for the velocity components are:

$$\tilde{v}_x = -\alpha\Bigg[\Big\{\Big[a + \sqrt{(\hat{n}-1)}b\Big]\cos\beta\lambda y$$
$$+ \Big[b - \sqrt{(\hat{n}-1)}a\Big]\sin\beta\lambda y\Big\}e^{\alpha\lambda y}$$
$$- \Big\{\Big[c - \sqrt{(\hat{n}-1)}d\Big]\cos\beta\lambda y$$
$$+ \Big[d + \sqrt{(\hat{n}-1)}c\Big]\sin\beta\lambda y\Big\}e^{-\alpha\lambda y}\Bigg]\sin\lambda x$$

$$\tilde{v}_y = [(a\cos\beta\lambda y + b\sin\beta\lambda y)e^{\alpha\lambda y}$$
$$+ (c\cos\beta\lambda y + d\sin\beta\lambda y)e^{-\alpha\lambda y}]\cos\lambda x \qquad (11.42)$$

From the third equation in (11.32) and (11.42) the stress component $\tilde{\sigma}_{xy}$ may be obtained, and from the stress equilibrium equations, the components $\tilde{\sigma}_{xx}$ and $\tilde{\sigma}_{yy}$ are obtained by differentiation and integration:

$$\tilde{\sigma}_{xy} = -2\bar{\eta}\alpha^2\lambda\Bigg[\Big\{\Big[a + \sqrt{(\hat{n}-1)}b\Big]\cos\beta\lambda y$$
$$+ \Big[b - \sqrt{(\hat{n}-1)}a\Big]\sin\beta\lambda y\Big\}e^{\alpha\lambda y}$$
$$+ \Big\{\Big[c - \sqrt{(\hat{n}-1)}d\Big]\cos\beta\lambda y$$
$$+ \Big[d + \sqrt{(\hat{n}-1)}c\Big]\sin\beta\lambda y\Big\}e^{-\alpha\lambda y}\Bigg]\sin\lambda x$$

$$\tilde{\sigma}_{yy} = 2\bar{\eta}\alpha\lambda[(a\cos\beta\lambda y + b\sin\beta\lambda y)e^{\alpha\lambda y}$$
$$- (c\cos\beta\lambda y + d\sin\beta\lambda y)e^{-\alpha\lambda y}]\cos\lambda x \qquad (11.43)$$

The even more complicated expressions for the layer-parallel normal component $\tilde{\sigma}_{xx}$ and the pressure $\tilde{p}$ are not used in solving for the velocity field for necking or folding, and are not given here.

The solution for low-slope or infinitesimal-amplitude necking refers in this case to the flow set up by a symmetric pinch-and-swell component (Fig. 11.2). The analysis of the folding of a single layer in Chapter 10 provides most of the details. Here, the mirror planes of symmetry immediately indicate that the vertical component of the perturbing velocity is odd in y when the coordinate origin is taken at the center of the layer and that it is even in x, so:

$$\tilde{v}_y(x, -y) = -\tilde{v}_y(x, -y)$$
$$\tilde{v}_y(x, y) = \tilde{v}_y(-x, y) \tag{11.44}$$

The first condition in (11.44) implies $c = a$, $d = -b$. The expressions for the velocity components may be simplified accordingly, giving:

$$\tilde{v}_x = -\alpha\left\{\left[a + \sqrt{(\hat{n} - 1)}b\right]\cos\beta\lambda y(e^{\alpha\lambda y} + e^{-\lambda\alpha y})\right.$$
$$\left. + \left[b - \sqrt{(\hat{n} - 1)}a\right] + \sin\beta\lambda y(e^{\alpha\lambda y} - e^{-\lambda\alpha y})\right\}\sin\lambda x$$

$$\tilde{v}_y = [a\cos\beta\lambda y(e^{\alpha\lambda y} - e^{-\alpha\lambda y})$$
$$+ (b\sin\beta\lambda y)(e^{\alpha\lambda y} + e^{-\alpha\lambda y})]\cos\lambda x \tag{11.45}$$

The stress components are:

$$\tilde{\sigma}_{xy} = -2\bar{\eta}\alpha^2\lambda\left\{\left[a + \sqrt{(\hat{n} - 1)}b\right]\cos\beta\lambda y(e^{\alpha\lambda y} - e^{-\alpha\lambda y})\right.$$
$$\left. + \left[b - \sqrt{(\hat{n} - 1)}a\right]\sin\beta\lambda y(e^{\alpha\lambda y} + e^{-\alpha\lambda y})\right\}\sin\lambda x$$

$$\tilde{\sigma}_{yy} = 2\bar{\eta}\alpha\lambda[a\cos\beta\lambda y(e^{\alpha\lambda y} + e^{-\alpha\lambda y})$$
$$+ b\sin\beta\lambda y(e^{\alpha\lambda y} - e^{-\alpha\lambda y})]\cos\lambda x \tag{11.46}$$

Using the same approximations as in the analysis for the buckling of a viscous layer, we obtain four relations from the boundary conditions at the upper sinusoidal surface:

$$-\alpha\left\{\left[a + \sqrt{(\hat{n} - 1)}b\right]\cos\beta\lambda h(e^{\alpha\lambda h} + e^{-\lambda\alpha h})\right.$$
$$\left. + \left[b - \sqrt{(\hat{n} - 1)}a\right]\sin\beta\lambda h(e^{\alpha\lambda h} - e^{-\lambda\alpha h})\right\}$$
$$= -\alpha_1\left[c_1 - \sqrt{(\hat{n} - 1)}d_1\right] \tag{11.47}$$

$$a\cos\beta\lambda h(e^{\alpha\lambda h} - e^{-\alpha\lambda h}) + b\sin\beta\lambda h(e^{\alpha\lambda h} + e^{-\alpha\lambda h}) = c_1 \tag{11.48}$$

$$-2\bar{\eta}\alpha^2\lambda\left\{\left[a + \sqrt{(\hat{n} - 1)}b\right]\cos\beta\lambda h(e^{\alpha\lambda h} - e^{-\alpha\lambda h})\right.$$
$$\left. + \left[b - \sqrt{(\hat{n} - 1)}a\right]\sin\beta\lambda h(e^{\alpha\lambda h} + e^{-\alpha\lambda h})\right\}$$
$$+ 2\bar{\eta}(\bar{D}_{xx} - \bar{D}_{yy})\lambda A(1 - R)$$
$$= -2\bar{\eta}_1\alpha_1^2\lambda\left[c_1 - \sqrt{(\hat{n}_1 - 1)}d_1\right] \tag{11.49}$$

$$2\bar{\eta}\alpha\lambda[a\cos\beta\lambda h(e^{\alpha\lambda h} + e^{-\alpha\lambda h})$$
$$+ b\sin\beta\lambda h(e^{\alpha\lambda h} - e^{-\alpha\lambda h})] = -2\bar{\eta}_1\alpha_1\lambda c_1 \tag{11.50}$$

Here, both the layer and the medium are power-law fluids. Since the coefficients for the medium may be eliminated between pairs of equations in (11.47) through (11.50), this system reduces to a pair of equations that may be solved for the coefficients a and b.

The interface evolution equation is developed as in the viscous folding example, yielding for the rate of change in amplitude, A, rather than slope, λA:

$$\frac{dA}{dt} = \left[-(1 + \xi) \right.$$
$$\left. + \frac{\hat{n}(2 + \xi)(1 - R)}{\left\{(1 - Q^2) + \frac{\sqrt{(\hat{n} - 1)}}{2\sin\beta k}[(1 + Q^2)(e^{\alpha k} - e^{-\alpha k}) + 2Q(e^{\alpha k} + e^{-\alpha k})]\right\}}\right]$$
$$\times \mathrm{Sgn}(\bar{D}_{xx})|\bar{D}_{xx}|A$$
$$= q(k; n, n_1, R, \xi)\mathrm{Sgn}(\bar{D}_{xx})|\bar{D}_{xx}|A \tag{11.51}$$

Here:

$$Q = \frac{\alpha_1\bar{\eta}_1}{\alpha\bar{\eta}} = \frac{\alpha_1}{\alpha}R \tag{11.52}$$

The principal argument $k = 2\pi(H/L)$ of the function q specifies the wavelength to layer thickness ratio of the cylindrical sinusoidal perturbation. The first three dimensionless parameters describe the rheological behavior of the layer and medium: n is the stress exponent of the layer, n_1 that of the medium, and R is the ratio of the effective viscosity of the medium to that of the layer. Finally, ξ describes the basic-state flow to which the pinch-and-swell component is responding. Since $\bar{D}_{xx}$ is greater than zero for axis-normal extension, $\xi > 0$ implies an additional axis-parallel extension, and $\xi < 0$ implies axis-parallel shortening. Note that the effective stress exponent of the layer, $\hat{n}$, is a function of both n and ξ (11.40); the stress exponent n_1 is "hidden" in the quantity Q. The function q may be termed the relative rate of amplification factor; it is dimensionless.

Since $\overline{D}_{yy} \neq -\overline{D}_{xx}$, the layer thickness, wavelength, and wavenumber satisfy the relations:

$$\frac{dH}{dt} = \overline{D}_{yy}H, \quad \frac{dL}{dt} = \overline{D}_{xx}L, \quad \frac{d\lambda}{dt} = -\overline{D}_{xx}\lambda \quad (11.53)$$

What seem like only moderate extensions of the model for initiation of folding of a single layer of viscous fluid embedded in a viscous medium, here for the complementary case of necking, lead to a somewhat daunting range in behavior. If the layer and medium are non-linear power-law fluids, two stress exponents are introduced, n and n_1, and if the basic-state flow has a component of stretching or shortening parallel to the perturbation axis, a feature not uncommon in natural deformation, the parameter ξ enters. In contrast, the behavior in the viscous folding model only varies with the viscosity ratio R. Thus, from a single parameter space, we must now consider a four-dimensional space!

In interpreting a set of data from trains of natural folds or pinch-and-swell structures, all four parameters may play a significant role. Thus, the relation (11.51), although relatively complicated, allows for a full study of the variation in behavior with the four parameters, the viscosity ratio R, the stress exponent of the layer n, that of the medium n_1, and the deformation rate ratio ξ. Both field data and experimental data such as those in Table 11.1 may be brought to bear. To treat necking in layer extension, we know that we must consider $n > 1$. In most examples presented here, the parameters are reduced to two by setting $n_1 = 1$, the Newtonian viscous limit, and $\xi = 0$. An exception is the result for mullions in a layer for which computed results are obtained later (Fig. 11.12), which only form if $n_1 > 1$, and for which the dependence on n_1 is key. Because the parameter $Q \sim \sqrt{n/n_1}$ plays a significant role in the relation (11.51), restriction to $n_1 = 1$ bypasses interesting behavior (Smith, 1977).

Perhaps remarkably, the result for amplification of a fold component is given by a relation identical to (11.51) except for a single change from a positive to a negative sign in the denominator of the second term in braces, just after the quantity $(1 - Q^2)$. This is simply a consequence of a symmetry in folding opposite to that expressed by (11.44), or, in folding, $\tilde{v}_y(x, -y) = \tilde{v}_y(x, y)$. Regular mullion structures (Fig. 10.10b) forming in shortening of a soft layer between stiff half-spaces are treated by assigning values of $R > 1$ in either of these two relations. Mullions may be approximately symmetric about the layer mid-plane, in which case (11.51) applies, or less commonly, asymmetric, in which case the relation with the sign change would apply. Given a set of natural pinch-and-swell structures, folds, or mullions, leading questions would be whether the present model could produce them and what ranges of parameters are necessary.

As in the viscous folding problem, it is useful to expand the relative rate of amplification factor, q, to low-order terms in k. The result is:

$$q \cong -(1 + \xi) + \frac{\hat{n}(2 + \xi)(1 - R)}{\left[2 + \dfrac{k^2}{6} + \dfrac{2Q}{\alpha k} + \dfrac{Qk}{3\alpha}\left(\dfrac{2}{n} + 1\right)\right]} \quad (11.54)$$

The free-plate result is obtained by setting $Q = R = 0$:

$$(q)_{\text{free plate}} \cong -(1 + \xi) + \hat{n}\left(1 + \frac{1}{2}\xi\right)\bigg/\left(1 + \frac{1}{12}k^2\right)$$

$$\cong (\hat{n} - 1)\left(1 - \frac{1}{12}k^2\right) + \xi\left[\frac{1}{2}\hat{n}\left(1 - \frac{1}{12}k^2\right) - 1\right]$$

$$\cong (\hat{n} - 1) + \xi\left(\frac{1}{2}\hat{n} - 1\right) \quad (11.55)$$

The last expression corresponds to the plane-sections-remain-plane approximation (11.10) but now contains information on the effect of additional shortening ($\xi < 0$) or extension ($\xi > 0$) along the axis of the perturbation. The second line indicates a wavenumber, k, dependent deviation from the plane sections result. The plane sections approximation for q, the last line in (11.55), is contoured in (Fig. 11.5) as a function of the intrinsic stress exponent, n, and the rate of deformation ratio, ξ. This shows a substantial decrease in instability, as measured by the relative rate of amplification q, away from a plane flow basic state, $\xi = 0$. This

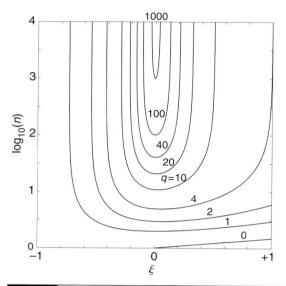

Fig 11.5 Contours of q for plane-sections-remain-plane approximation for the free plate in (n, ξ)-space.

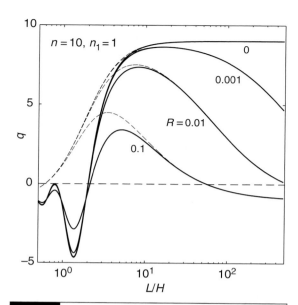

Fig 11.6 q-spectra for $n = 10$ and $R = 0, 0.001, 0.01$, and 0.1; heavy lines show the exact results, light lines the approximation for $k \ll 1$.

decrease is less for extension parallel to the pinch-and-swell axis ($\xi > 0$) than for shortening ($\xi < 0$) parallel to the axis. For example, if $n = 101, q = 100$ for plane flow, but only $q \cong 8$ for an axial rate of extension one-half that of the axis-normal extension, that is for $\xi = 0.5$. For axis-normal contraction, $\xi = -0.5$ and the relative rate of amplification factor is $q \cong 3$. Thus, the model suggests that pinch-and-swell structures are favored in nearly plane deformation.

The dependence on L/H, where $H = 2h$ is the thickness of the layer, is shown by plotting q versus L/H (Fig.11.6) for necking in plane flow for $n = 10, n_1 = 1$, and several values of R. The expansion for $k \ll 1$ yields a good approximation (dashed lines) down to $L/H \approx 10$. While the stress exponent $n = 10$ is large compared with values estimated in laboratory experiments, the necking instability is relatively weak, so that a large basic-state stretch is required to get significant amplification. For example, an amplification of 10 at the dominant wavelength at which q is a maximum, for $q_d = 9$ would require a stretch $S = \exp(\ln 10/q_d) = 1.29$.

We denote the variation of q with wavelength or wavenumber the q-spectrum. From it the position of maximum is at the dominant wavelength/thickness ratio, L_d/H, and the relative sharpness of the peak indicates how selective is

the amplification, and thus the regularity in an array of structures. The q-spectra for $R = 0.05$ and $n = 10, 100$, and $10\,000$, and ∞ (Fig. 11.7) show multiple maxima that become prominent for $n \geq 100$. These arise because of the increasing dominance in the variation of q with k (11.51) of the sinusoidal term, $\sin[k\sqrt{1 - (1/n)}] \cong \sin k$, $n \gg 1$ over the exponential term, $\exp(k\sqrt{1/n}) \cong 1$, $n \gg 1$. The transition between two modes of necking or folding, one at modest stress exponent n, and one at large stress exponent $n \geq 10$–100, is also tied to this transition in dependence. The second mode is one of resonance folding or necking in which: "The competent layer does not act mechanically as a coherent unit, but, instead, the irregularities on one interface produce motions that deform the other and vice versa" (Smith, 1979). This behavior is associated with the dominance of sinusoidal versus exponential variation in velocity and stress components in the y-direction, which result in the dependences of q on k just noted. It is only shown for $k \geq 1$, or for $L/H \leq 6$, when the sinusoidal dependence in k begins to become apparent.

The coherent layer mode is exemplified by the pure folding mode of a single viscous layer, as

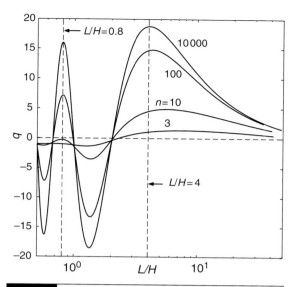

Fig 11.7 Multiple peaks in $q = q(L/H)$ as a function of $n =$ 10, 100, 10 000 and the $n \to \infty$ approximation for $R = 0.05$, n_1 $= 3$, $\xi = 0$. Velocity fields for the two maxima at $L/H = 4$ and 0.8 and the minimum at $L/H = 4/3$ are shown in Fig. 11.9.

illustrated by the perturbing velocity fields (Fig. 11.8). These are velocity fields in unconfined or free layers. Even though the sinusoidal perturbation in this case is only imposed at the upper surface, not directly indicated in the figure, a nearly pure folding mode, with approximately uniform vertical velocity at the fold hinges, develops at $L/H = 4$. At $L/H = 2$, the layer behaves approximately as a half-space, with the velocity decreasing exponentially away from the surface at which the shape perturbation is present. For the highly non-linear layer, the sinusoidal dependence results, as in Smith's description, at $L/H = 4$ or $k = \pi/2$, in a maximum vertical velocity at the lower surface and zero vertical velocity at the upper surface at which the shape perturbation is present. For $L/H = 2$, or $k = \pi$, the perturbing flow is distributed with uniform intensity throughout the layer, but no modification of the shape perturbation occurs. In the coherent mode in necking, because the rate of extension is nearly uniform on a section, the vertical velocity varies linearly through the section, in contrast to the uniform vertical velocity in folding, and is zero at the mid-point. For such cases the plane-sections-remain-plane approximation for $k \ll 1$ gives good results.

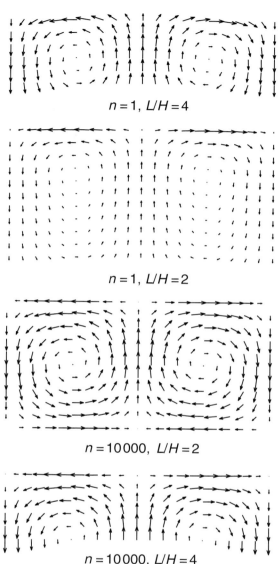

$n = 1, L/H = 4$

$n = 1, L/H = 2$

$n = 10000, L/H = 2$

$n = 10000, L/H = 4$

Fig 11.8 Coherent layer and resonance behaviors for layers with $n = 1$ and 10 000, $R = 0.05$ for folding at $L/H = 4$ and 2 driven by a sinusoidal perturbation at only the *upper* surface of the layer.

Before further considering resonance effects in necking, we first obtain results for folding and necking in the limit $n \to \infty$. Denote A_s as the amplitude of the pinch-and-swell mode and A_b for that of the folding mode. Taking account of the sign change in (11.51) for folding, and considering only plane flow ($\xi = 0$), (11.49) reduces in this limit for necking to:

$$\frac{dA_s}{dt} = \frac{\sqrt{n_1}}{R} \frac{(1-R)\,\mathrm{Sgn}(\bar{D}_{xx})\sin k\,|\bar{D}_{xx}|A_s}{1 + [R(k - \sin k)/2\sqrt{n_1}]}$$

$$\cong \frac{\sqrt{n_1}}{R}(1-R)\,\mathrm{Sgn}(\bar{D}_{xx})\sin k\,|\bar{D}_{xx}|A_s \qquad (11.56)$$

For folding:

$$\frac{dA_b}{dt} = -\frac{\sqrt{n_1}}{R} \frac{(1-R)\,\mathrm{Sgn}(\bar{D}_{xx})\sin k\,|\bar{D}_{xx}|A_b}{1 + [R(k - \sin k)/2\sqrt{n_1}]}$$

$$\cong -\frac{\sqrt{n_1}}{R}(1-R)\,\mathrm{Sgn}(\bar{D}_{xx})\sin k\,|\bar{D}_{xx}|A_b \qquad (11.57)$$

We may use these results to compute the rates of growth for the amplitudes of the upper and lower interfaces, A' and A'', where:

$$A' = A_b + A_s, \qquad A'' = A_b - A_s \qquad (11.58)$$

Using the approximations for $R \ll 0$:

$$\frac{dA'}{dt} \cong -\frac{\sqrt{n_1}}{R}(1-R)\,\mathrm{Sgn}(\bar{D}_{xx})\sin k\,|\bar{D}_{xx}|A''$$

$$\frac{dA''}{dt} \cong -\frac{\sqrt{n_1}}{R}(1-R)\,\mathrm{Sgn}(\bar{D}_{xx})\sin k\,|\bar{D}_{xx}|A' \qquad (11.59)$$

To re-confirm the sense of these relations, in folding $\mathrm{Sgn}(\bar{D}_{xx}) = -1$ and both A' and A'' are positive: the perturbation grows if $\sin k > 0$. In necking in extension, $\mathrm{Sgn}(\bar{D}_{xx}) = +1$ and A'' is negative, A' is positive: again, the perturbation grows if $\sin k > 0$.

The discrepancy from the approximations in (11.59) is due to the difference between the discarded terms in the denominators of (11.56) and (11.57), which are small if $R/\sqrt{n_1} \ll 1$. The sinusoidal dependence in (11.59) is reflected in a vertical dependence in the velocity field (Fig. 11.9) that corresponds to the propagation of disturbances at either layer surface, resulting in either cancellation or reinforcement as a function of wavenumber k. Here, as opposed to the cases in Fig. 11.8, a full pinch-and-swell perturbation is imposed, and both interfaces have sinusoidal shape perturbations. Resonance corresponds to the case of maximum reinforcement. Further, the simple dependency on k through the function $\sin k$ immediately allows us to read off the results. Maximum rate of amplification will occur for $\sin k = 1$, or for $k = \pi/2,\ 5\pi/2,\ \dots$, or $L/H = 4/1,\ 4/5,\ \dots$, with a maximum rate of decay in perturbation at $k = 3\pi/2,\ 7\pi/2,\ \dots$, or $L/H = 4/3$, $4/7,\ \dots$, and zero rate of change at $k = \pi,\ 2\pi,\ \dots$,

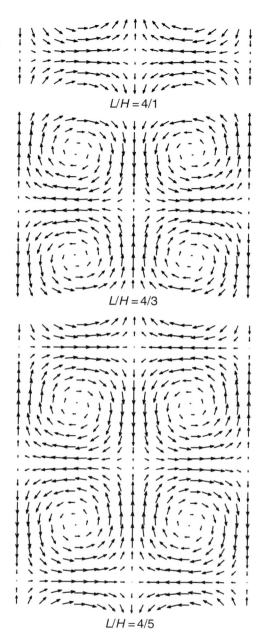

$L/H = 4/1$

$L/H = 4/3$

$L/H = 4/5$

Fig 11.9 Perturbing velocity distribution for necking in a layer with $n = 10\,000$ at $L/H = 4/1$, $4/3$, and $4/5$ showing resonance behavior.

or $L/H = 4/2,\ 4/4,\ \dots$ The results shown in Fig. 11.9 are equivalent to the peak positive and negative values in Fig. 11.7 at $L/H = 4/1$, $4/3$, and $4/5$. The case of neither growth nor decay, $L/H = 2$, is shown in Fig. 11.8.

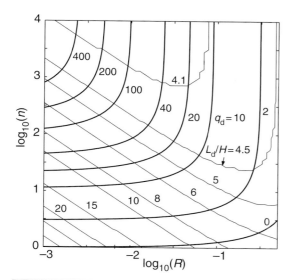

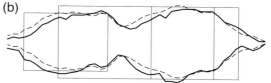

Fig 11.10 Contours of q_d and L_d/H in (n, R)-space for $n_1 = 1$.

Fig 11.11 (a) Boudin exposed in a shear zone (near Middletown, CT). (b) Boudin profile, with 2 : 1 vertical exaggeration: actual (light line) and symmetric (heavy line), with rectangles having same area and same maximum thickness, done for entire structure and two individual boudins. Photograph by R. C. Fletcher.

Comparison with natural structures requires that we consider the effect of the mechanical constraint of the embedding medium. This is summarized in Fig. 11.10 for the case of plane flow ($\xi = 0$) and a Newtonian viscous medium ($n_1 = 1$) by contouring the dominant wavelength to thickness ratio, L_d/H, at which the rate of amplification is maximum and the value of q for it, q_d, in (n, R)-space. This result allows an initial interpretation of a train of pinch-and-swell structures from which a mean neck-to-neck span to mean thickness could be estimated. Thus, associating this with the theoretical value of L_d/H, we may trace the appropriate contour of this quantity on the figure to obtain possible values of n and R. If we infer from the strong development of necking that the maximum relative rate of amplification q_d was large, e.g. $q_d > 20$, we may further limit the possible values of n and R to those corresponding to the upper-left portion of the figure.

In folding, a strong tendency of the layer to maintain uniform thickness after the locking in of a regular sequence of folds allows us to use the fold arc length to thickness ratios as those established at the end of selective amplification and the inception of finite amplitude folding. To estimate better the value of L_d/H for pinch-and-swell

structures, the corresponding distances between necks and the layer thickness attained before extreme attenuation of the necks may be estimated by returning the area between necks in the observed structures to a rectangle whose vertical dimension is the current maximum thickness. An impression of this operation may be obtained by examining Fig. 11.3.

This operation has been carried out for a natural boudin cross section (Fig. 11.11). The boudin, or pair of boudins, is in a pegmatite layer embedded in gneiss. The bulk deformation of the gneiss consisted of extension plus right-lateral (positive) shear, as indicated by right-dipping normal faults that produce a few sharp offsets in the upper and lower surfaces (Fig. 11.11a). The exposure is within a shallowly dipping right-lateral shear zone near Middletown, Connecticut. The boudin profile (Fig. 11.11b) was measured from an approximate median line, producing the actual slightly asymmetric form. A symmetric form was created by locally adjusting the profiles to lie at half the local layer thickness from the median plane. The adjusted profile differs by only a modest amount from the actual profile. The pair of boudins is separated from any other segments of the same layer by a distance at least comparable to its length. While part of the deformation is tied to the normal faulting, including the central neck between the boudins, the overall form is more suggestive of a continuous ductile necking. Detailed study to support or refute this suggestion has not been carried out by us. None-the-less, this hypothesis provides a useful example for the present discussion.

In Fig. 11.11b, we have constructed the rectangles approximating the initial boudin form for the entire structure, supposing the central neck to be a later feature, and for the two individual boudins or pinch-and-swell structures. Their aspect ratios are, for the entire structure, 4.2, and for the individuals, 2.3 on the left and 2.7 on the right. The value for the entire structure is consistent with model values of L_d/H for $n \gg 1$, but those for the individual structures are not. It might be suggested that the latter reflect the tendency for a mechanically isolated segment to divide in two sub-equal segments if it becomes unstable with respect to necking, in this case chiefly by faulting. The present model applies only to a continuous layer or a segment with very large aspect ratio, and does not apply directly to a process involving discrete faults (but see the next section).

The present model may also be applied to the initiation of the regular mullion structures shown in Fig. 10.2b. The lobe-and-cusp morphology indicates that the layer has the lower effective viscosity, or $R > 1$. These structures are produced in layer-parallel shortening, so that $\mathrm{Sgn}(\overline{D}_{xx}) = -1$. Using these and plane flow ($\xi = 0$), (11.51) then provides a relation describing the growth or decay of the pinch-and-swell perturbations whose selective amplification give rise to the mullions. Appreciable instability requires that the host be non-linear. We thus assign a typical stress exponent (Table 11.1) to the layer, $n = 3$, and determine the variation of q_d and L_d/H in (n_1, R)-space (Fig. 11.12). Note that $n_1 \geq 2$. This figure is read in the same manner as Fig. 11.10, with values of n and n_1 determining L_d/H and q_d, the "d" again denoting the dominant or most rapidly amplifying component.

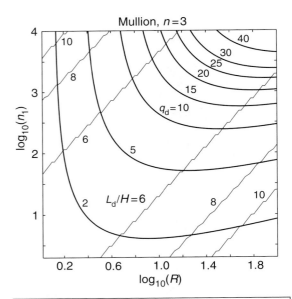

Fig 11.12 q_d and L_d/H for mullion structures for $n = 3$ and $n_1 \geq 2$.

The strength of the instability is small unless the host has a very large stress exponent, so that mullion structures such as those seen in Fig. 10.2b may be inferred to represent large amounts of layer-parallel shortening. This might explain the significant difference between the span-to-thickness ratio of these structures and the values of $L_d/H \geq 6$.

11.2.4 A model for large-scale crustal necking

Necking may manifest itself at crustal and lithospheric scales, on the Earth, on other planets and on the moon of Jupiter, Ganymede (Fink and Fletcher, 1981; Collins et al., 1998; Patel et al., 1999; Dombard and McKinnon, 2001). The strikingly regular succession of basins and ranges that form the dominant structure in the Basin and Range Province of the western United States (Fig. 11.13) have been interpreted as the result of necking of the strong brittle layer of the crust (Fletcher and Hallet, 1983). The crust is broken up into segments approximately 30 km in width (Fig. 11.14). These are superposed on a subtler necking at a scale >100 km in which the strong upper layer of the mantle lithosphere plays a significant role (Zuber

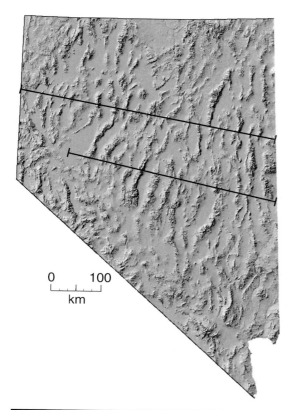

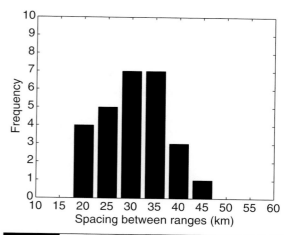

Fig 11.14 Histogram of spans between range centers (Fletcher and Hallet, 1983).

Fig 11.13 Basin-and-range structure in the state of Nevada; spans between range centers were measured on the transects (Fletcher and Hallet, 1983).

et al., 1986). The latter expresses itself as an alternation in dip of the dominant basin-bounding normal faults.

To model this process, we postulate that in the brittle crustal layer faulting was initially more distributed, with faults of all length scales giving a roughly continuous deformation at scales of a few kilometers or less. Thus, in the initial phase of extension a regular array of pinch-and-swell structures with spans of ~30 km forms. The development of major discrete normal fault zones bounding the basins is then superposed on this template.

A rigid-plastic layer undergoing extension affords an approximate model for the brittle behavior of the strong upper crustal layer. In the present model, we will simulate the lower ductile crust as a homogeneous Newtonian viscous half-space. More complicated and realistic models have been treated (Fletcher and Hallet, 1983; Zuber *et al.*, 1986). In contrast to necking of an embedded layer at the scale of an exposure, gravity plays an important role in crustal necking, and there is an essential asymmetry between boundary conditions at the top and base of the plastic layer. A further interesting effect involves the role of erosion, sediment transport, and deposition.

While the perturbing flow in a plastic layer at yield may be treated as that in a power-law layer in which the stress exponent n tends to infinity, it is instructive to use the plastic yield condition and flow law directly. For the plane basic state and perturbing flows considered here, these are given by (11.22). The layer is at yield in uniform shortening so that for the basic-state and perturbing stresses, the yield condition (11.22) gives, for mean and perturbing stresses:

$$\bar{\sigma}_{xx} - \bar{\sigma}_{yy} = 2K \, \mathrm{Sgn}\!\left(\bar{D}_{xx}\right)$$
$$\tilde{\sigma}_{xx} - \tilde{\sigma}_{yy} \cong 0 \tag{11.60}$$

Here K is the shear stress and it is independent of mean stress. The Airy stress function for the perturbing stress then satisfies:

$$\frac{\partial^2 \phi}{\partial y^2} - \frac{\partial^2 \phi}{\partial x^2} = 0 \tag{11.61}$$

The appropriate form of the solution for ϕ may be written:

$$\phi = -\left(\frac{1}{\lambda^2}\right)\left(\frac{K\lambda}{|\bar{D}_{xx}|}\right)(b\cos\lambda y + d\sin\lambda y)\cos\lambda x \quad (11.62)$$

The associated perturbing stress components are:

$$\tilde{\sigma}_{xx} = \tilde{\sigma}_{yy} = \left(\frac{K\lambda}{|\bar{D}_{xx}|}\right)(b\cos\lambda y + d\sin\lambda y)\cos\lambda x$$
$$(11.63)$$
$$\tilde{\sigma}_{xy} = \left(\frac{K\lambda}{|\bar{D}_{xx}|}\right)(b\sin\lambda y - d\cos\lambda y)\sin\lambda x$$

The perturbing stress components are generated from the yield condition and, by use of the Airy stress function, from the equations of stress equilibrium. The choice of the constant factors in (11.62) is merely to provide convenient expressions for both the stress and velocity components.

From the flow law in (11.22):

$$\bar{D}_{xx} = \bar{\Lambda}K\mathrm{Sgn}(\bar{D}_{xx})$$
$$\tilde{D}_{xx} = -\tilde{D}_{yy} \cong \tilde{\Lambda}K\mathrm{Sgn}(\bar{D}_{xx}) \quad (11.64)$$
$$\tilde{D}_{xy} \cong \bar{\Lambda}\tilde{\sigma}_{xy}$$

Substitution into the equation of compatibility (10.64) yields:

$$\frac{\partial^2\tilde{\Lambda}}{\partial y^2} - \frac{\partial^2\tilde{\Lambda}}{\partial x^2} \cong 2\lambda^2\frac{|\bar{D}_{xx}|\mathrm{Sgn}(\bar{D}_{xx})}{K^2}$$
$$\times (b\cos\lambda y + d\sin\lambda y)\cos\lambda x \quad (11.65)$$

This equation has both a homogeneous solution, for zero right-hand side, and the particular solution for the given right-hand side. When the result is substituted into the relations (11.64) and these are integrated, we obtain:

$$\tilde{v}_x = [(a - d + b\lambda y)\sin\lambda y - (c + b + d\lambda y)\cos\lambda y]\sin\lambda x$$
$$\tilde{v}_y = [(a + b\lambda y)\cos\lambda y + (c + d\lambda y)\sin\lambda y]\cos\lambda x$$
$$(11.66)$$

Note that the perturbing stress components (11.62) contain only two arbitrary constants b and d. These constants are fixed by the conditions on the vanishing of tractions at the top of the layer, on the surface $\zeta' = H + A'\cos\lambda x$. These relations give, to the present approximation:

$$\tilde{\sigma}_{yy}(x, H) \cong -\rho g A'\cos\lambda x$$
$$(11.67)$$
$$\tilde{\sigma}_{xy}(x, H) \cong -2K\mathrm{Sgn}(\bar{D}_{xx})(\lambda A')\sin\lambda x$$

Combining (11.62) and (11.67):

$$b = 2|\bar{D}_{xx}|A'\left[-S\frac{\cos k}{k} - \mathrm{Sgn}(\bar{D}_{xx})\sin k\right]$$
$$(11.68)$$
$$d = 2|\bar{D}_{xx}|A'\left[-S\frac{\sin k}{k} + \mathrm{Sgn}(\bar{D}_{xx})\cos k\right]$$

where as before $k = 2\pi(H/L)$. The four boundary conditions at the layer/half-space interface, $\zeta'' = A''\cos\lambda x$, are:

$$\tilde{v}_x(x,0) \cong \tilde{v}_x^{(1)}(x,0), \quad \tilde{v}_y(x,0) \cong \tilde{v}_y^{(1)}(x,0)$$
$$\tilde{\sigma}_{yy}(x,0) \cong \tilde{\sigma}_{yy}^{(1)}(x,0)$$
$$(11.69)$$
$$\tilde{\sigma}_{xy}(x,0) + 2K\mathrm{Sgn}(\bar{D}_{xx})(\lambda A'')\sin\lambda x$$
$$\cong \tilde{\sigma}_{xy}^{(1)}(x,0) + 4\eta_1\bar{D}_{xx}(\lambda A'')\sin\lambda x$$

Substituting from (11.66) and (11.62) together with expressions for a viscous half-space (Chapter 10) into (11.69) gives:

$$-(c + b) = -a_1, \quad a = a_1 - b_1$$
$$-\frac{K\lambda}{|\bar{D}_{xx}|}d + 2K\mathrm{Sgn}(\bar{D}_{xx})(\lambda A'') = -2\eta_1\lambda a_1 + 4\eta_1\bar{D}_{xx}(\lambda A'')$$
$$\frac{K\lambda}{|\bar{D}_{xx}|}b = 2\eta_1\lambda(a_1 - b_1)$$
$$(11.70)$$

From (11.70) the remaining two constants for the plastic layer, a and c, may be obtained.

The evolution equations for the two interface amplitudes A' and A'' are obtained as in the previous examples. Here, the results may be written out explicitly. They are moderately complex in form and a detailed exegesis of the terms has not been worked out, but some informative features may be pointed out. The evolution equations are:

$$\frac{dA'}{dt} = -\bar{D}_{xx}A' + 2\left[-S - \frac{S}{Rk}(1 - R\cos k\,\sin k)\right.$$
$$\left. + \mathrm{Sgn}(\bar{D}_{xx})\sin^2 k\right]|\bar{D}_{xx}|A'$$

$$\frac{dA''}{dt} = -\bar{D}_{xx}A'' + \frac{2}{R}\left[-S\frac{\cos k}{k} - \mathrm{Sgn}(\bar{D}_{xx})\sin k\right]|\bar{D}_{xx}|A'$$
$$(11.71)$$

The behavior depends upon three dimensionless groups. The strength ratio $R = 2\eta_1|\bar{D}_{xx}|/K$ is equivalent to the earlier effective viscosity ratio in models for folding and necking. Note, however, the interesting dependence on the absolute rate of shortening, since the shear strength K of the brittle upper crust is independent of rate. At slow rates of extension, R will be smaller, and the degree of instability will be larger. The dimensionless group $S = \rho g H/2K$ is the ratio of a lithostatic stress to the stress difference at yield in the plastic layer. A more realistic model for the strength of the crust would introduce a mean stress dependence on the strength. Effectively, only a cohesion-like quantity is used here, although its value may be assigned to account for a mean value of the strength of the brittle crustal layer that is dependent on the thickness H. Further discussion of this issue may be found in the papers cited earlier. The third dimensionless group is $k = 2\pi/(L/H)$.

Note that the relations (11.71) have the form:

$$\frac{dA'}{dt} = q_{11}A' + q_{12}A''$$
$$\frac{dA''}{dt} = q_{21}A' + q_{22}A'' \tag{11.72}$$

In the limiting case $S = 0$, (11.71) becomes:

$$\frac{dA'}{dt} = \mathrm{Sgn}(\bar{D}_{xx})|\bar{D}_{xx}|$$
$$\times \left[(-1 + 2\sin^2 k)A' + 2\left(1 - \frac{1}{R}\right)\sin kA'' \right]$$
$$\frac{dA''}{dt} = \mathrm{Sgn}(\bar{D}_{xx})|\bar{D}_{xx}|\left[-\frac{2}{R}\sin kA' - A'' \right] \tag{11.73}$$

Excluding the terms for kinematic amplification, with factors -1 in brackets, and a term of order unity in q_{11}, the dominant behavior for $R \ll 1$ exhibits resonance, in the sense that the amplification at each surface is driven by the amplitude at the opposite surface. This suggests that the damping of topography by erosion, sediment transport, and deposition may have a large effect on the necking instability. This damping may be incorporated into the evolution equations by simply adding a term to dA'/dt in (11.71). That is, the current state of motion depends on the current topography, not on its rate of change, and so the contribution to the latter by surface processes is simply additive.

A variety of models for topographic damping might be used. One first proposed by Culling (1960) and used by others to model the decay of fault scarps (Andrews and Hanks, 1985) supposes that the flux of material is proportional to slope. Conservation of mass, excluding differences in density between rock and sediments, then requires that the rate of change in elevation be proportional to the negative of the divergence of the volume flux. Any adjustment towards an "isostatic state," often included in models for the infilling of sedimentary basins and concomitant erosion at their periphery, is already included in the solution for the velocity field. Applying Culling's model on a component-by-component basis, we obtain:

$$\left(\frac{dA'}{dt}\right)_{\text{surface}} = -P\lambda^2 A' = -Mk^2|\bar{D}_{xx}|A'$$
$$M = P/\left(H^2|\bar{D}_{xx}|\right) \tag{11.74}$$

Here $M = P/\left(H^2|\bar{D}_{xx}|\right)$ enters as an additional dimensionless group and P is a diffusion constant. The quantity (11.74) is then added to q_{11}.

The value of the dimensionless group M might be estimated and the use of Culling's model for topographic decay at scales of approximately 10 to 100 km might be assessed by detailed study, but this is beyond the scope of the present treatment. More simply, if the rate of reduction by erosion is 1, 10, 100 m Ma^{-1}, or 1 km Ma^{-1} for a relief of 1 km at a wavelength of 30 km, a layer thickness $H = 10$ km, and a rate of deformation $|\bar{D}_{xx}| \approx 10^{-15}$ s^{-1}, then $M \approx 0.01, 0.1, 1$, or 10. The layer thickness, H, is irrelevant to the surface process but is conveniently used here to replace λ by k. Since the proposed relief may be large, its reduction by a factor of ten results in an increase in M by the same factor. Accordingly, $M \approx 1$–100 might be a reasonable range for this dimensionless number.

Evolution of the interfaces from arbitrary initial values $A'(0)$ and $A''(0)$ tends to produce a form that grows with the positive eigenvalue of the system (11.72) or:

$$q = \tfrac{1}{2}(q_{11} + q_{22}) + \sqrt{\tfrac{1}{4}(q_{11} - q_{22})^2 + q_{12}q_{21}}$$
$$\frac{A'}{A''} = \frac{q - q_{22}}{q_{21}} = \frac{q_{12}}{q - q_{11}} \tag{11.75}$$

Here the ratio of amplitudes associated with this eigenvalue is given by the second line. The dominant wavelength is that maximizing the eigenvalue q.

As with the necking of a single layer at $n \gg 1$, resonance leads to the excitation of multiple peaks in rate of amplification at a sequence of values of $L/H < 1$. Here, we shall consider only the maximum value of L_d/H. A question of principal interest is how the existence of the necking instability and its length scale constrains the dimensionless groups S, R, and M. Alternatively, we may ask which a priori estimates of these quantities, as of M above, would be consistent with necking at the basin-and-range scale $\sim 30\,km$. Overlap between these two sets of values would support the model.

An estimate for mean strength of the brittle crust in extension, using a friction angle of $30°$ and no cohesion is $K \approx \rho g H/3$. Including cohesion, K will be larger than this by a multiple greater than one and certainly less than two for $H \approx 10\,km$. Thus, we expect $3/2 \geq S \geq 3/4$, and for $\eta_1 \approx 10^{19}$ to $10^{21}\,Pa\,s^{-1}$ and $\overline{D}_{xx} \approx 10^{-15}\,s^{-1}$, $R \approx 0.0002$ to 0.02. The latter values are remarkably small relative to effective viscosity ratios obtained from interpretation of natural fold data; if $\overline{D}_{xx} \approx 10^{-14}\,s^{-1}$, $R \approx 0.002$–0.2. With these estimates in mind, we may illustrate application of the model to the basin-and-range structures by computing L_d/H, q_d, and $(A'/A'')_d$ for $S = 1$ over a wide range in R and M. Contours of these quantities, determined numerically, are shown in Fig. 11.15.

The regularity of basin-and-range structure (Fig. 11.12) suggests a strong necking instability, so that as previously discussed for folding (Chapter 10) we require $q_d \geq 20$. This quantity depends chiefly on R (Fig. 11.15) and the constraint requires $R \leq 0.05$. We may use the mean value of the measured spans as an estimate of L_d, since the amount of extension associated with the later-stage basin-and-range structure is modest. Since the smallest values of L_d/H are ≈ 4.6 to 4.8, this implies $H \approx 6.5\,km$. Although this is smaller than the typical depths to the brittle–ductile transition in continental crust of ≈ 10 to $15\,km$, it may be reasonable in view of the higher thermal gradient in this region. We thus conclude that the present simple model is a plausible one for the initiation of basin-and-range structure. Other models with a more realistic characterization of crustal rheological

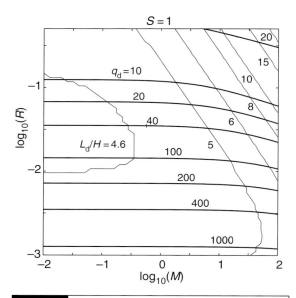

Fig 11.15 Contours of q_d and L_d/H for the crustal necking model in (R, M)-space for $S = 1$.

behavior (Fletcher and Hallet, 1983), but comparable to the present one, provide a better fit.

11.3 Coupling of viscous flow and macroscopic diffusional transport

Under a wide range of conditions, pressure solution is a significant mechanism of deformation in rocks that contain a large volume fraction of moderately soluble minerals such as calcite and quartz. Pressure solution taking place at the grain scale (Chapter 11, frontispiece) can result in pervasive ductile deformation. For example, in this sandstone, dissolution occurs on grain surfaces and on surfaces of the dark anastamosing solution seams approximately normal to the direction of maximum compression, horizontal in the figure. Dissolved material diffuses to grain surfaces subjected to the intermediate or least compression and precipitates there, often in the form of fibers, as here. Precipitation occurred onto the ends of the fibers as they incipiently pulled away from the sub-horizontal surfaces of the grains. The rate of deformation is determined by the rate of diffusive transport from sites of dissolution to those of re-precipitation, by the kinetics of dissolution and precipitation, by rates of mechanical adjustment, or by some combination of these. There is a dependence on grain size, with fine-grained rocks deforming more rapidly than coarse-grained rocks at the same stress. If both pressure solution and crystal plasticity contribute significantly to deformation, a coarser-grained rock may deform chiefly by the latter mechanism while a finer-grained rock deforms chiefly by the former. A rock deforming by pressure solution will behave approximately as a linear viscous fluid.

The sandstone (frontispiece) comes from a location in the internal part of the Cascades accretionary wedge, southeast of the topographic high point at Mt. Olympus (Washington, USA). There, the cleavage is nearly vertical and normal to the direction of plate convergence. The thin section is normal to the cleavage. The principal stretches for the strain produced by pressure solution are 0.7 normal to cleavage, 1.17 parallel to cleavage in the plane of the figure, and 0.98 in the direction normal to these (Feehan and Brandon, 1999). The product of the stretches is 0.80, which implies that 20% of the initial volume has been removed in the deformation. Since the observed deformation most likely took place after the rock was compacted to negligible porosity, volume loss must come from loss of dissolved material, chiefly quartz, from an initial volume of rock.

11.3.1 A model coupling deformation and diffusion in a viscous fluid

The specific behavior to be considered here relates to the segregation of material in sites such as boudin necks (Fig. 11.1b, Fig. 11.16). Figure 11.16 shows the neck region in a boudin in a rock consisting of inter-layered dark amphibolite and light felsic layers, and represents a case of multi-layer boudinage rather than that of a single stiff layer in a soft medium, the case studied in this chapter. The neck is shown by the sharp in-folding of layers on the right-hand side of the figure and by the infilling of the roughly lenticular boudin gap volume. When this occurred, the light-colored infilling may have been a melt. This local segregation may be an intermediary in the wholesale segregation of melt from a partly melted rock, the transport in this case being by Darcy flow rather

Fig 11.16 Multi-layer boudinage in gneiss showing segregation of material into boudin necks; horizontal span ~6 m. Photograph by R. C. Fletcher.

than diffusion. In this section, we treat the transport as diffusion; descriptions for either diffusion or Darcy flow are formally nearly equivalent.

Volume loss or gain involves the net transport of the dissolved component over a macroscopic distance $\gg$ grain size. This is the subject of interest to us here, although not at the scale required to produce the loss of silica in the rock volumes sampled by the sandstone described above. Rather, we will consider dissolution with negative dilatation and precipitation with positive dilatation with diffusional transport mediating between these at the scale of a structure in outcrop. Negative dilatation is shown schematically in Fig. 11.17, where the smaller volume on the right contains the same number of inert or insoluble marker particles.

To treat macroscopic transport by diffusion in a deforming rock, we make the following assumptions:

1. Pressure solution is pervasive, so that dilatation is continuous at the scale of interest. This assumption may be valid even if material is dissolved along discrete solution seams and precipitated into discrete veins, provided the scale of transport is much greater than the dimensions and spacing of the seams or veins dispersed within the rock volume.
2. Dilatation is isotropic. This assumption is less satisfactory if dissolution occurs on seams and precipitation in veins, since these are generally strongly aligned.

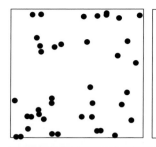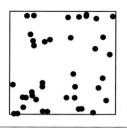

Fig 11.17 Schematic diagram of homogeneous negative dilatation with retention of inert marker particles. Area loss = volume loss = 20%.

3. Only plane deformation is treated, and dilatation is assumed isotropic in the plane of flow.
4. The material dissolving or precipitating makes up much of the rock and is uniformly available throughout the volume of interest.
5. Distortion of elements takes place as though the material were an isotropic incompressible viscous fluid: distortion and dilatation are additive parts of the rate of deformation, but otherwise not directly coupled.

With these assumptions, expressions for the rate of deformation are:

$$D_{xx} = \frac{1}{4\eta}(\sigma_{xx} - \sigma_{yy}) + D$$
$$D_{yy} = \frac{1}{4\eta}(\sigma_{xx} - \sigma_{yy}) + D \qquad (11.76)$$
$$D_{xy} = \frac{1}{2\eta}\sigma_{xy}$$

Here twice D is the rate of dilatation, referring to the rate of change in the area of an element in the plane of flow.

In the case of pressure solution, the rate of dilatation, twice D, is associated with dissolution, transport, and precipitation of the soluble, volumetrically dominant, mineral in the rock. A further assumption, point 4, is that there is no porosity within the material to act as a sink, nor can porosity be created by dissolution. Thus, dissolution or precipitation must be balanced by transport that at the scale of interest is by diffusion along intergranular fluid films. Then:

$$2D = -\left(\frac{\partial J_x}{\partial x} + \frac{\partial J_y}{\partial y}\right)V_0 \qquad (11.77)$$

J_x and J_y are the components of the macroscopic mass flux vector per unit depth and V_0 is the specific volume per unit mass of the soluble mineral.

Mass flux is related to the gradient of the bulk chemical potential of the dissolving or precipitating solid phase in the intergranular film, μ, or:

$$J_x = -M\frac{\partial \mu}{\partial x}, \quad J_y = -M\frac{\partial \mu}{\partial y}$$
$$\text{where } M \cong \frac{\kappa f}{\tau}\frac{c_0}{R'T'} \qquad (11.78)$$

Here κ is the diffusivity of the mineral component in aqueous fluid, f is an effective film porosity, τ is the film tortuosity, c_0 is the mean concentration of the solid component in the aqueous film, R' is the gas constant, and T' is the absolute temperature. If the kinetics of dissolution and precipitation are rapid, relative to transport, the mean chemical potential in an element of the rock may be written (Kamb, 1959a):

$$\mu \cong \mu_0 - \tfrac{1}{2}(\sigma_{xx} + \sigma_{yy})V_0 \qquad (11.79)$$

Combining (11.77), (11.78), and (11.79) we have:

$$D = \psi\left(\frac{\partial^2}{\partial x^2} + \frac{\partial^2}{\partial y^2}\right)(\sigma_{xx} + \sigma_{yy})$$
$$\text{where } \psi \cong \left(\frac{\kappa f}{\tau}\right)\frac{c_0 V_0^2}{4R'T'} \qquad (11.80)$$

The dimensions of ψ are $[\psi] = \text{M}^{-1}\text{L}^3\text{T}$.

Combining (11.78) through (11.80) and (11.76) yields the desired constitutive relations for the plane flow, including the diffusional transport of the soluble mineral component. An inhomogeneous distribution of pressure or mean stress in a viscous medium deforming in plane flow has been used to assess dissolution, diffusion, and precipitation within it (Stephansson, 1974), where the divergence of the gradient in mean stress is used as a measure of dilatation. However, as we have learned, the Airy stress function, ϕ, in such a material satisfies the biharmonic equation, so that:

$$\left(\frac{\partial^2}{\partial x^2} + \frac{\partial^2}{\partial y^2}\right)(\sigma_{xx} + \sigma_{yy}) = \left(\frac{\partial^2}{\partial x^2} + \frac{\partial^2}{\partial y^2}\right)\left(\frac{\partial^2\phi}{\partial x^2} + \frac{\partial^2\phi}{\partial y^2}\right) = 0$$
$$(11.81)$$

Thus, in the present formulation, such a stress distribution would give no dilatation, even though the gradient in mean stress is not zero. The relation (11.81) is obtained by substituting the stress components into the constitutive relations for an *incompressible* viscous fluid, and these in turn into the equation of compatibility. Repeating this here, but with the present constitutive relations, we obtain:

$$\left(\frac{\partial^2}{\partial x^2} + \frac{\partial^2}{\partial y^2}\right)^2 \left[1 - 2\eta\psi\left(\frac{\partial^2}{\partial x^2} + \frac{\partial^2}{\partial y^2}\right)\right]\phi = 0 \quad (11.82)$$

To treat examples of deformation and diffusional transport in layered rock configurations, we again seek a solution that is separable in x and y. This is:

$$\phi(x, y) = \left(\frac{2\eta\lambda}{\lambda^2}\right)\{[a + b(ly - 1)]e^{\lambda y} + me^{\nu\lambda y}$$

$$+ [c + d(ly + 1)]e^{-\lambda y} + ne^{-\nu\lambda y}\}\cos\lambda x$$

where $\nu = \sqrt{1 + \dfrac{1}{2\eta\psi\lambda^2}}$ (11.83)

The four terms containing the constants a, b, c, and d in this expression are identical to those used in Chapter 10, and satisfy the biharmonic equation. The remaining two terms containing m and n yield a non-zero dilatation rate, $2D$. The quantity $\eta\psi$ has the dimensions of a length squared, and we write $L^* = \sqrt{(2\eta\psi)}$.

The stress components derived from (11.83) are:

$$\sigma_{xx} = -2\eta\lambda\{[a + b(\lambda y + 1)]e^{\lambda y} + [c + d(\lambda y - 1)]e^{-\lambda y}$$
$$+ \nu^2(me^{\nu\lambda y} + ne^{-\nu\lambda y})\}\cos\lambda x$$

$$\sigma_{yy} = 2\eta\lambda\{[a + b(\lambda y - 1)]e^{\lambda y} + [c + d(\lambda y + 1)]e^{-\lambda y}$$
$$+ (me^{\nu\lambda y} + ne^{-\nu\lambda y})\}\cos\lambda x \quad (11.84)$$

$$\sigma_{xy} = -2\eta\lambda\{[(a + b\lambda y)]e^{\lambda y} - (c + d\lambda y)e^{-\lambda y}$$
$$+ \nu(me^{\nu\lambda y} - ne^{-\nu\lambda y})\}\sin\lambda x$$

The velocity components derived using (11.76) and (11.80) are:

$$v_x = -[(a + b\lambda y)e^{\lambda y} + (c + d\lambda y)e^{-\lambda y} + me^{\nu\lambda y}$$
$$+ ne^{-\nu\lambda y}]\sin\lambda x$$

$$v_y = \{[a + b(\lambda y - 1)]e^{\lambda y} - [c + d(\lambda y + 1)]e^{-\lambda y} \quad (11.85)$$
$$+ \nu(me^{\nu\lambda y} - ne^{-\nu\lambda y})\}\cos\lambda x$$

The rate of dilatation is:

$$2D = \frac{\partial v_x}{\partial x} + \frac{\partial v_y}{\partial y} = -\lambda(1 - \nu^2)(me^{\nu\lambda y} + ne^{-\nu\lambda y})\cos\lambda x$$

$$(11.86)$$

11.3.2 Necking of a power-law layer embedded in a viscous medium with macroscopic transport

To illustrate some aspects of the behavior of pervasive pressure solution (Fletcher, 1982), we return to the study of boudinage, which serves as a focus of interest and attention in this chapter. Consider the necking of a power-law fluid layer in a medium of the type formulated here. Pressure solution does not take place within the layer. The relations derived from the boundary conditions are nearly the same as in (11.47) through (11.50), but the right-hand sides are replaced according to:

$$\tilde{v}_x(x, h) \cong -(c_1 + g_1)\sin\lambda x$$

$$\tilde{v}_y(x, h) \cong -(c_1 + d_1 - \nu g_1)\cos\lambda x$$

$$\tilde{\sigma}_{yy}(x, h) \cong 2\eta_1\lambda(c_1 + d_1 + g_1)\cos\lambda x \quad (11.87)$$

$$\tilde{\sigma}_{xy}(x, h) \cong 2\eta_1\lambda(c_1 - \nu g_1)\sin\lambda x$$
$$-4\bar{\eta}\bar{D}_{xx}(\lambda A)(1 - \eta_1/\bar{\eta})$$

Here we have also used the restriction to a plane basic-state flow. Since there are now five coefficients to be fixed, the additional one in this case being g_1, the equivalent of n in the relations (11.83) to (11.86), another boundary condition is required. This is the vanishing of the normal component of the diffusional flux at the interface.

While there is a basic state of uniform extension, the rate of dilatation in the case of a layer in which diffusion does not occur is zero. Since there is a jump in layer-parallel normal stress, and hence mean stress, across the medium–layer interface, the condition of zero diffusional flux may not correspond to what is seen in a natural deformation. In extension, the mean stress in the layer is less than that in the medium, and the component of a soluble mineral in the medium would tend to diffuse into the stiff layer and precipitate. If such a situation were posited, the additional boundary condition would be on the continuity of the normal flux at the interface, but for simplicity, we exclude such diffusion.

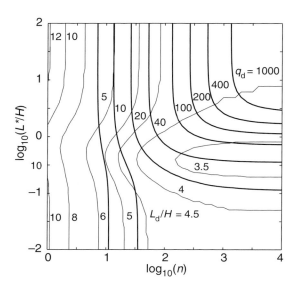

Fig 11.18 q_d and L_d/H contoured in $(n, L^*/H)$-space for necking for viscosity ratio $R = 0.05$.

In the absence of basic-state transport, the condition of zero normal flux at the interface, to first order in slope λA, is:

$$\tilde{J}_y^{(1)}(x, 0) \sim \frac{\partial}{\partial y}\left[\frac{1}{2}(\tilde{\sigma}_{xx}^{(1)} + \bar{\sigma}_{xx}^{(1)})\right]_{(x,0)} \cong 0 \qquad (11.88)$$

To the present approximation, this yields the condition:

$$d_1 - \frac{1}{2}\nu(\nu^2 - 1)g_1 = 0 \qquad (11.89)$$

The five equations obtained by combining (11.87) and (11.89) are solved numerically for the constants a, b, c_1, d_1, and g_1. The added complexity relative to the necking problem considered above suggests that closed-form results may be laborious to obtain and may not easily provide physical insight. We do not attempt this here.

The effect on necking of dilatation mediated by diffusional transport in the host is shown by contouring q_d and L_d/H in $(n, L^*/H)$-space at fixed viscosity ratio $R = 0.05$ (Fig. 11.18) using:

$$\frac{L^*}{H} = \sqrt{\frac{2\eta_1\psi}{H^2}} \qquad (11.90)$$

This is a suitable dimensionless group for the present problem. Here, the medium viscosity

enters, but parameters ψ and ν, which also refer to the medium, are not subscripted. At any layer stress exponent, n, q_d increases with L^*/H and the increase is significant for large n at which the necking instability is otherwise moderate to strong. This effect "saturates" as L^*/H becomes comparable to L_d/H, or at approximately $L^*/H = 10$. That is, as transport becomes efficient, the driving gradient itself is lowered, so L_d/H and q_d reach limiting values and then do not change as L^*/H increases further.

At large n, or the plastic layer limit, the instability becomes very large. Since much boudinage occurs by separation of the stiff layer into discrete segments by faults or shear zones, we might anticipate that this behavior is indeed characteristic of layers forming this type of boudin. The present model would thus be expected to provide a satisfactory model for any initial phase of continuous necking that might have preceded through-going faulting, as in the basin-and-range model.

The effect of diffusional mass transport in the medium on necking is further illustrated by plotting (Fig. 11.19) deformed grids and velocity fields for cases of no diffusion ($L^*/H = 0$) and vigorous diffusion ($L^*/H = 3.2$). Only the grid deformation due to the perturbing flow is shown; in (Fig. 11.19a), the apparent thickening in the swell of the layer or in the medium adjacent to the pinch would be offset by the uniform basic-state extension. Without diffusion ($L^*/H = 0$), the medium does not thin appreciably over the swell nor thicken over the pinch or neck, but with diffusion ($L^*/H = 3.2$), these effects are marked. Notice that the elements above the swell also shrink, while those over the neck undergo a positive dilatation. A third effect, associated with a partial reduction of the mechanical constraint from the medium in the case of diffusion, is that the perturbing deformation is markedly reduced away from the layer. The last effect is emphasized in the perturbing velocity fields (Fig. 11.19b); the medium velocity being much greater in the case of no diffusion except in the close vicinity of the layer.

A scalar measure of the strength of diffusive transport is afforded by the ratio of the net rate of diffusional volume transport towards the neck per unit depth across a surface at $x = L/4$ to the transport by the perturbing flow through the

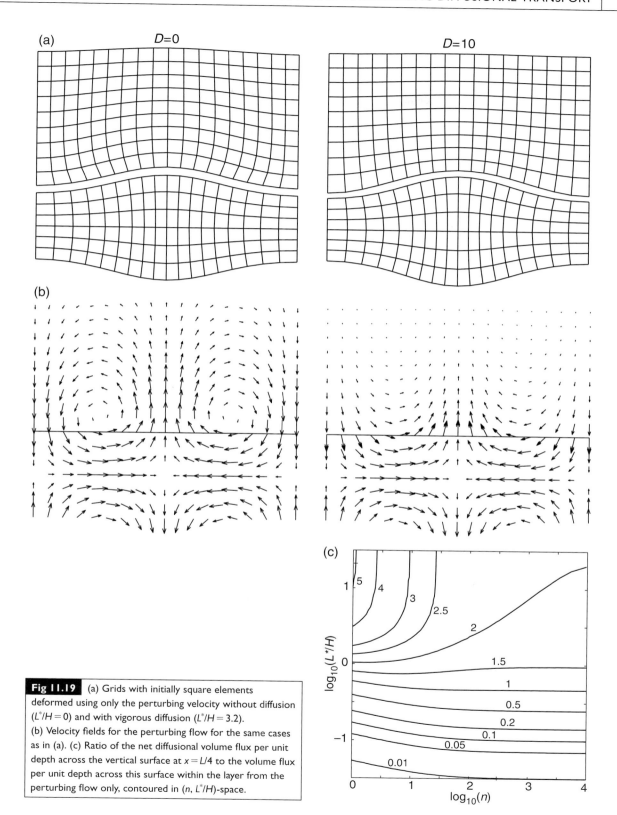

Fig 11.19 (a) Grids with initially square elements deformed using only the perturbing velocity without diffusion ($L^*/H = 0$) and with vigorous diffusion ($L^*/H = 3.2$). (b) Velocity fields for the perturbing flow for the same cases as in (a). (c) Ratio of the net diffusional volume flux per unit depth across the vertical surface at $x = L/4$ to the volume flux per unit depth across this surface within the layer from the perturbing flow only, contoured in $(n, L^*/H)$-space.

upper half of the necking layer towards the swell (Fig.11.19c). This number may be greater than unity because the diffusional flux must also counter the drag of material in the medium toward the swell. This suggests that a contribution of slip at the layer–medium contact, which would diminish such drag, may enhance the instability further; the effect is not studied here.

11.4 | Continuum properties of composite materials

Excluding volcanic glasses, rocks are made up of grains or crystals, and contain cracks and pores that *in situ* will be filled with liquid or gas. At a larger scale, rock masses are heterogeneous, from the relatively simple case of a layered sedimentary rock to the more complex internal structure of a strongly deformed metamorphic rock. Treatment of these materials as continuous media, the justification for which we have previously set forth, still leaves open questions. How may we estimate the bulk properties of rocks relevant to certain behavior, such as elastic deformation or flow, from the properties of the major component materials and their geometric configuration? As the configuration of its mechanical components changes in a ductilely deforming rock, can the evolution in macroscopic properties be determined?

These questions relate to the correlation of detailed observations of rock composition and structure with their constitutive behavior when the deformation of interest took place. For example, it is often remarked that the rheological behavior of a rock in ductile deformation is determined by its weakest component, such as quartz in granite. Can we find support for this idea through mechanical analysis of such a composite material? Such questions may be answered by direct laboratory experiment. But these are sufficiently expensive in time and resources to warrant discovering methods of estimation whose reliability may be tested against particular experimental results. Further, we need a conceptual basis with which to systematize experimental results and to think about natural deformation. In this section, we examine the simplest methods.

As a more concrete example, the sandstone in the frontispiece is made up of larger grains, chiefly of quartz, embedded in a fine-grained matrix rich in phyllosilicates and quartz, two components that might be expected to have had distinct mechanical behavior. The larger grains might have behaved as approximately rigid elements in a weak matrix. Evidently, though, the large grains may be dissolved. The large grains are elongate parallel to cleavage. Discontinuous seams depleted in fine-grained quartz, rich in phyllosilicates, and aligned along cleavage are a prominent if volumetrically minor additional component of the rock. The presence of these and the elongate grains argue against isotropy of the constitutive behavior, either in rheological or elastic behavior. In shear parallel to cleavage, the seams would possibly contribute to the deformation to a degree far outweighing their volumetric fraction. How might we quantify these features in producing a model for the bulk behavior?

11.4.1 Voight and Reuss estimates for the bulk viscosity of a composite of two viscous fluids

The simple procedures for estimating the bulk properties of composite materials used here do not always conform to the methodology so far presented, in which we advocate the formulation and solution of boundary value problems. In analyzing these problems, the judicious use of approximation is useful and often necessary, but conditions of traction continuity and continuity of displacement or velocity, if appropriate, are honored. In the estimation procedures introduced here, however, this use of approximation seems to have been taken too far!

As an example, imagine a composite material made up of two isotropic linear viscous fluids. For definiteness, imagine a configuration like that of sandstone, in which the quartz grains are replaced by one viscous fluid and the fine-grained matrix by the other. Suppose that grain contacts are welded: no slip or separation occurs along them. Also, set aside the processes of dissolution and precipitation that are central to the actual deformation of this rock. If there were a higher fraction of quartz grains, they would form more complex interconnected bodies of this component rather than isolated masses surrounded by the matrix component. The homogeneous mechanical elements of the composite will then consist of isolated bodies to rather complex interdigitated bodies consisting of amalgamations of grains composed of one or the other component. By our hypothesis, that each component may be approximated by an isotropic viscous fluid, the constitutive relations for the individual bodies are given. Boundary conditions on continuity of velocity or displacement and of traction at their interfaces would then be specified. However, the geometry of the composite body is so complex that determining the stress and velocity distribution within it arising from a prescribed bulk homogeneous stress or rate of deformation would be difficult to obtain, even by numerical means. Instead, we consider two simple means of estimating the bulk behavior that avoid difficulty.

In the Reuss estimate, the internal stress is taken to be homogeneous and hence equal to the macroscopic or applied stress. Here a point of view espoused by J. N. Goodier is taken. We do not say that the stress in the composite material is *assumed homogeneous* because it is a priori known not to be homogeneous, or highly unlikely to be so. Rather, we postulate a behavior or condition for the model, in this case, that the stress is homogeneous. We are free to postulate anything we like about the model, as that is completely independent of the natural example. Later, we can hope to understand to what extent the model corresponds to nature. The equations of stress equilibrium will be satisfied and the normal and shear stress components acting on interfaces within the composite will be continuous as required. However, because the components of the rate of deformation in the separate constituents are homogeneous, the conditions of velocity continuity at interfaces will generally not be satisfied, even in approximation. Thus, the estimate does not represent an attempt to solve the boundary value problem for the material of interest specified at the microscopic scale.

The macroscopic or bulk components of the rate of deformation are then taken as the averages over the volume distribution of the components. If the two-component viscous fluids have viscosities η_1 and η_2 and volume fractions f_1 and $f_2 = 1 - f_1$, the component D_{xx} will have the values in the two components:

$$D_{xx}^{(1)} = \frac{1}{2\eta_1} s_{xx}, \quad D_{xx}^{(2)} = \frac{1}{2\eta_2} s_{xx} \tag{11.91}$$

The macroscopic value of this component is then:

$$
\begin{aligned}
D_{xx} &= f_1 D_{xx}^{(1)} + f_2 D_{xx}^{(2)} \\
&= \frac{f_1}{2\eta_1} s_{xx} + \frac{f_2}{2\eta_2} s_{xx} = \frac{1}{2\eta_R} s_{xx}
\end{aligned}
\tag{11.92}
$$

Here, η_R is the Reuss estimate for the macroscopic viscosity:

$$\eta_R = \left(\frac{f_1}{\eta_1} + \frac{f_2}{\eta_2} \right)^{-1} \tag{11.93}$$

Note that nothing was said about the configuration of the composite. We might suppose that the configuration was consistent with the composite being isotropic, but the indefiniteness has a further meaning. Not only is the result (11.93) an estimate for a composite material made up of the specified volume fractions of the two components, it is the lowest estimate that one might obtain in any way. It is the lower bound on the bulk viscosity of such a mixture, as Burton Paul was apparently the first to prove (Paul, 1960).

An estimate of the bulk viscosity of the mixture, by a method first proposed by Voight, may be obtained by postulating, in this model, that the rate of deformation is homogeneous. In this case, the velocity field in the medium is continuous. The equations of stress equilibrium are satisfied in the sense that the stress is homogeneous in any volume of one or the other components, but the shear and normal tractions will not generally be equal across the interfaces between elements of the composite. Likewise, we do not specify the configuration of the composite.

Selecting a component of the deviatoric stress whose mean or macroscopic value is s_{xx} we have:

$$s_{xx}^{(1)} = 2\eta_1 D_{xx}, \quad s_{xx}^{(2)} = 2\eta_2 D_{xx} \tag{11.94}$$

But then:

$$s_{xx} = 2\eta_V D_{xx} = f_1 s_{xx}^{(1)} + f_2 s_{xx}^{(2)} = f_1 2\eta_1 D_{xx} + f_2 2\eta_2 D_{xx} \tag{11.95}$$

Therefore:

$$\eta_V = f_1 \eta_1 + f_2 \eta_2 \tag{11.96}$$

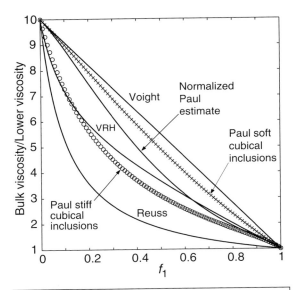

Fig 11.20 Estimates of bulk viscosity. VRH refers to the Voight–Reuss–Hill estimate.

$$\eta_n = \eta_V, \quad \eta_s = \eta_R \qquad (11.97)$$

Our present aim is to construct estimates for an isotropic composite material, so this association of the Voight and Reuss estimates with the principal viscosities of a layered, anisotropic material would seem no more than fortuitous. However, it does give us a strong clue as to a significant factor: the effect of the two-component geometry of the composite. By considering the layered configuration, we observe that in layer-parallel shortening or extension, both layer types support the bulk stress. Thus, if one component has a very much larger viscosity, its effect on the principal viscosity η_n will be large, if not dominant. The component with higher viscosity in this case may then make up the "load-bearing framework," with intervening layers of much smaller viscosity supporting little load. On the other hand, in layer-parallel shear, the resistance, or lack of it, may be principally associated with the low-viscosity component, with sheets of the high-viscosity component acting as isolated inclusions. Indeed, both components support the same load, in terms of layer-parallel shear stress. Thus, as might have been guessed beforehand, the geometry of the composite may have a great range even if it corresponds to isotropic bulk behavior, and this will have a major effect on the bulk viscosity. As suggested here, two principal types of configuration exist, those in which the high-viscosity component forms a connected load-bearing framework, and those in which it is present as isolated inclusions surrounded by a matrix of the low-viscosity component (Handy, 1994). We turn to another simple method of estimation that accounts for this difference.

The Voight estimate is an upper bound on the viscosity of the composite, a result also proved by Paul (1960).

A simple way of showing that the two estimates are bounds – and here we must be careful not to claim we have obtained a proof! – is to consider the case when one component is rigid, or has infinite viscosity. The Voight estimate indicates that no matter how small a volume of this material is contained in the composite, the composite itself will have infinite viscosity. The Reuss estimate indicates that no matter how small an amount of the material with finite viscosity is present, the viscosity of the composite will be finite. With regard to the supposition that the rheological behavior of a composite material is determined by the low-viscosity component in it, the Reuss and Voight estimates say quite opposite things. The Voight and Reuss bounds for the bulk viscosity are shown in Fig. 11.20 for materials consisting of two viscous fluids with $\eta_2 = 10\eta_1$ as a function of the volume fraction of the fluid with the lower viscosity, f_1.

The Voight and Reuss bounds on the viscosity of an isotropic composite may also be recognized as the exact principal viscosities of a composite made up of alternating layers of the two fluids, as used in Chapter 10 to model the gross mechanics of chevron folds, with:

11.4.2 Paul estimates for an isotropic viscous composite

The lack of dependence on the geometry of the configuration inherent in the Voight and Reuss estimates is not likely to be wholly appealing to the structural geologist. A simple method for obtaining estimates that takes something of the internal configuration into account has been proposed (Paul, 1960). This makes use of the strength-of-materials plane-sections-remain-plane approximation used in our initial analysis of necking. These estimates show the expected asym-

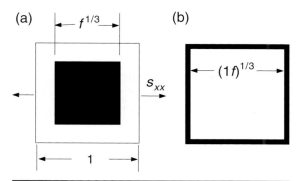

Fig 11.21 Central sections of composite cubes used in the Paul estimate for macroscopic viscosity for a volume fraction $f = 0.25$.

metry of behaviors for high-viscosity inclusions in low-viscosity material versus low-viscosity inclusions in high-viscosity material, an asymmetry not contained in the Voight and Reuss estimates.

Consider again a composite composed of two isotropic viscous components. Paul models a composite material in terms of a simple representative volume element (RVE) of it in the form of a unit cube. For definiteness, he also considered specific simple, if somewhat idealized, configurations of the components within this RVE. The component of viscosity η_1 might be in the form of a cube centered within the unit cube with the surrounding material of viscosity η_2 (Fig. 11.21a). The side of the cube will have dimension $f_1^{1/3}$. Let the macroscopic stress component $\sigma_{xx} > 0$ be applied to a pair of faces of the cube, and no other tractions applied to it. Suppose, as in the necking analysis, that plane sections remain plane, so that sheets of the cube containing only the exterior fluid of viscosity η_2 undergo a rate of extension:

$$D'_{xx} = \frac{1}{2\eta_2}\left(\frac{2}{3}\sigma_{xx}\right) = \frac{1}{3\eta_2}\sigma_{xx} \qquad (11.98)$$

Here $s_{xx} = \sigma_{xx} - \frac{1}{3}\sigma_{xx} = \frac{2}{3}\sigma_{xx}$ is the deviatoric stress component acting parallel to x. Sheets of fluid that contain an interior portion of fluid with viscosity η_1 undergo a rate of extension:

$$D''_{xx} = \frac{1}{3\eta_1}\sigma^{(1)}_{xx} = \frac{1}{3\eta_2}\sigma^{(2)}_{xx} \qquad (11.99)$$

To conform to the macroscopic applied stress, the average over the unit area of the section must be:

$$f_1^{2/3}\sigma^{(1)}_{xx} + (1 - f_1^{2/3})\sigma^{(2)}_{xx} = \sigma_{xx} \qquad (11.100)$$

Combining (11.100) and (11.99) we have:

$$D''_{xx} = [f_1^{2/3}(3\eta_1) + (1 - f_1^{2/3})(3\eta_2)]^{-1}\sigma_{xx} \qquad (11.101)$$

The mean rate of extension is the average of these taken along the x-direction:

$$D_{xx} = (1 - f_1^{1/3})D'_{xx} + f_1^{1/3}D''_{xx} = \frac{1}{3\eta_P^{(1)}}\sigma_{xx} \qquad (11.102)$$

Here $\eta_P^{(1)}$ is a Paul estimate with the 1-component as an inclusion in a matrix of the 2-component. Performing the indicated algebra:

$$\frac{\eta_P^{(1)}}{\eta_1} = \frac{f_1^{2/3} + (1 - f_1^{2/3})(\eta_2/\eta_1)}{f_1^{1/3} + [f_1^{2/3} + (1 - f_1^{2/3})(\eta_2/\eta_1)](1 - f_1^{1/3})} \qquad (11.103)$$

Another estimate is obtained by supposing the material with viscosity η_1 surrounds an inclusion of viscosity η_2, both with the same volume fractions as in the previous case (Fig. 11.21b). The result is given by:

$$\frac{\eta_P^{(2)}}{\eta_1} = \frac{g_1^{2/3}(\eta_2/\eta_1) + (1 - g_1^{2/3})}{g_1^{1/3} + [g_1^{2/3}(\eta_2/\eta_1) + (1 - g_1^{2/3})](1 - g_1^{1/3})}$$

where $g_1 = 1 - f_1$ $\qquad (11.104)$

The result is written to emphasize the symmetry between it and (11.103). These two estimates are also plotted in Fig. 11.20. They lie within the Voight and Reuss bounds, and, as further expected, the estimated viscosity for the case that the stiffer material surrounds inclusions of the softer, is larger than for the complementary configuration.

11.4.3. Discussion

Two more estimates may be constructed from the two pairs at hand: the Voight and Reuss bounds, and the two Paul estimates. The average of the Voight and Reuss bounds is called the Voight–Reuss–Hill estimate after its originator, Rodney Hill (Hill, 1965):

$$\frac{\eta_{VRH}}{\eta_1} = \frac{1}{2}\left(\frac{\eta_V}{\eta_1} + \frac{\eta_R}{\eta_1}\right) \qquad (11.105)$$

This estimate may be chosen if we have no information on the geometry of the composite, other than that it is consistent with bulk isotropic behavior, or that the sample of interest is selected randomly from a population with variable geometry but given volume fractions of the two components. The bounds provide information on the possible range of variation.

Another estimate may be obtained by placing Paul elements in series, so that the softer material is neither always an inclusion in the stiffer material or vice versa. The latter is more likely if f_1 is large, so we weight its contribution by f_1 and that of the former by $1-f_1$, obtaining:

$$\frac{\bar{\eta}_P}{\eta_1} = f_1 \frac{\eta_P^{(2)}}{\eta_1} + (1-f_1)\frac{\eta_P^{(1)}}{\eta_1} \qquad (11.106)$$

All six estimates are plotted in Fig. 11.20 as a function of the low-viscosity component volume fraction, f_1, for the case $\eta_2/\eta_1 = 10$. Note that the Voight and Reuss estimates manage to stay outside of the tangle of the other four estimates, which supports their nature as bounds. The largest difference in estimates occurs for higher volume fractions of the high-viscosity component, $1-f_1 > 0.5$. The difference between the Paul estimates, for which explicit configurations of the composite are associated, give us an impression of the joint effect of configuration and the variables f_1 and η_2/η_1. For example, a relative bulk viscosity of 5 corresponds to $f_1 = 0.25$ for the high-viscosity inclusion in a low-viscosity matrix configuration, but to $f_1 = 0.5$ for the low-viscosity inclusion in a high-viscosity matrix configuration, so that a range in volume fractions may be offset by the nature of the composite configuration. Again, at the same volume fraction, a substantial range in relative bulk viscosity may be achieved by changing the configuration.

As a rock consisting of two or more major mechanical components deforms, its internal geometry will change. If it began as an assemblage of equant grains or mineral aggregates or a more complex intermeshing configuration still consistent with bulk isotropic behavior, deformation will tend to produce a material with anisotropic properties. Instead of treating idealized configurations by the Paul method, the actual configuration of the rock might be sampled and a plane-sections-remain-plane analysis undertaken, both in extension parallel to geometrically estimated principal directions and in shear. This would provide a method of assessing the bulk anisotropic behavior, given known or postulated behavior of the components. The estimates discussed here may also be applied to non-linear materials, although computation of the Paul estimates is then rather complicated. In the special case that the two materials are power-law fluids and the stress exponents are equal, the computation becomes quite simple.

11.5 | Anisotropic fluids and internal instability

In the treatment of large-scale structures, such as accretionary wedges, it has been usual to approximate the rheological behavior, however varied within the structure, as isotropic. At the scale of an exposure, when layered and foliated rocks deform in a ductile manner, the resulting structures generally imply strong anisotropy, but to introduce such behavior into models for deformation at a much larger scale, it would be necessary to specify something of the initial disposition of layering and to keep track of it during the deformation. Further, with the development of small-scale structures, such as folds, which "break up" the layering or foliation within volumes large relative to the scale of folding, the bulk behavior at this scale will exhibit a smaller degree of anisotropy. Thus, the use of isotropic constitutive relations for deformation at the largest scales may be justified as an approximation.

There is still a strong motivation to study the consequences of anisotropic behavior in this and many other situations. For example, the formation of structures such as folds and internal boudinage in rocks that are foliated, layered, or otherwise anisotropic in their bulk behavior may be modeled as an instability in an anisotropic medium. The results may be used to interpret arrays of natural structures, many of which are quite complex in terms of spatial variation in length scales, structural morphology, and the intensity of structural development in a rock that might otherwise have been imagined to be initially an approximately homogeneous mass of layered sedimentary or metamorphic rock, gneiss, or schist.

11.5.1 Deformation of an anisotropic viscous fluid

Modeling of ductile deformation of a rock volume is appropriately treated using the constitutive relations for a continuum that captures the bulk rheological behavior at the scale of interest. Understanding that this approximation applies to a composite material, we realize that suitable constitutive relations may be needed to describe anisotropic behavior, as for a layered or foliated material, a composite mass with a strong shape fabric, or a polycrystalline material with lattice preferred orientation, or a material in which all of these elements contribute to rheological anisotropy. Further, all of these factors and others, such as composition, will contribute to inhomogeneity. In some cases, such inhomogeneity as in a volume of metamorphic or sedimentary rock may be approximated by a set of a discrete layers or bodies of other shape, e.g. inclusions, which are themselves homogeneous. This is useful when the contrast in mean properties of the discrete bodies is much greater than that exhibited by internal heterogeneity. Types of structures arising in this case, such as folds and pinch-and-swell structures, have been treated earlier in this chapter and in Chapter 10. In the present case, we consider the other alternative of a continuous variation in properties at the scale of interest.

We consider a body in which the degree of heterogeneity is small, and may therefore be treated as a perturbation on a homogeneous material. This restriction has four anticipated consequences:

1. Analysis may be carried out by linearization about a basic state and is therefore tractable.
2. Both in the analysis and in the physical interpretation of the results, any heterogeneous current distribution of properties, the associated velocity field, and the relations describing the evolving deformation and modification in the distributions of properties may be broken up into independent components, e.g. the Fourier components whose linear superposition gives the distribution or field.
3. Physical intuition is most readily obtained by focusing on the behavior of the individual components.
4. To interpret a naturally deformed rock mass,

we would initially explore the scales and patterns of the deformation and inferred constitutive behavior in terms of these components.

Consider an anisotropic linear viscous fluid described by relations introduced in Chapter 10:

$$D'_{xx} = \frac{1}{2\eta_n}s'_{xx}, \quad D'_{xy} = \frac{1}{2\eta_s}s'_{xy} \tag{11.107}$$

Here x' and y' are local axes in the material parallel to the principal axes of anisotropy. Consider continuous variations in three quantities: θ, the small deviation of the x'-axis from the x-axis of fixed reference axes x and y, and the two principal viscosities η_n and η_s. Write the latter as:

$$\eta_n = \overline{\eta}_n(1 + \delta_n), \quad \eta_s = \overline{\eta}_s(1 + \delta_s) \tag{11.108}$$

Here δ_n and δ_s are spatially varying fractional deviations from the mean values. Referred to x and y, the constitutive relations are:

$$4\eta_n D_{xx} = [(1 + m) + (1 - m)\cos 4\theta]s_{xx} + (1 - m)\sin 4\theta s_{xy}$$
$$4\eta_n D_{xy} = (1 - m)\sin 4\theta s_{xx} + [(1 + m) - (1 - m)\cos 4\theta]s_{xy} \tag{11.109}$$

Here $m = \eta_n/\eta_s$.

We now linearize these equations about a basic state with rate of deformation components $\overline{D}_{xx}$, $\overline{D}_{xy}$, deviatoric stress components $\overline{s}_{xx}$, $\overline{s}_{xy}$, orientation $\overline{\theta} = 0$, and principal viscosities $\overline{\eta}_n$, $\overline{\eta}_s$. For the perturbing quantities, we obtain:

$$4\overline{\eta}_n \tilde{D}_{xx} \cong 2\tilde{s}_{xx} + (1 - \overline{m})4\theta \overline{s}_{xy} - 2\delta_n \overline{s}_{xx}$$
$$4\overline{\eta}_n \tilde{D}_{xy} \cong 2\overline{m}\tilde{s}_{xx} + (1 - \overline{m})4\theta \overline{s}_{xx} - 2\overline{m}\delta_s \overline{s}_{xx} \tag{11.110}$$

Here $\overline{m} = \overline{\eta}_n/\overline{\eta}_s$. We may proceed further without assigning expressions for the variations of θ, δ_n, and δ_s by expressing the deviatoric stress components in terms of the Airy stress function, $\phi(x, y)$ and then substituting (11.110) into the equation of compatibility (10.64) for the rate of deformation. After expansion, we obtain:

$$\frac{\partial^4 \phi}{\partial y^4} + 2(2\overline{m} - 1)\frac{\partial^4 \phi}{\partial y^2 \partial x^2} + \frac{\partial^4 \phi}{\partial x^4}$$
$$= 4(\overline{m} - 1)\left[\left(\frac{\partial^2 \theta}{\partial y^2} - \frac{\partial^2 \theta}{\partial x^2}\right)\overline{s}_{xy} - 2\frac{\partial^2 \theta}{\partial x \partial y}\overline{s}_{xx}\right]$$
$$+ 2\left[\left(\frac{\partial^2 \delta_n}{\partial y^2} - \frac{\partial^2 \delta_n}{\partial x^2}\right)\overline{s}_{xx} - 2\overline{m}\frac{\partial^2 \delta_s}{\partial x \partial y}\overline{s}_{xy}\right] \tag{11.111}$$

The perturbation in principal axis orientation and those in the principal viscosities occur in separate terms, because any term containing a product of a perturbing quantity is deleted in the linearization. They may thus be thought of as giving separate effects even though for any volume element in the fluid both are required to specify the local rheological behavior. We might thus imagine one limiting situation in which the principal viscosities were perfectly homogeneous but the principal axis orientation varied, and another in which the opposite was true. This separation is no longer possible when the dimensionless quantities describing them are both too large for the linearized equations to hold.

In contrast to the many examples of boundary and initial value problems discussed in this text, we now consider an initial value problem for an unbounded volume of material. The initial value description now refers to the functions:

$$\theta = \theta(x, y), \quad \delta_n = \delta_n(x, y), \quad \delta_s = \delta_s(x, y) \qquad (11.112)$$

If one wishes to make a full investigation of inhomogeneity of this sort, a sensible first step is to consider two simpler cases, one in which the material is isotropic and all that is considered is a perturbation in viscosity, and the other in which the material is anisotropic, but the perturbations in the principal viscosities vanish. To illustrate the analysis and results further, we restrict attention to the latter case, described only by the perturbation in θ. Since the variations δ_n and δ_s are to be ignored, it is useful to think of them as zero and to replace $\bar{m}$ with m. Having worked through the analysis with several mathematical forms for the perturbation, we find that the appropriate elementary form for a component in this perturbation is the periodic band-like form:

$$\theta(x, y) = -\Theta \sin \lambda(x - \nu y) \qquad (11.113)$$

Here Θ is the amplitude or maximum value of the slope and $\nu = \tan \beta$, where β is the angle made with the normal to the mean plane of foliation, or the y-axis, with a counterclockwise angle negative. Such a perturbation is the only one that behaves as an independent component, or eigenmode, in a general plane deformation. The following analysis will show that this is the case.

A cylindrical surface to which the principal axes are tangent and normal that may be associated with (11.113) is:

$$\zeta(x, y) = \bar{y} + A \cos \lambda(x - \nu y) \qquad (11.114)$$

Here $\Theta = \lambda A$ and $\partial \zeta / \partial x = \tan \theta \cong \theta$. We may think of the trace of a cylindrical surface (11.114) as a foliation surface; its mean height, $\bar{y}$, above some reference level, which defines, in part, a material surface in the fluid, is treated differently from the independent coordinate y. An example of a set of foliation surfaces of the form (11.114) is shown in Fig. 11.22 for the case $\beta = -45°$.

The solution that we seek starts with the particular solution to (11.111), where only the first term on the right-hand side is considered. Substituting (11.113) into that term, it is then clear that $\phi \sim \sin \lambda(x - \nu y)$, and we obtain:

$$\phi = -\frac{(1/\lambda^2)(4m - 1)[(-\nu^2 + 1)\bar{s}_{xy} 2\nu \bar{s}_{xx}]\Theta \sin \lambda(x - \nu y)}{[1 + (2m - 1)\nu^2 + \nu^4]} \qquad (11.115)$$

Given the stresses:

$$\bar{s}_{xx} = \frac{1}{2}\left(\frac{\partial^2 \phi}{\partial y^2} - \frac{\partial^2 \phi}{\partial x^2}\right)$$

$$\bar{s}_{xy} = -\frac{\partial^2 \phi}{\partial y \partial x} \qquad (11.116)$$

We may then substitute into (11.110) and integrate to obtain the velocity components:

$$\bar{v}_x = \frac{-4(m - 1)\nu[2\nu \bar{D}_{xy} + (1 - \nu^2)\bar{D}_{xx}]}{[1 + 2(2m - 1)\nu^2 + \nu^4]} A \cos \lambda(x - \nu y)$$

$$\bar{v}_y = \frac{-4(m - 1)[2\nu \bar{D}_{xy} + (1 - \nu^2)\bar{D}_{xx}]}{[1 + 2(2m - 1)\nu^2 + \nu^4]} A \cos \lambda(x - \nu y) \qquad (11.117)$$

As in previous examples, the evolution of the interface may be determined from the relation:

$$\frac{\partial \zeta}{\partial t} = v_y(x, \zeta) - v_x(x, \zeta)\frac{\partial \zeta}{\partial x} \qquad (11.118)$$

The basic-state flow is:

$$\bar{v}_x = \bar{D}_{xx} x + 2\bar{D}_{xy} y$$
$$\bar{v}_y = -\bar{D}_{xx} y \qquad (11.119)$$

Carrying out the expansion of (11.118) to first order in slope, we obtain the evolution equations for the component:

Fig 11.22 Single component with $\beta = -45°$. The maximum slope is chosen large enough so that the structure is visually distinct.

Fig 11.23 Symmetric internal boudinage is the sum of two cylindrical perturbations with $\beta = -45°$ and $+45°$.

$$\frac{dA}{dt} = -\overline{D}_{xx}A - \frac{4(m-1)[2v\overline{D}_{xy} + (1-v^2)\overline{D}_{xx}]}{[1 + 2(2m-1)v^2 + v^4]}A$$

$$\frac{d\lambda}{dt} = -\overline{D}_{xx}\lambda, \quad \frac{dv}{dt} = \overline{D}_{xx}v + 2\overline{D}_{xy}, \quad \frac{d\overline{y}}{dt} = -\overline{D}_{xx}\overline{y}$$

$$(11.120)$$

Because this set of equations is complete and self-contained, it demonstrates that the component is in fact linearly independent of all others. A perturbation that is not a single linearly independent component, in a general plane flow, is the example of internal boudinage shown in Fig. 11.23, which combines a perturbation of the sort shown in Fig. 11.22 with another of equal amplitude and phase, but with β or v of opposite sign, $\beta = +45°$. In pure extension or shortening, the components will behave in a symmetric manner, but if there is a component of foliation-parallel shear, they will not and the independent evolution of the two parts becomes obvious.

The relations (11.120) may be integrated numerically to follow the evolution of the structure, as long as the slope remains small, here not on a single interface but throughout a volume of fluid. We now use the above results to illustrate structures that might be produced in an anisotropic material whose rheological behavior is approximated by an anisotropic viscous fluid.

As with the folding of a single layer, the behavior is most simply described by the rate of growth of amplitude or slope of a single component. Because two components of the basic-state rate of deformation may vary arbitrarily, it is useful to scale all relations with the maximum rate of shear, using dimensionless variables:

$$\overline{d}_{xx} = \overline{D}_{xx}/\overline{I}_2, \quad \overline{d}_{xy} = \overline{D}_{xy}/\overline{I}_2$$
$$\text{where } \overline{I}_2 = \sqrt{(\overline{D}_{xx}^2 + \overline{D}_{xy}^2)}$$

$$(11.121)$$

Focusing on amplitude rather than slope, we then examine the dimensionless quantity:

$$q(v; m, \overline{d}_{xx}) = \frac{1}{\overline{I}_2 A}\frac{dA}{dt}$$

$$= -\overline{d}_{xx} - \frac{4(m-1)[2v\overline{d}_{xy} + (1-v^2)\overline{d}_{xx}]}{[1 + 2(2m-1)v^2 + v^4]}$$

$$(11.122)$$

Because $\overline{d}_{xx}^2 + \overline{d}_{xy}^2 = 1$, the dependence on the basic state reduces to the single variable $\overline{d}_{xx}$.

In contrast to cases in which a layer of finite thickness H undergoes folding or necking, there is no dependence on an absolute length scale, since

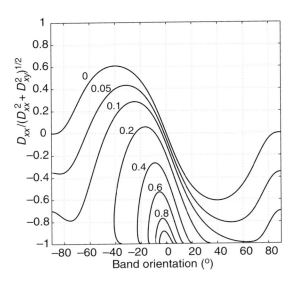

none exists. That is, in principle, structures may occur at any scale within the material. What is selected for in the bulk deformation is the most rapidly amplified band orientation, or, alternatively, that which has received the maximum cumulative amplification. In reality, in a rock like schist, the grain scale provides a lower limit on the scale of coherent structures produced, but often the schist will also exhibit a compositional lamination, so that structures may occur in response to several scales of microscopic structure that give anisotropy. Indeed, the largest perturbations are often present at one or both of these smallest scales at which coherent deformations can take place. Hence, structures will commonly occur at these scales, but, in principle, they may also occur at larger scales as is often observed (Price and Cosgrove, 1990).

The expected band-like structures may be represented for a given material, specified by the principal viscosity ratio m, as a function of the basic-state flow. Here we suppose that the components $\overline{D}_{xx}$ and $\overline{D}_{xy}$ are in constant proportion, or that $\overline{d}_{xx}$ is constant during the deformation. We may then contour q in $(\beta, \overline{d}_{xx})$-space (Fig. 11.24). In this figure, for $m = 4$, q has been normalized by the maximum value attained, $(q_d)_{max} = 14$. This occurs for foliation-normal shortening $\overline{d}_{xx} = 0$ for a

Fig 11.25 Crenulation simulation $m = 4$, vertical stretch is 1.2; initial undeformed area was square.

component with band orientation – or axial plane orientation – normal to the direction of shortening. Only positive values of q/q_{max} are shown. q may be negative, indicating decay in the amplitude of a perturbation. Negative contours are disposed in a pattern that has a center of symmetry about the point $\beta = \overline{d}_{xx} = 0$.

For combined states of deformation in which positive shearing is added to foliation-parallel shortening, the maximum shifts to a negative value of β, representing a fold structure that has a sense of axial plane orientation opposite to that of so-called drag folds. Further, the maximum rate of amplification decreases. The result predicts that folds may form in foliation-parallel shear alone, $\overline{d}_{xx} = 0$, but once the axial plane of a component rotates to normal to the foliation in the course of a finite deformation, its amplitude will then cease growing and begin to decay. Thus, any structures which form in foliation-parallel shear must "lock-in" by a mechanism as yet not identified to exist before decay sets in. Potential instability exists in combined foliation-parallel extension and shear, but the strength of instability in the present case is weak. Continued amplification with shear takes place in a basic-state flow with $\bar{d}_{xx} < -0.6$, and aggregate amplification will outweigh later decay for any value $\bar{d}_{xx} < 0$.

By integrating the relations (11.120) through a finite deformation, we may determine the amplitude and orientation history of a component. If an initial set of perturbations with random initial slope, λA, and phase, and chosen at equal intervals in orientation to foliation β are followed, the final form of foliation planes may be computed as a summation. An example is shown in Fig. 11.25 for foliation-normal shortening. The initial shape of the rock element was square. Fold axial planes are not perfectly normal to the direction of shortening and they are finite in extent, even as seen in this finite segment of the medium. They are nearly normal to the direction of shortening, as expected from the rate of shortening maximum there (Fig. 11.24).

At present, little quantitative interpretation of structures in foliated and multi-layer rocks has been carried out, and this field of study remains open. Figure 11.24 suggests that the continuity of axial planes and the distribution in their orientation for a given bulk shortening might afford some indication of the strength of anisotropy as described by the parameter m the basic-state deformation, and the character of the initial perturbation.

11.6 | Concluding remarks

This chapter has introduced a few of the factors which might be treated in more realistic models of rock deformation: (i) rheological non-linearity; (ii) dilatation at a macroscopic scale mediated by diffusional transport; (iii) bulk properties of a composite material; and (iv) instability in the deformation of an anisotropic material. The models formulated and analyzed are relatively simple and to a substantial degree build on material presented in earlier chapters. The first two topics were studied in application to the initiation of pinch-and-swell structures in extension, as well as to folds and mullions, to suggest the possibility of the study of a wide range of behavior in structures such as folds or boudinage. Overall, though, the presentation is one of brief sketches of restricted subject matter and methods. While these sketches often supply means of carrying out the modeling of naturally deformed rock, they also provide a means of gaining physical insight.

Chapter 12

Model development and methodology

Oblique aerial photograph of the eastern slope of Mt. Hillers in the Henry Mountains, Utah. The Black Mesa laccolith and Maiden Creek sill form the black, cliff-forming outcrops.

Three main approaches are needed to unscramble a complicated system. (1) One can take it apart and characterize all the isolated bits – what they are made of and how they work. (2) Then one can find exactly where each part is located in the system in relation to all the other parts and how they interact with each other. These two approaches are unlikely, by themselves, to reveal exactly how the system works. (3) To do this one must also study the behavior of the system and its components while interfering very delicately with its various parts, to see what effect such alterations have on behavior at all levels (Crick, 1988).

Nature, or what we might call natural reality, can appear to our senses as a very complicated system when we view geological structures in outcrop. Francis Crick (1988) also faced a complicated system when viewing the constituents of living cells. He suggests in his book *What Mad Pursuit* that one should first characterize all the parts of the system and then understand their geometric relationships. This is what we attempt to do as structural geologists when mapping structures in the field. In Chapters 2 and 3 some of the useful tools for mapping were described and the principles of differential geometry were introduced to provide the fundamental basis for characterization of structures. Unlike the cell in a test tube, many parts of typical geological structures are inaccessible because of limited exposure, and usually there are limited data on the temporal development of structures. Crick then suggests one must study the system as a whole to understand how it behaves when various parts are perturbed. This step is possible when the system is a cell in a test tube, but generally it is impossible when the system is a rock mass larger than a cubic meter. Consequently, we turn to laboratory and mathematical models of geologic structures to carry out this step in Crick's prescription for scientific inquiry. Models are constructed with specific features and attributes of the rock mass, and the model system is studied to understand how it works.

This chapter focuses on the development of mathematical models of geologic structures. In particular we consider the idealization of observed structures and the selection of general boundary conditions for model development. At the end of this chapter we present a methodology for the practice of structural geology that summarizes the underlying concepts that have been described and utilized throughout this book.

12.1 | Idealization of field observations

We begin this chapter by describing how G. K. Gilbert (1877) idealized the laccolithic intrusions in the Henry Mountains of southeastern Utah (Fig.

7.8). The frontispiece for this chapter is an oblique aerial photograph of the eastern flank of Mt. Hillers showing laccolithic intrusions at Black Mesa and Trachyte Mesa. Gilbert was one of the masters of scientific methodology in the practice of geology, and we have much to learn from studying the way he worked. We give an example of the procedure of idealization, recognizing that this will not provide one with all the knowledge required to implement the procedure. Indeed, to perfect this procedure requires considerable experience mapping structures in the field, and intimate familiarity with continuum mechanics. Nevertheless, we introduce the procedure now in a specific, and perhaps narrowly focused, manner using the example of Gilbert's discovery of laccolites (now called laccoliths) and his research into the origins of the Henry Mountains (Fig. 1.16). It is assumed that the reader is familiar with the introduction to Gilbert's research provided in Chapter 1 and with his conceptual model for laccoliths (Fig. 1.17).

12.1.1 G. K. Gilbert's field observations in the Henry Mountains

Gilbert arrived on the western edge of the Henry Mountains in mid August of 1875 by horseback. Intrigued by the range of mountains he saw to the east, Gilbert wondered if they might be a good place to consider the question of whether volcanic mountains were just piles of lava flows or perhaps the result of doming by injection of magma at depth. On August 18, 1875, Gilbert observed the sedimentary rocks circling the base of Mt. Ellsworth and dipping away from the summit (Fig. 12.1). The next day he speculated that Mt. Hillers must be capped with trachyte (igneous rock) and again observed the sedimentary units dipping steeply around the base of the mountain in contrast to their nearly horizontal aspect further from the mountain.

On August 21st Gilbert approached the base of Mt. Hillers and recorded in words and a sketch (Fig. 12.2) the scene that he observed:

Camp 38 is on the SE base of Hillers. We have found several minute springs in skirting the mountain and this one barely suffices us. It cannot be depended on as permanent ... The rock which rises toward Hillers from the south is the B cliff (Ferron Sandstone). It is

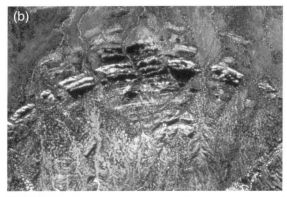

Fig 12.1 Photographs of the southwestern flank of Mt. Hillers. (a) From the ground looking toward the summit showing the upturned strata around the base of the mountain. (b) Aerial view showing prominent encircling strata. Photograph by D. D. Pollard.

lost in the "debris" without increasing the dip (7°) with which it approaches. But beyond are red and white sands – inferior rocks tilted almost to the vertical and interspersed with dikes. Moreover these sandstone hogbacks seem to trend in a curve around the mountain as far as they extend (Hunt, 1988a).

The juxtaposition of the flat-lying sedimentary rocks of the plateau and those somewhat older strata turned up nearly to vertical against the igneous core of the mountain was a dramatic sight. Clearly these mountains were not a simple pile of lava flows. The older sedimentary rocks apparently had been pushed up by the invading magma. This scene laid the groundwork for Gilbert's idealization of the mountains that would come the next day.

The view of Mt. Holmes from near Gilbert's campsite of August 22nd on the southern flank of Mt. Hillers is reproduced in a modern photograph (Fig. 12.3). He drew a sketch of this scene in his notebook (Fig. 12.4) and made the following comments:

Looking at it from a hill E of camp 38, I am impressed with the idea that the dikes are radial, diminishing outward. The dip of the sandstones is not greater at the center than on the flanks. It is just a tumor cracked in the middle. A main crack (dike) runs S (a–b), another NE (a–c), a third W (a–d). The S and W dikes show no flows and the adjacent sandstones are preserved by their hardness. Nothing below G.M. (Navajo Sandstone) shows but G.M. goes to the top (Hunt, 1988a).

By the time he wrote these lines the seed for Gilbert's conceptual model had germinated and, with the use of the word "tumor", he was almost ready to describe it.

The next step was taken when Gilbert produced the sketch in his notebook shown in Fig. 12.5 and compared his observations at Mt. Hillers and Mt. Holmes:

The types of Hillers and H.V. (Holmes) are somewhat different. The radial dikes of the latter are feebly represented by the thin radials of the former and the concentric dikes of Hillers do not appear in H.V. If Hiller be one extension of the H.V. type, then only the Trias was lifted and the Carboniferous either lay below the seat of action or below a disturbing reservoir (Hunt, 1988a).

This sketch was Gilbert's first attempt to draw the "disturbing reservoir" that he later termed a laccolite. There was no doubt in Gilbert's mind that these mountains were created by the injection of magma at depth to both lift and bend the overlying strata. He gathered further evidence on this field trip to support the hypothesis that "Hillers be an extension of the H.V. type" and that there exists a progressive evolution of flexural amplitudes from Mt. Holmes to Mt. Ellsworth to Mt. Hillers. It is clear that the concepts embodied in Fig. 12.5 were used as the basis for the reconstruction used as the frontispiece of Gilbert's final report (see Chapter 1, frontispiece). The final step that Gilbert took in the idealization procedure was to replace the mushroom-shaped laccolith and domed sedimentary strata (Fig. 12.5) with a cylindrical chamber of magma pushing upward on a rigid piston of flat-lying strata (Fig. 1.18).

12.1.2 Steps in the idealization procedure

The structural geologist usually starts with a direct field observation, although photographs (Figs. 12.1, 12.3) or field sketches and maps (Figs.

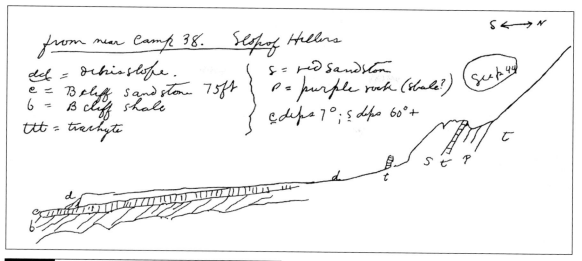

Fig 12.2 Sketch from the field notebooks of G. K. Gilbert in 1875 showing a cross section through the southwestern flank of Mt. Hillers (Hunt, 1988a). Compare this to Fig. 12.1. Reprinted from Hunt (1988a) with permission of The Geological Society of America.

12.2, 12.4) may be used to reproduce the scene for others. Of course what one sees directly in the field and then records on a photograph, sketch, or map should be recognizably similar, but many features of the scene are lost, while others are captured in these procedures. The act of recording the scene is a form of idealization. The photograph loses much of the three-dimensional view provided by one's eyes and may lose much of the color information as well as features hidden in shadows. Typically, sketches and maps record very little of the totality of a given scene. Yet, with a few lines and a bit of shading a skillful recorder such as Gilbert can transform the visible scene (Fig. 12.3) into a sketch (Fig. 12.4) that includes most of the geologically salient features.

An important question is why a particular scene that one stumbles across in the field should be more attractive than any other. Perhaps Gilbert chose to record the southern edge of Mt. Hillers (Fig. 12.2) because he believed it would enable him to address the issue of volcanic mountains raised by his boss, J. W. Powell. In any case, it is clear that Gilbert had a question in mind when he took the time to record the upturned strata and to marvel at this particular scene. He then focused on Mt. Holmes, possibly because it seemed to record an earlier stage in the process of uplift and doming. He noted that the dips of the layers were less at Mt. Holmes, that erosion had cut less deeply into this structure, and that the remaining strata carried completely over the top of the mountain. In contrast the top of Mt. Hillers had apparently been stripped of its overlying strata, so only igneous rock is exposed there.

Gilbert was engaged in working on the process of mountain building, so he sought out scenes that exemplified the stages in that process. In doing so he transformed spatial position and geometry into temporal sequence and motion: the changes in the geometry of the intrusions and deformed strata from Mt. Holmes to Mt. Ellsworth to Mt. Hillers recorded snapshots in time of the progressive evolution of laccoliths. This transformation of space for time is one of the most important tools of the structural geologist. Because we rarely are able to observe the deformation or flow of rock during the development of a structure, finding exposures that exemplify the different stages in such a development is a critical part of any field project.

Having chosen the scene to record, Gilbert began to throw away many of the things he observed directly in the field, as well as many of the things we can see in the photographs of Mt. Hillers and Mt. Holmes (Figs. 12.1, 12.3). In his sketches (Figs. 12.2, 12.4) only a few crucial items remain: the gently dipping strata of the plateau; the talus on the slopes; the more steeply dipping strata and interleaved sills flanking the mountains; the

Fig 12.3 Photograph of the northern flank of Mt. Holmes looking south toward the summit showing the inclined strata around the base of the mountain. Photograph by D. D. Pollard

Fig 12.4 Sketch from the field notebooks of G. K. Gilbert in 1875 showing a panorama of the northern flank of Mt. Holmes (Hunt, 1988a). Compare this to Fig. 12.3. Reprinted from Hunt (1988a) with permission of The Geological Society of America.

igneous core at Mt. Hillers and the vertical dikes at Mt. Holmes. No one would mistakenly claim that these sketches are photographs because the simple lines and patterns are mere representations. On the other hand, anyone with a modicum of geological experience would have no doubt that the sketch in Fig. 12.4 was made from the same scene recorded in the photograph in Fig. 12.3. Gilbert was a superb craftsman when it came to field sketches. They have sufficient lines to capture the essence of the geological features, while avoiding those lines that would simply clutter the image.

In the next step of his idealization (Fig. 12.5) Gilbert chose to throw away more things and, interestingly, he chose to add features that he did not observe! The dikes and sills that cut and interleaved the upturned strata on the flanks of the mountains are gone. Presumably, Gilbert decided that these intrusive forms were minor compared to the laccolith. The strata are completed over the top of the laccolith, a relationship he observed for the G.M. (Navaho Sandstone) at Mt. Holmes, but the strata are completely eroded from the top of Mt. Hillers. Furthermore, the talus is gone from the slope of the mountain. A feeder dike is added at the bottom of the laccolith, presumably because Gilbert believed that the magma had to flow up from below in some kind of channel. He had not seen such a feeder and had no way of knowing what shape or dimensions it might have. Perhaps the most interesting feature that Gilbert added, without direct evidence, is the flat bottom contact between the intruded igneous rock and the apparently undisturbed strata below.

In the final step, the broad flexure of the strata is replaced by the highly localized deformation of

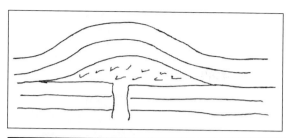

Fig 12.5 Sketch from the field notebooks of G. K. Gilbert in 1875 showing his conceptual model of a laccolith. Reprinted from Hunt (1988a) with permission of The Geological Society of America.

a cylindrical fault, cutting entirely through the overburden (Fig. 1.18). This fault forms the periphery of the laccolith as the overlying piston of sedimentary rock is pushed upward. The bending of the strata over the laccolith is completely ignored in this idealization. Indeed, there is no deformation of the strata except along the fault. Because of the geometry of the fault and the piston, the laccolith has a vertical side and a flat top, rather than the mushroom shape of the idealization shown in Fig. 12.5.

At each step in the procedure of idealization Gilbert made choices about what was important and what was not, about what should be added and what should be deleted. These choices have a profound effect on the nature of the analysis that is to follow and determine most of the results that will be forthcoming. By throwing away the sills interleaved with the upturned strata, that part of the intrusive process could not be addressed. By transforming the flexure of the strata into a fault, the resistance that bending might offer to the inflation of the laccolith was ignored. By replacing the magma with a static pressure distribution, the flow and heat transport of the magma is relegated to a lesser role. Choosing a fault to provide the resistance to uplift elevated the friction and strength of the sedimentary rocks to a more important role than the resistance to bending. Furthermore, the role of bedding-plane faults during bending was ignored. Exactly how and why Gilbert made these choices is not known, but they led him to conclusions about the origin of the Henry Mountains that otherwise would not have been obtained. Suffice it to say that one should

pay particular attention to such choices when engaged in the procedure of idealization.

Apparently the choices made by Gilbert in the final step of his idealization procedure (Fig. 1.18) were dictated by the solutions for boundary and initial value problems that were available to him, and the level of complexity that he felt was necessary to address his questions about laccoliths. This demonstrates the importance of being familiar with solutions to problems in mechanics and also the necessity for pragmatic decisions. Gilbert knew that engineers had developed solutions for the bending of elastic plates and his conceptualization in Fig. 12.5 includes bending as a prominent feature of the deformation, however, he chose to ignore bending. Furthermore, he was familiar with solutions for the flow of viscous fluids, but he chose to ignore the role that flow of the magma might play in the deformation. Apparently Gilbert believed that determining the relationship among the forces acting on a rigid body of simple geometric shape (Fig. 1.18) was sufficient to understand the origin of laccoliths. Working out the mechanics of the piston model led Gilbert to the hypothesis embodied in Eqn. (1.2): the laccolith radius is proportional to the depth of overburden. His field data proved to be consistent with this relationship (Table 1.1).

Choices made during the idealization procedure may be driven in part by practical considerations. For example, when is the report on this problem due on your thesis advisor's desk or your employer's desk? How long would it take one to learn the necessary principles and tools for an unfamiliar area of continuum mechanics in order to apply these to the particular problem? How much time would it take for the available computer to solve the problem that has been posed for a given set of boundary or initial conditions? How much would it cost to gather the necessary data to constrain the model? These and a host of other considerations can force some purely pragmatic decisions to be made that influence the outcome of an investigation.

As the idealization procedure continues, parameters and conditions are excluded from the definition of the problem, so the behavior of the model is likely to diverge from the behavior of the natural system. Therefore, confidence in the model results should diminish. If these parameters and conditions were included, the model may approach the actual behavior of the natural process more closely. On the other hand, the additional parameters and conditions may be less well constrained by actual data. A master of this kind of analysis, Art Lachenbruch, describes this dilemma in the following way:

In selecting a formal model there is a trade-off; as its complexity increases, we can usually conclude less from it with more confidence. In this paper we select a simple model and attempt to conclude a lot from it, while recognizing that the literal application of these conclusions is questionable, but that the insight is likely to be useful (Lachenbruch, 1973).

It is relatively easy, given the power of modern computers and the sophisticated tools available for modeling complex mechanical systems, to create a model of a geological process that is itself too complex to understand, or that is too poorly constrained by data. In hindsight it is clear that Gilbert's piston laccolith was simple enough to give him insight, and practical in the sense that the necessary field data could be gathered to test the hypothesis derived from the model.

In general terms the procedure we have described in this section is not new. Indeed, it can be traced back to the reductionist methodology first articulated by Descartes in 1619 (Davis and Hersh, 1986). It is one of the cornerstones of modern scientific research.

12.2 | Selection of general boundary conditions

General boundary conditions define the context of a problem, so the appropriate theoretical principles, fundamental laws, governing equations, and computational tools can be brought to bear on finding a solution. The selection of general boundary conditions is not a simple matter, and no easily written prescription can address all the variations and complexities one is likely to encounter. This procedure requires an understanding of both the field observations that serve to characterize the structures, and the physical principles and scaling relationships that underlie

possible models for these structures. Here we give examples, all based upon the structure that Gilbert set out to investigate over a hundred years ago in the Henry Mountains, and show how different questions, posed in the field about the same structure, lead to different choices for the context of modeling, that is to different general boundary conditions.

Because tectonic processes are multifaceted, often involving solid and fluid deformation, heat and mass transport, and chemical reactions, rarely is there a single choice of general boundary conditions that enables one to address all the interesting questions that arise from field observations. Furthermore, we are limited in our understanding of how these various processes are coupled together, and the solution methods for coupled problems may be difficult to implement. Finally, the solutions to coupled problems may be so complex that they are difficult to understand and therefore are not readily applied to the simple questions asked in the field. For all of these reasons we choose to break up tectonic processes into component parts following the methodology described in the quote at the beginning of this chapter (Crick, 1988). Each part is analyzed according to a particular choice of general boundary conditions. Thus, the selection of general boundary conditions is influenced by practical necessity and guided by an underlying reductionist philosophy of science.

Once we have made the choice to work within a particular area of continuum mechanics such as plate theory, elasticity theory, viscous fluid mechanics, or heat conduction, the most general differential equations for that area usually are simplified by eliminating certain variables or terms from these equations. This elimination may be based on field observations that justify, for example, the reduction of a three-dimensional structure to a two-dimensional approximation for that structure. Or, for example, the elimination may be based on a choice to ignore the initial and final phases of deformation during which a flow field changes in time, so a steady-state approximation can be used to describe the well-developed flow field that existed between these phases. In other cases dimensional analysis is used to quantify the relative importance of terms in the governing equations and eliminate those that are negligible. In this section we describe a variety of simplification procedures, and the methods that are employed to make and to justify these choices.

The procedure for idealization, described in the previous section, and the selection and simplification of general boundary conditions are not independent. The former is described as a field procedure and it should, for the most part, be undertaken during mapping or data collection, when the decisions can be evaluated by direct observations. The latter is described as an office procedure, and it is likely to be undertaken with a continuum mechanics textbook in hand. In fact most structural geologists, including Gilbert, intertwine these two procedures. Apparently Gilbert carried an engineering handbook into the field and presumably used it to help conceptualize and set up problems (Pyne, 1980). An idealization may be designed specifically to take advantage of a known solution, for example in elasticity theory or fluid mechanics. Later, having found a solution for a more realistic set of parameters, certain constraints imposed in the former idealization may be relaxed. In this way an analysis may progress, for example, from one employing a linear and isotropic viscous fluid (Chapter 10), to an anisotropic viscous fluid, to a fluid with more complex rheology (Chapter 11). This give-and-take relationship between the idealization of field observations and the selection of general boundary conditions for modeling is vital to the development of effective models and the analysis of structural data.

12.2.1 Plate theory: what controls the shape of the domed strata over a laccolith?

It is clear that Gilbert understood the strata over laccoliths in the Henry Mountains did not behave as rigid pistons (Fig. 1.18) because his conceptual model that preceded the piston laccolith shows the strata bent into a domed shape (Fig. 12.5). He noted that resistance to uplift for the piston model is proportional to the overburden thickness and speculated in his report of 1877 that resistance to bending might increase with some greater power of the overburden thickness.

I am led by the analogy of allied problems in mechanics to assume that the resistance of the body of strata varies with some power of its depth, but I am unable to say what power. So far as I am aware, neither mathematical analysis nor experimentation has been directed to the problem in question. According to Rankine "the resistances of flexure of similar cross-sections (of elastic beams) are as their breadths and as the squares of their depths" ("Applied Mechanics", page 316), and it is possible that the same law applies to the resistances which continuous strata oppose to the uplifts of domes. But it appears more probable that the greater complexity of the strains developed in the formation of domes causes the depth to enter into the formula with a higher power than second (Gilbert, 1877).

To address questions about the shape of the domed strata and their resistance to bending a number of models have been proposed since Gilbert's report based on a theory for the deflection of thin plates (Johnson, 1970; Pollard and Johnson, 1973; Koch et al., 1981; Kerr and Pollard, 1998).

The context, or general boundary conditions, for the analysis of thin plates is the engineering discipline called *strength of materials* or *plate theory*. Reference textbooks are available on this subject from the engineering literature (Timoshenko, 1958; Timoshenko and Woinowsky-Krieger, 1959). In Section 4.3.1 the dimensionless group for plate bending was derived, (4.45), and showed that displacements scale with the fourth power of the length and inversely with the elastic stiffness and the third power of the thickness. Thus, bending under distributed loads is most sensitive to the geometry of the plate.

To apply plate theory to the laccolith problem the sedimentary strata overlying the laccolith are idealized as a stack of n thin plates of thickness, h_i (Fig. 12.6a). Particular plates may or may not correspond to stratigraphic units, but each behaves as an independent mechanical unit, capable of slipping relative to adjacent mechanical units along bedding-plane faults. Unlike Gilbert's rigid piston, these plates deform according to linear elastic relationships among the stress and infinitesimal strain components defined by Hooke's Law (Chapter 8). For plates that are isotropic and homogeneous with respect to elastic properties, the two relevant material constants for each plate are Young's modulus, E_i, and Poisson's ratio, ν_i. The plates are bent by upward directed forces due

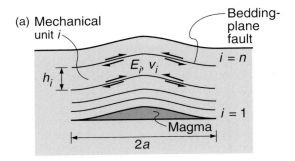

(a) Mechanical unit i

Bedding-plane fault

E_i, v_i

h_i

$i = n$

$i = 1$

Magma

$2a$

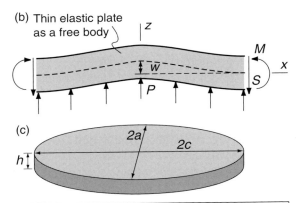

(b) Thin elastic plate as a free body

z

M

w

x

S

P

(c)

$2a$

$2c$

h

Fig 12.6 Idealized model for plate bending over a laccolith. (a) Cross section of multiple mechanical units with bedding-plane faults. (b) Cross section of a single mechanical unit. (c) Oblique view of plate model for a mechanical unit.

ution of tangential tractions on these cross sections of the plate. Thus, the equilibrium of the free body is determined by the vertical pressure acting across the plane of the plate, and the bending moments and shear forces acting on the lateral edges of the plate.

The vertical displacement of particles along the middle surface of the plate is referred to as the *deflection*, w, which is used to characterize the shape of the deformed plate. The governing equation for the deflection distribution, $w(x, y)$, of a single thin elastic plate subject to a pressure acting across the plane of the plate apparently was first derived by Navier in 1820 (Timoshenko, 1953, p. 121):

$$\frac{\partial^4 w}{\partial x^4} + 2\frac{\partial^4 w}{\partial x^2 \partial y^2} + \frac{\partial^4 w}{\partial y^4} = \frac{P(x,y)}{R} \qquad (12.1)$$

The plate is postulated to be in a state of static equilibrium so there are no (or negligible) accelerations of the middle surface in the z-direction. In (12.1) the term $R = Eh^3/12(1 - \nu)$ is the so-called *flexural rigidity* of the plate, a measure of the resistance to bending. Note that the flexural rigidity is proportional to Young's modulus and to the cube of the plate thickness. From the governing equation we see that the plate problem is two dimensional, that is the deflection and the pressure are functions of only two spatial coordinates. This fourth-order partial differential equation is solved for particular choices of boundary conditions to determine the distribution of deflection. It should be mentioned that this formulation is restricted to thin elastic plates, those that have lengths greater than about eight times their thickness, $2a/h > 8$, and to deflections that create slopes less than about 20°. For lesser ratios of length to thickness or greater slopes, simplifying postulates about the bending of the plate introduce errors in deflection that exceed 10%.

For the sake of this example, consider a stack of n plates all with the same elliptical shape in the (x, y)-plane (Fig. 12.6c). The long dimension of each plate is $2c$, and the short dimension is $2a$, so the general elliptical plan can vary from circular, $c = a$, to anticlinal, $c \gg a$. Gilbert conceived of the "ideal" laccolith as being circular in plan shape (Gilbert, 1877), whereas Hunt (1953) interpreted the laccoliths around the flanks of the five Henry

to the magma pressure distributed over a length $2a$, and this upward motion is resisted by the weight of the plates and their elastic stiffness. The plates slide over one another as they bend and the host rock below the level of the laccolith and to either side of the bending plates is treated as rigid.

A particular plate is shown isolated as a free body (Fig. 12.6b) with the coordinate system oriented so the x-axis and y-axis lie in the plane of the plate with the z-axis vertical, and the origin is at the center of the middle surface of the plate in the undeformed state. The normal component of traction on the bottom of the plate is equivalent to a distributed pressure, $P(x, y)$, and there are no shear components. The top of the plate is traction free and the distal edges are loaded by the bending moment, M, and shear force, S, necessary for static equilibrium (Timoshenko, 1958; Timoshenko and Woinowsky-Krieger, 1959). The bending moment accounts for the distribution of the normal tractions and the shear force accounts for the distrib-

Mountains as being "tongue-shaped" or roughly anticlinal in plan with long axes extending radially from the intrusive centers. The elliptical plan accounts for every shape from one of these end-members to the other. The boundary conditions at the distal edge of each plate are that both the deflection and the slope are zero.

A uniform distribution of pressure, $P = $ constant, is defined as the difference between the magma and lithostatic pressures, $P_m - P_w$. For plates that are able to slide freely over one another (no shear tractions across the interfaces), the flexural rigidity is the sum of the individual flexural rigidities, and we refer to this as the *effective flexural rigidity*, R_e (Pollard and Johnson, 1973):

$$R_e = \sum_{i=1}^{n} \frac{E_i h_i}{12(1 - \nu_i^2)} \qquad (12.2)$$

The plates are numbered from 1 to n starting at the base of the stack (Fig. 12.6); h_i is the thickness of the ith plate; and Young's modulus and Poisson's ratio for this plate are E_i and ν_i, respectively.

The solution to (12.1) for the deflection of any one of the uniformly loaded elliptical plates is (Love, 1944; Timoshenko and Woinowsky-Krieger, 1959):

$$w = \frac{(P_m - P_w)}{8R_e} \left\{ \frac{\left[1 - \left(\frac{x}{a}\right)^2 - \left(\frac{y}{c}\right)^2 \right]^2}{\left(\frac{3}{a^4} + \frac{2}{a^2 c^2} + \frac{3}{c^4} \right)} \right\} \qquad (12.3)$$

The two end-member cases simplify this two-dimensional problem to one spatial dimension where the deflection distributions are:

$$w = \frac{(P_m - P_w)}{24R_e}(a^4 - 2a^2 x^2 + x^4) \quad \text{(anticlinal)}$$
$$\qquad (12.4)$$

$$w = \frac{(P_m - P_w)}{64R_e}(a^4 - 2a^2 x^2 + x^4) \quad \text{(circular)} \quad (12.5)$$

The deflection distribution along any cross section in the (x, z)-plane is the same for the anticlinal plan shape. The deflection distribution along any radial line from the origin is the same for the circular plan shape. Note that the deflection is directly proportional to the driving pressure and to the fourth power of the half-length, a, so it is considerably more sensitive to changes in the length of the plate, than to changes in pressure.

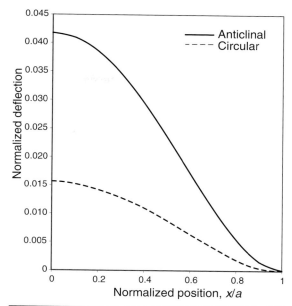

Fig 12.7 Plot of normalized vertical displacement (deflection) versus position for bending elastic plates with uniform distributed loads. Because of symmetry only half the distribution is shown.

The deflection is illustrated in Fig. 12.7 where the dimensionless deflection is plotted versus the dimensionless distance from the center of the bent plate for both the circular and anticlinal plans. Only positive values of x/a are shown because the solution is symmetric about $x/a = 0$. All deflection distributions for the general elliptical plan shape would fall between these two so the graph illustrates the entire spectrum of deflections for this model. The form of the model deflection is double hinged, that is a distal concave upwards hinge surrounds the edge of the dome and gradually changes to a limb of nearly constant dip where the curvature reverses sign to form the concave downward hinge marking the center of the dome. This form is qualitatively similar to the form envisioned by Gilbert in one of his idealizations of a laccolith (Fig. 12.5) and to the form illustrated in his restored section of Mt. Ellsworth (Chapter 1, frontispiece).

For a comparison of the model deflection distributions to field data we turn to maps and cross sections for the southern Henry Mountains (Jackson and Pollard, 1988, 1990). On the geologic and structural map of Mt. Holmes (Fig. 12.8) note that the sedimentary strata are continuous over the top of the dome, and the beds dip more or less in radial directions around the mountain. Furthermore, the magnitude of the dips is small far from the mountain, less than 10°; increases to over 20° on the steep flanks, and decreases to less than 10° near the top. The cross section along the line A'–A (Fig. 12.9) is based on the bedding attitudes measured at exposures around the mountain, and the geologic and topographic maps. This cross section reveals a form of bending that is similar to the plate model (Fig. 12.7). In addition to the doubly hinged structure the cross section reveals a gently dipping peripheral limb that extends 3–4 km beyond the lower hinge for all three of the southern Henry Mountains (Jackson and Pollard, 1990). This does not correlate with the simple plate model, and may indicate the presence of underlying sills and smaller laccoliths around the flanks of the central laccoliths.

The correlations between the plate model deflections and the cross-sectional shapes for Mt. Ellsworth and Mt. Hillers are more difficult to assess because the upper parts of these domes are eroded. Furthermore, whereas maximum limb dips of 20° at Mt. Holmes are just within the range permitted for the application of plate theory, the dips are between 50° and 55° at Mt. Ellsworth, and between 75° and 85° at Mt. Hillers. These intrusive structures have developed beyond the stage where elastic plate theory should be applied. However, if these domes passed through an earlier stage of development when, according to Gilbert's conceptual model, the sedimentary overburden was domed much like that at Mt. Holmes, plate theory would be applicable for this earlier stage.

The diameters of the southern Henry Mountains domes, $2a \approx 10$ to 14 km, are only two to three times the total overburden thickness, $h \approx 4$ km, yet applications of plate theory require a ratio of diameter to thickness greater than about eight. On the other hand the sedimentary section is composed of a multitude of sandstone, siltstone, and shale beds, and this bedding provides opportunities for the development of bedding-plane faults and shear zones within softer layers that would act to delaminate the overburden into thinner mechanical units. Bedding-plane fault zones are exposed within the sandstones and at formational contacts (Fig. 12.9), indicating that the overburden behaved in these places as a stack of mechanical units that could slip over one another. Measurements of bedding-plane faults at Mt. Holmes demonstrate that they are spaced from 150 to 200 m apart, so this may be a typical thickness of the mechanical units (Jackson and Pollard, 1988). In this way the total overburden thickness of about 4 km could be reduced to an *effective thickness*, h_e, that was considerably less than the diameter of the domes.

The effective thickness of a stack of bending plates is equal to the thickness of a single plate that would resist bending just as much as the entire stack. For mechanical units with the same elastic properties, E and ν, that are able to slide freely over one another, the flexural rigidity reduces to the following simple form:

$$R_e = \frac{E}{12(1-\nu^2)}\sum_{i=1}^{n} h_i^3 = \frac{E h_e^3}{12(1-\nu^2)} \qquad (12.6)$$

Note that the resistance to bending in this equation scales with the cube of the effective thickness. Thus, if the effective thickness is less than the total thickness, there can be a profound effect on the resistance to bending. For example, if $h = 4$ km, then $h^3 = 64$ km. However, if this overburden is delaminated into four equal mechanical units by bedding-plane faults, then $h_i = 1$ km each, $n = 4$, and $h_e^3 = 4$. Delamination into four mechanical units reduces the resistance to bending by a factor of 16. Because bedding-plane faults would offer frictional resistance to sliding and, as pointed out in the next section, these faults are unlikely to develop over the entire laccolith, this analysis over-estimates the reduction in flexural rigidity. None-the-less the mechanical effect of bedding-plane faults on the development of laccoliths is likely to be significant.

In summary, the plate theory provides insight concerning the resistance to bending of sedimentary strata over laccoliths, and the solution for uniform loading gives a deflection shape that is similar to the early stages of doming at

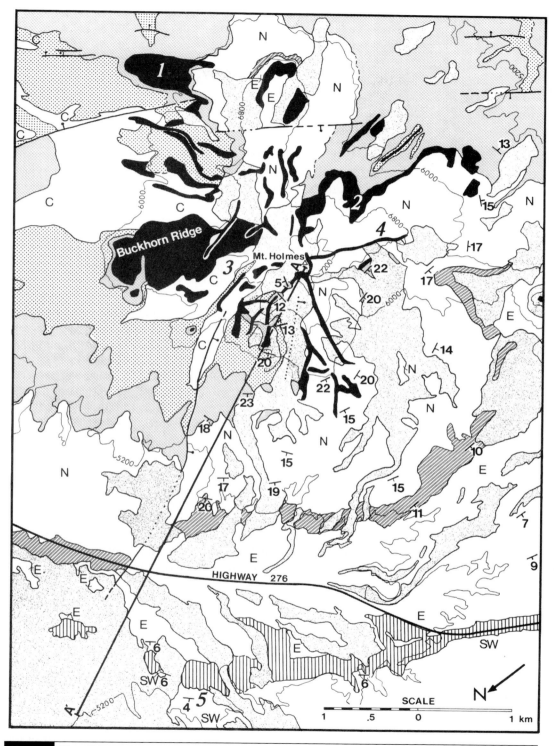

Fig 12.8 Map of Mt. Holmes in the southern Henry Mountains, UT. Black is diorite porphyry; white (N) is Navaho sandstone. Reprinted from Jackson and Pollard (1988) with permission of The Geological Society of America.

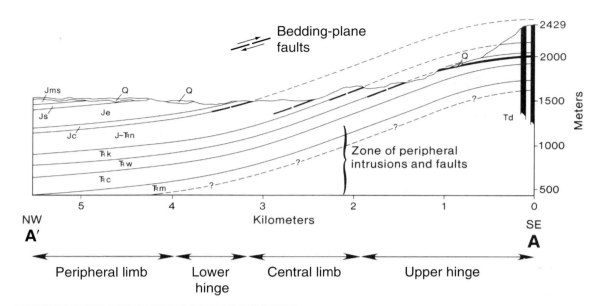

Fig 12.9 Cross section of Mt. Holmes identified as A'–A on Fig. 12.8. Note bedding-plane faults. Reprinted from Jackson and Pollard (1988) with permission of The Geological Society of America.

Mt. Holmes. To answer the question posed at the beginning of this section, the resistance to bending apparently exerts an important control on the shape of the domed strata, and this resistance is strongly dependent upon the thickness of the mechanical units in the sedimentary sequence. The shape of the domed strata also depends upon the pressure distribution in the laccolith, the distribution of slip between the mechanical units, and the nature of the boundary conditions at the distal edge of the laccolith, all of which have been investigated using plate theory (Pollard and Johnson, 1973; Koch *et al.*, 1981; Kerr and Pollard, 1998). Additional insights have been gained by addressing the sill–laccolith transition using elasticity theory (Zenzri and Keer, 2001).

12.2.2 Elasticity theory: how and where do bedding-plane faults form over sills?

Field observations of bedding-plane faults within strata overlying the laccoliths at the three southern Henry Mountains provide evidence that the overburden was sub-divided into mechanical units on the order of 200 m thick and capable of

sliding over one another (Jackson and Pollard, 1988). Plate theory indicates the importance of this delamination mechanism in reducing the effective thickness of the overburden and thereby reducing the resistance to bending so the laccolith can grow in amplitude. However, these mechanical units and the boundary conditions between them are prescribed in setting up a problem in plate theory, so one cannot address the questions posed in the title of this section. Instead one can use a model based on Gilbert's concept that the earliest stage in the development of laccoliths is the insinuation of a thin horizontal sill of magma between the strata (Fig. 12.10a). When the horizontal dimension, $2a$, of such a sill is less than the depth, d, the resistance to bending of the thick overburden is so great that opening of the sill is accommodated primarily by the elastic compression of the surrounding rock, both above and below the sill. The dashed lines in Fig. 12.10a schematically represent how bedding planes would displace upward and downward to accommodate opening of the sill. Note that the displacements decrease away from the sill and are negligible at Earth's surface.

The state of stress on horizontal planes around a model sill are calculated to determine where bedding-plane faulting might initiate (Jackson and Pollard, 1990). The context, or general boundary conditions, for this analysis is elasticity theory

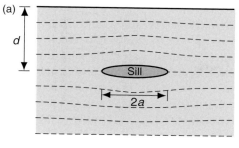

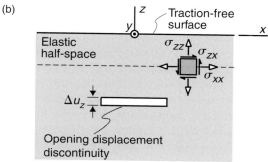

(Muskhelishvili, 1954; Timoshenko and Goodier, 1970; Barber, 1992). To apply elasticity theory to the problem of bedding-plane faulting the sedimentary units above and below the sill are idealized as part of a homogeneous and isotropic elastic body (Fig. 12.10b). Thus, differences in the elastic properties of the rocks making up the sedimentary sequence are ignored and the two isotropic elastic constants for the rock mass are taken as the shear modulus, G, and Lamé's constant λ (Chapter 8).

Navier's displacement equations of motion (7.135)–(7.137) written for quasi-static conditions and in the absence of body forces are:

$$G\frac{\partial^2 u_i}{\partial x_k \partial x_k} + (G + \lambda)\frac{\partial^2 u_k}{\partial x_i \partial x_k} = 0 \qquad (12.7)$$

Here the displacement components u_i are taken as u_x, u_y, and u_z and the distinction between spatial and material coordinates is ignored. From a solution to (12.7) for the displacement components the kinematic equations are used to compute the infinitesimal strain components and then

Hooke's Law is used to compute the stress components (Chapter 8). These stresses are the *supplementary stress field* due to opening of the model sill. A lithostatic stress field due to gravity acting on the body is added to find the total stress field.

The coordinate system is oriented so the x- and y-axes are horizontal, the z-axis is vertical, and the origin is at the traction-free surface (representing Earth's surface) directly above the model sill (Fig. 12.10b), which has a square tipline in this three-dimensional half-space. The sill lies in the $z = -d$ plane over the square area $-a < x < +a$ and $-a < y < +a$. Before opening, the upper and lower surfaces of the sill are an infinitesimal distance, ε, above and below the $z = -d$ plane. The boundary conditions, written in terms of the displacement components on these surfaces, produce an opening displacement discontinuity in the z-direction of magnitude Δu_z defined as:

$$\Delta u_z = u_z(z = -d + \varepsilon) - u_z(z = -d - \varepsilon) \qquad (12.8)$$

The upper surface of the model sill displaces in the positive z-direction, and the lower surface displaces in the negative z-direction, so the opening is Δu_z. Displacements of these two adjacent surfaces in x and y are zero. These boundary conditions describe what is commonly referred to as a *dislocation surface* or a surface of *displacement discontinuity*. The displacement components are continuous everywhere in the elastic body except for paths across the dislocation surface, at which there is an abrupt change in sign with no change in magnitude.

The solution for the rectangular dislocation surface (Okada, 1985) is too complicated to reproduce here but stress fields computed from this solution are illustrated in Fig. 12.11. The opening of the model sill induces changes in the state of stress everywhere in the surrounding region and the analysis seeks to identify those locations where stress changes on horizontal planes are conducive to bedding-plane faulting. The normal and shear stress components acting across horizontal planes in the model are σ_{zz} and σ_{zx}. Recall that the computed stresses represent the supplementary stress state, so the stress state due to gravity must be added to the normal components.

The component of shear stress induced on horizontal planes, σ_{zx}, would promote bedding-plane

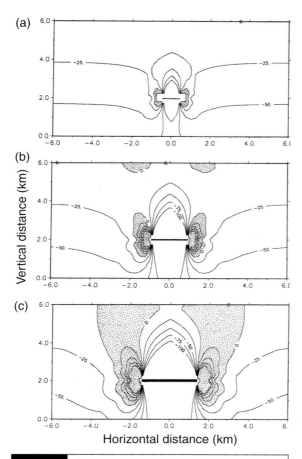

(a)

(b)

Vertical distance (km)

(c)

Horizontal distance (km)

Fig 12.11 Cross sections through a model sill with Coulomb stress contoured. Stippled region corresponds to that area where bedding-plane faults are predicted. Reprinted from Jackson and Pollard (1990) with permission of The Geological Society of America.

faulting, whereas the component of compressive normal stress, σ_{zz}, would resist faulting (Segall and Pollard, 1980; Oppenheimer et al., 1988). The relationship that quantifies this tendency for faulting is based on the Coulomb criterion (see Chapter 9) and is measured as the Coulomb stress, σ_C, which is calculated following (9.40):

$$\sigma_C = \left| \sigma_{zx} \right| + \mu_i [\sigma_{zz} + (\rho_r - \rho_w) g^* z] \quad (12.9)$$

Here μ_i is the coefficient of internal friction; ρ_r and ρ_w are the average mass density of the host rock and the groundwater, respectively; and g^* is the magnitude of the near-surface acceleration of gravity. Note that the normal stress is a combination of the

normal stress induced by opening of the sill (the supplementary stress state) and the ambient normal stress due to the weight of overburden (Anderson's standard state). The pore fluid pressure from a hydrostatic column of groundwater with water table at the free surface of the half-space reduces this normal stress to an effective normal stress. For the calculations used to produce Fig. 12.11 the constants are $\mu_i = 0.85$ and $(\rho_r - \rho_w) = 1.4 \times 10^3$ kg m^{-3}.

Contours of the Coulomb stress are plotted in Fig. 12.11 for a sill at a depth $d = 4$ km with lengths $2a = 1.0$, 3.0, and 4.0 km. The solution for the elastic boundary value problem of a crack with internal pressure suggests that the opening, Δu_z, should be proportional to the sill length for constant magma pressure, P. Here the ratio of opening to length is fixed at $\Delta u_z/a = 1/200$, so the three plots are for sills that are 5, 15, and 20 m thick, respectively. Regions of positive Coulomb stress are stippled to indicate where bedding-plane faulting is likely to develop. For $2a = 1.0$ km (Fig. 12.11a), the Coulomb stress is only positive in the immediate vicinity of the sill tips and the regions of stress concentration associated with sill opening are more or less symmetric above and below the tip. We would expect any bedding plane slip to be localized around the advancing tip of the sill. At distances from the center of the sill greater than its length, the stress field is dominated by the lithostatic stress of the rock and the hydrostatic stress of the groundwater, both of which are linear functions of depth. There, the contours of Coulomb stress are nearly horizontal and the values decrease at about -12 MPa km^{-1} from the surface. Immediately over and under the sill the Coulomb stress is negative due to the vertical compression of the rock as it accommodates the opening of the sill. The presence of the sill is virtually undetectable at Earth's surface.

Once the sill has advanced to a length of 3.0 km (Fig. 12.11b), the regions of positive Coulomb stress extend well above and below the sill tips. Also, two regions of positive Coulomb stress have developed at the free surface and extend about 500 m downward, toward the model sill tips. These changes indicate that the sill is starting to interact mechanically with the traction-free surface. At a length of 4.0 km (Fig.

12.11c), this interaction is significant and the regions of positive Coulomb stress extend from the surface to the sill tips, and these regions extend laterally to a distance of almost 4 km from the point immediately over the center of the sill. The overburden out to this distance is susceptible to the development of bedding-plane faults, except for the region immediately over the center of the sill where enhanced vertical compression would prevent frictional slip. Delamination is predicted to develop above the distal margin of the sill and not immediately over its center. This distribution of bedding-plane faulting would promote the formation of laccoliths with flat tops and monoclinal bending over their periphery (Koch *et al.*, 1981).

From the elasticity theory we understand that the stress perturbation associated with the lateral growth of a sill enhances the shear stresses and lowers the normal compressive stresses on horizontal bedding planes in such a way that faulting is likely on weak bedding planes above the advancing sill tip. As the sill approaches a length equal to the overburden thickness, the delamination spreads all the way to Earth's surface and we would anticipate a transition to laccolithic bending, accommodated by sliding of the mechanical units over one another along bedding-plane faults. Elasticity theory and the Coulomb failure criterion explain how and where these faults form, and this prediction is consistent with field observations of bedding-plane faults at Mt. Holmes in the Henry Mountains (Fig. 12.9).

12.2.3 Viscous fluid mechanics: how rapidly can magma flow into sills?

The questions asked in the previous two sections focus attention on host rock deformation during sill and laccolith formation. The mechanical role of the magma is reduced to providing a pressure on the stack of plates or on the elastic material surrounding the sill. In other words the mechanical action of the magma is replaced by the appropriate distribution of tractions in the form of a boundary condition. This is an effective way to simplify the mechanical system composed of both injecting magma and deforming host rock, but it necessarily means that one cannot address questions about the rate of development of the sill or

laccolith (Fig. 4.12). The context, or general boundary conditions, for the analysis of magma flow is that branch of fluid mechanics devoted to the flow of fluids with mechanical properties that include viscosity and strength. Reference textbooks on fluid mechanics provide the background for model development and include solutions for flow of materials with a variety of physical properties in conduits of various shapes (Lamb, 1945; Schlichting, 1979; Landau and Lifshitz, 1960; White, 1974).

In Section 4.3.2 we used dimensional analysis to identify Reynolds Number (4.55) as the scale factor for viscous flow in conduits (Reynolds, 1883; White, 1974). This dimensionless group is a ratio of inertial to viscous forces in the flowing fluid and is proportional to the conduit width, fluid density, and characteristic velocity, and inversely proportional to the Newtonian viscosity. Reynolds' laboratory experiments (Fig. 4.8c) demonstrated that the flow regime is laminar for numbers less than about 2000. The apparent viscosities of silicate liquids (magma) have been measured for a wide variety of chemical compositions and water contents over the range of melting temperatures (Shaw, 1963, 1969; Shaw *et al.*, 1968; Murase and McBirney, 1973; McBirney and Murase, 1984; Ryan and Blevins, 1987). Given the great viscosity of most magmas and the modest velocities for flow in sills the regime is likely to be laminar.

For the purpose of a simple example we consider an isothermal fluid, the model magma, flowing in a tabular conduit of length $2a$ and height $2h$, surrounded by rigid host rock (Fig. 12.12a). A feeder dike at the center of the sill supplies the magma. Of course hot magma emplaced into cold sedimentary rock will loose heat to the surroundings (Lovering, 1935, 1936; Jaeger, 1957, 1964b), but rock is a good insulator, so it is not unreasonable to postulate that the temperature change is insignificant over the time required for the sill to propagate to the transition length for laccolith formation. In Section 4.2.2 we reviewed the solution for conductive heat loss from a tabular intrusion of magma and showed that emplacement times on the order of a few days are consistent with this postulate (Delaney and Pollard, 1981, 1982). As the previous sections indicate, the sill grows in length and thickness as

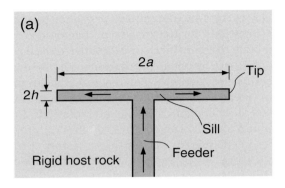

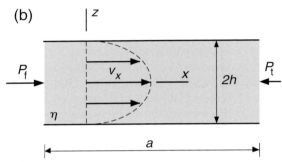

Fig 12.12 Idealized model for flow of viscous magma in a sill. (a) Geometry of sill conduit with feeder dike. (b) Velocity profile in model sill.

magma is injected from the feeder dike. Here the flow is determined for conduits with particular ratios of thickness to length, representing different moments during development of the sill. The solution does not describe the progressive development from an early stage to a later stage in this process and neglects the vertical component of velocity. We also neglect any consideration of the propagation mechanism or flow near the tip of the conduit, which is postulated to advance with the same velocity as the magma.

For the purpose of this example we postulate that the model magma has a constant density, ρ, and behaves like an isotropic Newtonian viscous fluid with constant viscosity, η. In other words this fluid obeys the Stokes condition described in Section 7.4.3 and the constitutive law given in (7.166). The viscosity of magma increases dramatically as temperature decreases, but we have already postulated an isothermal flow, so it is consistent to ignore changes in viscosity. Under these conditions Cauchy's Laws of Motion reduce to the Navier–Stokes equations (7.170) which describe

variations in space and time of the pressure and the velocity components. Flow through a sill is idealized in Fig. 12.12b as flow through a conduit with straight sides parallel to the x-axis and separated by a constant height, $2h$. Because the conduit is in the horizontal (x, y)-plane, the only non-zero component of gravitational acceleration is $g_z = g^*$. We postulate that the flow is entirely in the x-coordinate direction and that it is steady state, so the components of velocity are:

$$v_x = f(z), \quad v_y = 0 = v_z \tag{12.10}$$

Because v_y and v_z are both zero, the continuity equation (Section 7.3.2) insures that v_x does not vary in the x-direction. Because we postulate that all cross sections parallel to the (x, z)-plane are identical, v_x does not vary in the y-direction. Furthermore, the steady-state condition requires that v_x is not a function of time.

With these constraints on the gravitational and velocity vectors, the Navier–Stokes equations for the pressure and velocity distributions reduce to:

$$-\frac{\partial p}{\partial x} + \eta \frac{d^2 v_x}{dz^2} = 0, \quad -\frac{\partial p}{\partial y} = 0, \quad -\frac{\partial p}{\partial z} + \rho g^* = 0 \tag{12.11}$$

The first equation governs the rate of flow in the x-direction and the distribution of this velocity from the top to the bottom of the model sill. The second and third equations, respectively, require the pressure to be constant in the y-coordinate direction, and the pressure to vary linearly in the vertical z-direction in proportion to the unit weight of the magma. The distribution of velocity from the bottom to the top of the model sill is found by integration with a no-slip boundary condition at the conduit walls:

$$v_x = -\frac{h^2}{2\eta} \frac{\partial p}{\partial x}\left(1 - \frac{z^2}{h^2}\right) = v_x(\max)\left(1 - \frac{z^2}{h^2}\right) \tag{12.12}$$

The maximum velocity is at the center, $z = 0$, and is proportional to the square of the conduit thickness and the pressure gradient in the flow direction, and inversely proportional to the Newtonian viscosity. The distribution of velocity across the conduit is symmetric and parabolic (Fig. 12.12b).

We evaluate the velocity of magma flow in a sill, preceding the development of a laccolith, by putting (12.12) in the following form:

$$v_x(\text{max}) = -\frac{h^2}{2\eta}\left(\frac{P_t - P_f}{a}\right) \tag{12.13}$$

Here $2h$ and $2a$ are the thickness and length of the sill, whereas P_t and P_f are the magma pressures at the tip and the feeder. For the Henry Mountains examples, the sills that developed into the larger laccoliths formed at about 4 km depth where the lithostatic pressure would be about $P_w = 100$ MPa. The magma pressure in excess of the lithostatic pressure at this depth has been estimated to range from 30 to 70 MPa, based on the density of the magma, the density stratification of the host rock, and the depth to the source of the magma (Johnson and Pollard, 1973). Taking 50 MPa as representative of this excess pressure, the total magma pressure at the feeder of the sill would be $P_f = 150$ MPa. We postulate that the magma pressure would decrease to the lithostatic pressure at the tip of the sill, so $P_t = 100$ MPa. To be consistent with the previous section, we use a thickness to length ratio of $h/a = 1/200$. If the viscosity is taken as $\eta = 10^2$ MPa s, a value representative of silica-rich magma (Johnson and Pollard, 1973), a relatively short sill, $a = 200$ m, would have a maximum velocity of about 0.001 ms^{-1} (Fig. 12.13, square symbols). For this sill nearing the transition to laccolithic bending of the overburden, $a = 1500$ m, the lesser pressure gradient would tend to decrease the velocity, but this is more than compensated for by the greater sill thickness, so the maximum velocity would be about 0.01 m s^{-1}.

Magma viscosity is very sensitive to temperature and water content, and the constitutive properties of the magma are likely to be non-Newtonian (Johnson and Pollard, 1973). These factors are not well constrained for the intrusions in the Henry Mountains, so the value of viscosity chosen above could be in error by a couple orders of magnitude. Based on the linear relationship between viscosity and velocity found above, this would imply differences in velocity of a couple orders of magnitude. To illustrate this range of behaviors we plot velocities for $\eta = 10^0$ and for 10^4 MPas in Fig. 12.13. From this plot we conclude that the maximum flow velocity for a viscous magma

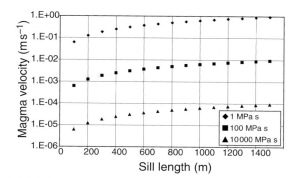

Fig 12.13 Plot of magma velocity versus sill length for three different viscosities.

would range between about 10^{-5} and 1 m s^{-1}. This implies that sills would take between about 10^3 s (~25 minutes) and 10^8 s (~5 years) to develop to the transition stage. While the time scale is not very well constrained, it clearly is a very short time compared to geologic eons.

The results we have just obtained ignore the deformation of the rock into which the magma is injected. A number of papers have treated the coupled problem of host rock deformation and magma flow during dike and sill emplacement (Spence and Turcotte, 1985; Lister, 1990; Lister and Kerr, 1991; Rubin, 1995). Comparing the energy consumed by fracturing, which is taken as independent of the intrusion length, and that consumed by viscous flow, which is taken as increasing linearly with intrusion length, it is clear that viscous dissipation will dominate beyond some critical length. For typical laboratory values of fracture energy this length is on the order of 1 m. However, it has been suggested that the fracture energy may not be constant and that the region of inelastic deformation at the tip of a dike or sill may increase in size with the length of the intrusion (Rubin, 1993). Under these conditions the fracture energy should not necessarily be neglected, particularly where geological evidence supports the development of such large regions of inelastic deformation (Delaney et al., 1986).

As sills propagate laterally and then bulge upward to form laccoliths, magma must be continually injected from below. This injection of magma results in the transport of heat from a source at greater depth into and throughout the shallow intrusion. To address questions about the cooling of the magma in tabular intrusions, and heating of the host rock, a number of models have been investigated, some that consider heat flow from a stagnant magma (Lovering, 1935, 1936; Jaeger, 1957, 1964b; Irvine, 1970), and others that consider the transport of heat within and from a flowing magma (Delaney and Pollard, 1982; Habert and De Saint-Blanquat, 2004). The context, or general boundary conditions, for these analyses is the subject of *heat transfer*, and there are many useful textbooks on this subject (Carslaw and Jaeger, 1959; Bird *et al.*, 1960).

12.3 | A methodology for the practice of structural geology

Newton's axiomatic framework allowed him to pursue a strategy in which he could construct a simplified, idealized mathematical model of the physical system he wanted to probe – in this case, the solar system. Using mathematics, Newton could work out the consequences of certain actions and compare them with measurements and empirical observations. That comparison, in turn, would suggest ways in which the model could be adjusted and refined to achieve even greater realism. In essence, this strategy of maintaining a right interplay between mathematical analysis and physical experience afforded a marvellously productive way of using mathematics to explain the workings of nature. Revolutionary in Newton's time, this kind of approach is taken for granted in modern research (Peterson, 1993).

The material presented in this textbook reveals two distinct views of structural geology. On the one hand we have described observations of structures: for example views through a microscope of tiny spherical objects that were deformed into ellipsoidal shapes as rocks were contorted into the South Mountain fold (Fig. 5.4), or photographs of exposures that show successive stages in the development of strike slip faults in granitic rock of the Sierra Nevada (Fig. 9.37). On the other hand we have described models of structures: for example a plot of principal stress trajectories associated with a pattern of dikes around the Spanish Peaks (Fig. 6.37), or a plot of displacement vectors associated with the 1999 Hector Mine earthquake (Fig.

8.15). The outcome of a structural investigation is judged to be successful if there is a compelling correspondence between the views provided by observation and modeling.

At times these different views of structural geology seem too disparate to be reconciled. The one is the world of boots and backpacks, rock saws and microscopes, maps and photographs, compasses and measuring tapes. The other is the world of vectors and tensors, material continua and differential equations, keyboards and computers, graphs and numbers. For some practitioners of structural geology a choice is made at an early stage in their education that closes the door on one of these worlds in favor of the other. One objective of this textbook is to encourage structural geologists to integrate these two worlds and discover the benefits of both.

A methodology for the practice of structural geology that integrates observations and modeling is illustrated in Fig. 12.14 as a set of ten stepping stones on a path with the suggestion that this be traversed in a counterclockwise sense starting at the top. Of course scientific investigations are rarely this well organized or rationalized. Instead of beginning with a field observation one may be inspired to investigate a new problem while reading a textbook on fluid mechanics or contemplating the solution to an elastic boundary value problem displayed as velocity vectors on a computer screen. Regardless of the source of inspiration one could argue that seeking the map or photograph or measurement in the field to confirm that the phenomenon in question occurs naturally in Earth's crust is a pre-requisite to launch an investigation. Thus, we find ourselves at the top of the diagram and suggest that this step of seeking data in the field should benefit from the techniques of field-based structural geology described in Chapter 2. Also, for the quantitative characterization of structures we advocate the use of differential geometry, some of which is described in Chapter 3.

Once launched along the path (Fig. 12.14) it is common to step off and move directly to a stepping stone out of sequence, or even to backtrack along the path. None-the-less this simple diagram provides a way to organize the primary scientific procedures employed by a structural geologist and to understand how they might relate to one

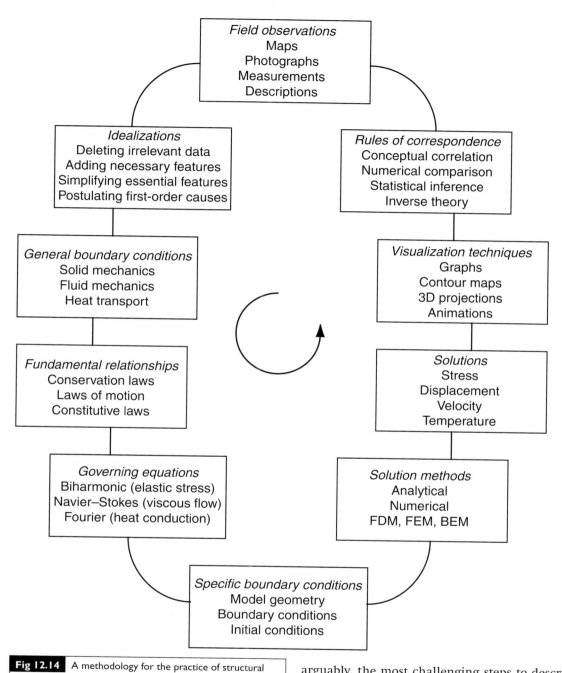

Fig 12.14 A methodology for the practice of structural geology.

another. For example, in Chapter 12 we have focused on two of the stepping stones near the beginning of the path: idealization of observed structures and selection of general boundary conditions for model development. These are, arguably, the most challenging steps to describe and, therefore, to teach. It is generally not possible to include all of the features of a structure in a model and those that are included usually are idealized. Idealization is given as the second step along the path and is a transition from observations to a model. It is largely done in the field during the process of mapping and measurement.

Here one postulates first-order cause-and-effect relationships and uses these to exclude observations that are deemed to be irrelevant.

The third step involves the selection of the branch of continuum mechanics that provides the general boundary conditions for modeling. Here the scaling arguments introduced in Chapter 4 should prove helpful, and the concepts of strain, rate of deformation, traction, and stress described in Chapters 5 and 6 must be understood. Although some sub-disciplines of continuum mechanics are spelled out on the third stepping stone, this list is not meant to be exclusive or to imply that coupled problems, for example of fluid flow and solid deformation, are unimportant. Indeed, the level of understanding of coupled problems among structural geologists and the modeling resources now available in terms of both hardware and software suggest that this will be a very fruitful area of investigation in the twenty-first century.

After selecting the theoretical context for an investigation one should focus on the fundamental relationships, two of which are described in Chapter 7 as the conservation laws of mass and momentum. This fourth step along the path commonly is overlooked, but it provides a touchstone that makes clear how the Laws of Motion have been formulated and how the constitutive laws are employed to reduce these to a specific set of governing equations identified with the fifth step along the path. At this point one has made an explicit commitment to a material behavior and perhaps simplified the equations of motion to exclude temporal or spatial variations in material properties. In this textbook we give considerable attention to the linear elastic material as described in Chapter 8 and the linear viscous material as described in Chapter 10. One of the most commonly employed governing equations in the elastic context is the biharmonic equation for the stress function in two dimensions. In the viscous context the Navier–Stokes equations are the benchmark.

In the sixth step one chooses a particular model geometry, which may reduce the governing equations to two or even one spatial dimension. Here one may eliminate time altogether, as in a quasi-static elastic problem or steady-state viscous flow problem. Then the specific boundary and/or initial conditions are selected to provide the constants of integration necessary to solve the governing equations. Sometimes, the specific boundary conditions may be constrained by field measurements, thereby establishing a direct link with the stepping stone at the top of the diagram. In other cases the specific boundary conditions are chosen arbitrarily, just to see what the outcome might be, and thereby learn about the behavior of the model structure. We have illustrated both of these approaches to modeling with examples throughout the text. In Chapters 8, 9, 10, and 11 we have employed methods that achieve analytical solutions to particular problems in elasticity theory or fluid mechanics. In the simpler cases these solutions are derived, but others are taken from the vast literature on these subjects without derivation to illustrate a particular point or concept in the context of the seventh stepping stone. In a few cases solutions were obtained by numerical methods but these methods are not even introduced here, much less developed from first principles. The finite-difference method (FDM), finite-element method (FEM), and boundary element method (BEM) have been exploited by engineers and scientists to find numerical solutions to boundary value problems (Timoshenko and Goodier, 1970; Crouch and Starfield, 1983; Hughes, 1987).

Whether found using analytical or numerical methods, the solutions themselves are the eighth step in this methodology and they provide the field quantities such as stress, displacement, velocity, and temperature as functions of the spatial coordinates and time. Only in rare instances are the distributions in space and time of these quantities so simple as to be understandable from an analytical equation. Therefore, one employs visualization techniques, the ninth stepping stone, that range from two-dimensional graphs and contour plots to three-dimensional projections and animations. Throughout this text we have used Matlab to aid in visualization. Because the scripts that produce these illustrations are available, visualization is a dynamic process in which the reader can adjust the boundary conditions or values of the parameters and see the response.

The last stepping stone along the path of Fig. 12.14 links the output of a modeling investigation to field observations through rules of correspondence (Margenau, 1977). These come in various forms and levels of mathematical and statistical rigor. In the simplest form a concept, such as the linear relationship between depth and diameter of laccoliths as conceived by Gilbert (Fig. 1.18), is tested by estimating the stratigraphic position of laccoliths in the Henry Mountains (Table 1.1). In a more quantitative evaluation the calculated slip directions for intersecting normal faults in an elastic model are compared to field measurements of slickenline orientations from the Chimney Rock area (Fig. 2.31). In another example, linear inverse theory is used to calculate the slip distribution on a fault model for the 1999 Hector Mine earthquake (Fig. 8.15) as constrained by surface displacement data from satellite radar images. The calculated slip distribution is then used as a boundary condition in a forward elastic model and the resulting surface displacements compared to those from the radar image. In all of these examples the correspondence proved sufficiently compelling to convince the structural geologist that the investigation was on the right track. Discrepancies, on the other hand, motivate further field work and modeling.

12.4 | Concluding remarks

In summary, we advocate a methodology that applies the extensive machinery of the physics and chemistry of the processes involved, most centrally rock deformation, both to suggest observations and to analyze, visualize, and interpret them. In this way, a coherent and self-consistent, if idealized, and non-unique, re-construction of the development of a geological structure may be achieved. We concede that tectonic processes and their products will not be completely described by mechanical models, but advocate the position that the mechanics must be complete. Thus, for prescribed initial and boundary conditions a forward model is generated that may produce likenesses of some of the observed geological structures and fabrics, to some satisfactory degree of approximation. If the forward model fails to produce satisfactory likenesses we learn that one or more of the postulates is inappropriate and must be excluded or modified. One cannot, however, exclude or modify the fundamental laws upon which the mechanical model is based. The general method we advocate is the construction of a sequence of quantitative models, graduated in their degree of detail, and successively providing an improved understanding.

References

Achenbach, J. D., 1973, *Wave Propagation in Elastic Solids*. New York: American Elsevier.

Ackermann, R. V., Schlische, R. W., and Withjack, M. O., 2001, The geometric and statistical evolution of normal fault systems: an experimental study of the effects of mechanical layer thickness on scaling laws. *Journal of Structural Geology* 23: 1803–19.

Aczel, A. D., 2000, *Mystery of the Aleph: Mathematics, the Kabbalah, and the Search for Infinity*. New York: Four Walls, Eight Windows.

Adams, F. and Nicholson, J., 1901, Experimental investigation into the flow of marble: *Philosophical Transactions of the Royal Society of London* 195: 363–401.

Aki, K. and Richards, P. G., 1980, *Quantitative Seismology: Theory and Methods*. San Francisco: W. H. Freeman.

Albritton, C. C., Jr., 1980, *The Abyss of Time: Changing Conceptions of the Earth's Antiquity after the Sixteenth Century*. San Francisco: Freeman, Cooper and Co.

Alpha, T. R., Vigil, J. R., and Buchholz, L., 1988, *Map Projections Via Hyper Card*, Open File Report 88-364. Menlo, CA: US Geological Survey.

Amadei, B. and Stephansson, O., 1997, *Rock Stress and its Measurement*. London: Chapman and Hall.

Anderson, D., 1975, Chemical plumes in the mantle. *Geological Society of America Bulletin* 86: 1593–1600.

Anderson, E. M., 1936, The dynamics of the formation of cone-sheets, ring-dykes, and caldron-subsidences. *Proceedings of the Royal Society of Edinburgh* 56: 128–56.

Anderson, E. M., 1951, *The Dynamics of Faulting and Dyke Formation with Application to Britain*. Edinburgh: Oliver and Boyd.

Anderson, E. M., 1972, *The Dynamics of Faulting and Dyke Formation with Applications to Britain*. New York: Hafner.

Anderson, T. L., 1995, *Fracture Mechanics*. Boca Raton: CRC Press.

Andrews, D. J. and Hanks, T. C., 1985, Scarp degradation by linear diffusion: inverse solution for age. *Journal of Geophysical Research* 90: 10 193–208.

Antonellini, M. and Aydin, A., 1994, Effect of faulting on fluid flow in porous sandstones: petrophysical properties. *American Association of Petroleum Geologists Bulletin* 78: 335–77.

Antonellini, M. and Aydin, A., 1995, Effect of faulting on fluid flow in porous sandstones: geometry and spatial distribution. *American Association of Petroleum Geologists Bulletin* 79: 642–71.

Antonellini, M. A., Aydin, A., and Pollard, D. D., 1994, Microstructure of deformation bands in porous sandstones at Arches National Park, Utah. *Journal of Structural Geology* 16: 941–59.

Archuleta, R., 1984, A faulting model for the 1979 Imperial Valley earthquake. *Journal of Geophysical Research* 89: 4559–85.

Argand, E., 1911, Les nappes de recouvrement des Alpes Pennines et leurs prolongements structuraux. *Beiträge zur geologischen Karte der Schweiz* 31: 1–25.

Arrowsmith, J. R., Pollard, D. D., and Rhodes, D. D., 1996, Hillslope development in areas of active tectonics. *Journal of Geophysical Research, B, Solid Earth and Planets* 101(3): 6255–75.

Arrowsmith, J. R., Rhodes, D. D., and Pollard, D. D., 1998, Morphologic dating of scarps formed by repeated slip events along the San Andreas Fault, Carrizo Plain, California. *Journal of Geophysical Research, B, Solid Earth and Planets* 103(5): 10 141–60.

Atkinson, B. K., 1987, *Fracture Mechanics of Rock*. London: Academic Press.

Atkinson, B. K. and Meredith, P. G., 1987, Experimental fracture mechanics data for rocks and minerals. In B. K. Atkinson, ed., *Fracture Mechanics of Rock*. London: Academic Press, pp. 477–525.

Aydin, A., 1977, Faulting in sandstone. Unpublished Ph.D. thesis, Stanford University.

Aydin, A., 1978, Small faults formed as deformation bands in sandstone. *Pure and Applied Geophysics* 116: 913–30.

Aydin, A., 2000, Fractures, faults, and hydrocarbon entrapment, migration and flow. *Marine and Petroleum Geology* 17(7): 797–814.

Aydin, A. and DeGraff, J. M., 1988, Evolution of polygonal fracture patterns in lava flows. *Science* 239: 471–6.

Aydin, A. and Eyal, Y., 2002, Anatomy of a normal fault with shale smear: implications for fault seal. *American Association of Petroleum Geologists Bulletin* 86(8): 1367–81.

Aydin, A. and Johnson, A. M., 1978, Development of faults as zones of deformation bands and as slip surfaces in sandstone. *Pure and Applied Geophysics* 116: 931–42.

Aydin, A. and Schultz, R. A., 1990, Effect of mechanical interaction on the development of strike-slip faults with echelon patterns. *Journal of Structural Geology* 12: 123–9.

Badoux, H., 1963, Les bélemnites tronçonées de

Leytron (Valais). *Bulletin de Géologie, Minéralogie, Géophysique et du Musée Géologique de l'Université de Lausanne* **138**: 1–7.

Bahat, D., 1991, *Tectonofractography*. New York: Springer-Verlag.

Bai, T. and Pollard, D. D., 2000a, Closely spaced fractures in layered rocks: initiation mechanism and propagation kinematics. *Journal of Structural Geology* **22**: 1409–25.

Bai, T. and Pollard, D. D., 2000b, Fracture spacing in layered rocks: a new explanation based on the stress transition. *Journal of Structural Geology* **22**: 43–57.

Bai, T., Pollard, D. D., and Gao, H., 2000, Explanation for fracture spacing in layered materials. *Nature* **403**: 753–6.

Barber, J. R., 1992, *Elasticity*. Dordrecht: Kluwer Academic.

Barton, N., 1973, Review of a new shear-strength criterion for rock joints. *Engineering Geology* **7**: 287–332.

Barus, C., 1891, The viscosity of solids. *US Geological Survey Bulletin* **73**.

Batchelor, G. K., 1967, *An Introduction to Fluid Mechanics*. Cambridge: Cambridge University Press.

Batt, G. E., Brandon, M. T., Farley, K. A., and Roden-Tice, M., 2001, Tectonic synthesis of the Olympic Mountains segment of the Cascadia wedge, using two-dimensional thermal and kinematic modeling of thermochronological ages. *Journal of Geophysical Research* **106**: 26 731–46.

Beckmann, P., 1971, *A History of π (pi)*. New York: Dorset Press.

Bell, J. S. and Babcock, E. A., 1986, The stress regime of the western Canadian Basin and implications for hydrocarbon production. *Bulletin of the Canadian Petroleum Geologists* **34**: 364–78.

Bell, R. J. T., 1920, *An Elementary Treatise on Coordinate Geometry of Three Dimensions*. London: Macmillan.

Bergbauer, S., 2002, The use of curvature for the analyses of folding and fracturing with application to the Emigrant Gap Anticline, Wyoming. Unpublished Ph.D. thesis, Stanford University.

Bergbauer, S. and Martel, S. J., 1999, Formation of joints in cooling plutons. *Journal of Structural Geology* **21**(7): 821–35.

Bergbauer, S. and Pollard, D. D., 2003, How to calculate normal curvatures of sampled geological surfaces. *Journal of Structural Geology* **25**: 277–89.

Bergbauer, S. and Pollard, D. D., 2004, A new conceptual fold–fracture model including prefolding joints, based on the Emigrant Gap anticline, Wyoming. *Geological Society of America Bulletin* **116**: 294–307.

Bieniawski, Z. T., 1984, *Rock Mechanics Design in Mining and Tunneling*. Rotterdam: A. A. Balkema.

Bieniawski, Z. T. and Bernede, M. J., 1979, Suggested methods for determining the uniaxial compressive strength and deformability of rock materials. *International Journal of Rock Mechanics and Mining Sciences and Geomechanics Abstracts* **16**(2): 135–40.

Billings, M. P., 1972, *Structural Geology*. Englewood Cliffs, NJ: Prentice-Hall.

Biot, M. A., 1961, Theory of folding of stratified visco-elastic media and its implications in tectonics and orogenesis. *Geological Society of America Bulletin* **72**: 1595–620.

Biot, M. A., 1965, *Mechanics of Incremental Deformation*. New York: John Wiley and Sons.

Birch, F., 1966, Compressibility: elastic constants. In S. P. Clark, ed., *Handbook of Physical Constants*. New York: The Geological Society of America, pp. 97–173.

Bird, R. B., Stewart, W. E., and Lightfoot, E. N., 1960, *Transport Phenomena*. New York: John Wiley and Sons.

Bott, M. H. P., 1959, The mechanics of oblique slip faulting. *Geological Magazine* **96**: 109–17.

Bourne, S. J., 2003, Contrast of elastic properties between rock layers as a mechanism for the initiation and orientation of tensile failure under remote compression. *Journal of Geophysical Research* **108**: 10.1029/2001JB001725.

Bourne, S. J. and Willemse, E. J. M., 2001, Elastic stress control on the pattern of tensile fracturing around a small fault network at Nash Point, UK. *Journal of Structural Geology* **23**: 1753–70.

Bowden, F. P. and Tabor, D., 1950, *The Friction and Lubrication of Solids*. Oxford: Clarendon Press.

Brace, W. F., 1964, Brittle fracture of rocks. In W. R. Judd, ed., *State of Stress in the Earth's Crust*. New York: Elsevier, pp. 111–74.

Brace, W. F. and Bombolakis, E. G., 1963, A note on brittle crack growth in compression. *Journal of Geophysical Research* **68**: 3709–13.

Brace, W. F. and Byerlee, J. D., 1966, Stick slip as a mechanism for earthquakes. *Science* **153**: 990–2.

Brandon, M. T., 2004, The Cascadia subduction wedge: the role of accretion, uplift, and erosion. In B. A. van der Pluijm and S. Marshak, eds., *Earth Structure: An Introduction to Structural Geology and Tectonics*. New York: W. W. Norton, pp. 566–74.

Braunstein, J. and O'Brien, G. D., 1968, *Diapirism and Diapirs: Memoir*. Tulsa, OK: American Association of Petroleum Geologists.

Bredehoeft, J. D., Wolff, R. G., Keys, W. S., and Shuter, E., 1976, Hydraulic fracturing to determine the regional *in situ* stress field, Piceance Basin, Colorado. *Geological Society of America Bulletin* **87**(2): 250–8.

Bridgman, P. W., 1931, *Dimensional Analysis*. New Haven, CT: Yale University Press.

Brodkey, R. S. and Hershey, H. C., 1988, *Transport Phenomena: A Unified Approach*. New York: McGraw-Hill.

Brown, E. T. and Hoek, E., 1978, Trends in relationships between measured *in situ* stresses and depth. *International Journal of Rock Mechanics and Mining Science* **15**: 211–15.

Buckingham, E., 1915, Model experiments and the forms of empirical equations. *Transactions of the American Society of Mechanical Engineers* **37**: 263–92.

Bürgmann, R. and Pollard, D. D., 1992, Influence of the state of stress on the brittle–ductile transition in granitic rock: evidence from fault steps in the Sierra Nevada, California. *Geology* **20**: 645–48.

Bürgmann, R. and Pollard, D. D., 1994, Strain accommodation about strike–slip fault discontinuities in granitic rock under brittle-to-ductile conditions. *Journal of Structural Geology* **16**: 1655–74.

Bürgmann, R., Pollard, D. D., and Martel, S. J., 1994, Slip distributions on faults: effects of stress gradients, inelastic deformation, heterogeneous host-rock stiffness, and fault interaction. *Journal of Structural Geology* **16**: 1675–90.

Byerlee, J., 1978, Friction of rocks. *Pure and Applied Geophysics* **116**: 615–26.

Calladine, C. R. and Drucker, D. C., 1962, Nested surfaces of constant rate of dissipation in creep. *Journal of Applied Mathematics* **29**: 79–84.

Carena, S. and Suppe, J., 2002, Three-dimensional imaging of active structures using earthquake aftershocks: the Northridge Thrust, California. *Journal of Structural Geology* **24**(4): 887–904.

Carslaw, H. S. and Jaeger, J. C., 1959, *Conduction of Heat in Solids*. Oxford: Clarendon Press.

Carter, N. L., Friedman, M., Logan, J. M., and Stearns, D. W., 1981, *Mechanical Behavior of Crustal Rocks (The Handin Volume)*, *Geophysical Monograph*. Washington, DC: American Geophysical Union, p. 326.

Cartwright, J. A., Trudgill, B. D., and Mansfield, C. S., 1995, Fault growth by segment linkage: an explanation for scatter in maximum displacement and trace length data from the Canyonlands grabens of SE Utah. *Journal of Structural Geology* **17**: 1319–26.

Cathles, L. M., 1975, *The Viscosity of the Earth's Mantle*. Princeton, New Jersey: Princeton University Press.

Cathles, L. M., 1977, An analysis of the cooling of intrusions by ground-water convection which includes boiling. *Economic Geology* **72**: 804–26.

Chandrasekhar, S., 1979, Beauty and the quest for beauty in science. *Physics Today* **July**: 25–30.

Chapple, W. M., 1968, A mathematical theory of finite-amplitude rock-folding. *Geological Society of America Bulletin* **79**: 47–68.

Chapple, W. M., 1978, Mechanics of thin-skinned fold-and-thrust belts. *Geological Society of America Bulletin* **89**: 1189–98.

Chinnery, M. A., 1961, The deformation of the ground around surface faults. *Bulletin of the Seismological Society of America* **51**: 355–72.

Chinnery, M. A., 1963, The stress changes that accompany strike-slip faulting. *Bulletin of the Seismological Society of America* **53**: 921–32.

Chinnery, M. A., 1966, Secondary faulting: I and II. *Canadian Journal of Earth Sciences* **3**: 163–90.

Choukroune, P. and Seguret, M., 1973, Tectonics of the Pyrenees: role of compression and gravity. In K. A. De Jong and R. Scholten, eds., *Gravity and Tectonics*. New York: John Wiley and Sons, pp. 141–56.

Clark, S. P. J., 1966, *Handbook of Physical Constants*. New York: The Geological Society of America.

Cloos, E., 1946, *Lineation: A Critical Review and Annotated Bibliography*, *Geological Society of America, Memoir* 18. Ann Arbor, MI: Edwards Brothers.

Cloos, E., 1947, Oolite deformation in the South Mountain Fold, Maryland. *Geological Society of America Bulletin* **58**: 843–918.

Cloos, E., 1971, Microtectonics along the western edge of the Blue Ridge, Maryland and Virginia. Baltimore, MD: The Johns Hopkins University Press.

Cobbold, P. R., Cosgrove, J. W., and Summers, J. M., 1971, Development of internal structures in deformed anisotropic rocks. *Tectonophysics* **12**: 23–53.

Cobbold, P. R., Durand, S., and Mourgues, R., 2001, Sandbox modelling of thrust wedges with fluid-assisted detachments. *Tectonophysics* **334**: 245–58.

Cocco, M. and Rice, J. R., 2002, Pore pressure and poro-elasticity effects in Coulomb stress analysis of earthquake interactions. *Journal of Geophysical Research* **107**: 1–17.

Collins, G. C., Head, J. W., III, and Pappalardo, R. T., 1998, The role of extensional instability in creating Ganymede grooved terrain: insights from Galileo high-resolution stereo imaging. *Geophysical Research Letters* **25**: 233–6.

Committee on the Future of the Global Positioning System, 1995, *The Global Positioning System: A Shared National Asset. Recommendations for Technical Improvements and Enhancements*. Washington, DC: Aeronautics and Space Engineering Board, National Research Council, National Academy Press.

Compton, R. R., 1962, *Manual of Field Geology*. New York: John Wiley and Sons.

Cooke, M., Mollema, P., Pollard, D. D., and Aydin, A., 2000, Interlayer slip and joint localization in East Kaibab Monocline, Utah: field evidence and results from numerical modeling. In J. W. Cosgrove and M. S. Ameen, eds., *Forced Folds and Fractures, Special Publication*. London: Geological Society, pp. 23–49.

Cooke, M. and Pollard, D. D., 1996, Fracture propagation paths under mixed mode loading within rectangular blocks of polymethyl methacrylate. *Journal of Geophysical Research* 101: 3387–400.

Cooke, M. L., 1997, Fracture localization along faults with spatially varying friction. *Journal of Geophysical Research, B, Solid Earth and Planets* 102(10): 22 425–34.

Cooke, M. L. and Underwood, C. A., 2001, Fracture termination and step-over at bedding interfaces due to frictional slip and interface opening. *Journal of Structural Geology* 23(2–3): 223–38.

Cotterell, B. and Rice, J. R., 1980, Slightly curved or kinked cracks. *International Journal of Fracture* 16: 155–69.

Coulomb, C. A., 1773, Sur une application des règles de maximis et minimis à quelques problèmes de statique relatifs à l'architecture. *Acad. Roy. des Sciences, Mémoires de math. et de physique par divers savants* 7: 343–82.

Couples, G., 1977, Stress and shear fracture (fault) patterns resulting from a suite of complicated boundary conditions with applications to the Wind River Mountains. *Pure and Applied Geophysics* 115: 113–33.

Couples, G. D. and Lewis, H., 1998, Lateral variations of strain in experimental forced folds. *Tectonophysics* 295: 79–91.

Cowan, D., 1992, Chairperson's message. *Structural Geology and Tectonics Division Newsletter*. Boulder CO: Geological Society of America, p. 1.

Cowie, P. A. and Scholz, C. H., 1992, Growth of faults by accumulation of seismic slip. *Journal of Geophysical Research* 97: 11 085–95.

Cowie, P. A. and Shipton, Z. K., 1998, Fault tip displacement gradients and process zone dimensions. *Journal of Structural Geology* 20: 983–97.

Crick, F., 1988, *What Mad Pursuit: A Personal View of Scientific Discovery*. New York: Basic Books.

Crider, J. G., 2001, Oblique slip and the geometry of normal-fault linkage: mechanics and a case study from the Basin and Range in Oregon. *Journal of Structural Geology* 23(12): 1997–2009.

Crider, J. G. and Pollard, D. D., 1998, Fault linkage: three-dimensional mechanical interaction between echelon normal faults. *Journal of Geophysical Research, B, Solid Earth and Planets* 103(10): 24 373–91.

Crouch, S. L. and Starfield, A. M., 1983, *Boundary Element Methods in Solid Mechanics: with Applications in Rock Mechanics and Geological Engineering*. London: George Allen and Unwin.

Cruikshank, K. M. and Aydin, A., 1995, Unweaving the joints in Entrada Sandstone, Arches National Park, Utah, USA. *Journal of Structural Geology* 17: 409–21.

Culling, W. E. H., 1960, Analytical theory of erosion. *Journal of Geology* 68: 336–44.

Dana, J. D., 1847a, Geological results of the Earth's contraction. *American Journal of Science* 3: 176–88.

Dana, J. D., 1847b, Geological results of the Earth's contraction. *American Journal of Science* 4: 88–92.

Dahlen, F. A., Suppe, J., and Davis, D., 1984, Mechanics of fold-and-thrust belts and accretionary wedges: cohesive Coulomb theory. *Journal of Geophysical Research* 89: 10 087–101.

Daly, R. A., Manger, G. E., and Clark, S. P. J., 1966, Density of rocks. In S. P. J. Clark, ed., *Handbook of Physical Constants*. New York: Geological Society of America, pp. 19–26.

Davatzes, N. C. and Aydin, A., 2003, Overprinting faulting mechanisms in high porosity sandstones of SE Utah. *Journal of Structural Geology* 25: 1795–813.

Davies, R. K. and Pollard, D. D., 1986, Relations between left-lateral strike-slip faults and right-lateral monoclinal kink bands in granodiorite, Mt. Abbot Quadrangle, Sierra Nevada, California. *Pure and Applied Geophysics* 124: 177–201.

Davis, D., Suppe, J., and Dahlen, F. A., 1983, Mechanics of fold-and-thrust belts and accretionary wedges. *Journal of Geophysical Research* 88: 1153–72.

Davis, E. E. and Lister, C. R. B., 1974, Fundamentals of ridge crest topography. *Earth and Planetary Science Letters* 21(4): 405–13.

Davis, G. H. and Reynolds, S. J., 1996, *Structural Geology of Rocks and Regions*. New York: John Wiley and Sons.

Davis, J. C., 1986, *Statistics and Data Analysis in Geology*. New York: John Wiley and Sons.

Davis, P. J. and Hersh, R., 1986, *Descartes' Dream*. Boston, MA: Houghton Mifflin.

Dawers, N. H., Anders, M. H., and Scholz, C. H., 1993, Growth of normal faults: displacement-length scaling. *Geology* 21: 1107–10.

De Sitter, L. U., 1964, *Structural Geology*. New York: McGraw-Hill Book Company.

DeGraff, J. M. and Aydin, A., 1987, Surface morphology of columnar joints and its significance to mechanics and directions of joint growth. *Geological Society of America Bulletin* 99: 605–17.

Delaney, P. T., 1990, Deep magma body beneath the summit and rift zones of Kilauea Volcano, Hawaii. *Science* **247**: 1265–372.

Delaney, P. T., Denlinger, R. P., Lisowski, M., *et al.*, 1998, Volcanic spreading at Kilauea, 1976–1996. *Journal of Geophysical Research* **103**: 18 003–23.

Delaney, P. T., Miklius, A., Arnadottir, T., Okamura, A. T., and Sako, M. K., 1993, Motion of Kilauea Volcano during sustained eruption from the Puu Oo and Kupaianaha vents, 1983–1991. *Journal of Geophysical Research* **98**: 17 801–20.

Delaney, P. T. and Pollard, D. D., 1981, Deformation of host rocks and flow of magma during growth of minette dikes and breccia-bearing intrusions near Ship Rock, New Mexico. *US Geological Survey Professional Paper* 1202, pp. 1–61.

Delaney, P. T. and Pollard, D. D., 1982, Solidification of basaltic magma during flow in a dike. *American Journal of Science* **282**: 856–85.

Delaney, P. T., Pollard, D. D., Ziony, J. I., and McKee, E. H., 1986, Field relations between dikes and joints: emplacement processes and paleostress analysis. *Journal of Geophysical Research* **91**(B5): 4920–38.

Dennis, J. G., 1987, *Structural Geology: An Introduction.* Dubuque, IA: William C. Brown.

Dieterich, J. H., 1969, Origin of cleavage in folded rocks. *American Journal of Science* **267**: 155–65.

Dieterich, J. H., 1979a, Modeling of rock friction: 1. Experimental results and constitutive equations. *Journal of Geophysical Research* **84**: 2161–8.

Dieterich, J. H., 1979b, Modeling of rock friction: 2. Simulation of preseismic slip. *Journal of Geophysical Research* **84**(B5): 2169–75.

Dieterich, J. H., 1981, Constitutive properties of faults with simulated gouge. In N. L. Carter, M. Friedman, J. M. Logan and D. W. Stearns, eds., *Mechanical Behavior of Crustal Rocks: the Handin Volume.* Washington, DC: American Geophysical Union, pp. 103–20.

Dieterich, J. H., 1986, A model for the nucleation of earthquake slip. *Geophysical Monograph* **37**: 37–47.

Dieterich, J. H., 1994, A constitutive law for rate of earthquake production and its application to earthquake clustering. *Journal of Geophysical Research, B, Solid Earth and Planets* **99**(2): 2601–18.

Dieterich, J. H. and Carter, N. L., 1969, Stress-history of folding. *American Journal of Science*, **267**: 129–54.

Dieterich, J. H. and Onat, E. T., 1969, Slow finite deformations of viscous solids. *Journal of Geophysical Research* **74**: 2081–8.

Dixon, J. M. and Summers, J. M., 1985, Recent developments in centrifuge modelling of tectonic processes: equipment, model construction techniques and rheology of model properties. *Journal of Structural Geology* **7**: 83–102.

Dombard, A. J. and McKinnon, W. B., 2001, Formation of grooved terrain on Ganymede: extensional instability mediated by cold superplastic creep. *Icarus* **154**: 321–36.

Donath, F. A., 1961, Experimental study of shear failure in anisotropic rocks. *Geological Society of America Bulletin* **72**: 985–90.

Donath, F. A. and Parker, R. B., 1974, Folds and folding. *Geological Society of America Bulletin* **75**: 45–62.

Duba, A. G., Durham, W. B., Handin, J. W., and Wang, H. F., 1990, *The Brittle–Ductile Transition in Rocks (The Heard Volume), Geophysical Monograph.* Washington, DC: American Geophysical Union, p. 243.

Emerman, S. and Turcotte, D. L., 1983, A fluid model for the shape of accretionary wedges. *Earth and Planetary Science Letters* **63**: 379–84.

Enever, J. R., Cornet, F., and Roegiers, J. C., 1992, ISRM commission on interpretation of hydraulic fracture records. *International Journal of Rock Mechanics and Mining Science* **29**: 69–72.

Engelder, T., 1993, *Stress Regimes in the Lithosphere.* Princeton, NJ: Princeton University Press.

Engelder, T., and Peacock, D. C. P., 2001, Joint development normal to regional compression during flexural-flow folding: the Lilstock buttress anticline, Somerset, England. *Journal of Structural Geology* **23**: 259–77.

Erdogan, F. and Sih, G. C., 1963, On the crack extension in plates under plane loading and transverse shear. *Journal of Basic Engineering, Transactions ASME* **85**: 519–27.

Eshbach, O. W., 1961, *Handbook of Engineering Fundamentals, Handbook Series.* New York: John Wiley and Sons.

Eshelby, J. D., 1957, The determination of the elastic field of an ellipsoidal inclusion, and related problems. *Proceedings of the Royal Society of London Series A* **241**: 376–96.

Evans, B. and Kohlstedt, D. L., 1995, Rheology of rocks. In T. J. Ahrens, ed., *Handbook of Physical Properties of Rocks.* Washington, DC: American Geophysical Union, pp. 148–65.

Faerseth, R. B., Knudsen, B.-E., Liljedahl, T., Midbøe, P. S., and Søderstrøm, B., 1997, Oblique rifting and sequential faulting in the Jurassic development of the northern North Sea. *Journal of Structural Geology* **19**(10): 1285–302.

Fairhurst, C., 1964, Measurement of *in situ* rock stresses with particular references to hydraulic fracturing. *Rock Mechanics and Engineering Geology* **2**: 129–47.

Farvolden, R. N. and Cherry, J. A., 1991, Opinion: are geology departments prepared for the 21st century? *Geology* **May**: 419.

Feehan, J. G. and Brandon, M. T., 1999, Contribution of ductile flow to exhumation of low *T*–high *P* metamorphic rocks: San Juan–Cascade Nappes, NW Washington State. *Journal of Geophysical Research* **104**: 10 883–901.

Feshbach, H. and Weisskopf, V. F., 1988, Ask a foolish question. *Physics Today* **October**: 9.

Fialko, Y. A., Khazan, Y., and Simons, M., 2001, Deformation due to a pressurized horizontal circular crack in an elastic half-space, with applications to volcano geodesy. *Geophysical Journal International* **146**: 181–90.

Fialko, Y. A. and Rubin, A. M., 1999, What controls the along-strike slopes of volcanic soft zones? *Journal of Geophysical Research* **104**: 20 007–20.

Fialko, Y. A., Sandwell, D. T., Agrew, D., Simons, M., Shearer, P., and Minster, B., 2002, Deformation on nearby faults induced by the 1999 Hector Mine earthquake. *Science* **297**: 1858–62.

Fink, J. H. and Fletcher, R. C., 1981, *A Mechanical Analysis of Extensional Instability on Ganymede*, Technical Memorandum 84211. Washington, DC: National Aeronautics and Space Administration, pp. 51–3.

Fisher, M. P. and Wiklerson, M. S., 2000, Predicting the orientation of joints from fold shape: results of pseudo-three-dimensional modeling and curvature analysis. *Geology* **28**: 15–18.

Fisher, R. A., 1953, Dispersion of a sphere. *Proceedings of the Royal Society of London Series A* **217**: 295.

Fletcher, R. C., 1974, Wavelength selection in the folding of a single layer with power-law rheology. *American Journal of Science* **274**: 1029–43.

Fletcher, R. C., 1982, Coupling of diffusional mass transport and deformation in a tight rock. *Tectonophysics* **83**: 275–91.

Fletcher, R. C. and Hallet, B., 1983, Unstable extension of lithosphere: a mechanical model for basin-and-range structure. *Journal of Geophysical Research* **83**: 275–91.

Fletcher, R. C. and Pollard, D. D., 1981, Anticrack model for pressure solution surfaces. *Geology* **9**: 419–24.

Fletcher, R. C. and Pollard, D. D., 1999, Can we understand structural and tectonic processes and their products without a complete mechanics? *Journal of Structural Geology* **21**: 1071–88.

Fleuty, M. J., 1964, The description of folds. *Proceedings of the Geologists' Association* **75**(4): 461–92.

Flodin, E. and Aydin, A., 2004, Faults with asymmetric damage zones in sandstone, Valley of Fire State Park, southern Nevada. *Journal of Structural Geology* **26**: 983–8.

Flugge, W., 1967, *Viscoelasticity*. London: Blaisdell.

Fossen, H. and Gabrielsen, R. H., 1996, Experimental modeling of extensional fault systems by use of plaster. *Journal of Structural Geology* **18**: 673–87.

Freund, L. B., 1979, The mechanics of dynamic shear crack propagation. *Journal of Geophysical Research* **84**: 2199–209.

Friedel, J., 1964, *Dislocations*. Oxford: Pergamon Press.

Friedman, M., Handin, J., and Alani, G., 1972, Fracture-surface energy of rocks. *International Journal of Rock Mechanics and Mining Science* **9**: 757–66.

Frocht, M. M., 1948, *Photoelasticity*. New York: John Wiley and Sons.

Fung, Y. C., 1965, *Foundations of Solid Mechanics, Prentice-Hall International Series in Dynamics*. Englewood Cliffs, NJ: Prentice-Hall.

Fung, Y. C., 1969, *A First Course in Continuum Mechanics*. Englewood Cliffs, NJ: Prentice-Hall.

Gallagher, J. J., Friedman, M., Handin, J., and Sowers, G. M., 1974, Experimental studies relating to microfracture in sandstone. *Tectonophysics* **21**: 203–47.

Gauss, K. F., 1827, Karl Friedrich Gauss, general investigations of curved surfaces. In J. C. Morehead, ed., *Investigations of Curved Surfaces of 1827 and 1825* (published in 1902). Princeton, NJ: Princeton University Library.

Ge, H. and Jackson, M. P. A., 1998, Physical modeling of structures formed by salt withdrawal: implications for deformation caused by slat dissolution. *American Association of Petroleum Geologists Bulletin* **82**: 228–50.

Gere, J. M. and Weaver, W. J., 1965, *Matrix Algebra for Engineers*. New York: Van Nostrand Reinhold.

Gilbert, G. K., 1877, *Report on the Geology of the Henry Mountains, US Geographical and Geological Survey of the Rocky Mountain Region*. Washington, DC: US Government Printing Office.

Gleick, J., 1987, *Chaos: Making a New Science*. New York: Viking Penguin.

Goodman, R. E., 1980, *Introduction to Rock Mechanics*. New York: John Wiley and Sons.

Goodman, R. E. and Shi, G.-H., 1985, *Block Theory and Its Application to Rock Engineering*. Englewood Cliffs, NJ: Prentice-Hall.

Gordon, J. E., 1976, *The New Science of Strong Materials*. Princeton, NJ: Princeton University Press.

Grachev, A. F., Magnitsky, V. A., Mukhamediev, S. A., and

Nikolaev, V. A., 2001, The effect of neotectonic movements on the gradients and curvatures of the northern Eurasian lithosphere surface. *Izvestiya–Russian Academy of Sciences, Physics of the Solid Earth*, **37**: 89–106.

Green, H. W. and Burnley, P. C., 1989, The mechanism of failure responsible for deep-focus earthquakes. *Nature* **341**: 733–7.

Gregory, B., 1990, *Inventing Reality: Physics as Language*. New York: John Wiley and Sons.

Griffith, A. A., 1921, The phenomena of rupture and flow in solids. *Philosophical Transactions of the Royal Society of London Series A* **221**: 163–98.

Griffith, A. A., 1924, The theory of rupture. In C. B. Biezeno and J. M. Burgers, eds., *First International Congress on Applied Mechanics*. Delft: J. Waltman, pp. 55–63.

Griggs, D. T., 1939, Creep of rocks. *Journal of Geology* **47**: 225–51.

Griggs, D. T. and Handin, J., 1960a, Observations on fracture and an hypothesis of earthquakes. In D. T. Griggs and J. Handin, eds., *Rock Deformation*, Memoir 79. New York: Geological Society of America, pp. 347–64.

Griggs, D. T. and Handin, J., 1960b, *Rock Deformation*, Memoir 79. New York: Geological Society of America, p. 382.

Grosfils, E. B. and Head, J. W., 1994, The global distribution of giant radiating dike swarms on Venus: implications for the global stress state. *Geophysical Research Letters* **21**: 701–4.

Groshong, R. H. Jr., 1975, Strain, fractures, and pressure solution in natural single layer folds. *Geological Society of America Bulletin* **86**: 1363–76.

Groshong, R. H. Jr., 1999, 3-D *Structural Geology: A Practical Guide to Surface and Subsurface Map Interpretation*. Berlin: Springer-Verlag.

Gross, M. R., 1993, The origin and spacing of cross joints: examples from Monterey Formation Santa Barbara Coastline, California. *Journal of Structural Geology* **15**: 773–51.

Gross, M. R., Fischer, M. P., Engelder, T., and Greenfield, R. J., 1995, Factors controlling joint spacing in interbedded sedimentary rocks: integrating numerical models with field observations from the Monterey Formation, USA. In M. S. Ameen, ed., *Fractography: Fracture Topography as a Tool in Fracture Mechanics and Stress Analysis*. London: Geological Society, pp. 215–33.

Grout, F. F., 1945, Scale models of structures related to batholiths. *American Journal of Science* **111**: 260–84.

Guglielmo, G., Vendeville, B. C., and Jackson, M. P. A., 2000, 3-D visualization and isochore analysis of extensional diapirs overprinted by compression. *American Association of Petroleum Geologists Bulletin* **84**: 1095–108.

Guiton, M. L. E., Sassi, W., Leroy, Y. M., and Gauthier, B. D. M., 2003, Mechanical constraints on the chronology of fracture activation in folded Devonian sandstone of the western Moroccan Anti-Atlas. *Journal of Structural Geology* **25**: 1317–30.

Gutscher, M., Kukowski, N., Malavieille, J., and Lallemand, S., 1998, Material transfer in accretionary wedges from analysis of a systematic series of analog experiments. *Journal of Structural Geology* **20**: 407–16.

Habert, G. and De Saint-Blanquat, M., 2004, Rate of construction of the Black Mesa bysmalith, Henry Mountains, Utah. In C. Breitkreuz and N. Petford, eds., *Physical Geology of High-Level Magmatic Systems*. London: Geological Society Special Publications **234**, pp. 163–174.

Hafner, W., 1951, Stress distributions and faulting. *Geological Society of America Bulletin* **62**: 373–98.

Hähner, G. and Spencer, N., 1998, Rubbing and scrubbing. *Physics Today* **51**(9): 22–7.

Haimson, B. C., 1968, Hydraulic fracturing in porous and nonporous rock and its potential for determining *in situ* stresses at great depth. Unpublished Ph.D. thesis, University of Wisconsin.

Haimson, B. C. and Fairhurst, C., 1967, Initiation and extension of hydraulic fractures in rocks. *Society of Petroleum Engineers Journal* **September**: 310–18.

Handin, J. and Hager, R. V., 1957, Experimental deformation of sedimentary rocks under confining pressure: tests at room temperature on dry samples. *American Association of Petroleum Geologists Bulletin* **41**: 1–50.

Handin, J. and Hager, R. V., 1958, Experimental deformation of sedimentary rocks under confining pressure: tests at high temperature. *American Association of Petroleum Geologists Bulletin* **42**: 2892–934.

Handin, J., Hager, R. V., Friedman, M., and Feather, J. N., 1963, Experimental deformation of sedimentary rocks under confining pressure: pore pressure tests. *American Association of Petroleum Geologists Bulletin* **47**: 717–55.

Handy, M. R., 1994, Flow laws for rocks containing two non-linear viscous phases: a phenomenological approach. *Journal of Structural Geology* **16**: 287–301.

Hanks, T. C., 1977, Earthquake stress drops, ambient tectonic stresses and stresses that drive plate motions. *Pure and Applied Geophysics* **115**: 441–58.

Happel, J. and Brenner, H., 1965, *Low Reynolds Number Hydrodynamics: With Special Applications to Particulate Media*. Englewood Cliffs, NJ: Prentice-Hall.

Harris, R. A. and Segall, P., 1987, Detection of a locked

zone at depth on the Parkfield, California, segment of the San Andreas fault. *Journal of Geophysical Research* 92(B8): 7945–62.

Harris, R. A. and Simpson, R. W., 1998, Suppression of large earthquakes by stress shadows: a comparison of Coulomb and rate-and-state failure. *Journal of Geophysical Research* 103: 24 439–51.

Haskell, N. H., 1937, The viscosity of the aesthenosphere. *American Journal of Science* 33: 22–8.

Hausman, D. M., 1998, *Causal Asymmetries*. Cambridge: Cambridge University Press.

Head, J. W., Crumpler, L. S., Aubele, J. C., Guest, J. E., and Saunders, R. S., 1992, Venus volcanism: classification of volcanic features and structures, associations, and global distributions from Magellan data. *Journal of Geophysical Research* 97: 13 153–97.

Heard, H. C., 1960, Transition from brittle fracture to ductile flow in Solenhofen limestone as a function of temperature, confining pressure, and interstitial fluid pressure. In D. T. Griggs and J. Handin, eds., *Rock Deformation*. Boulder, CO: Geological Society of America, pp. 193–226.

Hearmon, R. F. S., 1961, *An Introduction to Applied Anisotropic Elasticity*. Oxford: Oxford University Press.

Herget, G., 1993, Rock stresses and rock stress monitoring in Canada. In J. A. Hudson, ed., *Rock Testing and Site Characterization: Comprehensive Rock Engineering*. Oxford: Pergamon Press, pp. 473–96.

Hill, R., 1965, A self-consistent mechanics of composite materials. *Journal of the Mechanics and Physics of Solids* 13: 213–22.

Hillerman, T., 1990, *Coyote Waits*. New York: Harper and Row.

Hilley, G. E. and Strecker, M. R., 2004, Steady-state erosion of critical Coulomb wedges with applications to Taiwan and the Himalaya. *Journal of Geophysical Research* 109: doi:10.1029/2002JB002284.

Hilley, G. E., Strecker, M. R., and Ramos, V. A., 2004, Growth and erosion of fold-and-thrust belts, with an application to the Aconcagua Fold-and-Thrust Belt, Argentina. *Journal of Geophysical Research* 109: doi:10.1029/2002JB002282.

Hirth, J. P. and Lothe, J., 1982, *Theory of Dislocations*. New York: John Wiley and Sons.

Hoagland, R. G., Hahn, G. T., and Rosenfield, A. R., 1973, Influence of microstructure on fracture propagation in rock. *Rock Mechanics* 5: 77–106.

Hobbs, D. W., 1962, The strength of coal under biaxial compression. *Colliery Engineering* 39: 285–90.

Hodgson, R. A., 1961, Classification of structures on joint surfaces. *American Journal of Science* 259: 493–502.

Hoek, E., 1965, *Rock Fracture Under Static Stress Conditions*.

Pretoria: Natural Mechanical Engineering Research Institute, CSIR.

Hoek, E. and Bieniawski, Z. T., 1965, Brittle fracture propagation in rock under compression. *International Journal of Fracture Mechanics* 1: 137–55.

Hofmann-Wellenhof, B., Lichtenegger, H., and Collins, J., 1997, *Global Positioning System*. New York: Springer-Verlag.

Hoshino, K., Koide, H., Inami, K., Iwamura, S., and Mitsui, S., 1972, *Mechanical Properties of Japanese Tertiary Sedimentary Rocks Under High Confining Pressures*, Report 244. Kawasaki: Geological Survey of Japan.

Hossain, K. M., 1979, Determination of strain from stretched belemnites. *Tectonophysics* 60: 279–88.

Howarth, R. J., 1999, Measurement, portrayal and analysis of orientation data and the origins of early modern structural geology (1670–1967). *Proceedings of the Geologists' Association* 110: 273–309.

Hubbert, M. K., 1937, Theory of scale models as applied to the study of geologic structures. *Geological Society of America Bulletin* 48: 1459–520.

Hubbert, M. K., 1945, Strength of the Earth. *American Association of Petroleum Geologists Bulletin* 29: 1630–53.

Hubbert, M. K., 1951, Mechanical basis for certain familiar geologic structures. *Geological Society of America Bulletin* 62: 355–72.

Hubbert, M. K., 1972, *Structural Geology*. New York: Hafner.

Hubbert, M. K., 1974, Is being quantitative sufficient? In D. F. Merriam, ed., *The Impact of Quantification on Geology*. Syracuse, NY: Syracuse University, pp. 27–49.

Hubbert, M. K. and Willis, D. G., 1957, Mechanics of hydraulic fracturing. *Petroleum, Transactions AIME* 210: 153–66.

Hudleston, P. J., 1973, Fold morphology and some geometrical implications of theories of fold development. *Tectonophysics* 16(1–2): 1–46.

Hudleston, P. J., 1992, A comparison between glacial movement and thrust sheet or nappe emplacement and associated structures. In S. Mitra and G. W. Fisher, eds., *Structural Geology of Fold and Thrust Belts*. Baltimore, MD: The Johns Hopkins University Press, pp. 81–91.

Hudson, J. A., Crouch, S. L., and Fairhurst, C., 1972, Soft, stiff and servo-controlled testing machines: a review with reference to rock failure. *Engineering Geology* 6: 155–9.

Hughes, T. J. R., 1987, *The Finite Element Method*. Englewood Cliffs, NJ: Prentice-Hall.

Hunt, C. B., 1953, *Geology and Geography of the Henry Mountains Region, Utah, US Geological Survey Professional Paper*. Washington, DC: US Government Printing Office.

Hunt, C. B., 1988a, *Geology of the Henry Mountains, Utah, as Recorded in the Notebooks of G. K. Gilbert, 1875–76.* Boulder, CO: The Geological Society of America.

Hunt, C. B., 1988b, The laccolith-stock controversy: new results from the southern Henry Mountains, Utah. Discussion and reply. *Geological Society of America Bulletin* **100**: 1657–9.

Huntoon, P. W., 1982, The Meander anticline, Canyonlands, Utah: an unloading structure resulting from horizontal gliding on salt. *Geological Society of America Bulletin* **93**: 941–50.

Hurlbut, C. S. and Griggs, D. T., 1939, Igneous rocks of the Highwood Mountains, Montana. *Geological Society of America Bulletin* **50**: 1032–112.

Hytch, M. J., Putaux, J.-L., and Penisson, J.-M., 2003, Measurement of the displacement field of dislocations to 0.03 Å by electron microscopy. *Nature* **423**(15 May): 270–3.

Inglis, C. E., 1913, Stresses in a plate due to the presence of cracks and sharp corners. *Royal Institute of Naval Architects Transactions* **55**: 219–30.

Irvine, T. N., 1970, Heat transfer during solidification of layered intrusions: I. Sheets and sills. *Canadian Journal of Earth Science* **7**: 1031–61.

Irwin, G. R., 1957, Analysis of stresses and strains near the end of a crack traversing a plate. *Journal of Applied Mechanics* **24**: 361–4.

Irwin, G. R., 1958, Fracture. In S. Flugge, ed., *Encyclopedia of Physics*. Berlin: Springer-Verlag, pp. 551–90.

Jackson, M. D. and Pollard, D. D., 1988, The laccolith-stock controversy: new results from the southern Henry Mountains, Utah. *Geological Society of America Bulletin* **100**: 117–39.

Jackson, M. D. and Pollard, D. D., 1990, Flexure and faulting of sedimentary host rocks during growth of igneous domes, Henry Mountains, Utah. *Journal of Structural Geology* **12**: 185–206.

Jaeger, J. C., 1957, The temperature in the neighborhood of a cooling intrusive sheet. *American Journal of Science* **255**: 306–18.

Jaeger, J. C., 1964a, *Elasticity, Fracture and Flow with Engineering and Geological Applications*. London: Methuen.

Jaeger, J. C., 1964b, Temperatures outside a cooling intrusive sheet. *American Journal of Science* **257**: 44–54.

Jaeger, J. C. and Cook, N. G. W., 1979, *Fundamentals of Rock Mechanics*. London: Chapman and Hall.

Jaeger, J. C. and Hoskins, E. R., 1966a, Rock failure under the confined Brazilian test. *Journal of Geophysical Research* **71**: 2651–9.

Jaeger, J. C. and Hoskins, E. R., 1966b, Stresses and failure in rings of rock loaded in diametral tension or compression. *British Journal of Applied Physics* **17**: 685–92.

Johnson, A. M., 1970, *Physical Processes in Geology*. San Francisco, CA: Freeman, Cooper and Co.

Johnson, A. M. and Fletcher, R. C., 1994, *Folding of Viscous Layers*. New York: Columbia University Press.

Johnson, A. M. and Pollard, D. D., 1973, Mechanics of growth of some laccolithic intrusions in the Henry Mtns, Utah: Part I, Field observations, Gilbert's model, physical properties and flow of magma. *Tectonophysics* **18**: 261–309.

Johnson, C. E., Rohahn, C., and Sharp, R. V., 1982, Introduction, The Imperial Valley, California, Earthquake of October 15, 1979, *Professional Paper* 1254. Washington, DC: United States Geological Survey, pp. 1–3.

Johnson, K. M. and Johnson, A. M., 2000, Localization of layer-parallel faults in San Rafael swell, Utah, and other monoclinal folds. *Journal of Structural Geology* **22**: 1455–68.

Johnson, R. B., 1961, Patterns and origin of radial dike swarms associated with West Spanish Peak and Dike Mountain, south-central Colorado. *Geological Society of America Bulletin* **72**: 579–90.

Johnson, R. B., 1968, *Geology of the Igneous Rocks of the Spanish Peaks Region, Colorado*, Professional Paper 594G. Menlo, CA: US Geological Survey, pp. 1–47.

Jones, G., Fisher, Q. J., and Knipe, R. J., 1998, *Faulting, Fault Sealing and Fluid Flow in Hydrocarbon Reservoirs*, Special Publication 147. London: Geological Society, p. 319.

Jonsson, S., Zebker, H. A., Segall, P., and Amelung, F., 2002, Fault slip distribution of the 1999 M-w 7.1 Hector Mine, California, earthquake, estimated from satellite radar and GPS measurements. *Bulletin of the Seismological Society of America* **92**: 1377–89.

Kamb, W. B., 1959a, Theory of preferred crystal orientation developed by crystallization under stress. *Journal of Geology* **67**: 153–70.

Kamb, W. B., 1959b, Ice petrofabric observations from Blue Glacier, Washington, in relation to theory and experiment. *Journal of Geophysical Research* **64**: 1891–909.

Kanninen, M. F. and Popelar, C. H., 1985, *Advanced Fracture Mechanics*. New York: Oxford University Press.

Kattenhorn, S. A., Aydin, A., and Pollard, D. D., 2000, Joints at high angles to normal fault strike: an explanation using 3-D numerical models of fault-perturbed stress fields. *Journal of Structural Geology* **22**(1): 1–23.

Kattenhorn, S. A. and Pollard, D. D., 2001, Integrating

3-D seismic data, field analogs, and mechanical models in the analysis of segmented normal faults in the Wytch Farm oil field, southern England, United Kingdom. *American Association of Petroleum Geologists Bulletin* **85**(7): 1183–210.

Kelly, V. C., 1955, Monoclines of the Colorado Plateau. *Geological Society of America Bulletin* **66**: 789–804.

Kerr, A. D. and Pollard, D. D., 1998, Toward more realistic formulations for the analysis of laccoliths. *Journal of Structural Geology* **20**: 1783–93.

Kilgore, B. D., Blanpied, M. L., and Dieterich, J. H., 1993, Velocity dependent friction of granite over a wide range of conditions. *Geophysical Research Letters* **20**(10): 903–6.

Kind, D. and Quinn, T., 1999, Metrology: *quo vadis?* *Physics Today (Sixteenth Annual Buyers' Guide)* **52**: BG13–BG15.

King, G. C. P., Stein, R. S., and Lin, J., 1994, Static stress changes and the triggering of earthquakes. *Bulletin of the Seismological Society of America* **84**: 935–53.

King, W., 1875, Report on the superinduced divisional structure of rocks, called jointing, and its relation to slaty cleavage. *Royal Irish Academy Transactions* **25**: 605–62.

Kirby, S. H. and Kronenberg, A. K., 1987, Rheology of the lithosphere: selected topics. *Reviews of Geophysics* **25**: 1219–44.

Kirsch, G., 1898, Die Theorie der Elastizität und die Bedürfnisse der Festigkeitslehre. *Zeitschrift des Verlines Deutscher Ingenieure* **42**: 797–807.

Koch, F. G., Johnson, A. M., and Pollard, D. D., 1981, Monoclinal bending of strata over laccolithic intrusions. *Tectonophysics* **74**: T21–T31.

Koenig, E. and Pollard, D. D., 1998, Mapping and modeling of radial fracture patterns on Venus. *Journal of Geophysical Research* **103**: 15 183–202.

Kostrov, B. V. and Das, S., 1988, *Principles of Earthquake Source Mechanics*. Cambridge: Cambridge University Press.

Krantz, W. R., 1988, Multiple fault sets and three-dimensional strain: theory and application. *Journal of Structural Geology* **10**: 225–37.

Kranz, R. L., 1983, Microcracks in rocks: a review. *Tectonophysics* **100**: 449–80.

Krumbein, W. C. and Graybill, F. A., 1965, *An Introduction to Statistical Models in Geology*. New York: McGraw-Hill.

Labuz, J. F., Shah, S. P., and Dowding, C. H., 1987, The fracture process zone in granite: evidence and effect. *International Journal of Rock Mechanics and Mining Science* **24**: 235–46.

Lachenbruch, A. H., 1973, A simple mechanical model

for oceanic spreading centers. *Journal of Geophysical Research* **78**: 3395–417.

Lamb, H., 1945, *Hydrodynamics*. New York: Dover.

Landau, L. D. and Lifshitz, E. M., 1960, *Fluid Mechanics*. Reading: Addison-Wesley.

Lawn, B. R. and Wilshaw, T. R., 1975, *Fracture of Brittle Solids*. Cambridge: Cambridge University Press.

Lawson, A. C., 1908, *The California Earthquake of April, 18, 1906, Report of the State Earthquake Investigation Committee*. Washington, DC: Carnegie Institute of Washington, p. 641.

Lee, T.-C. and Delaney, P. T., 1987, Frictional heating and pore pressure rise due to fault slip. *Geophysical Journal of the Royal Astronomical Society* **88**: 569–91.

Lekhnitskii, S. G., 1963, *Theory of Elasticity of an Anisotropic Elastic Body*. San Francisco: Holden-Day.

Li, V. C., 1987, Mechanics of shear rupture applied to earthquake zones. In B. K. Atkinson, ed., *Fracture Mechanics of Rock*. San Diego, CA: Academic Press.

Lide, D. R., 2004, *CRC Handbook of Chemistry and Physics*. Boca Raton, FL: Chemical Rubber Company Press, Inc.

Linker, M. F. and Dieterich, J. H., 1992, Effects of variable normal stress on rock friction: observations and constitutive equations. *Journal of Geophysical Research, B, Solid Earth and Planets* **97**(4): 4923–40.

Lipschutz, M. M., 1969, *Theory and Problems of Differential Geometry, Schaum's Outline*. New York: McGraw-Hill.

Lisle, R. J., 1994, Detection of zones of abnormal strains in structures using Gaussian curvature analysis. *American Association of Petroleum Geologists Bulletin* **78**: 1811–19.

Lisle, R. J., 2000, Predicting patterns of strain from three-dimensional fold geometries: neutral surface folds and forced folds. In J. W. Cosgrove and M. S. Ameen, eds., *Forced Folds and Fractures*, Special Publication 169. London: Geological Society pp. 213–21.

Lister, J. R., 1990, Buoyancy-driven fluid fracture. *Journal of Fluid Mechanics* **210**: 263–80.

Lister, J. R. and Kerr, R. C., 1991, Fluid-mechanical models of crack propagation and their application to magma transport in dykes. *Journal of Geophysical Research* **96**: 10 049–77.

Liu, S. and Dixon, J. M., 1990, Centrifuge modelling of thrust faulting: strain partitioning and the sequence of thrusting in duplex structures. In R. J. Knipe, ed., *Deformation Mechanisms, Rheology and Tectonics*, Special Publication 54. London: Geological Society, pp. 431–44.

Liu, S. and Dixon, J. M., 1991, Centrifuge modelling of thrust faulting: structural variation along strike in fold-thrust belts. *Tectonophysics* **188**: 39–62.

Lockner, D. A. and Beeler, N. M., 2003, Rock failure and earthquakes. In W. H. K. Lee, H. Kanamori, P. C. Jennings, and C. Kisslinger, eds., *International Handbook of Earthquake and Engineering Seismology*, Part A. Amsterdam: Academic Press, pp. 505–38.

Love, A. E. H., 1944, A Treatise on the Mathematical Theory of Elasticity. New York: Dover.

Lovering, T. S., 1935, Theory of heat conduction applied to geological problems. *Geological Society of America Bulletin* **46**: 69–94.

Lovering, T. S., 1936, Heat conduction in dissimilar rocks and the use of thermal models. *Geological Society of America Bulletin* **47**: 87–100.

Maerten, F., Resor, P., Maerten, L., and Pollard, D. D., 2005, Inverting for slip on three-dimensional fault surfaces using angular dislocations. *Bulletin of the Seismological Society of America* in press.

Maerten, L., 2000, Variation in slip on intersecting normal faults: implications for paleostress inversion. *Journal of Geophysical Research* **105**: 25 553–65.

Maerten, L., Gillespie, P., and Pollard, D. D., 2002, Effects of local stress perturbation on secondary fault development. *Journal of Structural Geology* **24**: 145–53.

Maerten, L., Pollard, D. D., and Karpuz, R., 2000, How to constrain 3D fault continuity and linkage using reflection seismic data: a geomechanical approach. *American Association of Petroleum Geologists Bulletin* **84**: 1311–24.

Maerten, L., Pollard, D. D., and Maerten, F., 2001, Digital mapping of three-dimensional structures of the Chimney Rock fault system, central Utah. *Journal of Structural Geology* **23**: 585–92.

Maerten, L., Willemse, E. J. M., Pollard, D. D., and Rawnsley, K., 1999, Slip distributions on intersecting normal faults. *Journal of Strurctural Geology* **21**: 259–71.

Mallet, J. L., 2002, *Geomodeling*. Oxford: Oxford University Press.

Malvern, L. E., 1969, *Introduction to the Mechanics of a Continuous Medium*. Upper Saddle River, NJ: Prentice-Hall.

Manduit, T. and Brun, J. P., 1998, Growth fault/rollover systems: birth, growth, and decay. *Journal of Geophysical Research* **103**: 18 119–36.

Mardon, D., 1988, Localization of pressure solution and the formation of discrete solution seams. Unpublished Ph.D. thesis, Texas A&M University.

Margenau, H., 1977, *The Nature of Physical Reality: A Philosophy of Modern Physics*. Woodbridge, CT: Ox Bow Press.

Marrett, R. and Peacock, D. C. P., 1999, Strain and stress. *Journal of Structural Geology* **21**: 1057–63.

Marshak, S. and Mitra, G., 1988, *Basic Methods of Structural Geology*. Englewood Cliffs, NJ: Prentice-Hall.

Martel, S. and Boger, W. A., 1998, Geometry and mechanics of secondary fracturing around small three-dimensional faults in granitic rock. *Journal of Geophysical Research* **103**: 21 299–314.

Martel, S., Pollard, D. D., and Segall, P., 1988, Development of simple strike-slip fault zones in granitic rock, Mount Abbot quadrangle, Sierra Nevada, California. *Geological Society of America Bulletin* **99**: 1451–65.

Martel, S. J., 1990, Formation of compound strike-slip fault zones, Mount Abbot Quadrangle, California. *Journal of Structural Geology* **12**(7): 869–82.

Martel, S. J. and Pollard, D. D., 1989, Mechanisms of slip and fracture along small faults and simple strike-slip fault zones in granitic rock. *Journal of Geophysical Research* **94**: 9417–28.

Massonnet, D., Rossi, M., Carmona, C., et al., 1993, The displacement field of the Landers earthquake mapped by radar interferometry. *Nature* **364**: 138–42.

McBirney, A. R. and Murase, T., 1984, Rheological properties of magmas. *Annual Reviews of Earth and Planetary Sciences* **12**: 337–57.

McClay, K. and Bonora, M., 2001, Analog models of restraining stepovers in strike-slip fault systems. *American Association of Petroleum Geologists Bulletin* **85**: 233–60.

McClay, K. R., Waltham, D. A., Scott, A. D., and Abousetta, A. A., 1991, Physical and seismic modeling of listric fault geometries. In A. M. Roberts, G. Yielding, and B. Freeman, eds., *The Geometry of Normal Faults*, Special Publication 56. London: Geological Society, pp. 231–9.

McClay, K. R. and White, M., 1995, Analogue models of orthogonal and oblique rifting. *Marine and Petroleum Geology* **12**: 137–51.

McClintock, F. A. and Walsh, J. B., 1962, Friction on Griffith cracks in rocks under pressure. In *Fourth US Congressional Applied Mechanics, Proceedings*. Berkeley, CA: American Society of Mechanical Engineers, pp. 1015–21.

McConaughy, D. T. and Engelder, T., 2001, Joint initiation in bedded clastic rocks. *Journal of Structural Geology* **23**(2–3): 203–21.

McGarr, A. and Gay, N. C., 1978, State of stress in the Earth's crust. *Annual Reviews of Earth and Planetary Sciences* **6**: 405–36.

McGill, G. E. and Stromquist, A. W., 1979, The grabens of Canyonlands National Park, Utah: Geometry, mechanics, and kinematics. *Journal of Geophysical Research* **84**: 4547–63.

McIntyre, D. B. and Weiss, L. E., 1956, Construction of block diagrams to scale in orthographic projection. *Proceedings of the Geological Association* **67**: 142–55.

McKenzie, D. P., 1969, The relation between fault plane solutions for earthquakes and the directions of the principal stresses. *Bulletin of the Seismological Society of America* **50**: 595–601.

Means, W. D., 1976, *Stress and Strain*. New York: Springer-Verlag.

Mechtly, E. A., 1973, *The International System of Units: Physical Constants and Conversion Factors*, Special Publication SP-7012. Washington, DC: National Aeronautics and Space Administration.

Meier, M. F., Kamb, B., Allen, C. R., and Sharp, R. P., 1974, Flow of Blue Glacier, Olympic Mountains, Washington, USA. *Journal of Glaciology* **13**: 187–212.

Melosh, H. J., 1989, *Impact Cratering: A Geologic Process*. New York: Oxford University Press.

Meriaux, C. and Lister, J. R., 2002, Calculation of dike trajectories from volcanic centers. *Journal of Geophysical Research* **107**(B4): doi: 10.1029/2001JB000 436.

Meyers, R. D. and Aydin, A., 2004, The evolution of faults formed by shearing across joint zones in sandstone. *Journal of Structural Geology* **26**(5): 947–66.

Michell, J. H., 1899, On the direct determination of stress in an elastic solid, with application to the theory of plates. *Proceedings of the London Mathematical Society* **31**: 100–24.

Mogi, K., 1958, Relations between the eruptions of various volcanoes and the deformations of the ground surfaces around them. *Bulletin of Earthquake Research Institute, University of Tokyo* **36**: 99–134.

Mohr, O., 1882, Über die Darstellung des Spannungszustandes eines Körperelementes. *Civilingenieure* **28**: 113–56.

Mohr, P. J. and Taylor, B. N., 2003, The fundamental physical constants. *Physics Today* **56**(8): BG6–BG13.

Mollema, P. N. and Antonellini, M. A., 1996, Compaction bands: a structural analog for antimode I cracks in aeolian sandstone. *Tectonophysics* **267**: 209–28.

Moore, J. M. and Schultz, R. A., 1999, Processes of faulting in jointed rocks of Canyonlands National Park, Utah. *Geological Society of America Bulletin* **111**: 808–22.

Morris, A. P., Ferrill, D. A., and Henderson, D. B., 1996, Slip tendency analysis and fault reactivation. *Geology* **24**: 275–8.

Muller, J. R., Aydin, A., and Maerten, F., 2003, Investigating the transition between the 1967 Mudurnu Valley and 1999 Izmit earthquakes along the North Anatolian Fault with static stress changes. *Geophysical Journal International* **154**(2): 471–82.

Muller, O. H. and Pollard, D. D., 1977, The stress state near Spanish Peaks, Colorado, determined from a dike pattern. *Pure and Applied Geophysics* **115**: 69–85.

Murase, T. and McBirney, A. R., 1973, Properties of some common igneous rocks and their melts at high temperatures. *Geological Society of America Bulletin* **84**: 3563–92.

Murray, J. R. and Segall, P., 2002, Testing the time-predictable earthquake recurrence model by direct measurement of strain accumulation and release. *Nature* **28**: 287–91.

Murray, J. R., Segall, P., Cervelli, P., Prescott, W., and Svarc, J., 2001, Inversion of GPS data for spatially variable slip-rate on the San Andreas fault near Parkfield, CA. *Geophysical Research Letters* **28**: 359–62.

Muskhelishvili, N. I., 1954, *Some Basic Problems of the Mathematical Theory of Elasticity*, tr. J. R. M. Radok, Leyden: Noordhoff.

Nakamura, K., 1977, Volcanoes as possible indicators of tectonic stress orientation: principal and proposal. *Journal of Volcanology and Geothermal Research* **2**: 1–16.

Nakamura, K., Jacob, K. H., and Davies, J. N., 1977, Volcanoes as possible indicators of tectonic stress orientation: Aleutians and Alaska. *Pure and Applied Geophysics* **115**: 87–112.

Narr, W. and Suppe, J., 1991, Joint spacing in sedimentary rocks. *Journal of Structural Geology* **13**(9): 1037–48.

Nelson, R. A., 2003, Guide for metric practice. *Physics Today* **56**(8): BG15–BG16.

Nemat-Nasser, S. and Horii, H., 1982, Compression-induced nonplanar crack extension with application to splitting, exfoliation, and rockburst. *Journal of Geophysical Research* **87**: 6805–21.

Netz, R., 2000, The origins of mathematical physics: new light on an old question. *Physics Today* **June**: 32–7.

Neurath, C. and Smith, R. B., 1982, The effect of material properties on growth rates of folding and boudinage: experiments with wax models. *Journal of Structural Geology* **4**: 215–29.

Newton, I., 1999, *The Principia*. Berkeley, CA: University of California Press. (Originally published 1687, Cambridge: Cambridge University Press.)

Nicholson, R. and Ejiofor, I. B., 1987, The three-dimensional morphology of arrays of echelon and sigmoidal, mineral-filled fractures: data from north Cornwall. *Journal of the Geological Society, London* **144**: 79–83.

Nur, A. and Byerlee, J. D., 1971, An exact effective stress law for elastic deformation of rock with fluids. *Journal of Geophysical Research* **76**: 6414–19.

Nur, A., Ron, H., and Scotti, O., 1986, Fault mechanics and kinematics of block rotation. *Geology* **14**: 746–9.

Nye, J. F., 1953, The flow law of ice from measurements made in glacier tunnels, laboratory experiments, and the Jungfrau borehole experiment. *Proceedings of the Royal Society of London, Series A* **219**: 477–89.

Nye, J. F., 1985, *Physical Properties of Crystals*. Oxford: Clarendon Press.

Obert, L. and Duvall, W. I., 1967, *Rock Mechanics and the Design of Structures in Rock*. New York: John Wiley and Sons.

O'Connor, J. J. and Robertson, E. F., 2004, *The MacTutor History of Mathematics Archive*. St. Andrews, Fife: School of Mathematics and Statistics, University of St. Andrews.

Odé, H., 1957, Mechanical analysis of the dike pattern of the Spanish Peaks area, Colorado. *Geological Society of America Bulletin* **68**: 567–76.

Okada, Y., 1985, Surface deformation due to shear and tensile faults in a half-space. *Bulletin of the Seismological Society of America* **75**: 1135–54.

Olson, J. and Pollard, D. D., 1989, Inferring palaeo-stresses from natural fracture patterns: a new method. *Geology* **17**: 345–8.

Olson, J. E., 1993, Joint pattern development: effects of subcritical crack growth and mechanical crack inter-action. *Journal of Geophysical Research* **98**(B7): 12 251–65.

Olson, J. E. and Pollard, D. D., 1991, The initiation and growth of *en échelon* veins. *Journal of Structural Geology* **13**(5): 595–608.

Oppenheimer, D. H., Reasenberg, P. A., and Simpson, R. W., 1988, Fault plane solutions for the 1984 Morgan Hill, California, earthquake sequence: evidence for the state of stress on the Calaveras fault. *Journal of Geophysical Research* **93**: 9007–26.

Owen, S., Segall, P., Freymueller, J., *et al.*, 1995, Rapid deformation of the south flank of Kilauea Volcano, Hawaii. *Science* **267**: 1328–32.

Ozkaya, S. I., 2002, QUADRO: a program to estimate principal curvatures of folds. *Computers and Geosciences* **28**: 467–72.

Pachell, M. A., Evans, J. P., and Taylor, W. L., 2003, Kilometer-scale kinking of crystalline rocks in a transpressive convergent setting, Central Sierra Nevada, California. *Geological Society of America Bulletin* **115**: 817–31.

Pan, E., Amadei, B., and Savage, W. Z., 1995, Gravitational and tectonic stresses in anisotropic rock with irregular topography. *International Journal of Rock Mechanics and Mining Science* **32**: 201–14.

Patel, J., Pappalardo, R. T., Head, J. W., III, *et al.*, 1999, Topographic wavelengths of Ganymede groove lanes from Fourier analysis of Galileo images. *Journal of Geophysical Research, E, Planets* **104**: 24 057–74.

Paterson, M. S., 1978, *Experimental Rock Deformation: the Brittle Field*. New York: Springer-Verlag.

Patton, T. L., Logan, J. M., and Friedman, M., 1998, Experimentally generated normal faults in single-layer and multilayer limestone specimens at confining pressure. *Tectonophysics* **295**: 53–77.

Paul, B., 1960, Prediction of elastic constants of multi-phase materials. *Transactions of the Metallurgical Society of AIME* **218**: 36–41.

Paul, B., 1961, Modification of the Coulomb–Mohr theory of fracture. *Journal of Applied Mechanics* **28**: 259–68.

Peacock, D. C. P., 1991, Displacement and segment linkage strike-slip fault zones. *Journal of Structural Geology* **13**: 1025–35.

Peacock, D. C. P. and Marrett, R., 2000, Strain and stress: reply. *Journal of Structural Geology* **22**: 1369–78.

Peacock, D. C. P. and Sanderson, D. J., 1991, Displacements, segment linkage and relay ramps in normal fault zones. *Journal of Structural Geology* **13**: 721–33.

Peacock, D. C. P. and Sanderson, D. J., 1994, Geometry and development of relay ramps in normal fault systems. *American Association of Petroleum Geologists Bulletin* **78**: 147–65.

Pearl, J., 2000, *Causality: Models, Reasoning, and Inference*. Cambridge: Cambridge University Press.

Peck, L., Barton, C. C., and Gordon, R. B., 1985, Microstructure and the resistance of rock to tensile fracture. *Journal of Geophysical Research* **90**: 11 533–46.

Peng, S. and Johnson, A. M., 1972, Crack growth and faulting in cylindrical specimens of Chelmsford granite. *International Journal of Rock Mechanics and Mining Science* **9**: 37–86.

Peng, S. D., 1971, Stresses within elastic circular cylinders loaded uniaxially and triaxially. *International Journal of Rock Mechanics and Mining Science* **8**: 339–432.

Peterson, I., 1993, *Newton's Clock: Chaos in the Solar System*. New York: Freeman.

Petit, J.-P. and Barquins, M., 1988, Can natural faults propagate under mode II conditions? *Tectonics* **7**: 1243–56.

Petit, J.-P. and Mattauer, M., 1995, Palaeostress superim-position deduced from mesoscale structures in lime-stone: the Matelles exposure, Languedoc, France. *Journal of Structural Geology* **17**(2): 245–56.

Phillips, F. C., 1954, *The Use of Stereographic Projection in Structural Geology*. London: Edward Arnold.

Pinto da Cunha, A., 1990, *Scale Effects in Rock Masses*. Rotterdam: A. A. Balkema.

Poirier, J.-P., 1985, *Creep of Crystals: High-Temperature Deformation Processes in Metals, Ceramics and Minerals*. London: Cambridge University Press.

Poliakov, A. N. B., Dmowska, R., and Rice, J. R., 2002, Dynamic shear rupture interactions with fault bends and off-axis secondary faulting. *Journal of Geophysical Research* 107(B11): no. 2295, doi:10. 1029/2001JB000572.

Pollard, D. D., 2000, Strain and stress: discussion. *Journal of Structural Geology* 22: 1359–67.

Pollard, D. D. and Aydin, A., 1984, Propagation and linkage of oceanic ridge segments. *Journal of Geophysical Research* 89(B12): 10 017–28.

Pollard, D. D. and Aydin, A., 1988, Progress in understanding jointing over the past century. *Geological Society of America Bulletin* 100: 1181–204.

Pollard, D. D., Bergbauer, S., and Mynatt, I., 2004, Using differential geometry to characterize and analyze the morphology of joints. In J. W. Cosgrove and T. Engelder, eds., *The Initiation, Propagation, and Arrest of Joints and Other Fractures*, Special Publication 231. London: Geological Society, pp. 153–82.

Pollard, D. D., Delaney, P. T., Duffield, W. A., Endo, E. T., and Okamura, A. T., 1983, Surface deformation in volcanic rift zones. *Tectonophysics* 94: 541–84.

Pollard, D. D. and Johnson, A. M., 1973, Mechanics of growth of some laccolithic intrusions in the Henry Mountains, Utah, II. *Tectonophysics* 18: 311–54.

Pollard, D. D. and Muller, O. H., 1976, The effect of gradients in regional stress and magma pressure on the form of sheet intrusions in cross section. *Journal of Geophysical Research* 81: 975–84.

Pollard, D. D., Muller, O. H., and Dockstader, D. R., 1975, The form and growth of fingered sheet intrusions. *Geological Society of America Bulletin* 86: 351–63.

Pollard, D. D., 2000, Strain and stress: Discussion. *Journal of Structural Geology* 22: 1359–67.

Pollard, D. D. and Segall, P., 1987, Theoretical displacements and stresses near fractures in rock: with applications to faults, joints, veins, dikes, and solution surfaces. In B. K. Atkinson, ed., *Fracture Mechanics of Rock*. London: Academic Press, pp. 277–349.

Pollard, D. D., Segall, P., and Delaney, P. T., 1982, Formation and interpretation of dilatant echelon cracks. *Geological Society of America Bulletin* 93: 1291–303.

Potter, D. B. and McGill, G. E., 1978, Valley anticlines of the Needles District, Canyonlands National Park, Utah. *Geological Society of America Bulletin* 89: 952–60.

Prager, W., 1961, *Introduction to the Mechanics of Continua*. Boston, MA: Ginn and Co.

Prescott, W., 1993, Seeing earthquakes from afar. *Nature* 364: 100–1.

Price, E. J. and Bürgmann, R., 2002, Interactions between the Landers and Hector Mine, California, earthquakes from space geodesy, boundary element modeling, and time-dependent friction. *Bulletin of the Seismological Society of America* 92: 1450–69.

Price, E. J. and Sandwell, D. T., 1998, Small-scale deformations associated with the 1992 Landers, California, earthquake mapped by synthetic aperture radar interferometry phase gradients. *Journal of Geophysical Research* 103: 27 001–16.

Price, N., 1966, *Fault and Joint Development in Brittle and Semi-Brittle Rock*. Oxford: Pergamon Press.

Price, N. J. and Cosgrove, J. W., 1990, *Analysis of Geological Structures*. Cambridge: Cambridge University Press.

Price, R. A., 1973, Large-scale gravitational flow of supracrustal rocks, southern Canadian Rockies. In K. A. De Jong and R. Scholten, eds., *Gravity and Tectonics*. New York: John Wiley and Sons, pp. 491–502.

Pyne, S. J., 1980, *Grove Karl Gilbert: A Great Engine of Research*. Austin, TX: University of Texas Press.

Ragan, D. M., 1985, *Structural Geology: An Introduction to Geometrical Techniques*. New York: John Wiley and Sons.

Ramberg, H., 1960, Relationships between length of arc and thickness of ptygmatically folded veins. *American Journal of Science* 258: 36–46.

Ramberg, H., 1963, Fluid dynamics of viscous buckling applicable to folding of layered rocks. *American Association of Petroleum Geologists Bulletin* 47: 484–505.

Ramberg, H., 1967, *Gravity, Deformation and the Earth's Crust*. London: Academic Press.

Ramsay, J. G., 1967, *Folding and Fracturing of Rocks*. New York: McGraw-Hill.

Ramsay, J. G., 1987, *The Techniques of Modern Structural Geology*, Vol. 2, *Folds and Fractures*. London: Academic Press.

Ramsay, J. G., 1989, Emplacement kinematics of a granite diapir: the Chindamora batholith, Zimbabwe. *Journal of Structural Geology* 11: 191–210.

Ramsay, J. G. and Huber, M. I., 1983, *The Techniques of Modern Structural Geology*, Vol. 1, *Strain Analysis*. London: Academic Press.

Ranalli, G., 1987, *Rheology of the Earth: Deformation and Flow Processes in Geophysics and Geodynamics*. London: Allen and Unwin.

Rawnsley, K. D., Peacock, D. C. P., Rives, T., and

Petit, J.-P., 1998, Joints in the Mesozoic sediments around the Bristol Channel Basin. *Journal of Structural Geology* **20**: 1641–61.

Raymond, C. F., 1971, Flow in a transverse section of Athabasca glacier, Alberta, Canada. *Journal of Glaciology* **10**: 55–8.

Reches, Z., 1978, Development of monoclines: Part I. Structure of the Palisades Creek branch of the East Kaibab monocline, Grand Canyon, Arizona. *Geological Society of America Memoir* **151**: 235–71.

Reches, Z., 1983, Faulting of rocks in three-dimensional strain fields: II. Theoretical analysis. *Tectonophysics* **95**: 133–56.

Reches, Z. and Dieterich, J. H., 1983, Faulting of rocks in three-dimensional strain fields: I. Failure of rocks in polyaxial, servo-control experiments. *Tectonophysics* **95**: 111–32.

Reches, Z. and Johnson, A. M., 1978, Development of monoclines: Part II. Theoretical analysis of monoclines. *Geological Society of America Memoir* **151**: 273–311.

Renshaw, C. E., 2000, Fracture spatial density and the anisotropic connectivity of fracture networks. *Geophysical Monograph* **122**: 203–11.

Renshaw, C. E. and Harvey, C. F., 1994, Propagation velocity of a natural hydraulic fracture in a poroelastic medium. *Journal of Geophysical Research, B, Solid Earth and Planets* **99**(11): 21 659–77.

Renshaw, C. E. and Park, J. C., 1997, Effect of mechanical interactions on the scaling of fracture length and aperture. *Nature* **386**(6624): 482–4.

Renshaw, C. E. and Pollard, D. D., 1994, Numerical simulation of fracture set formation: a fracture mechanics model consistent with experimental observations. *Journal of Geophysical Research, B, Solid Earth and Planets* **99**(5): 9359–72.

Renshaw, C. E. and Pollard, D. D., 1995, An experimentally verified criterion for propagation across unbonded frictional interfaces in brittle, linear elastic materials. *International Journal of Rock Mechanics and Mining Science* **32**(3): 237–49.

Resnick, R. and Halliday, D., 1977, *Physics*, part 1, 3rd edn. New York: John Wiley and Sons.

Reynolds, O., 1883, An experimental investigation of the circumstances which determine whether the motion of water shall be direct or sinuous, and the laws of resistance in parallel channels. *Philosophical Transactions of the Royal Society of London* **174**: 935–82.

Ribe, N. M. and Christensen, U. R., 1999, The dynamical origin of Hawaiian volcanism. *Earth and Planetary Science Letters* **171**: 517–31.

Rice, J. R., 1968, Mathematical analysis in the mechanics of fracture. In H. Liebowitz, ed., *Fracture: An Advanced Treatise*, Vol. 2. New York: Academic Press, pp. 191–311.

Rice, J. R., 1980, The mechanics of earthquake rupture. In A. M. Dziewonski and E. Boschi, eds., *Physics of the Earth's Interior*. Delft: North Holland, pp. 555–649.

Rice, J. R., 1992, Fault stress states, pre-pressure distributions, and the weakness of the San Andreas fault. In B. Evans and T. F. Wong, eds., *Fault Mechanics and Transport Properties of Rocks*. New York: Academic Press, pp. 435–59.

Richardus, P. and Adler, R. K., 1972, *Map Projections For Geodesists, Cartographers and Geographers*. Amsterdam: North-Holland.

Rispoli, R., 1981, Stress fields about strike-slip faults inferred from stylolites and tension gashes. *Tectonophysics* **75**: T29–T36.

Roberts, A., 2001, Curvature attributes and their application to 3D interpreted horizons. *First Break* **19**: 85–100.

Robin, P.-Y. and Cruden, A. R., 1994, Strain and vorticity patterns in ideally ductile transpression zones. *Journal of Structural Geology* **16**: 447–66.

Robinson, L. H., 1959, The effect of pore and confining pressure on the failure process in sedimentary rock. *Quarterly of the Colorado School of Mines* **54**: 177–99.

Rubin, A. M., 1990, A comparison of rift-zone tectonics in Iceland and Hawaii. *Bulletin of Volcanology* **52**(4): 302–19.

Rubin, A. M., 1993, Tensile fracture of rock at high confining pressure: implications for dike propagation. *Journal of Geophysical Research* **98**: 15 919–35.

Rubin, A. M., 1995, Propagation of magma-filled cracks. *Annual Reviews of Earth and Planetary Sciences* **23**: 287–336.

Rubin, A. M. and Pollard, D. D., 1988, Dike-induced faulting in rift zones of Iceland and Afar. *Geology* **16**: 413–17.

Rudnicki, J. W., 1977, The inception of faulting in a rock mass with a weakened zone. *Journal of Geophysical Research* **82**: 844–54.

Rudnicki, J. W., 1979, Rotation of principal stress axes caused by faulting. *Geophysical Research Letters* **6**: 135–8.

Rudnicki, J. W., 1980, Fracture mechanics applied to the Earth's crust. *Annual Reviews of Earth and Planetary Sciences* **8**: 489–525.

Rummel, F., 1987, Fracture mechanics approach to hydraulic fracturing stress measurements. In B. K. Atkinson, ed., *Fracture Mechanics of Rock, Academic Press Geology Series*. London: Academic Press, pp. 217–39.

Rutter, E. H., 1983, Pressure solution in nature, theory

and experiment. *Journal of the Geological Society of London* **140**: 725–40.

Ryan, M. P. and Blevins, J. Y. K., 1987, *The Viscosity of Synthetic and Natural Silicate Melts and Glasses at High Temperatures and 1 bar (10^5 Pascals) Pressure and at Higher Pressures*, Bulletin 1764. Denver, CO: US Geological Survey.

Ryan, R. J. and Smith, P. K., 1998, A review of the mesothermal gold deposits of the Meguma Group, Nova Scotia, Canada. *Ore Geology Reviews* **13**: 153–83.

Sander, B., 1970, *An Introduction to the Study of Fabrics of Geological Bodies*. Oxford: Pergamon Press.

Sanford, A. R., 1959, Analytical and experimental study of simple geologic structures. *Geological Society of America Bulletin* **70**: 19–52.

Savage, J. C., Prescott, W. H., Lisowski, M., and King, N., 1979, Deformation across the Salton trough, California, 1973–1977. *Journal of Geophysical Research* **84**: 3069–79.

Savage, W. Z. and Swolfs, H. S., 1986, Tectonic and gravitational stresses in long symmetric ridges and valleys. *Journal of Geophysical Research* **91**: 3677–85.

Savage, W. Z., Swolfs, H. S., and Powers, P. S., 1985, Gravitational stresses in long symmetric ridges and valleys. *International Journal of Rock Mechanics and Mining Science* **22**: 291–302.

Scheidegger, A. E., 1962, Stresses in the Earth's crust as determined from hydraulic fracturing data. *Geologie und Bauwesen* **27**: 45–53.

Schlichting, H., 1979, *Boundary-Layer Theory*. New York: McGraw-Hill.

Scholz, C. H., 1990, *The Mechanics of Earthquakes and Faulting*. Cambridge: Cambridge University Press.

Segall, P. and Harris, R. A., 1986, Slip deficit on the San Andreas Fault at Parkfield, California, as revealed by inversion of geodetic data. *Science* **233**: 1409–13.

Segall, P., McKee, E. H., Martel, S. J., and Turrin, B. D., 1990, Cretaceous age of fractures in the Sierra Nevada batholith, California. *Geology* **18**: 1248–51.

Segall, P. and Pollard, D. D., 1980, Mechanics of discontinuous faults. *Journal of Geophysical Research* **85**: 4337–50.

Segall, P. and Pollard, D. D., 1983a, Joint formation in granitic rock of the Sierra Nevada. *Geological Society of America Bulletin* **94**: 563–75.

Segall, P. and Pollard, D. D., 1983b, Nucleation and growth of strike slip faults in granite. *Journal of Geophysical Research* **88**(B1): 555–68.

Segall, P. and Simpson, C., 1986, Nucleation of ductile shear zones on dilatant fractures. *Geology* **14**: 56–9.

Selby, S. M., 1975, *Standard Mathematical Tables*. Cleveland, OH: CRC Press, p. 756.

Shaw, H. R., 1963, Obsidian–H_2O viscosities at 1000 and 2000 bars in the temperature range 700° to 900°. *Journal of Geophysical Research* **68**: 6337–43.

Shaw, H. R., 1969, Rheology of basalt in the melting range. *Journal of Petrology* **10**: 510–35.

Shaw, H. R., Peck, D. L., Wright, T. L., and Okamura, R., 1968, The viscosity of basaltic magma: an analysis of field measurements in Makaopuhi lave lake, Hawaii. *American Journal of Science* **266**: 225–64.

Sheriff, R. E. and Geldart, L. P., 1995, *Exploration Seismology*. New York: Cambridge University Press.

Sherwin, J.-A. and Chapple, W. M., 1968, Wavelengths of single layer folds: a comparison between theory and observation. *American Journal of Science* **266**: 167–79.

Shipton, Z. K. and Cowie, P. A., 2001, Damage zone and slip-surface evolution over micron to km scales in high-porosity Navajo sandstone, Utah. *Journal of Structural Geology* **23**: 1825–44.

Sibson, R. H., 1986, Earthquakes and rock deformation in crustal fault zones. *Annual Reviews of Earth and Planetary Sciences* **14**: 149–75.

Sibson, R. H., 1987, Earthquake rupturing as a mineralizing agent in hydrothermal systems. *Geology* **15**: 701–4.

Sibson, R. H., 1989, Earthquake faulting as a structural process. *Journal of Structural Geology* **11**(1/2): 1–14.

Sieh, K., Jones, L., Hauksson, E., *et al.*, 1993, Near-field investigations of the Landers earthquake sequence, April to July 1992. *Science* **260**: 171–6.

Sih, G. C., 1973, *Handbook of Stress Intensity Factors*. Bethlehem, PA: Institute of Fracture and Solid Mechanics, Lehigh University.

Smith, R. B., 1975, Unified theory of the onset of folding, boudinage, and mullion structure. *Geological Society of America Bulletin* **86**: 1601–9.

Smith, R. B., 1977, Formation of folds, boudinage, and mullions in non-Newtonian materials. *Geological Society of America Bulletin* **88**: 312–20.

Smith, R. B., 1979, The folding of a strongly non-Newtonian layer. *American Journal of Science* **279**: 272–87.

Smoluchowski, M., 1909, Über ein gewisses Stabilitätsproblem der Elastizitätslehre und dessen Beziehung zur Entstehung von Faltengebirgen. *Anz. Akad. Wiss. Krakau, Math. Naturw.* **2**: 3 and 727.

Sokolnikoff, I. S., 1956, *Mathematical Theory of Elasticity*. New York: McGraw-Hill.

Sokoutis, D., 1987, Finite strain effects in experimental mullions. *Journal of Structural Geology* **9**: 233–42.

Sommer, E., 1969, Formation of fracture "lances" in glass. *Engineering Fracture Mechanics* **1**: 539–46.

Sosa, E. and Tooley, M., 1993, *Causation*. Oxford: Oxford University Press, p. 252.

Spence, D. A. and Turcotte, D. L., 1985, Magma-driven propagation of cracks. *Journal of Geophysical Research* **90**: 575–80.

Stein, R. S., Dieterich, J. H., and Barka, A. A., 1996, Role of stress triggering in earthquake migration on the North Anatolian Fault. *Physics and Chemistry of the Earth* **21**: 225–30.

Stein, R. S. and Lisowski, M., 1983, The 1979 Homestead Valley earthquake sequence, California: control of aftershocks and postseismic deformation. *Journal of Geophysical Research* **88**: 6477–90.

Stephansson, O., 1974, Stress-induced diffusion during folding. *Tectonophysics* **22**: 233–51.

Stephansson, O., 1993, Rock stress in the Fennoscandian shield. In J. A. Hudson, ed., *Comprehensive Rock Engineering*. Oxford: Pergamon Press, pp. 445–59.

Sternlof, K. R., Chapin, J. R., Pollard, D. D., and Durlofsky, L. J., 2004, Permeability effects of deformation band arrays in sandstone. *American Association of Petroleum Geologists Bulletin* **88**(9): 1315–29.

Stoker, J. J., 1969, *Differential Geometry*. New York: Wiley-Interscience.

Struik, D. J., 1961, *Lectures on Classical Differential Geometry*. Reading, MA: Addison-Wesley.

Tada, H., Paris, P. C., and Irwin, G. R., 1973, *The Stress Analysis of Cracks Handbook*. Hellertown, PA: Del Research Corp.

Tapponnier, P. and Brace, W. F., 1976, Development of stress-induced microcracks in Westerly granite. *International Journal of Rock Mechanics and Mining Science* **13**: 103–12.

Taylor, W. L. and Pollard, D. D., 2000, Estimation of *in situ* permeability of deformation bands in porous sandstone, Valley of Fire, Nevada. *Water Resources Research* **36**(9): 2595–606.

Taylor, W. L., Pollard, D. D., and Aydin, A., 1999, Fluid flow in discrete joint sets: field observations and numerical simulations. *Journal of Geophysical Research, B, Solid Earth and Planets* **104**(12): 28 983–29 006.

Terzaghi, K., 1943, *Theoretical Soil Mechanics*. New York: John Wiley and Sons.

Thatcher, W. and Bonilla, M., 1989, Earthquake fault slip estimation from geologic, geodetic and seismological observations: implications for earthquake mechanics and fault segmentation, US Geological Survey, Open File Report 89–315. Menlo Park, CA: pp. 386–99.

Thomas, A. L. and Pollard, D. D., 1993, The geometry of echelon fractures in rock: implications from laboratory and numerical experiments. *Journal of Structural Geology* **15**: 323–34.

Thomson, W., 1891, Electrical units of measurement: lecture delivered at the Institution of Civil Engineers on May 3, 1883. *Nature Series, Popular Lectures and Addresses*, Vol. 1, *Constitution of Matter*. London: MacMillan, pp. 80–134.

Tikoff, B. and S. F. Wojtal, 1999, Displacement of control of geologic structures. *Journal of Structural Geology* **21**: 959–67.

Timoshenko, S., 1953, *History of Strength of Materials*. New York: McGraw-Hill.

Timoshenko, S., 1958, *Strength of Materials. I. Elementary Theory and Problems*. Princeton, NJ: Van Nostrand.

Timoshenko, S. and Goodier, J. N., 1970, *Theory of Elasticity*. New York: McGraw-Hill.

Timoshenko, S. and Woinowsky-Krieger, S., 1959, *Theory of Plates and Shells*. New York: McGraw-Hill.

Timoshenko, S. and Young, D. H., 1968, *Elements of the Strength of Materials*. Princeton, NJ: Van Nostrand.

Treagus, S. H. and Lisle, R. J., 1997, Do principal surfaces of stress and strain always exist? *Journal of Structural Geology* **19**: 997–1010.

Treagus, S. H. and Treagus, J. E., 2002, Studies of strain and rheology of conglomerates. *Journal of Structural Geology* **24**: 1541–67.

Treiman, J., Kendrick, K., Bryant, W., Rockwell, T., and McGill, S., 2002, Primary surface rupture associated with the Mw 7.1 16 October 1999 Hector Mine earthquake, San Bernardinno County, California. *Bulletin of the Seismological Society of America* **92**: 1171–191.

Truesdell, C., 1961, Stages in the development of the concept of stress. In *Problems of Continuum Mechanics*. Philadelphia, PA: Society for Industrial and Applied Mathematics, pp. 556–64.

Truesdell, C. and Noll, W., 1965, The non-linear field theories of mechanics. In S. Flugge, ed., *Encyclopedia of Physics*, Vol. 3, No. 1. Berlin: Springer-Verlag.

Trusheim, F., 1960, Mechanism of salt migration in northern Germany. *American Association of Petroleum Geologists Bulletin* **44**: 1519–40.

Tullis, T. E., 1988, Rock friction constitutive behavior from laboratory experiments and its implications for an earthquake prediction field monitoring program. *Pure and Applied Geophysics* **126**: 555–88.

Tullis, T. E. and Tullis, J., 1986, Experimental rock deformation techniques. In B. E. Hobbs and H. C. Heard, eds., *Mineral and Rock Deformation: Laboratory Studies, The Paterson Volume, Geophysical Monograph*. Washington, DC: American Geophysical Union, pp. 297–324.

Turcotte, D. L. and Schubert, G., 1982, *Geodynamics: Applications of Continuum Physics to Geological Problems*. New York: John Wiley and Sons.

Turner, F. J. and Weiss, L. E., 1963, *Structural Analysis of Metamorphic Tectonites*. New York: McGraw-Hill.

Twiss, R. J. and Moores, E. M., 1992, *Structural Geology*. New York: W. H. Freeman and Co.

Van Dyke, M., 1982, *An Album of Fluid Motion*. Stanford, CA: The Parabolic Press.

Varberg, D. and Purcell, E. J., 1992, *Calculus with Analytical Geometry*. Englewood Cliffs, NJ: Prentice-Hall.

Vendeville, B. C., Ge, H., and Jackson, M. P. A., 1995, Scale models of salt tectonics during basement-involved extension. *Petroleum Geosciences* **1**: 179–83.

Venkatraman, B. and Patel, S. A., 1970, *Structural Mechanics with Introduction to Elasticity and Plasticity*. New York: McGraw-Hill.

Wang, W.-H. and Davis, D. M., 1996, Sandbox model simulation of forearc evolution and noncritical wedges. *Journal of Geophysical Research* **101**: 11 329–39.

Wallace, R. E., 1951, Geometry of shearing stress and relation to faulting. *The Journal of Geology* **59**: 118–30.

Weertman, J., 1996, *Dislocation Based Fracture Mechanics*. River Edge, NJ: World Scientific.

Weertman, J. and Weertman, J. R., 1964, *Elementary Dislocation Theory*. New York: Macmillan.

Weinberger, R., 2001, Joint nucleation in layered rocks with non-uniform distribution of cavities. *Journal of Structural Geology* **23**: 1241–54.

Weyl, H., 1987, *The Continuum: A Critical Examination of the Foundation of Analysis*. Kirksville, MO: The Thomas Jefferson University Press, p. 94.

White, F. M., 1974, *Viscous Fluid Flow*. New York: McGraw-Hill.

Whitehead, J. A. Jr. and Luther D. S., 1975, Dynamics of laboratory diapir and plume models. *Journal of Geophysical Research* **80**: 705–17.

Whitney, C. S., 1943, Discussion on paper by V. P. Jensen. *Journal of the American Concrete Institute* **39**: 548.

Wilczek, F., 2004, Whence the force F = ma II: Rationalizations. *Physics Today* **V**: 10–11.

Willemse, E. J. M., 1997, Segmented normal faults: correspondence between three-dimensional mechanical models and field data. *Journal of Geophysical Research* **102**(1): 675–92.

Willemse, E. J. M., Peacock, D. C. P., and Aydin, A., 1997, Nucleation and growth of strike-slip faults in limestones from Somerset, UK. *Journal of Structural Geology* **19**: 1461–77.

Willemse, E. J. M. and Pollard, D. D., 1998, On the orientation and patterns of wing cracks and solution surfaces at the tips of a sliding flaw or fault. *Journal of Geophysical Research* **103**: 2427–38.

Willemse, E. J. M., Pollard, D. D., and Aydin, A., 1996, Three-dimensional analyses of slip distributions on normal fault arrays with consequences for fault scaling. *Journal of Structural Geology* **18**(2–3): 295–309.

Williams, M. L., 1957, On the stress distribution at the base of a stationary crack. *Journal of Applied Mechanics, Transactions ASME* **24**: 109–14.

Wilson, G. and Cosgrove, J. W., 1982, *Introduction to Small-Scale Geological Structures*. London: George Allen and Unwin.

Wiltschko, D. V. and Sutton, S. J., 1982, Deformation by overburden of a coarse quartzite conglomerate. *Journal of Geology* **90**: 725–33.

Wong, T.-F., 1982a, Effects of temperature and pressure on failure and post-failure behavior of Westerly granite. *Mechanics of Materials* **1**: 3–17.

Wong, T.-F., 1982b, Micromechanics of faulting in Westerly granite. *International Journal of Rock Mechanics and Mining Sciences* **19**: 49–64.

Wood, D. S. and Oertel, G., 1980, Deformation in the Cambrian slate belt of Wales. *Journal of Geology* **88**: 309–26.

Woodford, A. O., 1956, What is Geologic Truth? *Journal of Geological Education* **4**(1): 5–8.

Woodworth, J. B., 1896, On the fracture system of joints, with remarks on certain great fractures. *Boston Society of Natural Historical Proceedings* **27**: 163–83.

Wosser, T. D., Campi, D. E., Fovince, M. A., and Smith, W. H., 1982, *Damage to Engineered Structures in California, The Imperial Valley, California, Earthquake of October 15, 1979*, Professional Paper 1254. Washington, DC: US Geological Survey.

Wu, H. and Pollard, D. D., 1995, An experimental study of the relationship between joint spacing and layer thickness. *Journal of Structural Geology* **17**(6): 887–905.

Yeats, R. S., Sieh, K., and Allen, C. R., 1997, *The Geology of Earthquakes*. New York: Oxford University Press.

Zakarevicius, A., 2000, Skaitmeniniai vertikaliuju zemes plutos deformaciju rodikliai. *Geodezija ir Kartografija* [Digital values of vertical crustal deformations. *Geodesy and Cartography*] **26**: 57–9.

Zebker, H. A., Rosen, P. A., Goldstein, R. M., Gabriel, A., and Werner, C. L., 1994, On the derivation of co-seismic displacement fields using differential radar interferometry: the Landers earthquake. *Journal of Geophysical Research* **99**: 19 617–43.

Zenzri, H. and Keer, L. M., 2001, Mechanical analyses of the emplacement of laccoliths and lopoliths. *Journal of Geophysical Research, B, Solid Earth and Planets* **106**(7): 13 781–92.

Zheng, Z., Kemeny, J., and Cook, N. G. W., 1989, Analysis of borehole breakouts. *Journal of Geophysical Research* **94**: 7171–82.

Ziv, A. and Rubin, A. M., 2000, Stability of dike intrusion along preexisting fractures. *Journal of Geophysical Research* **105**(3): 5947–61.

Zoback, M. D., 1985, Well bore breakouts and *in-situ* stress. *Journal of Geophysical Research* **90**: 5523–30.

Zoback, M. D., Zoback, M. L., Mount, V. S., *et al.*, 1987, New evidence on the state of stress of the San Andreas fault system. *Science* **238**: 1105–11.

Zoback, M. L., 1992, First- and second-order patterns of stress in the lithosphere: the world stress map project. *Journal of Geophysical Research* **97**: 11 703–28.

Zoback, M. L., Zoback, M. D., Adams, J., *et al.*, 1989, Global patterns of tectonic stress. *Nature* **341**: 291–8.

Zuber, M. T., Parmentier, E. M., and Fletcher, R. C., 1986, Extension of continental lithosphere: a model for two scales of basin and range deformation. *Journal of Geophysical Research* **91**: 4826–38.

Index